THE

Bed and Breakfast

GUIDE

WHICH? BOOKS

Which? Books is the book publishing arm of Consumers' Association, which was set up in 1957 to improve the standards of goods and services available to the public. Everything Which? publishes aims to help consumers, by giving them the independent information they need to make informed decisions. These publications, known throughout Britain for their quality, integrity and impartiality, have been held in high regard for four decades.

Independence does not come cheap: the guides carry no advertising, and no B&B, hotel, restaurant or pub can buy an entry in our guides, or treat our inspectors to free meals or accommodation. This policy, and our practice of rigorously re-researching our guides for each edition, helps us to provide our readers with information of a standard and quality that cannot be surpassed.

THE GOOD Bed and Breakfast GUIDE

Elsie Dillard and Susan Causin

WHICH? BOOKS

CONSUMERS' ASSOCIATION

Which? Books are commissioned and researched by
Consumers' Association and published by
Which? Ltd,
2 Marylebone Road, London, NW1 4DF

Distributed by The Penguin Group:
Penguin Books Ltd, 27 Wrights Lane, London W8 5TZ

Published in association with
The K.S. Giniger Company Inc, New York, NY 10107, USA

First edition 1988, reprinted 1988
Revised first edition 1989
Second edition March 1990, reprinted July 1990
Third edition April 1992, reprinted September 1992
Fourth edition April 1994
Fifth edition April 1996
Sixth edition April 1998

British Library Cataloguing in Publication Data
A catalogue record for this book is available
from the British Library

ISBN 0 85202 693 5

Photoset by Tradespools Ltd, Frome, Somerset
Printed and bound in England by Clays Ltd, St Ives plc

Cover photograph by Michael Dunne/Elizabeth Whiting and Associates
Cover design and text illustrations by Paul Saunders

Contents

Introduction 7

The top 20 13

London 15

England 27

Scotland 427

Wales 535

Channel Islands 587

Indexes 595
  1. B&Bs by county 597
  2. B&Bs by name 615

Report forms 631 and 667

Maps 639

ABOUT THE EDITORS

Elsie Dillard and Susan Causin are both British-born, married to Americans and living in Seattle, Washington. From 1976 to 1995, Elsie Dillard ran the Elsie from England Travel Agency, specialising in personalised tours of Britain. Susan Causin worked for the British Tourist Authority in London for 11 years before settling in the USA.

They spend much of the year in Britain, and have undertaken extensive trips to find the best available bed-and-breakfast accommodation, in a great number of cases following 'leads' provided by readers. Their researches led to the first edition of *The Good Bed and Breakfast Guide*, published in 1988. This all-new, sixth edition has been completely revised and updated.

Introduction

The very first edition of *The Good Bed and Breakfast Guide* was published in 1988 to a warm welcome from members of the public hungering after truly independent advice on good-value places to stay in Britain. And that is exactly what the *Guide*, ten years on and now in its sixth edition, continues to deliver.

Once again it has been fully re-researched and rewritten to present close to 1,200 of the best B&Bs over the length and breadth of Britain and the Channel Islands. Readers' recommendations play a large part in bringing potential new entries to our attention, and keeping us updated about places which featured in the previous edition. These recommendations are backed up by independent inspections; no free hospitality is accepted, B&Bs make no payment for inclusion (as they do for many of our competitors), and details about each entry are painstakingly checked for accuracy (although we do welcome feedback if we get something wrong!). And that is about as independent as one can get.

Better and better

We have been pleasantly surprised how, with each new edition of the *Guide*, standards of B&Bs have continued to improve. First of all is the comfort factor. From what our readers tell us (and inspectors confirm), beds and other furnishings are more comfortable, B&Bs are warmer (with guests in most cases now able to control heating in bedrooms) and better lit, and plumbing more up to date. Seldom these days will visitors find 'baths not permitted after 8pm and not without owners' permission'. . . .

Perhaps even more important, B&Bs are providing a more accommodating service to visitors than ever before. Because they are family homes in which guests are looked after by the owners themselves, B&Bs have always had the advantage of being able to provide a more personal service (and for less cost) than a hotel. Nowadays, flexibility and sensitivity to guests' needs are even more to the fore. Breakfasts, for example, increasingly are served at a time to suit, and – with a little notice – owners will usually cater to various dietary needs. Contrast that with a few years ago, when no-substitute fry-ups were served at, say, 8 to 8.30am full stop.

Most B&Bs will provide free maps and local information; some in rural areas will even lend bicycles, fishing gear or wellington boots. Many proprietors are willing to pick up guests from train and coach stations and ferries, or look after cars of those who have used the B&B as a stepping-off and returning point for a trip by plane or boat. In short, B&Bs are becoming better-value, more comfortable and plainly more pleasurable to stay in. You will find a list of our 20 favourites on page 13.

But not all is lightness and cheer

The picture is not entirely rosy, however. The surly host, the meagre, no-choice breakfast, grubby rooms, noise and discomfort are still facts of life at some B&Bs (not, we hasten to add, at those that feature in the guide you are now reading). What do readers complain about most?

At the top of the list is the invisible, 'I-can't-be-bothered' host, who appears only to hand over the key when you arrive and receive payment when you go. Friendliness, warmth and helpfulness are all distinctly absent. Second in the line of fire is confusion over bookings, especially if arrangements have been made over the telephone. Misunderstandings arise over prices, types of rooms booked and even dates booked. Some B&Bs take a very 'relaxed' attitude to keeping records, and it is no joke when guests turn up after a long, tiring journey to find their booked room let to someone else and the B&B full. Readers are especially peeved, too, when they leave messages on a B&B's answerphone but never have their call returned.

Another grievance is noise, from traffic and trains outside to rattling plumbing and raucous fellow guests through thin walls within the B&B. Yet another problem is lighting – usually inadequate bedside lighting, although one reader tells us that one B&B was so dim that 'we had to use a cigarette lighter to find the keyhole' and 'my husband had to shave in the afternoon'. Small rooms also come in for a slamming. After addition of *en suite* facilities at one establishment, the already compact bedrooms were reduced to 'cupboard size'. Several readers have told us about *en suite* shower-rooms which are so tiny that a normal-sized adult cannot stand up straight.

In addition, the paucity of breakfasts at some establishments has generated a number of letters. One reader complains that 'it seemed rather mean to offer juice *or* cereal – staff were quite adamant that we could not have both', while another informs us that 'other guests were supplementing their breakfasts by robbing unoccupied tables'.

And finally, according to several letters sent to us, the all-round 'B&B from hell' still exists. Summing up a stay that had proved memorable for all the wrong reasons, one couple writes:

'All that was needed to complete our weekend was the appearance of Norman Bates's mother wielding a butcher's knife.' As we say above, that B&B and the others just referred to are not among those you will find in *The Good Bed and Breakfast Guide.*

How entries are chosen

Our criteria for selecting a B&B for the *Guide* have not changed over its six editions: what we look for are a warm welcome, cleanliness, a friendly atmosphere and, wherever possible, an attractive location or a building that is itself of some historical or architectural interest. We also consider value for money. Although as a general guideline we have set a limit of £30 per person sharing a twin or double room, we have included some B&Bs that charge more, usually on the grounds that they offer a very high standard of accommodation, or are in expensive areas such as London, Edinburgh, Bath or Rye.

The types of B&Bs chosen continue to cover a wide range, from working farms and city-centre guesthouses offering good-value, no-frills accommodation, to country houses complete with swimming-pools, croquet lawns and tennis courts. There are converted lighthouses and oasthouses, inns and restaurants-with-rooms offering excellent food, and modest suburban homes where guests are treated as part of the family. At some places visitors can meet others around one big dining-table, or perhaps while enjoying drinks around a fire; elsewhere, candlelit evening meals at elegant individual tables are offered; while at others the main draw might be a magnificent setting, attractive gardens, a barnyard full of tame animals for the children to meet, a town or area of special historical interest, or wonderful beaches nearby.

Inevitably, some of the B&Bs which featured in the previous edition have been dropped, for a variety of reasons. A change of ownership may have come too late for our inspection programme, or there may have been a lowering of standards, or a jump in prices. Some establishments have left the *Guide* simply because their owners have retired. In other cases there may have been no change at all – only the fact that other, better B&Bs have appeared in the area.

More than 300 entries – around a quarter of the total – are new to this edition, and are clearly flagged in the book. A great many of these have been brought to our attention by readers. Although we have tried to be as fair and objective as possible in our choosing, some worthy establishments inevitably will have been excluded simply because we have not heard about them. In this regard, we cannot over-stress how invaluable your reports and letters are. As in our sister publications, *The Good Food*

Guide and *The Which? Hotel Guide*, reader feedback forms an essential part of our research programme, and we thank all of you who have taken the trouble to write in. For those of you new to contributing, note that report forms are at the back of the book, or just write a letter – no stamp is required if your letter is mailed in the UK. Alternatively, email us on *guidereports@which.co.uk.*

Something to watch out for is the attempt by some B&Bs to 'solicit' letters; they may even photocopy our report forms and hand them out to guests. We can spot these easily, and give them no credence. But genuine reports from readers, prompted only by a desire to share details of a pleasant stay at a B&B – or to give us fresh details about a place – are given full attention.

How to use the Guide

The best way to use the *Guide* is to start with the maps at the back of the book. Once you have made a note of the localities that most suit your needs, turn to the appropriate page in the main part of the book to find the entry or entries under that locality. (In London, B&Bs are listed by name of establishment rather than by locality.) As an additional aid, there are two indexes at the back of the book, the first listing B&Bs by county and the second by name of B&B.

In the entries themselves, 'NEW ENTRY' indicates that the B&B was not in the previous edition (although its owners may have been, at a different address). Directions to the establishments have been improved where necessary, giving more details to the immediate locality. In some cases, the route is so complex that we have suggested you ask the B&B proprietors for directions.

The descriptive part of the entries usually includes some facts about setting, the house itself, décor and furnishings, the atmosphere, any special features, and whether evening meals are offered. If the B&B has no car park, we try to indicate where guests may park. If one-night bookings are not accepted at certain times of the week or year, that is mentioned.

The following information is set out at the bottom of each entry: owners' names; months when open (when, for example, we say 'Mar to Nov', that means the B&B is open from the beginning of March to the end of November); room details; prices per room, and any children's reductions and prices of evening meals if available; credit and debit cards accepted; any restrictions on children, dogs and smoking; whether there is a car park, plus amenities for guests such as a garden they can use, games room, tennis court and swimming-pool. If the words '(*The Good Food Guide*)' appear at the very end of an entry, that means that the B&B also features in the 1998 edition of *The Good Food Guide*.

New to this *Bed and Breakfast Guide* under room details is a more precise listing of bath/shower facilities. If, for example, the details say, '3 double, 1 with bath/shower, 1 with private bathroom, 1 with wash-basin', that means that one of the rooms has *en suite* facilities, one has a separate bathroom exclusively for that room's use, and one has a wash-basin (and shares a bathroom with other guests). 'Tea/coffee' in the room details – also new to this edition – indicates that facilities for making a hot drink are available in bedrooms. (Many B&Bs may have such facilities instead in the kitchen or lounge area.) TVs in rooms are also mentioned. 'Lounge' refers to a communal room (or rooms) in which guests can relax, watch TV, read or chat, and may vary from a large, elegantly furnished drawing-room exclusively for guests' use to a cosy sitting-room shared with the owners.

Tourist boards: an update

In the last *Guide* we commented on the criteria of classification and grading schemes run by the tourist boards. We are glad to hear that the Wales and Scottish tourist boards are proposing to grade all establishments, including B&Bs, on quality rather than on facilities, as has been the case to now. The English Tourist Board is combining quality and facilities for their assessment of hotels, but sticking largely to quality for B&Bs and guesthouses. The changeover to the new way of assessing should by complete by the year 2000.

One of the several 'quality' categories to be introduced by the English Tourist Board will be 'service and hospitality – guest care', which will cover services such as supplying information on the local area, extending a warm, cheerful welcome (including an offer of refreshment on arrival), and so on. We commend the introduction of such an assessment since it is hospitality of this kind that B&Bs are all about, and *should* offer their guests. But other 'quality' categories proposed by the English Tourist Board are a little less re-assuring. For example, in order to achieve a top 'level 5' quality rating, an establishment would need a 'professional finish' to décor, 'co-ordinated sanitary ware', a 'degree of luxury' for window dressings, 'professionally fitted individual thermostatic controlled heating' in bedrooms, and so on.

The upshot is that – in England, at any rate – the pressures on B&Bs to 'upgrade' will apparently continue, with the result that in some cases character, good value and a friendly, informal atmosphere will succumb in the rush to install the 'mod cons' needed for a better rating. Why can't tourist boards give B&Bs their own category – one that would give full marks for, say, a warm and friendly atmosphere, accommodating service, cleanliness and good upkeep of facilities, excellent, good-choice breakfasts plus something special such as a brilliant setting or fascinating architecture – rather than continue to set standards of décor and furnishings that are inappropriate for most B&Bs?

Slighted singles

Something that continues to niggle as we travel around Britain is the single supplement. (Each entry in the *Guide* clearly indicates prices for single rooms and single occupancy.) This extra charge might make sense when a lone traveller wants to book a double room in high season. But how can B&Bs justify charging a hefty supplement for a small single room, which is often less comfortable than others in the establishment – or for a double room when a single guest arrives late in the evening? We applaud those B&Bs, sadly in the minority, that do *not* penalise the lone traveller by levying this extra fee. Our hope is that such enlightenment among a few will soon become the norm.

Staying current

Once again, a sincere thank you to all of you who have written to us about your experiences in B&Bs; your recommendations and comments have helped a great deal in preparing this *Good Bed and Breakfast Guide*. From your letters it was quite evident that most of you had made good use of the last edition in your travels around Britain, though we could not help but notice that a few people were relying on old guides. Some B&Bs in the current edition have steadfastly retained their high standards and have featured in every edition since the first, but, at the same time, a great many others have faded from the scene. Yet we receive letters from readers puzzled why such-and-such place is not as we describe it, or is no longer doing B&B, or is not in our book. Our answer is: please do not rely on an out-of-date *Guide*. Stay current and you will be well equipped to enjoy your stays at that unique institution, the great British B&B.

The top 20

The B&Bs listed below are the Editors' 20 favourites. Each has something special to recommend it: perhaps a particularly beautiful or intriguing house, a magnificent setting, imaginative meals, or hosts that are willing to do that little bit extra to make a stay especially pleasurable.

London

25 Eglington Road, London E4

England

Bales Mead, West Porlock, Somerset
Barn House, Broadway, Hereford & Worcester
Buckman Brow, Millom, Cumbria
Gate House, North Bovey, Devon
Holmwood, Woodstock, Oxfordshire
Kirkwood Guest House, Windermere, Cumbria
Manorhouse, Beyton, Suffolk
Old Railway Station, Petworth, West Sussex
Sandy Laithe, Tosside, North Yorkshire
Spursholt House, Romsey, Hampshire
Starston Hall, Starston, Norfolk
Still Cottage, Somerton, Somerset
Tregain, Portloe, Cornwall
Villiers, Burwash, East Sussex

Scotland

Catalina, Strathy, Highland
Corry Lodge, Broadford, Isle of Skye
Skirling House, Skirling, South Lanarkshire

Wales

Bwthyn, Menai Bridge, Isle of Anglesey
Lakeside, Llanrug, Gwynedd

London

SWISS HOUSE HOTEL, LONDON

Avonmore Hotel **map 12**

66 Avonmore Road, W14 8RS
TEL: (0171) 603 4296/3121 FAX: (0171) 603 4035

Avonmore is a small, pleasant hotel in a quiet residential street, and owner Margaret McKenzie keeps the place in tip-top condition. The recently upgraded interior features solid-oak furnishings. Bedrooms are well equipped with a range of facilities, including mini bars. Breakfast is served in the basement dining-room, which also has a licensed bar. Avonmore is conveniently placed for both Olympia and Earl's Court, and West Kensington Underground station is only a few minutes' walk away.

OWNER: Margaret McKenzie OPEN: all year ROOMS: 1 single, with wash-basin; 2 double, both with bath/shower; 3 twin, all with bath/shower; 3 family, 2 with bath/shower, 1 with wash-basin; tea/coffee and TV in all bedrooms; lounge with TV TERMS: single £48–£75, twin/double £70–£85, family room £80–£85; deposit: 1 night's charge CARDS: Amex, MasterCard, Switch, Visa DETAILS: children welcome; no dogs; garden

Bickenhall Hotel **map 12**

119 Gloucester Place, W1H 3PJ
TEL: (0171) 935 3401 FAX: (0171) 224 0614

This tasteful Georgian terraced building is in a central location, only a short distance from Baker Street Station, in the West End. The reception includes an elegantly furnished sitting-area with a period fireplace. Room sizes range from small singles to huge family rooms, and most of the bedrooms have *en suite* showers and all have TVs. Simple breakfasts are served, and guests can relax in the garden and patio at the back of the hotel.

OWNER: Irene Aghabegian OPEN: all year ROOMS: 5 single, 3 with shower; 4 double, 3 with shower; 8 twin, 7 with shower; 3 family, all with shower; tea/coffee and TV in all bedrooms; lounge with TV TERMS: single £40–£65, single occupancy £50–£70, twin/double £55–£85, family room £95–£110; children under 2 free; deposit: 1 night's charge CARDS: Amex, Diners, MasterCard, Visa DETAILS: children welcome; small dogs welcome; garden

Collin House **map 12**

104 Ebury Street, SW1W 9QD TEL/FAX: (0171) 730 8031

Readers continue to endorse the simple, good-value accommodation offered at this Victorian terraced property, which enjoys a location that is both central and fairly quiet. Bedrooms vary in size, most have *en suite* showers, and three are on the ground floor. Dafydd and Beryl Thomas are helpful and friendly people, and are happy to recommend local restaurants and wine bars. They have also provided a good supply of local information. Collin House is close to Victoria Station, and within easy walking distance of Buckingham Palace. There is no private parking, but they can offer a special rate at a nearby public car park.

OWNERS: Dafydd and Beryl Thomas OPEN: all year ROOMS: 3 single, all with shower; 4 double, 2 with shower, 2 with wash-basin; 5 twin, 3 with shower, 2 with wash-basin; 1 family, with wash-basin TERMS: single £45–£55, single occupancy £50–£55, twin/double £55–£70; deposit: 1 night's charge CARDS: none DETAILS: children welcome; no dogs; no smoking in breakfast room

Concorde Hotel

map 12

50 Great Cumberland Place, W1H 7FD

TEL: (0171) 402 6169 FAX: (0171) 724 1184

NEW ENTRY

Situated right in the heart of central London, one minute's walk from Oxford Street, Marble Arch and Hyde Park, Concorde Hotel offers unfussy, reasonably priced accommodation. All bedrooms have bath or shower *en suite*, plus cable TV, a safe, and direct-dial telephone. Buffet-style continental breakfast is served in the basement, and there is a tiny bar open in the evenings. Guests also have use of a pleasant lounge, warmed by an open fire and supplied with daily newspapers.

OWNER: Mrs Parker OPEN: all year exc Christmas ROOMS: 10 single, 3 double, 12 twin, 2 family; all rooms with bath/shower, tea/coffee and TV; lounge with TV TERMS: single/single occupancy £68, twin/double £78, family room from £98; deposit required CARDS: Amex, Delta, Diners, MasterCard, Switch, Visa DETAILS: children welcome; dogs by arrangement

Enrico Hotel

map 12

79 Warwick Way, SW1V 1QP TEL: (0171) 834 9538 FAX: (0171) 233 9995

This pleasant, immaculately maintained Victorian hotel offers excellent-value accommodation and makes a good base for exploring London and taking out-of-town day trips, being in the environs of Victoria rail and coach stations. Bedrooms are modest in size and simply furnished; some have shower cubicles and wash-basins, and there are shared bathrooms and WCs on each floor. Breakfast is served in the pleasantly decorated dining-room.

OWNERS: Mr G. Desira OPEN: all year ROOMS: 4 single, all with wash-basin; 13 double, 6 with shower (no WC), 7 with wash-basin; 9 twin, 3 with shower (no WC), 6 with wash-basin; lounge with TV TERMS: single £30, single occupancy £35, twin/double £35–£45; babies free; deposit: 1 night's charge CARDS: MasterCard, Switch, Visa DETAILS: children welcome; no dogs; no smoking in breakfast room

La Gaffe

map 12

107–111 Heath Street, Hampstead, NW3 6SS

TEL: (0171) 435 8965 FAX: (0171) 794 7592

NEW ENTRY

Built in 1734 as a shepherd's cottage, La Gaffe has been run as a hotel, café, bar and Italian restaurant by the Stellas for more than 35 years. It can be found a short walk up the steep hill from Hampstead Underground station, and right on the edge of Hampstead Heath. All eighteen bedrooms are *en suite* and have TV and telephone. Continental breakfast is included in the room rates, with a small surcharge for a cooked breakfast instead, and it is served in the bar area. It is a short journey on the Underground to central London.

OWNER: Bernardo Stella OPEN: all year ROOMS: 4 single, 6 double, 4 twin, 4 four-poster; all rooms with bath/shower, tea/coffee and TV TERMS: single £50–£60, single occupancy £60–£70, twin/double £75–£85, four-poster £110–£120; children sharing with parents £5; deposit: 1 night's charge or credit card details CARDS: Amex, Delta, Diners, MasterCard, Switch, Visa DETAILS: children welcome; no dogs; no smoking

Harlingford Hotel

map 12

61–63 Cartwright Gardens, WC1H 9EL
TEL: (0171) 387 1551 FAX: (0171) 387 4616

Harlingford, originally three separate houses in a Georgian terrace, has been in the Davies family for 40 years. It is situated in an attractive leafy crescent in the heart of Bloomsbury, and is clean, comfortable and well maintained. One reader was particularly impressed with the breakfast and the level of care and attention shown by staff. Bedrooms are simply decorated and have a good range of facilities. There is a large breakfast room overlooking the gardens and a lounge with TV. Guests also have access to the crescent gardens, where there are tennis courts. King's Cross, St Pancras and Euston stations are very close, and the Piccadilly Line runs directly to Heathrow Airport from nearby Russell Square.

OWNER: Mr A.W. Davies OPEN: all year ROOMS: 17 single, 9 double, 5 twin, 12 family; all rooms with bath/shower exc 1 single with wash-basin; tea/coffee and TV in all bedrooms; lounge with TV TERMS: single £63–£65, single occupancy £77–£80, twin/double £77–£80, family room £87–£98; deposit: 1 night's charge CARDS: Amex, Delta, MasterCard, Switch, Visa DETAILS: children welcome; no dogs

Lincoln House Hotel

map 12

33 Gloucester Place, W1H 3PD
TEL: (0171) 486 7630 FAX: (0171) 486 0166

Lincoln House is situated in a Georgian terrace on busy Gloucester Place, not far from Oxford Street, Marble Arch and Hyde Park. Accommodation is comfortable, bedrooms are well equipped (facilities include satellite TV and direct-dial telephone), and most have *en suite* shower-rooms. Full English breakfast is served in the attractive dining-room, and the house is decorated throughout with beautiful silk flower arrangements.

OWNER: Joseph Sheriff OPEN: all year ROOMS: 10 single, 7 with shower, 3 with wash-basin; 6 double, 5 with shower, 1 with private bathroom; 3 twin, 2 with shower, 1 with wash-basin; 3 family, 2 with shower, 1 with wash-basin; tea/coffee and TV in all bedrooms; lounge with TV TERMS: single £45–£69, twin/double £59–£89, family room £89–£105; deposit: 1 night's charge CARDS: Amex, Diners, MasterCard, Switch, Visa DETAILS: children welcome; no dogs; no smoking in breakfast room

Melrose House **map 3**

89 Lennard Road, SE20 7LY **NEW ENTRY**
TEL: (0181) 776 8884 FAX: (0181) 325 7636

An old chandelier from a pub adorns the attractively decorated entry hall of this Victorian villa, in a quiet, tree-lined residential street. Bedrooms are well appointed and have comfortable beds with warm duvets. Breakfast is served at a large pine table in the elegant dining-room, which has its original fireplace, or in the conservatory, overlooking the well-tended garden, with its waterfall, pond and herbaceous borders. Frances Roberts is happy to assist guests in every way she can – recommending places to eat, or arranging theatre tickets and car hire, for example. Crystal Palace park, with its concert arena and dinosaur statues, is within easy walking distance, and central London is less than half an hour away by train.

OWNER: Frances Roberts OPEN: all year ROOMS: 3 double, all with shower; 1 twin, with private bathroom; 1 family, with shower; tea/coffee and TV in all bedrooms; lounge TERMS: single occupancy £20–£30, twin/double £35–£45, family room £45–£55; no children under 1; deposit: 1 night's charge CARDS: none DETAILS: children welcome; no dogs; smoking in 1 lounge only; car park; garden

Mentone Hotel **map 12**

54–55 Cartwright Gardens, WC1H 9EL
TEL: (0171) 387 3927 FAX: (0171) 388 4671

Mentone Hotel is part of a Georgian terraced crescent in the Bloomsbury area of central London, close to the British Museum. Most of the bedrooms have *en suite* facilities, and all are well equipped. There is a pleasant basement breakfast room, and a lounge with TV. Euston, King's Cross and St Pancras stations are nearby, and fax and email facilities are available at reception.

OWNERS: Mr and Mrs Tyner OPEN: all year ROOMS: 10 single, 6 with bath/shower, 4 with wash-basin; 12 double, all with bath/shower; 14 twin, all with bath/shower; 5 family, all with bath/shower; 2 rooms suitable for wheelchair-users; tea/coffee and TV in all bedrooms; lounge with TV TERMS: single £39–£55, single occupancy £55–£60, twin/double £55–£69, family room £80–£90; deposit: 1 night's charge or credit card details CARDS: Amex, Delta, MasterCard, Switch, Visa DETAILS: children welcome; no dogs; no smoking in dining-room; garden

Oxford House Hotel **map 12**

92–94 Cambridge Street, SW1V 4QG
TEL: (0171) 834 6467/9681 FAX: (0171) 834 0225

Oxford House is in the middle of Pimlico, in a quiet residential street close to Victoria rail and coach stations. It offers simple accommodation, with shared bathrooms, but bedrooms are of a good size and attractively decorated. There is also a pleasant basement breakfast room and a TV lounge on the ground floor. The owners are friendly and helpful people, and though there are no parking facilities, they can arrange for half-price parking at the nearby public car park.

OWNER: Yunus Kader OPEN: all year ROOMS: 2 single, 5 double, 4 twin, 6 family; all rooms with wash-basin; lounge with TV TERMS: single £32–£34, twin/double £42–£45, family room £57–£78; deposit: credit card details CARDS: MasterCard, Visa DETAILS: children welcome; dogs by arrangement

Parkland Walk Guest House **map 12**

12 Hornsey Rise Gardens, N19 3PR
TEL: (0171) 263 3228 FAX: (0171) 263 3965

Parkland Walk offers visitors a truly alternative experience – owners Laurence and Penny Solomons can arrange for guests to unwind at the end of a busy day with shiatsu, massage, aromatherapy and more besides, from local trained therapists. The Solomons go out of their way to ensure guests' comfort at their large Victorian house, which has views across the city from its back garden, and provide plenty of local information. Bedrooms are nicely decorated, and the double can be used as a family room. Breakfast, ordered the night before, is served in the dining-room. The area is well served by buses, and Archway Underground station is within walking distance. Highgate Cemetery, Hampstead Heath and Alexandra Palace are all under two miles away.

OWNERS: Laurence and Penny Solomons OPEN: all year ROOMS: 2 single; 1 double/family, with private bathroom; 1 twin, with shower; tea/coffee and TV in all bedrooms and lounge TERMS: single £28–£32, single occupancy £40–£50, twin/double £55–£65, family room £65–£75; children under 5 free, reductions for older children; deposit: 1 night's charge CARDS: Amex DETAILS: children welcome; no dogs; no smoking; garden

Parkwood Hotel **map 12**

4 Stanhope Place, W2 2HB TEL: (0171) 402 2241 FAX: (0171) 402 1574

Parkwood is a small, friendly, comfortable hotel very centrally placed, just off Bayswater Road, close to Hyde Park, Marble Arch and Oxford Street. The house is well maintained and has been redecorated throughout since the last edition of the *Guide*. Bedrooms have direct-dial telephones and most are *en suite*. Breakfast is served in the basement dining-room, which is decorated with old posters, and on fine days guests can take advantage of the picnic tables outside on the terrace. It should be noted that there is no lift, and plenty of stairs to climb, although two bedrooms are on the ground floor.

OWNER: Peter Evans OPEN: all year ROOMS: 5 single, 1 with bath/shower; 1 double, with bath/shower; 7 twin, all with bath/shower; 5 family, 4 with bath/shower; tea/coffee and TV in all bedrooms; lounge with TV TERMS: single/single occupancy £45–£65, twin/double £55–£80, family room £75–£90; children under 2 free on weekends only; deposit required CARDS: MasterCard, Switch, Visa DETAILS: children welcome; no dogs; no smoking in dining-room and reception area

Romany House Hotel **map 12**

35 Longmoore Street, SW1V 1JQ TEL/FAX: (0171) 834 5553

Legend has it that Romany House was once a highwaymen's haunt, but today it is a small, family-run B&B offering basic accommodation at a very reasonable price. It is a very old building, possibly dating from the fifteenth century, and stands on the corner of a quiet side street, not far from Victoria Station. Good breakfasts are served on attractive china in the basement dining-room. All rooms have wash-basins and share the use of three bathrooms; most now have TVs.

OWNER: Jaffer Jeraj OPEN: all year exc Christmas ROOMS: 2 single, 6 double, 2 twin; all rooms with wash-basin; TV in most bedrooms TERMS: single/single occupancy £25, twin/double £35; children's reductions by arrangement; deposit: 1 night's charge CARDS: none DETAILS: children welcome; no dogs; garden

17 Ovington Street **map 12**

17 Ovington Street, SW3 2JA TEL: (0171) 584 2722 **NEW ENTRY**

This small, narrow terraced house is situated in a quiet residential street in South Kensington, close to Harrods, Hyde Park, and the Victoria & Albert, Natural History and Science Museums. The house is furnished in keeping with its character and decorated in soft, neutral colours. Accommodation comprises a good-sized twin-bedded basement room with a wash-basin and toilet, plus a single room on the first floor. Guests can relax in the beautifully furnished sitting-room, and breakfast is served in the kitchen, which leads out to a small patio, set with tables and chairs. Margaret Parsons does not usually offer bed-and-breakfast in July and August, but advises that guests phone to check availability if they wish to visit at this time. There are three Underground stations close by.

OWNER: Margaret Parsons OPEN: all year exc July, Aug and Christmas ROOMS: 1 single; 1 twin, with WC and wash-basin; TV in both bedrooms TERMS: single £35–£40, single occupancy £45, twin £65–£70; deposit required CARDS: none DETAILS: children welcome; no dogs; no smoking

Swiss House Hotel **map 12**

171 Old Brompton Road, SW5 0AN
TEL: (0171) 373 2769 FAX: (0171) 373 4983

Although Swiss House Hotel is on the busy Old Brompton Road, it aims to create a country-house atmosphere, with trailing ivy and window boxes outside, and attractive dried-flower displays throughout the interior. Bedrooms are comfortable, and all have *en suite* facilities. Buffet-style continental breakfast is served in the basement dining-room, and from midday a selection of snacks is also available. Swiss House is in the heart of Kensington, and there are two Underground stations close by.

OWNER: Peter Vincenti OPEN: all year ROOMS: 4 single, 3 double, 4 twin, 4 family; all rooms with shower exc 1 twin with private bathroom; TV in all bedrooms and lounge TERMS: single £42–£59, single occupancy £65, twin/double £74–£82, family room £82–£110; children under 3 free; deposit: 1 night's charge or credit card details CARDS: Amex, Delta, Diners, MasterCard, Switch, Visa DETAILS: children welcome; dogs welcome; no smoking in dining-room and some bedrooms; garden

Terstan Hotel

map 12

29–31 Nevern Square, SW5 9PE
TEL: (0171) 835 1900 FAX: (0171) 373 9268

The Terstan Hotel is well placed for both Earl's Court and Olympia exhibition halls. It is a family-run hotel in an attractive square, with access to the square's garden. It has friendly, helpful staff and continues to provide good value. The pleasant bedrooms are well decorated, and other amenities include a bar with TV open until 1am, a pool room, a small lounge and a breakfast room. There is lift access to all floors.

OWNER: Mr S. Tabaka OPEN: all year exc Christmas ROOMS: 22 single, 10 with bath/shower, 12 with wash-basin; 8 double, 13 twin, 5 family, all with bath/shower; tea/coffee and TV in all bedrooms; lounge TERMS: single £32–£46, single occupancy £52–£55, twin/double £62–£65, family room £71–£78; deposit or written confirmation required CARDS: Amex, Delta, MasterCard, Switch, Visa DETAILS: children welcome; no dogs; no smoking in dining-room; games room

Thanet Hotel

map 12

8 Bedford Place, WC1B 5JA
TEL: (0171) 636 2869 FAX: (0171) 323 6676

NEW ENTRY

This elegant Georgian terraced house is between Russell Square and Bloomsbury Square, a stone's throw from the British Museum. The Orchards are experienced hoteliers and provide a warm, friendly and informal atmosphere, and some of the best-value bed-and-breakfast accommodation in the area. Bedrooms are comfortable and well equipped, with firm beds, good lighting, TV and direct-dial telephones. Breakfast is of the English kind, and is good and generous. Note that bedrooms at the front of the house may be disturbed by some traffic noise at certain times of the day. Oxford Street is a short walk away, and there is a public car park at the end of the street.

OWNER: Richard Orchard OPEN: all year ROOMS: 4 single, 4 double, 4 twin, 3 family; all rooms with bath/shower, tea/coffee and TV TERMS: single £57, twin/double £75, family room £81–£99; deposit: credit card details CARDS: Amex, Delta, MasterCard, Switch, Visa DETAILS: children welcome; no dogs

25 Eglington Road **map 3**

25 Eglington Road, North Chingford E4 7AN
TEL: (0181) 529 1140 FAX: (0181) 508 3837

This large Edwardian house is in the north-east London suburb of Chingford, less than half an hour by train from central London. It stands in attractive landscaped gardens with a small open-air swimming pool, heated by solar power. The Clapps are a very hospitable couple, providing trays of goodies and nightcap decanters in bedrooms, and will give lifts to and from the station. Helen Clapp is a qualified London tour guide and glad to help guests plan days out. The two bedrooms are in excellent decorative order, and the bathrooms have been upgraded to include a power shower. Both breakfast and generous, imaginative evening meals are available. Nearby Epping Forest offers pleasant walks and horse riding.

OWNERS: Helen and Drummond Clapp OPEN: all year exc Christmas ROOMS: 1 single, 1 double; both rooms with private bathroom and tea/coffee; lounge with TV TERMS: single/single occupancy £32.50, twin/double £65; dinner £15; deposit: 1 night's charge CARDS: none DETAILS: no children under 12; no dogs; guide dogs only; no smoking upstairs; garden; swimming-pool

Vicarage Private Hotel **map 12**

10 Vicarage Gate, Kensington, W8 4AG
TEL: (0171) 229 4030 FAX: (0171) 792 5989

This small private hotel is in an excellent location in an attractive garden square, just a few minutes' walk from Kensington High Street. It is a fine Victorian house with an impressive facade and entrance hall, and a very pleasant atmosphere. Each floor has a shower-room and WC, and all of the good-sized bedrooms have wash-basins. Hair-dryers and irons can be provided on request. There is a small sitting-room on the ground floor, and a large dining-room in the basement where full English breakfast is served. Hot drinks are available all day.

OWNERS: Martin and Eileen Diviney OPEN: all year ROOMS: 7 single, 2 double, 6 twin, 3 family; all rooms with wash-basin; lounge with TV TERMS: single £40–£42, twin/double £64–£68, family room from £88; deposit: 1 night's charge CARDS: none DETAILS: children welcome; no dogs; no smoking in dining-room

Westminster House Hotel **map 12**

96 Ebury Street, SW1W 9QD TEL/FAX: (0171) 730 4302

Jane and Glyn Jones are cheerful hosts, and provide a good standard of accommodation in this elegant Regency house. Four of the fresh, comfortable bedrooms have *en suite* showers; the others share two recently revamped shower-rooms. There is no lounge for guests to use, but all the bedrooms have TVs. Breakfasts are served in the bright ground-floor dining-room. The hotel is well situated, only a few minutes' walk from Victoria coach and rail stations, and close to all the famous sights of Westminster.

OWNERS: Glyn and Jane Jones OPEN: all year exc Christmas ROOMS: 2 single, with wash-basin; 3 double, 1 with shower, 2 with wash-basin; 3 twin, 1 with shower, 2 with wash-basin; 2 family, both with shower; tea/coffee in and TV in all bedrooms TERMS: single £48, twin/double £58–£68, family room £78–£88; deposit: 1 night's charge CARDS: Amex, Delta, MasterCard, Switch, Visa DETAILS: children welcome; no dogs; smoking in bedrooms only

England

ROSEGARTH, WEST GRAFTON

ACTON Suffolk — map 6

Durham Cottage

Melford Road, Acton CO10 0BA TEL: (01787) 370142
3m NE of Sudbury, between A134 and B1115

This terracotta-coloured house is convenient for visiting two of Suffolk's prettiest villages – Long Melford and Lavenham. Guests are welcomed by Vanessa and Hugh Tatum to their family home with a hot drink on arrival, and Gus the collie joins in the greeting. The good-sized bedrooms have sloping ceilings, and are tastefully decorated with attractive wallpapers; mineral water and fresh milk are nice touches. TV is available on request. Breakfast is served in the dining-room/lounge, and there are several places for evening meals within the area.

OWNERS: Vanessa and Hugh Tatum OPEN: May to Sept ROOMS: 1 double, 1 twin; both rooms with tea/coffee; lounge with TV TERMS: single/single occupancy £20, twin/double £35; children's reductions according to age; deposit: £10 per room CARDS: none DETAILS: children welcome; no dogs; smoking in lounge only; car park; garden

AFFPUDDLE Dorset — map 2

Old Vicarage

Affpuddle DT2 7HH TEL/FAX: (01305) 848315
just S of A35 on B3390

The Old Vicarage was rebuilt in 1792 after it was destroyed by fire. It is a mellow-brick house standing in a one-and-a-half-acre garden next to a picturesque church. Anthea Hipwell is a delightful lady, very anxious to please her guests, and runs a beautifully furnished and comfortable house. One of the spacious bedrooms has *en suite* facilities and the other two have their own private bathroom. Breakfast is served at a long table in the dining-room, or on the patio in summer. Dinner is not available in the summer months, but is provided on request during winter. The Old Vicarage lies about a mile from the A35 in the Piddle Valley, and is an excellent location for exploring Thomas Hardy country.

OWNERS: Anthea and Michael Hipwell OPEN: all year exc Christmas ROOMS: 3 double, 1 with bath/shower, 2 with private bathroom; tea/coffee and TV in all bedrooms TERMS: single occupancy £25–£28, double £40–£45; dinner (winter only) £7 to £12; deposit: £10 CARDS: none DETAILS: no children under 10; no dogs; car park; garden

---

B&B rates specified in the details at the end of each entry are given (as applicable) for a single room, for single occupancy of a double room, and then per room in the case of two people sharing a double or twin-bedded room, or for a family room. Because double rooms with four-poster beds often cost more, those are listed separately.

ALDEBURGH Suffolk map 6

Brightside

147 Saxmundham Road, Aldeburgh IP15 5PB
TEL: (01728) 454058

Brightside is a well-kept bungalow, with a patio and neat, attractive garden, owned by a friendly couple who enjoy welcoming guests into their home. The two spacious bedrooms are well equipped and have *en suite* facilities. Wholesome breakfasts offering fresh fruit, locally made sausages, free-range eggs, and home-made jams and marmalades are served in the dining-room.

OWNERS: A.H. Melson and Mrs E.G. Mill OPEN: Easter to end Oct ROOMS: 2 double; both rooms with bath/shower, tea/coffee and TV TERMS: single occupancy £20, twin/double £40; deposit: £10 CARDS: none DETAILS: no children under 14; dogs by arrangement; car park; garden

Ocean House

NEW ENTRY

25 Crag Path, Aldeburgh IP15 5BS
TEL: (01728) 452094 FAX: (01728) 453909

Ocean House is in a superb location, right on the seafront and very close to the town centre. It was built around 1860, and at one time was divided into two properties, but Juliet and Phil Brereton bought both parts and restored it to its original condition. They decorated and furnished it in period style, with old rocking horses, Turkish rugs and a fine display of African scenes brought back from Zimbabwe. Two bedrooms have views of the beach and sea, and there is a games room with table tennis in the basement. Bicycles are available for guests to borrow, and musical visitors have use of a grand piano. Breakfast includes home-made bread, scones and preserves, and dinners are available by arrangement. Early reservations are recommended for this popular B&B, particularly for the Aldeburgh Festival in June. There is a £10 supplement for one-night bookings.

OWNERS: Phil and Juliet Brereton OPEN: all year ROOMS: 2 double, 1 with bath/shower, 1 with wash-basin; 1 twin, with bath/shower; tea/coffee and TV in all bedrooms TERMS: single occupancy £25–£50, twin/double £35–£60; dinner £7.50–£10; deposit: £25 CARDS: none DETAILS: no children; no dogs; no smoking; games room

Wateringfield

Golf Lane, Aldeburgh IP15 5PY TEL: (01728) 453163

Built in 1934, Wateringfield is a superbly decorated house, approached up a private road, and standing in an acre of landscaped garden with sun terraces. The beautifully appointed bedrooms have attractive wallpapers and plush carpets, and all overlook the garden or the adjoining golf course. Good breakfasts are served in the parquet-floored dining-room. Linda Connah is very helpful and will assist visitors with itineraries. Keen walkers will find footpaths to Snape, or towards the RSPB reserve on the North Warren. A self-catering studio flat is also available.

OWNER: Linda Connah OPEN: Mar to Nov ROOMS: 1 single, with wash-basin; 2 double, 1 with bath/shower, 1 with wash-basin; 2 twin, 1 with bath/shower, 1 with private bathroom; tea/coffee and TV in all bedrooms TERMS: single £20, single occupancy £25–£30, twin/double £36–£40; deposit: £10 per person CARDS: none DETAILS: children welcome; no dogs; no smoking; car park; garden

ALDFIELD North Yorkshire — map 8

Bay Tree Farm

Aldfield HG4 3BE TEL/FAX: (01765) 620394
off B6265, 3m SW of Ripon

This seventeenth-century stone farmhouse is on the edge of the Yorkshire Dales, within easy walking distance of Fountains Abbey and Studley Deer Park. The main outbuildings on the 400-acre farm are a mile away from the farmhouse and the converted barn that houses the guest accommodation. It has its own reception area and dining-room, and a sitting-room with french windows opening on to the garden. There are six bedrooms, tastefully decorated and furnished and all *en suite*. Substantial breakfasts are served at a large antique oak table. A converted stable block provides self-catering accommodation for two people.

OWNERS: Val and Andrew Leeming OPEN: all year ROOMS: 3 double, 2 twin, 1 family; all rooms with bath/shower and TV; lounge TERMS: single occupancy £25, twin/double £40–£50, family room £40–£50; children's reductions according to age; dinner £12; deposit: £5 per night CARDS: Visa DETAILS: children welcome; dogs welcome; no smoking; car park; garden

ALLERFORD Somerset — map 1

Fern Cottage — NEW ENTRY

Allerford TA24 8HN TEL/FAX: (01643) 862215
off A39 Porlock to Minehead road

This traditional Exmoor cottage is thought to date from the late sixteenth century, and is next to the post office on the narrow road through the small village of Allerford (which takes its name from the alder trees that grow along the river). The house has a welcoming atmosphere and the Hamiltons are excellent hosts. Each of the individually furnished bedrooms has its own character and *en suite* facilities. There are two sitting-rooms, one with a log fire and a smaller one with TV, and the attractive dining-room has a big table where guests are seated as well as, occasionally, non-residents for dinner. Breakfast offers a varied choice, including waffles, smoked fish, omelettes and home-made jams and marmalades. The speciality of the house is the wine cellar, with a selection of 60 different wines to choose from to accompany dinner. Allerford is a picturesque National Trust village within the Exmoor National Park, and a wonderful area for walking.

OWNERS: Jean and Ian Hamilton OPEN: all year exc Christmas ROOMS: 3 double/twin/family, all with bath/shower and tea/coffee; lounge with TV TERMS: single occupancy £36.50; twin/double/family from £53; dinner £12.50; deposit: 20% CARDS: Delta, MasterCard, Switch, Visa DETAILS: no children under 11; dogs in bedrooms only; no smoking; car park

ALMONDSBURY South Gloucestershire **map 2**

Abbotts Way Guest House

Gloucester Road, Almondsbury BS12 4JB TEL/FAX: (01454) 613134

Abbotts Way is a modern Georgian-style house with 12 acres of land and superb views, across fields of sheep, to the two Severn bridges. It is a bright, elegant house providing a high standard of accommodation. The spacious bedrooms are beautifully furnished and decorated with soft colours, and most have *en suite* facilities with power showers. There is a comfortable TV lounge and a conservatory where breakfast is served. Guests are welcome to enjoy the lovely garden and patio, and the sauna. The owners plan to install an indoor swimming-pool in 1998.

OWNERS: Pam and Geoff Watkins OPEN: all year ROOMS: 2 single, 2 double, 1 twin, 1 family; all rooms with shower exc 1 single with private bathroom; tea/coffee and TV in all bedrooms; lounge with TV TERMS: single £23–£28, single occupancy £28, twin/double £45, family room £45–£50; children under 12 free; deposit: credit card details CARDS: Amex, Delta, Diners, MasterCard, Visa DETAILS: children welcome; no dogs; no smoking; car park; garden

ALNMOUTH Northumberland **map 11**

Bilton Barns

Bilton, Alnmouth NE66 2TB TEL: (01665) 830427 FAX: (01665) 830063
1½m W of Alnmouth on minor road to Shilbottle

The approach to Bilton Barns, part of a 400-acre mixed farm, is up a half-mile private drive. The setting is peaceful, with views of Alnmouth and Warkworth bays. Traditional and antique furniture give the house a solid air, and bedrooms are well proportioned. All three have *en suite* showers plus TVs, are decorated in pale pastels and overlook either the coast or the countryside. A good place to relax is the lounge, with its open fire and comfortable furniture; there is also a sun room which guests may use. Evening meals can be arranged, with children's portions and vegetarian options available by request. The farm also has two self-catering cottages.

OWNER: Dorothy Jackson OPEN: Easter to Nov ROOMS: 2 double, 1 twin; all rooms with bath/shower, tea/coffee and TV; lounge TERMS: single occupancy £22–£25, twin/double £39–£44; reductions for children according to age if sharing with parents; dinner £11; deposit: £10 per person CARDS: none DETAILS: children welcome; no dogs; smoking in lounge only; car park; garden

The Grange

Northumberland Street, Alnmouth NE66 2RJ TEL/FAX: (01665) 830401

Jennifer and Peter Cossins took over The Grange in April 1996 and are maintaining the high standards set by the previous owners at this impressive eighteenth-century house in walled gardens overlooking the Aln estuary. The spacious bedrooms are elegantly furnished, and two have four-poster beds and *en suite* bathrooms; one of these and another room are suitable for families. An attractive drawing-room has window seats to take advantage of the view. Excellent breakfasts are served, and there are several eating-establishments nearby. Three self-catering units are also available, one of which is in a Grade II-listed building.

OWNERS: Peter and Jennifer Cossins OPEN: all year exc Christmas ROOMS: 1 single, with wash-basin; 1 double, with wash-basin; 2 four-poster, both with bath/shower; 1 family, with wash-basin; tea/coffee and TV in all bedrooms; lounge TERMS: single £22, single occupancy £25–£45, twin/double £42–£54, four-poster £50–£54, family room from £44–£54; reductions for children sharing with parents; deposit: £25 CARDS: none DETAILS: children welcome; no dogs; no smoking; car park; garden

ALNWICK Northumberland **map 11**

Charlton House

2 Aydon Gardens, South Road, Alnwick NE66 2NT TEL: (01665) 605185

Kate Jones continues to maintain high standards in this tall, imposing semi-detached Victorian house sitting in its own pretty garden close to the centre of town. Because the Joneses live in an extension, guests have the entire house to themselves. All bedrooms have *en suite* facilities and most have an original fireplace; hand-made patchwork quilts lend a homely air. Guests have use of a large lounge with satellite TV, piano and open fire. Evening meals are no longer available, but breakfast remains a banquet: choose from full English, continental, filled crêpes and (in season) Craster kippers. Kate Jones is a friendly host, happy to offer visitors information on nearby places of interest.

OWNERS: Kathleen and Ben Jones OPEN: all year exc Christmas ROOMS: 1 single, 3 double, 1 twin; all rooms with bath/shower, tea/coffee and TV; lounge with TV TERMS: single £19, single occupancy £25, twin/double £38 CARDS: none DETAILS: no children; no dogs; no smoking; car park; garden

ALPORT Derbyshire **map 9**

Rock House

NEW ENTRY

Alport DE45 1LG TEL: (01629) 636736
off B5056, 3m S of Bakewell

This impressive, Grade II-listed eighteenth-century house stands beside a great crag of tufa (a large rock outcrop), formed 300 million years ago. The house was formerly part of the Duke of Rutland's estate, and is beautifully maintained and furnished in keeping with its period and character. Several original features remain, such as flagstone floors and oak beams. Breakfast is served on fine china in the bright dining-room, and there are several pubs close by serving food. All three bedrooms have their own bathrooms. This is a popular spot for anglers and walkers, and is close to Bakewell, Chatsworth and the heart of the Peak District.

OWNERS: Jan and Tony Statham OPEN: all year ROOMS: 1 double, 2 twin; all rooms with private bathroom and tea/coffee; lounge with TV TERMS: single occupancy £20, twin/double £40; deposit: £20 CARDS: none DETAILS: no children; no dogs; no smoking; car park; garden

ALSTONEFIELD Staffordshire **map 5**

Stanshope Hall

Stanshope, nr Alstonefield DE6 2AD
TEL: (01335) 310278 FAX: (01335) 310470
off A515 Ashbourne to Buxton road, on minor road 1m S of Alstonefield towards Ilam

Set in the heart of the Peak District, in the beautiful Manifold Valley, Stanshope Hall makes an interesting place to stay. Parts of this listed house date back to the sixteenth century, though most of the current building came later, and features include an eighteenth-century stone staircase, Georgian shutters, and the Victorian fireplace in the drawing-room. Local artists have painted murals in many of the rooms, and the bedrooms each have their own decorative theme: the king-sized double room has a medieval/moorish design, the other double has Regency-style stripes, and the twin has an Egyptian feel. All bedrooms have *en suite* bathrooms, also with individual décor. As well as breakfast, evening meals using local and free-range produce, including fruit and vegetables from the owners' own kitchen garden, are served. Vegetarian options are available and the house is licensed, though guests may bring their own wine for a £2 corkage fee.

OWNERS: Naomi Chambers and Nick Lourie OPEN: all year exc Christmas ROOMS: 2 double, 1 twin; all rooms with bath/shower, tea/coffee and TV; lounge TERMS: single occupancy £25–£35, twin/double £50–£70; two-thirds reduction for children sharing with parents; dinner £21; deposit: £10 per person per night CARDS: Delta, MasterCard, Switch, Visa DETAILS: children welcome; no dogs; no smoking in bedrooms; car park; garden

---

We welcome your feedback about B&Bs you have stayed in. Please make use of the report forms at the end of the book – or use your own stationery if you prefer – and mail your report to: The Editors, The Good Bed and Breakfast Guide, *FREEPOST, 2 Marylebone Road, London NW1 1YN. (No stamps are needed if mailed within the UK.) Recommendations for B&Bs for our next edition are very welcome. Please let us know if you need more report forms and we will send you a fresh supply.*

ALTON BARNES Wiltshire **map 2**

Newtown House

Alton Barnes SN8 4LB TEL/FAX: (01672) 851391
from Marlborough take A4 W, after 2m turn left at Fyfield, signposted Lockeridge and Alton Barnes; house on right after approx 3m

Newtown House is a restaurant-with-rooms, in a converted late-nineteenth-century farmhouse in the middle of nowhere, high on the Marlborough Downs and overlooking the Vale of Pewsey. Originally two cottages, the house has been extended and is surrounded by an attractive garden. Interesting furniture and paintings adorn the interior, the two comfortable bedrooms all enjoy lovely views, and the elegant drawing-room is large and comfortably furnished. The restaurant is open for dinner to residents from Tuesday to Saturday and to non-residents on Thursday, Friday and Saturday evenings. The area is excellent for riding and walking. The Ridgeway long-distance path runs close by the house, and the Wansdyke, an ancient Roman barrier, is less than half a mile away. Picnic hampers can be provided by arrangement.

OWNERS: Jeremy and Lorraine Shutter OPEN: all year exc Christmas ROOMS: 2 double, 1 with shower, 1 with private bathroom; lounge TERMS: single occupancy £30–£35, double £55–£65; dinner £19 CARDS: none DETAILS: no children under 14; no dogs; smoking in lounge only; car park; garden

ALTRINCHAM Greater Manchester **map 8**

Marron Guest House

15 Manchester Road, Altrincham WA14 4RG TEL: (0161) 941 5603

The Bartles are a friendly couple, offering good-value accommodation in an area where it is often hard to find. Their Victorian house is on the main road near the centre of Altrincham, just five minutes' walk from the station. It is decorated to a high standard and well maintained, and the front door has its attractive original stained glass still in place. There is no guest lounge, but the large bedrooms have TV and easy chairs. One of the rooms has both a single and a double bed, and can be let to families. Only breakfast is served, but there are plenty of eating establishments nearby. Manchester and its airport are both within easy reach.

OWNERS: Mr and Mrs R.W. Bartle OPEN: all year ROOMS: 2 double, 2 twin; tea/coffee and TV in all bedrooms TERMS: single occupancy £25–£28, twin/double £42–£44, family room £60–£62; deposit: 10% per room CARDS: none DETAILS: no children under 7; no dogs; no smoking in dining-room; car park

---

'Bath / shower' in the details under each entry means that the rooms have en suite *facilities. 'Private bathroom' signifies that a room has a bathroom for its exclusive use. The B&B may have other, shared bathroom facilities as well. We list 'wash-basins' for rooms that have them but do not have* en suite *or private facilities.*

AMBLESIDE Cumbria **map 8**

Cherry Garth

Old Lake Road, Ambleside LA22 0DH
TEL: (01539) 433128 FAX: (01539) 433885

This white-painted Victorian house has a beautiful landscaped garden, and a view of Loughrigg Fell. The spacious bedrooms offer clean and pleasant accommodation, and are comfortably furnished, some with exposed stone walls, and some with four-poster beds made by a local craftsman. There are now three additional bedrooms, and a new guest lounge. Breakfast is served between 8am and 9am, and includes home-baked bread and blueberry muffins. It is an easy walk to the village and guests have free membership of the nearby Low Wood Leisure Centre.

OWNERS: Nigel and Jackie Gorton OPEN: all year ROOMS: 4 double, 1 twin, 6 four-poster, 1 family; all rooms with bath/shower exc 2 double with private bathroom; tea/coffee and TV in all bedrooms; lounge with TV TERMS: single occupancy £30–£45, twin/double £44–£65, four-poster £60–£90, family room £60–£80; deposit: 1 night's charge CARDS: Delta, MasterCard, Switch, Visa DETAILS: children welcome; no smoking in bedrooms; car park; garden

Fern Cottage

6 Waterhead Terrace, Ambleside LA22 0HA TEL: (01539) 4330077

Maureen Rushby took over this small, well-maintained house in early 1997 and, according to one visitor, 'could not do more to make her guests comfortable and very well fed'. Outside, window boxes are a blaze of colour in summer, and within, the house is like a 'new pin', with newly installed carpets and freshly decorated bedrooms. The three guest rooms all have wash-basins and share a bathroom. Ample cooked breakfasts are served in the small dining-area in the lounge, and Maureen is happy to recommend local pubs and restaurants for evening meals. A good selection of leaflets on what to see and do in the area can be found in the house, which is just a couple of minutes' walk away from the head of Lake Windermere. There is a free car park nearby, and a 'pay and display' one within 100 yards.

OWNER: Maureen Rushby OPEN: all year exc Christmas ROOMS: 2 double, 1 twin; all rooms with wash-basin and tea/coffee; lounge with TV TERMS: single occupancy £18–£20, twin/double £28–£33; children's reductions by arrangement; deposit: £10 per person CARDS: none DETAILS: no children under 5; dogs by arrangement; no smoking

Old Vicarage **NEW ENTRY**

Vicarage Road, Ambleside LA22 9DH
TEL: (01539) 433364 FAX: (01539) 434734

This interesting large Victorian house is set in an acre of peaceful, secluded gardens in the centre of Ambleside. It has been tastefully renovated, and has retained its old-fashioned charm. The lounge has an original marble fireplace, a piano, a small snooker table and plenty of books and games. Bedrooms have a mixture of modern and antique furniture, and all have *en suite* bathrooms. Laundry facilities are also available. The Old Vicarage has membership of the local leisure club, with swimming-pool, gymnasium and sauna.

OWNERS: Ian and Helen Burt OPEN: all year ROOMS: 4 double, 2 twin, 4 four-poster; all rooms with bath/shower; lounge TERMS: single occupancy £30–£32.50, twin/double £50–£55, four-poster £55–£59; half-price for children sharing with parents; deposit: £20 per person CARDS: Delta, MasterCard, Switch, Visa DETAILS: children welcome; dogs welcome; smoking in lounge only; car park; garden

Riverside Lodge

Rothay Road, Rothay Bridge, Ambleside LA22 0EH TEL: (01539) 434208
on A593, by Rothay Bridge on W side of town

This creeper-covered early-Georgian house stands on the banks of the River Rothay, surrounded by mature trees and gardens. Inside, the house is cosy and characterful, with old beams, and tasteful furnishings and décor. There are five well-equipped bedrooms, one of which is on the ground floor. Breakfast is served in the attractive dining-room that overlooks the river, and the lounge is warmed by an open fire on cool days. Legend has it that Bonnie Prince Charlie rested here. The minimum booking is two nights at weekends, and three nights at bank holiday weekends. Five self-catering cottages are also available, just across the river.

OWNERS: Alan and Gillian Rhone OPEN: all year exc Christmas ROOMS: 4 double, 1 twin; all rooms with bath/shower, tea/coffee and TV; lounge TERMS: twin/double £50–£60; deposit: £20 per person CARDS: MasterCard, Visa (3% surcharge on credit cards) DETAILS: no children; no dogs; no smoking in public rooms; car park; garden

ARDINGLY West Sussex — map 3

Old Knowles — NEW ENTRY

Church Lane, Ardingly RH17 6UR TEL/FAX: (01444) 892259
in village take Steet Lane to church, then unmade-up road; house on right

Almost at the end of a rough lane leading past the church is this idyllic 600-year-old brick-built house. It is surrounded by a fine garden with a tennis court, and exudes an air of peace and tranquillity. The Parvins have lived here on and off for the past 20 years, and Old Knowles is very much their family home, which they are happy to share with guests. The most popular of the three guest bedrooms is the enormous room above the garage, with its sitting and kitchen areas, as well as *en suite* shower. Of the two bedrooms in the main house, one has a private bathroom and the other an *en suite* shower. Fruit, a welcoming glass of sherry and appetising breakfasts are all included in a stay.

OWNER: Rosemary Parvin OPEN: all year ROOMS: 2 double, both with shower; 1 twin, with private bathroom; tea/coffee and TV in all bedrooms; lounge with TV TERMS: single occupancy £25–£30, twin/double £45–£50 CARDS: none DETAILS: no children under 8; well-behaved dogs welcome; car park; garden; tennis

ARLINGTON East Sussex **map 3**

Bates Green

Tye Hill, Arlington BN26 6SH TEL/FAX: (01323) 482039
off A22 / A27, 3m NW of Polegate; from village find lane signposted Arlington Turkeys and Bates Green Farm

This attractive, former gamekeeper's cottage, dating from the eighteenth century and restored and enlarged in 1922, is on a 130-acre working sheep and turkey farm, in a quiet location close to the tiny village of Arlington. Carolyn McCutchan is a keen gardener and her lovely garden is open to the public under the National Gardens Scheme. An ancient woodland renowned for its wonderful bluebells is also on the property, and there is a hard tennis court. The three bedrooms have pleasant views, and the sitting-room has a log fire that blazes in winter. Breakfast is served in the attractive dining-room, and light suppers and sandwiches are also available by arrangement. Guests are welcomed on arrival with tea and home-made cakes. Bates Green is close to the South Downs and eight miles from Eastbourne and Glyndebourne.

OWNER: Carolyn McCutchan OPEN: all year exc Christmas ROOMS: 1 double, 2 twin; all rooms with bath and shower, tea/coffee and TV; lounge TERMS: single occupancy £25–£48, twin/double £45–£54 CARDS: none DETAILS: no children under 10; no dogs; no smoking; car park; garden; tennis

ARNSIDE Cumbria **map 8**

Willowfield

The Promenade, Arnside LA5 0AD TEL: (01524) 761354
from M6 junction 35 take A6 to Milnthorpe, then B5282 to Arnside

This Victorian stone house is in a quiet cul-de-sac, with views to the Lakeland hills over the Kent estuary. The ambience is warm and friendly, and the rooms are comfortable; some now have new furniture and duvets. There is a lounge, and four-course dinners, including vegetarian options, are served in a separate dining-room. Owner Ian Kerr has on display several of his own photographs of the view from the house at sunset. This is a popular area for walking, bird-watching and exploring the lakes. No one-night bookings are taken on Saturdays.

OWNERS: Ian and Janet Kerr OPEN: all year ROOMS: 2 single, both with wash-basin; 3 double, all with bath; 3 twin, all with shower; 2 family, 1 with shower, 1 with wash-basin; tea/coffee and TV in all bedrooms TERMS: single £20–£22, single occupancy £35–£37, twin/double £44–£50, family room £48–£54; dinner £12; deposit: £30 per room CARDS: Delta, MasterCard, Visa DETAILS: children welcome; well-behaved dogs only; no smoking; car park; garden

ASHTON KEYNES Wiltshire **map 2**

Two Cove House

Ashton Keynes SN6 6NS TEL/FAX: (01285) 861221
off A419 Cirencester to Swindon road

Two Cove House is a comfortable, old-fashioned family home which was built in the sixteenth century as a Cotswold manor-house, and is set in a garden full of rare and unusual shrubs. The house has historical associations with the Civil War. The attractively furnished large, beamed drawing-room is in the oldest part of the building, and guests also have the use of a small lounge, which has detailed wall maps and lots of brochures to help with activity planning. A walled patio leads off this room, and barbecues are sometimes held here in summer. Most of the good-sized bedrooms have *en suite* facilities. Dinner is served by arrangement, with the Hartlands often joining their guests; early supper is provided for children under ten who are not allowed at dinner.

OWNERS: Peter and Elizabeth Hartland OPEN: all year exc Christmas ROOMS: 2 double, 1 with bath/shower, 1 with private bathroom; 1 twin, 1 family, both with bath/shower; tea/coffee in all bedrooms; TV in most bedrooms and lounge TERMS: single occupancy £27–£34, twin/double £48–£56, family room £64–£66; children's reductions; dinner £17.50; deposit: £10 per person CARDS: none DETAILS: children welcome; dogs by arrangement; no smoking in dining-room; car park; garden

ASHWATER Devon **map 1**

Renson Mill

Ashwater EX21 5ER TEL/FAX: (01409) 211665
8m N of Stowford Cross intersection on A30 between Launceston and Okehampton; phone for more precise directions

Overlooking open countryside about a mile north of the village of Ashwater, this converted grain mill and barn offers as guest accommodation a large twin-bedded room with its own *en suite* bathroom and small sitting-room with a TV. The latter can be used as a separate bedroom, and both rooms have direct access from the courtyard. There is also a conservatory, and guests take breakfast in the farmhouse-style kitchen, once the place where corn was ground in the house's working mill days. Imaginative evening meals are available if booked ahead. The Archers are a welcoming couple who lived before retirement in the Far East, and keep lots of birds and dogs. The garden now has a croquet lawn.

OWNERS: Sonia and Geoffrey Archer OPEN: all year exc Christmas ROOMS: 1 twin, with bath/shower, tea/coffee and TV TERMS: twin £50; children's reductions by arrangement; dinner £13; deposit: £50 CARDS: none DETAILS: children by arrangement; no dogs; no smoking; car park; garden

ASTON MAGNA Gloucestershire map 5

Newlands Farmhouse NEW ENTRY

Aston Magna GL56 9QQ TEL: (01608) 650964
off A429, 3m NW of Moreton-in-Marsh

This delightful Cotswold-stone house, dating from the sixteenth century, stands in a pretty walled garden in a quiet village, a few minutes' drive from Moreton-in-Marsh. The house stood derelict for two years prior to being taken over in 1985 by the Hessels, who have lovingly restored it, cleverly combining old-world charm – thick stone walls and flagstone floors – with modern comforts. There is an antique dough bin, settle and monks' table in the sitting-room, which has a TV. The three large bedrooms have a bright décor and are spotlessly clean. Breakfast only is served, but a portfolio of local restaurants has been compiled by the thoughtful owners.

OWNERS: Mr and Mrs Hessel OPEN: Mar to end Nov ROOMS: 2 double, 1 twin; all rooms with wash-basin, tea/coffee; lounge with TV TERMS: single occupancy £27, twin/double £38–£42 CARDS: none DETAILS: no children; no dogs; no smoking; car park; garden

AVETON GIFFORD Devon map 1

Court Barton Farmhouse

Aveton Gifford TQ7 4LE TEL/FAX: (01548) 550312

John and Jill Balkwill are the third generation of the family to live at this charming, creeper-covered, Grade II-listed sixteenth-century stone farmhouse, which is next to the village church. An imposing arched porchway, a flagstone hallway and a spiral staircase all add character to the house. Bedrooms are simply furnished and decorated, and the comfortable lounge is well stocked with books and magazines. Visitors are welcome to use the swimming-pool and games room. Court Barton Farmhouse has a friendly atmosphere and particularly welcomes children.

OWNERS: John and Jill Balkwill OPEN: all year exc Christmas ROOMS: 1 single, 2 double, 2 twin, 2 family; all rooms with bath/shower, tea/coffee and TV; lounge with TV TERMS: single/single occupancy £20–£30, twin/double £40–£52, family room £60–£78; reductions for children sharing with parents; deposit: 1 night's charge CARDS: Delta, MasterCard, Switch, Visa DETAILS: children welcome; no dogs; no smoking in dining-room; car park; games room; garden; swimming-pool

---

The end details for each entry state whether or not dogs are allowed, but it is always best to check when booking.

AXMINSTER Devon **map 2**

Millbrook Farm

Chard Road, Axminster EX13 5EG
TEL: (01297) 35351 FAX: (01297) 35739
on A358, just N of Axminster

This thatched former farmhouse, set in terraced gardens in a rural spot just outside Axminster on the main road, is very old indeed: parts of it date back to the beginning of the tenth century. It offers comfortable accommodation in attractive bedrooms, each with satellite TV and video, and some of the rooms can take an additional bed if required. Evening meals, using home-grown produce, are available by arrangement, and are served in the beamed dining-room. There is a small conservatory, and the lounge has an inglenook fireplace and beams. The garden has children's swings and lots of places to sit.

OWNERS: Sybil and John Gay OPEN: all year exc Christmas ROOMS: 2 double; 1 twin, with bath/shower; tea/coffee and TV in all bedrooms; lounge with TV TERMS: single occupancy £20–£22, twin/double £33–£39; reductions for children under 11 sharing with parents; dinner £11.50; deposit: £10 per room CARDS: none DETAILS: children welcome; no dogs; no smoking; car park; garden

AYLSHAM Norfolk **map 6**

Old Bank House

3 Norwich Road, Aylsham NR11 6BN TEL: (01263) 733843

This elegant, early seventeenth-century red-brick building was originally part of an inn, then later Aylsham's private bank, and Enid Parry has created a warm and friendly atmosphere in her home. Among several interesting features in the house are the pillared hall, the minstrel's gallery and Queen Anne panelling. The three bedrooms are traditionally decorated; the double room has an *en suite* Victorian bathroom, and one of the beds in the family room is a half-tester. In the cellar are table tennis, a dartboard and a sauna. For children, there are toys in the sitting-room, and a swing in the walled garden. Breakfasts include a selection of home-made jams and marmalades, and dinner is also available if pre-booked; children's helpings and vegetarian choices can be provided.

OWNERS: Mr and Mrs Parry OPEN: all year exc Christmas ROOMS: 1 double, with bath; 1 twin, with wash-basin; 1 family, with wash-basin; TV in all bedrooms; lounge TERMS: single occupancy £25, twin/double £38–£44, family room £38–£48; children under 2 free, £12 for ages 2–14; deposit: £10 CARDS: none DETAILS: children welcome; dogs welcome by arrangement; smoking in lounge only; car park; games room; garden

---

If we know a B&B has an alcohol licence, we say so. Most unlicensed B&Bs that offer evening meals allow guests to bring their own wine to dinner. If you wish to do this, ask the B&B when you book.

BABWORTH Nottinghamshire map 9

Barns Country Guest House

Morton Farm, Babworth, nr Retford DN22 8HA
TEL: (01777) 706336 FAX: (01777) 709773
on B6420, 2m E of A1

This creeper-clad eighteenth-century barn has been restored with care and retains the beams and original bricks. It is set in a quiet location outside the town of Retford. The well-appointed rooms are colour-co-ordinated with warm floral patterns, and furnished in antique pine. The former single room has been incorporated into a large family room with two double beds, and a king-sized four-poster bedroom is now available. Breakfasts are cooked on the Aga and served in the beamed dining-room with its real fire. A visit to the Bassetlaw Museum in Retford, which specialises in local history and archaeology, is suggested.

OWNER: Rosalie Brammer OPEN: all year exc Christmas ROOMS: 3 double, 1 twin, 1 four-poster, 1 family; all rooms with bath/shower, tea/coffee and TV; lounge TERMS: single occupancy £32–£35, twin/double £42–£45, four-poster £50–£65, family room £50–£60; deposit: £10 per person CARDS: Amex, Delta, MasterCard, Visa DETAILS: children welcome; no dogs; no smoking; car park; garden

BACONSTHORPE Norfolk map 6

Chestnut Farmhouse

The Street, Baconsthorpe NR25 6LH TEL: (01263) 577614
off A148, 3m S of Holt

Situated in a quiet village six miles from the Norfolk coast, this whitewashed farmhouse was built in the seventeenth century. Some of the furniture has been made by Roger Bacon, who also sells it from his workshop on the property. The two spacious bedrooms have *en suite* showers, TV and a sitting-area. Margaret Bacon serves splendid breakfasts consisting of fruit, yoghurts, cereals and a large cooked platter. The Strawberry Parlour, where light lunches and afternoon teas are available in the summer, is open to the public, and was one of the top 11 places in the Tea Council's Award Programme for 1997. Chestnut Farmhouse has a warm and friendly atmosphere and makes a good base for exploring the area; the ruins of Baconsthorpe Castle are nearby.

OWNERS: Margaret and Roger Bacon OPEN: all year ROOMS: 1 double, 1 twin; both rooms with shower, tea/coffee and TV TERMS: twin/double £48–£54; deposit required CARDS: none DETAILS: no children; no dogs; no smoking; car park; garden

---

Breakfast at B&Bs tends to mean a cooked breakfast of bacon, eggs, toast and so on, although many establishments also offer a good choice of cereals, yoghurts, fruit and other options. If you have special dietary requirements, it is best to discuss these when you make a booking.

BAMBURGH Northumberland map 10

Glenander

27 Lucker Road, Bamburgh NE69 7BS
TEL: (01668) 214336 FAX: (01668) 214100

Glenander is on the outskirts of the village of Bamburgh, a short walk from the impressive castle. Eileen McDougal has many years of experience in the hotel trade, which ensures her guests are provided with just about every comfort in an informal and relaxed atmosphere. The attractive pastel bedrooms have *en suite* bathrooms, TVs and hair-dryers. Breakfasts are served in the pine-furnished dining-room, and a portfolio of local eating establishments has been compiled. The large lounge is where guests can unwind at the end of the day. In the village are a picturesque golf course and a museum dedicated to local hero Grace Darling, who is buried in the churchyard.

OWNER: Eileen McDougal OPEN: all year exc Christmas ROOMS: 1 double, 2 twin; all rooms with bath and shower, tea/coffee and TV; lounge with TV TERMS: single occupancy £25–£40, twin/double £42–£56; deposit: £20 per person CARDS: none DETAILS: no children under 5; dogs welcome; no smoking

Greengates

34 Front Street, Bamburgh NE69 7BJ TEL: (01668) 214535

Claire Manson took over Greengates after the last edition of the *Guide* went to press, and she has done much to upgrade the premises. Every room has been redecorated; pretty pastels now predominate in the bedrooms, which have new carpets and curtains, and now are all either *en suite* or with a private bathroom. One bedroom is on the ground floor. The house overlooks the cricket green, and also has fine views of the castle. Guests can watch TV or just relax in the lounge, which has an open fire. Mrs Manson, who hails from Northumberland, is happy to share her knowledge of the area with her guests. Bicycle hire can be arranged.

OWNER: Claire Manson OPEN: all year ROOMS: 1 double, with private bathroom; 1 twin, with private bathroom; 1 family, with shower; tea/coffee in all bedrooms; lounge with TV TERMS: single occupancy £25–£35, twin/double £37–£45, family room £50; children's reductions by arrangement; deposit: £20 CARDS: none DETAILS: children welcome; dogs welcome; no smoking; car park

BARDFIELD END GREEN Essex map 3

Wellcroft

Bardfield End Green CM6 3PX TEL: (01371) 830548
from B184 at Thaxted take Bardfield road for ½m, take left turn at triangle; house is on right after ¼m

Standing in an acre of traditional gardens with herbaceous borders and surrounded by open farmland, Wellcroft is an enchanting 300-year-old country cottage. The only bedroom is twin-bedded, with its own sitting-room, TV and luxury bathroom. Visitors also have the use of the lounge which has oak beams, an open fireplace and a grandfather clock (silent at night). Ruth Gooch-Harris is a charming host who looks after her guests well. Breakfast is cooked on the Aga, and low-fat and special diets can be catered for with advance notice. This is an excellent base from which to explore rural Essex and Suffolk. Of special interest in nearby Thaxted is the ancient church and Guildhall.

OWNER: Ruth Gooch-Harris OPEN: all year exc Christmas ROOMS: 1 twin, with bath, tea/coffee and TV; lounge with TV TERMS: single occupancy £24, twin £44; deposit: £10 CARDS: none DETAILS: no children; no dogs; no smoking; car park; garden

BARNARD CASTLE Co Durham map 10

Marwood View

98 Galgate, Barnard Castle DL12 8BJ TEL: (01833) 637493
on access road, just off main road through village

Readers especially commend the warm welcome and the 'plentiful, well-prepared and presented' food at this Grade II-listed Victorian house, which stands within its own well-stocked garden just off the main road. Bedrooms are tastefully decorated in soft pastel fabrics; the bedspreads and curtains have been made by Sheila Kilgarriff. Evening meals, by arrangement, are served in the dining-room at 6.30–7pm, and 'dietary foibles' and other requirements are accommodated graciously. For those who wish to work off their dinner, there is a sauna and fitness area in the converted cellar; for those who wish to take it easy, there's satellite TV in the lounge and all the bedrooms. Off-street parking is limited, but unrestricted free parking is available on the access road just outside.

OWNERS: John and Sheila Kilgarriff OPEN: all year ROOMS: 2 single, 1 with shower, 1 with private bathroom; 3 double, all with shower; tea/coffee and TV in all bedrooms; lounge with TV TERMS: single £18, single occupancy £25, twin/double £36–£38; dinner £12 (less for children); deposit: £10 for 1-week bookings or bank holidays CARDS: none DETAILS: children under 10 by arrangement only; no dogs; no smoking; car park; garden

BARNHAM West Sussex map 3

Tamarisk Cottage NEW ENTRY

Lake Lane, Barnham PO22 0AL TEL/FAX: (01243) 553186
off B2132, 2m N of Bognor Regis

Tamarisk Cottage, a 300-year-old typical Sussex farm cottage is set on a quiet country lane. The tastefully furnished house has a comfortable drawing-room with an open log fire, and a dining-room with an inglenook fireplace where breakfast and evening meals, using vegetables and fruits from the lovely flint-walled garden, are served. The twin-bedded ground-floor suite, with a separate entrance, comprises an *en suite* shower-room and sitting-room, and has a telephone and TV. Additionally, there are a double and a single room on the first floor. Chichester, Goodwood, Arundel and the sea are all within easy reach. Judy and Michael Simmonds are welcoming and obliging hosts and can give advice on the South Downs Way and other walks, as they are keen walkers themselves.

OWNERS: Judy and Michael Simmonds OPEN: all year exc Christmas ROOMS: 1 single, with private bathroom; 1 double, with private bathroom; 1 twin, with bath/shower; tea/coffee and TV in all bedrooms; lounge with TV TERMS: single £20–£25, single occupancy £25–£30, twin/double £50, family room £60–£70; half-price for small children; deposit: 10% CARDS: none DETAILS: children welcome; no dogs; no smoking; car park; garden

BARNSTAPLE Devon **map 1**

Bradiford Cottage NEW ENTRY

Halls Mill Lane, Bradiford, Barnstaple EX31 4DP TEL/FAX: (01271) 345039
from N Barnstaple take A361 towards Braunton, right at first major traffic lights towards Bradiford, sharp left at next junction, across bridge; after 200yds turn right; first house on left

Dating from the seventeenth century, Bradiford Cottage lies at the end of a short narrow lane in the little village of Bradiford, which is on the edge of Barnstaple. It has been converted from a traditional farm building that once had farmers' living quarters at one end and animals at the other. The original slate floors have been retained. The entrance to the house is into the attractive, square-shaped dining-room, while, at the other end, the large, comfortable drawing-room leads out to a secluded garden and patio. The bedrooms are bright and well furnished, and share a bathroom and a shower-room, with an extra WC on the ground floor. A relaxed atmosphere prevails in this family home, where Jane Hare enjoys welcoming visitors. Several self-catering units are also available in the farm buildings on the other side of the lane. A public footpath from the cottage leads to the Tarka Trail, and Bradiford is well placed for beaches, golf, fishing and walking.

OWNERS: Jane and Tony Hare OPEN: all year exc Christmas and New Year ROOMS: 2 single, 1 double, 1 family/twin; all rooms with wash-basin, tea/coffee and TV; lounge with TV TERMS: single £15–£17, single occupancy £20–£25, twin/double £30–£34, family room £34–£50; half-price for children sharing with parents; deposit: 50% CARDS: none DETAILS: no children under 8; no dogs; no smoking; car park; garden

---

If you intend to spend several days at a B&B, it is worth asking whether there are reduced rates, particularly if the period is midweek or off-season. It is always best to check prices, especially for single occupancy, when booking. If we know of any particular payment stipulations, we mention them in the details at the end of the entry. We asked the proprietors to estimate their 1998 prices in the autumn of 1997, so the rates may have changed since publication. If a deposit is required for an advance booking, this is stated in the details.

BARTON ON SEA Hampshire map 2

Bank Cottage NEW ENTRY

Grove Road, Barton on Sea BH25 7DN TEL/FAX: (01425) 613677
follow A337 4m W of Lymington, take first left after roundabout; Grove Rd is first turning from sea on right; Bank Cottage first house on left up steep driveway

This small, two-storey house is tucked away on a quiet road, across which lies a peaceful meadow. It is only 100 yards from the cliff's edge, and the back bedrooms overlook the sea. The Neaths offer a warm welcome, and are always willing to advise guests about local places of interest. They provide comfortable accommodation; all rooms have *en suite* showers and TVs. Riding and sailing are on offer nearby, and there is a nearby pub and café for evening meals. A cliff-top walk runs all the way to Milford on Sea.

OWNERS: Mr and Mrs R.J. Neath OPEN: all year exc Christmas ROOMS: 2 double, 1 twin; all rooms with shower, tea/coffee and TV; lounge TERMS: single occupancy £25, twin/double £39–£45; 33% reduction for children; deposit: 10% CARDS: none DETAILS: no children under 9; no dogs; no smoking; car park; garden

BASHLEY Hampshire map 2

Yew Tree Farm

Bashley Common Road, Bashley BH25 5SH TEL/FAX: (01425) 611041
on B3058, 1m E of A35 Lyndhurst to Christchurch road

Imaginative à la carte evening meals and a truly attractive setting heighten the appeal of this eighteenth-century thatched New Forest smallholding located about four miles from the coast. It is surrounded by 12 acres of grazing land bounded by traditional hedges, and there is usually a spare stable for a visiting horse. The roof was re-thatched in 1997 – the first time it has had to be done since 1970, when the present owners moved in. Frequent renovation and decoration, much of it done by Mrs Matthews herself, have ensured that standards have been kept high. Although there is no guest lounge, the two bedrooms are roomy and comfortable, with *en suite* facilities, TVs and armchairs; and breakfasts are served in bedrooms until 11am. Dinners, by arrangement, are taken in the hall or bedrooms, and may feature items such as spit-roasted Suffolk duckling, a variety of game dishes, vegetarian options, and Denhay Farm ham (a local speciality). On fine days, visitors are welcome to sit out in the patio and take in the enchanting cottage garden.

OWNERS: Mr and Mrs Gordon Matthews OPEN: all year exc owners' holidays (phone to check) ROOMS: 1 double, 1 twin; both rooms with bath/shower, tea/coffee and TV TERMS: single occupancy £40–£45, twin/double £60–£70; dinner £20–£25; deposit sometimes required CARDS: none DETAILS: no children; no dogs; no smoking; car park; garden

BASSINGTHORPE Lincolnshire map 6

Sycamore Farm

Bassingthorpe NG33 4ED TEL: (01476) 585274
off A1, just off B6403, 6m SE of Grantham

The atmosphere is relaxed and informal at this red-brick Victorian farmhouse, part of a 450-acre mixed beef, sheep and barley farm, which has been in the family for four generations. Guests receive a warm welcome with a cup of tea or coffee on arrival, and the Robinsons are happy to provide local knowledge. There are three spacious, spotlessly clean bedrooms with traditional and antique furniture; two have *en suite* bathrooms. The comfortable lounge contains board games, a piano and TV. Breakfast is served at a single large table, and there are several places within easy driving distance for evening meals. The Robinsons are happy for guests to explore the farm.

OWNERS: Phil and Sue Robinson OPEN: Mar to end Nov ROOMS: 2 double, 1 with bath/shower, 1 with private bathroom; 1 twin, with bath/shower; tea/coffee and TV in all bedrooms; lounge with TV TERMS: single occupancy £25, twin/double £40–£45; deposit required for long bookings only CARDS: none DETAILS: no children under 10; no dogs; no smoking; car park; garden

BATH Bath & N.E. Somerset map 2

Bloomfield House

146 Bloomfield Road, Bath BA2 2AS
TEL: (01225) 420105 FAX: (01225) 481958

This grand, Grade II-listed building, built in the 1820s by one of Bath's leading architects, is on a quiet residential street close to the city centre. Bridget and Malcolm Cox have restored it to its former glory, retaining many of the original features, but adding modern comforts. Most of the beautifully furnished bedrooms are on the second floor, each with direct-dial telephone and mahogany-panelled private bathrooms, and four have four-poster beds. There is a large drawing-room for guests' use, and two self-catering apartments are also available. Breakfast is served in the dining-room, which has old maps decorating the walls.

OWNERS: Bridget and Malcolm Cox OPEN: all year ROOMS: 1 single, with bath/shower; 2 double, 1 with bath/shower, 1 with private bathroom; 1 twin, with bath/shower; 4 four-poster, 2 with bath/shower, 2 with private bathroom; tea/coffee and TV in all bedrooms TERMS: single/single occupancy £45–£55, twin/double £80–£85, four-poster £75–£95; deposit: 50% CARDS: Delta, MasterCard, Switch, Visa DETAILS: no children; no dogs; no smoking; car park; garden

---

If a B&B offers off-street car parking, we note 'car park' at the end of the entry. If nearby on-street parking must be used, in most cases we give details in the descriptive text.

Cranleigh

159 Newbridge Hill, Bath BA1 3PX
TEL: (01225) 310197 FAX: (01225) 423143

This beautifully refurbished Victorian house is about a mile from the city centre in a peaceful situation. Bedrooms are decorated with rich fabrics made by Chris Webber, and have comfortable beds. One room has a luxury four-poster bed with a peach and pewter-grey canopy, while the family room has a settee and armchairs, and there are two rooms on the ground floor. The Webbers are a friendly, charming couple who are happy to provide information on the area for guests. Breakfast offers plenty of choice, starting with a help-yourself selection, laid out on the antique sideboard, followed by a variety of cooked courses. The large dining-room incorporates a sitting-area with TV. Guests also have use of the garden. During March and October the minimum booking at weekends is two nights.

OWNERS: Arthur and Christine Webber OPEN: all year exc Christmas ROOMS: 1 double, 2 twin, 1 four-poster, 1 family; all rooms with shower, tea/coffee and TV; lounge TERMS: twin/double £65–£70, four-poster £70–£75, family room £65–£100; deposit: £30 CARDS: MasterCard, Visa DETAILS: no children under 5; no dogs; no smoking; car park; garden

---

Greenways

1 Forester Road, Bathwick, Bath BA2 6QF TEL/FAX: (01225) 310132

This pleasant late-Victorian house has retained most of its period features. It is in a quiet area of town, just ten minutes' walk from the centre, and owner Mrs Goldsmith is a very friendly lady. There are three attractively decorated bedrooms, all with *en suite* facilities, and a guests' lounge that is comfortably furnished with antiques, and has a large fireplace. Breakfasts are served in the conservatory or, weather permitting, in the secluded garden.

OWNERS: Mrs P.A. Goldsmith OPEN: all year exc Christmas ROOMS: 2 double, 1 twin; all rooms with bath/shower; lounge with TV TERMS: single occupancy £35–£40, twin/double £45–£55; reductions for children sharing with parents; deposit: £10 CARDS: none DETAILS: children welcome; no dogs; car park; garden

---

Haydon House

9 Bloomfield Park, Bath BA2 2BY TEL/FAX: (01225) 444919 and 427351

High standards continue at this stylish and friendly Edwardian house set on a quiet residential street about a mile south of the city centre. Guests just arriving will be met by a host of colour – the garden and hanging baskets are magnificent – while the interior shows that a good eye for elegant yet unfussy co-ordination has been at work. Bedrooms are themed – blueberry, strawberry, elderberry, gooseberry and mulberry – with everything matching impeccably; all five are *en suite* and are comfortably kitted out with telephones, bathrobes, TVs and coffee/tea-making facilities. The spacious pink lounge, with an outlook over the very pretty terrace and lawns, is well stocked with magazines. There is also a study which is open to guests. Breakfasts, which include options such as eggs-just-about-any-way-you-want-them, porridge with rum, and pancakes with maple syrup, are served at one long, polished table – or, when weather permits, on the sun terrace. Unrestricted parking is available on the street outside.

OWNERS: Gorden and Magdalene Ashman-Marr OPEN: all year ROOMS: 2 double, 1 twin, 1 four-poster, 1 family; all rooms with bath/shower, tea/coffee and TV; lounge TERMS: single occupancy £45–£55, twin/double £60–£80, four-poster £70–£80, family room from £80; deposit: 1 night's charge or credit card details CARDS: Amex, Delta, MasterCard, Visa DETAILS: children by arrangement; no dogs; no smoking; garden

Leighton House

139 Wells Road, Bath BA2 3AL TEL: (01225) 314769 FAX: (01225) 443079

Colin and Marilyn Humphrey took over this handsome Victorian residence in the summer of 1996 and immediately set about refurbishing it. They installed double-glazing, direct-dial telephones in the bedrooms, and laid specially made carpets throughout. The house was built in 1873 and is set in an attractive garden, overlooking the city and surrounding hills. The large, comfortable lounge has plenty of books and maps to help visitors plan their stay, and the individually decorated bedrooms are spacious and well equipped. The town centre is only ten minutes' walk or a short bus ride away.

OWNERS: Colin and Marilyn Humphrey OPEN: all year exc 2–3 weeks in Jan ROOMS: 4 double, 3 twin, 1 family; all rooms with bath and shower; lounge TERMS: single occupancy £47–£60, twin/double £62–£75, family room £72–£110; deposit: £20 per person or credit card details CARDS: Delta, MasterCard, Switch, Visa DETAILS: no children under 8; no dogs; no smoking; car park; garden

Meadowland

36 Bloomfield Park, Bath BA2 2BX TEL/FAX: (01225) 311079

This immaculate 1930s-style villa lies about a mile from the city centre in a leafy residential area, in half an acre of secluded gardens. The house has been decorated with elegance, and the large, pale-yellow drawing-room with its wide selection of books and magazines is a good place to relax in. Bedrooms are individually decorated to a high standard and are well appointed; two overlook the gardens and one – a large double at the back – has good views of Bath's Regency crescents. Breakfast, served in the pretty dining-room, might include Scotch pancakes and potato scones, as well as more traditional items. Meadowland is one mile from the train station and about 300 yards from the bus route into the city centre.

OWNER: Catherine Andrew OPEN: all year exc Christmas ROOMS: 2 double, 1 twin; all rooms with bath/shower, tea/coffee and TV; lounge with TV TERMS: single occupancy £45–£50, twin/double £60–£70; deposit or credit card details required CARDS: MasterCard, Visa DETAILS: no children under 5; no dogs; no smoking; car park; garden

Somerset House

35 Bathwick Hill, Bath BA2 6LD
TEL: (01225) 466451 FAX: (01225) 317188

This restaurant-with-rooms is an elegant Regency listed mansion set in a large attractive garden reputedly containing the largest Judas tree in England, plus a mini-railway. It is located just three-quarters of a mile from the centre of Bath. Food plays a large part in a stay here, and room prices now include the price of evening meals (except on Sunday, between November and May, when it includes lunch). One reader was 'particularly impressed with the home-made everything, including the marmalade'. The restaurant, which is licensed, is also open to the public. Nine comfortable bedrooms, all with *en suite* facilities, and two well-furnished lounges retain their original grand proportions. Themed 'special interest and activity weekends' – based, for example, on canals, local railways or even Jane Austen – are offered from time to time.

OWNERS: Jean, Jonathan and Malcolm Seymour OPEN: all year ROOMS: 1 single, 5 double, 4 twin, 2 family; all rooms with bath/shower, tea/coffee and TV; lounge with TV TERMS: D,B&B single £43.50–£51, single occupancy £59.50–£67, twin/double £87–£102, family room £116–£136; half-price for children 3–10, two-thirds for ages 10–13; deposit: £20 per person CARDS: Amex, MasterCard, Visa DETAILS: children welcome; small dogs welcome but not in public rooms; no smoking; car park; garden

---

Wellsgate

NEW ENTRY

131 Wells Road, Bath BA2 3AN
TEL: (01225) 310688 FAX: (01225) 310143

Although on a busy main road, Wellsgate stands above it and is surprisingly quiet. It is a Victorian house with an extensive, pretty rear garden, and enjoys views of the abbey and city. Breakfast – full English, continental or vegetarian – is served in the pretty conservatory-style room at the back of the house, and an elegantly furnished lounge is provided for guests' use. The three *en suite* bedrooms are comfortably appointed and can also be used as singles or family rooms, and garaging or off-street parking is provided. Wellsgate is a ten-minute walk from the city centre and is also on a bus route.

OWNER: Mrs E.G. Long OPEN: all year exc Christmas ROOMS: 3 double/twin; all rooms with bath/shower, tea/coffee and TV; lounge with TV TERMS: single/single occupancy £20–£35, twin/double £40–£52, family room £58–£65; deposit: £25 CARDS: MasterCard, Visa DETAILS: children welcome; no dogs; no smoking; car park; garden

---

If a B&B accepts credit cards, we list them in the details at the end of an entry – or specify no cards are accepted if that is so. There may be a surcharge if you pay by credit card. It is always best to check when booking whether the card you want to use will be accepted.

BATHFORD Bath & N. E. Somerset **map 2**

Eagle House

NEW ENTRY

23 Church Street, Bathford BA1 7RS TEL/FAX: (01225) 859946

Set in the beautiful conservation village of Bathford only three miles from Bath, Eagle House is an impressive listed Georgian house standing in one and a half acres of gardens, and combining comfort and elegance with a welcoming atmosphere. The bedrooms are spacious, well equipped and overlook the garden or countryside. Guests can browse through brochures, read the newspaper or play CDs and cassettes in the magnificent drawing-room. Continental, or cooked breakfast at a small extra charge, is served in the dining-room, and there is a second smaller sitting-room for guests' use; both these rooms look out over the terraced gardens. A further two bedrooms, each with private bathroom, are available in the walled garden cottage, which also has a sitting-room and kitchen; bookings are for a minimum of two nights.

OWNERS: John and Rosamund Napier OPEN: all year exc Christmas ROOMS: 2 single, 3 double, 2 twin, 1 family; all rooms with bath/shower, tea/coffee and TV; 2 lounges TERMS: single £35–£42, single occupancy £42–£56, twin/double £42–£74, family room £54–£74; free for children sharing with parents; deposit required for weekend bookings CARDS: MasterCard, Visa DETAILS: children welcome; dogs welcome; no smoking in some bedrooms; car park; garden; tennis

BATTLE East Sussex **map 3**

Abbey View

NEW ENTRY

Caldbec Hill, Battle TN33 0JS TEL/FAX: (01424) 775513

Set on a hill above Battle, Abbey View is a modernised 1920s house. The interior has been virtually gutted and now provides neat, meticulously clean accommodation in smallish rooms, one enjoying pleasant rural views to the abbey. Guests have a couple of different sitting-areas at their disposal, and breakfast only is served at separate tables in the dining-room, which has access to the terrace and garden. It is only a short downhill walk into the centre of Battle, whose attractions include the abbey (overlooking the site of the Battle of Hastings), the local museum, and Buckleys Yesterdays World' featuring shops, displays and exhibits from 1850 to 1950.

OWNERS : Chris and Janet Whiteman OPEN: all year ROOMS: 2 double, 1 with bath/ shower, 1 with private bathroom; 1 twin, with bath/shower; tea/coffee and TV in all bedrooms; lounge with TV TERMS: single occupancy £25–£35; twin/double £46–£50; deposit required CARDS: Delta, MasterCard, Visa DETAILS: no childen under 12; no dogs; no smoking; car park; garden

---

We state at the end of an entry whether children are welcome, and explain any age restrictions. If there are reduced rates for children, this is mentioned; if no reductions are specified, assume you will have to pay full rates for children.

Kitchenham Farm

Ashburnham TN33 9NP TEL/FAX: (01424) 892221
off A271, 4m W of Battle

This ivy-clad Georgian farmhouse, built in 1770, is surrounded by over 800 acres of farmland, and is part of the Ashburnham Estate. It has a welcoming, relaxed atmosphere, and the sitting-room has a large open fireplace and TV. One bedroom has *en suite* facilities and the other two share a shower-room, and there is an additional ground-floor WC. Evening meals are served by arrangement. Coarse fishing is available on the river which runs through the farm. Guests are welcome to explore the farm and stroll through the meadows and woods.

OWNERS: Monty and Amanda Worssam OPEN: all year exc Christmas ROOMS: 1 double, with wash-basin; 2 twin, 1 with bath, 1 with wash-basin; tea/coffee in all bedrooms; lounge with TV TERMS: single occupancy £25, twin/double £36–£44; children under 2 free, other reductions according to age; deposit required CARDS: none DETAILS: children welcome; no dogs; no smoking; car park; garden

BEADNELL Northumberland **map 10**

Shepherds Cottage

NEW ENTRY

Beadnell NE67 5AD TEL: (01665) 720497
on B1340 Alnwick–Seahouses road ¾m W of Beadnell village

This is a new venture for the owners, who took over the business in late 1996. The house stands in an acre of gardens on the coastal road, a couple of miles from Seahouses. It was formerly a Georgian lodge, and the surrounding land is owned by the Duke of Northumberland. The bedrooms have a cottagey feel, with bright pastel colours, and pine furniture; all three have new *en suite* showers and are on the ground floor. Guests have their own entrance to the house. The sitting-cum-dining-room has french windows leading on to a terrace, where breakfast is sometimes served when weather permits. Castles, quiet sandy beaches and water sports are all within striking distance.

OWNERS: D. Birchall and B. Seaward-Birchall OPEN: all year ROOMS: 2 double, 1 twin; all rooms with shower, tea/coffee and TV TERMS: single occupancy £25, twin/double £40–£44; deposit: 50% CARDS: none DETAILS: no children under 12; dogs by arrangement; no smoking; car park; garden

BEDALE North Yorkshire **map 9**

Hyperion House

88 South End, Bedale DL8 2DS TEL: (01677) 422334

This red-brick detached house on the south side of Bedale offers three prettily decorated bedrooms, plus a well-furnished lounge to relax in and a warm welcome from the Deans. One double room has a king-sized bed and an *en suite* bathroom that has been recently fully refurbished, and another double has sole use of a bathroom; the twin is chiefly used for overflow from the other rooms. Children from 10 upwards are welcome, but, as there is no family room, must be confident enough to sleep in a room on their own. Ron Dean knows a great deal about the local area, and is happy to supply maps, walking books and advice – plus videos of places of interest that guests may watch. Generously sized full Yorkshire breakfasts are offered, with special diets catered for. Residents have their own entrance, and are given their own key.

OWNERS: Sheila and Ron Dean OPEN: Mar to Jan exc Christmas and New Year ROOMS: 2 double, 1 with bath/shower, 1 with private bathroom; 1 twin, with wash-basin; tea/coffee and TV in all bedrooms; lounge with TV TERMS: single occupancy £30–£35, twin/double £36–£42; £12 for children 10–14; deposit: £20 per room CARDS: none DETAILS: no children under 10; no dogs; no smoking; car park; garden

Southfield

96 South End, Bedale DL8 2DS TEL: (01677) 423510

Southfield is a well-maintained house a few minutes' walk from the town centre. Mrs Keighley is a friendly host, who likes to chat with guests. Tea is offered on arrival, and in the evening hot chocolate is served in the comfortable lounge. Two bedrooms now have *en suite* showers. Historic Bedale House is nearby, and Jervaulx Abbey is a short drive away.

OWNERS: Arthur and Marjorie Keighley OPEN: all year exc Christmas ROOMS: 1 single; 2 double, both with shower; 1 twin, with wash-basin; tea/coffee in all bedrooms; lounge with TV TERMS: single £18, single occupancy £20, twin/double £36–£40 CARDS: none DETAILS: no children; no dogs; no smoking; car park; garden

BEERCROCOMBE Somerset — map 2

Frog Street Farm

Beercrocombe TA3 6AF TEL/FAX: 01823 480430

leave A358 at Hatch Inn and follow Station Road, take first left and continue past turning to Beercrocombe

The oldest parts of this attractive, wistaria-covered Somerset longhouse date back to the fifteenth century. It is on a 130-acre dairy farm, and the name comes from a corruption of the Anglo-Saxon for 'meeting-place'. Some interesting features remain, including Jacobean panelling, beams and inglenook fireplaces. The bedrooms are comfortable and simply decorated. A large dining-room, two sitting-rooms and a small writing-room, which used to house the cider press, provide plenty of space for relaxing; dinner is served at 7 o'clock. There are good views from the house and it is surrounded by a lawned garden. Nearby Tintinhull House and Muchelney Abbey are well worth a visit.

OWNERS: Henry and Veronica Cole OPEN: Apr to Oct ROOMS: 2 double, 2 twin; all rooms with bath/shower and tea/coffee; lounge with TV TERMS: single occupancy £30, twin/double £50–£54; dinner £16 CARDS: none DETAILS: no children under 11; no dogs; no smoking; car park; garden

Whittles Farm

Beercrocombe TA3 6AH TEL/FAX: (01823) 480301

on A358 turn at sign for Beercrocombe, fork right down Radigan Lane then first left after railway bridge

This attractive virginia-creeper-covered farmhouse dates from the sixteenth century, though the front part of the house was added in the nineteenth century. It is on a 200-acre working dairy farm, a mile from the village, set in pretty countryside on the edge of the Blackdown hills. Breakfast is served in the large dining-room at one table, and dinner is eaten in the smaller, cosy dining-room at the rear of the house, which has an open fire. A small selection of wines is available at dinner. Bedrooms are spacious, prettily decorated and furnished with easy chairs. Guests also have use of a comfortable sitting-room and a drawing-room. The farm is seven miles from Taunton.

OWNER: Claire Mitchem OPEN: all year exc Christmas ROOMS: 2 double, 1 twin; all rooms with bath; lounge with TV TERMS: single occupancy £30–£32, twin/double £48–£52; dinner £15; deposit: 10% CARDS: none DETAILS: no children; no dogs; smoking in 1 lounge only; car park

BELLINGHAM Northumberland map 11

Westfield House

Bellingham, nr Hexham NE48 2DP TEL/FAX: (01434) 220340

This large Victorian house, built for a wealthy grocer, is approached along a tree-lined drive with lovely views all around. Several original features remain, including some interesting fireplaces. The ground-floor family bedroom has pine furniture which formerly belonged to David Minchin's grandmother, and one room has a four-poster bed. The Minchins are a most accommodating couple, and provide a friendly, relaxing atmosphere. They have put together a very useful pocket guide on where to go and what to see in the area. The sitting-room overlooks the garden, where guests can relax in warm weather. Evening meals are health-conscious and imaginative, and breakfasts are substantial.

OWNERS: David and June Minchin OPEN: all year ROOMS: 2 double, 2 twin, 1 four-poster, 1 family; all rooms with shower, tea/coffee and TV; lounge with TV TERMS: twin/double £52, four-poster £52; children under 2 free; dinner £15; deposit required CARDS: MasterCard, Visa DETAILS: children welcome; dogs by arrangement; no smoking; car park; garden

BELSAY Northumberland map 10

Bounder House NEW ENTRY

Belsay NE20 0JR TEL: (01661) 881267
on A696 ½m N of Belsay take B6309 and follow 'B&B' signs for 2m

Set in farming country, Bounder House is a 12-acre smallholding supporting pigs and sheep. The house was built in the late 1980s with stones from the original farm building, and offers good-value accommodation. The bedrooms are prettily decorated and well furnished. The two doubles have *en suite* showers, one room has a microwave and a fridge, and another a microwave. Breakfast is served in the lounge/dining-room, and for evening meals there are several pubs within a four-mile drive. Kath Fearns is a friendly, outgoing lady who extends a warm welcome to her guests. Pick-up from Newcastle Airport can be arranged, and a self-catering cottage that sleeps four is also available. Belsay Hall, Castle and Gardens are worth visiting.

OWNERS: Ian and Kath Fearns OPEN: all year ROOMS: 2 double, both with shower; 1 twin; 1 family; tea/coffee and TV in all bedrooms; lounge with TV TERMS: single occupancy £25, twin/double £35, family room £45–£55; reductions for children sharing with parents; deposit required in high season CARDS: none DETAILS: children welcome; dogs by arrangement; no smoking; car park; garden

BEOLEY Hereford & Worcester map 5

Cherrypit

Cherry Pit Lane, Beoley B98 9DH TEL/FAX: (01527) 62454
on B4101, on N outskirts of Redditch

Cherrypit is a handsome mock-Tudor house set in a peaceful six-acre garden. A large patio overlooks a fish pond, and an array of wildlife can often be glimpsed in the grounds. The well-proportioned bedrooms are neatly decorated, and there is one *en suite* room in an annexe. Evening meals are served between 6 and 8pm in a separate dining-room, and there is a cosy television lounge, complete with open fire, for guests to use.

OWNERS: Don and Anne Howles OPEN: all year ROOMS: 2 single, both with wash-basin; 2 twin, 1 with shower, 1 with wash-basin; tea/coffee and TV in all bedrooms; lounge with TV TERMS: single/single occupancy £17–£20, twin/double £34–£50; children under 5 free, half-price for ages 5–12; dinner £10 CARDS: none DETAILS: children welcome; dogs by arrangement; no smoking; car park; garden

---

If you are forced to turn up later than planned, please telephone to warn the proprietor. It is always best to book a room in advance, even in winter. B&Bs with few rooms may close at short notice for periods not specified in the details.

BERRYNARBOR Devon map 1

Sloley Farm NEW ENTRY

Castle Hill, Berrynarbor EX34 9SX TEL/FAX: (01271) 883032
in centre of village turn opposite church up Castle Hill; house ¼m on right

This seventeenth-century farmhouse is set in three lovely acres and stands just outside Berrynarbor, three-times winner of Devon's 'Best-Kept Village' award. The village has a thirteenth-century pub (which serves evening meals) and a twelfth-century church. Sloley Farm is comfortably furnished – all bedrooms are *en suite*, and one is on the ground floor – and the owners, in the view of one visitor, are 'kind and welcoming'. Their lounge with its wood-burning stove is shared with residents, and both excellent breakfasts and, if arranged in advance, good old-fashioned home-cooked evening meals, using produce from their own garden, are available, with vegetarians well catered for. Walkers are particularly welcome here, with all levels of walks suggested; packed lunches can be provided and pick-ups at the end of a day's walking arranged, and there are drying facilities. Guests arriving by train at Barnstaple can arrange to be met, and there is a half-hourly bus service from Ilfracombe to Berrynarbor. The property also has self-catering stone cottages.

OWNERS: Jill and Brian Mountain OPEN: all year ROOMS: 2 double, 1 twin; all rooms with shower and tea/coffee; lounge with TV TERMS: single occupancy £16–£22, twin/double £32–£44; dinner £12.50; deposit required CARDS: none DETAILS: no children; no dogs; no smoking; car park; garden

BERWICK East Sussex map 3

Dawes House NEW ENTRY

Berwick BN26 5QS TEL: (01323) 871276
take Alfriston turning off A27; house is second drive on left

This partly thatched, partly half-tiled house was once a dairy, and can be found next to the winery, not far from the old village of Alfriston. Dawes House is set in the scenic Cuckmere Valley in an attractive garden, and has very charming owners. The house is full of beams and low doorways, suitably padded to protect unwary heads. The drawing-room has a log fire, and both breakfast and evening meals, by arrangement, are served in the elegantly furnished dining-room. One of the comfortable bedrooms is on the ground floor and has its own entrance. The house is close to Glyndebourne, Newhaven, Lewes and Eastbourne.

OWNERS: Mr and Mrs Michael Wardroper OPEN: all year exc Christmas and Jan ROOMS: 1 double, 1 family; all rooms with bath/shower and tea/coffee; TV in family room and lounge TERMS: single occupancy £25, twin/double £45–£50, family room £45–£50; dinner £12.50 CARDS: none DETAILS: no children under 10; dogs by arrangement; no smoking; car park; garden

BERWICK ST JAMES Wiltshire map 2

The Mill House NEW ENTRY

Berwick St James SP3 4TS TEL: (01722) 790331
on B3083, between A36 and A303, 9m NW of Salisbury

This charming house, built in 1785, is at the end of the sleepy, pretty village of Berwick St James. In summer, the garden is full of hundreds of old-fashioned roses, and there are 12 acres of nature reserve for guests to explore, including a wildflower meadow, where birds, waterfowl and deer can be seen. The atmosphere is friendly and welcoming, and the accommodation comfortable. Guests can fish or swim in the mill pool. Stonehenge is a lovely three-and-a-half mile walk away.

OWNERS: Diana Gifford Mead and Michael Mertens OPEN: all year ROOMS: 2 single, 1 with private bathroom, 1 with wash-basin; 4 double, all with bath/shower; 1 twin, with bath/shower; 1 family, with bath/shower; tea/coffee and TV in all bedrooms; lounge with TV TERMS: single £20, single occupancy £25–£35, twin/double £40–£60, family room £65–£85; deposit: £10 CARDS: none DETAILS: no children under 5; no dogs; car park; garden

BERWICK-UPON-TWEED Northumberland map 11

Dervaig Guest House

1 North Road, Berwick-upon-Tweed TD15 1PW TEL: (01289) 307378

Readers continue to endorse this B&B, especially the excellent cooked breakfasts, which are served in the pretty breakfast room with its lace tablecloths, pretty crockery, original casement shutters and attractive coving. The house dates from the 1800s, is peacefully situated in a quiet part of Berwick and is well maintained. Double-glazing makes things even quieter. The sitting-room features a grand-daughter clock and is a pleasant room in which to relax after a busy day. Bedrooms are roomy and have armchairs and comfortable high beds. The Nobles have helpfully prepared a list of local eating establishments, including how long it will take to get there by foot or car.

OWNERS: Mick and Betty Noble OPEN: all year ROOMS: 2 double, both with bath/shower; 3 family, 2 with bath/shower, 1 with private bathroom; tea/coffee and TV in all bedrooms; lounge TERMS: single occupancy £30–£45, double £40–£52, family room £55–£70; half-price for children under 10; deposit: £20 CARDS: none DETAILS: children welcome; no dogs; car park; garden

Funnywayt'mekalivin NEW ENTRY

41 Bridge Street, Berwick-upon-Tweed TD15 1ES TEL/FAX: (01289) 308827

This gem of a hideaway is tucked down a cobbled side street in the centre of town, almost at the harbour's edge, and ten minutes' walk from the railway station. The two simple but elegant *en suite* guest bedrooms are decorated in soft colours and antique pine; both have

TVs. Elizabeth Middlemiss used to run a restaurant from the property which featured in *The Good Food Guide*; she now provides an outside catering service and will also cook evening meals for guests, but only if arranged with very good notice, and these may not always be available. Meals are served in the kitchen, which has its original wood floors. A free car park is close by.

OWNER: Elizabeth Middlemiss OPEN: all year ROOMS: 2 double, 1 with bath, 1 with shower; tea/coffee and TV in all bedrooms TERMS: double £45–£50; dinner £25; deposit: £10 per night CARDS: Switch, Visa DETAILS: children welcome; dogs welcome; no smoking

3 Scott's Place

3 Scott's Place, Berwick-upon-Tweed TD15 1LQ TEL: (01289) 305323

Improvements are ongoing at this quietly situated, pleasant stone townhouse just two minutes from the town centre. The twin room has a new carpet, soft furnishings and matching duvets. Bedrooms are comfortable, with spacious *en suite* facilities, and musical guests may play the piano in the lounge. Jeanette and Paul Blaaser are a retired couple who work together to provide good-value, friendly hospitality. Paul was a catering lecturer for 25 years and makes the home-baked cake served with tea on guests' arrival. There is a good choice at breakfast, including kippers and smoked haddock. Pre-arranged evening meals are available, and a speciality dessert is Jeanette's bread-and-butter pudding served with home-made ice-cream. There is no private car park, but a residents' parking permit can be provided. Tabby the ginger cat has proved popular with guests.

OWNER: Jeanette Blaaser OPEN: all year ROOMS: 2 double, 1 twin; all rooms with bath/shower, tea/coffee and TV; lounge TERMS: single occupancy £20–£35, twin/double £34–£45; dinner £10.50; deposit: £10 per room CARDS: none DETAILS: no children; no dogs in public rooms; no smoking in dining-room; garden

BETHERSDEN Kent map 3

Little Hodgeham

Smarden Road, Bethersden TN26 3HE TEL: (01233) 850323

10m W of Ashford on A28 Bethersden road turn right at Bull pub, then continue towards Smarden for 2m; house on right

The setting is idyllic: a delightful half-acre garden with roses, wild heathers, a sunken patio and a pond complete with waterfall and ducks, all surrounded by wooded farmland. Charm too extends to the 500-year-old cottage, with its old beams, inglenook fireplace and air of cosiness and comfort. The cottagey bedrooms with their pleasant views of the garden or outdoor swimming-pool are furnished to a high standard; one is a four-poster, and all are *en suite*. Besides the lounge, patio and garden, guests can relax in the library or the small conservatory. Although Erica Wallace prepares only light suppers these days by arrangement, she is happy to direct guests to places for evening meals. The outdoor (unheated) pool is open from May to August. Coarse-fishing is available for those who bring their own rods.

OWNER: Erica Wallace OPEN: mid-Mar to Aug ROOMS: 1 double, 1 twin, 1 four-poster; all rooms with bath/shower and tea/coffee; lounge with TV TERMS: single occupancy £46, twin/double £71, family room from £71; dinner £12.50; deposit: £20 per person CARDS: none DETAILS: children welcome; dogs in barn only; no smoking in dining-room; car park; garden; swimming-pool

BEVERLEY East Riding of Yorkshire map 9

Eastgate Guest House

7 Eastgate, Beverley HU17 0DR
TEL: (01482) 868464 FAX: (01482) 871899

Eastgate Guest House is located on a residential side-street very close to the town centre. Julie Anderson, whose family has been running the establishment for the past 30 years, offers comfortable accommodation in a warm and relaxed atmosphere. Many of the bedrooms have *en suite* facilities, and they all have TVs and bedside lights. The guest lounge contains an extensive assortment of interesting books, including many giving useful information on the local area. There are plenty of places for evening meals within walking distance, as well as many historical buildings; including the Picture Playhouse, one of the oldest working cinemas in the country. There is on-street parking or free parking at the nearby train station.

OWNER: Julie Anderson OPEN: all year ROOMS: 4 single, all with wash-basin; 7 double, 6 with shower, 1 with wash-basin; 1 twin, with wash-basin; 3 family, all with wash-basin; tea/coffee and TV in all bedrooms; lounge with TV TERMS: single/single occupancy £17–£23, twin/double £30–£46, family room £30–£50; reductions for children sharing with parents; deposit: £10 per room CARDS: none DETAILS: children welcome; dogs welcome; smoking in lounge only; garden

BEYTON Suffolk map 6

Manorhouse NEW ENTRY

The Green, Beyton IP30 9AF TEL: (01359) 270960
off A14, 4m E of Bury St Edmunds; in Beyton opposite green and next to village pond

This Suffolk longhouse, parts of which date from the late fifteenth century, does not have a B&B sign outside: look for 'Manorhouse entrance' across from the village green. The hospitality and warmth extended by Kay Dewsbury is exceptional, and it is not unusual for visitors to extend their stay. One reader enormously enjoyed relaxing in the hammock in the large, secluded back garden – which also has more conventional garden seating for the less laid-back. Two well-appointed *en suite* bedrooms are offered, both with seating-areas, and the twin has beams. As we went to press, plans were well under way to add another two rooms on the ground floor of a barn conversion. Excellent breakfasts, featuring free-range eggs from the Manorhouse's own hens and a large selection of teas, are served whenever guests want in the dining-room with its huge, old-fashioned fireplace flanked with stones taken from the ruins of Bury Abbey. Dinners are available by arrangement for guests staying a few days; otherwise, the Dewsburys will happily supply their own 'where to eat' list.

OWNERS: Kay and Mark Dewsbury OPEN: all year exc Christmas ROOMS: 1 double, 1 twin; both rooms with bath/shower, tea/coffee and TV; lounge TERMS: single occupancy £27–£30, twin/double £40–£45; children's reductions by arrangement; dinner £14 CARDS: none DETAILS: no children under 6; no dogs; no smoking; car park; garden

BICKINGTON Devon — map 1

Penpark

Bickington TQ12 6LH TEL: (01626) 821314 FAX: (01626) 821101
just off A38 between Ashburton and Bovey Tracey; follow signs for Widecombe in the Moor; Penpark is ½m on right at top of hill

This elegant country house on the edge of Dartmoor was designed by Sir Clough Williams-Ellis in 1928. It has five and a half acres of mature gardens and woodland, with magnificent views of hills in one direction, and as far as the sea in the other. Bedrooms are beautifully furnished and decorated in soft, restful colours, and a reporter found his room 'exceptionally large'. The twin room has a balcony, sofa and armchairs. Breakfast is served in the family dining-room, as is dinner (available by arrangement). There is a table-tennis table for guests' use in the cellar, and a full-sized hard tennis court in the grounds. It is advisable to call in advance for directions.

OWNER: Madeleine Gregson OPEN: all year exc Christmas ROOMS: 1 single, 1 double, 1 twin; all rooms with private bathroom, tea/coffee and TV; lounge with TV TERMS: single £22–£24.50, twin/double £44–£49; children under 2 free, half-price for ages 2–10; deposit required CARDS: none DETAILS: children welcome; no dogs; no smoking; car park; garden; tennis

BIDDENDEN Kent — map 3

River Hall Coach House

Biddenden TN27 8JE TEL: (01580) 291565 FAX: (01580) 292137
from Biddenden, take A262 S towards Tenterden, take first left by Dashmonden Place, continue 1m then turn left by Guy House; house is third property on right

The oldest part of this attractive part-tiled house dates back to the fifteenth century, and was moved from the centre of Biddenden to its present site about a hundred years ago. The lower part of the building originally served as a market place, and the upper part, which is now a spacious, attractive bedroom, was used as a meeting-house.

Breakfast and dinner are served either in the dining-room or the spacious conservatory, which overlooks the terrace and garden. Bill and Sara Sleigh are very welcoming hosts. There are many National Trust properties to visit in the area, including Sissinghurst Castle. Ashford and Dover are within easy driving distance.

OWNERS: Bill and Sara Sleigh OPEN: all year exc Christmas ROOMS: 2 twin; both rooms with bath/shower, tea/coffee and TV; lounge TERMS: single occupancy £33–£35, twin £52–£56; dinner £19.50 CARDS: none DETAILS: no children under 12; no dogs; no smoking; car park; garden

BIDEFORD Devon — map 1

Lower Winsford House

Abbotsham Road, Bideford EX39 3QP
TEL: (01237) 475083 FAX: (01237) 425802
just off A39 towards Bideford

This substantial, whitewashed mid-nineteenth-century residence was originally a farmhouse. It has large gardens and a pretty courtyard, and the house is comfortably and attractively decorated. Guests have use of two sitting-rooms, one with TV, and breakfast is served at one table in the dining-room. Lower Winsford House lies on the edge of the village of Abbotsham, in a rural setting, half a mile from the old port and market town of Bideford and three miles from the beach at Westward Ho!. Nearby Torrington is the home of Dartington Crystal and Rosemoor Gardens, owned by the Royal Horticultural Society.

OWNER: Margaret Ogle OPEN: Easter to Sept ROOMS: 2 double, 1 with shower, 1 with wash-basin; 1 twin, with bath/shower; tea/coffee in all bedrooms; TV in 1 bedroom and lounge TERMS: single occupancy £25, twin/double £38–£42; reductions for children 5–14 by arrangement; deposit required CARDS: none DETAILS: no children under 5; no dogs; no smoking; car park; garden

BINHAM Norfolk — map 6

Field House — NEW ENTRY

Walsingham Road, Binham NR21 0BU TEL: (01328) 830639
on B1388 midway between Binham and Great Walsingham

Set in eight acres of beautiful parklike grounds, this listed Georgian farmhouse has fine views over countryside. It offers three large, well-appointed guest bedrooms, all with period furniture, armchairs, fridges and TV. The family suite has its own bathroom and two bedrooms, a double and a twin. The enormous lounge has log fires, plus a piano which guests may play, and plenty of books and magazines. Breakfasts and dinners prepared by Fiona Thompson – who focuses on fresh, local produce – are served in the dining-room, which overlooks the garden; high tea for children is also offered.

Reporters tell us she is a most congenial host, happy to share knowledge of the area with guests, and that her cooking is 'first-class'. Binham is an excellent example of a Norfolk flint village.

OWNER: Fiona Thompson OPEN: all year exc Christmas ROOMS: 1 double, 1 twin, 1 family; all rooms with bath/shower, tea/coffee and TV; lounge TERMS: single occupancy £32–£34, twin/double £48–£52, family room from £48 plus children's charges; children's reductions according to age; dinner £15, children's teas £2.50; deposit: £10 per booking CARDS: none DETAILS: children welcome; no dogs; smoking in lounge only; car park; garden

BINTON Warwickshire map 5

Gravelside NEW ENTRY

Binton CV37 9TU TEL: (01789) 750502 and 297000 FAX: (01789) 298056
off B439 Stratford-upon-Avon to Evesham road

Gravelside is a beautifully converted barn, on a hill with views over to the Malvern Hills and the Cotswolds. All the bedrooms, plus a lounge and dining-room, are in the barn, and there are kitchen facilities for preparing light snacks. The house is impeccably maintained and luxuriously furnished with bleached-ash furniture, custom-made for the barn. Pictures on the stairs depict Binton in a bygone era. Two brown labradors form a friendly welcoming committee. All the bedrooms have TVs, fridges and *en suite* power-showers, and are tastefully decorated; one is on the ground floor. The well-tended garden and all-weather tennis court are available for residents' use. The owners live in the main house and are happy to assist guests in every way they can. Imaginative breakfasts are served in the dining-room, and a pub is nearby for evening meals.

OWNERS: Denise and Guy Belchambers OPEN: all year ROOMS: 2 double, 1 twin; all rooms with bath/shower, tea/coffee and TV TERMS: single occupancy £35–£40, twin/double £50–£60; deposit: 25% CARDS: MasterCard, Visa DETAILS: no children under 12; no dogs; no smoking; car park; garden; tennis

BISCOMBE Somerset map 2

Merlands

Biscombe TA3 7PZ TEL/FAX: 01823 601606
from Hemyock follow sign to Churchingford, turn left at sign for Biscombe, then first right

The Morleys, a welcoming, friendly couple, built their cottage-style country house themselves in 1990. It is a 'green' house, with heat provided by environmentally friendly solar panels, and is in a rural location in the beautiful Blackdown Hills. The grounds incorporate woodland, a wildflower meadow and a stream, and walks in the area might include sightings of wildlife. Breakfast only is provided, but Mrs Morley is happy to indicate good eating-places in the nearby villages, and provide other local information. The lounge has an inglenook fireplace and a door to the garden, and the bedrooms are comfortable.

OWNERS: B.L. and P.W.G. Morley OPEN: Mar to Oct ROOMS: 2 double; both rooms with bath/shower and tea/coffee; lounge with TV TERMS: single occupancy £20–£25, double £40; half-price for children sharing with parents; deposit required CARDS: none DETAILS: no children under 8; no dogs; no smoking; car park; garden

BLACKPOOL Lancashire **map 8**

Beaucliffe Hotel

NEW ENTRY

20–22 Holmfield Road, North Shore, Blackpool FY2 9TB
TEL: (01253) 351663

This large, turn-of-the-century corner house is close to Queen's Promenade and the beach. The atmosphere is informal and friendly, and there is a bar/lounge and a non-smoking TV lounge. All the good-sized bedrooms have *en suite* showers, and are well appointed and comfortable with white furniture. A varied dinner menu is offered, and vegetarians can be catered for with advance notice. The Siddalls work hard at maintaining this good-value hotel, and are happy to provide information on what to do and see in the area. Weekend bookings are for a minimum of two nights.

OWNERS: Don and Vida Siddall OPEN: all year, exc owners' holidays ROOMS: 6 double, 3 twin, 4 family; all rooms with shower, tea/coffee and TV; 2 rooms suitable for wheelchair-users; lounge with TV TERMS: twin/double/family £34–£57; children under 4 free, half-price for ages 4–12 sharing parents' room; dinner £6; deposit: £15 per person CARDS: none DETAILS: children welcome; small dogs only; no smoking in dining-area; car park; garden

Grosvenor View

7–9 King Edward Avenue, North Shore, Blackpool FY2 9TD
TEL: (01253) 352851

It is a five-minute ride by bus or tram, or a fifteen minute stroll, to the centre of Blackpool from Grosvenor View, which is near Queen's Promenade in the North Shore area. Some of the bedrooms have *en suite* showers, including one ground-floor single. There are two lounges for residents, one of which is for smokers. The bright dining-room is where breakfasts and reasonably priced evening meals – these might include main courses such as roast leg of pork, and vegetable lasagne – are served; special diets can be catered for and children's portions provided. The Jacksons extend a warm welcome to guests, and run their business with cheerful efficiency.

OWNERS: Dave and Sheila Jackson OPEN: all year ROOMS: 2 single, 1 with shower, 1 with wash-basin; 8 double, 4 with shower, 4 with wash-basin; 5 twin, 4 with shower, 1 with wash-basin; 2 family, 1 with shower, 1 with wash-basin; tea/coffee in all bedrooms; 2 lounges with TV TERMS: single £16.50–£22, single occupancy £33–£44, twin/double £33–£44, family room £49–£64; reductions for children under 16; dinner £6; deposit: £10 per person CARDS: Amex, MasterCard, Visa DETAILS: children welcome; no dogs; smoking in 1 lounge only; car park; garden

Sunray

42 Knowle Avenue, Blackpool FY2 9TQ
TEL: (01253) 351937 FAX: (01253) 593307

Located less than two miles north of the Tower and just off Queen's Promenade, this small family-run hotel offers nine well-appointed guest bedrooms. Eight have *en suite* showers and one an *en suite* bath, and all have tea/coffee-making facilities and TVs. Breakfasts and, by arrangement, evening meals are served in the dining-room at individual tables; vegetarian options are available if requested in advance. Guests can relax from a day out at Blackpool's many attractions in the light and airy guest lounge, which has a TV.

OWNERS: Jean and John Dodgson OPEN: all year exc Christmas ROOMS: 3 single, 2 double, 2 twin, 2 family; all rooms with bath/shower, tea/coffee and TV; lounge with TV TERMS: single/single occupancy £25–£28, twin/double £50–£56, family room from £50; dinner £12 CARDS: Amex, MasterCard, Visa DETAILS: children welcome; no dogs; car park; garden

BLADON Oxfordshire **map 5**

Manor Farmhouse NEW ENTRY

9 Manor Road, Bladon OX20 1RU TEL/FAX: (01993) 812168
after entering Bladon on A4095 take last left turn in village (Manor Rd); farmhouse on second bend

Quietly situated at the edge of the village – look for the handsome house behind the iron railings – this Grade II-listed farmhouse dating from the early eighteenth century offers good-value accommodation. Guests have their own entrance and can come and go as they please. The two bedrooms are reached up a spiral staircase and share a shower-room; the larger room, the double, has a cast-iron bed and wicker furniture. Breakfasts are served at a large refectory table in the attractive dining-room. Keep an eye out for the interesting display of watercolours, which were painted by Mrs Stevenson's mother. Helen Stevenson herself is always very happy to assist guests with sight-seeing itineraries. Two pubs in the village serve food.

OWNER: Helen Stevenson OPEN: all year exc Christmas ROOMS: 1 double, 1 twin; tea/coffee and TV in both bedrooms TERMS: single occupancy £25–£35, twin/double £35–£50; children's reductions by arrangement; deposit: £20 CARDS: none DETAILS: children welcome; no dogs; no smoking; car park; garden

To find an entry in the Guide, *go to the maps at the back of the book. Entries are plotted on the maps under their closest village, hamlet or city, except in London, where they are listed by name of B&B. After choosing your localities, go to the relevant section of the book (England, Scotland, Wales etc.), where localities are listed in alphabetical order (by B&B name order in London). There is also an index at the back of the book.*

BLIDWORTH Nottinghamshire map 5

Holly Lodge

Ricket Lane, Blidworth NG21 0NQ
TEL: (01623) 793853 FAX: (01623) 490977
¼m N of where B6020 crosses A60

Once upon a time this was a Victorian hunting-lodge; now it provides comfortable and well-maintained B&B accommodation. The house is set in 15 acres of woodlands and fields which guests are welcome to explore. All four bedrooms are on the ground floor in the restored stables, and overlook the courtyard; one is suitable for disabled visitors. A twin room with its own bathroom is in the main house. Breakfast is served in the pretty dining-room, which leads to the conservatory. Guests have the use of a tennis court, and a sitting-room which has been attractively refurbished.

OWNER: Ann Shipside OPEN: all year ROOMS: 2 single, 2 double, 1 twin; all rooms with bath/shower or private bathroom; 1 room suitable for wheelchair-users; tea/coffee and TV in all bedrooms; lounge with TV TERMS: single £30–£32, twin/double £43–£46; deposit: 50% or credit card details CARDS: Amex, MasterCard, Visa DETAILS: children welcome; no dogs; no smoking; car park; garden; tennis

BLUBBERHOUSES North Yorkshire map 9

Scaife Hall Farm NEW ENTRY

Blubberhouses LS21 2PL TEL: (01943) 880354
just off A59, 9½m W of Harrogate

Scaife Hall is a working farm set in attractive countryside on the edge of the Yorkshire Dales. The Ryders have lovingly restored the stone-built farmhouse, and now offer a high standard of accommodation. The three *en suite* bedrooms have been individually decorated in fresh patterns of green, blue and pink, and have pine furnishings. There is a snug television lounge with a log-fire and richly-patterned carpet; breakfasts are served in a separate dining-room. Guests are welcome to explore the surrounding farmland, which is inhabited by Swaledale sheep and Suckler cattle.

OWNER: Christine Ryder OPEN: all year exc Christmas ROOMS: 2 double, 1 twin; all rooms with bath/shower and tea/coffee; lounge with TV TERMS: single occupancy £30, twin/double £40; £12 for children under 10 CARDS: none DETAILS: children welcome; no dogs; no smoking; car park

---

We welcome your feedback about B&Bs you have stayed in. Please make use of the report forms at the end of the book – or use your own stationery if you prefer – and mail your report to: The Editors, The Good Bed and Breakfast Guide, *FREEPOST, 2 Marylebone Road, London NW1 1YN. (No stamps are needed if mailed within the UK.) Recommendations for B&Bs for our next edition are very welcome. Please let us know if you need more report forms and we will send you a fresh supply.*

BLYTHE BRIDGE Staffordshire **map 5**

The Limes **NEW ENTRY**

Cheadle Road, Blythe Bridge ST11 9PW TEL: (01782) 393278
on A521, 5m SE of Stoke-on-Trent

Set in a beautiful landscaped garden, this large Victorian house is furnished with antiques and offers elegant, comfortable accommodation. Several original features remain, such as stained-glass windows, rich ornate woodwork and fireplaces. Bedrooms are spacious, two have their own shower units, and there is an additional bathroom plus two WCs. On arrival, guests are greeted with a hot drink and biscuits, served in the drawing-room. On fine days guests can sit out on the furnished patio. The Potteries and Stoke-on-Trent are both a short drive away.

OWNER: Rosemary Williams OPEN: all year exc Christmas ROOMS: 1 single, with shower (no WC); 1 double, with shower (no WC); 1 family, with wash-basin; lounge with TV TERMS: single £21–£22, single occupancy £22–£25, twin/double £37–£38, family room £47–£57; deposit: £10–£15 CARDS: none DETAILS: no children under 5; no dogs; smoking in lounge only; car park; garden

BOMERE HEATH Shropshire **map 7**

Fitz Manor

Bomere Heath SY4 3AS TEL/FAX: (01743) 850295
take A5 to Montford Bridge, just NW of Shrewsbury; then A4380 to Forton; turn right after 1m; 1m further on to Fitz Manor

Five hundred years old and still going strong, this black and white timbered manor-house set in a pretty Tudoresque garden complete with rosebeds, herbaceous borders and long lawns gives off an air of homeliness mixed with grandeur. The house is filled with character, and the ambience is warm and unpretentious. The two sitting-rooms sport an assortment of furniture; on chilly days a fire is lit. The dining-room is enormous, and guests may share a candlelit dinner at one table with other residents, and perhaps with their hosts too. One of the three bedrooms has good views of the Severn Valley and Welsh hills. An outdoor heated swimming-pool is open from mid-May to mid-September, and for the slightly less energetic there is a pool table in the house.

OWNERS: Dawn and Neil Baly OPEN: all year ROOMS: 1 single, with wash-basin; 2 twin; tea/coffee in all bedrooms; lounge with TV TERMS: single £20–£25, single occupancy £25, twin £40–£50; dinner £12.50 CARDS: none DETAILS: children welcome; no dogs; no smoking; car park; games room; garden; swimming-pool

---

If there are any bedrooms with TV, or with tea / coffee-making facilities, we mention this in the details at the end of an entry.

BOSHAM West Sussex **map 3**

Critchfield House **NEW ENTRY**

Bosham Lane, Old Bosham PO18 8HG TEL/FAX: (01243) 572370
off A259, 4m W of Chichester

This attractive rambling house, dating from the early eighteenth century, is in a lovely, peaceful location, five minutes' walk from the harbour. It has a large garden with a putting-green in front. Mrs Field is a keen golfer and a very welcoming, helpful host. The house is furnished and decorated to a high standard, and the bedrooms are very comfortable; the two twin-bedded rooms can also be used as doubles. Freshly squeezed juices, fruit salad and home-made marmalade and jams feature at breakfast, which is served at a communal table in the antique-filled, oak-beamed dining-room. Guests have their own entrance and staircase, and a pretty paved sun terrace. Bosham is one of the oldest villages in Sussex, and the tomb of King Canute's eight-year-old daughter can be found in the church, which was built during his reign in the eleventh century.

OWNER: Janetta Field OPEN: Mar to Oct ROOMS: 1 double, with private bathroom; 2 twin, 1 with shower, 1 with private bathroom; tea/coffee and TV TERMS: single occupancy £25–£35, twin/double £45–£60; deposit: £10 per room per night CARDS: none DETAILS: no children under 8; dogs welcome in 1 room only; no smoking; car park; garden

Kenwood **NEW ENTRY**

Main Street, Bosham PO18 8PH
TEL: (01243) 572727 FAX: (01243) 572738
just N of A259, 3m W of Chichester

Although just off the main coastal road, this substantial Victorian house is a quiet place, surrounded by a large, rather wild garden. The décor and furnishings also have a Victorian flavour, and the house has a friendly, welcoming atmosphere. Breakfast is served in one of two conservatories, where there is a fridge and a microwave for guests' use if they wish to prepare other meals themselves. In the other conservatory is a pool table. Bedrooms are spacious and well equipped, and most have *en suite* facilities. The solar-heated covered swimming-pool resembles an exotic oasis, surrounded by colourful plants, and there are tables and chairs for poolside relaxing.

OWNERS: Sheena and Barry Godden OPEN: all year ROOMS: 1 single, 3 double, 2 twin, 1 four-poster, 1 family; all rooms exc 3 with bath/shower; 2 rooms suitable for wheelchair-users; tea/coffee and TV in all bedrooms; lounge with TV TERMS: single/ single occupancy £25–£30, twin/double £40–£50, four-poster £45–£50, family room £50–£60; half-price for children sharing with parents CARDS: none DETAILS: children welcome; guide dogs only; smoking in 1 room only; car park; games room; garden; swimming-pool

Any smoking restrictions that we know of are given in the details at the end of the entry.

White Barn

Crede Lane, Bosham PO18 8NX TEL/FAX: (01243) 573113
from A259 turn at sign for Bosham, then left after ¾m and left again at Crede Lane

White Barn is an architecturally interesting house built in the early 1970s on a peaceful private road in the Saxon harbour village of Bosham. The Trotmans are welcoming, hospitable hosts, and the house has a warm and relaxing atmosphere. There are two twin-bedded rooms in the main building, plus a double-bedded beamed studio in the garden. Dinners are served at a communal table in the dining-area, which overlooks the patio and landscaped garden, and the sitting-room has a log fire for winter evenings. Guests may bring their own wine to dinner, and special diets may be catered for with notice.

OWNERS: Antony and Susan Trotman OPEN: all year exc Christmas ROOMS: 1 double, 2 twin; all rooms with bath/shower, tea/coffee and TV; lounge with TV TERMS: single occupancy £40–£60, twin/double £56–£70; dinner £19.50; deposit: £20; per person CARDS: MasterCard, Visa DETAILS: no children under 10; no dogs; no smoking; car park; garden

BOSTON Lincolnshire **map 6**

Fairfield Guest House

101 London Road, Boston PE21 7EN TEL: (01205) 362869

Only a mile from town, this large Victorian house stands in its own grounds. The Blakeys took over the property in January 1997, and have plans to upgrade and improve the house and to add more bedrooms. There is a pleasant lounge decorated with floral wallpaper, and a small sitting-area in the entrance hall. The ten bedrooms are of a good size and have firm beds. Substantial breakfasts start with a help-yourself buffet, followed by traditional cooked dishes.

OWNERS: Norman and Lorraine Blakey OPEN: all year ROOMS: 4 single, all with wash-basin; 3 double, 1 with shower, 2 with wash-basin; 1 twin, with wash-basin; 2 family, 1 with shower, 1 with wash-basin; tea/coffee and TV in all bedrooms; lounge with TV TERMS: single/single occupancy £17, twin/double £32–£36; £8 for children aged 3–11; deposit: £10 CARDS: none DETAILS: children welcome; small dogs welcome; no smoking in dining-room; car park; garden

BOTALLACK Cornwall **map 1**

Manor Farm

Botallack TR19 7QG TEL: (01736) 788525
on B3306, 1m N of St Just

Joyce Cargeeg has been offering B&B at this attractive, granite-built seventeenth-century farmhouse for nearly 50 years. The farm, which featured as 'Nampara' in the TV series *Poldark* and as 'Roslyn Farm' in *Penmarric*, is on the edge of the small village of Botallack, and the lane past the farm leads straight down to the sea, cliffs and moorlands. The house has personality and atmosphere, with lots of antique furniture: the dining-room has a beamed ceiling and open fireplace, and the cosy bedrooms are named after local tin-mines. Substantial breakfasts with plenty of choice are served. John Wesley tried to preach from the garden wall, and was pelted by the villagers.

OWNER: Joyce Cargeeg OPEN: all year ROOMS: 1 double, with private bathroom; 1 twin, with bath/shower; 1 four-poster, with bath/shower; tea/coffee and TV in all bedrooms; lounge TERMS: single occupancy £35, twin/double/four-poster £46; deposit: 10% CARDS: none DETAILS: children welcome; no dogs; smoking in 1 room only; car park; garden

BOURNE Lincolnshire **map 6**

Bourne Eau House

30 South Street, Bourne PE10 9LY TEL: (01778) 423621
in Bourne town centre opposite the cenotaph

Elizabethan, Jacobean, Georgian and Victorian influences can be noted at this elegant Grade II-listed house, located next door to a twelfth-century abbey and not far from the grassy ruins of Hereward the Wake's castle. Inside, antique furniture plus old beams, stone-mullioned windows and inglenooks add to the impression of age and refinement, though the guest accommodation on offer provides full modern comforts. The three bedrooms are well appointed, with *en suite* facilities, TVs, flowers, toiletries, fruit and more. Excellent evening meals, cooked by Dawn Bishop, can be booked, and are served in the lofty Elizabethan dining-room with its high-backed chairs, antique refectory table and gargantuan fireplace. Often the Bishops join their guests at dinner. Residents also have the use of a drawing-room and music room, and may wander through the beautiful garden down to the Bourne Eau stream to watch the waterfowl.

OWNERS: Dr and Mrs G.D. Bishop OPEN: all year exc Christmas ROOMS: 1 double, 2 twin; all rooms with bath/shower, tea/coffee and TV; lounge TERMS: single occupancy £32.50–£35; twin/double £65–£70; children's reductions according to age; dinner £22.50 CARDS: none DETAILS: children welcome; no dogs; no smoking; car park; garden

Mullions

123 North Road, Bourne PE10 9BU
TEL: (01778) 393978 FAX: (01778) 393990
on A15 Sleaford to Peterborough road

Mullions is a large mid-1950s-built detached house standing in peaceful gardens on the edge of town. All the rooms have mullioned windows and some have leaded lights; the house's oak doors are reputed to have come from Buckminster Hall. The attractive bedrooms are decorated with antique pine, satinwood and oak furniture and have *en suite* showers; one room has the sole use of a

WC as there is not one in the room itself. There is a large lounge for guests' use, and breakfast and evening meals, if pre-arranged, are served in the separate dining-room. Vegetarian and special diets can be catered for, and children's portions are available. Mullions is unlicensed, but guests may bring their own wine to dinner. Rocky the terrier and Cinders the fluffy friendly cat are part of the family. The Essexes always maintain very high standards, and a reporter tell us that 'nothing is too much trouble for them'.

OWNERS: Liz and Jim Essex OPEN: all year ROOMS: 2 double, 1 twin; all rooms with shower, tea/coffee and TV; lounge with TV TERMS: single occupancy £23–£30, twin/double/family room £36–£60; deposit: for long visits only; dinner £14 CARDS: none DETAILS: no children under 6; no dogs; no smoking; car park; garden

BOURNEMOUTH Dorset map 2

Parklands Hotel

4 Rushton Crescent, Bournemouth BH3 7AF TEL/FAX: (01202) 552529

This friendly hotel just north of Bournemouth town centre has easy access by car or bus. The Clarks are a helpful couple who are assisted by their two sons and a daughter-in-law. Off the entrance way is a comfortable lounge equipped with TV and a small bar. Beyond lies the dining-room, where breakfast and dinner are served. The pleasant bedrooms are on the ground and first floors and have hair-dryers, TVs and telephones. Four rooms now have double-glazing, four have power-showers and two four-poster beds. Rushton Crescent is a quiet street just off the main road.

OWNERS: Alan and Sylvia Clark OPEN: all year ROOMS: 2 single, 3 double, 3 twin, 2 four-poster, 1 family; all rooms with bath/shower exc 3 with wash-basin; tea/coffee and TV in all bedrooms; lounge with TV TERMS: single £17–£25, single occupancy £20–£25, twin/double £34–£44, four-poster £44–£50, family room £38–£44; dinner £8; deposit: £10 per person minimum CARDS: Amex (4% surcharge), MasterCard, Visa DETAILS: no children under 6; no dogs; no smoking in dining-room; car park; garden

Sandhurst

16 Southern Road, Southbourne, Bournemouth BH6 3SR
TEL: (01202) 423748

Sandhurst is on a quiet road close to the sea. A cliff lift provides easy access to the long beach, and the centre of Southbourne is only two minutes' walk in the opposite direction; the centre of Bournemouth is only a short drive away. The cream-and-red painted detached house is decorated in summer with flowering tubs and window boxes. There is a comfortable sitting-room with TV, and a dining-room where home-cooked dinners are served. The bedrooms vary in size but all are neat and cosy, and most are *en suite*.

OWNERS: Colin and Jean du Faur OPEN: Mar to Oct ROOMS: 1 single, with wash-basin; 3 double, 2 with bath/shower, 1 with private bathroom; 1 twin, with bath/shower; 2 family, both with bath/shower; 1 room suitable for wheelchair-users; tea/coffee and TV in all bedrooms; lounge with TV TERMS: single £18–£20, single occupancy

£25–£35, twin/double £36–£40; babies free, reductions for children under 8; dinner £8; deposit: £15 per person CARDS: none DETAILS: children welcome; no dogs; smoking in lounge only; car park

BOURTON-ON-THE-WATER Gloucestershire **map 5**

Larch House

Station House, Bourton-on-the-Water GL54 2AA TEL: (01451) 821172
just off A429 Stow-on-the-Wold to Northleach road

Built from local stone, Larch House is a well-maintained house in an acre of attractive garden, just two minutes' walk from the village. The house is stylishly decorated, and the good-sized bedrooms have matching fabrics, white furniture and large *en suite* bathrooms. A bedroom over the garage is suitable for those who like their privacy. There is a comfortable lounge, and breakfast is served in the dining-room overlooking the garden. Dorothy and David Pulham are friendly hosts, happy to help with itineraries and recommend places for evening meals.

OWNERS: Dorothy and David Pulham OPEN: all year exc Christmas ROOMS: 1 double, 1 twin, 1 family; all rooms with bath/shower, tea/coffee and TV; lounge with TV TERMS: twin/double £40, family room £50–£55; reductions for children sharing with parents; deposit: £40 CARDS: none DETAILS: children welcome; no dogs; no smoking; car park

Windrush Farm

Bourton-on-the-Water GL54 3BY TEL/FAX: (01451) 820419
on A436, 1½m W of Bourton-on-the-Water

Windrush Farm is an attractive Cotswold-stone farmhouse with mullioned windows on a 150-acre working arable farm. The owners work as a team, and David enjoys talking to guests and helping to plan trips. The spacious house has recently been redecorated, and has a TV lounge containing plenty of brochures on places to visit. Both bedrooms have countryside views and *en suite* showers, and have floral chintz wallpapers, curtains and bedspreads. Excellent cooked breakfasts are served at one table in the dining-room. There are several eating-places in the village for evening meals. No one-night bookings are taken at weekends.

OWNERS: David and Jenny Burrough OPEN: Mar to Dec exc Christmas ROOMS: 1 double, 1 twin; both rooms with shower and tea/coffee; lounge with TV TERMS: single occupancy £30, twin/double £40; deposit: £20 CARDS: none DETAILS: no children; no dogs; no smoking; car park; garden

'Bath / shower' in the details under each entry means that the rooms have en suite *facilities. 'Private bathroom' signifies that a room has a bathroom for its exclusive use. The B&B may have other, shared bathroom facilities as well. We list 'wash-basins' for rooms that have them but do not have* en suite *or private facilities.*

BOVEY TRACEY Devon map 1

Front House Lodge

East Street, Bovey Tracey TQ13 9EL TEL/FAX: (01626) 832202

Front House Lodge, a listed building dating from 1540, is in the centre of the historical town of Bovey Tracey. Legend has it that Charles I was billeted here before a battle. The Campbells are friendly people and have decorated their house in idiosyncratic fashion: pink and floral chintzes set the tone, and the house is crammed with silk and dried flowers, dolls, china and much else besides. Some of the bedrooms have wonderful views, and one has a free-standing Victorian bath. There is a large sitting-room which leads into the licensed bar, and evening meals are served, by arrangement, in the dining-room. Barbecues sometimes take place in the pretty garden. Bovey Tracey is not far from the resort of Torquay.

OWNERS: Gail and Ian Campbell OPEN: all year ROOMS: 3 double, with bath/shower; 2 twin, 1 with bath/shower, 1 with private bathroom; 1 family, with bath/shower; tea/coffee and TV in all bedrooms; lounge with TV TERMS: single occupancy £25–£30, twin/double £40–£48, family room £57–£72; dinner £12.50–£15 CARDS: Amex, MasterCard, Visa DETAILS: children welcome; no dogs; no smoking; car park; garden

BOWNESS-ON-WINDERMERE Cumbria map 8

Elim House NEW ENTRY

Biskey Howe Road, Bowness-on-Windermere LA23 2JP
TEL: (01539) 442021

This 150-year-old house built from traditional Lakeland stone is situated on a quiet side street about ten minutes' walk from Lake Windermere and close to shops and restaurants. The pretty garden has been a winner in the 'Windermere in Bloom' contest. The good-sized bedrooms, most of which are *en suite*, are spotlessly clean and have a mixture of traditional and modern furnishings. The top-floor rooms, with their sloping beamed ceilings, are particularly charming. Breakfast, cooked by Jack Collins, is served in the pink-hued breakfast room. Limited private parking is available; otherwise, there is free parking on the street outside.

OWNER: J.R.B. Collins OPEN: all year exc Christmas ROOMS: 5 double, 3 with shower, 2 with wash-basin; 3 four-poster, all with shower; tea/coffee and TV in all bedrooms TERMS: twin/double £45, four-poster £60; deposit: £50 CARDS: none DETAILS: no children; no dogs; no smoking; car park

Fairfield NEW ENTRY

Brantfell Road, Bowness-on-Windermere LA23 3AE
TEL/FAX: (01539) 446565

This attractive, large house stands in a secluded half-acre garden, just a few minutes' walk from the village and the lake. It was at one time the home of Annie Garnett, watercolourist, gardener and designer. Major refurbishment of the property has been undertaken, and the house is impeccably maintained. Bedrooms are well appointed: each has *en suite* or private facilities, plus hair-dryers, radio alarms and TVs. Substantial breakfasts are served in the bright, predominately pink dining-room; vegetarian and special diets can be catered for. There is a small residents' bar and an elegant lounge where an open fire burns on chilly evenings. The patio area in the garden is a tranquil spot in which to relax. The Hoods are extremely helpful and dedicated to ensuring their guests enjoy their stay. A minimum of three nights must be booked over bank holidays. Four self-catering units are also available.

OWNERS: Ray and Barbara Hood OPEN: all year exc Christmas ROOMS: 1 single, 4 double, 1 twin, 1 four-poster, 2 family; all rooms with bath/shower exc 1 with private bathroom; tea/coffee and TV in all bedrooms; lounge with TV TERMS: single £23–£30, single occupancy £33–£40, twin/double £46–£60, four-poster/family room £50–£64; babies free, reductions for older children according to age; deposit: £30 per room CARDS: MasterCard, Visa DETAILS: children welcome; no dogs; no smoking; car park; garden

Storrs Gate House

Longtail Hill, Bowness-on-Windermere LA23 3JD TEL: (01539) 443272
at junction of A592 and B5284, opposite the marina

Storrs Gate House was built 100 years ago of local stone, and stands in two acres of secluded gardens. It is well maintained and three of the simply furnished but comfortable bedrooms have *en suite* facilities; the other two share a bathroom. Evening meals are not served, but there are several eating-establishments within walking distance. Coffee can be enjoyed in the bright lounge, which has a coal fire and TV. The Kilduffs provide good-value accommodation and are always happy to assist guests with advice on places to visit.

OWNERS: Philip and Betty Kilduff OPEN: Mar to mid-Nov ROOMS: 3 double, 2 with shower; 2 family, 1 with shower; tea/coffee and TV in all bedrooms; lounge with TV TERMS: twin/double £32–£46, family room £45–£69; half-price for children sharing with parents; deposit: £20 CARDS: none DETAILS: children welcome; no dogs; smoking in lounge only; car park; garden

BOXTED Essex **map 6**

Round Hill House NEW ENTRY

Church Road, Boxted CO4 5ST TEL/FAX: (01206) 272392
2m off A134 Sudbury to Colchester road at Great Horksley

This large bungalow was built around 1930 and stands in a well-tended garden with views over Dedham Vale. The elegant drawing-room is a wonderful place in which to relax, and for musical guests there is a piano. Pre-booked candlelit dinners are served in the dining-room, which has a large picture window. There are friendly dogs, a tennis court and stabling, and children are welcome to use the barn, where games can be played. Mrs Carter has thought of everything for her guests' comfort, and is particularly helpful with information on local walks, such as the Essex Way to Dedham.

OWNERS: Jeremy and Mary Carter OPEN: all year ROOMS: 1 double, with private bathroom; 1 twin, 1 family, both with bath/shower; tea/coffee in all bedrooms; lounge with TV TERMS: single occupancy £25, twin/double £42–£45, family room £50–£60; children's reductions from Nov to end Mar; dinner £15; deposit: £10 for Saturday-night bookings CARDS: none DETAILS: children welcome; dogs by arrangement; smoking in lounge only; car park; garden; tennis

BRADFORD-ON-AVON Wiltshire map 2

Bradford Old Windmill

4 Masons Lane, Bradford-on-Avon BA15 1QN
TEL: (01225) 866842 FAX: (01225) 866648
off A363, 3m NW of Trowbridge

The uniqueness of the building, the welcome and friendliness of the owners and the high standard of accommodation all combine to make this converted windmill an excellent base for visiting this corner of England. It stands high above Bradford-on-Avon with wonderful views over the town. The conversion work was carefully carried out to retain the original atmosphere and features of the building, with the *en suite* bathrooms and spiral staircase cleverly fitted into the shape of the house. The bedrooms have been done up with flair and imagination, one having a waterbed and another a round bed. The single bedroom has now been incorporated into the double room. The large, bright dining-room, with one big table, has french doors leading out on to a small patio and neatly kept garden with tables and chairs, and there is a spacious, comfortable sitting-room. Dinner is available three times a week.

OWNERS: Priscilla and Peter Roberts OPEN: Mar to Dec exc Christmas ROOMS: 3 double; all rooms with bath/shower, tea/coffee and TV TERMS: single occupancy £65–£79, double £75–£89; children's reductions if sharing with parents; deposit: 1 night's charge CARDS: Amex, MasterCard, Visa DETAILS: no children under 6; no dogs; no smoking; car park; garden

Priory Steps NEW ENTRY

Newtown, Bradford-on-Avon BA15 1NQ
TEL: (01225) 862230 FAX: (01225) 866248
off the A363, 3m NW of Trowbridge

Built on the side of a hill, Priory Steps is a large, three-storey Cotswold-stone house, converted from six seventeenth-century weavers' cottages. There is a delightful walled garden to the rear, and a series of terraces lead down to the valley below. Within, staircases and corridors abound, and Carey Chapman loves the excuse of continually upgrading the rooms, as it is a reason for buying more antiques. Diana is a qualified chef and offers a combination of English and continental dishes for dinner, served at one table in the elegant dining-room, which has doors out to the patio. There are views of the garden from most of the bedrooms, all of which have *en suite* facilities. No one-night bookings are possible at weekends.

OWNERS: Carey and Diana Chapman OPEN: all year ROOMS: 3 double, 2 twin; all rooms with bath/shower, tea/coffee and TV TERMS: single occupancy £50, twin/double £66 (£75 for 3 people); dinner £18 CARDS: MasterCard, Visa DETAILS: no children; no dogs; smoking in library only; car park; garden

BRADFORD PEVERELL Dorset **map 2**

Dower House

Bradford Peverell, nr Dorchester DT2 9SF TEL: (01305) 266125

take Bradford Peverell turning off A37, at T-junction after ¼m turn left; house is first on right

This fine, old listed house stands in four acres of partially walled gardens right in the centre of the attractive village of Bradford Peverell. The Eatons are a charming, welcoming couple who offer guests tea and home-made cakes on arrival. The house has a relaxed feel; the cosy, book-lined sitting-room has a log fire, and the bedrooms are very comfortable and all have their own bathrooms. Home-made bread and preserves and home-produced honey feature at breakfast time. The house is only eight miles from the sea and beautiful cliff-top walks.

OWNERS: Michael and Kips Eaton OPEN: Mar to end Nov ROOMS: 1 single, 1 double, 1 twin; all rooms with private bathroom and tea/coffee; lounge with TV TERMS: single/single occupancy £17.50–£20, twin/double £35–£40; deposit required CARDS: none DETAILS: children under 8 by arrangement only; no dogs; no smoking; car park; garden

BRADWELL Derbyshire **map 8**

Stoney Ridge

NEW ENTRY

Granby Road, Bradwell S33 9HU TEL: (01433) 620538

take A625 from Castleton; after 1½m turn right into B6049; after entering Bradwell turn right into Gore Lane, continue up hill, sharp left into Granby Rd; fourth house on right

Large, landscaped gardens with mature shrubs and ponds, plus a heated indoor swimming-pool, are special attractions at this immaculately kept large, 25-year-old B&B in the heart of the Peak District National Park. The bedrooms have fine views, are decorated in light shades of green and peach, and have firm beds and fitted wardrobes. The enormous lounge, with a rocking chair and furnished in soft grey, leads out on to a balcony adorned with hanging baskets and tubs – a fine place to enjoy breakfast or coffee on warm days. Helen Plant extends a warm welcome along with a cup of tea or coffee to guests on arrival.

OWNER: Helen Plant OPEN: all year ROOMS: 3 double, all with bath/shower; 1 twin, with private bathroom; tea/coffee and TV in all bedrooms; lounge with TV TERMS:

single occupancy £28, twin/double £46–£50; deposit required CARDS: Delta, MasterCard, Switch, Visa DETAILS: no children under 10; dogs welcome; car park; garden; swimming-pool

BRAFFERTON North Yorkshire **map 9**

Laurel Farm

Brafferton YO6 2NZ TEL/FAX: (01423) 360436
on edge of village reached by minor road off A19 at Easingwold, or A1 at Boroughbridge, 16m NW of York

This impressive listed farmhouse, built in the mid-eighteenth century and lovingly restored by Sam and Annie Key, is just outside the village. It stands on a courtyard with stables, and has an attractive garden, with a tennis court and croquet lawn. Beyond the garden is 25 acres of pasture, bounded by the River Swale, where guests can enjoy a quarter of a mile of private fishing. Guest accommodation includes a double room, a twin room, and a suite comprising a double room, single room and bathroom. The Keys enjoy entertaining and are both accomplished cooks; guests can join them for candlelit dinners by arrangement. The house is licensed, and evening drinks may be taken on the south-facing terrace with its views of the Vale of York.

OWNERS: Sam and Annie Key OPEN: Mar to Nov ROOMS: 1 double, 1 twin, 1 four-poster, 1 family; all rooms with bath/shower, tea/coffee and TV; lounge TERMS: single occupancy £25, twin/double/four-poster £50, family room from £50; dinner £19.50 CARDS: none DETAILS: children welcome; smoking in bedrooms only; car park; games room; garden; tennis

BRAMFIELD Suffolk **map 6**

Broad Oak Farm

Bramfield IP19 9AB TEL: (01986) 784232
3m S of Halesworth, take A144 to Bramfield then turn off at Queen's Head pub, and continue for ¾m

The listed sixteenth-century farmhouse is at the end of a half-mile private road, surrounded by meadows and a well-tended garden with a tennis court. Many original features remain, such as oak beams and a Tudor fireplace. There is a good collection of books to browse through in the comfortable residents' lounge, and evening meals are served by arrangement. Guests also have the use of a games room with a small snooker table, a table-tennis table and a dartboard. Broad Oak Farm makes a good base for exploring this interesting area, and the attractive coastal town of Southwold is within striking distance.

OWNERS: Peter and Pat Kemsley OPEN: all year ROOMS: 1 double, with bath/shower; 2 twin, 1 with bath/shower, 1 with wash-basin; tea/coffee in all bedrooms; lounge with TV TERMS: single occupancy £20, twin/double £30–£36; children's reductions according to age; dinner £9; deposit required CARDS: none DETAILS: children welcome; dogs welcome; no smoking in bedrooms; car park; games room; garden; tennis

BRAMHOPE West Yorkshire map 8

The Cottages

Moor Road, Bramhope, nr Leeds LS16 9HH TEL: (0113) 284 2754
leaving Leeds on A660, turn left at St Giles' church in Bramhope and go up hill to Moor Rd

Although located in a rural area, this B&B is convenient for those wishing to visit Leeds, Harrogate and Bradford, or to use Leeds/ Bradford Airport. Originally a terrace of eighteenth-century farm cottages, it has been fully renovated and offers five well-appointed guest bedrooms, all of which are *en suite* and have TVs, quality duvets and pine and oak furniture. Residents have the use of a cosy beamed lounge with a stone fire place. Generous breakfasts are served in the attractive dining-room. Guests are extended a friendly welcome and are invited to make use of the large, landscaped garden and have a look at the orchard.

OWNERS: Sue and David Adams OPEN: all year exc Christmas ROOMS: 4 double, 1 twin; all rooms with bath/shower, tea/coffee and TV; lounge with TV TERMS: single occupancy £30, twin/double £44 CARDS: none DETAILS: no children under 10; no dogs; no smoking; car park; garden

BRAN END Essex map 3

Elmcroft Guest House

Bran End, Stebbing CM6 3RJ TEL/FAX: (01371) 856450
from A120 between Great Dunmow and Braintree follow signs to Stebbing; continue through village; B&B 1m from church

'After an excellent breakfast, we walked around the grounds, fed the fish and the ducks and decided to stay another night,' was how one couple summed up their experience at this welcoming B&B. Situated in the small hamlet of Bran End just outside the historic village of Stebbing, Elmcroft sits on a hill in five acres of land that boasts a large, natural fish-filled pond, a stream and loads of wildlife. It offers three spacious and immaculate guest bedrooms, all on the ground floor and sharing a bathroom. Excellent breakfasts prepared by Elaine Preou are served in the lounge/dining-room. The guest accommodation has a separate entrance, and there is plenty of information on hand in the entrance hall about local places to eat and visit. Stebbing, a ten-minute walk away, has a number of buildings dating from Elizabethan times, and its even-earlier (fourteenth-century) church is well worth a visit.

OWNER: Elaine Preou OPEN: all year ROOMS: 1 single, with wash-basin; 2 twin; tea/ coffee and TV in all bedrooms; lounge with TV TERMS: single £16–£17, single occupancy £18–£19, twin £32–£34; children's reductions; deposit: £10 CARDS: none DETAILS: children welcome; no dogs; no smoking in 1 bedroom and in dining-room; car park; garden

BRANSCOMBE Devon **map 2**

Hole Mill

Branscombe EX12 3BX TEL: (01297) 680314
in village take lane by post office for ¾m over 2 cattle grids and past Hole House

This large, whitewashed seventeenth-century house set in beautiful hilly countryside incorporates a converted watermill and miller's cottage. It is accessed via a narrow and sometimes steep lane. Within, it is charmingly furnished (look out for the 'mice models'); there are beams everywhere, and the bedrooms overlook the garden and stream. The Harts make every effort to make guests feel at home. Breakfast – which, besides traditional items, may feature vegetarian sausages, black pudding, duck or goose eggs and field mushrooms – is at a time to suit: the record so far, we are told, is 2.20pm. Refreshments during the day are available in the sitting-room, the garden or the rebuilt terrace. The sitting-room has a TV and an inglenook fireplace, and two of the bedrooms have high brass and iron beds. The Harts are keen wildlife observers and know all about the animals, birds and hedgerow plants seen in the immediate area. On warm evenings visitors are invited to sit out in the garden, have a glass of wine (bring your own) and count the bats.

OWNERS: Rod and Amanda Hart OPEN: all year ROOMS: 2 double, 1 with wash-basin; 1 twin, with wash-basin; lounge with TV TERMS: single occupancy £22–£33, twin/double £32–£38; children's reductions by arrangement; deposit: £15 for first night, £10 per subsequent night CARDS: none DETAILS: no children under 6; dogs by arrangement; no smoking; car park; garden

BREDWARDINE Hereford & Worcester **map 5**

Bredwardine Hall

Bredwardine HR3 6DB TEL/FAX: (01981) 500596
on A438 take turning signposted Hay-on-Wye and Bredwardine; continue over river bridge to centre of village

The Batsons took over this impressive mid-nineteenth-century manor-house in mid-1996, and have dedicated themselves to building on the high standards set by the previous owners. Guests receive a warm welcome and are looked after well. The house is set in its own ample wooded grounds near the River Wye and the Golden Valley. Entrance is to a rather grand hall and imposing staircase, and the drawing-room with its floor-to-ceiling windows offers good views of the garden and countryside. The five well-appointed, good-sized bedrooms are all either *en suite* or with private bathroom. A courtesy cocktail bar can be found in the dining-room, where breakfasts and (by arrangement) home-cooked evening meals are served.

OWNERS: A.J. and L.Y. Batson OPEN: all year exc Christmas ROOMS: 2 double, 1 with bath/shower, 1 with private bathroom; 1 twin, 2 family, both with bath/shower; tea/coffee and TV in all bedrooms; lounge TERMS: single occupancy £29–£31, twin/double £46–£52, family room £46–£52 plus children's charge; half-price for children sharing with parents; dinner £14; deposit required CARDS: none DETAILS: no children under 6; dogs welcome; smoking in lounge only; car park; garden

BRIDGWATER Somerset **map 2**

Cokerhurst Farm

87 Wembdon Hill, Bridgwater TA6 7QA TEL/FAX: (01278) 422330
just off A39 in Wembdon, 1½m W of Bridgwater

Although just outside the town of Bridgwater, this sixteenth-century longhouse has a peaceful location on a 100-acre farm, run by Diana and Derrick Chappell with the assistance of their three daughters. A large walled garden provides a sheltered spot to sit and take in the views of the rolling Quantock Hills. The three comfortable bedrooms are reached by a spiral staircase, and the beamed breakfast room has a sitting-area with TV. There is a small lake in the grounds. The Chappells operate a 'pick your own' business, and guests can indulge themselves with strawberries and raspberries.

OWNERS: Diana and Derrick Chappell OPEN: all year exc Christmas ROOMS: 1 double, 1 twin, 1 family; all rooms with bath/shower, tea/coffee and TV; lounge with TV TERMS: single occupancy £20–£22.50, twin/double £40–£45, family room £45–£75; £5 for children under 5, £10 for ages 5–10; deposit: £10 CARDS: none DETAILS: children welcome; no dogs; no smoking; car park; garden

BRIDLINGTON East Riding of Yorkshire **map 9**

Etherleigh

13 Wellington Road, Bridlington YO15 2BA TEL: (01262) 673583

A warm welcome is extended to visitors at this tall Victorian house in the heart of this old port and fishing town. The Tates offer modestly priced, comfortable guest accommodation in the form of eight bedrooms, some with *en suite* facilities and all with TVs. For relaxing after a day out in town, there is a pleasant lounge, which also has a TV and a fireplace made by George Tate. Exceptionally good-value dinners (as well as breakfasts) are served in the licensed dining-room, and there is a small residents' bar. Limited off-street parking is available on a first-come, first-serve basis.

OWNERS: Mr and Mrs G.W. Tate OPEN: all year ROOMS: 1 single, with wash-basin; 2 double, both with wash-basin; 2 twin, 1 with shower, 1 with wash-basin; 3 family, all with shower; tea/coffee and TV in all bedrooms; lounge with TV TERMS: single/single occupancy £13.50, twin/double £27–£35, family room £35 plus children's charge;

reductions for children sharing with parents; dinner £4.50; deposit: £10 per person CARDS: none DETAILS: children welcome; dogs welcome; smoking in lounge only; car park

Glen Alan Hotel

21 Flamborough Road, Bridlington YO15 2HU TEL: (01262) 674650

This child-friendly small hotel offers reasonably priced accommodation and food, and is close to both the town centre and beach. The licensed dining-room is open from 5.30 to 7pm, and guests may wish to enjoy a preprandial drink at the cosy Tudor Bar. A baby-listening service is available, and the tastefully decorated lounge has a TV. The comfortable bedrooms are now all either *en suite* or with private bathroom, and have hair-dryers, TVs and tea/coffee-making facilities. There is no private parking, though on-street parking is unrestricted.

OWNERS: Roy and Judy Jones OPEN: all year ROOMS: 4 double, 1 twin, 4 family; all rooms with bath/shower exc 1 double with private bathroom; tea/coffee and TV in all bedrooms; lounge with TV TERMS: single/single occupancy £21, twin/double £42, family room from £42; reductions for children sharing with parents; dinner £6 (less for children); deposit: £20 per person CARDS: Amex, Delta, Diners, MasterCard, Visa DETAILS: children welcome; no dogs; no smoking in dining-room

The Ryburn

31 Flamborough Road, Bridlington YO15 2JH TEL: (01262) 674098

This large Victorian residence is close to the sea and within easy walking distance of the town centre. Janet and Bernard Fozzard are a very hospitable couple who have created a welcoming ambience in this well-maintained hotel. Some of the large, well-appointed bedrooms have Sanderson wallpapers, and the Fozzards plan to add further *en suite* facilities; two rooms have private entrances and balconies, and one of the bedrooms is on the ground floor. The comfortable lounge has a TV and a small licensed bar. Breakfasts and good-value home-cooked dinners are served in the dining-room.

OWNERS: Janet and Bernard Fozzard OPEN: all year ROOMS: 2 single, both with wash-basin; 3 double, 2 with shower, 1 with wash-basin; 1 twin, with shower; 4 family, 2 with shower, 2 with wash-basin; tea/coffee and TV in all bedrooms; lounge with TV TERMS: single £17–£21, twin/double £34–£42, family room from £34; children's reductions according to age; dinner £7 CARDS: none DETAILS: children welcome; no dogs; smoking in lounge only; car park; garden

BRIGHTON East Sussex map 3

Franklins

41 Regency Square, Brighton BN1 2FJ TEL: (01273) 327016

The owners are friendly and welcoming, and the house, in a terrace just off Regency Square, has a relaxed atmosphere. Bedrooms vary in size and are comfortably furnished and well appointed, all having small *en suite* bathrooms and direct-dial telephones. The pleasant sitting-room has comfortable sofas and is adjoined to the small breakfast room; both have their original fireplaces. Breakfasts are 'lovely and big', evening meals are available by arrangement, and room service is offered between 11am and 11pm. Franklins is convenient for the town centre and the seafront.

OWNERS: Sandra Williams and Katrina Cole OPEN: all year exc Christmas ROOMS: 1 single, 4 double, 1 family; all rooms with bath/shower and tea/coffee; lounge with TV TERMS: single/single occupancy £32–£45, double £38–£60, family room £60–£70; reductions for children sharing with parents; dinner £10–£25; deposit: 1 night's charge minimum CARDS: none DETAILS: children welcome; no dogs

BRISTOL Bristol **map 2**

Lawns Guest House

91 Hampton Road, Redland, Bristol BS6 6JG TEL: (0117) 973 8459

This spacious and comfortable Georgian residence with Victorian additions has interesting original features, such as plaster ceilings with decorative cornices. It stands in a large secluded garden, but is only a mile from the city centre. Mrs Moran extends a warm welcome to her guests, and 'cooks the most wonderful breakfasts'. There is a TV room with a wide selection of reading material. The large bedrooms are airy and spotlessly clean. Mrs Moran is president of the local flower club, and looks after her garden, which guests are welcome to use. It is advisable to use the frequent local bus service for visiting the city, rather than going by car.

OWNERS: John and Nell Moran OPEN: all year exc Christmas ROOMS: 1 single, with wash-basin; 1 double, with wash-basin; 3 twin, 1 with shower, 2 with wash-basins; tea/coffee and TV in all bedrooms; lounge with TV TERMS: single £24, single occupancy £24–£32, twin/double £39–£43, family room £45 CARDS: none DETAILS: children welcome; guide dogs only; car park; garden

BROADWAY Hereford & Worcester **map 5**

Barn House

NEW ENTRY

152 High Street, Broadway WR12 7AJ TEL/FAX: (01386) 858633

This beautiful country house stands in sixteen acres of gardens and paddocks, in the heart of the town of Broadway. It was renovated in the seventeenth century, and parts of the house date back to medieval times. Its historical features include oak beams, casement shutters and a huge Tudor fireplace. The spacious bedrooms are well appointed, with king-sized beds, pine furniture and built-in wardrobes. A large, heated indoor pool is available for guests to use between March and October, and there is also a croquet lawn. Afternoon teas are served in the attractive garden, which is open to the public as part of the National Garden Scheme; and there are plenty of establishments which serve evening meals within walking distance.

OWNERS: Mark and Jane Ricketts OPEN: all year ROOMS: 3 double, 2 with bath/ shower, 1 with private bathroom; 1 twin, with bath/shower; tea/coffee and TV in all bedrooms; lounge with TV TERMS: single occupancy £35–£65, twin/double £55–£75 CARDS: none DETAILS: children welcome; dogs welcome in some bedrooms; smoking in 1 lounge only; car park; garden; swimming-pool

---

Leasow House

Laverton Meadow, Broadway WR12 7NA
TEL: (01386) 584526 FAX: (01386) 584596
take B4632 from Broadway towards Cheltenham, then take road signposted Wormington and Dumbleton; house is first on right

This beautiful Cotswold-stone farmhouse dates back to the early 1600s, but has been renovated to provide modern facilities. It is a relaxing, informal place, set in the heart of the countryside, on the county border with Gloucestershire. The luxurious bedrooms all have king-sized beds; some are in the beautifully restored farm outbuildings, which have their original oak beams and bare stone walls. One bedroom, the Bull Pen, has been equipped for wheelchair-users. The drawing-room/library has a well-stocked bookcase, leather sofas and chairs, and is provided with complimentary sherry. Good breakfasts are served in the dining-room, overlooking the garden and towards open countryside. The Meekings are a friendly couple, happy to assist with itineraries and recommend places for evening meals.

OWNERS: Barbara and Gordon Meekings OPEN: all year ROOMS: 3 double, 2 twin, 2 family; all rooms with bath/shower; 1 room suitable for wheelchair-users; lounge TERMS: single occupancy £35–£45, twin/double £53–£62, family room £60–£73; children's reductions according to age; deposit: £30 per room CARDS: Amex, MasterCard, Visa DETAILS: children welcome; dogs by arrangement; no smoking; car park; garden

---

Whiteacres

Station Road, Broadway WR12 7DE TEL: (01386) 852320
on A44 Evesham road, on edge of village

This spacious turn-of-the-century house is set back off the main road, just outside Broadway. The house is well maintained, and the bedrooms have soft pastel furnishings. Three of the bedrooms have four-posters, two overlook the garden and one very spacious room is on the ground floor. Breakfast is served in the dining-room, which has a collection of interesting plates and french doors leading out to the patio and garden. There is a comfortable guest lounge with a gas fire. Plenty of places for evening meals can be found nearby, and it is an ideal base for exploring the Cotswolds.

OWNER: Helen Richardson OPEN: Mar to Oct ROOMS: 2 double, 1 twin, 3 four-poster; 1 room with bath/shower, 5 with shower; all rooms with tea/coffee and TV; lounge with TV TERMS: single occupancy £25–£30, twin/double £38–£40, four-poster £40–£42 CARDS: none DETAILS: no children; no dogs; smoking in lounge only; car park; garden

BROBURY Hereford & Worcester map 5

Brobury House

Brobury HR3 6BS TEL: (01981) 500595 FAX: (01981) 500229
from A438, 8m W of Hereford turn at sign for Bredwardine; house is by Bredwardine Bridge

This beautiful Victorian country house, bought by an American family in the early 1970s, stands in ten acres of formal gardens with spectacular views over the River Wye. The business is now managed by Leonora Weaver, the owner's daughter, and she is happy to prepare a traditional American pancake breakfast. Bedrooms are spacious and furnished to a high standard, and named after the Okarmas' children. Located in the coach-house is an art gallery with a sizeable collection of antique prints and watercolours dating back to 1820. Guests have use of the gardens, and fishing can be arranged on the River Wye.

OWNER: Mrs M. Okarma OPEN: all year ROOMS: 2 single, both with shower; 2 double, both with bath/shower; 2 twin, both with wash-basin; tea/coffee in all bedrooms; TV in 1 double bedroom; lounge TERMS: single £25, twin/double £60–£90 CARDS: MasterCard, Visa DETAILS: no children; no dogs; no smoking; car park; garden

BROCKENHURST Hampshire map 2

Caters Cottage

Latchmoor, Brockenhurst SO42 7UP TEL: (01590) 623225
from Brockenhurst take B3055 towards Bournemouth, go under railway bridge then turn right after 75yds on to a gravel track

Caters Cottage, hidden away in the peaceful heart of the New Forest, is approached down a rough gravel track several hundred yards long. The pleasant whitewashed building has lawns to the side and views of undulating moorland and forest. The bedrooms are simply furnished. Breakfast is served at a long refectory table in a panelled rectangular room which serves as both dining- and sitting-room. The Onslows are happy to collect guests from Brockenhurst station. Beaulieu motor museum is a short drive away, and the car ferry to the Isle of Wight can be taken from nearby Lymington.

OWNERS: Mr and Mrs Onslow OPEN: all year exc Christmas ROOMS: 1 single, 1 double, 1 twin; all rooms with wash-basin, tea/coffee and TV; lounge with TV TERMS: single £20–£21, single occupancy £29, twin/double £38–£40; babies free; deposit CARDS: none DETAILS: children welcome; dogs welcome; no smoking in bedrooms; car park; garden

---

Breakfast at B&Bs tends to mean a cooked breakfast of bacon, eggs, toast and so on, although many establishments also offer a good choice of cereals, yoghurts, fruit and other options. If you have special dietary requirements, it is best to discuss these when you make a booking.

BROSELEY Shropshire **map 5**

Broseley Guest House

The Square, Broseley TF12 5EW TEL: (01952) 882043
after entering town on B4373 turn right at crossroads by church and continue to town square

This big brick house stands in the centre of Broseley, a characterful early-industrial town with a charming mish-mash of architectural styles and a wooded, hilly setting. The guesthouse offers seven well-appointed bedrooms: all are *en suite* and have TVs, mini-bars and direct-dial telephones. The double bedrooms and one twin can also be used as family rooms. Evening meals are available with prior notice, and vegetarians can be catered for. There is a TV-free guest lounge to relax in. Ironbridge is just a short drive away.

OWNERS: Geoff and Laurie Nixey OPEN: all year exc Christmas ROOMS: 2 single, 3 double, 2 twin; all rooms with bath/shower, tea/coffee and TV; lounge TERMS: single £26–£29, single occupancy £32–£35, twin/double £44–£48; reductions for children according to age if sharing with parents; dinner £12.50; deposit: £20 or credit card details CARDS: MasterCard, Visa DETAILS: children welcome; £1 fee for dogs; no smoking in some bedrooms and public areas; garden

BROUGHTON IN FURNESS Cumbria **map 8**

Garner House

Church Street, Broughton in Furness LA20 6HJ TEL: (01229) 716462
on A595, just W of village

Garner House is a Victorian property standing in secluded walled gardens on the outskirts of the village. Both bedrooms are decorated with William Morris wallpaper, and have *en suite* facilities. In the lounge are a marble fireplace and a grandfather clock, while another grandfather clock can be found halfway up the stairs, and the dining-room boasts an elegant crystal chandelier from Sweden, where Maud Barrett was born. Alan Barrett was formerly leader of the local rescue team and ensures that guests wishing to undertake fell walks are well prepared. There is a furnished terrace in the garden for sitting outside on fine days.

OWNERS: Maud and Alan Barrett OPEN: all year exc Christmas ROOMS: 1 double, with bath; 1 twin, with shower; tea/coffee and TV in both bedrooms; lounge with TV TERMS: single occupancy £24, twin/double £40; deposit: £10 per person CARDS: none DETAILS: no children under 7; dogs welcome; garden

---

B&B rates specified in the details at the end of each entry are given (as applicable) for a single room, for single occupancy of a double room, and then per room in the case of two people sharing a double or twin-bedded room, or for a family room. Because double rooms with four-poster beds often cost more, those are listed separately.

BRYHER Isles of Scilly **map 1**

Bank Cottage

Bryher TR23 0PR TEL/FAX: (01720) 422612

This 400-year-old traditionally built cottage is close to the seashore and has impressive views of the western rocks and the Atlantic. The simple bedrooms are light and airy, and prettily decorated. Most of them have *en suite* showers, and sea views. The dining-room has a low, beamed ceiling, and the lounge is a bright, comfortable room leading out on to the terrace and the garden, which is filled with colourful flowers. Mr Mace is a diver and collects sea urchins to sell all over the world. Bryher is the smallest of the five inhabited Isles of Scilly, under a mile across and less than two from north to south. The minimum stay at Bank Cottage is three nights, or one week during the summer months.

OWNERS: Mr and Mrs M.G. Mace OPEN: Easter to Nov ROOMS: 1 single, with wash-basin; 1 double, with shower; 3 twin, 2 with shower, 1 with wash-basin; tea/coffee and TV in all bedrooms; lounge with TV TERMS: single £35–£36, twin/double £37–£42; deposit: 25% CARDS: none DETAILS: no children under 8; no dogs; smoking in bedrooms only; garden

---

Soleil D'or

Bryher TR23 0PR TEL: (01720) 422003

Soleil D'or is a short distance from the beach on the eastern shore of Bryher. It is a small, modern bungalow offering comfortable accommodation in a relaxed and informal atmosphere. All the bedrooms have wonderful sea views, and the lounge has a TV. Meals include local produce whenever possible. Bryher has a contrasting landscape and is a friendly island with a small working community; visitors are welcome to join in island activities. There are boat trips to the Bishop Rock lighthouse and to follow the weekly gig races, and wildlife-watchers can enjoy seeing seals as well as puffins and other sea-birds.

OWNER: Angela Street OPEN: Easter to late Oct ROOMS: 2 double, 1 twin; all rooms with bath/shower, tea/coffee and TV; lounge with TV TERMS: single occupancy £22–£26, twin/double £44–£48; reductions for children in early and late season; dinner £8; deposit required CARDS: none DETAILS: children welcome; no dogs; no smoking in dining-room; garden

---

If you intend to spend several days at a B&B, it is worth asking whether there are reduced rates, particularly if the period is midweek or off-season. It is always best to check prices, especially for single occupancy, when booking. If we know of any particular payment stipulations, we mention them in the details at the end of the entry. We asked the proprietors to estimate their 1998 prices in the autumn of 1997, so the rates may have changed since publication. If a deposit is required for an advance booking, this is stated in the details.

BUCKFASTLEIGH Devon map 1

Kilbury Manor Farm NEW ENTRY

Colston Road, Buckfastleigh TQ11 0LN
TEL: (01364) 644079 FAX: (01364) 644059
from town centre follow Old Totnes Rd S for 1m, continue into Colston Rd; Kilbury Manor Farm is just on left

This seventeenth-century Devon longhouse, surrounded by meadows and a stream, is situated at the beginning of a narrow, four-mile lane. The bedrooms are attractively furnished, and the one bedroom which allows smoking and dogs is in a converted barn which adjoins the house. Suzanne Lewis is an excellent cook and makes good use of home-grown vegetables and herbs in imaginative evening meals. Breakfast is also a treat and features organic sausages, plus an excellent choice for vegetarians. Suzanne also runs cookery courses from September to June. A £2 supplement is charged for one-night or same-day bookings between April and October.

OWNERS: Graham Rice and Suzanne Lewis OPEN: all year exc Jan ROOMS: 2 double, both with bath/shower; 1 family, with private bathroom; tea/coffee and TV in all bedrooms; lounge TERMS: single occupancy £22.50–£25, twin/double £38–£42, family room £50–£64; dinner £15.50; deposit: £21 per person CARDS: none DETAILS: children welcome; dogs by arrangement in 1 bedroom only; smoking in 1 bedroom only; car park; games room; garden

BUCKLAND MONACHORUM Devon map 1

Store Cottage

The Village, Buckland Monachorum PL20 7NA TEL/FAX: (01822) 853117
village signposted off A386 between Yelverton and Horrabridge

This attractive stone cottage, part of a small terrace said to be over 300 years old, is almost next to the church in the centre of the attractive, unspoilt village of Buckland Monachorum. The front door leads straight into the cosy sitting-room, with its log fire and low, beamed ceiling; breakfast is served here at a table by the window. The two bright bedrooms have *en suite* facilities and are surprisingly spacious, very well equipped and comfortably furnished. Annabel and John Foulston are friendly, hospitable people. They are knowledgeable about the area and only too pleased to help guests plan a day out, and also have on hand a wealth of tourist information and maps for guests to browse through. Buckland Monachorum is not far from Plymouth and is in an ideal location for exploring Dartmoor.

OWNERS: Annabel and John Foulston OPEN: all year exc Christmas ROOMS: 1 double, 1 twin; both rooms with bath/shower, tea/coffee and TV; lounge TERMS: single occupancy £25–£30, twin/double £40 CARDS: none DETAILS: no children under 12; dogs by arrangement; no smoking; car park; garden

---

The end details for each entry state whether or not dogs are allowed, but it is always best to check when booking.

BUCKLAND NEWTON Dorset — map 2

Holyleas House — NEW ENTRY

Buckland Newton, Dorchester DT2 7DP TEL: (01300) 345214
on B3143, opposite village cricket pitch

Holyleas is an old stone-built former farmhouse standing in half an acre of lovely walled gardens. The peaceful village of Buckland Newton is surrounded by rolling hills and is close to the long-distance Wessex Ridgeway footpath. Both sitting- and dining-rooms are comfortably furnished and elegant, with a blazing log fire in the sitting-room in the winter. Mrs Bunkall runs the house in a quiet and efficient manner. The spacious bedrooms are well equipped and have the use of two bathrooms. Dinner can be served by arrangement. Sherborne and Dorchester are both about ten miles away, and the coast can be reached in half an hour.

OWNER: Tia Bunkall OPEN: all year exc Christmas ROOMS: 1 single; 1 double; 1 twin, with washbasin; tea/coffee in all bedrooms; lounge with TV TERMS: single £20, single occupancy £25–£30, twin/double £40–£44; children's reductions according to age; dinner £10; deposit: £10 CARDS: none DETAILS: children welcome; dogs by arrangement; no smoking; car park; games room; garden

BUILDWAS Shropshire — map 5

Bridge House

Buildwas TF8 7BN TEL: (01952) 432105
on B4360 in Buildwas near junction with A4169 Telford to Shrewsbury bypass

Full of character, comfort and charm, this seventeenth-century Grade II-listed, half-timbered, creeper-clad house with views over the River Severn offers four well-appointed and spacious *en suite* bedrooms. Individually decorated, all have sitting-areas and TVs; one has a display of antique swords, bayonets and knives hung beside its Victorian bath. For relaxation, the very pleasant lounge with its pretty brick fireplace, original oak panelling, pot-plants and comfortable chairs is just the thing. A pub serving evening meals is a couple minutes away by car.

OWNER: Janet Hedges OPEN: all year exc Christmas and New Year ROOMS: 2 double, 1 twin, 1 family; 2 rooms with bath and 2 with shower; tea/coffee and TV in all bedrooms; lounge with TV TERMS: single occupancy £30–£35, twin/double £48–£55, family room £78–£85; children's reductions according to age; deposit required CARDS: none DETAILS: children welcome; no dogs; no smoking in dining-room; car park; garden

---

We state at the end of an entry whether children are welcome, and explain any age restrictions. If there are reduced rates for children, this is mentioned; if no reductions are specified, assume you will have to pay full rates for children.

Hill View Farm

Buildwas TF8 7BP TEL: (01952) 432228
on A4169 between Buildwas and Much Wenlock

Part of a working farm, this attractive red-brick house with its creepers and climbing roses offers comfortable, no-frills accommodation. The three bedrooms share two bathrooms, although, if guests wish one room can be let with a private bathroom. New carpets and some new furniture have been installed since the last edition of the *Guide*. Breakfasts are substantial, and are served in the dining-room-cum-lounge. The Priory at Much Wenlock and the town of Ironbridge are close by.

OWNERS: John and Rosemarie Hawkins OPEN: all year exc Christmas ROOMS: 2 double, 1 twin; all rooms with wash-basin and tea/coffee; lounge with TV TERMS: single occupancy £16–£20, twin/double £32–£35; reductions for children under 13; deposit: £10 CARDS: none DETAILS: children welcome; no dogs; no smoking; car park; garden

BULMER North Yorkshire **map 9**

Grange Farm

Bulmer YO6 7BN TEL/FAX: (01653) 618376
on A64 turn at sign to Castle Howard, then left to Bulmer and first left

This red-brick farmhouse, part of a working dairy farm on the Castle Howard Estate, offers three pleasant, simple guest bedrooms, a comfortable TV lounge to relax in and a warm welcome, especially to families with children. The double room can also be used as a family room. For the energetic, there is a games room with table tennis, a pool table and weights. Breakfasts are served in the dining-room with its antique sideboard. Children are welcome to visit the farm animals.

OWNER: Janet M. Foster OPEN: all year exc Christmas ROOMS: 1 single, 1 double, 1 twin; all rooms with wash-basin, tea/coffee and TV; lounge with TV TERMS: single/ single occupancy £16, twin/double £32; family room from £32; free for children under 3, reductions for older children CARDS: none DETAILS: children welcome; well-behaved dogs welcome; smoking in lounge only; car park; games room; garden

Lower Barn

Wandales Lane, Bulmer YO6 7ES TEL: (01653) 618575
leave A64 4m SW of Malton at sign for Bulmer, turn left after village church

This 200-year-old stone-built barn has been thoughtfully converted and now offers excellent B&B accommodation for up to six people. The roomy bedrooms are tastefully furnished and have *en suite* showers, though not their own WCs. There is a guest lounge complete with a TV and a wood-burning stove, and a pretty walled garden where guests may sit and enjoy the view over the Rydale countryside. Isabel Hall provides good-value, home-cooked evening meals at a time to suit residents.

OWNER: Isabel Hall OPEN: all year exc Christmas ROOMS: 2 double, 1 twin; 2 rooms with shower (not WC), 1 with wash-basin; tea/coffee in all bedrooms; TV in 2 bedrooms and lounge TERMS: single occupancy £16–£22, twin/double £30–£32; £8 for children; dinner £6 CARDS: none DETAILS: no children under 5; no dogs; no smoking; car park; garden

BURCOMBE Wiltshire map 2

Manor Farm

Burcombe SP2 0EJ TEL: (01722) 742177 FAX: (01722) 744600
just off A30, 6m W of Salisbury

Manor Farm stands in a walled garden on the edge of the village, in a quiet spot with views of fields and farms. It is built of grey stone and has been extended since its days as an early-Edwardian cottage, and is now a very comfortable house, with a friendly and welcoming atmosphere. The two bedrooms are now *en suite*, and there is an attractive sitting-room with lots of plants and access to the pretty garden. Manor Farm is an ideal spot for walking and for those searching for some peace and quiet, yet there are plenty of places of interest nearby, such as Wilton House, Stonehenge and the New Forest.

OWNER: Sue Combes OPEN: Mar to end Nov ROOMS: 1 double, 1 twin; both rooms with shower, tea/coffee and TV; lounge with TV TERMS: single occupancy £25–£30, twin/double £40–£44; children's reductions according to age; deposit: £5 per person CARDS: none DETAILS: children welcome; no dogs; no smoking; car park; garden

BURFORD Oxfordshire map 2

Chevrons

Swan Lane, Burford OX18 4SH TEL: (01993) 823416

Chevrons (the name comes from the medieval paintings in the guests' lounge) is tucked away on a side street just off the High Street of this beautiful, busy, historic town. The building dates back to the early sixteenth century, and still has some of the original doors. The two bedrooms are well maintained and share a bathroom. There is also a walled rose garden for guests' use. Sheila and John Roberts offer a warm welcome, and although only breakfast is served, there are plenty of eating establishments in the town.

OWNERS: Sheila and John Roberts OPEN: all year ROOMS: 1 double, 1 twin; both rooms with wash-basin, tea/coffee and TV; lounge TERMS: single occupancy £26–£27, twin/double £36; deposit required CARDS: none DETAILS: children welcome; dogs by arrangement; no smoking; garden

BURLEY Hampshire — map 2

Holmans

Bisterne Close, Burley BH24 4AZ TEL/FAX: (01425) 402307
off A31 / A35, 4m SE of Ringwood

This large, modern family house is in a quiet location just outside the village of Burley in the New Forest. It has four acres of attractive gardens, and stabling for four horses available for guests arriving on horseback or in carriages. The three comfortable bedrooms are all *en suite*, and residents have use of a lounge with TV. Breakfast is taken at a large mahogany table in the dining-room. Although evening meals are not provided, there is a pub nearby with a local reputation for good food. The area is ideal for riding and carriage driving.

OWNERS: Robin and Mary Ford OPEN: all year exc Christmas ROOMS: 2 double, 1 twin; all rooms with bath/shower and tea/coffee; lounge with TV TERMS: single occupancy £30, twin/double £42–£50; reductions for children under 8 sharing with parents; deposit: £5 per person CARDS: none DETAILS: children welcome; no dogs in bedrooms; no smoking; car park; garden

BURNHAM-ON-SEA Somerset — map 2

Priors Mead

23 Rectory Road, Burnham-on-Sea TA8 2BZ TEL/FAX: (01278) 782116
from M5 junction 22 follow main road towards Burnham-on-Sea; after third roundabout turn right into Berrow Rd; Rectory Rd is second right

Peter and Felicity (known as Fizz) Alexander are a welcoming couple and their large Edwardian house, standing in an attractive garden, has a relaxed atmosphere. Bedrooms are large and well equipped, the hall is furnished with a sofa and armchairs, and there is a baby grand piano in the dining-room. Guests sit round a large table for breakfast; alternatively, there are two small tables for couples. The garden incorporates a croquet lawn and unheated swimming-pool. The town, beach, tennis and golf courses are all within walking distance. John Cleese lived here as a child during the war.

OWNERS: Peter and Felicity Alexander OPEN: all year exc Christmas ROOMS: 1 double, with private bathroom; 1 twin; 1 family; tea/coffee and TV in all bedrooms; lounge TERMS: single occupancy £19–£20, twin/double £32–£36, family room from £32; £12 for children under 12 in family room; deposit: £10 CARDS: none DETAILS: children welcome; no dogs; no smoking; car park; garden; swimming-pool

---

'NEW ENTRY' indicates that a B&B was not in the previous edition (although its owners may have been, at a different address).

If you are forced to turn up later than planned, please telephone to warn the proprietor. It is always best to book a room in advance, even in winter. B&Bs with few rooms may close at short notice for periods not specified in the details.

BURTON LAZARS Leicestershire map 5

The Grange

New Road, Burton Lazars LE14 2UU TEL/FAX: (01664) 560775
from A606 1m S of Melton Mowbray turn E at Burton Lazars church

Set in large formal gardens and with good views over the open countryside, The Grange is an attractive wistaria-clad country house. Each of the four guest bedrooms is colour-themed and co-ordinated: the Blue Room has a four-poster bed; the Yellow Room is a double with a balcony; the Pink Room is a large double that can also be used as a family room; and the Burgundy Room, with twin beds, is on the ground floor and is suitable for wheelchair-users. All the rooms have *en suite* facilities and TVs. Guests also have the use of a sitting-room with an open fire and access to the garden. Pam Holden is a cordon bleu cook and does wonderful things with Stilton; evening meals are available if pre-arranged, and the B&B is licensed.

OWNER: Pam Holden OPEN: all year ROOMS: 2 double, 1 twin, 1 four-poster; all rooms with bath/shower, tea/coffee and TV; 1 room suitable for wheelchair-users; lounge TERMS: single occupancy £29.50, twin/double/four-poster £44.50, £5 for each child sharing with parents; dinner £15 CARDS: none DETAILS: children welcome; no dogs; smoking in lounge only; car park; garden

BURWASH East Sussex map 3

Villiers NEW ENTRY

High Street, Burwash TN19 7ET TEL: (01435) 882624

This seventeenth-century Grade II-listed house was completely restored in the mid-1990s, and has been furnished and decorated to a very high standard. Right in the centre of the charming little village of Burwash opposite the tea shop, it was itself a shop until recently. Of the two guest bedrooms, the double has a sitting-room and private bathroom, while the twin, which is in the attic, is normally let to accommodate any overflow from the double and is a more basic room. Sue Jennings, a retired nurse, is a welcoming host and shares the upstairs drawing-room, which has an inglenook fireplace, with guests. The ground-floor dining-area is where breakfast – including free-range eggs, 'Burwash Beauty' sausages and home-made marmalade – is usually served, or in fine weather on the terrace with its splendid views. Smoking is permitted only in one lounge. Residents may use the house and garden throughout the day. The village has three pubs that serve food, all within a few minutes' walk.

OWNER: Sue Jennings OPEN: all year exc Christmas and New Year ROOMS: 1 double, with private bathroom; 1 twin; tea/coffee and TV in both bedrooms; lounge with TV TERMS: single occupancy £15–£20, twin/double £30–£40; very young children charged for breakfast only CARDS: none DETAILS: children welcome; no dogs; smoking in 1 lounge only; car park; garden

BURY ST EDMUNDS Suffolk map 6

South Hill House NEW ENTRY

43 Southgate Street, Bury St Edmunds IP33 2AZ
TEL: (01284) 755650 FAX: (01284) 752718

With its flagstone floors, origins from medieval times and Georgian additions, South Hill House is full of character. It became an Academy for Young Ladies in the mid-1800s, and Charles Dickens used to come and read to the students; it is believed to be the school mentioned in *The Pickwick Papers*. It later became a boys' boarding school, and the bell tower dating from that time can still be seen in the garden. Furnished comfortably with antique and traditional pieces, the house offers three large, *en suite* bedrooms. The family room is well equipped with a double bed, two single beds, a cot, settee and armchair, plus *en suite* bathroom. Breakfasts include locally made sausages and are served family-style at a refectory table. Sarah Green is an accommodating host, and provides guests with their own keys.

OWNERS: Sarah and Anthony Green OPEN: all year exc Christmas ROOMS: 1 double, 1 twin, 1 family; all rooms with bath/shower, tea/coffee and TV TERMS: single occupancy £28–£32, twin/double £40–£42, family room £44; reductions for children according to age if sharing with parents; deposit: £15 CARDS: none DETAILS: children welcome; no dogs; no smoking; car park; garden

BUSLINGTHORPE Lincolnshire map 9

East Farm House

Middle Rasen Road, Buslingthorpe LN3 5AQ TEL: (01673) 842283
from Middle Rasen follow sign to Lissington; house on right after 2m

This nineteenth-century Grade II-listed farmhouse is in a remote and peaceful spot, approached by a private lane. Gill and Jim Grant are a congenial and down-to-earth couple, and have a conservation award for their 400-acre arable farm and nature trail. There is plenty of wildlife to be seen about, including squirrels, partridges and a resident kestrel. The entrance to the house is made from quarry tiles, and the beamed sitting-room has a Worcester sandstone fireplace. Substantial breakfasts and, by arrangement, evening meals are served in the bright dining-room. Vegetarians can be catered for with notice. The two large bedrooms have traditional furnishings and floral wallpaper. There is a tennis court for guests' use, and a self-catering holiday cottage on the farm.

OWNER: Gill Grant OPEN: all year exc Christmas ROOMS: 1 double, with shower; 1 twin, with private bathroom; tea/coffee and TV in both bedrooms; lounge with TV TERMS: single occupancy £20–£25, twin/double £38–£40; half-price for children; dinner £12; deposit required CARDS: none DETAILS: children welcome; dogs welcome; no smoking; car park; garden; tennis

BUXTON Derbyshire **map 9**

Coningsby

6 Macclesfield Road, Buxton SK17 9AH TEL/FAX: (01298) 26735

The guest bedrooms have names: there's the luxurious Ivory Room with its spa bath, plus the Green, Blue and Pink rooms, all *en suite* and with satellite TV. Coningsby is a handsome Victorian house standing in a neat garden about half a mile from the town centre and very close to the Pavilion Gardens. The interior is furnished in mainly Edwardian style, and guests have their own comfortable licensed lounge. Dinners, which must be pre-booked, are served in the red-toned dining-room, as are good Derbyshire breakfasts, which might feature smoked salmon and scrambled eggs as one of 'Linda's Special Breakfast of the Day' as well as many other options.

OWNERS: Dr and Mrs J. Harry OPEN: Mar to Nov ROOMS: 3 double, 1 twin; all rooms with bath/shower, tea/coffee and TV; lounge with TV TERMS: single occupancy £50, twin/double £55–£70; dinner £15; deposit required CARDS: none DETAILS: no children; no dogs; no smoking; car park; garden

---

Grosvenor House

1 Broad Walk, Buxton SK17 6JE TEL/FAX: (01298) 72439

Grosvenor House is a grand Victorian building set in a conservation area within easy walking distance of the centre of the spa town of Buxton, and with views across Pavilion Gardens and the River Wye towards the Opera House. Bedrooms are all decorated and furnished to a high standard, and the larger 'de luxe' rooms are front-facing and have opulent period furniture. Breakfast and dinner are served in the licensed dining-room, and guests planning a visit to the opera can order dinner early. The elegant and tastefully furnished lounge is well stocked with local information, books and games. The Fairbairns also run a coffee shop next door, which is open to the public.

OWNERS: Graham and Anne Fairbairn OPEN: all year ROOMS: 5 double, 1 twin, 2 family; all rooms with bath/shower, tea/coffee and TV; lounge TERMS: single occupancy £42.50–£50, twin/double £50–£70, family room £70–£90; children's reductions according to age; dinner £15; deposit: minimum 10% CARDS: none DETAILS: no children under 8; guide dogs only; smoking in lounge only; car park; garden

---

Hawthorn Farm Guest House

Fairfield Road, Buxton SK17 7ED TEL: (01298) 23230
on A6, N of town centre

This attractive building, with thick stone walls, dates from around 1600 and has been in the Smith family for ten generations. It is still very much the same as when it was built, with leaded windows, beams and some very low doorways. The dining-room has a carved oak fireplace and a grandfather clock, and the comfortable lounge has a stone fireplace. Six bedrooms, four of which are *en suite*, are on the ground floor in an annexe, while the rest are in the main house. The guesthouse is ten minutes' walk from the centre of Buxton, and a regular bus service passes by the front door. The nearby thirteenth-century church of St Peter is worth a visit.

OWNER: David Smith OPEN: Apr to Oct ROOMS: 4 single, all with wash-basin; 2 double, both with wash-basin; 2 twin, 1 with wash-basin, 1 with shower; 4 family, all with shower; tea/coffee in all bedrooms; TV in some bedrooms and lounge TERMS: single £21–£22, single occupancy £30–£40, twin/double £42–£48, family room from £48; reductions for children sharing with parents according to age; deposit: £10 CARDS: none DETAILS: children welcome; dogs in bedrooms only; no smoking in dining-room; car park; garden

Netherdale

16 Green Lane, Buxton SK17 9DP TEL: (01298) 23896

This splendid detached Victorian house, named after a Scottish dale, is on a quiet side street, just a few minutes' walk from the centre of town. The bedrooms in the main house are very spacious and have curtains made by owner Gwenda Stewart, dressing-tables and TV, and most are *en suite*. Examples of Gwenda's embroidery are offered for sale, and meals are a highlight: four-course dinners, served in the licensed dining-room, feature delicious home-made desserts.

OWNERS: John and Gwenda Stewart OPEN: all year exc Christmas and New Year ROOMS: 2 single; 6 double, 5 with bath/shower; 2 family, both with bath/shower; tea/coffee and TV in all bedrooms; lounge with TV TERMS: single £21–£23, single occupancy £30, twin/double £42–£44, family room £60–£65; reductions for children sharing with parents; dinner £14; deposit: £15 per room CARDS: none DETAILS: children welcome; no dogs; no smoking; car park; games room; garden

Stoneridge NEW ENTRY

9 Park Road, Buxton SK17 6SG TEL: (01298) 26120

This peaceful Edwardian house is in a conservation area close to the opera house and town centre. Patty and Alex Hoskin spent three years converting the house from a private residence to make it suitable for B&B. They are friendly hosts and have created an informal atmosphere. The house is furnished in keeping with its era, and the four rooms all have *en suite* facilities, and are provided with plenty of brochures and information on the area. Excellent breakfasts are served in the dining-room, which has a cast-iron fireplace, and a complimentary glass of sherry is offered in the evening in the comfortable lounge, which leads on to the terrace. Guests arriving by train can arrange to be picked up from either Buxton or Macclesfield.

OWNERS: Patty and Alex Hoskin OPEN: all year exc Christmas and Jan ROOMS: 2 double, 1 twin, 1 family; all rooms with bath/shower, tea/coffee and TV; lounge with TV TERMS: single occupancy £26–£27, twin/double £35–£39, family room £42.50–£54; deposit: 1 night's charge CARDS: none DETAILS: children welcome; dogs welcome; no smoking; car park; garden

BYFORD Hereford & Worcester — map 5

Old Rectory

Byford HR4 7LD TEL: (01981) 590218 FAX: (01981) 590499
off A438, 7m W of Hereford

Charles and Audrey Mayson have created a friendly atmosphere at the Old Rectory, and run the house in an informal and relaxed way. It was built in 1830, is set in a large landscaped garden, with a magnificent cedar tree, and enjoys rural views. Bedrooms are spacious and all have *en suite* facilities, easy chairs and books. Dinner is served, with children's portions and vegetarian options available, although the Maysons are happy to arrange reservations at one of the many local restaurants, if required. Fishing can be arranged on the nearby River Wye, and the Wye Valley Walk passes by the house. The town of Hay-on-Wye, famous for its bookshops, and the historical city of Hereford, are both a short drive away.

OWNERS: Mr and Mrs C. Mayson OPEN: Mar to Nov ROOMS: 2 double, 1 twin; all rooms with bath/shower, tea/coffee and TV; lounge TERMS: single occupancy £25–£40, twin/double £37–£45; children's reductions by arrangement; dinner £12; deposit: £20 CARDS: none DETAILS: children welcome; no dogs; no smoking; car park; garden

CADNAM Hampshire — map 2

Walnut Cottage

Old Romsey Road, Cadnam SO4 2NP TEL/FAX: (01703) 812275
at Cadnam roundabout take A3090 to Copythorne, then first left

Walnut Cottage is a 150-year-old white, brick-built cottage on a quiet lane in an attractive garden. It is a comfortable and welcoming family home furnished with antiques, with a pleasant bright, light sitting-room and fireplace. An alternative place to sit is the central hall with its comfortable chairs. Breakfast is served at one large table in the small dining-room. The three bedrooms all have *en suite* facilities, and one is on the ground floor. Plenty of information is available on what to do and see in the vicinity. Good food can be found at a pub 150 yards down the road. Walnut Cottage is not far from the M27 and is well placed for visiting the New Forest and Southampton.

OWNERS: Eric and Charlotte Osgood OPEN: all year exc Christmas ROOMS: 1 double, 2 twin; all rooms with bath/shower and tea/coffee; 1 room suitable for wheelchair-users; lounge with TV TERMS: single occupancy £28, twin/double £43; deposit: £10 CARDS: none DETAILS: no children under 14; no dogs; no smoking in two bedrooms; car park; garden

---

Many B&Bs are in remote places, and although in many cases we provide directions, it is always advisable to ask for clear instructions when booking.

CALDBECK Cumbria **map 10**

Swaledale Watch

Whelpo, Caldbeck CA7 8HQ TEL: (01697) 478409
on B5299, 1m W of Caldbeck

Located not far from the Cumbrian Way in the heart of the Lake District National Park, this 300-acre working dairy and sheep farm offers comfortable, well-furnished guest accommodation. The house itself stands near a stream and old stone bridge. All four bedrooms have *en suite* facilities as well as good-quality carpets and fabrics; the attractive curtains have been made by a family friend and add flair to the rooms. The guest lounge has been extended and provides fine views over open country; it has a *chaise longue* and TV – plus an open fire, as does the dining-room. One bedroom, the 'honeymoon suite', has a four-poster bed with a lace canopy, and a jacuzzi. Evening meals by arrangement are available, and packed lunches can be provided – useful for visitors who might want to spend a day exploring the farm or trekking off into the rolling Lakeland fells.

OWNERS: Mr and Mrs A. Savage OPEN: all year exc Christmas ROOMS: 1 twin, 1 four-poster, 2 family; all rooms with bath/shower, tea/coffee and TV; lounge with TV TERMS: single occupancy £18–£21, twin £36, four-poster £38–£42, family room from £36 plus children's charge; children's reductions according to age; dinner £11; deposit required for new customers CARDS: none DETAILS: children welcome; no dogs; no smoking; car park; garden

CAMBRIDGE Cambridgeshire **map 6**

De Freville House

166 Chesterton Road, Cambridge CB4 1DA
TEL: (01223) 354993 FAX: (01223) 321890

A high standard of B&B is offered at this tasteful Victorian residence, only a short trek away from the town centre, the colleges and the River Cam. Ann Hunter is a congenial host who has been running the place for almost 20 years. The spacious spick-and-span bedrooms are well-maintained, and almost all have *en suite* showers. Look out for the Hunters' collection of antique clocks on display around the house. Guests can relax in the pleasant garden and patio area; free on-street parking is available.

OWNER: Ann Hunter OPEN: all year exc Christmas ROOMS: 1 single, 5 double, 1 twin; all rooms with shower exc 1 double with private bathroom; tea/coffee and TV in all bedrooms; lounge with TV TERMS: single £32, single occupancy £35, twin/double £45–£55; deposit: £10 CARDS: none DETAILS: no children under 10; no dogs; no smoking; garden

If any bedrooms are suitable for wheelchair-users, we mention this in the details at the end of the entry.

Netley Lodge

NEW ENTRY

112 Chesterton Road, Cambridge CB4 1BZ TEL: (01223) 363845

This Edwardian town house, close to the River Cam and only a mile from the city centre, is run by Danuta and Joe Mikolajczyk, who are a very welcoming couple. The house is well maintained, in good decorative order and furnished in a traditional style. Guest rooms have comfortable beds, and the *en suite* family bedroom is on the ground floor.

OWNER: Danuta Mikolajczyk OPEN: all year exc Christmas ROOMS: 1 single, with private bathroom; 2 twin, 1 with bath/shower, 1 with private bathroom; 1 family, with bath/shower; tea/coffee and TV in all bedrooms TERMS: single £22, single occupancy £30, twin/double £38, family room £55; deposit: 1 night's charge CARDS: none DETAILS: no children under 2; no dogs; no smoking; car park; garden

CANTERBURY Kent

map 3

Oriel Lodge

3 Queen Avenue, Canterbury CT2 8AY TEL/FAX: (01227) 462845
approaching Canterbury on A2 take left turn 400 metres after first roundabout

Just a five-minute walk from the town centre and Canterbury West Station, Oriel Lodge stands in a quiet, tree-lined street within view of the cathedral. It is a large detached Edwardian house built in the style of William Morris and, within, furnishings and décor reflecting the William Morris influence. All six bedrooms have TVs and tea/coffee facilities; two are *en suite* and the others have shared bathrooms next to them. Breakfasts are served in the large lounge/dining room, which has an open hob-grate fireplace; complimentary afternoon teas are also provided. The Rishworths' keen interest in gardening is reflected in their own pretty garden. A minimum of two nights must usually be booked during bank holidays and on summer weekends.

OWNERS: Keith and Anthea Rishworth OPEN: all year ROOMS: 1 single, with wash-basin; 3 double, all with wash-basin; 1 twin, with shower; 1 family, with shower; tea/coffee and TV in all bedrooms; lounge TERMS: single £23–£30, single occupancy £26–£38, twin/double £39–£59, family room £66–£80; half-price for children 6–11 sharing with parents; deposit: 25% CARDS: MasterCard, Visa DETAILS: no children under 6; no dogs; smoking in lounge only; car park; garden

Zan Stel Lodge

140 Old Dover Road, Canterbury CT1 3NX TEL: (01227) 453654

This unusual looking pebble-dashed Edwardian house with its striking bay windows is next to Kent County Cricket ground and about ten minutes' walk from the city centre and the famous cathedral. At one time the property was a bricklayers' school (that explains the windows), and the walls surrounding the garden have inset fireplaces of different designs, which were the work of apprentices. The house is comfortable and well-kept, and the rooms have their original fireplaces. The Stedmans are delightful, cheerful people and love looking after their guests. Dinner is not available, but there is a good selection of places to eat in town.

OWNERS: Zandra and Ron Stedman OPEN: all year exc Christmas ROOMS: 1 double, with shower; 1 twin, with private bathroom; 2 family, 1 with shower, 1 with private bathroom; tea/coffee and TV in all bedrooms; lounge TERMS: single occupancy £30–£45, twin/double £40–£50, family room £54–£72; deposit: £10 CARDS: none DETAILS: children welcome; no dogs; no smoking; car park; garden

CARLISLE Cumbria map 10

Avondale

3 St Aidan's Road, Carlisle CA1 1LT TEL: (01228) 523012
just off A69 by St Aidan's church

'Avondale is absolutely top notch,' wrote an enthusiastic reporter of this Edwardian house on a quiet tree-lined road, just outside the town centre. Michael and Angela Hayes have created a home-from-home atmosphere in their impeccably maintained house, which is furnished in period style. The sitting-room has leaded windows and the 'large and luxurious' bedrooms all have fireplaces. Evening meals are available if arranged in advance, and the owners are happy to recommend places to eat out in Carlisle. The garden makes an attractive place to sit and enjoy sunny weather.

OWNERS: Michael and Angela Hayes OPEN: all year exc Christmas ROOMS: 1 double, with private bathroom; 2 twin, 1 with bath, 1 with private bathroom; tea/coffee and TV; lounge with TV TERMS: single occupancy £20–£25, twin/double £40–£44; dinner £8.50; deposit: £20 CARDS: none DETAILS: children welcome; no dogs; no smoking in bedrooms; car park

Blackwell Farm

Blackwell, Durdar, Carlisle CA2 4SH TEL: (01228) 24073
from M6 junction 42 follow sign to Dalston, turn right at Black Lion pub then left at White Ox pub

Part of a 200-year-old dairy farm, this unpretentious family home ensures a comfortable stay. The atmosphere is relaxed, with cups of tea and biscuits provided on arrival. The snug bedrooms are modestly furnished, and there is a TV lounge for guests' use. Residents are welcome to explore the farm, and children may make friends with the many animals kept on the property, including cats, dogs and calves. The Westmorlands provide filling breakfasts, and three family pubs serving evening meals lie within two miles. Blackwell Farm sits on the edge of the racecourse, just outside the cathedral city of Carlisle.

OWNER: Andrea Westmorland OPEN: all year exc Christmas ROOMS: 1 double, 1 family; tea/coffee in both bedrooms; lounge with TV TERMS: single occupancy £16–£17, double £32–£34, family from £32; children's reductions by arrangement CARDS: none DETAILS: children welcome; dogs welcome; no smoking in bedrooms or bathrooms; car park

Courtfield House

169 Warwick Road, Carlisle CA1 1LP TEL: (01228) 22767

This Victorian red-brick house is on a main road, within easy walking distance of the town centre. It is colourfully decorated outside, with flower tubs and window boxes, and the theme continues inside with dried-flower arrangements throughout the house. Bedrooms are colour-co-ordinated and have *en suite* facilities; there are plans to add a single bedroom. Three-course dinners are served, with children's portions and vegetarian options always available.

OWNERS: Eric and Marjorie Dawes OPEN: all year exc Christmas ROOMS: 2 double, 1 twin, 3 family; all rooms with shower, tea/coffee and TV; lounge with TV TERMS: single occupancy £22–£25, twin/double £35–£38, family room £45–£55; half-price for children under 12; dinner £10 CARDS: none DETAILS: children welcome; no dogs; smoking in lounge only; car park

Fern Lee

NEW ENTRY

9 St Aidan's Road, Carlisle CA1 1LT TEL/FAX: (01228) 511930

This large Victorian corner house has been impeccably restored by Mike and Wendy Pattinson. Bedrooms are individually decorated with floral wallpapers, and duvets have Jacobean patterns. All are *en suite* and have satellite TV. High chairs and travel cots are available. Generous breakfasts are served at separate tables in the dining-room. Fern Lee is close to the M6, and just ten minutes' walk from the city centre and the bus and railway stations. There is an 18-hole golf course less than 200 yards from the house.

OWNERS: Mike and Wendy Pattinson OPEN: all year exc Christmas ROOMS: 1 single, 2 double, 2 twin, 1 four-poster, 2 family; all rooms with bath/shower, tea/coffee and TV; 1 room suitable for wheelchair-users; lounge with TV TERMS: single £22–£25, twin/double £40, four-poster £40–£45, family room £45–£54; half-price for children sharing with parents; dinner £10; deposit: 10% CARDS: none DETAILS: children welcome; no dogs; smoking in 2 rooms only; car park

Howard House

27 Howard Place, Carlisle CA1 1HR TEL/FAX: (01228) 512550

A comfortable old-fashioned ambience pervades this good-value B&B, which is in a quiet residential area just five minutes' walk from Carlisle's bus and rail stations. Those who arrive by car will find unrestricted parking on nearby streets (the Fishers will provide a residential parking pass). The house was built in the 1800s and is well maintained, with interesting items such as an extensive plate collection and old pictures of the town adding to the atmosphere. One bedroom has a six-foot four-poster bed, and the top-floor bedrooms, with their yellow and green décor, are particularly attractive. Guests relaxing in the parlour-like lounge may be privileged to meet one of the three friendly cats who live here. Evening meals, if pre-arranged, are served in the separate dining-room. Mr Fisher, who has an interest in local genealogy, is happy to share his knowledge with guests.

OWNERS: Sandra and Lawrence Fisher OPEN: all year ROOMS: 2 single, 1 with private bathroom; 1 twin, with shower; 1 four-poster, with shower; 2 family, both with wash-basin; tea/coffee and TV in all bedrooms; lounge with TV TERMS: single £16–£18, single occupancy £30, twin £34–£44, four-poster £36–£44, family room £40–£50; reductions for children under 12; dinner £9; deposit: £15 CARDS: MasterCard, Switch, Visa DETAILS: children welcome; no dogs

CARNFORTH Lancashire map 8

Thwaite End Farm

Carnforth LA5 9TN TEL: (01524) 732551
on A6 2½m S of Carnforth

This attractive, seventeenth-century farmhouse is situated on a main road two and a half miles from Carnforth. It is part of a small working beef and sheep farm, which has been run by the Irelands for over 20 years. The beamed bedrooms both have *en suite* showers, and are comfortably appointed with traditional furniture. Breakfasts are served at separate tables in the dining-room, which contains an original sandstone fireplace. Evening meals are available at several nearby pubs. Thwaite End Farm is an ideal base for visiting the Lake District and the Yorkshire Dales.

OWNER: Mrs A. Ireland OPEN: all year exc Christmas ROOMS: 1 double, 1 twin; both rooms with shower, tea/coffee and TV; lounge with TV TERMS: single occupancy £20–£25, twin/double £40–£44 CARDS: none DETAILS: no children; no dogs; smoking in lounge only; car park; garden

CASTLE ACRE Norfolk map 6

Willow Cottage

Stocks Green, Castle Acre PE32 2AE TEL: (01760) 755551
just off A1065, 4m N of Swaffham

This listed, 270-year-old property is next to the medieval church of St James in the middle of the charming village of Castle Acre. Several original features remain, such as the oak beams in the cosy bedrooms, two of which overlook the green. On the ground floor is a tea-shop, serving home-made cakes and scones. The village is in the outer bailey of the eleventh-century castle, and most of the houses in the village are built from the flints and stones of the castle ruins. There are lovely walks along the River Nar and nearby Peddars Way. Also worth exploring are the ruins of the twelfth-century priory, founded by William the Conqueror's son-in-law.

OWNER: Peter Foster OPEN: Feb to Nov ROOMS: 2 double, 2 twin; all rooms with wash-basin; lounge with TV TERMS: single occupancy £18–£20, twin/double £30–£34, family room £45; children's reductions by arrangement; deposit required CARDS: none DETAILS: children welcome; dogs by arrangement; garden

CASTLE DONINGTON Leicestershire map 5

Weaver's Lodge

65 Station Road, Castle Donington DE74 2NL TEL: (01332) 812639
on B6540 (main street through village)

High standards continue at this well-designed, comfortable guesthouse with a neat, white exterior set off by award-winning floral displays. The house was once a weaver's cottage, and retains some original features such as a bare-brick fireplace in the dining-room. Although it is on the village's main street, double-glazing keeps the noise down. Bedrooms are airy and bright, prettied up with wicker and pine furniture; the two single rooms share a bathroom, and the double has an *en suite* shower. Residents have the use of a lounge with TV. Three-course evening meals can be pre-arranged, and the guesthouse is licensed.

OWNERS: Mr and Mrs David Daley OPEN: all year ROOMS: 2 single, both with wash-basin; 1 double, with shower; tea/coffee and TV in all bedrooms; lounge with TV TERMS: single £22, single occupancy £27.50, twin/double £45; dinner £9.50; deposit: £10 per person per night CARDS: none DETAILS: no children; no dogs; no smoking in bedrooms; car park

CASTLE HEDINGHAM Essex map 6

Pannells Ash NEW ENTRY

Sudbury Road, Castle Hedingham CO9 3AD TEL: (01787) 460364
from Castle Hedingham take B1058 towards Bury St Edmunds for 1m; cottage is on right

This long, pink-painted fifteenth century farmhouse, part of a working arable farm, stands in a well-tended garden one mile from Castle Hedingham. The Redgewells are an accommodating couple who welcome visitors with a hot drink and biscuits. The house has been beautifully restored, retaining original features such as oak beams, sloping floors, low doors and an open fireplace. There are two lounges, one with a TV, lots of books and magazines to browse through, and access to the patio and garden. The three bedrooms are roomy and comfortable, and share two bathrooms; the twin can be made into a family room. Breakfasts are prepared on the Aga and served family-style in the kitchen/dining-room. Sylvia Redgewell makes her own preserves, and her speciality jam comes from the rare bullace (wild plum) trees in the garden.

OWNER: Mrs S.N. Redgewell OPEN: all year exc Christmas ROOMS: 1 single, with wash-basin; 1 double; 1 twin/family room; lounge with TV TERMS: single £16–£18, single occupancy £25, twin/double £32–£34, family room £38–£48; reductions for very young children; deposit required for bookings of 3 nights or more CARDS: none DETAILS: children welcome; no dogs; no smoking; car park; garden

---

Any smoking restrictions that we know of are given in the details at the end of the entry.

CASTLETON South Yorkshire **map 9**

Bargate Cottage

Market Place, Castleton S33 8WQ
TEL: (01433) 620201 FAX: (01433) 621739
entering village on A625 from Hope, proceed through sharp left bend, past school, take lane at left of Nags Head public house into Market Place, continue to top; house on left

Virtually uninhabitable when they took it over in the late 1980s, this seventeenth-century cottage sitting at the foot of the Castle hill has been something of a labour of love for the Newsomes. They have painstakingly restored it, injecting comfort while retaining a great deal of the house's original character: thick stone walls, creaky floors, an inglenook fireplace and beamed ceilings all add to the atmosphere. Bedrooms are of a good size and prettified with colourful duvets and curtains (made by Sylvia) plus a resident rag doll or teddy bear on every bed. One room is on the ground floor. A comfortable, cosy lounge has a TV, and there is a conservatory that overlooks the terraced garden. Generous evening meals are cooked by Derek and served in the dining-room at individual tables; alternatively, he will be happy to point you towards a plethora of eating-places within easy reach.

OWNERS: Derek and Sylvia Newsome OPEN: all year exc Christmas ROOMS: 1 double, 1 twin, 2 four-poster; all rooms with bath/shower, tea/coffee and TV; lounge with TV TERMS: single occupancy £39, twin/double £43, four-poster £47; half-price for children under 12 sharing with parents; dinner £10.50; deposit: £20 CARDS: none DETAILS: children welcome; no dogs; no smoking; car park; garden

CATLOWDY Cumbria **map 10**

Bessiestown Farm

Catlowdy CA6 5QP TEL/FAX: (01228) 577219
on B6318, 5m E of Canonbie, 8m NE of Longtown

Bessiestown Farm lies just a few miles from the Scottish border, on the edge of the Kielder Forest, surrounded by moorland, and is a working beef and sheep farm. The house is decorated with many interesting items, including paintings by a local artist. Bedrooms are spacious and well equipped, all with *en suite* facilities. Excellent breakfasts are served, as are four-course dinners every night except Sunday. Guests have use of a TV lounge, a licensed bar lounge and a conservatory. The indoor heated swimming-pool is open from May to September, there is a games room with table tennis and a pool table, and riding can be arranged at the local riding centre. Around the courtyard are three self-catering cottages, converted from redundant farm buildings.

OWNERS: Jack and Margaret Sisson OPEN: all year exc Christmas ROOMS: 2 double, 1 twin, 1 family; all rooms with bath/shower, tea/coffee and TV; lounge with TV TERMS: single occupancy £31–£35, twin/double £45–£48, family room £60–£70; dinner Mon to Sat £11; deposit: £20 per room per night CARDS: MasterCard, Visa DETAILS: children welcome; no dogs; no smoking; car park; games room; garden; swimming-pool

CHACOMBE Northamptonshire map 5

Berry Furze

NEW ENTRY

12 Silver Street, Chacombe OX17 2JR TEL: (01295) 710145
leave M40 at junction 11, take A361 signposted Daventry; after ¾m turn right signposted Chacombe

Berry Furze is a comfortable modern bungalow standing in a colourful, secluded garden in a quiet lane leading to a ford. The bedrooms are bright and airy, have good beds and are either *en suite* or have a private bathroom. For TV addicts, there's one in the guest lounge and one of the bedrooms. Breakfast is served family-style until 10am in the dining-room with its pleasant views of the garden. Brian and Noelene Cummins treat guests as friends, and provide lots of information about the area.

OWNERS: Mr and Mrs B.J. Cummins OPEN: all year exc Christmas ROOMS: 3 double, 2 with shower, 1 with private bathroom; tea/coffee in all bedrooms; TV in 1 bedroom and lounge TERMS: single occupancy £22, double £40; dinner £11; deposit: 50% CARDS: none DETAILS: no children; dogs by arrangement; no smoking; car park; garden

CHAGFORD Devon map 1

Glendarah House

Lower Street, Chagford TQ13 8BZ
TEL: (01647) 433270 FAX: (01647) 433483

Glendarah is a substantial Victorian house with a comfortable, peaceful atmosphere. It is on the edge of the small town of Chagford, on the north-eastern edge of Dartmoor. Within, soft tones predominate, and there is a small bar and a quiet sitting-room where guests can relax. Breakfast is served in the dining-room, which enjoys the morning sun and has views of the large garden and the hills beyond. One of the bedrooms is in the Coach House annexe. Chagford is a pretty Dartmoor village and makes a good centre for walking. One-night bookings are not usually taken at weekends during the high season.

OWNERS: Julia and Raymond Bellenger OPEN: all year exc 1 week Nov, Christmas and 1 week Jan ROOMS: 3 double, 3 twin; all rooms with bath/shower, tea/coffee and TV; lounge TERMS: single occupancy £23–£32, twin/double £45–£60; deposit: £10 per room per night CARDS: Delta, MasterCard, Visa DETAILS: no children under 10; dogs in coach-house room only; no smoking; car park; garden

---

Breakfast at B&Bs tends to mean a cooked breakfast of bacon, eggs, toast and so on, although many establishments also offer a good choice of cereals, yoghurts, fruit and other options. If you have special dietary requirements, it is best to discuss these when you make a booking.

CHARD Somerset — map 2

Yew Tree Cottage NEW ENTRY

Hornsbury Hill, Chard TA20 3DB TEL: (01460) 64735 FAX: (01460) 68029
1m N of Chard on A358 Chard to Ilminster road

This unpretentious house set in a pretty one-acre garden stands at the top of a hill on the outskirts of Chard just off the main road. The three bedrooms are decorated in restful pale colours, and are all *en suite*. Breakfasts are taken in an attractive glassed-in garden room at the back of the house, which opens out to a narrow terrace and the garden. Evening meals are available with 24-hours' notice, or Jenny and John Wright will be happy to recommend nearby restaurants or inns. There is also a residents' TV lounge where, on chilly days, a fire is lit. Self-catering accommodation is available.

OWNERS: Jenny and John Wright OPEN: all year exc Christmas ROOMS: 2 double, 1 twin; all rooms with bath/shower and tea/coffee; lounge with TV TERMS: single occupancy £36, twin/double £36–£42; dinner £12; deposit: 1 night's charge CARDS: none DETAILS: no children under 12; no dogs; no smoking; car park; garden

CHARING Kent — map 3

Barnfield

Charing TN27 0BN TEL/FAX: (01233) 712421
take A20 from Charing roundabout towards Maidstone, then first left down Hook Lane for 2½m

Barnfield, a fifteenth-century house which has been in the Pym family since 1936, is on a 30-acre sheep farm, in peaceful and beautiful countryside. It has the full monty of beams and inglenook fireplaces that go with a building of this age. Bedrooms are simply furnished and share one small bathroom. Guests have use of a large combined lounge/dining-room, with comfortable chairs and shelves full of books. Outside there is a hard tennis court. Riding can be arranged nearby, and this is a good area for country walks.

OWNERS: Martin and Phillada Pym OPEN: all year exc Christmas ROOMS: 2 single, 2 double, 1 twin; all rooms with wash-basin and tea/coffee; lounge with TV TERMS: single £22–£25, single occupancy £30, twin/double £40–£44; reductions for children sharing with parents; deposit: £10 per night CARDS: none DETAILS: children welcome; no dogs; no smoking; car park; garden; tennis

CHEADLE Staffordshire — map 5

Ley Fields Farm

Leek Road, Cheadle ST10 2EF TEL: (01538) 752875
on A522 Leek road, 2m N of Cheadle

This attractive listed Georgian farmhouse is set on a working dairy farm, surrounded by beautiful countryside. The atmosphere and level of comfort and cleanliness were described as 'excellent' by a reporter.

All bedrooms are *en suite*, and one of the family rooms is in an annexe and has its own lounge. The main guest lounge is spacious and has open fires. Dinner is no longer served, but there are plenty of eating-establishments nearby and Kathryn Clowes is happy to make recommendations.

OWNER: Kathryn Clowes OPEN: all year exc Christmas ROOMS: 1 double, 2 family; all rooms with bath/shower, tea/coffee and TV; lounge with TV TERMS: single occupancy £19–£20, twin/double £36–£38, family room £56–£58; reductions for children sharing with parents; deposit required CARDS: none DETAILS: children welcome; no dogs; no smoking; car park; garden

CHEDDLETON Staffordshire — map 5

Choir Cottage

Choir House, Ostlers Lane, Cheddleton ST13 7HS TEL: (01538) 360561
3m S of Leek, off A520 opposite Red Lion pub into Hollow Lane, past church and left into Ostlers Lane; house is on right

Seventeenth-century Choir Cottage stands in the former herb garden of Choir House, the home of William and Elaine Sutcliffe. Accommodation comprises two rooms with four-poster beds and *en suite* facilities; both rooms have their own private entrance, and one is suitable for families. Guests also have use of a comfortable lounge with an interesting collection of china and a beautiful antique grandfather clock. Evening meals are provided if pre-arranged. Choir Cottage makes a convenient base for visiting Alton Towers, the Peak District and the Potteries.

OWNERS: William and Elaine Sutcliffe OPEN: all year exc Christmas ROOMS: 2 four-poster; both rooms with bath/shower, tea/coffee and TV TERMS: single occupancy £30–£35, four-poster £50–£55; half-price for children; deposit: 1 night's charge CARDS: none DETAILS: babies and children over 4 welcome; no dogs; no smoking; car park; garden

CHELMSFORD Essex — map 3

Aarandale Guest House

9 Roxwell Road, Chelmsford CM1 2LY TEL: (01245) 251713

Aarandale was taken over in 1997 by Mrs Perera, an enthusiastic lady who enjoys welcoming guests to her home. She has previously lived in South Africa, and various artefacts brought back from there are on display in the dining-room. Bedrooms are warm and comfortable and, as the *Guide* went to press, Mrs Perera was planning to add *en suite* facilities to the double room. Dinner is served by arrangement, and guests visiting the town centre should take advantage of the convenient bus service.

OWNERS: Mrs M. Perera OPEN: all year exc Christmas ROOMS: 5 single, 1 with bath/shower, 4 with wash-basin; 1 double, with wash-basin; tea/coffee and TV in all bedrooms TERMS: single £20–£25, single occupancy £25, twin/double £38; dinner £7 CARDS: none DETAILS: children welcome; no dogs; car park

CHELTENHAM Gloucestershire map 5

Hannaford's

20 Evesham Road, Cheltenham GL52 2AB
TEL: (01242) 515181 and 524190 FAX: (01242) 25757

This mid-nineteenth-century townhouse is near Cheltenham racecourse and within easy walking distance of the town centre. It has retained much of its original character in features such as ornate ceilings and marble fireplaces. The immaculately kept bedrooms are richly furnished and well equipped. Breakfast is served in the bright dining-room. Guests have use of a TV lounge and a licensed bar/lounge, and there are facilities for business functions. The owners speak French and Italian.

OWNER: Dorothy Crowley OPEN: all year exc Christmas ROOMS: 2 single, 1 double, 4 twin, 1 family; all rooms with bath/shower, tea/coffee and TV; lounge with TV TERMS: single/single occupancy £35–£45, twin/double £55–£65, family room £55–£75; reductions for children sharing with parents CARDS: Amex, Diners, MasterCard, Visa DETAILS: children welcome; no dogs; no smoking in some bedrooms and dining-room

CHERITON BISHOP Devon map 1

Horselake Farm NEW ENTRY

Cheriton Bishop EX6 6HD TEL/FAX: (01647) 24220
entering village from east off A30, take right turn signposted Parish Church, turn right at T-junction towards Froggy Mill, turn left after bridge into farm

Idyllically pretty with its thatched roof and whitewashed cob, this sixteenth-century farmhouse – originally two cottages – is full of old beams and uneven floors. Each guest bedroom has a different theme: one has an oriental motif; another (with a four-poster bed) is decorated in dark greens and blues and has a gold-star-studded ceiling; and the third (the *en suite* Rose Room) has an intriguing bathtub built into one side of the room, accessed through a narrow archway. High ceilings and beams feature in both drawing-room and dining-room. Breakfasts and (if pre-arranged) evening meals are served at the old refectory table; alternatively, there are two restaurants and a pub nearby. Outside are a very pretty garden, apple orchards and a heated swimming-pool. The Stephenses grow apples commercially, keep sheep and run an Arabian horse stud.

OWNER: Nola Stephens OPEN: all year exc Christmas ROOMS: 1 double, with bath/shower; 1 twin, with wash-basin; 1 four-poster, with wash-basin; all rooms with tea/coffee and TV; lounge with TV TERMS: single occupancy £17–£20, twin/double £34–£44, four-poster £40; children under 5 free; dinner £10; deposit: 10% CARDS: none DETAILS: children welcome; no dogs; no smoking; car park; games room; garden; swimming-pool

---

If there are any bedrooms with TV, or with tea/coffee-making facilities, we mention this in the details at the end of an entry.

CHESTER **Cheshire** **map 7**

Chester Town House

23 King Street, Chester CH1 2AH
TEL: (01244) 350021 FAX: (01244) 342095

A well-appointed, tastefully decorated interior, a genuinely welcoming atmosphere, and a superb location in a conservation area of this charming old town all help to make a stay at Chester Town House memorable. Set within the ancient city walls in an area of cobbled streets, shops and restaurants, the house is within easy walking distance of the town centre. The cottage-style bedrooms all have *en suite* facilities plus TVs, toiletries, and amenities such as hair-dryers, telephones and trouser presses. Breakfasts – continental or traditional full English – are served in the breakfast room, and guests can relax in the conservatory-style lounge. Visitors arriving by car can park in the free residential car park across the street.

OWNER: Mrs M.V. Bellis OPEN: all year exc Christmas ROOMS: 2 single, 3 double, 1 twin; all rooms with bath/shower, tea/coffee and TV; lounge TERMS: single £30–£35, twin/double £45–£48; deposit: £20 or credit card details CARDS: MasterCard, Visa DETAILS: children welcome; dogs welcome; car park

---

Holly House Guest House

Stone Place, Hoole, Chester CH2 3NR TEL: (01244) 328967

'Very good value' was one visitor's verdict on this Georgian-style house in a cul-de-sac not far from a main road, and about a mile from the city centre. It is convenient for the railway station, a bus into Chester runs close by, and off-street parking is available for those arriving by car. Bedrooms are pleasantly decorated in pastels; three have *en suite* facilities. There is no lounge, but guests may browse through books and literature on what to see and do set out near a window seat on the landing. Marilyn Rudham is a pleasant and friendly host who runs her B&B in a professional way, and is happy to recommend venues for evening meals. Breakfasts are served in the no-smoking dining-room.

OWNER: Marilyn Rudham OPEN: all year ROOMS: 1 single, with shower; 2 double, both with shower; 1 family, with wash-basin; tea/coffee and TV in all bedrooms TERMS: single £19, single occupancy £23, twin/double £32–£35, family room £38; children under 5 free, half-price for children over 5; deposit: £10 CARDS: none DETAILS: children welcome; no dogs; no smoking in dining-room; car park; garden

---

Mitchell's of Chester

Green Gables, 28 Hough Green, Chester CH4 8JQ
TEL/FAX: (01244) 679004
on A5104 on S side of city

This elegant Victorian house, close to the town centre, has a sweeping staircase and fine moulded cornices. Furniture is also from the Victorian era, including an old sewing machine and grandfather clock. The original marble fireplace remains in the dining-room, where good breakfasts are served at one large banqueting table. The lounge has a log fire and looks out to some unusual vaults tunnelling under the well-maintained garden. The spacious bedrooms are decorated in rich colours and have *en suite* showers. There is reading material and a video library for guests' use. Visiting the centre of Chester is best done by public transport or on foot.

OWNERS: Colin and Helen Mitchell OPEN: all year exc Christmas ROOMS: 1 single, 1 double, 1 twin, 1 family; all rooms with shower and TV; lounge with TV TERMS: single £27, single occupancy £32, twin/double £42, family room £52–£58; children's reductions according to age; deposit: £20 CARDS: MasterCard, Visa DETAILS: children welcome; no dogs; smoking in lounge only; car park; garden

CHESTERFIELD Derbyshire — map 8

Abigail's Guest House

62 Brockwell Lane, Chesterfield S40 4EE TEL: (01246) 279391

Abigail's is a red-brick house, dating from the turn of the century, standing on top of a hill, just outside the centre of Chesterfield. Two bedrooms are on the ground floor. The conservatory dining-room overlooks the garden, which has two ponds and a waterfall, and panoramic views down the hill towards the town and beyond. As well as breakfast, evening meals can be served, by arrangement, with vegetarian options available on request. The bus to town stops right outside the front door; alternatively, a ten-minute walk will take you there.

OWNERS: Gail and Mike Onza OPEN: all year ROOMS: 2 single, 3 double, 2 twin; all rooms with bath/shower, tea/coffee and TV; lounge with TV TERMS: single £21.50–£24, single occupancy £24, twin/double £39.50; children under 2 free, half-price for ages 2–12; deposit required for bookings of 1 week or more CARDS: none DETAILS: children welcome; dogs welcome; smoking in lounge only; car park; garden

Sheeplea Cottage Farm

Baslow Road, Eastmoor, Chesterfield S42 7DD TEL: (01246) 566785
on A619, 5m W of Chesterfield

This stone-built Derbyshire cottage overlooks Chatsworth House, and was once part of the Chatsworth Estate. It is part of a 30-acre smallholding which supports Jacob sheep and horses. Veronica Worrall extends a warm welcome, and guests are treated as visiting friends. The bedrooms have attractive duvets and pretty curtains made by Veronica, and a mixture of traditional and antique furniture. The house has many interesting features, including a large tapestry set in an old carved frame made from dark wood. Breakfasts are served in the small lounge, and include free-range eggs from the farm chickens. A local inn provides evening meals.

OWNER: Veronica Worrall OPEN: Mar to Oct ROOMS: 1 double, 1 twin; both rooms with wash-basin, tea/coffee and TV; lounge TERMS: single occupancy £20, twin/double £32; deposit required CARDS: none DETAILS: no children under 8; no dogs; no smoking; car park; garden

CHESWICK Northumberland map 11

Ladythorne House

Cheswick TD15 2RW TEL: (01289) 387382
4m S of Berwick-upon-Tweed

This fine listed Georgian house stands in a lovely garden surrounded by open countryside, with views over the Cheviot Hills, and is close to miles of sandy beaches. It has all the modern comforts, including recently installed central heating, yet retains many original features, such as the inglenook fireplace and ceiling rose. The house is well maintained by the family and has a friendly and informal atmosphere; Mr Parker senior looks after the garden and does the cooking. The bedrooms have a mix of antique and traditional furniture, and the front ones have far-reaching views. There are two TV lounges, one non-smoking. Interested guests may read a brief history of Ladythorne House, published by Berwickshire Naturalists. Evening meals are served at a pub a mile away.

OWNERS: Neville and Valerie Parker, and Mr R.C. Parker OPEN: all year ROOMS: 1 single, 1 double, 2 twin, 2 family; all rooms exc single with wash-basin; 2 lounges, 1 with TV TERMS: single/single occupancy £12–£14.50, twin/double £24–£29, family room £43.50; children under 2 free, reductions for older children according to age; deposit: £10 per booking CARDS: none DETAILS: children welcome; dogs welcome with own bedding; smoking in 1 lounge only; car park; garden

CHICHESTER West Sussex map 3

Chichester Lodge

Oakwood, Chichester PO18 9AL TEL: (01243) 786560
take B2178 out of Chester, and 1½m after Salthill Rd take left into Oakwood School drive

Chichester Lodge is an attractive single-storey building set in a pretty one-and-a-half-acre garden. It was originally the lodge to a manor-house which is now a boy's school (the Dridges have no connection with the school). The four small bedrooms are charmingly decorated, with *en suite* facilities, and one has a four-poster bed. Breakfast is served either in the dining-room or in the breakfast room. Guests can relax in the garden room, the pleasant conservatory, or the garden in summer. The house is convenient for Goodwood Racecourse.

OWNER: Jeannette Dridge OPEN: all year ROOMS: 3 double, 1 four-poster; all rooms with bath/shower; tea/coffee and TV in most bedrooms; garden-room TERMS: single occupancy £35, double/four-poster £45–£50; deposit: £10 CARDS: none DETAILS: no children; no dogs; no smoking; car park; garden

CHIDDINGFOLD Surrey **map 3**

Greenaway

Pickhurst Road, Chiddingfold GU8 4TS
TEL: (01428) 682920 FAX: (01428) 605078

Only a few minutes' walk from the picturesque village green, Greenaway is a charming seventeenth-century house with low-beamed ceilings. It is beautifully furnished throughout, and the comfortable and attractively decorated sitting-room overlooks the garden. Bedrooms are simple; all have TVs and one has *en suite* facilities. Breakfast can be served in either the lovely dining-room or in the kitchen. John and Sheila Marsh are a delightful, welcoming couple. Petworth House is just a few miles away, and Chiddingfold is within easy reach of London.

OWNERS: John and Sheila Marsh OPEN: all year ROOMS: 1 single; 1 double, with bath; 1 twin; TV in all bedrooms and lounge TERMS: single £35, single occupancy £40–£50, twin/double £55–£75; deposit: 50% CARDS: MasterCard, Switch, Visa DETAILS: children welcome; dogs welcome; no smoking; car park; garden

CHIDEOCK Dorset **map 2**

Chimneys

Main Street, Chideock DT6 6JH TEL: (01297) 489368

This partly thatched, partly tiled guesthouse dates from the late sixteenth century and was converted in 1930 from three cottages. It is set in a pretty front garden, with half an acre at the back with fruit trees and bushes. Although the house is on the main road, double-glazing keeps out most of the traffic noise. The interior is spacious, but the simply furnished bedrooms and the bathrooms are quite compact. The sitting-room has a traditional beamed ceiling, and evening meals are served in the panelled dining-room/bar. The village of Chideock lies in a valley and is only five minutes from the sea; much of the surrounding coastline is owned by the National Trust.

OWNERS: Trevor and Jenny Yerworth OPEN: all year exc Christmas ROOMS: 3 double, 2 with shower, 1 with wash-basin; 1 twin, 1 four-poster, both with shower; tea/coffee and TV in all bedrooms; lounge with TV TERMS: single occupancy £22–£25, twin/double £34–£50, four-poster £54; reductions for children over 5 sharing with parents; deposit: £20 CARDS: none DETAILS: no children under 5; no dogs; no smoking; car park

---

We welcome your feedback about B&Bs you have stayed in. Please make use of the report forms at the end of the book – or use your own stationery if you prefer – and mail your report to: The Editors, The Good Bed and Breakfast Guide, *FREEPOST, 2 Marylebone Road, London NW1 1YN. (No stamps are needed if mailed within the UK.) Recommendations for B&Bs for our next edition are very welcome. Please let us know if you need more report forms and we will send you a fresh supply.*

CHIDHAM West Sussex **map 3**

Easton House

Chidham Lane, Chidham PO18 8TF TEL/FAX: (01243) 572514
turn off A259 5m W of Chichester at Chidham Lane, then 1m on left

You will find this Tudor house down a quiet lane just a few minutes' walk from the harbour in the village of Chidham. The house is full of pictures, china, cats and music – guests are welcome to play the Bechstein piano, the cello or double bass. The atmosphere is informal and visitors are made to feel at home. The lounge has a TV, and residents may make use of the attractive garden. One of the two cosy bedrooms has an *en suite* bathroom. In summer bookings must be for a minimum of two nights. Chichester, which is about six miles away, offers a good choice of places for evening meals.

OWNER: Mary Hartley OPEN: all year exc Christmas ROOMS: 1 double, with bath; 1 twin, with wash-basin; tea/coffee in both bedrooms; lounge with TV TERMS: single occupancy £19–£32, twin/double £38–£42; half-price for children under 10 CARDS: none DETAILS: children welcome; dogs by arrangement; no smoking; car park; garden

Old Rectory

Cot Lane, Chidham PO18 8TA TEL/FAX: (01243) 572088
turn S off A259 down Cot Lane at Barleycorn pub, continue for 1m

The Old Rectory is reached down a quiet, leafy country lane and has a welcoming, relaxed atmosphere. It is a spacious house in a lovely garden, opposite the Saxon church of St Mary in this pretty little village. Most of the large, well-furnished bedrooms have *en suite* facilities or private use of a bathroom. A spacious formal drawing-room has a TV, and breakfast is served in the dining-room. A conservatory leads out to the garden, beyond which is a swimming-pool and a croquet lawn. The village pub serves food and is within a few minutes' walk. Chidham is in the middle of a small peninsula, which juts out into Chichester Harbour, and is a wonderful area for bird-watching, sailing and walking.

OWNERS: Peter and Anna Blencowe OPEN: Mar to Jan ROOMS: 2 single, both with wash-basin; 3 double/twin, 2 with bath/shower, 1 with private bathroom; tea/coffee in all bedrooms; TV in most bedrooms and lounge TERMS: single £18–£20, single occupancy £21–£30, twin/double £42–£50; children's reductions by arrangement CARDS: none DETAILS: children welcome; dogs welcome; smoking in lounge only; car park; garden; swimming-pool

To find an entry in the Guide, *go to the maps at the back of the book. Entries are plotted on the maps under their closest village, hamlet or city, except in London, where they are listed by name of B&B. After choosing your localities, go to the relevant section of the book (England, Scotland, Wales etc.), where localities are listed in alphabetical order (by B&B name order in London). There is also an index at the back of the book.*

CHILGROVE West Sussex **map 3**

Post Office Cottage

NEW ENTRY

Chilgrove, nr Chichester PO18 9HU
TEL: (01243) 535309 FAX: (01243) 535305
on B2141 from Chichester; on entering the village take first right, then left at the pillarbox; cottage is next to the cricket-pitch

This attractive seventeenth-century Sussex-flint cottage was once the village school and, more recently, the post office. It is on the edge of the peaceful hamlet of Chilgrove in a lovely large garden. The cottage is very comfortable and the Hernimans are welcoming people; Paul Herniman makes made-to-measure shoes. The beamed bedroom has *en suite* spacious facilities and can be let as either a double or a twin. Guests have their own entrance. Breakfast is served in the small dining-room, or in the garden in summer, and residents can relax in the large drawing-room with its inglenook fireplace. Liz Herniman also organises the village cricket club. Chilgrove is six miles north-west of Chichester, and sailing, golf, horse-riding and racing are all available locally.

OWNER: Liz Herniman OPEN: all year exc Christmas ROOMS: 1 twin/double, with bath/shower, tea/coffee and TV TERMS: single occupancy £25–£40, twin/double £50–£60; children half-price; deposit: 20% CARDS: none DETAILS: children welcome; no dogs; no smoking; car park; garden

CHIPPING CAMPDEN Gloucestershire **map 5**

Rosary Cottage

High Street, Chipping Campden GL55 6AL TEL: (01386) 841145

This fourteenth-century cottage was the first house to be built in the small town of Chipping Campden, and the High Street was later built around it. Bedrooms have pine furniture and co-ordinated pastel fabrics. Breakfast is served in the cosy dining-room, which has a grandfather clock. There are no TVs in this interesting house, which has kept much of its original charm in oak beams and thick stone walls. Chipping Campden is wonderfully placed for touring the Cotswolds.

OWNER: Rosemary Spencer OPEN: all year ROOMS: 2 double, 1 twin; all rooms with bath/shower and tea/coffee TERMS: single occupancy £35, twin/double £44 CARDS: none DETAILS: children welcome; no dogs; no smoking

Sparlings

Leysbourne, Chipping Campden GL55 6HL
TEL: (01386) 840505 FAX: (01386) 841676

Situated at the north end of the High Street, Sparlings is a seventeenth-century listed building. The house has been tastefully restored and retains many original features, such as flagstone floors and oak beams. It is immaculately kept, with a comfortable TV lounge, and the two bedrooms are well appointed, each having a private bathroom. Breakfast only is served, but there are plenty of eating places within walking distance. The house does not have its own parking, so visitors should ask in advance about parking arrangements.

OWNER: Geoffrey E. Douglass OPEN: all year ROOMS: 1 double, 1 twin; both rooms with private bathroom and tea/coffee; lounge with TV TERMS: single occupancy £27–£28, twin/double £46.50–£49.50 CARDS: none DETAILS: no children under 6; no dogs; smoking in lounge only; garden

CHIVELSTONE Devon **map 1**

South Allington House

Chivelstone TQ7 2NB TEL: (01548) 511272 FAX: (01548) 511421
turn off A38 for Kingsbridge, take main Dartmouth road; turn right at Frogmore, follow signs to E. Prawle until Chivelstone, turn left; ½m to B&B

This sizeable house is part of a working farm, and is peacefully set in pleasant Devonshire countryside. Sheep graze almost up to the door, and there is a pretty little pond in the front. The Bakers have maintained their high standards, and the bedrooms are well appointed: two have four-poster beds and all have electric blankets. The guest lounge has a log fire and TV, and first-class breakfasts are served in a large dining-room. Facilities for croquet and bowls are available, and self-catering accommodation is still on offer in the east wing of the house. One-night bookings are not available in high summer.

OWNERS: Edward and Barbara Baker OPEN: closed 2 months of the year, check when booking ROOMS: 1 single, 4 double, 2 twin, 2 four-poster; all rooms with bath/shower exc single and 1 twin with private bathrooms; tea/coffee in all bedrooms; TV in some bedrooms and lounge TERMS: single £20–£21, single occupancy £30–£40.50, twin/double £42–£48, four-poster £54–£56; reductions for children sharing with parents CARDS: none DETAILS: children welcome; no dogs; no smoking; car park; garden

CHOP GATE North Yorkshire **map 9**

Hillend Farm

Chop Gate TS9 7JR TEL: (01439) 798278
on B1257, 6m S of Stokesley

Hillend is high on the North Yorkshire Moors near the remote village of Chop Gate, surrounded by beautiful walking country. Six footpaths pass through the 106-acre farm, which takes in part of one of the few remaining oak forests and remnants of old jet mines. Bride Stones, an ancient stone circle, is 20 minutes' walk away. Bedrooms, both of which are *en suite*, are decorated in white and pink, and the sitting-room has an open fire. Evening meals are no longer served, but there are several eating-establishments in the village.

OWNERS: Mr and Mrs Johnson OPEN: Mar to Nov ROOMS: 1 double, 1 family; both rooms with bath/shower and tea/coffee; lounge with TV TERMS: single occupancy £25, double £40–£44, family room £40–£44; half-price for children; deposit: £20 CARDS: none DETAILS: children welcome; dogs by arrangement; smoking in lounge only; car park; garden

CHUDLEIGH Devon map 1

Oakfield

Exeter Road, Chudleigh TQ13 0DD TEL/FAX: (01626) 852194
off A38, 1m NE of Chudleigh

Oakfield, an attractive mid-nineteenth-century country house, stands in 20 acres of landscaped gardens, orchard and paddocks on the outskirts of Chudleigh. It has spacious, beautifully furnished and decorated bedrooms, each with its own character and supplied with fresh fruit and flowers; one has a half-tester bed. Visitors have use of a large, elegant drawing-room, a library and a billiard room. Although the house is grand, the Johnson-Kings are a most welcoming couple and treat their guests like friends. The extensive garden has a small heated swimming-pool in a sheltered position close to the house, and a loggia where guests can sit on fine evenings. A local restaurant is recommended by the Johnson-Kings for evening meals. Oakfield is well placed for exploring Dartmoor, and golf, fishing and riding are all available nearby.

OWNER: Patricia Johnson-King OPEN: Easter to Oct ROOMS: 2 twin, 1 four-poster; all rooms with bath/shower, tea/coffee and TV; lounge TERMS: single occupancy £50, twin £60–£70; deposit: £10 per person CARDS: none DETAILS: no children under 12; no dogs; no smoking; car park; games room; garden; swimming-pool

CHURCHAM Gloucestershire map 5

Edgewood House NEW ENTRY

Churcham GL2 8AA TEL: (01452) 750232
on A40, Gloucester to Ross-on-Wye road, 4m W of Gloucester

This large, detached 1930s house has two acres of park-like grounds with mature trees, shrubs and colourful flowers. Bedrooms are pine-furnished and the beds have bright duvets. Breakfast is served in the dining-room, which leads on to the conservatory, and there is a guests' lounge, warmed by a gas fire on chilly evenings. An abundance of leaflets provides information on what to see and do in the area. Edgewood House is near a viewing point for the Severn Bore Tidal Wave and opposite the Highnam Woods RSPB reserve.

OWNERS: Mr and Mrs P. Stevens OPEN: all year ROOMS: 1 double, with shower; 1 twin, with private bathroom; 1 family, with shower; tea/coffee in all bedrooms; lounge with TV TERMS: single occupancy £25–£29, double £40–£45, twin £38–£42, family room from £20–£22.50 per person; deposit: 25% CARDS: none DETAILS: no children under 8; no dogs; no smoking; car park; garden

CHURCH STRETTON Shropshire map 5

Brookfields Guest House

Watling Street North, Church Stretton SY6 7AR TEL: (01694) 722314

Brookfields has the benefit of being just a stroll from the town centre and yet offering lovely views over the countryside and the Stretton Hills. The house itself is set in half an acre of pretty landscaped gardens. Four comfortable *en suite* bedrooms are offered, all with TVs and amenities such as hair-dryers and clock radios. One bedroom is on the ground floor. There is a guest lounge, and the bright dining-room, which overlooks the Long Mynd – popular with hill-walkers and hang-gliding enthusiasts – is where breakfasts are served.

OWNERS: Carol and Stewart Blower OPEN: all year ROOMS: 2 double, 1 twin, 1 family; twin and double rooms with shower, family room with bath; tea/coffee and TV in all bedrooms; lounge TERMS: single occupancy £27–£35, twin/double £45–£47, family room from £55; children's reductions according to age CARDS: none DETAILS: children welcome; dogs by arrangement; no smoking in bedrooms; car park; garden

CIRENCESTER Gloucestershire map 2

Wimborne House

91 Victoria Road, Cirencester GL7 1ES TEL/FAX: (01285) 653890

Just a few minutes' walk from the town centre, this nineteenth-century detached house standing in its own gardens offers four well-appointed *en suite* bedrooms. One has a four-poster bed, and all have TVs, are colour-co-ordinated in pastels and furnished in pine. Guests also have use of a sitting-room on the first floor. Good-value evening meals are available by arrangement, and vegetarian options can be requested.

OWNERS: Dianne and Marshall Clarke OPEN: all year exc Christmas ROOMS: 3 double, 1 twin, 1 four-poster; all rooms with bath and shower, tea/coffee and TV; lounge TERMS: single occupancy £20–£28, twin/double £30–£40, four-poster £40–£45; dinner £7.50; deposit: £10 per person CARDS: none DETAILS: no children under 10; no dogs; no smoking; car park; garden

CLARE Suffolk map 6

Ship Stores

22 Callis Street, Clare CO10 8PX TEL: (01787) 277834
on B1063, 200 metres from church

Set in the small, picturesque town of Clare, Ship Stores was converted out of three seventeenth-century, timber-framed cottages. The main building encompasses the old village shop, and there are also adjoining tea-rooms. All of the refurbished bedrooms have *en suite* showers and TVs, and two of the rooms are in a ground-floor annexe across the courtyard. The guest lounge has a TV and video, and free films are provided. A wide variety of freshly prepared breakfasts are available, including vegetarian options. Evening meals are on offer by request; alternatively, there are a couple of pubs within walking distance that serve food. The area is popular with antique hunters.

OWNERS: Debra and Colin Bowles OPEN: all year ROOMS: 3 double, 1 twin, 1 family; all rooms with shower, tea/coffee and TV; 2 rooms suitable for wheelchair-users; lounge with TV TERMS: single occupancy £25–£39, twin/double £39–£44, family room £64; babies free, half-price for children under 10, reductions for older children sharing with parents; dinner £8.50; deposit: £10 CARDS: Delta, MasterCard, Switch, Visa DETAILS: children welcome; no dogs; no smoking in bedrooms; car park

CLAYDON Suffolk map 6

Redbrae NEW ENTRY

The Slade, Claydon IP6 0EX TEL: (01473) 830310
just off A14, 5m NW of Ipswich

This large modern bungalow is in two parts with a corridor joining them, and stands in a large garden with a pond, a patio and a play area for children. It is in a peaceful hamlet with rural views, and is only a mile from the village and a few minutes' drive from Ipswich. There is a public footpath to Barham Church in front of the house, and a wooded bridle walk. The three bedrooms have modern furnishings; the double room in the main bungalow shares a bathroom and lounge with the owner. The twin and family rooms are in the other section and share a bathroom, lounge and kitchen. Joan Hassell is a congenial host and a keen tennis player. Breakfasts, and pre-booked dinners, are served family-style and can be taken in the dining-room or conservatory. Vegetarian choices and children's portions can be arranged. A pub in the village also serves good evening meals. One half of the B&B can also be let out as a two-bedroomed self-catering unit.

OWNER: Joan Hassell OPEN: all year ROOMS: 1 double, 1 twin, 1 family; tea/coffee and TV in all bedrooms; lounge with TV TERMS: single occupancy £20, twin/double £36, family room from £36; £10 for children sharing with parents; dinner £10; deposit: £50 for bookings of 1 week and over CARDS: none DETAILS: children welcome; no dogs; no smoking; car park; garden

CLEETHORPES N.E. Lincolnshire map 9

Brentwood Guest House

9 Princes Road, Cleethorpes DN35 8AW TEL: (01472) 693982

Only five minutes from the beach, this black-and-white Victorian house provides clean, serviceable accommodation. The modestly furnished bedrooms range in size from average to large family rooms. A TV lounge is available for visitors' use. Breakfast, and pre-arranged home-cooked traditional evening meals, are served at separate tables in the bright dining-room. As Brentwood is unlicensed, guests are welcome to bring their own wine to dinner. Suzanne and Kevin Brown offer a very friendly welcome to their visitors.

OWNERS: Kevin and Suzanne Brown OPEN: all year ROOMS: 2 double, 4 twin, 3 family; all rooms with wash-basin, tea/coffee and TV; lounge with TV TERMS: single occupancy £16–£20, twin/double £32, family room £35–£49; half-price for children under 12 sharing parents' room; dinner £6; deposit: £5 per room CARDS: none DETAILS: children welcome; dogs welcome with own bedding

CLIFTON Derbyshire map 5

Collycroft Farm

Clifton, nr Ashbourne DE6 2GN TEL: (01335) 342187
just off A515, 2m S of Ashbourne

Collycroft is a mid-eighteenth-century farmhouse on a 250-acre beef and dairy farm on the edge of the Peak District. There are footpaths through the surrounding meadows, and guests can enjoy use of the pretty garden and patio. The house has lovely old-fashioned furnishings, and there is a comfortable lounge for residents' use. One bedroom has *en suite* facilities, while the other two have private use of large bathrooms. Breakfast, which may include home-made jams, can be served at different times to suit guests' needs. Prince Charles once visited the farm and enjoyed tasting Mary Hollingsworth's home-made damson gin (not damson jam, as we said by error in the last edition!). The farm is a short drive from Ashbourne, where there are several pubs and restaurants.

OWNER: Mary Hollingsworth OPEN: all year ROOMS: 1 double, with shower; 1 twin, with private bathroom; 1 family, with private bathroom; tea/coffee and TV in all bedrooms; lounge with TV TERMS: single occupancy £20, twin/double £36–£40, family room £36–£40; children £10 in family room; deposit required CARDS: none DETAILS: children welcome; no dogs; no smoking in bedrooms; car park; garden

CLIFTON-UPON-TEME Hereford & Worcester map 5

Pitlands Farm NEW ENTRY

Clifton-upon-Teme WR6 6DX TEL: (01886) 812220
from Worcester take A443 towards Tenbury, turn into B4204, go right at Martley, continue over river bridge; B&B is ½m on right

This charming thatched farmhouse stands in beautiful rolling countryside, less than a mile from the unspoilt village of Clifton-upon-Teme. The large garden and orchards are inhabited by sheep and turkeys, and fly-fishing is available on a private trout pool. The dining-room-cum-lounge area dates back to the fifteenth century. There are two comfortable bedrooms, one of which is an enormous oak-beamed family room with an open fire. Diane and John Mann have a good sense of humour, and guests are treated as visiting friends. Four self-catering units are also situated on the property, and the local village pubs serve evening meals. As we were going to press plans were in progress to make one twin and the family *en suite* with shower, leaving the remaining twin with a private bathroom.

OWNERS: Diane and John Mann OPEN: Mar to Oct ROOMS: 2 twin, 1 family; tea/coffee in all bedrooms; TV in some rooms and lounge TERMS: single occupancy £17, twin £34, family from £34 CARDS: none DETAILS: children welcome; no dogs; no smoking in bedrooms; car park; garden

CLINT GREEN Norfolk **map 6**

Clinton House

Well Hill, Clint Green NR19 1RX TEL: (01362) 692079

from Dereham head S on B1135; at Yaxham take sign for Matishall, then turn right at school and continue for 200 metres

This immaculately kept 200-year old whitewashed, shuttered house is in a peaceful Norfolk hamlet. The garden has a lawn with colourful rose beds, a willow and an old well; a grass tennis court and croquet lawn are available for guests' use. The beamed lounge has an inglenook fireplace, which is used on cold days. The bedrooms are beautifully decorated and have every comfort and, although none has *en suite* facilities, there are two bathrooms exclusively for guests. The annexe room is no longer available. Breakfast is served in the conservatory. It should be noted that the house is not open between 11am and 4pm.

OWNERS: John and Margaret Searle OPEN: all year exc Christmas ROOMS: 1 double, 1 twin, 1 family; all rooms with wash-basin, tea/coffee and TV; lounge with TV TERMS: single occupancy £20–£22, twin/double £32–£34, family room £41–£45; babies free, half-price for older children; deposit required CARDS: none DETAILS: children welcome; no dogs; no smoking; car park; garden; tennis

CLITHEROE Lancashire **map 8**

Brooklyn NEW ENTRY

32 Pimlico Road, Clitheroe BB7 2AH TEL: (01200) 428268

Flower-filled baskets and window boxes decorate this pleasant detached Victorian townhouse, just a few minutes' walk from the centre of the historic market town of Clitheroe. Pam Glendinning is a congenial and welcoming host. Bedrooms have stripped-pine furniture and floral duvets, the lounge is well furnished and guests have use of the walled garden in summer. Full cooked or continental breakfast is served, and dinner can be provided by arrangement.

OWNERS: Robert and Pam Glendinning OPEN: all year ROOMS: 1 single, 1 double, 2 twin; all rooms with bath/shower, tea/coffee and TV; lounge TERMS: single/single occupancy £25–£30, twin/double £40–£45; children under 5 free, half-price for ages 5–12; dinner £10; deposit required CARDS: Delta, MasterCard, Switch, Visa DETAILS: children welcome; no dogs; no smoking

CLUN Shropshire **map 5**

Old Farmhouse, Woodside

Clun SY7 0JB TEL: (01588) 640695

in village in front of church turn into Vicarage Rd; after 300yds turn right, signposted Woodside; farmhouse ½m on left

Built in the seventeenth century as a labourer's cottage and later extended, the farmhouse is set in a large, pretty garden with a stream and a natural pool. A six-foot stone wall separates the old part of the building from the new. From the house are pleasant views over the Clun Valley. Two guest bedrooms are offered, one suitable for families, and residents also have the use of a TV lounge, off which is a conservatory that leads into the garden. Home-cooked evening meals are available if booked in advance, and are, along with breakfast, served in the separate dining-room.

OWNER: R.H. Wall OPEN: Mar to Oct ROOMS: 1 double, 1 family; both rooms with wash-basin and tea/coffee; lounge with TV TERMS: single occupancy £18, double £30–£34, family room £30–£34 plus children's charge; children under 5 free, half-price for ages 5–10; dinner £9; deposit required CARDS: none DETAILS: children welcome; dogs welcome; no smoking; car park; garden

COCKERMOUTH Cumbria **map 10**

Wythop Mill Cottage **NEW ENTRY**

Wythop Mill, Cockermouth CA13 9YP TEL: (01768) 776174

This cosy, Grade II-listed seventeenth-century cottage is by a water mill and stream in the midst of beautiful walking country. Owner Sheila Collier formerly ran Old Bank House in Hayfield (listed in the last edition of the *Guide*) and has set out to offer the same high standard of accommodation that she provided there. She restored the cottage herself, decorating and furnishing it in keeping with its character, combining its old world charm with modern comforts. One of the two pretty bedrooms has *en suite* facilities, the other a private bathroom. There is a guests' lounge, and breakfast, prepared on the Aga, is served in the separate dining-room, where a Cumbrian Court cupboard displays the date 1676.

OWNER: Sheila Collier OPEN: Mar to Nov ROOMS: 2 double, 1 with bath/shower, 1 with wash-basin; tea/coffee and TV in both bedrooms; lounge with TV TERMS: single occupancy £25–£30, double £30–£35 CARDS: none DETAILS: children welcome; well-behaved dogs welcome; no smoking; car park; garden

---

'Bath / shower' in the details under each entry means that the rooms have en suite *facilities. 'Private bathroom' signifies that a room has a bathroom for its exclusive use. The B&B may have other, shared bathroom facilities as well. We list 'wash-basins' for rooms that have them but do not have* en suite *or private facilities.*

COLCHESTER Essex map 3

Four Sevens Guest House

28 Inglis Road, Colchester CO3 3HU TEL/FAX: (01206) 546093
in town off B1022 Maldon road

Improvements are ongoing to this light and spacious Victorian residence on a quiet tree-lined street, only a few minutes' walk from the town centre. The lounge has been refurbished with new settees and armchairs. The immaculate bedrooms have pine furnishings and attractive duvets. All have satellite TV, and video recorders can be provided on request, with a huge selection of tapes available. Large breakfasts and pre-arranged dinners are served in the dining-room; vegetarians can be catered for and guests may bring their own wine to dinner. Parking permits are provided.

OWNER: Calypso Demetri OPEN: all year exc Christmas ROOMS: 3 double/family, 1 with shower, 2 with wash-basin; 3 twin, 1 with shower, 2 with wash-basin; tea/coffee and TV in all bedrooms TERMS: single occupancy £30–£35, twin/double £35–£45, family room £50–£60; half-price for children; dinner £15 CARDS: none DETAILS: no children under 2; no dogs; smoking in some bedrooms only; garden

Old Manse

15 Roman Road, Colchester CO1 1UR TEL: (01206) 545154

The Old Manse is situated in a quiet square, within walking distance of the town centre, and has a Roman wall at the end of the garden. Wendy Anderson is a thoughtful host who provides guests with tea trays and home-made cakes. The three tastefully decorated bedrooms have antique furniture and TV; one room is on the ground floor. The comfortable sitting-room has a piano, which musical guests are welcome to play. Breakfast is served at a large table, and there are several places for evening meals within walking distance. Parking is available on the road with a permit provided by the owners.

OWNER: Wendy Anderson OPEN: all year exc Christmas ROOMS: 1 double, with private bathroom; 2 twin; tea/coffee and TV in all bedrooms TERMS: single occupancy £25–£28, twin/double £36–£44; deposit required CARDS: none DETAILS: no children under 5; no dogs; no smoking

COLLINGTON Hereford & Worcester map 5

The Granary

Church House Farm, Collington HR7 4NA TEL: (01885) 410345
off B4214, 3m N of Bromyard

Positioned in a lovely and tranquil part of the Kyre Valley, the Granary is part of a 200-acre working farm. It offers five well-appointed *en suite* rooms, all on the ground floor in a sensitively converted barn. Beamed ceilings and pastel shades add to their appeal. Two of the rooms are suitable for disabled visitors. Dinners, which must be pre-booked, are served by candlelight in the licensed dining-room, which is also open to non-residents for dinners and Sunday lunch. One visitor found that dining here was a 'romantic' experience, and especially commended the puddings.

OWNER: Margaret Maiden OPEN: all year ROOMS: 1 double, 4 twin; all rooms with bath/shower, tea/coffee and TV; 2 rooms suitable for wheelchair-users; lounge with TV TERMS: single occupancy £20, twin/double £40–£40; reductions for children by arrangement; dinner £10–£15; deposit: £10 per person CARDS: none DETAILS: children welcome; dogs by arrangement; no smoking in dining-room; car park

COMBE MARTIN Devon **map 1**

Holdstone Farm

Hunters Inn Road, Combe Martin EX34 0PE TEL: (01271) 883423
off A399, 2m N of Combe Martin

This beef and sheep farm has been around since the twelfth century and is in a secluded position, high up on the downs. The house has a welcoming, friendly and homely atmosphere, added to by low ceilings and an inglenook fireplace in the guests' lounge. There are two fresh and bright bedrooms, which share a bathroom, and although there are no drink-making facilities in the bedrooms, tea and coffee are always available when required. Evening meals are served by arrangement in the attractive dining-room, and Sunday lunch is also available. Cliffs, sandy beaches and the resort of Ilfracombe are nearby.

OWNER: Jayne Lerwill OPEN: all year exc Christmas ROOMS: 1 double, 1 family; lounge with TV TERMS: single occupancy £18–£20, twin/double £36–£38, family room £60–£64; dinner £12; deposit: minimum £20 CARDS: none DETAILS: children welcome; no dogs; no smoking; car park; garden

COMBWICH Somerset **map 2**

Moxhill Farmhouse NEW ENTRY

Combwich TA5 2PN TEL: (01278) 652285 FAX: (01278) 653942
take A39 from Bridgwater, turn off N into Cannington; farm is 1½m on left before right turn to Combwich.

Visitors to Moxhill Farmhouse find a warm and friendly welcome, and comfortably furnished bedrooms with lots of extras, such as fruit, bottled water and shampoo. The 250-year-old farmhouse, which is part of a dairy farm run by Nigel Venner, stands in a peaceful area surrounded by flat farmland, only five miles from Bridgwater. Carol Venner has a good reputation for her cooking and provides an extensive dinner menu, including vegetarian options and children's portions. The house is licensed and has a well-stocked wine cellar. Bedrooms have easy chairs, good lights for reading and TV, and there is a lounge, also with TV.

OWNERS: Carol and Nigel Venner OPEN: all year ROOMS: 1 single, 2 double, 2 family; all rooms with bath/shower, tea/coffee and TV; lounge with TV TERMS: single £20–£22, single occupancy £21–£26, double £40–£44, family room £40–£44 plus children's charges; children under 2 free, half-price for ages 2–12 sharing with parents; dinner £9–£18; deposit: £10 per person CARDS: none DETAILS: children welcome; dogs by arrangement; no smoking; car park; garden

COMPTON ABBAS Dorset **map 2**

Old Forge

Fanners Yard, Chapel Hill, Compton Abbas SP7 0NQ
TEL/FAX: (01747) 811881
just off A350, 3m S of Shaftesbury

Tim and Lucy Kerridge have sensitively converted these former wheelwright and carriage-builder's premises to create simple yet attractive accommodation. The house was built around 1700 from local stone in the hamlet of Compton Abbas, on the edge of Fontmell Down. There are lots of old beams and sloping ceilings throughout the house, pretty bedrooms, and a comfortable breakfast/sitting-room with a wood-burning stove. A pergola in the courtyard makes a pleasant place for sitting outside. The old forge itself, just across the road, is now a museum. Tim restores vintage cars at the back of the property in a converted lorry shed. The area provides good walking, with National Trust chalk downland nearby, and bicycle hire is available. One-night bookings are not taken at weekends or bank holidays.

OWNERS: Tim and Lucy Kerridge OPEN: all year ROOMS: 1 single, with private bathroom; 1 double, with private bathroom; 1 family, with shower; tea/coffee in all bedrooms; TV in double bedroom and lounge TERMS: single £25–£27.50, single occupancy £35–£40, double £40–£50, family room £60–£67.50; deposit: £20 CARDS: none DETAILS: children welcome; dogs by arrangement; no smoking; car park; garden

CONISTON Cumbria **map 8**

Arrowfield Country Guest House

Little Arrow, Coniston LA21 8AU TEL: (01539) 441741
on A593, 1¾m S of Coniston

Just under two miles from Coniston, Arrowfield is a good base from which to explore the Lake District. All around are fine views of this beautiful area, and the house itself, dating from Victorian times, stands in its own pretty gardens. Malcolm and Stephanie Walton continue to upgrade the premises, putting in new carpets and curtains since the last edition of the *Guide*. Bedrooms are spacious and well appointed; one double has a king-sized bed. Guests have the use of a comfortable lounge, complete with open fire. Breakfasts, served in the separate dining-room, are substantial and offer good choice: opt for full English, including eggs from the Waltons' own free-range hens and honey from their bees, or for continental with hot croissants. Bread and preserves are home-made.

OWNERS: Malcolm and Stephanie Walton OPEN: Feb to Nov ROOMS: 1 single, 3 double, 1 twin; all rooms with bath/shower, tea/coffee and TV; lounge with TV TERMS:

single £20–£23, single occupancy £35, twin/double £40–£46; children's reductions according to age; deposit: £10 per person CARDS: none DETAILS: children welcome; no dogs; no smoking; car park; garden

Cruachan

NEW ENTRY

Collingwood Close, Coniston LA21 8DZ TEL: (01539) 441628
entering Coniston on A593 from Ambleside, take first left before fire station; house on left

Named after a mountain in Scotland, Cruachan is a modern house standing in a quiet cul-de-sac close to the centre of the village, and has grand views of the Old Man of Coniston. Within, all is light and airy, and the colour-co-ordinated bedrooms give off something of an air of luxury with their quality linens, firm beds and pine furniture. All have *en suite* showers and TVs. Guests have the use of a lounge/dining-room, where breakfasts are served. These may feature poached haddock and poached eggs, plus a cooked vegetarian option, as well as traditional choices. Those arriving via pedal-power can park their cycles in a secure storage room, and walkers returning from a wet day on the hills can make use of drying facilities.

OWNERS: Alan and Lillian Grant OPEN: all year exc Christmas ROOMS: 2 double, 1 twin; all rooms with shower, tea/coffee and TV; lounge TERMS: single occupancy £25–£30, twin/double £40–£50; children's reductions according to age; deposit: £20 CARDS: none DETAILS: children welcome by arrangement; no dogs; no smoking; car park; garden

Townson Ground

Coniston LA21 8AA TEL: (01539) 441272
take Hawkshead road from Coniston to head of lake, turn right on road marked 'Brantwood'; first house on left

Townson House stands in two acres of formal gardens, surrounded by trees, on the eastern bank of Coniston Water, one mile from the village. It is now run by Richard Nelson, son of the former owners, and his wife Wendy, and they have redecorated and made improvements to this attractive sixteenth-century house. Bedrooms are decorated in pastel colours and have pine furniture, and the top-floor room has oak beams and a sloping ceiling. The enormous lounge has two fireplaces, and breakfast is served in the beamed dining-room. Laundry facilities are available, and there are three self-catering cottages available.

OWNERS: Richard and Wendy Nelson OPEN: all year exc Christmas ROOMS: 1 single, with wash-basin; 2 double, both with bath/shower; 1 twin, with bath/shower; 1 family, with bath/shower; tea/coffee and TV in all bedrooms; lounge TERMS: single £20–£25, twin/double £40–£52, family room from £62; reductions for children sharing with parents; deposit: 1 night's charge CARDS: Delta, MasterCard, Switch, Visa DETAILS: no children under 3; dogs by arrangement; no smoking in public rooms; car park; garden

COOKHAM DEAN Berkshire map 3

Primrose Hill NEW ENTRY

Bradcutts Lane, Cookham Dean SL6 9TL TEL: (01628) 528179
off A404, 3m N of Maidenhead

This large house on top of a hill, on the outskirts of Cookham Dean, has an attractive garden with a croquet lawn and a summer house. The two pine-furnished bedrooms share a bathroom, and there is an additional WC on the ground floor. There are two lounges, one with a wood-burning stove and TV, the other a quiet room with an open fire. There are lots of interesting things to look at in the house, including a display of ancestral portraits on the galleried landing. Sir Stanley Spencer, the well-known artist, was born in Cookham, and there is a gallery dedicated to him in the village – a visit is recommended.

OWNER: Diana Benson OPEN: all year exc Christmas ROOMS: 1 single, 1 family; both rooms with wash-basin and TV; lounge with TV TERMS: single/single occupancy £18–£20, family room £40–£45; deposit: £5 CARDS: none DETAILS: children welcome; dogs welcome with own bedding and not left unattended in rooms; no smoking; car park; garden

COOMBE KEYNES Dorset map 2

April Thatch NEW ENTRY

Coombe Keynes, nr Lulworth Cove BH20 5PP TEL/FAX: (01929) 463412
off B3071 Wool to Lulworth road, 1½m from Wool

This pretty, Grade II-listed thatched cottage, surrounded by a pleasant garden, is at the edge of the quiet hamlet of Coombe Keynes. Accommodation is simple but tastefully decorated and furnished, and what makes it stand out is the warmth and friendliness of Helen Cooper and her husband Terry. Both have a good sense of humour and are considerate hosts, and will pick up guests from Wool station. April Thatch is within easy reach of Lulworth Cove and in a good area for walking.

OWNER: Helen Cooper OPEN: all year ROOMS: 2 double, 1 with shower, 1 with wash-basin and WC; tea/coffee in both bedrooms; TV in 1 bedroom and lounge TERMS: single occupancy £20–£25, double £35–£40; children's reductions by arrangement; deposit: 1 night's charge CARDS: none DETAILS: children welcome; dogs welcome to sleep in hallway; no smoking; car park; garden

---

If you intend to spend several days at a B&B, it is worth asking whether there are reduced rates, particularly if the period is midweek or off-season. It is always best to check prices, especially for single occupancy, when booking. If we know of any particular payment stipulations, we mention them in the details at the end of the entry. We asked the proprietors to estimate their 1998 prices in the autumn of 1997, so the rates may have changed since publication. If a deposit is required for an advance booking, this is stated in the details.

COPTHORNE West Sussex map 3

Linchens

New Domewood, Copthorne RH10 3HF TEL/FAX: (01342) 713085
from M3 junction 10 take A264 towards East Grinstead; after Shell Garage on right turn left into private New Domewood road, then first right and, after sharp bend to left, Linchens is first house on right

Linchens, built in the 1960s, is a large chalet-style house on an upmarket estate and is set in three-and-a-half-acres of mature and well-maintained gardens. The bedrooms are bright, good-sized rooms, all with a sitting-area. Breakfast is taken at one table in the owner's sitting-room, which overlooks the garden. The Smyths are knowledgeable about the local area and will do transfers to or from Gatwick for an extra charge, and will also provide parking while visitors are away. Linchens is a 15-minute drive from the airport.

OWNERS: John and Sally Smyth OPEN: all year exc Christmas ROOMS: 2 double/twin/family, 1 with bath/shower, 1 with private bathroom; tea/coffee and TV in both bedrooms TERMS: single occupancy £32.50–£37.50, twin/double £50–£52.50, family room £65–£72.50; deposit: £10 CARDS: MasterCard, Visa DETAILS: children welcome; dogs welcome; no smoking; car park; garden

CORBRIDGE Northumberland map 10

Clive House NEW ENTRY

Appletree Lane, Corbridge NE45 5DN TEL: (01434) 632617

This creeper-covered house, only five minutes' walk from the village, was built in 1848 and was part of the village school. The entrance has an exposed stone wall and red Victorian décor. The well-appointed bedrooms have floral wallpapers and pine furniture, and one has a four-poster bed. Breakfast is served in a very large beamed galleried room, which was the original schoolhouse. The sitting-room overlooks the garden and has a fine display of paintings by local artist Penny Ward. Corbridge church dates from the seventh century and is well worth a visit.

OWNER: Mrs Ann Hodgson OPEN: all year exc Christmas ROOMS: 1 double, 1 twin, 1 four-poster; all rooms with bath/shower, tea/coffee and TV; lounge with TV TERMS: single occupancy £30–£35, twin/double £40–£44, four-poster £44; deposit: £20 per booking CARDS: none DETAILS: no children; no dogs; no smoking; car park

Town Barns NEW ENTRY

Off Trinity Terrace, Corbridge NE45 5HP TEL: (01434) 633345
leave A69 at Stagshaw road exit, continue ½m into Corbridge; follow signs to Roman sight through village; Town Barns just outside up private lane

There is a touch of luxury about this 25-year-old house made of local stone. In a secluded setting yet near the village centre, it is approached by a private lane, and has fine views of the Tyne Valley and surrounding countryside. Author Catherine Cookson lived here from 1978 to 1981. The spacious and well-appointed bedrooms, which are accessed from the galleried landing, are furnished in yew and mahogany, and colour-co-ordinated in pastels. The family room consists of two adjoining rooms with *en suite* facilities. The large, well-furnished lounge has a real fire for chilly evenings, and overlooks the heated indoor swimming-pool, which is open for guests' use during the summer. Breakfasts are served in the separate dining-room.

OWNERS: Tony and Dorothy Wilson OPEN: Mar to Oct ROOMS: 2 double, 1 family; all rooms with bath/shower, tea/coffee and TV; lounge with TV TERMS: single occupancy £25–£35, double £44–£46, family room from £44–£46; reductions for children sharing with parents; deposit: £10 per person CARDS: none DETAILS: children welcome; no dogs; no smoking; car park; games room; garden; swimming-pool

CORNFORTH Co Durham **map 10**

Ash House

24 The Green, Cornforth DL17 9JH TEL: (01740) 654654
off A177/A688, 4m S of Durham, near A1 junction 61

Delia Slack continues to provide a warm welcome to guests, who appreciate her friendly helpfulness. Having run her B&B since 1975, she knows the area well and will happily advise on places to visit. The house dates from the Victorian era, and stands in a tranquil spot opposite the green in this pretty conservation village. Bedrooms are of a good size, and dressed up in floral fabrics; one room has a four-poster bed. Breakfast is served in the dining-room, and guests will find many eating-places for evening meals nearby.

OWNERS: Mr and Mrs D. Slack OPEN: all year ROOMS: 1 twin, 1 four-poster, 1 family; all rooms with wash-basin, tea/coffee, and TV TERMS: single occupancy £22–£30, twin £36, four-poster £45, family room £50; £10 for children under 10; deposit: £10 CARDS: none DETAILS: children welcome; dogs welcome; car park; garden

CORSHAM Wiltshire **map 2**

Pickwick Lodge Farm

Guyers Lane, Corsham SN13 0PS
TEL: (01249) 712207 FAX: (01249) 701904
take A4 towards Bath from Corsham, turn right into Guyers Lane, follow lane to end, house on right

A half-mile track leads to this lovely old Cotswold-stone farmhouse. The rear part of this listed house dates from the seventeenth century, with the front having been added much later. Pickwick Lodge is part of a 300-acre arable and beef farm, which guests are welcome to explore. From the lounge, steps lead down into the attractive dining-room, where breakfasts are served, and one of the large double bedrooms, which can also be used as family rooms, is on the ground floor. Nearby are the Wiltshire White Horse, Avebury and Stonehenge. The picturesque villages of Lacock and Castle Combe are also within easy reach, and Bath is just a 15-minute drive away.

OWNERS: Guy and Gill Stafford OPEN: all year exc Christmas ROOMS: 2 double, 1 with bath/shower, 1 with private bathroom; 1 twin, with private bathroom; tea/coffee and TV in all bedrooms TERMS: single occupancy £20–£25, twin/double from £36–£40; babies free, half-price for children under10 sharing with parents; deposit or letter of confirmation required CARDS: none DETAILS: children welcome; dogs by arrangement; no smoking; car park; garden

CORTON Suffolk map 6

Church Farm NEW ENTRY

Corton NR32 5HX TEL/FAX: (01502) 730359

off A12 between Lowestoft and Great Yarmouth

This attractive nineteenth-century farmhouse, part of a working arable farm, is located not far from the Suffolk coast and its sandy beaches. Guests may enjoy the pleasant rose gardens and patio outside and, within, are accommodated graciously in one of the four spacious double bedrooms. Decorated in soft pastel colours, the rooms are comfortably appointed, with *en suite* facilities or private bathroom, plus armchairs, TVs and radio alarms. One has a sea view, and one very large room is in a tastefully converted farm building. Generous breakfasts are served on fine china in the elegant dining-room.

OWNERS: Lis and Mick Edwards OPEN: Mar to Nov ROOMS: 4 double, 3 with bath/ shower, 1 with private bathroom; tea/coffee and TV in all bedrooms TERMS: single occupancy £25–£30, double £38–£40; deposit: £20 CARDS: none DETAILS: no children; no dogs; no smoking; car park; garden

COTGRAVE Nottinghamshire map 5

Jerico Farm NEW ENTRY

Fosse Way, Cotgrave NG12 3HG TEL/FAX: (01949) 81733

100 metres off A46 down farm drive 1m N of junction of A46 with the A606 Nottingham to Melton Mowbray road

This large, red-brick modern house is part of a 130-acre mixed working farm supporting wheat and barley, sheep and cattle. Coarse fishing is available on the property. Bedrooms are fair-sized and decorated in soft colours. The sitting-room has a wood-burning stove and overlooks the garden. Substantial farmhouse breakfasts are served in the conservatory; special dietary needs can be catered for with advance notice. Mrs Herrick is an accommodating host who has prepared a portfolio, complete with menus, on nearby places to eat.

OWNERS: Sally and David Herrick OPEN: all year exc Christmas ROOMS: 1 double, with wash-basin; 2 twin, 1 with shower, 1 with wash-basin; tea/coffee and TV in all bedrooms; lounge with TV TERMS: single occupancy £21–£27, twin/double £36–£40; deposit: £10 per room per night or credit card details CARDS: Delta, MasterCard, Switch, Visa DETAILS: no children under 5; no dogs; no smoking; car park; garden

COTHERSTONE Co Durham — map 10

Glendale — NEW ENTRY

Cotherstone DL12 9UH TEL: (01833) 650384

follow B6277 from Barnard Castle 3m to Cotherstone; take East Briscoe Rd from village; B&B is first house on the right

This modern stone-built house is set in a half-acre of colourful gardens, and is surrounded by peaceful countryside. The well-appointed bedrooms are fully *en suite*, and have TVs. Full English breakfasts are served at separate tables in a cosy dining-room, which has a wood-burning stove. There is also a sitting-area on a galleried landing where guests are served a hot drink and slice of home-baked cake on arrival. Evening meals are available at the local pub, and the Rabbitts are happy to provide information about suitable alternatives. Glendale is an ideal base for walks, bird-watching and visiting the nearby Bowes Museum and Raby Castle.

OWNERS: David and Morlene Rabbitts OPEN: all year ROOMS: 3 double; all rooms with bath/shower, tea/coffee and TV; lounge TERMS: single occupancy £16–£22, double £32; deposit: £6 per room per night CARDS: none DETAILS: no children; no dogs; no smoking; car park; garden

COVENTRY West Midlands — map 5

Abigail Guest House

39 St Patrick's Road, Coventry CV1 2LP TEL: (01203) 221378

This Victorian terraced guesthouse is situated withing walking distance of Coventry cathedral and the city centre, and offers good-value accommodation. The house is kept spotlessly clean, and the comfortable bedrooms all have wash-basins and TVs. Double glazing has been installed, helping to make the house quiet and peaceful. Abigail Guest House is close to the railway and bus stations and well positioned for visiting Coventry and Warwick universities. Guests are advised to request instructions for navigating the one-way system when booking.

OWNERS: Roger and Julie Griffiths OPEN: all year exc Christmas and New Year ROOMS: 3 single, 1 double, 1 twin, 1 family; all rooms with wash-basin, tea/coffee and TV; lounge with TV TERMS: single £17–£19, single occupancy £18–£25, twin/double £32–£37, family room £34–£45; children under 5 free; half-price for ages 5–11; deposit: 1 night's charge in high season CARDS: none DETAILS: children welcome; well-behaved dogs welcome; no smoking in dining-room; garden

If a B&B offers off-street car parking, we note 'car park' at the end of the entry. If nearby on-street parking must be used, in most cases we give details in the descriptive text.

Crest Guest House

39 Friars Road, Coventry CV1 2LJ
TEL: (01203) 227822   FAX: (01203) 227244

It is easy to spot this red-brick villa among all the others: it's the one with the royal-blue woodwork and the lovingly landscaped garden full of colourful shrubs and flowers. Although in a quiet cul-de-sac, this immaculate guesthouse is only ten minutes' walk from the cathedral and the Transport Museum. The welcome here is especially warm, and Peggy Harvey's genuine enthusiasm for making her guests' stay happy is clearly visible. The bedrooms, all of which have TVs, have new, rich-coloured curtains and matching duvets; the two single rooms share a bathroom and the twin rooms are *en suite*. The cosy and comfortable lounge with its log-effect fire is also where generous breakfasts are served. Visitors coming by car should be sure when making a reservation to request instructions for navigating the one-way system.

OWNERS: Alan and Peggy Harvey   OPEN: all year exc Christmas   ROOMS: 2 single, both with wash-basin; 2 twin, both with shower; tea/coffee and TV in all bedrooms; lounge   TERMS: single £22–£26, single occupancy £30–£35, twin £45–£50; deposit: £10 per person   CARDS: none   DETAILS: children welcome; dogs by arrangement; no smoking; car park; garden

COWES   Isle of Wight — map 2

Northlands

52 Baring Road, Cowes PO31 8DJ   TEL/FAX: (01983) 293764

This large Victorian house has spectacular views over the Solent. The Kellys are hospitable, welcoming people and this family house has a relaxed atmosphere. Ian is a native of the island and is more than happy to share his knowledge of its attractions and sailing facilities with his guests. Both he and Christine enjoy entertaining and serve good home-cooked dinners, and they join their guests in the dining-room. An attractive wide staircase leads up to the three beautifully furnished bedrooms, one of which has *en suite* facilities.

OWNERS: Ian and Christine Kelly   OPEN: all year exc Christmas   ROOMS: 1 double; 2 twin, 1 with bath/shower; TV in all bedrooms and lounge   TERMS: single occupancy £30–£45, twin/double £50–£70; dinner £18.50; deposit: £50   CARDS: MasterCard, Switch, Visa   DETAILS: no children under 8; no dogs; car park; garden

COXWOLD   North Yorkshire — map 9

School House

Coxwold YO6 4AD   TEL: (01347) 868356
6m E of A19, between Thirsk and Easingwold

Located on the outskirts of a pretty village in the heart of the North York Moors National Park, School House is a former coaching-inn dating from the seventeenth century. It is a long, stone-built cottage with many pieces of furniture and other items in keeping with its origins, including a large collection of plates and brass. It also offers three attractive guest bedrooms, with sloping roofs and pastel décor. All have TVs, and share two bathrooms. Home-cooked evening meals can be booked in advance. Shandy Hall, the home of Lawrence Sterne, author of *Tristram Shandy*, can be visited in the village, which also has a beautiful old church.

OWNERS: John and Jean Richardson OPEN: all year exc Christmas ROOMS: 1 double, 1 twin, 1 family; all rooms with wash-basin; tea/coffee and TV bedrooms TERMS: single occupancy £20, twin/double £36, family room £36–£46; children's reductions by arrangement; dinner £11 CARDS: none DETAILS: children welcome; dogs welcome; no smoking in dining-room; car park; garden

CRACKINGTON HAVEN Cornwall **map 1**

Nancemellan

Crackington Haven EX23 0NN TEL/FAX: (01840) 230283
from A39 at Wainhouse Corner, 7m S of Bude, follow signs W for Crackington Haven

Nancemellan is a very welcoming place, surrounded by nine acres of beautiful gardens, and just 500 yards from the beach in a wonderful position at the entrance to the village. The large and attractive house has lovely views, and the Ruffs are charming hosts who enjoy looking after their guests. The bedrooms also have lovely views, and the comfortable lounge is beautifully furnished. Breakfast is served in the large family kitchen. This a wonderful place for those who enjoy walking, beaches or just getting away from it all.

OWNERS: Eddie and Lorraine Ruff OPEN: Apr to Oct ROOMS: 2 double, 1 with bath, 1 with private bathroom; 1 twin, with private bathroom; tea/coffee and TV in all bedrooms; lounge TERMS: single occupancy £25–£40, twin/double £44–£60 CARDS: none DETAILS: no children; no dogs; no smoking; car park; garden

Trevigue Farm

Crackington Haven EX23 0LQ TEL/FAX: (01840) 230418
1½m S of Crackington Haven on minor road

The 500-acre farm has been in existence since before the Norman Conquest, and is mentioned in the Domesday Book, but the farmhouse is much younger, dating from the early sixteenth century. It is built around a cobbled courtyard in a hollow, a mile and a half from the tiny village of Crackington Haven, and only a few hundred yards away from dramatic cliffs. Janet Crocker restored the house herself, and now runs the business with her daughter-in-law Gayle. Bedrooms have beams and sloping walls, and the sitting-room has deep sofas, a log-burning fire, books and TV. Janet loves cooking and enjoys preparing both traditional and more innovative meals. Trevigue Farm is also licensed to hold weddings.

OWNERS: Janet Crocker and Gayle Crocker OPEN: all year exc Christmas ROOMS: 2 double, 2 twin; all rooms with bath/shower and tea/coffee; TV in double bedrooms and lounge TERMS: single occupancy £40–£50, twin/double £50–£70; dinner £25; deposit required CARDS: none DETAILS: no children under 12; no dogs; no smoking; car park

Treworgie Barton

Crackington Haven EX23 0NL TEL/FAX: (01840) 230233
from A39 at Wainhouse Corner 7m S of Bude, follow signs W for Crackington Haven, take first right and right again

Treworgie Barton is reached by a long, narrow private road, about two miles from the beach and the village of Crackington Haven. The sixteenth-century farmhouse originally belonged to the Prior of Launceston and was taken over by Henry VIII. It has a very pretty, small walled garden, and is set in peaceful countryside. Pam Mount is a friendly host and a wonderful cook, providing four-course evening meals using local produce, served in the traditional, antique-furnished dining-room, which has a granite fireplace. Tony Mount is happy to help guests plan their day. There are four pretty bedrooms, one of which has a four-poster bed. Behind the house are the farm buildings and beyond that the wooded Millock Valley, where there are opportunities for lovely walks.

OWNER: Pam Mount OPEN: Apr to Sept (Nov, Feb and Mar advance booking only) ROOMS: 1 double, with bath/shower; 1 twin, with private bathroom; 1 four-poster, with bath/shower; 1 family, with bath/shower; tea/coffee and TV in all bedrooms; lounge TERMS: single occupancy £25–£36, twin/double £36–£40, family room £46–£65; dinner £15; deposit: £20–£50 CARDS: none DETAILS: no children under 10; no dogs; no smoking; car park; garden

CRAFTHOLE Cornwall

map 1

The Bungalow

NEW ENTRY

Cliff Road, Crafthole PL11 3BY TEL: (01503) 230334
½m W of Crafthole on the Downderry road

Aptly named, the Bungalow is a wooden, chalet-style building standing in a windswept garden in a magnificent setting. The house was originally used by troops during World War I and extended in the 1920s. Angie Harvey's parents moved here in 1947, and both she and her sister, who helps out with the B&B during holiday times, were born here. From the verandah are splendid views, and a narrow lane leads down to a sheltered beach. The house is comfortable and spotlessly clean, and the atmosphere warm and welcoming; guests are greeted with tea and cakes on arrival. The two bedrooms share a WC and shower-room, and although the house is not centrally heated, the bedrooms have electric heaters. Angie Harvey does home-baking for people in the neighbourhood, and guests get the benefit of freshly made bread for breakfast. One reader was pleased to find such a 'delightful' B&B away from the crowded tourist areas. The coastal footpath runs close by.

OWNER: Angie Harvey OPEN: early Apr to late Oct ROOMS: 1 double, 1 twin, both with wash-basin; lounge with TV TERMS: single occupancy £15, twin/double £30 CARDS: none DETAILS: no children; no dogs; no smoking; car park; garden

CRANBROOK Kent **map 3**

Folly Hill Cottage NEW ENTRY

Friezley Lane, Hocker Edge, Cranbrook TN17 2LL TEL/FAX: (01580) 714299
from A21 take A262 through Goudhurst; after approx 3m Friezley Lane is just before roundabout at A229 junction

At the end of a narrow wooded lane about three miles from Cranbrook in peaceful countryside, Folly Hill Cottage is an enchanting place. It was built in 1880, but has been added to over the years, and now provides comfortable guest accommodation in a get-away-from-it-all atmosphere. One bedroom has an *en suite* bathroom, plus dressing-room, small balcony and splendid views, while the other has its own private bathroom. Guests also have the use of a small TV room with a fridge. The de Carles are friendly, welcoming people, and Sonia de Carle is happy, with 24-hours' notice, to prepare good home-cooked meals – either two or three courses – served in the dining-room at a communal table. Alternatively, guests may opt for sandwiches and coffee, or be advised by their hosts on restaurants and pubs in the area. Visitors are welcome to use the unheated outdoor swimming-pool and lovely garden in summer. Two nights' minimum booking over weekends is required from Easter through September.

OWNER: Sonia de Carle OPEN: all year exc Christmas ROOMS: 2 twin, 1 with bath/shower, 1 with private bathroom; tea/coffee in both bedrooms; TV in 1 bedroom and lounge TERMS: single occupancy £25–£30, twin £38–£46; dinner £10–£15; deposit: 20% CARDS: none DETAILS: no children under 10; no dogs; no smoking; car park; swimming-pool

The Oast NEW ENTRY

Hallwood Farm, Cranbrook TN17 2SP TEL: (01580) 712416
off A229, 1½m S of Cranbrook

The Oast is well off the beaten track, set down a private drive and surrounded by orchards, pastures and fields. Part of a 200-acre mixed farm, the house dates from the seventeenth century and now offers two spacious, elegantly furnished guest bedrooms, both with generously sized *en suite* facilities. Residents enjoy good breakfasts – poached haddock might be featured along with full English or continental options – in the lovely beamed dining-room, which also has a sitting-area and TV. The Wickhams are welcoming hosts, and ensure their guests are comfortable and well looked after. Note that single-night bookings are not taken for Fridays or Saturdays. The

B&B is well placed for the Bedgebury Pinetum and Sissinghurst Gardens, and Cranbrook's church is worth a visit; in addition, the village has a good selection of eating places for evening meals.

OWNERS: Mr and Mrs N. Wickham OPEN: Feb to Nov ROOMS: 1 double, 1 twin; both rooms with bath/shower, tea/coffee and TV TERMS: single occupancy £30, twin/double £40 CARDS: none DETAILS: no children under 5; no dogs; no smoking; car park

CRANLEIGH Surrey

map 3

Bookers Lee

Guildford Road, Alfold, Cranleigh GU6 8JS TEL: (01483) 272442
off A281, 2m W of Cranleigh, 9m S of Guildford

Bookers Lee is a smart late-Georgian house in three acres of well-kept gardens, just outside the small town of Cranleigh. The Carrs are friendly and welcoming, and the house has a relaxed atmosphere, and décor and furnishings of a very high standard. Breakfasts are particularly good and are different every day. The lounge and dining-room are spacious, light, and beautifully decorated and furnished. Guests also have use of a drying-room. Attractions within easy driving distance include several stately homes and the Royal Horticultural Society gardens at Wisley.

OWNERS: Andrew and Margaret Carr OPEN: all year exc Christmas ROOMS: 1 double, 1 twin; both rooms with private bathroom, tea/coffee and TV; lounge TERMS: single occupancy £25, twin/double £40–£45; £15 for children CARDS: none DETAILS: no children under 8; dogs in stable only; no smoking; car park; garden

CREED Cornwall

map 1

Creed House

Creed TR2 4SL TEL: (01872) 530372
from A390 at Grampound, turn on to Creed Lane, signposted Creed; after 1m, turn left at church; house is on left

Creed House stands in five acres of lovely landscaped gardens, with large lawns, walled herbaceous gardens and a stream which feeds several ponds. It is a large Georgian country house, situated on a quiet, narrow lane, about a mile from the village of Grampound. The Croggons are charming, welcoming people, and do everything possible to ensure their guests are comfortable. Until they bought the house, it was the rectory to the nearby fourteenth-century church of St Crida. Bedrooms are well proportioned and simply and tastefully furnished with antiques. Breakfast is served in the dining-room in summer or in the attractive farmhouse-style kitchen in the colder months. Guests have use of the drawing-room, as well as the entire garden to relax in, and there are tennis courts.

OWNERS: Mr and Mrs William Croggon OPEN: all year exc Christmas ROOMS: 3 double/twin, 1 with bath/shower, 2 with private bathroom; lounge with TV TERMS: single occupancy £30, twin/double £55–£60 CARDS: none DETAILS: no children under 10; no dogs; no smoking; car park; garden; tennis

CREWKERNE Somerset map 2

Broadview Gardens

43 East Street, Crewkerne TA18 7AG TEL: (01460) 73424

This unusual colonial-style bungalow, built in 1926, is in an elevated position overlooking Crewkerne. Steps lead up to the front door, which opens directly into the dining-room. The lounge is at the back of the house and overlooks the acre of terraced gardens (occasionally open to the public under the National Gardens Scheme) with interesting shrubs and plants and a water garden. Gillian and Robert Swann are a very friendly couple, and have a reputation for good home-cooked evening meals. The house is very comfortable and has been furnished and decorated with the owners' collections of china, rugs and pictures. Broadview Gardens is on the outskirts of Crewkerne, and the gardens at Clapton Court are just a few minutes' drive away.

OWNERS: Gillian and Robert Swann OPEN: all year ROOMS: 2 double, 1 with shower, 1 with private bathroom; 1 twin, with bath/shower; tea/coffee and TV in all bedrooms; lounge TERMS: single occupancy £35–£46, twin/double £50–£56; dinner £14; deposit: 1 night's charge or credit card details CARDS: Delta, MasterCard, Visa DETAILS: children welcome; dogs by arrangement; no smoking; car park; garden

CROCKERTON Wiltshire map 2

Tanhouse Cottage

Crockerton BA12 8AU TEL: (01985) 214816
on A350, 1m S of Warminster

This former farmhouse, dating from the seventeenth century, is a pretty whitewashed building, on the edge of the Longleat Estate, only a couple of miles from Longleat House. The large double bedroom can also accommodate families, while the remaining three rooms are quite small; there is one shared bathroom upstairs, with another available downstairs as well as a separate WC. The cosy oak-beamed sitting-room is shared with the owners. Freshly prepared, home-cooked evening meals are served in the pretty dining-room, by arrangement. The cottage backs on to a main road, so it can be rather noisy, but the surrounding countryside is quiet and peaceful, and there is a small attractive, cottage-style enclosed garden, where breakfast is served on warm mornings.

OWNER: Sheila Dickinson OPEN: all year exc Christmas ROOMS: 2 single, 1 double/family, 1 twin; all rooms with wash-basin; lounge with TV TERMS: single £20, single occupancy £25, twin/double £40, family room £50; £10 for children; dinner £12.50; deposit: £10 CARDS: none DETAILS: children welcome; dogs welcome; no smoking in bedrooms; car park; garden

CROMER Norfolk — map 6

Beachcomber

17 Macdonald Road, Cromer NR27 9AP TEL: (01263) 513398

Just a short walk to the centre of this seaside town and close to the beach, this Edwardian house is conveniently situated. It offers seven guest bedrooms plus, if pre-arranged, good-value evening meals. Most of the bedrooms, which are individually decorated in both rich colours and pastels, have *en suite* showers and all have TVs. The non-*en suite* rooms share a bathroom. There is also a guest lounge with a TV and, for those wanting a quiet space, a sitting-room with lots of books to dip into. Cromer is famous for its fresh crabs, and the Norfolk Shire Horse Centre is nearby.

OWNER: Anne Weinle OPEN: all year exc Christmas ROOMS: 1 single, with wash-basin; 4 double, 3 with shower, 1 with wash-basin; 1 twin, with shower; 1 family, with bath/shower; tea/coffee and TV in all bedrooms; lounge with TV TERMS: single £16–£18, single occupancy £25–£36, twin/double £32–£40, family room from £36 plus children's charge; children's reductions by arrangement; dinner £8.50; deposit: £20 CARDS: none DETAILS: children welcome; no dogs; smoking in lounge only; garden

CROOK Cumbria — map 8

Birksey Brow

Crook LA8 8LQ TEL: (015394) 43380

from Kendal take B5384 4m W to Crook, pass through village; with Sun Inn on right go ½m up hill past village hall and church

Birksey Brow is a creeper-covered stone-built house in 36 acres of fell and walking land with wonderful views. The Browns are a friendly couple who also run a small stock-rearing farm. The elegant house has a warm atmosphere, and all the good-sized bedrooms, two of which are *en suite*, have mountain views. Fresh fruit and flowers are in the bedrooms and honeymooners receive special attention. Afternoon teas are available, and excellent breakfasts include home-made jams and marmalades, with vegetarians catered for. Dinner is available by prior arrangement and guests may bring their own wine as Birksey Brow is unlicensed. Over bank holiday weekends only three-night bookings are taken.

OWNERS: Robin and Dany Brown OPEN: all year exc Christmas ROOMS: 1 double, with bath/shower; 2 twin, 1 with bath/shower, 1 with private bathroom; tea/coffee and TV in all bedrooms; lounge with TV TERMS: single occupancy £35–£42, twin/double £50–£64, family room £60–£80; dinner £17.50–£20; deposit: £25 CARDS: none DETAILS: no children under 8; no dogs; smoking in lounge only; car park; garden

CROOKHAM Northumberland **map 11**

Coach House

Crookham TD12 4TD TEL: (01890) 820293 FAX: (01890) 820284
just off A697, 5m E of Coldstream

The Coach House makes an excellent base for touring beautiful Northumberland. Lynne Anderson has created a warm and welcoming ambience in this creatively converted complex of farm buildings around a courtyard. The former coach-house itself is now a large sitting-room with the original open-raftered roof. Log fires keep it warm on cool evenings. Bedrooms are large, some have windows overlooking the courtyard. Most are on the ground floor, and three are equipped for wheelchair-users; one, smaller room even has a roll-in shower with its own specially designed wheelchair. Lynne plans to add a further *en suite* bedroom. Four-course dinners and substantial breakfasts are highly recommended.

OWNER: Lynne Anderson OPEN: Easter to Oct ROOMS: 4 double, 3 with bath/shower, 1 with wash-basin; 5 twin, 4 with bath/shower, 1 with wash-basin; 3 rooms suitable for wheelchair-users; tea/coffee and TV in all bedrooms TERMS: single occupancy £23–£36, twin/double £46–£72; children's reductions according to age; dinner £16.50; deposit: £10 per person CARDS: Visa DETAILS: children welcome; dogs welcome by arrangement; no smoking in dining-room; car park; garden

CROWHURST East Sussex **map 3**

Brakes Coppice Farm **NEW ENTRY**

Forewood Lane, Crowhurst TN33 0SJ TEL/FAX: (01424) 830347
1m SW of A2100 Battle to Hastings road

Set in peaceful countryside, with pleasant views towards the sea, Brakes Coppice Farm is reached down a long drive three miles from Battle. The small, well-equipped bedrooms all have *en suite* facilities. Breakfast is served in the large dining-room at individual tables, and a comfortably furnished lounge is also available. The Ramsdens also run an outside catering-equipment business, which is particularly busy with weddings during the summer months.

OWNER: Fay Ramsden OPEN: all year exc Christmas and New Year ROOMS: 1 single, 1 double, 1 twin; all rooms with bath/shower, tea/coffee and TV; lounge TERMS: single £30, single occupancy £35, twin/double £45–£50 CARDS: none DETAILS: no children under 12; no dogs; no smoking; car park; garden

If a B&B accepts credit cards, we list them in the details at the end of an entry – or specify no cards are accepted if that is so. There may be a surcharge if you pay by credit card. It is always best to check when booking whether the card you want to use will be accepted.

CROYDE Devon — map 1

Combas Farm

Putsborough, Croyde EX33 1PH TEL: (01271) 890398
signposted on minor road from Croyde to Putsborough

This attractive seventeenth-century farmhouse is in a beautiful position on a well-preserved track in a quiet valley. It is covered with wistaria and a grapevine and has a colourful garden and orchard. The Adamses keep a 140-acre cattle and sheep farm and grow fruit, vegetables and herbs for the kitchen. Both the dining-room and sitting-room have open stone fireplaces (one with a bread oven). All bedrooms are *en suite*; two are suitable for families, and there is a 'cabin room' with bunk beds for children. Babysitting can be arranged. Putsborough Sands beach, which stretches for three miles to Woolacombe, is only a mile away, and much of the surrounding land and coastline is owned by the National Trust.

OWNERS: John and Gwen Adams OPEN: Mar to Nov ROOMS: 2 double, 1 with bath/shower, 1 with private bathroom; 2 family/twin, both with shower; lounge with TV TERMS: single occupancy £18–£21, twin/double £36–£42, family room £54–£63; dinner £9.50; deposit: 20% CARDS: none DETAILS: children welcome; no dogs; smoking in lounge only; car park; garden

CUSOP Hereford & Worcester — map 5

Lansdowne House

Cusop, Hay-on-Wye HR3 5RF TEL: (01497) 820125
from Hay-on-Wye take B4348 and immediately turn right into narrow lane signposted 'Cusop and Cusop Dingle'; after 600 metres turn left, signposted 'ancient church of St Mary'; Lansdowne on left after 100 metres

Popular for visitors to Hay-on-Wye – the famous book town is just a walk away across the fields – Lansdowne is an attractive Victorian house peacefully placed in a lovely rural setting. You can see for miles across fields and hills. Guests are met with biscuits and a drink upon arrival, and readers tell us the Flacks are most accommodating hosts. Superlative breakfasts are served in the conservatory or, when weather allows, on the patio overlooking the large pretty garden, which guests are welcome to use. The two guest bedrooms, both with *en suite* facilities, TVs, and complimentary tea/coffee, mineral water and fresh fruit, are immaculate.

OWNERS: Margaret and Rob Flack OPEN: all year exc Christmas ROOMS: 1 double, 1 twin; both rooms with bath/shower, tea/coffee and TV TERMS: single occupancy £21–£22, twin/double £32–£34; deposit: £10 CARDS: none DETAILS: children welcome by arrangement; no dogs; no smoking; car park; garden

---

Any smoking restrictions that we know of are given in the details at the end of the entry.

DANEHILL East Sussex **map 3**

Sliders Farm

Furner's Green, nr Danehill TN22 3RT
TEL: (01825) 790258 FAX: (01825) 790125
off A275 East Grinstead to Lewes road, 1m S of Danehill

Situated down a quiet lane, this listed sixteenth-century farmhouse has exposed beams and inglenook fireplaces, and has been cleverly adapted to provide twentieth-century comforts. David and Jean Salmon are very friendly and helpful hosts. The bedrooms are spacious and comfortably furnished, and there is a large guests' lounge with a billiard table and log fire. Facilities also include a hard tennis court, heated swimming-pool and private trout lakes. There are two self-catering units in a seventeenth-century barn conversion in the grounds. Sliders Farm is within easy reach of Wakehurst Place and the Bluebell Railway. Bookings of more than one night are preferred.

OWNERS: David and Jean Salmon OPEN: all year exc Christmas ROOMS: 2 double, 1 twin; all rooms with bath/shower, tea/coffee and TV; lounge TERMS: single occupancy £28–£34, double/twin £38–£56; dinner £14; deposit: £10 per room CARDS: none DETAILS: children welcome; no dogs; smoking in lounge only; car park; garden; swimming-pool; tennis

DARLINGSCOTT Warwickshire **map 5**

Lower Farm

NEW ENTRY

Darlingscott CV36 4PN TEL/FAX: (01608) 682750
off A429, 2m NW of Shipston on Stour

This eighteenth-century home set in the unspoilt village of Darlingscott, on the edge of the Cotswolds, has been renovated and refurbished to a high standard. The large oak-beamed bedrooms are beautifully furnished and have built-in wardrobes. The top-floor rooms, with sloping ceilings, are particularly attractive. A fine collection of prints and interesting pictures are displayed throughout the house. Guests are welcome to take advantage of the well-tended garden and patio. Ken and Jackie Smith are warm and friendly hosts, and pay great attention to detail. They used to run a restaurant, and breakfast is 'quite superb'. Vegetarians and those with special dietary requirements can be catered for with notice. Lower Farm is ideally placed for visiting the lovely villages and gardens in the area.

OWNERS: Jackie Smith OPEN: all year exc Christmas ROOMS: 2 double, 1 twin; all rooms with bath/shower, tea/coffee and TV TERMS: single occupancy £25–£30, twin/double £40–£45; deposit required CARDS: none DETAILS: no children under 8; no dogs; no smoking; car park; garden

---

The end details for each entry state whether or not dogs are allowed, but it is always best to check when booking.

DARTMOUTH Devon **map 1**

Broome Court

Broomhill, Dartmouth TQ6 0LD TEL: (01803) 834275
off B3122, approx 1½m W of Dartmouth

Set in beautiful, undulating Devon countryside, in an acre of grounds with outstanding views, Broome Court consists of attractive old converted farm buildings which surround a flower-filled courtyard with a goldfish pond in the centre. It stands in a quiet lane about a mile and a half outside Dartmouth towards Totnes. Jan Bird extends a warm, friendly greeting to guests, and runs an immaculate house. It has been attractively furnished, mostly in pine, and there are pine floors on the ground level. The spacious bedrooms have fresh flowers and bottled water, and guests have the use of two large lounges, one of which has an open fire on chilly days. A hearty breakfast is served in the old farmhouse kitchen. Special arrangements can be made for guests interested in golf and nearby leisure facilities.

OWNERS: Jan Bird and Thomas Boughton OPEN: all year exc Christmas ROOMS: 2 double, 1 twin; all rooms with bath/shower, tea/coffee and TV; 2 lounges, 1 with TV TERMS: single occupancy £35–£40, twin/double £55–£60; deposit: £25 CARDS: none DETAILS: no children under 12; dogs by arrangement; smoking in lounges only; car park; garden

Campbells

NEW ENTRY

5 Mount Boone, Dartmouth TQ6 9PB TEL/FAX: (01803) 833438
from A3122 in Dartmouth turn right into Townstal Rd; first left

This turn-of-the-century semi-detached house stands in a wonderful position above the town with panoramic views of Dartmouth and the estuary. The Campbells are a charming couple who previously ran a B&B in Scotland and moved here in 1995. Breakfast is served in the pleasant dining-room with access to the terrace and garden, and includes 'as little or as much' of what you want, from muesli to locally smoked kipper fillets to (in season) fresh fruit from the garden. Evening meals are also available with prior notice. Both the dining-room and the two double bedrooms have splendid views. There are no easy chairs in the bedrooms, nor TVs, and the B&B has no lounge, but if guests have something particular they want to watch on the box they can be accommodated in the owner's sitting-room. A spare bed can be provided 'in case he snores'. Guests are asked not to arrive between noon and 4pm.

OWNER: Angela Campbell OPEN: Easter to mid-Oct ROOMS: 2 double, both with bath/shower and tea/coffee TERMS: single occupancy £30–£60, double £60; dinner £25; deposit: 1 night's charge CARDS: none DETAILS: no children; dogs by arrangement; no smoking in dining-room; car park; garden

If any bedrooms are suitable for wheelchair-users, we mention this in the details at the end of the entry.

Ford House

44 Victoria Road, Dartmouth TQ6 9DX TEL/FAX: (01803) 834047

Imaginative dinners and breakfasts are a draw at this ivy-covered Regency house set up a steep hill only 500 yards from Dartmouth's historic quay. The three tastefully decorated rooms all have *en suite* facilities, telephones and fridges, and the lounge with its open fire has views into the garden. At dinner, which is served between 7 and 10pm, guests eat together at the large mahogany table, and the set menu might take in dishes such as scallops in a puff pastry case served with a cream and basil sauce, then duck breasts with a green peppercorn sauce, followed by a good choice of desserts. Ford House is unlicensed, but guests may bring their own wine (there is no corkage charge). Breakfast is served from 8am (9am Sunday) until noon, and items such as devilled kidneys and poached smoked haddock are available if ordered in advance.

OWNER: Richard Turner OPEN: Mar to Oct ROOMS: 1 double, 2 twin; all rooms with bath and shower, tea/coffee and TV; lounge TERMS: single occupancy £45–£70, twin/double £55–£70 (lower rates require min stay of 5 nights); children's reductions by arrangement; dinner £25; deposit: £50 CARDS: Amex, MasterCard, Visa DETAILS: children welcome; dogs welcome; car park; garden

Hedley House **NEW ENTRY**

Newcomen Road, Dartmouth TQ6 9BN TEL: (01803) 835849

In an excellent position – just 400 yards from the town centre and near Dartmouth Castle – and enjoying superb views of the Dart Estuary, Hedley House offers three attractively furnished and very comfortable *en suite* guest bedrooms. It is a small terraced Georgian house run by a friendly couple who give their guests a very warm welcome. They are happy to provide many facilities on request, from daily newspapers to ice, as well as advice on good walks, restaurants and interesting places to visit. Breakfasts, one reader writes, are 'delicious'. The walk into the town centre takes five minutes, with an uphill return. A minimum of two nights must be booked from April to September.

OWNERS: Robert and Marilyn Bird OPEN: all year ROOMS: 3 double, 2 with bath, 1 with shower; all rooms with tea/coffee; lounge with TV TERMS: single occupancy £45–£60, twin/double £60–£80; deposit: 25% for first visit CARDS: none DETAILS: no children; no dogs; no smoking; garden

B&B rates specified in the details at the end of each entry are given (as applicable) for a single room, for single occupancy of a double room, and then per room in the case of two people sharing a double or twin-bedded room, or for a family room. Because double rooms with four-poster beds often cost more, those are listed separately.

DAWLISH Devon **map 1**

Oak Cottage

Luscombe Hill, Dawlish EX7 0PX TEL: (01626) 863120
from end of M5 at Exeter take A38 then A380 Torquay road; after 2m take B3192 Teignmouth road, take second left to Dawlish; Oak Cottage is third house on left after 1½m

Oak Cottage stands in an acre of beautifully landscaped gardens, set above the village of Dawlish and close to the sea. The fine stone building has been converted out of four nineteenth-century workers' cottages that once stood on the Luscombe Estate. These origins explain the recurring sets of stairs and doors, which give the house a structure that lends well to providing two exceptionally comfortable and unusual guest bedrooms. Both are fully *en suite* with quality beds, one of which is six-feet long, and have pleasant views over the surrounding countryside. A whirlpool bath is also available in one of the rooms. Freshly prepared dinners are served in the dining-room, and guests might also sample home-produced marmalades and preserves at breakfast. The garden, with views of the sea, has a terrace, pond and croquet lawn. Oak Cottage is an ideal base for walks in Dartmoor and the Exe Estuary.

OWNERS: Tony and Liz Williams OPEN: all year exc Christmas ROOMS: 1 double, 1 twin; both rooms with bath, tea/coffee and TV; lounge with TV TERMS: single occupancy £37, twin/double £54; dinner £15; deposit: 10% CARDS: none DETAILS: no children; dogs by arrangement; smoking in lounge only; car park; garden

DEDHAM Essex **map 3**

May's Barn Farm

May's Lane, off Long Road West, Dedham CO7 6EW TEL: (01206) 323191
on B1029 1m from Dedham heading towards Arleigh turn left into Long Road West, then left again after ¼m

Tranquilly located in Constable country, this traditionally furnished farmhouse offers spacious and comfortable guest accommodation. The house is part of a 300-acre working arable farm. The double bedroom has its own bathroom, while the twin is *en suite*. The green and gold lounge with its TV, open fire, books and games is a good place to relax in. The light and airy dining-room is where guests can tuck into good farmhouse breakfasts featuring home-made marmalade and jam. A footpath from Dedham village leads to Flatford Mill, famous for its associations with Constable.

OWNER: Jean Freeman OPEN: all year exc Christmas ROOMS: 1 double, with private bathroom; 1 twin, with bath/shower; tea/coffee and TV in both bedrooms; lounge with TV TERMS: single occupancy £24–£25, twin/double £39–£41; deposit: £10 CARDS: none DETAILS: no children under 12; no dogs; no smoking in bedrooms or dining-room; car park; garden

DENT Cumbria — map 8

Stone Close

Main Street, Dent LA10 5QL TEL: (01539) 625231 FAX: (01539) 726567

Peter and Kay Rushton took over Stone Close early in 1997, and are committed to maintaining the same high standards set by the previous owners. The seventeenth-century whitewashed stone building was originally two cottages, and still retains much of its original character. There are three guest bedrooms, and the ground floor is given over to a licensed tea-shop, also open to the public during the daytime, serving excellent lunches and snacks, including home-made cakes and pastries, throughout the day. Stone Close has no private parking but there is a public car park nearby. Dolly's Cottage next door provides self-catering accommodation for up to three people.

OWNERS: Kay and Peter Rushton OPEN: all year ROOMS: 1 single, 1 double, 1 family; all rooms with wash-basin and tea/coffee TERMS: single £17.75–£20, single occupancy £20–£25, twin/double £29.50–£33, family room £34–£40; dinner £8.50; deposit: £10 per room CARDS: Delta, MasterCard, Switch, Visa DETAILS: children welcome; dogs welcome (1 per room); no smoking; games room

DETHICK Derbyshire — map 5

Manor Farmhouse

Dethick DE4 5GG TEL: (01629) 534246

from M1 junction 28 take A38 to Alfreton, then A615 signposted Matlock, then after 5m turn left to Dethick

One reader commends the 'excellent breakfast' and 'very welcoming' atmosphere at this 300-year-old farmhouse set at the edge of the Peak District. Built from the ruins of a thirteenth-century manor, the house has plenty of atmosphere – low doors, thick stone walls – though rooms are well appointed and comfortable. The bedrooms are decorated in pastels, and are either *en suite* or have a private bathroom. The guest lounge has a TV. Evening meals are available by arrangement, though there is a large choice of places in the area that serve food. Sir Anthony Babington, famous for his part in the unsuccessful plot to free Mary Queen of Scots, once lived in the house.

OWNERS: Mr and Mrs H. Groom OPEN: all year exc Christmas ROOMS: 1 double, with bath/shower; 2 twin, 1 with bath/shower, 1 with private bathroom; TV in 2 bedrooms and lounge TERMS: single occupancy £30–£35, twin/double £45–£48; one-third reduction for children; dinner £9; deposit: £10 per person CARDS: none DETAILS: no children under 8; guide dogs welcome; no smoking; car park; garden

---

If we know a B&B has an alcohol licence, we say so. Most unlicensed B&Bs that offer evening meals allow guests to bring their own wine to dinner. If you wish to do this, ask the B&B when you book.

DOVER Kent map 3

Linden Guest House

231 Folkestone Road, Dover CT17 9SL TEL/FAX: (01304) 205449

Just five minutes' drive from the centre of Dover and the ferries, and ten minutes from the Channel Tunnel, this three-storey terraced Victorian town house on a busy road offers well-appointed accommodation. The interior is attractively decorated and the bedrooms have double-glazing. Dover Castle can be seen floodlit at night from the rear of the house, and guests have use of a secure car park. The Walkdens provide a free courtesy collection from the bus and coach stations and the ferry terminal.

OWNERS: Jean and Roger Walkden OPEN: all year exc Christmas ROOMS: 1 single, with wash-basin; 3 double, 2 with shower, 1 with wash-basin; 1 family, with shower; tea/coffee and TV in all bedrooms; lounge with TV TERMS: single £16–£22, single occupancy £25–£30, double £32–£45, family room £40–£65; children's reductions by arrangement; deposit: £10 or credit card details CARDS: Delta, MasterCard, Switch, Visa DETAILS: children welcome; small dogs only by arrangement; no smoking in dining-room; car park; garden

Tower House

98 Priory Hill, Dover CT17 0AE TEL: (01304) 208212

'Doreen Wraight is a friendly and helpful person who provides a warm welcome and good breakfast,' writes one visitor to this unusual guesthouse. In former days a water tower, it stands in a pretty garden with splendid views of the castle, docks and surrounding hilly countryside. Bedrooms are light and prettily decorated with chintzy curtains and bedspreads. There is a double room, and family suite comprising a double and a single room which can be let separately. Breakfast can be provided early for guests catching ferries.

OWNERS: Ron and Doreen Wraight OPEN: all year exc Christmas ROOMS: 1 double, 1 family; both rooms with shower TERMS: twin/double £32–£42, family room £40–£50; deposit: £10; per room CARDS: none DETAILS: children welcome; no dogs; no smoking; garden

DOWNHAM MARKET Norfolk map 6

Dial House

Railway Road, Downham Market PE38 9EB
TEL: (01366) 388358 FAX: (01366) 382238
400yds from railway station

The Dial House, displaying its sundial on the front of the house, is a Grade II-listed Georgian building. The Murrays are friendly hosts who greet their guests with tea or coffee on arrival. The comfortable TV lounge has a marble fireplace, and there are lots of books and brochures on the area. Three well-appointed, good-sized bedrooms all have armchairs; two have *en suite* facilities, and the third has exclusive use of a bathroom. Breakfasts feature home-made jams and bread. Evening meals are available (except between Christmas Eve and New Year's Day), and all diets can be catered for; there is no alcohol licence, but guests may bring their own wine.

OWNERS: Ann and David Murray OPEN: all year ROOMS: 1 double, with bath/shower; 2 twin, 1 with bath/shower; tea/coffee and TV in all bedrooms; lounge with TV TERMS: single occupancy £20–£28, twin/double £30–£38; dinner £12; deposit: £20 or 10% CARDS: none DETAILS: children welcome; no dogs in public rooms; no smoking; car park; garden

DOWNTON Hampshire **map 2**

Cottage Bed & Breakfast NEW ENTRY

Angel Cottage, Angel Lane, Downton BH25 5PT TEL: (01425) 629506
on A337, 4m W of Lymington

Angel Cottage is a 150-year-old red-brick building in a quiet, rural setting in an attractive garden, close to the sea and next door to the golf course. The house has a very pleasant, relaxed and friendly feel to it, and is warm and light. Mrs Jelley was a chef, and will do evening meals with enough notice. As she has a young son, families are very welcome, with all the children mixing in. The *en suite* double room is in the main house, and the *en suite* family room is in a self-contained oak barn and has a kitchenette. Breakfast is served in the conservatory, and the sitting-room is available to guests at any time.

OWNERS: Mr and Mrs Jelley OPEN: all year ROOMS: 1 double, 1 family; both rooms with shower, tea/coffee and TV TERMS: single occupancy £35–£45, double £44–£50, family room £44–£60; £10 for children under 10, £15 for ages 10–12; deposit: 1 night's charge CARDS: none DETAILS: children welcome; smoking in conservatory only; car park; garden

DOWNTON Wiltshire **map 2**

The Warren

15 High Street, Downton SP5 3PG TEL: (01725) 510263
7m from M27 junction 1, or off A338 Salisbury to Ringwood road

The Warren is a listed brick building, parts of which date from the thirteenth century, which has been carefully enlarged and modernised over the centuries. The Baxters are welcoming hosts, and the spacious house has exposed beams and antique furnishings. An early fireplace was uncovered in the small sitting-room. The large bedrooms are well decorated, and one has a 500-year-old half-tester bed. Breakfast is served in the breakfast room, which has french windows leading to a large rear garden with an expanse of lawns and borders ending with views of the church. The Warren lies in the middle of the pretty village of Downton, which is on the River Avon and is only a mile and a half from the New Forest.

OWNERS: John and Elizabeth Baxter OPEN: all year exc Christmas ROOMS: 2 double, 1 with bath/shower, 1 with wash-basin; 2 twin, both with wash-basin; 1 four-poster, with bath/shower; 1 family, with wash-basin; tea/coffee in all bedrooms; lounge with TV TERMS: single occupancy £27–£32, twin/double £40, four-poster £40–44, family room £40–£65; £12.50 for children aged 5–12 sharing with parents; deposit: £10 per room CARDS: none DETAILS: no children under 5; dogs on leads only and not in breakfast room; no smoking in breakfast room or bathrooms; car park; garden

DREWSTEIGNTON Devon map 1

Ford House

Drewsteignton EX6 6RD TEL: (01647) 281243
off A30, just N of Drewsteignton

This former manor-house, just outside the picturesque village of Drewsteignton, on the northern edge of Dartmoor, is set in 15 acres of lovely gardens and woodland. Bedrooms are simply and tastefully decorated, and all have spacious *en suite* bathrooms. There is a relaxing sitting-room, and a Victorian conservatory where guests may sit and enjoy a pre-dinner drink. The dining-room, which was formerly the winter kitchen, has a built-in range with tile surround. The house is reached down a series of narrow lanes, and may be difficult to find, so the Pages will send directions at the time of booking. National Trust-owned Castle Drogo is nearby.

OWNERS: Michael and Jacqueline Page OPEN: all year exc Christmas ROOMS: 3 double, 3 twin; all rooms with bath/shower and tea/coffee; lounge with TV TERMS: single occupancy £30, twin/double £60; dinner £16.50; deposit: 10% CARDS: none DETAILS: no children under 14; no dogs; no smoking; car park; games room; garden

DULVERTON Somerset map 1

Town Mills

Dulverton TA22 9HB TEL: (01398) 323124

Dulverton is a small town on the edge of Exmoor National Park, and this Georgian mill house is in a quiet position close to the town centre. There is no lounge or dining-room, but guests have unrestricted use of their spacious bedrooms; two have log fires, and one is on the ground floor and has its own sitting-room and *en suite* facilities. Breakfast is also served in the bedrooms. The area is ideal for walking and riding.

OWNER: Jane Buckingham OPEN: all year ROOMS: 4 double, 3 with shower, 1 with wash-basin; 1 twin; with wash-basin; tea/coffee and TV in all bedrooms TERMS: single occupancy £20–£36, twin/double £35–£46; reductions for children if sharing with parents; deposit required CARDS: none DETAILS: children welcome; no dogs; smoking in bedrooms only; car park; garden

---

If you are forced to turn up later than planned, please telephone to warn the proprietor. It is always best to book a room in advance, even in winter. B&Bs with few rooms may close at short notice for periods not specified in the details.

DUNSTER Somerset map 1

Dollons House

Church Street, Dunster TA24 6SH
TEL: (01643) 821880 FAX: (01643) 822016

This attractive listed house in the centre of the medieval village of Dunster was once the village pharmacy, and also produced a delicious marmalade which was ordered by the Houses of Parliament. The house has elm beams and reed ceilings, and has been attractively decorated and furnished. Everything is spotlessly clean and each of the bright, chintzy bedrooms has its own theme: for example there is a tulip room, and a teddy bear room with a mural of a bear painted by the owner's daughter. The first-floor sitting-room has doors out on to a small terrace with views of woods and hills, and breakfast is served in the ground-floor dining-room. The Bradshaws are a friendly couple and run a craft shop which takes up the two front rooms of Dollons. As there is no parking at the house, arriving guests need to unload their luggage, then use the nearby public car park.

OWNERS: Major and Mrs Humphrey Bradshaw OPEN: all year exc Christmas ROOMS: 2 double, 1 twin; all rooms with bath/shower, tea/coffee and TV; lounge with TV TERMS: single occupancy £35–£38, twin/double £50–£55; deposit: £10 or 10% CARDS: Delta, MasterCard, Visa DETAILS: no children; no dogs; no smoking; garden

---

Spears Cross Hotel

West Street, Dunster TA24 6SN TEL/FAX: (01643) 821439

The entrance to this listed fifteenth-century house is on Dunster's main street, close to the castle. A terraced garden leads up to the castle mound, and a collection of model houses decorates the terraces. The bedrooms are prettily furnished and have antique brass or pine beds; two have the original thin wooden walls, which have had an extra layer added for soundproofing, and another room has beautiful exposed beams. Breakfast is served in the attractive dining-room. Next to the beamed lounge with its inglenook fireplace is the licensed bar.

OWNERS: John and Christine Rathbone OPEN: Feb to mid-Dec ROOMS: 1 double, 1 twin, 1 family; all rooms with bath/shower, tea/coffee and TV; lounge with TV TERMS: single occupancy £21–£33, twin/double £42–£50; half-price for children; deposit: £20 CARDS: Delta, MasterCard, Switch, Visa DETAILS: children welcome; dogs by arrangment; no smoking; car park; garden

DURHAM Co Durham map 10

Georgian Town House

10 Crossgate, Durham DH1 4PS TEL/FAX: (0191) 386 8070

This stylish B&B is on a residential street yet just a short, steep climb from Durham's bus and railway stations, and five-minutes' walk from the cathedral. It is a Grade II-listed eighteenth-century house and, within, presents both comfort and quirkiness. Stencilled motifs cover the walls: these include ivy trailing up the stairs, and pillars in the bright conservatory (where breakfasts are served, accompanied by classical music). The bedrooms are well appointed, with modern furniture enhanced by colourful touches, such as candles, co-ordinated fabrics and dried flowers. Smoking is permitted only in the sitting-room. On-street parking is free.

OWNER: Mrs J.A. Weil OPEN: all year exc Christmas ROOMS: 3 double, 3 twin; all rooms with bath/shower, tea/coffee and TV; lounge TERMS: single occupancy £40–£45, twin/double £50–£55; deposit: £10 per room CARDS: none DETAILS: children welcome; no dogs; smoking in lounge only; garden

EASINGWOLD North Yorkshire **map 9**

Old Vicarage

Market Place, Easingwold YO6 3AL
TEL: (01347) 821015 FAX: (01347) 823465
just off A19, 12m NW of York

'Very comfortable, quiet and a good welcome' was one reader's verdict on her stay at this beautifully maintained eighteenth-century house in the Vale of York. An air of simple elegance pervades, along with a gracious and welcoming atmosphere. The house, built of hand-made bricks, is set in extensive grounds: guests may amble out to a croquet lawn and a walled rose garden. Bedrooms are spacious and comfortably furnished; all are *en suite*, have TVs, tea/coffee-making facilities and clock-radios, and beds have patchwork quilts. The drawing-room has a grand piano: musical evenings have been known to occur. Breakfasts are served in the pleasant dining-room, which overlooks the garden.

OWNERS: John and Christine Kirman OPEN: all year exc Christmas ROOMS: 1 single, 3 double, 2 twin; 5 rooms with shower, 1 with bath and shower; tea/coffee and TV in all bedrooms; lounge TERMS: single £25–£28, single occupancy £35–£40, twin/double £45–£58; children's reductions according to age; deposit: £10 per person CARDS: none DETAILS: children welcome; no dogs; no smoking; car park; garden

EAST BARKWITH Lincolnshire **map 9**

Bodkin Lodge

Torrington Lane, East Barkwith LN8 5RY TEL: (01673) 858249

An environmental theme permeates this extended and completely renovated and refurbished pre-war bungalow in the heart of the Lincolnshire countryside. The Stamps are conservation-minded, and are happy to direct guests to a nearby nature trail with all its attendant wildlife. They also provide two well-appointed *en suite* guest bedrooms, each with a TV, antique furniture, hair-dryer, heated towel rail and tea/coffee-making facilities. Both rooms – but especially the double – have excellent views over the fields, and are in their own self-contained wings of the house. The TV-free guest lounge is a good place to relax in, with its deep sofas and open fire. Dinners here are by arrangement and are superb; they are served in the candlelit dining-room, and Anne Stamp is happy to cater for vegetarians with advance notice.

OWNERS: Richard and Anne Stamp OPEN: all year exc Christmas and New Year ROOMS: 1 double, 1 twin; both rooms with bath/shower, tea/coffee and TV; lounge TERMS: single occupancy £25–£30, twin/double £45–£50; dinner £13; deposit: £20 CARDS: none DETAILS: no children under 8; no dogs; no smoking; car park; garden

EASTBOURNE East Sussex map 3

Beachy Rise

5 Beachy Head Road, Eastbourne BN20 7QN TEL: (01323) 639171

Just off a busy road leading to Beachy Head, this unpretentious semi-detached late-Victorian house is in a conservation area not far from the town centre. Outside is a south-facing patio, where guests can sit on fine days and enjoy the garden with its apple trees. Within, there is a sense of spaciousness and comfort. Residents may relax in the sitting-room with its satellite TV, and enjoy breakfasts as well as – if pre-arranged – three-course evening meals, which are served in the licensed dining-room with its views of the garden. Bedrooms all have either *en suite* showers or a private bathroom, and most have their original fireplaces as well as TVs. Some of the double rooms are large enough to be used as family rooms. Unrestricted on-street parking is available, though at times it might be difficult to find a space. The house is about a ten-minute walk from the sea.

OWNERS: Mr and Mrs R.F. Cooke OPEN: all year exc Christmas ROOMS: 5 double, 4 with shower, 1 with private bathroom; 1 family, with shower; tea/coffee and TV in all bedrooms; lounge with TV TERMS: single occupancy £20–£22, double £40–£44, family room from £40; children under 3 free, reductions for ages 4–13 according to age; dinner £10; deposit: £10 CARDS: Visa DETAILS: children welcome; dogs by arrangement; smoking in bedrooms only; garden

EAST COKER Somerset map 2

Holywell House NEW ENTRY

Holywell, East Coker, nr Yeovil BA22 9NQ
TEL: (01935) 862612 FAX: (01935) 863035
turn off A30 Yeovil to Crewkerne road, just W of Yeovil, signposted East Coker, continue for 2½m, house is opposite Foresters Arms

This large Georgian house, built of local hamstone, has been lovingly restored. The Somervilles moved here in 1990, and Mr Somerville created the gorgeous three-acre garden from scratch. It has a stream running through and includes bog gardens, plus herb, organic vegetable and fruit gardens, as well as herbaceous borders and many specially selected trees, and it is open to the public under the National Gardens Scheme. The house is extremely comfortable and has a welcoming and friendly atmosphere. Guests have a choice of three well-equipped bedrooms: the Pine Room, with its wonderful old fitted pine wardrobe; the twin-bedded Cottage Suite, which has a galleried sitting-room and is suitable for four people; and the Master Suite with its mahogany-panelled, Victorian-style bathroom. Both the sitting- and dining-rooms are elegantly furnished, and dinner is available by prior arrangement, featuring produce from the garden. Of interest nearby is the RNAS museum at Yeovilton, Cricket St Thomas Wildlife Park, and the town of Sherborne.

OWNER: Jackie Somerville OPEN: all year exc Christmas ROOMS: 2 double, 1 twin; all rooms with bath/shower, tea/coffee and TV; lounge TERMS: single/single occupancy £35–£40, twin/double £60–£65; dinner £17; deposit required CARDS: none DETAILS: no children; no dogs; no smoking in public rooms; car park; garden; tennis

EAST COWES Isle of Wight **map 2**

Crossways House

Crossways Road, East Cowes PO32 6LJ TEL/FAX: (01983) 298282

Crossways House, formerly part of the Osborne royal estate, was built as a residence for Queen Victoria's Admiral Master of Arms, and later used as a school for the Osborne naval cadets. It is a substantial house standing in its own grounds, just off the main road, close to Osborne House. The Baldwins are a friendly couple, and extend a warm welcome to their guests. Most bedrooms are on the ground floor. The house incorporates 'Memories' restaurant, open for lunch and dinner, and a lounge bar where visitors can sample the collection of over 40 whiskies and 25 brandies. A tea garden is located in the grounds.

OWNERS: Mike and Hilary Baldwin OPEN: all year ROOMS: 2 double, both with bath/shower; 4 twin, 3 with bath/shower, 1 with private bathroom; 1 family; tea/coffee and TV in all bedrooms; lounge with TV TERMS: single occupancy £27.50–£30, twin/double £45, family room £45–£60; children's reductions according to age; dinner £9 CARDS: Amex, Diners, MasterCard, Visa DETAILS: children welcome; no dogs; car park; garden

EAST KNOYLE Wiltshire **map 2**

Moors Farmhouse

East Knoyle SP3 6BU TEL: (01747) 830385 FAX: (01747) 830877
just W of East Knoyle on minor road to Gillingham

This attractive, creeper-clad stone farmhouse is on a working dairy farm, with an old-fashioned farmyard that guests can enjoy. Situated in a quiet position on the northern edge of Blackmore Vale, it has lovely views. The oldest part of the house dates back to the seventeenth century, and the first-floor extension, reached by an outside staircase, was added after the Napoleonic Wars, for the purpose of storing cheese. The extension now functions as the guest accommodation, comprising a suite of a twin-bedded room, bathroom, and sitting-room with a wood-burning stove. Extra beds can be added to accommodate families. Riding is available, and Moors Farmhouse is ideal for country lovers seeking peace and quiet.

OWNER: June Reading OPEN: all year exc Christmas ROOMS: 1 twin, with bath/shower, tea/coffee and TV TERMS: twin £44; children £14 CARDS: none DETAILS: children welcome; no dogs; car park; garden

EAST MEON Hampshire map 2

Drayton Cottage

East Meon GU32 1PW TEL: (01730) 823472
E of A32 on minor road from West Meon to East Meon

Substantial breakfasts and a very colourful, well-kept garden add to the attractiveness of this B&B, located on a small country road just a mile away from the pretty Domesday village of East Meon with its Norman church. Originally two cottages, the 200-year-old flint and chalk building now is arranged so that guests use one end and the Rocketts live at the other. Both bedrooms face the River Meon; the *en suite* twin room can be made into a large double as it has zip-locked twin beds, and the double has its own bathroom. There is a small conservatory as well as a guest lounge and small dining-room.

OWNER: Joan Rockett OPEN: all year exc Christmas ROOMS: 1 double, with private bathroom; 1 twin, with shower; tea/coffee and TV in both bedrooms; lounge TERMS: single occupancy £22–£24, twin/double £40–£44; deposit: £10 per person CARDS: none DETAILS: no children; no dogs; no smoking in bedrooms; car park; garden

EAST PRAWLE Devon map 1

Hines Hill

East Prawle TQ7 2BZ TEL/FAX: (01548) 511263
from Kingsbridge follow A379 to Frogmore, then signs to East Prawle; Hines Hill is on the left 200yds down road towards sea

Hines Hill is an attractive house built in 1937, and stands on a 400-foot cliff with far-reaching views of the coastline. Many years of foreign travel by the owners have produced an interesting collection of antique and oriental furniture. The ground floor has been opened up to provide a large lounge/dining-room, with doors out to the terrace, taking full advantage of the lovely sea views. Two of the three comfortable bedrooms have *en suite* facilities, and the third has the sole use of a bathroom. David is a retired pilot and Sylvia used to run a restaurant here. Her favoured style is French provincial, but menus include dishes from other countries where she has lived. Dinner is served at one table, in a dinner-party atmosphere. The garden is full of interesting plants, and there is a small beach below the house as well as the South-West coastal path. Visitors return here not only for the food and views, but also for the opportunity to relax in an atmosphere of warmth and friendliness.

OWNERS: Sylvia and David Morris OPEN: Mar to Oct ROOMS: 2 double, 1 with bath/shower, 1 with private bathroom; 1 twin, with bath/shower; tea/coffee and TV in all bedrooms TERMS: single occupancy £20–£43.50, twin/double £40–£58; dinner £12; deposit CARDS: none DETAILS: no children under 12; no dogs; no smoking; car park; garden

EAST WITTERING West Sussex map 3

Bayside NEW ENTRY

Tamarisk Walk, East Wittering PO20 8DQ TEL: (01243) 670786

Bayside is a 70-year-old bungalow with an attractive garden, set in a quiet area just across the road from the beach. Jenny Pine extends a warm and friendly welcome and runs a very relaxed and comfortable house. Guests have a TV lounge to relax in and are free to use the kitchen for making drinks. Those who do not wish to go out and about are welcome to use the house all day. The three bedrooms share a bathroom and there is a separate WC. Breakfast is served in the dining-room. Sailing and diving tuition can be arranged.

OWNER: Jenny Pine OPEN: all year ROOMS: 1 single; 2 double; TV in all bedrooms and lounge TERMS: single/single occupancy £18–£20, double £36–£40 CARDS: none DETAILS: no children; dogs welcome; no smoking in bedrooms; car park; garden

EAST WITTON North Yorkshire map 9

Dale View

38 East Witton, nr Leyburn DL8 4SH TEL: (01969) 624113
on A6108, 3m SE of Leyburn

A reader who visited Dale View in June had a thoroughly enjoyable time, in spite of awful weather. 'This is in no small measure because of the kindness and level of service offered by the Dunthornes,' she wrote. The cosy cottage is at the end of a terrace overlooking the green in the tiny village of East Witton. It is lavishly decorated throughout and maintained to a high standard, and Terry Dunthorne is responsible for the stencilled decorations on the bedroom furniture. The comfortable guests' lounge is adorned with a collection of plates and prints and has a hand-built grandfather clock. Breakfasts are served at individual tables in the small dining-area, and other meals can be had at the highly recommended Blue Lion pub, 200 yards away.

OWNERS: Mr and Mrs T. Dunthorne OPEN: all year exc Christmas ROOMS: 1 double, 1 twin; both rooms with bath/shower, tea/coffee and TV; lounge with TV TERMS: twin/double £46; deposit: 30% CARDS: none DETAILS: no children; no dogs; no smoking; car park; garden

---

If there are any bedrooms with TV, or with tea / coffee-making facilities, we mention this in the details at the end of an entry.

EBRINGTON Gloucestershire **map 5**

Holly House

Ebrington GL55 6NL TEL: (01386) 593213
from Chipping Campden take B4035 E towards Shipston on Stour; after garden centre turn left to Ebrington

This comfortable, turn-of-the-century house stands in a small village with an ancient church, two miles from Chipping Campden. The three *en suite* bedrooms are all situated on the ground floor and can accommodate wheelchair-users. A new lounge complete with TV and video is now available for guests to use. Breakfasts are served in the separate dining-room, and can also be taken in the bedrooms on request. A local pub serves evening meals Monday to Saturday; the Hutsbys will provide Sunday dinners by arrangement. Hidcote Gardens and Snowshill Manor are nearby.

OWNERS: Candida and Jeffrey Hutsby OPEN: all year exc Christmas ROOMS: 1 double, 1 twin, 1 family; all rooms with bath/shower, tea/coffee and TV; all rooms suitable for wheelchair-users; lounge with TV TERMS: single occupancy £25–£36, twin/double £36–£40, family room £46–£60; children's reductions according to age if sharing with parents; Sun dinner £15; deposit: £10 per night CARDS: none DETAILS: children welcome; well-behaved dogs welcome; no smoking; car park; garden

ELSING Norfolk **Map 6**

Bartles Lodge

Church Farm, Church Street, Elsing NR20 3EA TEL: (01362) 637177
off B1110, 5m NE of Dereham; opposite church

This black and white bungalow is set in 12 acres of land encompassing a peaceful landscaped garden and two lakes. The small, comfortable bedrooms have excellent facilities, all have *en suite* bath or shower, and most have views of the garden. Guests can relax in the large conservatory overlooking the grounds, and full English breakfasts are served in the adjacent dining-room. Coarse fishing can be arranged at either of the private lakes for a small fee during the summer, and fishing is free between November and March. Bartles Lodge is in the quiet village of Elsing, and the Norfolk Rural Life Museum is nearby. Evening meals are available at the local inn; one-night bookings are usually not accepted in August and September.

OWNERS: David and Annie Bartlett OPEN: all year ROOMS: 2 double, 3 twin, 1 four-poster, 1 family; all rooms with bath/shower and TV; lounge TERMS: single occupancy £27–£35, twin/double £45, four-poster £56, family room £58; deposit: £20 for 2 nights or more CARDS: MasterCard, Visa DETAILS: no children under 10; dogs by arrangement; no smoking in dining-room; car park; garden

---

Many B&Bs are in remote places, and although in many cases we provide directions, it is always advisable to ask for clear instructions when booking.

ELY Cambridgeshire **map 6**

Black Hostelry

Cathedral Close, The College, Ely CB7 4DL
TEL: (01353) 662612 FAX: (01353) 665658

This unique place, situated on the south side of Ely cathedral, is a fine example of a domestic medieval building still in use. Once an infirmary for Benedictine monks, it became a canon's house in the sixteenth century. It now offers modernised accommodation consisting of one suite incorporating bedroom, lounge and bathroom, which is used as a double, twin or family; and a double room with a private bathroom. The suite has Norman arches and a Tudor fireplace, and those staying in the double can enjoy their breakfast in a medieval undercroft. Both rooms overlook the surrounding, peaceful gardens. The Black Hostelry is in walking distance of shops and restaurants in the town.

OWNERS: Canon and Mrs D. Green OPEN: all year exc Christmas ROOMS: 1 double, 1 double/twin/family; both rooms with private bathroom, tea/coffee and TV; lounge with TV TERMS: single occupancy/double £49, double/twin/family suite £49 plus children's charge; £10 for children sharing with parents; deposit: £10 CARDS: none DETAILS: children welcome; dogs welcome; car park; garden

Springfields

Ely Road, Little Thetford, Ely CB6 3HJ
TEL: (01353) 663637 FAX: (01353) 663130
off A10, 2m S of Ely

High standards continue to be maintained at this modern ranch-style bungalow, which offers three well-appointed and elegantly decorated guest bedrooms. All are on the ground floor in an addition to the house, have TVs, either *en suite* facilities or private bathrooms, and pleasant views of the well-manicured garden. The dining-room, with its collections of interesting plates and glasses, is where breakfast is served. The Baileys treat their guests with warmth and friendliness, and welcome new arrivals with a hot drink.

OWNERS: Mr and Mrs Derek Bailey OPEN: all year exc Christmas ROOMS: 1 double, with shower; 2 twin, both with private bathroom; tea/coffee and TV in all bedrooms TERMS: single occupancy £30, twin/double £50; deposit: £10 per person CARDS: none DETAILS: no children under 12; no dogs; no smoking; car park; garden

We welcome your feedback about B&Bs you have stayed in. Please make use of the report forms at the end of the book – or use your own stationery if you prefer – and mail your report to: The Editors, The Good Bed and Breakfast Guide, *FREEPOST, 2 Marylebone Road, London NW1 1YN. (No stamps are needed if mailed within the UK.) Recommendations for B&Bs for our next edition are very welcome. Please let us know if you need more report forms and we will send you a fresh supply.*

ETCHINGHAM East Sussex map 3

King John's Lodge

Sheepstreet Lane, Etchingham TN19 7AZ
TEL: (01580) 819232 FAX: (01580) 819562
turn off A21 at Flimwell and follow A2087 to Ticehurst; turn left past church and first left again; house on left after 1m

King John II of France is said to have been held prisoner here for several years in the mid-fourteenth century. The oldest part of the house dates back to that period, although most of it is Jacobean and there are Edwardian additions. The Cunninghams are responsible for the sympathetic renovation, and have retained original features such as the leaded lights in the mullioned windows. Jill is also the inspiration behind the four acres of spectacular gardens, which include a secret garden and a wild garden with rosewalk and a lily pond. Full English breakfast is served in the Elizabethan dining-room or on the sun terrace, and four-course dinners are available by arrangement. One of the three bedrooms, which is in the oldest part of the house, has an open loft containing a bed as well as twin beds below, and is ideal for a family. Guests have use of the tennis court, croquet lawn and swimming-pool. The garden is sometimes open to the public as part of the National Gardens Scheme, and there are plants and garden ornaments for sale.

OWNERS: Jill and Richard Cunningham OPEN: all year exc Christmas ROOMS: 2 double, 1 with bath/shower, 1 with private bathroom; 1 twin, with private bathroom; 1 family, with bath/shower; tea/coffee in all bedrooms; lounge with TV TERMS: single occupancy £40–£45, twin/double/family £60–£70 plus children's charge; children's reductions by arrangement; dinner £24; deposit usually required CARDS: none DETAILS: no children under 7; no dogs; smoking in 1 lounge only; car park; garden; swimming-pool; tennis

EVESHAM Hereford & Worcester map 5

Brookside

Hampton, Evesham WR11 6ND TEL: (01386) 443116
just off A44 Evesham to Pershore road

Brookside occupies a peaceful location by the River Isbourne, less than a mile from the centre of Evesham. Bedrooms are brightly decorated and modestly furnished. One of the single rooms is on the ground floor and has its own WC and wash-basin, and there are three bathrooms for guests' use. A cosy sitting-room is supplied with tea/coffee-making facilities and a small fridge. Modestly priced dinners are served by arrangement, with children's portions and vegetarian options available with notice. On sunny days, guests can sit out in the large garden.

OWNERS: Mick and Lynne Mathers OPEN: all year exc Christmas ROOMS: 2 single, 1 double, 2 twin, 1 family; all rooms with wash-basin; TV in some bedrooms and lounge TERMS: single £16–£18, single occupancy £20–£25, twin/double £30–£34, family room

£40–£45; half-price for children sharing with parents; dinner £8.50; deposit required CARDS: none DETAILS: no babies under 1; no dogs; smoking in lounge only; car park; garden

Church House

Greenhill Park Road, Evesham WR11 4NL TEL: (01386) 40498

Decorated and furnished sensitively in keeping with its origins, this fine Victorian house standing very close to the town centre continues to maintain its high standards. It offers three comfortable *en suite* rooms, each with a TV, plus a charming blue-curtained sitting-room with a log fire and antiques. First-class breakfasts include home-made jams. The Shaws work together to ensure visitors are well looked after, and Mrs Shaw speaks fluent Spanish and French.

OWNERS: Mr and Mrs E.M. Shaw OPEN: all year exc Christmas ROOMS: 1 double, 1 twin, 1 family; all rooms with bath/shower, tea/coffee and TV; lounge with TV TERMS: single occupancy £26–£35, twin/double £38–£46, family room £56–£65; half-price for children under 12; deposit by arrangement CARDS: none DETAILS: children welcome; well-behaved dogs welcome; no smoking in dining-room; car park; garden

EXETER Devon map 1

The Edwardian

30–32 Heavitree Road, Exeter EX1 2LQ
TEL/FAX: (01392) 276102 and 254699

An Edwardian theme, appropriately enough, runs through this immaculately clean B&B within a stone's throw of the city centre. Décor and furnishings in keeping with the era – including antique brass or period wooden bedsteads in some rooms, plus an assortment of collectables – add to the feel of yesteryear, although the comforts on offer are modern enough. Most of the rooms have *en suite* facilities, and three have four-poster beds; many have direct-dial telephones and hairdryers, and all have TVs. Some rooms have views of the cathedral. Breakfasts – continental, vegetarian or full English – are served at separate tables in one of the two adjoining dining-rooms, and there is a blue-hued, tastefully decorated guest lounge with TV. The Rattenburys hail from Exeter, and are happy to share their considerable knowledge of the city and the surrounding area with their visitors.

OWNERS: Michael and Kay Rattenbury OPEN: all year exc Christmas ROOMS: 2 single, 5 double, 2 twin, 3 four-poster; all rooms with bath/shower exc 1 single with private bathroom; tea/coffee and TV in all bedrooms; lounge with TV TERMS: single £24–£36, single occupancy £34–£38, twin/double £44–£48, four-poster £48–£50, family room £54–£65; deposit: 20% CARDS: Amex, MasterCard, Visa DETAILS: children welcome; dogs welcome; no smoking in dining-rooms; car park; garden

Any smoking restrictions that we know of are given in the details at the end of the entry.

Raffles Hotel

11 Blackall Road, Exeter EX4 4HD TEL/FAX: (01392) 270200

This large, semi-detached Victorian house in a quiet residential area is a very comfortable place with a friendly atmosphere. It still has many original features, including the stairway and the hall floor-tiles, and is beautifully decorated and furnished with antiques. The attractive bedrooms all have TVs and *en suite* bathrooms. Breakfasts and, by arrangement, evening meals are served in the small dining-room. Guests can relax in the secluded rear garden with its wistaria-covered arches, or in the lounge. The town centre and cathedral are only ten minutes' walk away.

OWNERS: Richard and Susan Hyde OPEN: all year ROOMS: 2 single, 2 double, 2 twin, 1 family; all rooms with shower, tea/coffee and TV; lounge with TV TERMS: single £30–£32, twin/double £44–£46, family room £50–£54; half-price for children sharing with parents; dinner £14 CARDS: Amex, Diners, MasterCard, Visa DETAILS: children welcome; dogs welcome; car park; garden

FARNINGHAM Kent **map 3**

The Bakery

High Street, Farningham, nr Dartford DA4 0DH TEL: (01322) 864210
from M25 junction 3 take A20; house opposite churchyard

The Bakery is a whitewashed, part-weatherboarded seventeenth-century cottage in the centre of the attractive village of Farningham. The house retains its original flagstone floors, and the elegantly simple bedrooms have armchairs. The attractive walled garden, which is open to the public once a year, has a croquet lawn and borders the cricket ground. Mrs Lovering was born in Portugal and speaks four languages as well as English. She is an artist and her work is on sale in her studio in the grounds. Brands Hatch is a mile away, and Lullingstone Castle and Biggin Hill are nearby attractions.

OWNERS: Mr and Mrs Lovering OPEN: all year exc Christmas ROOMS: 1 single; 1 double, with wash-basin; 1 twin, with wash-basin TERMS: single £20–£25, single occupancy £25, twin/double £40–£55; reductions for children sharing with parents; deposit: £10 per person CARDS: none DETAILS: no children under 8; no dogs; no smoking; car park; garden

FAR SAWREY Cumbria **map 8**

West Vale

NEW ENTRY

Far Sawrey LA22 0LQ TEL: (01539) 442817
on B5285, 2m SE of Hawkshead

This traditional Lakeland stone house, built in the 1890s, is a short distance from the car ferry across Windermere, and has views of Grizedale Forest, mountains and fields dotted with sheep. Bedrooms are prettily decorated with delicate prints and pastels. All have *en suite* shower and are supplied with an information pack on the area. There is also a TV lounge, with an open fire, and a small licensed lounge bar. Breakfast and, by arrangement, dinner are served, and vegetarians can be catered for. Alternatively, a pub in Near Sawrey serves food. The area is associated with Beatrix Potter and is a designated area of outstanding natural beauty.

OWNER: Mrs I. Forbes OPEN: Mar to Oct ROOMS: 3 double, 2 twin, 1 family; all rooms with shower and tea/coffee; lounge with TV TERMS: single occupancy £23, twin/double £46; one-third reduction for children under 11; dinner £11; deposit: £15 per person CARDS: none DETAILS: no children under 7; guide dogs only; no smoking in dining-room; car park; garden

FAVERSHAM Kent **map 3**

Frith Farm House

Otterden, Faversham ME13 0DD
TEL: (01795) 890701 FAX: (01795) 890009
from A20 after Lenham, turn left to Warren St, continue 3m following signs to Eastling village

This attractive late-Georgian farmhouse is in six acres of formal gardens, with an ornamental pond, summer house and cherry orchard. The house is approached up a gravel driveway and sits high on the North Downs. The Chesterfields are a very welcoming couple and their house has three beautifully furnished and comfortable guest bedrooms. Breakfast is served in the vine-covered conservatory, and excellent home-cooked dinners, by prior arrangement, in the dining-room where Markham Chesterfield's china collection is displayed. The elegant lounge has been furnished in keeping with the period of the house and is a perfect place in which to relax. Horse-riding can be arranged. Otterden is a tiny place between the A2 and A20, and it is advisable to ask for directions when booking.

OWNERS: Markham and Susan Chesterfield OPEN: all year ROOMS: 1 double, 1 twin, 1 four-poster; all rooms with shower, tea/coffee and TV; lounge TERMS: single occupancy £35–£39, twin/double £52–£56, four-poster £56–£60; dinner £19.50; deposit: £10 per person per night CARDS: MasterCard, Visa (3% surcharge on credit cards) DETAILS: no children under 10; no dogs; no smoking; car park; garden

---

The Granary

Plumford Lane, Faversham ME13 0DS TEL/FAX: (01795) 538416
from M2 junction 6 take left turn to Faversham, at T-junction turn left, then first left into Brogdale Rd, then first left signposted Plumford; house ½m along on right

Until recently the Granary was part of a working farm, and stands peacefully in a pretty part of rural Kent, surrounded by a large garden and an orchard. It is an attractively converted stone building adjoining the neighbouring oast house and offers tasteful, immaculate guest accommodation. The three bedrooms have either *en suite* showers or a private bathroom, and all have TVs. A large timber verandah off the lounge has grand views over the countryside. The Brightmans provide a warm welcome, and the house has a relaxed and friendly atmosphere. Good breakfasts are served in the farmhouse-style dining-room, and several pubs in the area provide evening meals.

OWNER: Annette Brightman OPEN: all year exc Christmas ROOMS: 1 double, 1 twin, both with shower; 1 family, with private bathroom; tea/coffee and TV in all bedrooms; lounge with TV TERMS: single occupancy £25–£30, twin/double £44, family room £54; babies free, reductions for older children sharing with parents; deposit: £10 per night CARDS: Delta, MasterCard, Switch, Visa DETAILS: no children under 12 exc babies; no dogs; no smoking; car park; garden

FELIXSTOWE Suffolk map 6

Primrose Gate NEW ENTRY

263 Ferry Road, Felixstowe IP11 9RX
TEL: (01394) 271699 FAX: (01294) 283614

This modern, unpretentious house is adjacent to Felixstowe Golf Course and the beach, and overlooks the River Deben in a quiet part of town.The bedrooms are spotlessly clean, and have modern furniture, armchairs and TV. Guests in summer are greeted with a drink served on the patio in the lovely garden, and long-stay visitors have free use of the outdoor swimming-pool. Generous breakfasts feature fresh fruit, yoghurt and traditional cooked fare, including free-range eggs from the owner's chickens. They are served family-style in the dining-room overlooking the garden and the countryside beyond. The Ferry Boat Inn nearby serves modestly priced evening meals, and other restaurants can be found in the town.

OWNER: Lesley Berry OPEN: all year ROOMS: 1 single, 1 double, 1 twin; all rooms with private bathroom; tea/coffee and TV TERMS: single £18, single occupancy £19, twin/double £33; children's reductions according to age CARDS: none DETAILS: children welcome; no dogs; no smoking; car park; garden; swimming-pool

FENITON Devon map 2

Colestocks House

Colestocks, Feniton EX14 0JR TEL: (01404) 850633 FAX: (01404) 850901
2m N of A30 at Payhembury exit, 4m W of Honiton

This delightful thatched sixteenth-century listed house with later additions stands in two acres of immaculately maintained gardens, surrounded by a high wall. Guests have the use of a putting-green, golf nets and croquet lawn. The comfortable sitting-room, with french windows opening out to the garden, has a good selection of books, and there is a lounge bar. Evening meals with a German flavour are served in the dining-room. The *en suite* bedrooms are spacious, one has a four-poster and two are on the ground floor. Golfers have a choice of 11 courses within a 20-mile radius. There is a riding school in the village, and fishing can be arranged locally.

OWNERS: Gordon and Ursula Broster OPEN: Apr to Oct ROOMS: 2 single, 3 double, 3 twin; all rooms with bath/shower, tea/coffee and TV; lounge TERMS: single £27.50, single occupancy £37.50, twin/double £55–£61; dinner £15 CARDS: Master Card, Visa DETAILS: no children under 10; no dogs; smoking in bar only; car park; garden

FIFEHEAD MAGDALEN Dorset map 2

Apple Tree Cottage

Fifehead Magdalen SP8 5RT TEL/FAX: (01258) 820689
1m S of A30 and 7½m W of Shaftesbury

This tastefully and comfortably furnished modern stone-built cottage is set in an 'away-from-it-all' hamlet among Dorset's picturesque hills and fields. Directions for getting here are a little complex: best to ask for clarification when booking. The car park is opposite the front door. The two bedrooms share a bathroom; the twin is the larger and has a TV, while the double is quite small but has the benefit of a fine view. Evening meals can be pre-booked and, along with breakfasts, are served in the dining-room. The B&B is well positioned for some beautiful walks, and for visits to Longleat and Stourhead.

OWNER: Mrs M. Wootton OPEN: all year ROOMS: 1 double, 1 twin; tea/coffee in both bedrooms; TV in twin room TERMS: single occupancy £20–£25, twin/double £35–£45; dinner £12–£15; deposit required CARDS: none DETAILS: no children; dogs by arrangement; car park; garden

FILLINGHAM Lincolnshire map 9

Church Farm

Fillingham DN21 5BS TEL: (01427) 668279 FAX: (01427) 668025
off B1398, 9m N of Lincoln

Christine and Bill Ramsay have lived on this 144-acre arable farm for over 30 years, but only started offering B&B in 1994. They are friendly hosts and their nineteenth-century farmhouse has a warm and welcoming ambience. It stands in an acre of secluded gardens on the edge of the village of Fillingham, where John Wycliffe, the fourteenth-century religious reformer, was rector. Bedrooms are comfortable, furnished with stripped pine, and the lounge has a TV and open fires. Breakfasts include home-made lemon curd and marmalade, and home-cooked dinners are served with prior notice in the bright, blue-striped dining-room. Children's portions and vegetarian meals can be provided on request, and guests may bring their own wine as there is no licence. The historic city of Lincoln is a short drive away.

OWNERS: Christine and Bill Ramsay OPEN: all year exc Christmas ROOMS: 1 single; 1 double, with shower; 1 twin; tea/coffee in all bedrooms; TV in 1 bedroom and lounge TERMS: single £20, single occupancy £20–£25, twin/double £32–£38; dinner £11; deposit: £10 CARDS: none DETAILS: no children under 5; no dogs; no smoking; car park; garden

FINCHAM Norfolk **map 6**

Rose Cottage

Downham Road, Fincham PE33 9HF TEL: (01366) 347426
on A1122, 4m E of Downham Market

On the edge of the village, this brick Georgian cottage stands in its own pleasant grounds, with a well-tended garden. It is warm and inviting, and the immaculate bedrooms have folk-weave bedspreads; one has *en suite* facilities. Angela Vaughan-Arbuckle speaks fluent German. Breakfast only is served, but several places for evening meals are nearby. There are plenty of walks in the vicinity, and a converted stable is also available as self-catering accommodation.

OWNER: Angela Vaughan-Arbuckle OPEN: all year exc Christmas ROOMS: 2 twin, 1 with shower, 1 with private bathroom; tea/coffee and TV in both bedrooms TERMS: single occupancy £18–£20, twin £30; babies up to 6 months free, children's reductions by arrangement; deposit: £10 CARDS: none DETAILS: children welcome; small dogs welcome; no smoking; car park; garden

FINDON West Sussex **map 3**

Findon Tower

Cross Lane, Findon BN14 0UG TEL: (01903) 873870
off A24 at S end of Findon into Cross Lane; house 200yds on left

A gravel drive leads to this Edwardian country house, clad in Sussex hanging tiles, with the eponymous tower, surmounted by a spire, housing its front entrance. From the hall beyond, an oak staircase leads to a balustraded landing. Delightful flower arrangements grace the communal rooms, which have views of the garden – the house is peacefully situated within its own grounds. The bedrooms are high-ceilinged and comfortably furnished, with plenty of hanging space and tea/coffee-making facilities (a hot drink is also offered on arrival). Guests have the use of a spacious sitting-room with TV, a dining-room where a full English breakfast is served at one long table, and a snooker room with a full-sized table. The Smiths are very welcoming and provide books and information leaflets about the area. Findon itself, an attractive old village in horse-breeding country, offers several possibilities for evening meals.

OWNERS: Thurza and Tony Smith OPEN: all year exc Christmas ROOMS: 2 double, 1 with bath/shower, 1 with private bathroom; 1 twin, with bath/shower; tea/coffee in all bedrooms; lounge with TV TERMS: single/single occupancy £25–£30, twin/double £40–£50; £7.50–£10 for children sharing with parents; deposit: £10 minimum CARDS: none DETAILS: children welcome; dogs by arrangement; no smoking; car park; games room; garden

The end details for each entry state whether or not dogs are allowed, but it is always best to check when booking.

FLAMBOROUGH East Riding of Yorkshire — map 9

Revidge — NEW ENTRY

North Marine Road, Flamborough YO15 1BA TEL: (01262) 850107

Revidge is a pleasant detached house in a peaceful setting, with a well-tended garden, complete with fish-pond and koi carp. The Spencers are a down-to-earth couple who provide a very friendly welcome and good-value accommodation in their spotlessly clean home. The guest lounge has a TV and a fine display of cross-stitch items made by Pauline. The blue-and-cream bedrooms have plenty of cupboard space. Substantial breakfasts are served, and packed lunches can be arranged; several pubs in Flamborough are within a ten-minute walk for evening meals. This is a popular venue for bird-watchers and walkers, and there is a golf course nearby; arrangements can be made for fishing and golf.

OWNER: Pauline Spencer OPEN: Mar to Nov ROOMS: 2 double, both with wash-basin, tea/coffee and TV; lounge with TV TERMS: single occupancy £15, double £26 CARDS: none DETAILS: children welcome; no smoking in dining-room; car park; garden

FLEET Hampshire — map 3

8 Chinnock Close

8 Chinnock Close, Fleet GU13 9SN TEL: (01252) 613646
4m S of M3 junction 4

Built over 30 years ago, 8 Chinnock Close is part of a housing development on the edge of Fleet, laid out with lots of trees. Guests use one end of the house, which includes a restful TV lounge with doors leading out to the patio and small back garden. The bedrooms are pleasantly furnished and share a bathroom and a shower-room. The Nixes live at the other end of the house, which is where they make miniatures and figures for dolls' houses, some of which can be found around the house. Enthusiasts come here specifically to watch the Nixes at work. This is a popular place for business people and very convenient for the Farnborough Air Show. There is a large selection of eating-places close by.

OWNERS: Mr and Mrs R. Nix OPEN: all year ROOMS: 1 single, 1 double, 1 twin; tea/coffee in all bedrooms; lounge with TV TERMS: single/single occupancy £16, twin/double £32 CARDS: none DETAILS: children welcome; no dogs; no smoking; car park; garden

---

We state at the end of an entry whether children are welcome, and explain any age restrictions. If there are reduced rates for children, this is mentioned; if no reductions are specified, assume you will have to pay full rates for children.

FORD Northumberland **map 10**

Estate House

Ford Village, Ford TD15 2QG TEL/FAX: (01890) 820414
on B6353, 3m W of Lowick

The Burtons are continuing to upgrade this delightful Victorian country house, and are excellent hosts. The house is impeccably maintained and stands in a large, well-landscaped garden. The sitting-room overlooks the garden, as do two of the bedrooms. There is a log fire for cool evenings, plus an organ expertly played by John Burton. Guests are usually greeted with a complimentary hot drink upon arrival. Two of the bedrooms have *en suite* facilities; all have TVs and armchairs. Breakfast includes home-baked bread, but dinner is no longer available; the Burtons can recommend some good places to eat nearby. Guests have access to the castle, which is situated just beyond the garden gate.

OWNERS: John and Maureen Burton OPEN: all year exc Christmas ROOMS: 2 double, 1 with bath/shower, 1 with wash-basin; 2 twin, 1 with bath/shower, 1 with wash-basin; tea/coffee and TV in all bedrooms; lounge TERMS: single occupancy £20–£30, twin/double £40–£52; deposit: £10 per person CARDS: none DETAILS: no children under 12; no dogs; no smoking; car park; garden

FORDINGBRIDGE Hampshire **map 2**

Green Patch

NEW ENTRY

Furze Hill, Fordingbridge SP6 2PS
TEL: (01425) 652387 FAX: (01425) 656594
just off A338 Salisbury to Ringwood road

This attractive country house has eight acres of grounds and garden, with direct access to the New Forest. The spacious bedrooms are comfortable, and there is an enormous conservatory for guests' use. Breakfast is served in the panelled dining-room or, weather permitting, on the patio which is a sheltered, sunny spot. Green Patch has a free and easy atmosphere, and there is plenty of sitting/relaxing space available throughout the day. Horses are welcome, and riding and pony-trekking can be arranged nearby. Light suppers can be arranged. As the house is difficult to find, it is advisable to ask for directions when booking.

OWNER: Meg Mulcahy OPEN: all year exc Christmas ROOMS: 3 double/twin/family, 1 with bath/shower, 2 with private bathroom; tea/coffee and TV in all bedrooms TERMS: single occupancy £25–£30, twin/double £40–£45, family room £55–£65; babies with own cot and food free; deposit: £25 CARDS: none DETAILS: children welcome; dogs welcome; no smoking; car park; garden

---

If you are forced to turn up later than planned, please telephone to warn the proprietor. It is always best to book a room in advance, even in winter. B&Bs with few rooms may close at short notice for periods not specified in the details.

FOUR ELMS Kent **map 3**

Knowlands

Five Fields Lane, Four Elms TN8 6NA TEL/FAX: (01732) 700314
off B2027, 2m NE of Edenbridge

Knowlands is a large nineteenth-century house with three and a half acres of well-maintained gardens, surrounded by wooded countryside in the beautiful Weald of Kent. There is a hard tennis court in the grounds, as well as a small lake, a summer house and many rose beds. The house is furnished in period style and the two comfortable bedrooms have their original fireplaces. Breakfast and dinner are served. Nearby tourist attractions include Chiddingstone and Hever Castles, Chartwell and Penshurst Place.

OWNERS: John and Ann Haviland OPEN: all year exc Christmas ROOMS: 2 double, both rooms with wash-basin, tea/coffee and TV; lounge with TV TERMS: double £55; dinner £16.50; deposit: 10% CARDS: none DETAILS: children welcome; no dogs; no smoking; car park; garden; tennis

FOWEY Cornwall **map 1**

Carneggan House

Lanteglos PL23 1NW TEL/FAX: (01726) 870327
4m from Pelynt on the Polruan road

Carneggan is in peaceful countryside, only a short distance from the sea, midway between Polruan and Polperro. This eighteenth-century former farmhouse is surrounded by six acres of grounds. There is a restful drawing-room with an open fireplace, and home-cooked evening meals are served in the dining-room by prior arrangement. The comfortably equipped bedrooms have night-storage heaters, and the largest has lovely views. A 20-minute walk across National Trust-owned farmland leads to several unspoilt beaches, and both Polperro and Polruan can be reached along the coastal path.

OWNER: Sue Shakerley OPEN: Feb to Nov ROOMS: 1 double, with bath/shower; 2 twin, 1 with bath/shower, 1 with private bathroom; TV in all bedrooms TERMS: single occupancy £27–£33, twin/double £44–£56; babies free, half-price for children under 12; dinner from £10; deposit: 50% CARDS: Amex, MasterCard, Visa DETAILS: children welcome; dogs by arrangement; no smoking in dining-room; car park; garden

Lanherriot Farm

NEW ENTRY

Fowey PL23 1JT TEL/FAX: (01726) 832637
from A390 take B3269 towards Fowey; after 5m at mini-roundabout take left on to road marked Fowey Docks; turn left at sign for Penventinue, follow past Penventinue Farm, pass through gateway marked Lanherriot Farm; continue to unmarked gate after right bend

Set in peaceful and remote countryside, with breathtaking views, 200-year-old Lanherriot Farm is one and a half miles from the old harbour town of Fowey. The Parnwells are extremely welcoming and the house has a warm and comfortable atmosphere. Children are very welcome, and especially love the donkeys and the outdoor heated swimming-pool (open from May to September) on the sheltered patio set in a wonderful garden. Jenny, who is also a caterer, prepares imaginative evening meals on the Aga, including vegetarian options if requested, served in the small dining-room. The three bedrooms in the main house share a bathroom and a shower-room, and there is a separate WC. For families, there is a suite in a building across the yard consisting of a main room with a sofa bed and another twin-bedded room, plus bathroom.

OWNERS: Mr and Mrs D.J. Parnwell OPEN: Mar to Nov ROOMS: 2 double; 1 twin; 1 family, with private bathroom; tea/coffee in all bedrooms; TV in 2 rooms TERMS: single occupancy £20–£25, twin/double £30–£37, family room £60–£80; reductions for children sharing with parents; dinner £9.50; deposit required for bookings of 3 days or more CARDS: none DETAILS: children welcome; no dogs; no smoking in bedrooms; car park; garden; swimming-pool

FOXTON Leicestershire map 5

Old Manse

37 Swingbridge Street, Foxton LE16 7RH TEL: (01858) 545456
on A6 follow sign for Foxton 1m N of Market Harborough; turn right after church and cross bridge

Guests continue to applaud the high standards and warm welcome found at this seventeenth-century house which used to be the residence of the Baptist minister. It is on the edge of the village in park-like grounds, with a canal running along the bottom. The well-furnished lounge has a log fire, an array of plants and an elegant collection of antique furniture, including a *chaise longue*. The large bedrooms are tastefully decorated in soft pastels and have comfortable beds; two have *en suite* showers. The Pickerings are a charming couple who often invite guests into their private lounge. Breakfasts only are served, but there is a pub close by for evening meals. Foxton was originally a hill-top settlement, and the Old Manse is actually on the historic village trail, which contains all the interesting local buildings.

OWNERS: Peter and Rita Pickering OPEN: all year exc Christmas ROOMS: 1 double, with private bathroom; 2 twin, both with shower; tea/coffee and TV in all bedrooms; lounge with TV TERMS: single occupancy £25, twin/double £40; half-price for children sharing with parents; deposit: £10 CARDS: none DETAILS: children welcome; no dogs; no smoking; car park; garden

To find an entry in the Guide, *go to the maps at the back of the book. Entries are plotted on the maps under their closest village, hamlet or city, except in London, where they are listed by name of B&B. After choosing your localities, go to the relevant section of the book (England, Scotland, Wales etc.), where localities are listed in alphabetical order (by B&B name order in London). There is also an index at the back of the book.*

FRAMLINGHAM EARL Norfolk **map 6**

Oakfield

Yelverton Road, Framlingham Earl NR14 7SD TEL: (01508) 492605
travelling SE on A146 3m from Norwich, turn right at Gull pub, keep left then turn left at top of lane

Oakfield is a modern bungalow in half an acre of attractive lawned garden. It is surrounded by two meadows, one with wild flowers and a fish pond. The well-maintained bedrooms are of a good size, and the twin and bathroom have been refurbished. A conservatory has been added, where excellent breakfasts are served, and there is a separate lounge with a TV. Plenty of pubs and restaurants nearby offer evening meals. Mrs Thompson is a superb host, and guests are well taken care of in this warm and friendly establishment.

OWNER: Mrs R.A. Thompson OPEN: all year exc Christmas ROOMS: 1 single; 1 double, with shower; 1 twin; tea/coffee in all bedrooms; lounge with TV TERMS: single £22–£25, single occupancy £30–£40, twin/double £40–£45; deposit: 1 night's charge CARDS: none DETAILS: no children under 10; no dogs; no smoking; car park; garden

FRAMPTON ON SEVERN Gloucestershire **map 5**

Old School House

NEW ENTRY

Whittles Lane, Frampton on Severn GL2 7EB TEL: (01452) 740457
entering village from A38, take first left; 300yds from end of green, turn right into Whittles Lane

The Old School House, parts of which date from the 1800s, is tucked away in a small village that reputedly has the longest village green in England. The gardens are delightful, and guests are encouraged to make use of them on fine days. The good-sized bedrooms are tastefully decorated in predominantly yellow and blue; both are *en suite*. Comfort and elegance characterise the sitting-room, which has a TV. Free-range eggs feature at breakfast, which sometimes is served in the garden. Three friendly dogs live here. There are places for evening meals within walking distance.

OWNERS: Mr and Mrs W.G. Alexander OPEN: all year exc Christmas and New Year ROOMS: 2 twin; both rooms with bath/shower and tea/coffee; lounge with TV TERMS: single occupancy £25, twin £50 CARDS: none DETAILS: no children under 10; well-behaved dogs only; no smoking in bedrooms; car park; garden

FRANT East Sussex **map 3**

Henley Farm

Frant TN3 9EP TEL: (01892) 750242
on B2099, 1½m S of Frant

This weatherboarded house is approached through an attractive wistaria-covered arch. Originally an oasthouse dating from the early 1800s, it is in a rural setting only four miles from the historic town of

Tunbridge Wells. There is a large pretty garden, a patio for sitting out and a tennis court which Ann Fleming describes as '*very* elderly'. This family home has a welcoming atmosphere and the four bedrooms all have *en suite* facilities. Frant is handy for visits to Sissinghurst Castle and Penshurst Place.

OWNER: Ann Fleming OPEN: all year exc Christmas ROOMS: 2 single, 1 double, 1 twin; all rooms with bath, tea/coffee and TV TERMS: single £19–£20, twin/double £38–£40; babies free, half-price for children under 12 CARDS: none DETAILS: children welcome; dogs by arrangement; no smoking in bedrooms; car park; garden; tennis

---

Old Parsonage

Church Lane, Frant TN3 9DX TEL/FAX: (01892) 750773

take A267 S from Tunbridge Wells for 2m; in Frant turn left into Church Lane

This substantial Georgian house, with a secluded walled garden and an enormous terrace, is off a quiet lane in a pretty twelfth-century village. Built by the Marquess of Abergavenny for his son, who was the parish rector between 1820 and 1845, it remained the rectory until bought by the present owners in 1987. The house is beautifully furnished, and contains many interesting photos, paintings and prints; the large drawing-room is packed with local historical photographs and tapestries. Tea and biscuits are offered to guests on arrival in the large conservatory overlooking the garden. Breakfast is served in the dining-room, and the comfortable bedrooms are spacious with *en suite* facilities. There is a restaurant just opposite, and a couple of pubs nearby that do evening meals. No one-night bookings are taken over weekends in high season.

OWNERS: Tony and Mary Dakin OPEN: all year ROOMS: 1 twin, 2 four-poster; all rooms with bath/shower, tea/coffee and TV; lounge TERMS: single occupancy £45–£55, twin £59–£69, four-poster £64–£72 CARDS: MasterCard, Visa DETAILS: children welcome; dogs welcome; smoking in conservatory only; car park; garden

FREMINGTON Devon **map 1**

Muddlebridge House

Fremington EX31 2NQ TEL/FAX: (01271) 376073

on B323, 3m W of Barnstaple, midway between Bickington and Fremington

Muddlebridge House stands in two acres of attractive grounds, and offers a wealth of amenities for families. It is a substantial Regency country house and is said to have derived its name from the nearby pack-horse bridge. The house has three spacious bedrooms, all with *en suite* showers: Torridge Room has one double and one single bed, Taw Room has twin beds, and Tarka Room is a two-room suite for families. There is also a separate bathroom exclusively for guests' use, and a sitting/dining-room where breakfast is served. Residents are also welcome to use the games room, which has facilities for snooker, table tennis and darts. The grounds also contain six self-catering cottages, attractive gardens and an indoor heated swimming-pool (bring your own swimming-towels). B&B guests are welcome to share the other facilities provided for the self-catering visitors, of sauna, fully equipped laundry room and a 'pets corner' complete with pygmy goats, ducks and bunnies. Bicycle hire can be arranged. No one-night bookings are accepted in August.

OWNERS: Graham and Ruth Macdonald OPEN: Apr to Nov ROOMS: 1 double, 1 twin, 1 family; all rooms with shower, tea/coffee and TV; lounge TERMS: single occupancy £22–£28, twin/double £40–£48; half-price for children under 13 sharing with parents; deposit: 25% CARDS: none DETAILS: children welcome (children under 2 by arrangement); no dogs; no smoking; car park; games room; garden; swimming-pool

FRESHWATER Isle of Wight **map 2**

Brookside Forge Hotel

Brookside Road, Freshwater PO40 9ER TEL: (01983) 754644

David and Jacqui Reynolds took over this large brick-built guesthouse in 1995 and are friendly and accommodating hosts. The house is set in a large garden in a quiet, leafy road close to the centre of Freshwater and just opposite the local swimming-pool and tennis courts. It offers ten small, well-equipped bedrooms, all of them with *en suite* showers (one with a bath as well), and there is a comfortable lounge with TV. A terraced lawn with seating is a good place for relaxing on fine days, and there is a patio bar. This is a child-friendly place, with cots and high chairs if required, a swing and games area in the garden, and children's tea at 5.30. Evening meals are also on offer, served at seven in the dining-room. Visitors arriving on the ferry without a car can arrange to be collected. A two-bedroomed self-catering cottage is also available.

OWNERS: David and Jacqui Reynolds OPEN: all year ROOMS: 1 single, 4 double, 3 twin, 2 family; all rooms with bath/shower, tea/coffee and TV; lounge with TV TERMS: single £18–£19.50, single occupancy £25, twin/double £36–£39, family room £36–£50; children's reductions according to age; dinner £9; deposit or credit card details required CARDS: MasterCard, Visa DETAILS: children welcome; smoking in some rooms only; car park; garden

Yarlands Country House

Victoria Road, Freshwater PO40 9PP TEL: (01983) 752574

Formerly the rectory, Yarlands is a handsome eighteenth-century country house set back from the road, with a wide driveway in front. It stands in two and a half acres of lovely, secluded gardens stretching down to the River Yar. The Fairmans are a welcoming couple who take a great deal of care to ensure their guests are comfortable, and put much effort into maintaining both the house and garden. There is a residents' bar and a comfortable lounge with views of the garden; each has an open fire for chilly days. The house is popular with business people. All six of the good-sized rooms have *en suite* facilities and TVs, and are furnished in pine. Evening meals, using where possible fresh produce from the garden, are served in the large dining-room.

OWNERS: John and Pat Fairman OPEN: Mar to Oct ROOMS: 2 double, 2 twin, 2 family; all rooms with bath/shower, tea/coffee and TV; lounge TERMS: single occupancy £32–£33, twin/double £54–£56, family room from £54; half-price for children sharing with parents; dinner £12; deposit: 10% CARDS: Delta, MasterCard, Switch, Visa DETAILS: no children under 3; no dogs; no smoking in dining-room or lounge; car park; garden

FRIETH Buckinghamshire **map 3**

Little Parmoor Farm

Frieth RG9 6NL TEL: (01494) 881600 FAX: (01494) 883634
from Henley-on-Thames take A4155 Marlow road, turn left to Hambleden, in village take Frieth road; farm on left

This brick and flint farmhouse is surrounded by attractive gardens and 220 acres of working stock and grain land, and was originally built in the sixteenth century. It has a relaxed and friendly atmosphere, children are welcome, and cots and high chairs can be provided. The three individually decorated bedrooms have a wealth of oak beams, and one has an old brass bed. Breakfast is served family-style and includes home-made jams and marmalade. Nearby pubs are available for evening meals. Little Parmoor Farm is well placed for visiting Henley and Marlow, and is an ideal spot for nature lovers. At weekends a minimum of two nights must be booked.

OWNERS: Frances and Roger Emmett OPEN: all year exc Christmas ROOMS: 1 single; 1 double, with shower; 1 twin; tea/coffee in all bedrooms; lounge with TV TERMS: single £20–£25, single occupancy £30–£40, twin/double £42–£46; £10 reduction for children; deposit: £20 CARDS: Visa DETAILS: children welcome; no dogs; no smoking; car park; garden

FRINTON-ON-SEA Essex **map 3**

Uplands Guest House

41 Hadleigh Road, Frinton-on-Sea CO13 9HQ
TEL: (01255) 674889

Uplands is a large semi-detached 1920s house in a quiet street, and stands in a pleasant landscaped garden, just three minutes' walk from the sea. It is comfortable and well furnished, and there are plenty of flowers around the house, giving it a warm and friendly ambience. The comfortable TV lounge leads to a bar/sun-room. The good-sized bedrooms are decorated in autumnal colours. Breakfasts, and dinners (with wine available by the glass or the bottle), are served in the bright dining-room. Transport to and from the station can be arranged.

OWNER: Mrs S.M. Creates OPEN: all year exc Christmas ROOMS: 3 single, all with wash-basin; 2 double, 1 with shower, 1 with wash-basin; 3 twin, all with shower; tea/

coffee in all bedrooms; lounge with TV TERMS: single £22–£27.50, single occupancy £27.50–£40, twin/double £44–£55; dinner £10.50 to £12; deposit: £10 per person CARDS: none DETAILS: no children; no dogs; no smoking; car park; garden

FRITH COMMON Hereford & Worcester map 5

Hunthouse Farm

Frith Common WR15 8JY TEL/FAX: (01299) 832277
off A456 halfway between Bewdley and Tewbury Wells; ½m W of Clows Top turning to Frith Common

'Absolutely first class in every respect' was one couple's verdict of their stay at this immaculate sixteenth-century listed farmhouse with stunning views over surrounding countryside. Moreover, 'breakfast was better than [at] *any* hotel'. Hunthouse is a working farm, and the house is full of atmosphere: there are low beams, open fires, and plenty of warm hospitality on offer from the Keels, who greet arriving guests with cakes and a hot drink. All three bedrooms are *en suite*, attractively decorated with matching fabrics and have tea/coffee-making facilities. Visitors just back from perhaps an energetic walk down country lanes can take it easy in the sitting-room with its wood-burning stove and TV.

OWNER: Jane Keel OPEN: all year exc Christmas ROOMS: 2 double, 1 with bath, 1 with shower; 1 twin, with shower; tea/coffee in all bedrooms; lounge with TV TERMS: single occupancy £30, twin/double £36–£40; deposit required CARDS: none DETAILS: no children under 8; no dogs; no smoking in bedrooms; car park; garden

FRITTENDEN Kent map 3

Maplehurst Mill NEW ENTRY

Mill Lane, Frittenden TN17 2DT TEL/FAX: (01580) 852203
turn E off A229 Maidstone to Hastings road just S of Staplehurst, signposted Frittenden; after 1m at bend in road turn right opposite white house, turn right again at end of lane; house is first on right

Earliest records of a watermill on this site date back to 1309, but the oldest part of the present building dates from the fifteenth century, and the mill itself was reconstructed in 1756. It is set in 11 acres of landscaped gardens, in a lovely position at the end of Mill Lane, and the three bedrooms all overlook the water and surrounding countryside. One has a four-poster bed, and another, on the ground floor, is suitable for wheelchairs. The first-floor drawing-room has a grand piano and overlooks the stream and wheel. Candlelit dinners are served in the beamed dining-room, with an inglenook fireplace and antique furniture. Organically grown vegetables and herbs come from the garden, and a good selection of English cheeses and English wines are offered. Guests have use of the heated open-air swimming-pool.

OWNERS: Heather and Kenneth Parker OPEN: all year exc Christmas ROOMS: 1 double, 1 twin, 1 four-poster; all rooms with bath and shower, tea/coffee and TV;

1 room suitable for wheelchair-users; lounge TERMS: single occupancy £39–£45, twin/double £58–£70, four-poster £58–£70; dinner £19; deposit: £10 per person CARDS: MasterCard, Visa DETAILS: no children under 12; no dogs; no smoking; car park; garden; swimming-pool

---

Old Rectory

Frittenden, Cranbrook TN17 2DG TEL/FAX: (01580) 852313
between A229 and A274, 2½m N of Sissinghurst and 3m SW of Headcorn

Two of the guest bedrooms at this comfortable red-brick house are now *en suite* and one has a private bathroom. Built in the 1800s, the Old Rectory is set in a large garden and has good views of the hills beyond. The Barnetts are, in the words of one reader, 'friendly without being intrusive', while another guest was impressed with their excellent and helpful knowledge about the local area. Meals too come in for praise, and dinner (by arrangement) is served at two tables in the dining-room; vegetarian choices are available on request, and diners may bring their own wine. In summer there is croquet and badminton in the garden. Single-night bookings are not accepted, and visitors must stay a minimum of two nights.

OWNERS: Alex and Joy Barnett OPEN: Easter to late Oct ROOMS: 1 double, with shower; 2 twin, 1 with shower, 1 with private bathroom; tea/coffee in all bedrooms; lounge with TV TERMS: single occupancy £30–£35, twin/double £48–£52; dinner £12–£14; deposit: £50 CARDS: none DETAILS: no children; no dogs; no smoking; car park; garden

FYLINGTHORPE North Yorkshire map 9

Croft Farm

Church Lane, Fylingthorpe YO22 4PW TEL: (01947) 880231
1m E of A171, 4m S of Whitby

Set in the North Moors National Park, Croft Farm enjoys splendid views over the old smugglers' village of Robin Hood's Bay and the sea. The house was modernised in the 1970s and is part of a small working stock farm. Three guest bedrooms are offered, all in excellent decorative order, some with new white fitted furniture; the double room has an *en suite* shower and the single room and family suite share a bathroom. Guests have two lounges to relax in, and they can tuck into hearty farmhouse breakfasts in the open-plan beamed dining-room. For those not wanting to travel far for an evening meal, there's an inn in the village. Self-catering accommodation that sleeps four is available in a cottage on the farm.

OWNERS: John and Pauline Featherstone OPEN: Easter to mid-Oct ROOMS: 1 single, with wash-basin; 1 double, with shower; 1 family, with wash-basin; tea/coffee in all bedrooms; lounge with TV TERMS: single £17.50–£19.50, single occupancy £19.50–£21.50, double £35–£43, family room £47–£50; reductions for children sharing with parents; deposit: £10 per person, 1-night bookings payable in advance CARDS: none DETAILS: no children under 5; dogs in kennels only; no smoking; car park; garden

GAWSWORTH Cheshire **map 8**

Rough Hey Farm

Leek Road, Gawsworth SK11 0JQ TEL: (01260) 252296
off A523, 3m S of Macclesfield

Set on the edge of the Pennines and commanding wonderful views, Rough Hey has a long and interesting history. It was listed in the Domesday Book, and extended in the eighteenth century. These days it offers comfortable guest accommodation, and a warm, friendly atmosphere provided by Phyllis Worth, who has been welcoming visitors here for over a dozen years. Bedrooms, especially the double, are generously proportioned, and *en suite* facilities have now been added to the twin. Guests have the use of a lounge/dining-room, where there's a TV and where breakfasts are served. The local pub, which does evening meals, can be reached down a farm track. The house is part of 300-acre sheep farm.

OWNER: Phyllis Worth OPEN: all year exc Christmas ROOMS: 2 single, both with wash-basin; 1 double, with bath/shower; 1 twin, with bath/shower; tea/coffee and TV in all bedrooms; lounge with TV TERMS: single £18, single occupancy £26, twin/double £36; reductions for children sharing with parents; deposit: £10 CARDS: none DETAILS: children welcome; no dogs; no smoking; car park; garden

GAYHURST Buckinghamshire **map 5**

Mill Farm

Gayhurst MK16 8LT TEL/FAX: (01908) 611489
take B526 out of Newport Pagnell for 2m, turn left at sign for Haversham; Mill Farm is first on left

Kaye Adams has been providing comfortable B&B in her family home for almost 20 years. The seventeenth-century house is part of a 500-acre working mixed farm, and is close to the Ouse Valley. The homely bedrooms all have TVs, and most have pleasant views over the surrounding countryside. Guests are welcome to tour the farm, and a hard-tennis court is available for the more active. Woburn Abbey and Safari Park are nearby.

OWNER: Kaye Adams OPEN: all year ROOMS: 1 single, with wash-basin; 1 double, with private bathroom; 1 twin, with shower; 1 family, with wash-basin; tea/coffee and TV in all bedrooms; lounge TERMS: single/single occupancy £18–£20, twin/double £35–£40; children's reductions according to age when sharing with parents; deposit: £10 per person CARDS: none DETAILS: children welcome; dogs welcome; smoking in 1 bedroom only; car park; garden; tennis

Breakfast at B&Bs tends to mean a cooked breakfast of bacon, eggs, toast and so on, although many establishments also offer a good choice of cereals, yoghurts, fruit and other options. If you have special dietary requirements, it is best to discuss these when you make a booking.

GLOSSOP Derbyshire map 8

Stanley Farm

NEW ENTRY

Chunal Lane, Glossop SK13 6JY TEL: (01457) 863727
on A264 Glossop to Chapel-en-le-Frith road

Set high in the hills with panoramic views of the Peak District, Stanley Farm is part of a 22-acre working farm, and is far enough back from the road to be free of traffic noise. The house was completely restored in 1983 and the atmosphere is warm and inviting. The three bedrooms have TVs and tea and coffee making facilities; one is *en suite* and the other two share a bathroom. Breakfasts, and dinner by prior arrangement, are served in the large dining-room/lounge, which has oak beams and a piano. Bunk-bed accommodation for groups is available in a converted barn.

OWNERS: Bill and Norma Brown OPEN: all year ROOMS: 1 double, with shower; 1 twin; 1 family; tea/coffee and TV in all bedrooms; lounge with TV TERMS: single occupancy £20, twin/double £35, family room £44; babies free, half-price for children under 11; dinner £8.50 CARDS: none DETAILS: children welcome; no dogs; no smoking; car park; garden

GLOUCESTER Gloucestershire map 5

Lulworth Guest House

12 Midland Road, Gloucester GL1 4UF TEL: (01452) 521881

A convenient location and good value are plus marks at this white-fronted, three-storey guesthouse not far from the centre of Gloucester. The train and bus stations are about half a mile away, and a park and a leisure centre are very close by. All but one of the tidy bedrooms have *en suite* facilities and all have TVs; two bedrooms are on the ground floor. Breakfast – traditional full English or, if requested, other options – is served in the dining-room on the lower ground floor. There's also a residents' lounge with satellite TV. Guests are given their own front-door keys, and the house has a secure car park at the rear.

OWNER: Mrs M.I. Dickinson OPEN: all year exc Christmas ROOMS: 1 single, 2 double, 2 twin, 3 family; all rooms with bath/shower exc 1 double with wash-basin; tea/coffee and TV in all bedrooms; lounge with TV TERMS: single/single occupancy £18–£20, twin/double £32–£35, family room from £42–£44; reductions for children sharing family room with parents; deposit: £10 per room CARDS: none DETAILS: children welcome; dogs by arrangement and not in public rooms; no smoking in dining-room; car park

---

B&B rates specified in the details at the end of each entry are given (as applicable) for a single room, for single occupancy of a double room, and then per room in the case of two people sharing a double or twin-bedded room, or for a family room. Because double rooms with four-poster beds often cost more, those are listed separately.

GOATHLAND North Yorkshire map 9

Glendale House

Goathland YO22 5AN TEL: (01947) 896281
2m W of A169 on minor road 5m S of Sleights

This large, stone house features as the home of the doctor in the TV series *Heartbeat*, and dates from 1860. Sandra Simmonds is a very welcoming host who greets guests with a hot drink on cold days. The immaculate bedrooms are decorated with pretty floral wallpapers, and one now has *en suite* facilities. The house has a warm and homely atmosphere, and the lounge has an open fire. Cooked breakfasts are served, and light supper trays can be provided in the lounge by arrangement. This is a lovely spot from which to visit the moors and to travel on the North Yorkshire Moors railway.

OWNERS: Sandra and Keith Simmonds OPEN: all year exc Christmas ROOMS: 1 double, with wash-basin; 2 family, 1 with shower, 1 with wash-basin; tea/coffee in all bedrooms; lounge with TV TERMS: single occupancy £25, double/family room £38 plus children's charge; children under 5 free, half-price for ages 5–14 if sharing with parents CARDS: MasterCard, Visa DETAILS: children welcome; no dogs; smoking in lounge only; car park; garden

GOUDHURST Kent map 3

Mill House

Church Road, Goudhurst TN17 1BN TEL: (01580) 211703
on A262 Goudhurst to Biddenden road, almost opposite church

Standing in two acres of pretty gardens and right next to the cricket ground, this former millhouse is a red-brick, tile-hung building dating from the sixteenth century. A smugglers' tunnel in the grounds is part of its historical heritage, along with old gnarled oak doors and an inglenook fireplace in the beamed lounge. The accommodation is comfortable and roomy; one of the doubles also has a single bed and can be used as a twin. Sissinghurst, Penshurst Place and Leeds Castle are within striking distance.

OWNER: Sally Russell OPEN: all year exc Dec ROOMS: 2 double; both rooms with bath/shower, tea/coffee and TV; lounge TERMS: single occupancy £40–£45, double £40–£45, family room £40–£65; reductions for children according to age; deposit required CARDS: none DETAILS: children welcome; no dogs; no smoking; car park; garden

West Winchet NEW ENTRY

Winchet Hill, Goudhurst TN17 1JX
TEL: (01580) 212024 FAX: (01580) 212250
on B2079, 2m N of Goudhurst

The Parkers live in a ground-floor wing of a handsome Victorian mansion, which is set in six acres of parkland two miles from Goudhurst. A number of readers have written to praise the warmth and hospitality extended by Annie and Jeremy Parker, and the quiet and seclusion of the property. The twin-bedded *en suite* room has french windows out to the terrace and garden, and is suitable for guests who may be less able-bodied; while the double (also on the ground floor) has an adjoining private bathroom. The twin can also be used as a family room, and both bedrooms have TVs. Excellent breakfasts are served at a dining-table in the large, comfortable drawing-room, which in the evening is an excellent place for guests to relax in after a day's visit to, perhaps, Sissinghurst Castle, Scotney Castle or Bedgebury Pinetum. No one-night bookings are accepted at weekends from June through August.

OWNERS: Jeremy and Annie Parker OPEN: all year exc Christmas ROOMS: 1 double, with private bathroom; 1 twin/family, with shower; tea/coffee and TV in both bedrooms; lounge TERMS: single occupancy £30–£35, twin/double £45–£50, family room £65–£70; £15 per night for children aged 5–15 sharing with parents; deposit required for advance bookings CARDS: none DETAILS: no children under 5; well-behaved dogs by arrangement; no smoking; car park; garden

GRANGE-OVER-SANDS Cumbria map 8

Somerset House

Kents Bank Road, Grange-over-Sands LA11 7EY TEL: (01539) 532631
from M6 junction 36 take A590 slip road to Grange

Somerset House offers reasonably priced accommodation, and is conveniently located within a short walk of the promenade. All of the modestly furnished rooms have comfortable beds with electric blankets, and the four twin rooms have *en suite* shower cubicles (though not their own WCs). One twin can be used as a family room. Guests can relax in either of the two lounges; one has a small bar. Evening meals are served in the elegant dining-room. Grange is a sleepy seaside town, with some lovely views over the Kent Estuary. Guests can park in a nearby car park, for which permits are available.

OWNERS: Elizabeth O'Neil and Rose-Marie Wilkinson OPEN: all year exc Christmas ROOMS: 2 single, both with wash-basin; 2 double, both with wash-basin; 4 twin, all with shower (not WC); tea/coffee and TV in all bedrooms; lounge TERMS: single £16.50–£19, single occupancy £25, twin/double £30–£37; half-price for children sharing with parents; dinner £8; deposit: £10 per room CARDS: none DETAILS: children welcome; no dogs in dining-room; no smoking in 1 lounge and dining-room; garden

Thornfield House

Kents Bank Road, Grange-over-Sands LA11 7DT TEL: (01539) 532512

Gary and Ann Holden took over this pleasant, welcoming house in 1996. They are an enthusiastic couple and immediately set about upgrading the guest accommodation. Bedrooms are attractively decorated in co-ordinated pastel colours, and three now have *en suite* facilities. Some of the rooms have views of Morecambe Bay, and the footpath to the promenade passes close by the house. Breakfasts are served in a separate dining-room, and dinner is also available, with vegetarian options by arrangement. The Holdens are an artistic couple and Ann makes decoupage greeting cards for sale.

OWNERS: Gary and Ann Holden OPEN: Mar to Nov ROOMS: 1 single, with wash-basin; 1 double, with shower; 2 twin, both with shower; 1 family, with wash-basin; tea/coffee and TV in all bedrooms; lounge TERMS: single £18.50–£22, single occupancy £37–£44, twin/double £37–£44, family room from £34; half-price for children 4–10 sharing with parents; dinner £9; deposit: £10 per person CARDS: none DETAILS: no children under 4; no dogs; no smoking; car park; garden

GRASMERE Cumbria

map 8

Rothay Lodge

White Bridge, Grasmere LA22 9RH TEL: (01539) 435341

This former 'gentleman's residence', built in 1830, is five minutes' walk from the centre of Grasmere. A conservatory extension to the comfortable lounge overlooks the spacious gardens, which bridge Greenhead Ghyll. All bedrooms have *en suite* bath, shower or both, and one is on the ground floor. A collection of watercolours from local artists is on display throughout the house. Drying facilities are provided for walkers. Only breakfast is served, but the Allans have menus from local restaurants available to help guests choose where to eat out.

OWNERS: Jean and Bill Allan OPEN: Feb to Nov ROOMS: 4 double, 1 twin; all rooms with bath/shower and TV; lounge TERMS: single occupancy £30–£40, twin/double £45–£53; reductions for children sharing with parents; deposit: £45 CARDS: none DETAILS: no children under 10; no dogs; no smoking; car park; garden

GRAYRIGG Cumbria

map 8

Punchbowl House

Grayrigg LA8 9BU TEL/FAX: (01539) 824345
on A685, 5m NE of Kendal

Set in the centre of this small village in lovely sweeping countryside, this nineteenth-century stone-built house is handily positioned for tours of the Yorkshire Dales or the Lake District. It has been tastefully furnished, and the roomy bedrooms are decorated in soft pastels. One has an *en suite* shower, and all have TVs. Home-cooked evening meals can be booked with 24-hours' notice, and focus on local produce; a sample menu could be leek and potato soup to start, then lamb and rosemary casserole, finishing with rum-and-walnut-filled pancakes with chocolate sauce. Full English breakfasts start the day off heartily. Walkers are welcome here, and returnees after a wet day will appreciate the drying-facilities. A self-catering suite sleeping up to six is available in an annexe.

OWNERS: Mr and Mrs I. Johnson OPEN: all year ROOMS: 2 double, 1 with shower, 1 with wash-basin; 1 twin, with wash-basin; tea/coffee and TV in all bedrooms; lounge TERMS: single occupancy £16–£30, twin/double £32–£38; dinner £13.50; deposit: £10 per room CARDS: none DETAILS: no children; no dogs; no smoking; car park

GREAT CHART Kent map 3

Worten House

Great Chart TN23 3BU TEL: (01233) 622944

from M20 junction 9 take A20 towards Charing for 1m, then turn left signposted Godinton, then second turning on right

Worten House is in a quiet and peaceful spot with good views over farmland. It probably dates from the eighteenth century and is an attractive red-brick and stone building with a charming walled garden. Within, it is a pleasantly furnished, comfortable family home, with two large, bright bedrooms which share a bathroom and two WCs. Guests have use of a sitting-room with a TV and a large, secluded garden. Evening meals are available with 24 hours' notice. Great Chart has good access by train and is two miles west of Ashford, but it is advisable to telephone for directions if coming by car.

OWNERS: Denise and Charles Wilkinson OPEN: all year exc Christmas ROOMS: 2 twin, both with wash-basin, tea/coffee; lounge with TV TERMS: single occupancy £25, twin £40; dinner £15 CARDS: none DETAILS: children welcome; no dogs; no smoking in bedrooms; car park; garden

GREAT DUNMOW Essex map 3

Homelye Farm

Braintree Road, Great Dunmow CM6 3AW

TEL: (01371) 872127 FAX: (01371) 876428

from A120 1m E of Great Dunmow turn into lane opposite water tower; farm at bottom of lane

A working mixed farm, Homelye provides ideal accommodation for visitors who value privacy, as the guest rooms are in converted stables not far from the house. Each of the three bedrooms has a separate entrance, and all are comfortably appointed with *en suite* showers, fridges and TVs. Good farmhouse breakfasts are served in the main house. Every leap year in July the famous Dunmow Flitch Trials – a tradition originating from the twelfth century and intended to encourage matrimony – take place in the town. Homelye is handy for Stansted Airport. A pub and a restaurant nearby serve evening meals.

OWNER: Tracy Pickford OPEN: all year exc Christmas ROOMS: 1 single, 1 double, 1 twin; all rooms with shower; tea/coffee and TV in all bedrooms; lounge TERMS: single £20–£23.50, single occupancy £25–£30, twin/double £40–£47; children's reductions by arrangement; deposit: £5 per person per night CARDS: none DETAILS: children welcome; no dogs; no smoking; car park; garden

GREAT MALVERN Hereford & Worcester map 5

Elm Bank

52 Worcester Road, Great Malvern WR14 4AB TEL: (01684) 566051
set back from A449 between Great Malvern and Malvern Link stations

Richard and Helen Mobbs have created a warm and friendly atmosphere in their splendid Regency home, which has views of the Malvern hills. Many original features of the house remain, including a charming curved staircase. Bedrooms are large, well maintained and tastefully decorated and furnished. Breakfast is served in the elegant dining-room, the bright lounge is well stocked with books and local information, and on fine days guests are welcome to take advantage of the well-tended garden.

OWNERS: Richard and Helen Mobbs OPEN: all year ROOMS: 3 double, 2 twin, 1 family; all rooms with bath/shower exc 1 twin with private bathroom; tea/coffee and TV in all bedrooms; lounge TERMS: single occupancy £24–£45, twin/double £35–£48, family room £48–£68; children under 2 free, reductions according to age for older children; deposit required CARDS: Delta, MasterCard, Switch, Visa DETAILS: children welcome; dogs by arrangement; smoking in lounge only; car park

GREAT SNORING Norfolk map 6

Red House

Great Snoring NR21 0AH TEL: (01328) 820641
off A148, 3m NE of Fakenham

The Red House, a large, red-brick Georgian building in the village of Great Snoring, is furnished mostly with interesting antique pieces, including a dining-table that was once owned by Charles Dickens. Mark Wells is a descendant of Edward II, and Mrs Wells has many interesting stories to tell about the many family portraits around the house. Accommodation comprises one immaculately kept double bedroom. Guests are offered early-morning tea, excellent breakfasts are served in the dining-room on fine china, and dinner is also available by arrangement.

OWNER: Rev and Mrs Mark Wells OPEN: all year exc Christmas ROOMS: 1 double, with bath/shower; lounge with TV TERMS: single occupancy £22, double £44; dinner £9.50; deposit: £5 CARDS: none DETAILS: no children; dogs by arrangement; no smoking; car park; garden

GREAT THURLOW Suffolk map 6

Old Vicarage NEW ENTRY

Great Thurlow CB9 7LE TEL: (01440) 783209
on A1307 Withersfield to Great Thurlow road

This 200-year old large former vicarage is approached up a private lane bordered by chestnut trees, and stands in six acres of grounds, with a garden and woodlands. It is comfortable and traditionally furnished with antiques. The spacious bedrooms have armchairs, and a TV can be provided on request. The lounge has a log fire which is lit on cool evenings, and there is a piano which musical guests can play. Mrs Sheppard is a helpful host and, being a professional cook, provides excellent breakfasts cooked on the Aga, as well as dinners (if pre-booked) which feature vegetables and fruit from the garden. Meals are served in the dining-room/lounge. Three friendly dogs also live here.

OWNERS: Sam and Jane Sheppard OPEN: all year exc Christmas ROOMS: 1 single, with bath/shower; 2 double/twin, 1 with private bathroom, 1 with wash-basin; tea/ coffee in all bedrooms; lounge with TV TERMS: single £22–£25, single occupancy £25, twin/double £44; dinner £15–£18; deposit: 1 night's charge CARDS: none DETAILS: no children under 7; dogs by arrangement; no smoking; car park; garden

GREAT YARMOUTH Norfolk map 6

Senglea Lodge

7 Euston Road, Great Yarmouth NR30 1DX TEL: (01493) 859632

This neat, well-maintained guesthouse offers excellent-value accommodation just minutes from the town centre. *En suite* facilities have been added to the four-poster/family rooms, which have lace canopies and attractive matching curtains made by Julia Formosa. All the bedrooms have satellite TV. The lounge/dining-room is warm and comfortable, and modestly priced home-cooked dinners are available at 5.30pm; Senglea is licensed. Car parking is available across the street.

OWNERS: Julia and Joe Formosa OPEN: all year exc Christmas ROOMS: 4 double, 2 with shower, 2 with wash-basin; 1 twin,with wash-basin; 2 family/four-poster, both with shower; tea/coffee and TV in all bedrooms; lounge with TV TERMS: single occupancy £12.50–£15, twin/double £25–£30, four-poster £28–£30, family room £35–£45; children's reductions according to age; dinner £5; deposit: £10 CARDS: none DETAILS: children welcome; no dogs; garden

GREENHAM Somerset map 2

Greenham Hall

Greenham TA21 0JJ TEL: (01823) 672603 FAX: (01823) 672307
off A38, 4m W of Wellington

Greenham Hall is an impressive Victorian country house built in a Gothic-revival style, complete with battlements and a tower, from which there are panoramic views of the village and surrounding countryside. The large, well-maintained garden has many interesting plants, and is a good place to unwind. The Ayres are welcoming hosts, and Peter, who was born in Africa, has decorated the walls with photographs of African wildlife. There is a huge hallway, and a breakfast/sitting-room with TV. The spacious bedrooms, though somewhat sparsely furnished, also have fine views. Local pubs and restaurants in the area are available for evening meals. Guests are offered a cup of tea on arrival and, in fine weather, afternoon tea can be taken on the terrace.

OWNERS: Caro and Peter Ayre OPEN: all year ROOMS: 3 double, 2 with bath/shower, 1 with wash-basin; 2 twin, 1 with bath/shower; 1 family, with private bathroom; lounge with TV TERMS: single occupancy £25–£30, twin/double £38, family room £43–£48; reductions for children sharing with parents; deposit required for bank holiday weekends only CARDS: none DETAILS: children welcome; small dogs by arrangement; car park; garden

GREENHOW HILL North Yorkshire map 9

Mole End

Greenhow Hill HG3 5JQ TEL: (01423) 712565
on B6265 between Pateley Bridge and Grassington

Set back from the road behind a traditional dry-stone wall and wide gate, this well-maintained modern house offers three comfortable guest bedrooms, all with good beds and TVs. The *en suite* twin-bedded room has both a bath and a power-shower, and has the best view. Substantial breakfasts, catering well for vegetarians, are served in the sitting-cum-dining-room, which enjoys a panoramic outlook over the countryside. A pub serving evening meals is just a couple of minutes' walk away, and Pateley Bridge with its assortment of eating-places is not far by car.

OWNERS: Dennis and Elaine Knowles OPEN: all year exc Christmas ROOMS: 1 double; 2 twin, 1 with bath/shower; tea/coffee and TV in all bedrooms; lounge TERMS: single occupancy £21–£24, twin/double £34–£38; deposit: 10% CARDS: none DETAILS: no children under 12; dogs welcome with own bedding; smoking in lounge only; car park; garden

GRINGLEY ON THE HILL Nottinghamshire map 9

Old Vicarage

Gringley on the Hill DN10 4RS TEL: (01777) 817248
next to village church, just off A631 between Gainsborough and Bawtry

This elegant former vicarage is set in three acres of gardens, including a rock garden, an orchard and a tennis court, in the middle of the village of Gringley on the Hill. The house is luxuriously furnished, and guests are greeted by William the African grey parrot. Other resident animals are a Shetland pony, a Welsh Cob pony and two dogs, Henry and Tatiana. One of the double rooms has an adjoining room with a single bed, and the two can be taken together as a family suite. Helena Simmonds grows her own vegetables for use in the dinners she prepares on the Aga. Vegetarian options are available, and the house is licensed to serve alcohol.

OWNERS: John and Helena Simmonds OPEN: all year exc Christmas ROOMS: 1 double, 2 twin; all rooms with bath/shower and tea/coffee; lounge with TV TERMS:

single occupancy £31, twin/double £52; children under 2 free, half-price for ages 2–12; dinner £18; deposit: £10 per booking CARDS: MasterCard, Visa DETAILS: children welcome; dogs by arrangement; no smoking; car park; garden

GRITTLETON Wiltshire **map 2**

Church House

Grittleton SN14 6AP TEL: (01249) 782562 FAX: (01249) 782546
from M4 junction 17 take A429 towards Malmesbury, then first left, continue 3½m to village

This elegant Bath-stone Georgian house was formerly the rectory and stands in the middle of the pretty village of Grittleton. It is surrounded by 11 acres of gardens and pasture in which there is a large heated and covered swimming-pool which is floodlit at night. In addition, croquet is available in the summer. Church House is ideal for small groups of friends or families with older children, and is well worth a visit for Anna Moore's excellent, unpretentious cooking, featuring organic vegetables and fruit. There is a spacious sitting-room, and dinner is served in a party atmosphere at the large dining-room table. The well-proportioned, simply furnished bedrooms have their own facilities, screened off in a corner of the room. Church House is located between the church and the pub, and is close to Badminton. Anna Moore is a fount of local and general knowledge and has all kinds of recommendations of interesting places to visit, such as Sheldon Manor, Westonbirt Arboretum, and Ilford Manor.

OWNERS: Dr and Mrs Michael Moore OPEN: all year ROOMS: 1 double, 3 twin; all rooms with bath/shower, tea/coffee and TV; lounge TERMS: single occupancy £32.50, twin/double £56.50; dinner £16.50; deposit or credit card details required CARDS: none DETAILS: no children under 12 exc babies; no dogs; no smoking in dining-room or drawing-room; car park; garden; swimming-pool

GULWORTHY Devon **map 1**

Hele Farm

Gulworthy PL19 8PA TEL: (01822) 833084
from Tavistock take A390 for 2½m W, turn right at crossroads, then second left

Hele Farm is an eighteenth-century, slate-fronted building standing in a large garden, at the end of a dead-end lane and a long gravel track. It is a 150-acre dairy farm in an isolated position, and is in the process of converting to organic production of beef and milk. The house offers unpretentious farmhouse comfort, with two clean, bright and attractive *en suite* bedrooms. Downstairs there is one large, comfortable room for guests, half of which used to be the old dairy, with a big dining-table at one end, and a sitting area at the other. Rosemary Steer is very welcoming to families with small children and provides a children's play room.

OWNER: Rosemary Steer OPEN: Mar to Oct ROOMS: 1 double, 1 twin; both rooms with bath/shower; tea/coffee in both bedrooms; lounge with TV TERMS: twin/double £34–£40; reductions for children according to age CARDS: none DETAILS: children welcome; no smoking; car park; garden

GURNARD Isle of Wight

map 2

Hillbrow

Tuttons Hill, Gurnard, nr Cowes PO31 8JA TEL: (01983) 297240

This former maternity home, built in the 1930s, has fine views over farmland to the Solent. The house is very clean, neat and well furnished, and bedrooms are well-equipped, with most *en suite*. Evening meals and light snacks are available, as well as breakfast. There is also an outdoor table-tennis table. Horse riding and golf can be arranged, and the centre of Cowes is only 15 minutes' walk away.

OWNERS: Val and Paul Mortlock OPEN: all year exc Christmas ROOMS: 1 single, with wash-basin; 1 double, with shower; 2 twin, 1 with shower, 1 with wash-basin; 1 family, with shower; tea/coffee and TV in all bedrooms; lounge with TV TERMS: single £19, single occupancy £24–£28, twin/double £38–£46; children's reductions according to age; dinner £8.50; deposit: £20 per person CARDS: none DETAILS: children welcome; no dogs; no smoking in dining-room; car park; garden

HADLOW Kent

map 3

Leavers Oast

NEW ENTRY

Stanford Lane, Hadlow TN11 0JN TEL/FAX: (01732) 850924
on A26, 6m NE of Tonbridge

The oast and barn were built around 1880 and converted to a private residence in 1960. The Turners transformed it again in 1987, bringing the house up to a high standard of comfort. Leavers Oast is surrounded by fields and farmland, and stands in a pleasant garden with a pond. The house has a welcoming atmosphere, and readers tell us that Mrs Turner is a 'considerate and helpful' lady who greets new arrivals with tea and cakes. The bedrooms are spacious, well appointed and comfortable; one double room and a twin-bedded room share a bathroom, while the second, *en suite* double is in the barn. Excellent breakfasts are taken in the kitchen, and evening meals, by prior arrangement, are served in the elegant dining-room, preceded by a complimentary drink. Although there is no separate residents' lounge, guests are welcome to share the Turners' huge, lovely drawing-room, and to sit out in the garden. A surcharge of £5 is levied on one-night stays in summer.

OWNERS: Anne and Denis Turner OPEN: all year ROOMS: 2 double, 1 with bath/shower; 1 twin; tea/coffee and TV in all bedrooms TERMS: single occupancy £40–£45, twin/double £34–£58; dinner £17.50; deposit: £25 CARDS: none DETAILS: no children under 12; no dogs; no smoking; car park; garden

HALTWHISTLE Northumberland map 11

Ald White Craig Farm

Haltwhistle NE49 9NW TEL/FAX: (01434) 320565
from A69 follow signs for Hadrian's Wall at eastern end of Haltwhistle; farm about ½m from the wall

Mrs Laidlow has lived here for over 35 years and continues to extend her own delightful brand of northern hospitality to guests. Ald White Craig is a seventeenth-century croft sitting high above Haltwhistle, surrounded by farmland where sheep and cattle graze, and with good views of the South Tyne Valley. Bedrooms have been upgraded, with the twin room (which has its own door to the patio) newly decorated with Victorian-style wallpaper and its *en suite* bathroom refurbished with maroon-coloured fittings. The double room, which has an *en suite* shower, has a lovely lace-canopied bed. An open fire burns on chilly days in the beamed lounge, which has a fine display of porcelain. Advance bookings must be for a minimum of two nights, although one-night casual bookings, when available, are accepted. The farm has five self-catering cottages. A nearby inn is handy for evening meals.

OWNER: J.I. Laidlow OPEN: all year exc Christmas ROOMS: 1 double, 1 twin; both rooms with bath/shower, tea/coffee and TV; lounge TERMS: single occupancy £29, twin/double £44; deposit: £20 or credit card details CARDS: Delta, MasterCard, Visa DETAILS: children welcome; guide dogs only; no smoking; car park; garden

HAMPTON IN ARDEN West Midlands map 5

The Hollies

Kenilworth Road, Hampton in Arden B92 0LW
TEL: (01675) 442681 FAX: (01675) 442941
just off A452, 2m S of junction with A45, take road signposted Balsall Common

The Hollies is a simple modern house, attractively decorated with welcoming floral displays in tubs and baskets outside. Inside, the décor is mostly in pastel shades. Bedrooms are a little on the small side, but have well-planned storage space and most have *en suite* showers. The guests' lounge has satellite TV. Jim and Tina are a friendly couple who live in a separate house close by. The Hollies is only a few miles from the National Exhibition Centre, Birmingham International station and the airport.

OWNERS: Jim and Tina Fitzpatrick OPEN: all year exc Christmas ROOMS: 1 single, with wash-basin; 5 double, 4 with shower, 1 with wash-basin; 2 twin, both with shower; 2 family, both with shower; tea/coffee and TV in all bedrooms; lounge with TV TERMS: single £20–£25, single occupancy £25–£28, twin/double £40–£45, family room £45–£50; deposit: £10 per room CARDS: none DETAILS: children welcome; no smoking in 4 bedrooms; car park; garden

HAMPTON LUCY Warwickshire map 5

Sandbarn Farm

Hampton Lucy CV35 8AU TEL: (01789) 842280
4½m going NE from Stratford-upon-Avon on A439, ignore first right to Hampton Lucy and continue to crossroads, then turn right and after 1½m farm on right

With glorious views towards the Cotswolds, this large sixteenth-century, red-brick property stands in ten acres of open countryside. The house has a mixture of antique and traditional furniture. The spacious bedrooms are well appointed, and the top-floor rooms, with their sloping ceilings, are particularly attractive; two adjoining bedrooms are ideal for a family. There is a television lounge, and excellent breakfasts are served in the charming dining-room.

OWNER: Mrs H.P. Waterworth OPEN: all year exc Christmas ROOMS: 1 single; 3 double, 2 with bath/shower, 1 with private bathroom; 4 twin, 2 with bath/shower; 2 family, both with bath/shower; tea/coffee in all bedrooms; lounge with TV TERMS: single £25, single occupancy £40, twin/double £50, family room £75–£100; deposit: 25% CARDS: none DETAILS: no children under 5; dogs by arrangement; smoking in lounge only; car park

HANLITH North Yorkshire map 8

Coachman's Cottage

Hanlith BD23 4BP TEL: (01729) 830538
take A65 from Skipton to Malham, then turn right in Kirkby Malham opposite Victoria pub

This 300-year old whitewashed cottage is in an unspoilt hamlet on the Pennine Way, with beautiful views. The house has thick stone walls and oak beams, and guests are welcomed with tea and home-made scones. Two of the bedrooms in the main house have sloping ceilings, and one has a king-sized bed. The other two are in a barn conversion, one having its own sitting-room; all have floral wallpapers and curtains. The lounge has a TV and a log fire, and the furniture is a mix of antique and traditional. Breakfast is served from 7.30 to 9 and offers a wide choice; there is a pub about 400 yards away for evening meals.

OWNERS: Glyn and Monica Jenkins OPEN: all year exc Christmas ROOMS: 3 double, 1 with shower; 1 twin, with private bathroom; tea/coffee and TV in all bedrooms; lounge with TV TERMS: twin/double £40–£42; deposit: £10 CARDS: none DETAILS: no children under 8; no dogs; no smoking; car park; garden

---

If a B&B accepts credit cards, we list them in the details at the end of an entry – or specify no cards are accepted if that is so. There may be a surcharge if you pay by credit card. It is always best to check when booking whether the card you want to use will be accepted.

HARGRAVE Cheshire map 7

Greenlooms Cottage

Martins Lane, Hargrave CH3 7RY TEL: (01829) 781475
from A41 2m S of Chester turn at sign for Waverton by antiques shop, then right after golf course

'Two delightful *en suite* bedrooms in a pretty cottage in a quiet country lane. Warm, comfortable atmosphere. Excellent, innovative evening meal and substantial breakfast with home-made preserves. A very friendly and relaxed stay in splendid countryside.' So reads the report from one pleased *Guide* reader, who sums it all up with '*quite* the best I've stayed in'. The only thing to add is that the cottage is 150 years old and furnished in keeping with its character; it has a cosy guest sitting-room with a TV; and the Newmans modestly describe those innovative evening meals (which need to be pre-booked) as 'straightforward, traditional English cooking'. Greenlooms Cottage is handy for visits to Chester and Beeston Castle.

OWNERS: Peter and Deborah Newman OPEN: all year ROOMS: 1 double, 1 twin; both rooms with shower and tea/coffee; lounge with TV TERMS: single occupancy £20, twin/double £40; dinner £10; deposit: £10 CARDS: none DETAILS: children welcome; no dogs; no smoking; car park; garden

HARROGATE North Yorkshire map 9

The Alexander

88 Franklin Road, Harrogate HG1 5EN
TEL: (01423) 503348 FAX: (01423) 540230

This impeccably maintained semi-detached Victorian residence offers accommodation of a high standard with good décor, furnished in keeping with the character of the house. In front is a small garden with a pond. All the rooms have double-glazing, and there is an attractive rosewood sideboard in the sunny sitting/dining-room. The spacious bedrooms have pink floral wallpapers and bed linen, plush headboards, attractive dried-flower arrangements and brass candlestick lamps on the walls; three have *en suite* showers. Parking is available on the road.

OWNERS: Richard and Lesley Toole OPEN: all year ROOMS: 2 single, both with wash-basin; 1 double, 2 family, all rooms with shower; tea/coffee and TV in all bedrooms; lounge with TV TERMS: single £22–£25, single occupancy £35–£44, twin/double £44–£46, family room £44; children's reductions by arrangement; deposit CARDS: none DETAILS: children welcome; no dogs; no smoking

---

We state at the end of an entry whether children are welcome, and explain any age restrictions. If there are reduced rates for children, this is mentioned; if no reductions are specified, assume you will have to pay full rates for children.

Knabbs Ash

Skipton Road, Felliscliffe, Harrogate HG3 2LT
TEL: (01423) 771040 FAX: (01423) 771515
off A59, 6m W of Harrogate, ½m E of the Millstones restaurant

Once a working farm, Knabbs Ash is a renovated farmhouse less than a mile from the main road. The 20-acre smallholding has grazing land for sheep, and a few hens. The house is beautifully maintained, and the luxurious bedrooms are decorated with quality curtains and coronets made by Sheila. The elegant sitting-room has an open fire, and a stunning view of the Nidderdale valley through the patio doors. Delicious breakfasts are served at separate pine tables, and there is a beautiful old pine dresser with a fine display of china. Sheila Smith is a very welcoming lady who enjoys meeting people and is happy to help guests plan their itineraries.

OWNER: Sheila Smith OPEN: all year exc Christmas ROOMS: 2 double, 1 twin; all rooms with bath/shower, tea/coffee and TV; lounge with TV TERMS: single occupancy £30–£35, twin/double £42–£45; deposit required CARDS: none DETAILS: no children under 10; no dogs; no smoking; car park; garden

Lynton House

42 Studley Road, Harrogate HG1 5JU TEL: (01423) 504715

This welcoming, good-value guesthouse with its pretty potted flowers and hanging baskets at the front is on a quiet, leafy street not far from the exhibition halls and conference centre. Attractive pictures are displayed here and there in the house, and the dining-room, where breakfast is served, has a large fish tank. Five guest bedrooms are offered, all with wash-basins, TVs, toiletries and tea/coffee-making facilities. There is no separate residents' lounge, but guests are welcome to share the family sitting-room with the McLoughlins if they wish. Plenty of eating-places for evening meals can be found in Harrogate.

OWNERS: John and Joan McLoughlin OPEN: Mar to Nov ROOMS: 2 single, 1 double, 1 twin, 1 family; all rooms with wash-basin, tea/coffee and TV TERMS: single £18–£20, single occupancy £28, twin/double £36, family room £46; deposit required CARDS: none DETAILS: no children under 9; no dogs; no smoking

HARTBURN Northumberland map 10

Baker's Chest

Hartburn NE61 4JB TEL: (01670) 772214 FAX: (01670) 772363
on B6343, 7m W of Morpeth

Located in the village of Hartburn, this attractive detached sandstone house is in pretty countryside. Within, the charming owners have created a warm family ambience. Sue Cansdale is very creative, and several of her paintings and collages are displayed around the house which is furnished with antiques and a collection of ornaments. Guests can relax in the TV lounge, with its marble fireplace and a spinning wheel, and are served breakfast in the dining-room, which has a grandfather clock and overlooks the garden. The two bedrooms in the main house have new power-showers, and guests also have the option of staying in one of the two self-catering cottages. Hartburn is well placed for visiting Hadrian's Wall, and is an ideal spot for nature-lovers, as there are many walks in the area, where one may spot deer and red squirrels.

OWNERS: Richard and Sue Cansdale OPEN: all year exc Christmas ROOMS: 1 double, 1 twin; both with shower and tea/coffee; lounge with TV TERMS: single occupancy £20–£35, twin/double £38–£40; deposit: £10 per person CARDS: none DETAILS: children welcome; dogs by arrangement; no smoking; car park; garden

HARTINGTON Derbyshire map 5

Manifold House

Hulme End, Hartington SK17 0EZ TEL/FAX: (01298) 84662
on B5054, 1¼m W of Hartington

This stone-built house, set in its own colourful and leafy gardens, can be found in the heart of the pretty and peaceful hamlet of Hulme End. Mike and Ann Baber have been running the bed and breakfast for over ten years, and continue to maintain a warm and informal atmosphere. The comfortable bedrooms are immaculately kept, and the double now has an *en suite* shower. The family and single share a bathroom, though they are not normally let at the same time. Breakfasts are served in large portions, and evening meals featuring home-grown vegetables are available by arrangement. Alton Towers, Chatsworth House and Haddon Hall are within a 20-minute drive.

OWNERS: Mike and Ann Baber OPEN: all year exc Christmas ROOMS: 1 single; 1 double, with shower; 1 family; TV in all bedrooms TERMS: single £19–£20, single occupancy £25–£30, double £44–£48, family from £38; children's reductions according to age; dinner £10.50; deposit required on bank holidays only CARDS: none DETAILS: children welcome; no dogs; no smoking in bedrooms; car park; garden

Raikes Farm

Hulme End, Hartington SK17 0HJ TEL/FAX: (01298) 84344
on B5054 halfway between Hartington and Hulme End

This ivy-clad, stone-built old farmhouse is well positioned for visits to Dovedale, Beresford Dale and the Tissington Trail. Dating from the sixteenth century, it is full of character, with exposed beams, thick walls and uneven floors, plus antiques such as a grandfather clock and a 300-year-old fruitwood settle. The twin room and one double bedroom have *en suite* facilities, and another double room has a WC and wash-basin; all are good-sized and comfortable and have TVs. Good farmhouse breakfasts are served in the dining-room, and guests also have the use of a TV lounge. Non-couch-potatoes can explore the 12-acre garden, or do some serious walking or biking further afield. A secure storeroom is available for bikes, and there's a drying-room. Stilton cheese fans might wish to try the locally made version in Hartington.

OWNERS: Alan and Valerie Shipley OPEN: all year exc Christmas ROOMS: 2 double, 1 with shower, 1 with wash-basin (and WC); 1 twin, with shower; tea/coffee and TV in all bedrooms; lounge with TV TERMS: single occupancy £23, twin/double £40–£44; half-price for children; dinner £12; deposit: £10 per person CARDS: none DETAILS: children welcome; dogs welcome with own bedding; no smoking; car park; garden

HARTLAND Devon **map 1**

West Titchberry Farm

Hartland EX39 6AU TEL: (01237) 441287

from A39 Bideford to Bude road, take B3248 signposted Hartland; at Lighthouse Cross take right fork, following signs for Hartland Point and Lighthouse for 4½m

This 150-acre farm, with sheep, pigs and dairy cows, is on the rugged north Devon coast only half a mile from Hartland Point and the lighthouse. The farmhouse was built around 1760 and is a typical eighteenth-century Devon longhouse. John and Yvonne Heard provide simple accommodation, a friendly welcome and excellent value. The kitchen and dining-room have beamed ceilings, and the cosy TV lounge has a wood-burning stove. Dinners or light evening meals, using produce from the farm, are available by arrangement. Guests have use of a games room and may explore the farm, and in spring children can help feed the lambs. A self-catering cottage is also available. West Titchberry Farm is within easy access of many of the area's outstanding beauty spots, including the picturesque village of Clovelly.

OWNERS: John and Yvonne Heard OPEN: all year exc Christmas ROOMS: 1 double, with wash-basin; 1 twin; 1 family, with wash-basin; tea/coffee in all bedrooms; lounge with TV TERMS: single occupancy £15–£20, twin/double £30, family room from £30; children's reductions according to age; dinner £7.50; deposit required CARDS: none DETAILS: children welcome; no dogs; no smoking in dining-room or bedrooms; car park; games room; garden

HARWICH Essex **map 3**

Reids of Harwich

3 West Street, Harwich CO12 3DA TEL: (01255) 506796

This Victorian house is located in the centre of Harwich, opposite the High Lighthouse, and is very handy for rail and bus stations and the ferries. It no longer houses the shop and gallery, though pictures of local scenes by owner Gordon Reid can still be viewed, displayed throughout the freshly decorated house. The spacious lounge, with a TV and a wealth of information on local places of interest, is on the first floor and has as its centrepiece a large marble fireplace. The three bedrooms are on the second floor and share a bathroom and a shower-room. Traditional full English breakfast is served, though a vegetarian version can be provided on request, and plenty of eating-places for evening meals are within walking distance. Reids has no off-street parking, but there's a free public car park nearby plus on-street parking.

OWNER: Gordon J. Reid OPEN: Apr to Oct ROOMS: 1 single, 1 double, 1 twin; all rooms with wash-basin, tea/coffee and TV; lounge with TV TERMS: single £16, single occupancy £25, twin/double £32 CARDS: none DETAILS: no children under 12; no dogs

HASLEMERE Surrey — map 3

Deerfell

Blackdown Park, Fernden Lane, Haslemere GU27 3LA
TEL: (01428) 653409 FAX: (01428) 656106
take A286 Haslemere to Midhurst road; then turn left into Fernden Lane just after the West Sussex border

Deerfell is a stone building with a garden having lovely views across the South Downs. It was once the coach house to Blackdown Park, which is still a privately owned house, and the entrance to it and other converted houses is through two large gates and down a long, rough driveway, two and a half miles from the start of Fernden Lane. There is a sitting-room, two attractive *en suite* bedrooms, and breakfast is served in the dining-room or conservatory. Evening meals are available by arrangement.

OWNERS: Mr and Mrs D. Carmichael OPEN: mid-Feb to mid-Dec ROOMS: 1 double/twin, 1 twin/family; both rooms with bath/shower, tea/coffee and TV; lounge TERMS: single occupancy £25, twin/double £40, family room £45; reductions for children sharing with parents in family room; dinner £9; deposit required for bookings of 3 nights and over CARDS: none DETAILS: children welcome; no dogs; no smoking; car park; garden

HATFIELD PEVEREL Essex — map 3

The Wick

Terling Hall Road, Hatfield Peverel CM3 2EZ TEL: (01245) 380705
just off A12, 3m SW of Witham

The Wick is a delightful listed sixteenth-century farmhouse in a rural setting, surrounded by a large garden containing duck ponds and a stream. A terrace has recently been added where guests may sit on warm days. The house has lots of character, and the drawing-room has an inglenook fireplace and plenty of books. The two well-furnished, beamed bedrooms share a large bathroom. Linda Tritton is a friendly, outgoing lady who offers tea or coffee on arrival. Imaginative breakfasts might include toasted bagels, croissants, fruit salad and cereal, followed by a cooked platter. Evening meals are served with advance notice, and children's helpings and vegetarian choices can be provided by arrangement. The Wick is not licensed, but guests may bring their own wine to dinner .

OWNER: Linda Tritton OPEN: all year exc Christmas ROOMS: 2 twin, 1 with wash-basin; tea/coffee and TV in 1 bedroom; lounge with TV TERMS: single occupancy £20–£25, twin £40–£50; dinner £10–£12.50 CARDS: none DETAILS: no children under 10; no dogs; no smoking upstairs; car park; garden

HAVERIGG Cumbria map 8

Dunelm Cottage

Main Street, Haverigg LA18 4EX TEL: (01229) 770097

from M6 junction 36 take A590 signposted Barrow, then Workington road, then Millom road to Haverigg; cottage on left in village

Dunelm Cottage was skilfully converted to a guesthouse in 1990 from two old village properties. It is on the coast and within easy reach of the Lake District. The three petite bedrooms are prettily furnished and have flowered pastel duvets; they share a bathroom and shower-room. Mrs Fairless is an accomplished cook, and imaginative evening meals are served in a separate dining-room; as Dunelm is unlicensed, guests are welcome to bring their own wine to dinner. A speciality line of Christmas cakes and puddings made on the premises is available for purchase. The harbour is within walking distance and Hoodbarrow Nature Reserve is nearby; packed lunches can be provided. Parking is in the village car park, which is opposite the house.

OWNER: Mrs J. Fairless OPEN: all year ROOMS: 1 double, 2 twin; all rooms with wash-basin and tea/coffee; lounge with TV TERMS: single occupancy £25–£27, twin/double £42–£44; dinner £12; deposit: £10 CARDS: none DETAILS: no children under 10; dogs by arrangement only; no smoking in bedrooms

HAWES North Yorkshire map 8

Brandymires

Muker Road, Hawes DL8 3PR TEL: (01969) 667482

on A684, just N of Hawes on road signposted to Muker

Loads of books to browse through, a grandfather clock, a comforting real fire in a marble fireplace on chilly days, plus splendid views and the warmest of welcomes all help to make a stay at this mid-nineteenth-century stone-built house memorable. Bedrooms are large and have their own sitting-areas; two have four-poster beds. The sitting-room is a good place for relaxation, and, like the bedrooms, remains TV-free. Evening meals can be arranged (every day except Thursday) and there is a short wine list. Breakfasts feature home-made bread and preserves.

OWNERS: Gail Ainley and Ann Macdonald OPEN: early Feb to early Nov ROOMS: 1 double, 1 twin, 2 four-poster; all rooms with wash-basin and tea/coffee; lounge TERMS: single occupancy £27, twin/double/four-poster £38; dinner £12; deposit: £15 CARDS: none DETAILS: no children; dogs by arrangement; no smoking; car park

Tarney Fors Farm House

Tarney Fors, Hawes DL8 3LS TEL: (01969) 667475
on B6255, 1½m W of Hawes

Genuinely far from the madding crowd, this converted Dales longhouse offers three comfortable double rooms plus good home-cooked meals, and plenty of peace and quiet. All around are splendid views over the fells, and walkers will find this ideal country. Free-range eggs, locally made sausages, black pudding and home-baked bread are among the items that feature at breakfast, and dinners, which need to be pre-booked, also focus on fresh, local supplies where possible; vegetarians are catered for. Light snacks can be ordered from the tea shop on the premises, and meals are taken in the licensed dining-room with its beams, flagstone floor and old-fashioned range. On fine days guest may enjoy after-dinner coffee in the terraced garden. Residents also have the use of a lounge with a TV and open fire. One of the double *en suite* rooms can also be used as a family room. 'Tarney Fors' is an approximation of 'forced water' – appropriate, since the house's water comes from a spring nearby.

OWNERS: Alan and Sue Harpley OPEN: Mar to Nov ROOMS: 3 double, 2 with shower, 1 with private bathroom; tea/coffee in all bedrooms; lounge with TV TERMS: single occupancy £38.50–£42, double £48–£52; reductions for children 7–15 sharing with parents; dinner £16.50; deposit: £25 per room or credit card details CARDS: Delta, MasterCard, Visa DETAILS: no children under 7; no dogs; no smoking; car park; garden

HAWKHURST Kent map 3

Conghurst Farm

Hawkhurst TN18 4RW TEL: (01580) 753331 FAX: (01580) 754579
from A21 take A268 E; 1½m after Hawkhurst turn right at Shell garage, continue 1½m down Conghurst Lane; house is on left-hand side

The oldest part of Conghurst Farm dates from 1350, and the property has been in the Piper family for hundreds of years, with family records in the local church going back to AD900. The house has been enlarged continually over the years, and a stone coat of arms, which was originally on the outside wall, is now in the family sitting-room. Conghurst is a 500-acre working sheep and arable farm down a quiet lane, with beautiful country views. The Pipers are very accommodating but unobtrusive hosts. Guests can use the drawing-room with its log fire, or there is a smaller room with a TV. The three spacious bedrooms are attractively decorated, and one has its own small sitting-room. Imaginative home-cooked dinners are available by arrangement. Sissinghurst and Bodiam Castles are in the area, and Cranbrook, Tenterden and Rye are nearby.

OWNER: Rosemary Piper   OPEN: all year exc Christmas   ROOMS: 1 double, with private bathroom; 2 twin, 1 with bath/shower, 1 with private bathroom; tea/coffee and TV in all bedrooms   TERMS: single occupancy £30, twin/double £48–£55; dinner £11.50–£13.50   CARDS: none   DETAILS: no children under 12; no dogs; no smoking; car park; garden

HAWORTH   West Yorkshire   **map 8**

Hill Top

NEW ENTRY

Haworth Moor, Haworth BD22 0EL   TEL: (01535) 643524
500yds W of Haworth, up long lane

This seventeenth-century renovated farmhouse is the only house on Haworth Moor, and has superb views over the Lower Laithe reservoir and hills beyond. Tastefully converted, it provides very comfortable accommodation. Several original features remain, such as flagstone floors and fireplaces. There is a snug sitting-room and an enormous lounge/dining-room which features a beautiful carved French cupboard and a grandfather clock. The three large, comfortable bedrooms all have *en suite* shower-rooms and TVs. A hot drink is provided in the evening, as well as upon arrival. Breakfast includes home-baked bread, and home-made jams and marmalade, and dinner can be provided by arrangement. Brenda Fox is a very accommodating lady who does everything possible to ensure her guests' comfort.

OWNER: Brenda Fox   OPEN: all year   ROOMS: 2 double, 1 twin; all rooms with shower, tea/coffee and TV; lounge   TERMS: single occupancy £25–£35, twin/double £38–£43; dinner £10; deposit required for bank holiday weekend bookings   CARDS: none   DETAILS: children welcome; dogs by arrangement; no smoking; car park; garden

Hole Farm

NEW ENTRY

Dimples Lane, Haworth BD22 8QS   TEL/FAX: (01535) 644755

Hole Farm is a 12-acre smallholding in an elevated position, approached up a bumpy lane, with views over the village and surrounding hills. The farm is inhabited by horses, foals, cows, turkeys and ducks. With just two letting-rooms, guests are assured of personal service from Janet Milner, who is a welcoming host offering home-made cakes on arrival. The bedrooms are furnished to a high standard in keeping with the character of the house, and both have *en suite* showers. This is a wonderful place from which to explore this lovely part of Yorkshire, and the village is only ten minutes' flat walk from the farm. Adults only are permitted in the main house, but children are welcome in the self-catering cottages. No one-night bookings are taken over bank holidays.

OWNER: Janet Milner OPEN: all year exc Christmas ROOMS: 1 double, 1 twin; both rooms with shower, tea/coffee and TV; lounge TERMS: single occupancy £25, twin/double £40 CARDS: none DETAILS: no children under 12; no dogs; no smoking; car park; garden

Moorfield Guest House

80 West Lane, Haworth BD22 8EN TEL/FAX: (01535) 643689

The footpath across Parson's Field, used by the Brontës on their way to the waterfall and Top Withens, runs a few yards from this detached Victorian house. All the bedrooms enjoy views over Brontë country, and are well equipped and comfortable. The family room is a large double with an adjacent single, plus bathroom. The dining-room opens out on to the terrace and the lovely garden, which itself overlooks the village cricket field. Evening meals are no longer served, but a list of recommended local restaurants is available, and the lounge has a small bar. The conservatory is a lovely spot in which to relax and enjoy the views, and has a wealth of local brochures and Brontë books.

OWNERS: Barry and Pat Hargreaves OPEN: all year exc Christmas ROOMS: 1 single, with shower; 3 double, 2 with shower, 1 with private bathroom; 2 twin, 1 family; both with shower; TV in all bedrooms; lounge TERMS: single £18–£25, single occupancy £20–£25, twin/double/family room £34–£40; children's reductions according to age CARDS: MasterCard, Visa DETAILS: children welcome; no dogs; no smoking in bedrooms or dining-room; car park; garden

HAYDON BRIDGE Northumberland map 10

Geeswood House

Whittis Road, Haydon Bridge NE47 6AQ TEL: (01434) 684220
off A69, 6m W of Hexham

In an elevated position, this early-nineteenth-century house is set in a beautifully landscaped garden that slopes down to Langley Burn and its waterfall. The house is immaculately kept, and the three comfortable bedrooms are of a good size and furnished in soft pastels; they share two bathrooms which are exclusively for guests' use. The lounge has an unusual fireplace, and there is an attractive galleried staircase. Home-made bread and fresh produce feature in the delicious breakfasts and evening meals, which are cooked on the Aga; vegetarian options can be arranged if booked in advance. Guests are welcome to bring their own wine to dinner, as Geeswood House is unlicensed.

OWNERS: John and Doreen Easton OPEN: all year exc Christmas ROOMS: 1 double, 2 twin; all rooms with wash-basin; lounge with TV TERMS: single occupancy £24, twin/double £36; dinner £11; deposit: £10 CARDS: none DETAILS: no children under 10; no dogs; no smoking; garden

HAZELBURY BRYAN Dorset **map 2**

Droop Farm

Hazelbury Bryan DT10 2ED TEL: (01258) 817244 FAX: (01258) 817806
off A357 / B3143, 4m SW of Sturminster Newton

This lovely fifteenth-century thatched farmhouse lies close to the village church and enjoys open farmland views across the Blackmore Vale. Maureen Kirby is a charming, welcoming host. Meals are served in the beamed dining-room, which has an inglenook fireplace and an original nineteenth-century bread oven. Breakfast features local free-range eggs, home-made yoghurt and Dorset honey; dinner can be provided if arranged in advance, or there are plenty of pubs and restaurants in the area. Accommodation comprises a suite with a twin-bedded and a double room sharing an *en suite* bathroom, and is suitable for a couple or a group of friends. There is also an attractive sitting-room. A converted barn provides self-catering accommodation for four adults.

OWNERS: Maureen and Jim Kirby OPEN: all year ROOMS: 1 double, 1 twin; both rooms with bath, tea/coffee and TV; lounge TERMS: single occupancy £20–£22, twin/double £40–£44; dinner £14.50 CARDS: none DETAILS: no children under 10; no dogs; smoking in dining-room only; car park; garden

HAZLETON Gloucestershire **map 5**

Windrush House

Hazleton GL54 4EB TEL: (01451) 860364
from A40 midway between Andoversford and Northleach take minor road signposted Hazleton, then first left and first right

Built from Cotswold stone and furnished with a compatible blend of modern and antique, Windrush House is peacefully located in the pretty hamlet of Hazleton. Four comfortable guest bedrooms are offered: two have *en suite* showers, and a roomy double on the ground floor has an adjacent WC. Guests may relax in the TV lounge, or in the separate sitting-room, where there is a piano. Imaginative three-course evening meals can be arranged (featuring, perhaps, fresh tomato soup with pesto to start, then sauté chicken breast in Grand Marnier served with apples and almonds, followed by a selection of desserts from the trolley, or cheeses), and are served in the dining-room with its fine views of the rolling countryside. In winter, riding weekends can be arranged. Jim, the golden labrador, won first prize in his class at Crufts in 1997.

OWNER: Mrs S.M. Harrison OPEN: all year exc mid-Dec to mid-Jan ROOMS: 2 double, 1 with shower, 1 with wash-basin; 2 twin, 1 with shower, 1 with wash-basin; tea/coffee in all bedrooms; lounge with TV TERMS: single occupancy £25–£30, twin/double £40–£50; dinner £20; deposit: £10 per room CARDS: none DETAILS: no children; no dogs; no smoking; car park; garden

HEADCORN Kent map 3

Vine Farm

Waterman Quarter, Headcorn TN27 9JJ
TEL: (01622) 890203 FAX: (01622) 891819
take A274 from Headcorn towards Tenterden, take first right at crossroads signposted Waterman Quarter, then ¾m

The oldest part of this attractive, long-timbered farmhouse dates from 1560, and the house retains much of its original character, with low-beamed ceilings and an enormous Elizabethan fireplace in the dining-room. It is positioned very peacefully off a quiet country lane, with the River Hammer running along one side of the property. The 50-acre farm supports sheep, and both the river and small lakes, which were once silted-up ponds, are now stocked with fish. Jane Harman is a very keen gardener, and guests are welcome to relax in the colourful garden on fine days. Dinners can be arranged in the autumn and winter. The two spacious bedrooms are attractively furnished and decorated, and both have *en suite* showers and TVs. An old barn has been converted into self-catering accommodation.

OWNER: Jane Harman OPEN: all year exc Christmas ROOMS: 1 double, 1 twin; both rooms with shower, tea/coffee and TV TERMS: single occupancy £30–£32, twin/double £40–£44; dinner £15 to £18 (not in summer); deposit: £10 or credit card number CARDS: MasterCard, Visa DETAILS: no children; no dogs; no smoking; car park; garden

HEASLEY MILL Devon map 1

Heasley House

Heasley Mill EX36 3LE TEL: (01598) 740213 FAX: (01598) 740677
from A361 Barnstaple to Tiverton road, take North Molton turning, then 2m N

Heasley House is set in a quiet hamlet, in a peaceful spot on the very edge of Exmoor. It is a substantial, listed Georgian house, originally the copper-mine captain's home. It has a pleasant, friendly atmosphere, and John and Jane Ayres, owners since 1995, have made a lot of changes, including replacing almost all the furniture. Six of the simply furnished bedrooms are *en suite*, and one room is on the ground floor. The dining-room has exposed beams and a large fireplace, and guests sit at long communal tables. One of the two lounges has a TV, and there is a pretty terraced garden with pleasant views where guests can relax after a day's outing. Self-catering accommodation is available in the house next door.

OWNERS: John and Jane Ayres OPEN: all year exc Christmas and Feb ROOMS: 4 double, 3 twin, all rooms with bath/shower exc 1 with wash-basin; tea/coffee in all bedrooms; 2 lounges, 1 with TV TERMS: single £24–£26, single occupancy £32.50; twin/double £57–£71; dinner £14.50; deposit £25 CARDS: none DETAILS: no children under 10; dogs welcome; smoking in TV room only; car park; garden

HELMSLEY North Yorkshire

map 9

Stilworth House

NEW ENTRY

1 Church Street, Helmsley YO6 5AD TEL: (01439) 771072

This impressive-looking Georgian house close to the market square overlooks the castle and the church. Three of the bedrooms are in a converted building facing a beautiful garden, and are prettily decorated with dainty fabrics, coronets and matching wallpaper. All five bedrooms have *en suite* showers and TVs. Breakfasts are served in a separate dining-room, which leads to a conservatory. Guests also have the use of a large lounge with an open fire and TV; in the lounge are french doors leading to the garden. The Cleveland Way starts near Helmsley, and the Prisoner of War Museum at Malton is an easy drive away.

OWNER: Carol Swift OPEN: all year exc Christmas ROOMS: 3 double, 1 twin, 1 family; all rooms with shower, tea/coffee and TV; lounge with TV TERMS: single occupancy £30–£40, twin/double £40–£50, family room £50–£60; deposit: £20 per person CARDS: none DETAILS: children by arrangement; no dogs; no smoking in public rooms; car park; garden

HEMSBY Norfolk

map 6

Old Station House

North Road, Hemsby NR29 4EZ TEL: (01493) 732022
just off B1159, 7m N of Great Yarmouth

This well-maintained, white-painted Edwardian house stands well off the road behind its neat front garden. It is ideally situated for touring the Norfolk Broads and the Great Yarmouth area. Mrs Lake offers a warm and friendly welcome, and the modestly furnished bedrooms are clean and comfortable, and share a bathroom and two WCs. A large TV lounge contains lots of books, and overlooks the garden and patio, where guests can sit on sunny days.

OWNERS: Mr and Mrs A. Lake OPEN: Easter to end Oct ROOMS: 2 double, 1 family; all rooms with wash-basin and tea/coffee; lounge with TV TERMS: single occupancy £20–£25, double £30–£34, family room £40–£45; children's reductions according to age; deposit: £10 per person CARDS: none DETAILS: children welcome; no dogs; no smoking; car park; garden

HENLEY-ON-THAMES Oxfordshire

map 3

Alftrudis

8 Norman Avenue, Henley-on-Thames RG9 1SG TEL/FAX: (01491) 573099

Standing in a private tree-lined gravel road, only three minutes from the town centre and river, Alftrudis is an immaculately kept Victorian house. Sue Lambert does all the decorating herself and has made the attractive curtains. The fresh and bright bedrooms are furnished with flair and two have *en suite* facilities. Breakfast is served in the dining-room, which overlooks the garden. Sue Lambert is happy to provide information on the area and recommend places for evening meals.

OWNER: Sue Lambert OPEN: all year ROOMS: 2 double, 1 with shower, 1 with private bathroom; 1 twin, with shower; tea/coffee and TV in all bedrooms; lounge with TV TERMS: single occupancy £30–£40, twin/double £40–£50; half-price for children sharing with parents; deposit: £10 per night CARDS: none DETAILS: no children under 8; no dogs; no smoking; car park

Lenwade

3 Western Road, Henley-on-Thames RG9 1JL TEL/FAX: (01491) 573468

Only five minutes' walk from the town centre, this attractive semi-detached, turn-of-the-century house is in a quiet residential area. The red-brick house is well maintained, and has a beautiful stained-glass window in the hall, and stripped pine doors. The pleasant bedrooms are decorated in warm colours; all have TVs, and cots can be provided. There is a comfortable TV lounge, and breakfast is served at one large table in the dining-room with its garden views. Mrs Williams is a friendly host who ensures the house has a welcoming, informal atmosphere.

OWNERS: John and Jacquie Williams OPEN: all year ROOMS: 2 double, 1 with shower, 1 with wash-basin; 1 twin, with shower; tea/coffee and TV in all bedrooms; lounge with TV TERMS: single occupancy £25–£40, twin/double £40–£50; free for children under 5, reductions by arrangement for older children sharing with parents; deposit: £10 CARDS: none DETAILS: children welcome; dogs by arrangement; smoking in bedrooms only; garden

The Rise **NEW ENTRY**

Rotherfield Road, Henley-on-Thames RG9 1NR
TEL: (01491) 579360 FAX: (01491) 578691

Built only 12 years ago using old timbers, bricks and doors, this large, luxurious Georgian-style house stands in several acres of magnificent gardens. The house has been beautifully furnished with antiques, and the spacious bedrooms have *en suite* bathrooms, TVs and easy chairs, plus many amenities from trouser-presses and hair-dryers to umbrellas and shoe-cleaning kits. The ground-floor bedroom has its own entrance and overlooks the garden. Guests have the use of their own lounge with a TV, and a dining-room where cooked breakfasts are served, which might include kedgeree, kippers or kidneys, as well as traditional full English and porridge.

OWNER: Shelagh Stanbridge OPEN: all year ROOMS: 1 double, 1 twin, 1 family; all rooms with private bathroom; 1 room suitable for wheelchair-users; tea/coffee and TV in all bedrooms; lounge with TV TERMS: single occupancy £38, twin/double £48, family room £50–£55; deposit: £10; per room CARDS: none DETAILS: children welcome; no dogs; no smoking; car park; garden

Watermans

NEW ENTRY

Harpsden Way, Henley-on-Thames RG19 1NX TEL/FAX: (01491) 578741

Guests can be assured of a warm welcome at this 1920s-built black and white timbered Tudor-style country house, standing in an acre of beautiful gardens. Within, elegance and comfort prevail, with furnishings a tasteful combination of antique and traditional. Bedrooms are decorated with flair; all are *en suite*, have good beds, TVs and armchairs. The sitting-room leads out on to the garden and terrace, where there is a covered heated swimming-pool plus a tennis court for guests' use in summer months. Breakfasts are imaginative, and Mrs Tristem is happy to recommend places to eat in Henley.

OWNERS: Mr and Mrs Tristem OPEN: Apr to Oct ROOMS: 2 double, 1 twin; all rooms with bath/shower, tea/coffee and TV; lounge with TV TERMS: single occupancy £30–£35, twin/double £45–£50; deposit: 1 night's charge for advance bookings CARDS: none DETAILS: children welcome; no dogs; car park; garden; swimming-pool; tennis

HENSTRIDGE Somerset **map 2**

Quiet Corner Farm

Henstridge BA8 0RA TEL: (01963) 363045 FAX: (01963) 343400
at junction with A30, take A357 S, then second left into Vale Lane leading into Oakvale Lane, then 150yds on right

This attractive Victorian house has wonderful views across the Blackmoor Vale and is hidden away on the edge of Henstridge, between Sherborne and Shaftesbury. The smallholding has a collection of stone farm buildings and extends to roughly five acres, supporting Shetland ponies. There is a lovely garden with tables and chairs, and an orchard with cider-apple trees. Guests have use of a sitting-room with TV, and another sitting-area can be found in the flagstoned entrance hall. Breakfast is served in the Garden Room, reached through the kitchen, and on the terrace in fine weather. The three bedrooms are traditionally furnished. Although dinner is not available, the Thompsons are happy to provide supper for small children by arrangement. No one-night bookings are possible on Fridays and Saturdays in July and August. In the grounds are also two well-equipped self-catering cottages which have been converted from barns.

OWNERS: Patricia and Brian Thompson OPEN: all year ROOMS: 2 double, 1 with bath/shower, 1 with wash-basin; 1 twin, with wash-basin; tea/coffee in all bedrooms; lounge with TV TERMS: single occupancy £25, twin/double £40–£42, family room £48–£64; children's reductions; deposit: £10 per room CARDS: none DETAILS: children welcome; no dogs; no smoking; car park; garden

---

Many B&Bs are in remote places, and although in many cases we provide directions, it is always advisable to ask for clear instructions when booking.

HEREFORD **Hereford & Worcester** **map 5**

Charades

34 Southbank Road, Hereford HR1 2TJ TEL: (01432) 269444
from city centre take A44 / A465 NE; turn right into Southbank Rd after crossing railway bridge; house on right where road veers to right

A stay at this imposing home in a quiet residential area just a few minutes' walk from the town centre was thought good value by one visitor. Built in the mid-nineteenth century, the house still boasts a grape-patterned iron staircase and, in the spacious lounge, a beautiful ceiling rose. Bedrooms are good-sized too, with flower-patterned curtains; the doubles have *en suite* facilities, and all rooms have TVs. The lounge now has new carpets and curtains. Guests tuck into breakfast at individual tables in the dining-room, which looks out over the secluded garden; from there are good views over Hereford to the Black Mountains.

OWNER: Mrs B. Mullen OPEN: all year ROOMS: 4 double, all with bath/shower; 2 twin, both with wash-basin; tea/coffee and TV in all bedrooms; lounge with TV TERMS: single occupancy £20–£25, twin/double £36–£42; reductions for children according to age; deposit: £10 CARDS: none DETAILS: no children under 5; dogs by arrangement; car park; garden

Chesley House

NEW ENTRY

9 Southbank Road, Hereford HR1 2TJ TEL/FAX: (01432) 274800
approaching Hereford on A4103, turn left off Aylestone Hill into Southbank Rd; house is 50yds on left

Just a few minutes from the town centre, this Victorian house retains the original ceramic tiles in the entrance way and dining-room. Recent upgrading has resulted in new carpets and freshly decorated rooms. The bedrooms are average in size, and have either *en suite* shower or bath. One room, with a Victorian theme, is particularly attractive. Breakfast is served family-style, and there is a TV-free sitting-room for guests to relax in. Rae and Nicholas Jones are pleasant and accommodating, and always happy to assist guests with planning itineraries. Ben the sheltie is friendly. A secure space for cycles is provided.

OWNERS: Mr and Mrs N. Jones OPEN: all year ROOMS: 1 double, 2 twin; 2 rooms with bath, 1 with shower; tea/coffee and TV in all bedrooms; lounge TERMS: single occupancy £22, twin/double £40; deposit: £10 CARDS: none DETAILS: children welcome; no dogs; car park; garden

Grafton Villa Farm

NEW ENTRY

Grafton, nr Hereford HR2 8ED TEL: (01432) 268689
off A49, 2m S of Hereford

This eighteenth-century farmhouse is at the end of a private lane, set in an acre of gardens with beautiful views, on a 200-acre sheep farm two miles from Hereford. The ambience is warm and friendly, the rooms furnished with antiques, and on chilly days a log fire burns in the lounge. The three well-equipped bedrooms are named after the local woodlands that can be seen from the window, and Jennie Layton made the colour co-ordinated bedspreads and bedroom curtains. Guests can collect their own freshly laid eggs for breakfast each morning, and an inn 300 yards away serves evening meals.

OWNERS: Jennie Layton OPEN: Feb to Oct ROOMS: 2 double, 1 with bath/shower, 1 with private bathroom; 1 twin, with bath/shower; tea/coffee and TV in all bedrooms TERMS: single occupancy £25, twin/double £39–£41; deposit: £10 per room CARDS: none DETAILS: children welcome; no dogs; no smoking; car park; garden

HERMITAGE Dorset **map 2**

Almshouse Farm

Hermitage, nr Sherborne DT9 6HA TEL/FAX: (01963) 210296
off A352 at turning signposted Hermitage, 6m S of Sherborne

This large, Grade II-listed stone farmhouse stands in peaceful countryside overlooking the Blackmore Vale, about halfway between Sherborne and Dorchester. It was originally part of a sixteenth-century monastery and retains many original features, including oak beams and a magnificent inglenook fireplace. Almshouse is a working 160-acre farm, and owners John and Jenny Mayo are happy for guests to watch the farming activities. They are cheerful people, who have been offering comfortable accommodation for nearly 30 years. Breakfast is served at separate tables in the dining-room. The house is surrounded by an attractive garden. The Cerne Abbas Giant is only a few miles away.

OWNER: Jenny Mayo OPEN: Feb to Dec ROOMS: 2 double, both with bath/shower; 1 twin, with private bathroom; tea/coffee and TV in all bedrooms; lounge with TV TERMS: single occupancy £25–£30, twin/double £38–£44; reductions for children sharing with parents; deposit: £10 per person per night CARDS: none DETAILS: children welcome; no dogs; no smoking in dining-room; car park; garden

HEXHAM Northumberland **map 11**

East Peterel Field Farm NEW ENTRY

Yarridge Road, Hexham NE46 2JT
TEL: (01434) 607209 FAX: (01434) 601753
from main street in Hexham take road towards Whitley Chapel; after ½m take right fork; after 2m take right turning just past crossroads

Reached up a quiet country lane, this charming converted farmhouse is in a peaceful position with distant views over the surrounding countryside. Susan Carr is a gracious host who provides a high standard of accommodation. The *en suite* bedrooms are beautifully furnished, and decorated in rich, warm colours. The enormous kitchen, where breakfast is served, can seat up to 40 people; dinners are taken in a separate dining-room. Susan is a gourmet cook and her evening meals have met with praise. Six times a year, between

Febraury and May, she plays host at cooking demonstrations, which attract famous culinary names. Guests have the use of a large drawing-room in high season, and a snug lounge during the rest of the year. East Peterel Field is part of a stud farm, and horse-riding can be arranged at the stables 200 yards up the road. Slaley golf-course is just four miles away.

OWNERS: Susan and David Carr OPEN: all year exc Christmas ROOMS: 2 double, 1 twin; all rooms with bath/shower, tea/coffee and TV; lounge with TV TERMS: single £34–£38, single occupancy £34, twin/double £50–£54; dinner £18.50 CARDS: none DETAILS: children welcome; no dogs; smoking in lounge only; car park; garden

---

Middlemarch

Hencotes, Hexham NE46 2EB TEL/FAX: (01434) 605003

Middlemarch is a listed Georgian house in the centre of town, overlooking the River Sele and the Abbey. The house is impeccably maintained, retaining its original flagstoned entrance, and has been tastefully restored by Eileen Elliott, who won a Civic Society Award in 1990 for its restoration. Furnishings are in keeping with the building, and the very large bedrooms are decorated in soft spring colours; one has a four-poster bed. The large drawing-room has ample information available on things to do in the area. Breakfast is served in the family kitchen, but there are several eating-establishments within walking distance.

OWNER: Eileen Elliott OPEN: all year ROOMS: 1 double, with wash-basin; 2 twin, 1 with bath/shower, 1 with wash-basin; 1 four-poster, with bath/shower; 1 family; tea/coffee and TV in most bedrooms; lounge TERMS: single occupancy £26–£42, twin/double/family room £42, four-poster £52; deposit: £10 per person CARDS: none DETAILS: no children under 10; small dogs by arrangement; no smoking; car park

---

West Close House

Hextol Terrace, Hexham NE46 2AD TEL: (01434) 603307

This detached 1920s villa is situated in a quiet, leafy cul-de-sac, ten minutes' walk from the centre of Hexham. It has lovely secluded gardens with tall beech hedges and a revolving summerhouse. The interior of the house is well maintained and double glazing has been added. Bedrooms are very comfortable, and one has an *en suite* shower-room. The dining-room, which has a small sitting-area in a bay window, and the lounge overlook the garden. Breakfast offers a choice between wholefood continental and traditional English, and light suppers are available by arrangement. Several eating-establishments are within walking distance. At the time of going to press, the owners were undertaking major refurbishments.

OWNER: Patricia Graham-Tomlinson OPEN: all year ROOMS: 2 single, both with wash-basin; 2 double, 1 with shower; tea/coffee in all bedrooms; lounge with TV TERMS: single £18–£20, double £42–£48; deposit: £5 per person per night CARDS: none DETAILS: no children under 10; no dogs; no smoking; car park; garden

HIGHAM Suffolk — map 6

The Bauble

Higham CO7 6LA TEL: (01206) 337254 FAX: (01206) 337263
on B1068, just N of A12, 7m N of Colchester

This charming period property is in the heart of Constable country on the Suffolk/Essex border. It stands in one-and-a-half acres of beautiful secluded gardens, with three ornamental ponds, a tennis court and heated swimming-pool (available after 5pm). The house has a warm, relaxed atmosphere, is well maintained and furnished mostly with antiques. The three bedrooms are well appointed, two have *en suite* facilities, and the third has the use of a private bathroom; all have TVs and bathrobes. The comfortable lounge has a log fire in winter, and imaginative breakfasts are served in the dining-room, which has a display of Penny's flower arrangements. The Watkinses are delightful hosts who greet guests with a cup of tea on arrival.

OWNERS: Nowell and Penny Watkins OPEN: all year exc Christmas ROOMS: 1 single, with bath/shower; 2 twin, 1 with bath/shower, 1 with private bathroom; lounge with TV TERMS: single £25–£30, single occupancy £30–£35, twin £40–£45 CARDS: none DETAILS: no children under 12; no dogs; no smoking; car park; garden; swimming-pool; tennis

HIGH HALDEN Kent — map 3

Hales Place

High Halden, nr Ashford TN26 3JQ
TEL: (01233) 850219 FAX: (01233) 850716
off A28 in High Halden, following brown signs to Art Studio

This large house dating from the sixteenth century is set in eleven acres of gardens and paddocks, with two wildlife ponds. Bedrooms are attractively furnished, and there is a small library and two sitting-rooms, the larger of which has an inglenook fireplace. Roger Green is an artist, and has converted some of the stables and barns into art studios and a gallery. Ellen Green, who comes from Germany, looks after the accommodation and is an experienced cook, making her own preserves, chutneys and bread. Evening meals include organically grown fruit and vegetables from the kitchen garden, and supplies of cream and honey come from nearby producers. After dinner, guests are welcome to join Roger in his private cinema and watch films from his large collection.

OWNERS: Roger and Ellen Green OPEN: all year exc Christmas ROOMS: 3 twin, 2 with bath/shower, 1 with private bathroom; lounge with TV TERMS: single occupancy £30–£35, twin/double £50–£54; babies with own cot free CARDS: MasterCard, Visa DETAILS: children welcome; no dogs; no smoking; car park; garden

---

The end details for each entry state whether or not dogs are allowed, but it is always best to check when booking.

HIGHNAM Gloucestershire map 5

Linton Farm

Highnam GL2 8DF TEL: (01452) 306456
on A40, 2m W of Gloucester, 200yds from Newent turning

No fancy frills, just good, modestly priced old-fashioned hospitality in a pleasant, informal atmosphere are on offer at Linton Farm. The comfortable red-brick farmhouse, dating back to the eighteenth century, is on an 800-acre arable farm, just outside Gloucester, and is furnished with antiques and solid old-fashioned pieces. None of the three bedrooms has a private bathroom, but there are two bathrooms shared between them, exclusively for guests' use. Only breakfast is served, but Gloucester has a number of pubs and restaurants and is a short drive away. Visitors are welcome to walk around the farm.

OWNER: Caroline Keene OPEN: all year ROOMS: 1 single; 1 double, with wash-basin; 1 family; tea/coffee and TV in all bedrooms TERMS: single/single occupancy £17, twin/double £34, family room £34–£60; children's reductions by arrangement; deposit required CARDS: none DETAILS: children welcome; well-behaved dogs welcome with own bedding; no smoking; car park; garden

HINTLESHAM Suffolk map 6

College Farm

Hintlesham IP8 3NT TEL/FAX: (01473) 652253
on A1071, ½m beyond Hintlesham village towards Hadleigh

Rosemary Bryce, who hails originally from Australia, has been providing a convivial welcome to guests at this pink-washed listed Tudor farmhouse for over a decade now. Part of a 600-acre mixed farm, the house was once owned by Cardinal Wolsey and retains a great deal of character, with sloping floors, oak beams, 'duck-your-head' doors and – in the sitting-room – an inglenook fireplace where log fires burn on chilly days. One of the three impeccably maintained bedrooms is *en suite*, while the other two share a bathroom; all have electric blankets. Free-range eggs and home-made marmalade feature at the substantial breakfasts. Guests are welcome to explore the farm, and will find marked footpaths to guide them; croquet and other outdoor games are also available.

OWNER: Rosemary Bryce OPEN: mid-Jan to mid-Dec ROOMS: 1 single, with wash-basin; 1 double, with bath/shower; 1 family, with wash-basin; tea/coffee in all bedrooms; lounge with TV TERMS: single £17.50–£19, single occupancy £23–£26, double £36–£42, family room £45–£55; £12 CARDS: Diners DETAILS: no children under 10; no dogs; no smoking; car park; garden

If you are forced to turn up later than planned, please telephone to warn the proprietor. It is always best to book a room in advance, even in winter. B&Bs with few rooms may close at short notice for periods not specified in the details.

HINTON CHARTERHOUSE Bath & N.E. Somerset map 2

Green Lane House

Hinton Charterhouse BA3 6BL TEL: (01225) 723631 FAX: (01225) 723773
off B3110, 4m S of Bath

Green Lane House was originally three terraced Bath-stone cottages, built in the early eighteenth century right in the middle of the conservation village of Hinton Charterhouse. There are four guest bedrooms, two of which have *en suite* showers, as well as a cosy sitting-room and a small breakfast room. Guests also have use of the garden at the rear of the house. Two nearby inns serve evening meals, and the village is a short drive from Bath, Wells, Longleat House and Farleigh Castle. There is no private parking, but guests may park their cars in the street outside the house.

OWNERS: Christopher and Juliet Davies OPEN: all year ROOMS: 2 double, 1 with shower, 1 with wash-basin; 2 twin, 1 with shower, 1 with wash-basin; tea/coffee in all bedrooms; lounge with TV TERMS: single occupancy £28–£42, twin/double £40–£54; children's reductions by arrangement; deposit: £10 per person or credit card details CARDS: Amex, MasterCard, Visa DETAILS: no babies; no dogs; no smoking; garden

HITCHAM Suffolk map 6

Hill Farmhouse

Bury Road, Hitcham IP7 7PT TEL: (01449) 740651
leave B1115 Stowmarket to Hadleigh road at White Horse pub in Hitcham; follow road signed to Bury for ½m; farmhouse on right

'Comfort and space, and peace' are the words one visitor found to describe a stay at this rambling old farmhouse set in three acres of grounds. The main building is Georgian with Victorian additions, and the guest accommodation is now all in an adjacent cottage, an oak-timbered building dating from the fifteenth century. All the immaculate bedrooms are *en suite*, and have TVs and very pleasant countryside views. Evening meals, as well as 'delicious' breakfasts, are served in the dining-room, and are normally three courses with a couple of choices at each stage; on Tuesday and Thursday less-expensive two-course set meals are offered instead. Guests can relax in the sitting-room with its beams and inglenook fireplace.

OWNERS: Philippa and Andrew McLardy OPEN: Mar to Oct ROOMS: 1 double, 2 twin; two rooms with bath, 1 with shower; tea/coffee and TV in all bedrooms; lounge TERMS: twin/double £32–£40; reductions for children under 12 sharing with parents; dinner £6.50 Tue and Thurs, £11 other days; deposit: 25% CARDS: none DETAILS: children welcome; dogs welcome; no smoking in 1 bedroom and dining-room; car park; garden

If there are any bedrooms with TV, or with tea / coffee-making facilities, we mention this in the details at the end of an entry.

HOLBROOK Suffolk map 6

Highfield NEW ENTRY

Harkstead Road, Holbrook IP9 2RA TEL: (01473) 328250
on B1080, 5m S of Ipswich

This attractive 1930s house stands in an acre of garden overlooking the Stour valley. The house is traditionally furnished, and there is a display of paintings by local artists. The three spacious bedrooms are decorated in good taste, all having king-sized or super-king-sized beds – Honeysuckle has a private balcony, Jasmine can alternate as a twin, and Wisteria has a cottagey décor. All have radio-alarms, TVs, lovely views and a fridge with fresh milk for early-morning tea. Breakfasts feature locally made sausages and freshly baked croissants. The Morrises are charming hosts, and are happy to provide maps and information about local places of interest, or to recommend suitable establishments for evening meals. The nearby Shotley Peninsula provides excellent facilities for sailing, fishing, wind-surfing and bird-watching. There are numerous walks in the area, including footpaths to the Stour estuary.

OWNERS: Bryan and Sally Morris OPEN: all year exc Christmas and New Year ROOMS: 3 double/twin; 2 rooms with bath/shower, 1 with private bathroom; tea/coffee and TV in all bedrooms; lounge with TV TERMS: single occupancy £27–£33, twin/double £35–£42; deposit required CARDS: none DETAILS: no children; no dogs; no smoking; car park; garden

HOLFORD Somerset map 2

Quantock House

Holford TA5 1RY TEL: (01278) 741439
just off A39, 13m NW of Bridgwater; turn left between garage and pub

Built in the seventeenth century, Quantock House is very pretty, with its thatched roof and large colourful cottage garden. Holford is a picturesque village on the ege of the Quantock Hills, and is perfectly placed for walking and riding expeditions. The attractively furnished interior is decorated with embroidery made by Mrs Laidler. Two of the bedrooms have *en suite* facilities, and the beds are covered with patchwork quilts. Guests have use of a comfortable, beamed lounge/dining-room, which has an inglenook fireplace and doors out to the garden. Evening meals are served by arrangement in winter only.

OWNER: Mrs P. Laidler OPEN: all year exc Christmas ROOMS: 1 double, with bath/shower; 1 twin, with bath/shower; 1 family, with private bathroom; tea/coffee and TV in all bedrooms; lounge TERMS: single occupancy £25–£30, twin/double/family room from £40; half-price for children sharing with parents; dinner £12; deposit: 50% CARDS: none DETAILS: children welcome; dogs welcome; no smoking; car park; garden

---

Any smoking restrictions that we know of are given in the details at the end of the entry.

HOLMESFIELD Derbyshire — map 9

Horsleygate Hall

Horsleygate Lane, Holmesfield S18 7WD TEL: (0114) 289 0333
off A61, midway between Chesterfield and Sheffield

This attractive stone house was built in 1783, with later additions, and stands in two acres of secluded terraced garden, with a stream and ponds, on the edge of the Peak District. There are several areas for sitting out on fine days. The interior incorporates modern comforts while retaining much of the house's original charm and atmosphere. The spacious bedrooms have new beds and are decorated in co-ordinating colours. Guests have the use of a lounge with TV and can partake of excellent breakfasts cooked on the Aga. Several pubs are nearby for evening meals. Margaret Ford is a relaxed, unpretentious lady who has created an informal atmosphere in her lovely home.

OWNERS: Margaret and Robert Ford OPEN: all year exc Christmas ROOMS: 1 double, with bath/shower; 1 twin, 1 family; both with wash-basin; tea/coffee in all bedrooms; lounge with TV TERMS: single occupancy £25–£27, twin/double £39–£45, family room £40–£48; children's reductions by arrangement; deposit: £15 CARDS: none DETAILS: no children under 5; no dogs; no smoking; car park; garden

HOLMFIRTH West Yorkshire — map 9

Holme Castle

Holme Village, Holmfirth HD7 1QG
TEL: (01484) 680680 FAX: (01484) 686764
on A6024, 2½m SW of Holmfirth

Holme Castle is not a castle at all, but a Victorian building that gets its name from its distinctive tower and castellated roof. It is located in a conservation area within the Peak District National Park, and is peacefully set overlooking the beautiful Holme Valley. The theme of environmental awareness is evident here, and the hotel has won awards for its efforts to promote conservation and ecological good sense. Not surprisingly, 'eat real food' is a tenet the owners practise, with guests happily getting the benefit of fresh, mostly local produce at breakfast and pre-arranged dinners. The latter can be either an informal two-course affair, or three courses served elegantly with silver and white linen; a wine list complements the food nicely. There is a comfortable parquet-floored lounge with an open fire – and service bells still in working order – and the eight well-appointed bedrooms all have good views. Most are *en suite*, with the other three sharing a bathroom. A cot (available for a one-off fee of £5) and high chair are available for the very young, and older children can play on the climbing frame in the garden.

OWNERS: Jill Hayfield and John Sandford OPEN: all year ROOMS: 1 single, with wash-basin; 4 double, 3 with bath/shower, 1 with wash-basin; 2 twin, both with bath/shower; 1 family, with wash-basin; room service for tea/coffee; TV in all bedrooms and lounge TERMS: single £30, single occupancy £45–£50, twin/double £50–£65, family room

£60–£75; babies free (exc for one-off fee of £5 for cot), £15 for children sharing parents' room; dinner £13.50–£20.50; deposit: 50% or credit card details CARDS: Amex, MasterCard, Visa (2.5% surcharge on credit cards) DETAILS: children welcome; no dogs; no smoking; car park; garden

HOLY ISLAND Northumberland — map 11

Britannia House

Holy Island TD15 2RX TEL: (01289) 389218

This attractive cream and brown corner-house is a popular choice with visitors to Holy Island. It is situated on the green, close by the ruins of an eleventh-century Benedictine church and monastery. The well-maintained bedrooms are comfortably furnished, and two have *en suite* facilities. The guest sitting-room has an open fire and TV. In summer Pauline Patterson runs a tea room featuring home-made cakes and fresh sandwiches. Visitors should remember that Holy Island cannot be reached from the mainland at high tide, and should be sure to check the tide tables in advance.

OWNERS: Mr and Mrs R. Patterson OPEN: Mar to Oct ROOMS: 2 double, both with shower; 1 twin, with wash-basin; tea/coffee in all bedrooms; lounge with TV TERMS: single occupancy £18, twin/double £36; children's reductions by arrangement; deposit: £10 CARDS: none DETAILS: children welcome; no dogs; smoking in lounge only; car park

North View

Holy Island TD15 2SD TEL: (01289) 389222

Situated in the centre of the village, North View is a modernised sixteenth-century farmhouse. Several original features remain, including a beamed entrance way, inglenook fireplace and an antique dresser in the dining-room. The colour-co-ordinated bedrooms are tastefully furnished and have comfortable beds; all have *en suite* showers. Breakfast and three-course, freshly made dinners are served in the licensed dining-room. The garden includes a patio, and is a pleasant place in which to relax on warm days. Holy Island is a great spot for bird-watching, and of special interest is the eleventh-century ruined priory. The owners will advise guests of safe times for crossing the three-mile causeway to the island, and by arrangement will collect those arriving from the mainland coach or train station.

OWNER: Rene Richardson OPEN: all year exc Christmas ROOMS: 2 double, 1 twin; all rooms with shower, tea/coffee and TV; lounge TERMS: single occupancy £30, twin/double £48–£50; deposit: £10 per night for new customers; dinner £11–£14 CARDS: MasterCard, Visa DETAILS: children welcome; no dogs; no smoking; car park; garden

---

If we know a B&B has an alcohol licence, we say so. Most unlicensed B&Bs that offer evening meals allow guests to bring their own wine to dinner. If you wish to do this, ask the B&B when you book.

Rose Villa

NEW ENTRY

Fiddlers Green, Holy Island TD15 2RZ TEL: (01289) 389268
access island via Beal on mainland; causeway is passable only at low tide

Its spotlessness and its 'pleasant, friendly' hosts are what prompted one visitor to Rose Villa to write to us, and inspection confirms that it is true. This nineteenth-century house with a red-tiled roof stands on the green by the church, and offers three immaculate bedrooms, two of which are *en suite* – plus the warm hospitality of Barbara Kyle. One of the double rooms is large enough for an extra bed to be moved in to accommodate families. Smoked fish and fresh fruit feature at breakfast as well as more traditional offerings, all served in the cosy beamed dining-room. Brandy the labrador is friendly. Parking is available on the village green outside the house. When making a reservation, be sure to check for safe crossing times from the mainland. Lindisfarne Castle and Priory are close by, as is everything else on this three-mile-long island.

OWNERS: George and Barbara Kyle OPEN: all year exc Christmas ROOMS: 2 double, 1 with bath/shower, 1 with private bathroom; 1 twin, with shower; tea/coffee and TV in all bedrooms TERMS: single occupancy £20–£25, twin/double £34–£36; children under 5 free, reductions for older children CARDS: none DETAILS: children welcome; no dogs; no smoking

HOOKE Dorset *map 2*

Watermeadow House

NEW ENTRY

Bridge Farm, Hooke, nr Beaminster DT8 3PD TEL/FAX: (01308) 862619
off A356, 3½m E of Beaminster

Watermeadow House, part of a working dairy farm, is a large Georgian-style house, built in the 1990s by the Wallbridges. It is on the edge of the village of Hooke with its tiny fifteenth-century church, and is surrounded by attractive gardens, fields and farmland. The family room is particularly large and bright, and the double room has a king-sized bed. Breakfast is served in the sun-lounge, which has views over the garden, and there is an elegant drawing-room. Visitors may want to have a look at the Roman fort at nearby Eggardon Hill, or try out various walks through the woods, along country lanes, or over the hills.

OWNER: Pauline Wallbridge OPEN: Apr to Oct ROOMS: 1 double, with private bathroom; 1 family, with bath/shower; tea/coffee and TV in both bedrooms; lounge with TV TERMS: double £40–£44, family room from £40; children's reductions if sharing with parents; deposit: £15 CARDS: none DETAILS: children welcome; no dogs; no smoking; car park; garden

If a B&B offers off-street car parking, we note 'car park' at the end of the entry. If nearby on-street parking must be used, in most cases we give details in the descriptive text.

HORSEY Norfolk — map 6

Old Chapel

Horsey Corner, Horsey NR29 4EH TEL: (01493) 393498
on B1159, m N of Horsey village

Located on National Trust land just outside Horsey, the Old Chapel is just a ten-minutes' brisk walk to the dunes and sea. Used for Methodist worship from 1910 to the late 1950s, it is now a friendly yet professionally run house offering three good-sized guest bedrooms. All have good rural views (one is named Sunrise, and another Sunset) and TVs; in addition, all three are suitable for use by disabled guests. The large double has a shower *en suite*. Dinners can be arranged, and are served at seven in the dining-room with its beams and cosy atmosphere. Visitors will find plenty of interest in Horsey, including a Saxon church and Old School House.

OWNER: H.M. Webster OPEN: all year ROOMS: 2 double, 1 with shower, 1 with wash-basin; 1 twin, with wash-basin; all rooms with tea/coffee and TV, and all suitable for wheelchair-users TERMS: single occupancy £19.50–£31.50, twin/double £29–£42; dinner £12; deposit: 33% CARDS: none DETAILS: children welcome; well-behaved dogs welcome; no smoking; car park; garden

HORSINGTON Somerset — map 2

Manor Farm House — NEW ENTRY

Horsington BA8 0EB TEL/FAX: (01963) 370366
just S of Wincanton on the A357 Templecombe road

Although right on the busy A357, Manor Farm House is amazingly quiet and tranquil. A beautiful early-Victorian stone house, it is set in 20 acres overlooking Blackmore Vale. It has a pleasant garden, with a walled area where organic vegetables are grown, as well as a tennis court. Mrs Cranfield-Frampton is very friendly and provides good home-cooked meals from locally produced ingredients. Four-course evening meals are served by arrangement in the dining-room and, weather permitting, breakfast can be taken outside. This comfortable family home has a large drawing-room with a grand piano, and the owners operate an open-house policy for their guests. Horse-riding and trout-fishing are available, and there are many places of interest nearby.

OWNER: Ruth Cranfield-Frampton OPEN: all year ROOMS: 1 double, 1 twin, both rooms with private bathroom and tea/coffee; lounge TERMS: single occupancy £25–£35, twin/double £40–£50; dinner £25; deposit CARDS: none DETAILS: no children; no dogs; smoking in lounge only; car park; garden; tennis

---

B&B rates specified in the details at the end of each entry are given (as applicable) for a single room, for single occupancy of a double room, and then per room in the case of two people sharing a double or twin-bedded room, or for a family room. Because double rooms with four-poster beds often cost more, those are listed separately.

HUDDERSFIELD **West Yorkshire** **map 9**

The Mallows

55 Spring Street, Springwood, Huddersfield HD1 4AZ TEL: (01484) 544684

This attractive listed building dates back to 1823, and is tucked away on a quiet, newly cobbled street just a short walk from the city centre. An attic conversion with skylight windows houses the two standard twin rooms and the single. The other bedrooms have *en suite* showers; all the rooms are comfortably furnished and have TVs. Margaret Chantry offers a warm welcome, and is full of suggestions about interesting things to do in Yorkshire. Excellent breakfasts are served in the dining-room, which retains much of its period flavour.

OWNER: Margaret Chantry OPEN: all year exc Christmas and New Year ROOMS: 1 single, with wash-basin; 1 double, with shower; 4 twin, 2 with shower, 2 with wash-basin; tea/coffee and TV in all bedrooms TERMS: single £17.50, single occupancy £19.50–£29.50, twin/double £30–£40 CARDS: none DETAILS: no children; no dogs; smoking in some bedrooms only; car park

HUNSTANTON **Norfolk** **map 6**

Sutton House

24 Northgate, Hunstanton PE36 6AP TEL/FAX: (01485) 532552

Only a short walk from the sea, this large, double-fronted Edwardian house stands in a quiet back-street in the town of Hunstanton. Three of the bedrooms have sea views; all are *en suite* and have TVs. One of the double rooms is on the first-floor, and opens out to a small balcony which overlooks the street. Breakfasts and pre-arranged evening meals are served at separate tables in the licensed dining-room; there is also a small bar area, and an attractive residents' lounge with wicker furnishings. Guests are made to feel instantly at home by the warm and accommodating owners.

OWNERS: Pat and Mike Emsden OPEN: closed 2 weeks Nov, 3 weeks Jan–Feb ROOMS: 1 single, 2 double, 2 twin, 3 family; all rooms with bath/shower, tea/coffee and TV; lounge with TV TERMS: single £25–£30, single occupancy £30, twin/double £45–£50, family room £55–£70; half-price for children; dinner £12–£15 CARDS: none DETAILS: children welcome; dogs welcome; car park

HUNTON **Kent** **map 3**

The Woolhouse

Grove Lane, Hunton ME15 0SE TEL: (01622) 820778 FAX: (01622) 820645
from Maidstone take B2010 to Yalding, take turning to Hunton; house is on left

Dating from the seventeenth century, this listed converted barn originally belonged to a wealthy wool merchant. The house is down a quiet lane in the middle of hop country and overlooks a lake; its porch and fences are covered with clematis and honeysuckle. The four beamed bedrooms are decorated with pretty wallpapers and have old pine furniture. The country atmosphere is continued in the garden room, where breakfast is sometimes served, and there is a first-floor drawing-room with a TV. Mrs Wetton is a picture framer and has her studio in a wing of the house.

OWNERS: Gavin and Anne Wetton OPEN: all year exc Christmas ROOMS: 1 single, with bath/shower; 1 double, with bath/shower; 2 twin, 1 with bath/shower; lounge with TV TERMS: single £23–£25, single occupancy £25–£30, twin/double £46–£50 CARDS: none DETAILS: no children; dogs by arrangement; car park; garden

HUTTON-LE-HOLE North Yorkshire **map 9**

Hammer & Hand

Hutton-le-Hole YO6 6UA TEL: (01751) 417300 FAX: (01751) 417711
3m N of A170 between Helmsley and Pickering

Built in 1784 as the village beer-house, this listed Georgian house is in a sheltered spot, facing the green in this unspoilt, picturesque village. Many original features remain, such as flagstone floors, cruck ceiling beams and oak panelling. The rooms have period furniture, and the comfortable sitting-room has an inglenook fireplace with an open log fire. The tastefully decorated *en suite* bedrooms, one recently refurbished with William Morris wallpaper, have views of either the village green or open moorland. Breakfast is served in the Old Tap Room, and dinner is available at 7pm; vegetarian dishes can be requested in advance, and there is a wine list. Further bedrooms are scheduled to be added during 1998 in the house next door. The house is well placed for visiting the North Yorkshire Moors National Park, York and the coastal resorts of Whitby and Scarborough.

OWNER: Anne Willis OPEN: all year ROOMS: 3 double, 1 twin; all rooms with bath/shower, tea/coffee and TV; lounge with TV TERMS: single occupancy £30–£33, twin/double £40–£46; dinner £13.50; deposit: £20 per room CARDS: none DETAILS: children welcome; dogs in bedrooms only; no smoking; car park; games room; garden

IDEN East Sussex **map 3**

Barons Grange

Readers Lane, Iden TN31 7UU TEL: (01797) 280478
turn W off B2082 Rye to Wittersham road in Iden, then take first right

Part of a 400-acre farm with sheep, orchards and cornfields, Barons Grange is a listed Georgian farmhouse in peaceful countryside down a quiet country lane, only a pleasant ten-minute stroll to the village. An acre of well-tended gardens includes a hard tennis court, croquet lawn and heated swimming-pool. The Ramuses, who in the past have won Olympic and Commonwealth medals for sailing and horse eventing, offer a warm welcome and an ideal environment for relaxation. The pretty bedrooms are comfortable, and guests have use of a sun loggia on the south-facing side of the house, which overlooks the garden and where breakfast is frequently served. There is also a large lounge, with an inglenook fireplace, and a dining-room with a large dark table and heavy leather chairs.

OWNERS: James and Joy Ramus OPEN: all year exc Christmas ROOMS: 2 double, 1 twin; all rooms with bath/shower, tea/coffee and TV; lounge TERMS: single occupancy £22.50–£27.50, twin/double £35–£55 CARDS: none DETAILS: no children under 12; dogs by arrangement; no smoking; car park; garden; swimming-pool; tennis

ILAM Staffordshire

map 5

Beechenhill Farm

Ilam DE6 2BD TEL/FAX: (01335) 310274

take A515 N from Ashbourne, after 1m turn left, after 5m turn right, continue 1m; farm has postbox at end of drive on left

Wonderful views, excellent food and comfortable accommodation in a separate guest wing all add to the appeal of a stay at this 92-acre sheep and dairy farm about one mile north of the pretty village of Ilam. The house itself is long and low, with creepers around the front door, and the guest wing has its own front entrance, a lounge/breakfast room with TV, and upstairs two *en suite* bedrooms. The family room is decorated with stencils by Sue Prince, who does illustrations for children's books. Hearty breakfasts include 'Beechenhill porridge' plus grilled options, yoghurt and more. Visitors are welcome to explore the farm – as long as 'no dangerous' activities are taking place – and may get to meet Florence the goat. Self-catering cottages, one of which can accommodate wheelchair-users, are also available.

OWNER: Sue Prince OPEN: Feb to Nov ROOMS: 1 double, 1 family; both rooms with shower and tea/coffee; lounge with TV TERMS: single occupancy £25–£30, double £40–£50, family room £40–£68; reductions for children according to age; deposit: £20 CARDS: none DETAILS: children welcome; no dogs; no smoking; car park; garden

IPSWICH Suffolk

map 6

Burlington Lodge

30 Burlington Road, Ipswich IP1 2HS
TEL: (01473) 251868 FAX: (01473) 411960

This large detached Victorian house was once home to the Suffolk artist Edward Smythe. It is situated on the corner of a quiet street, only five minutes' walk from the town centre and is well maintained. The good-sized bedrooms have modern furniture and individual décor, with one double room on the ground floor. All the bedrooms have showers and wash-basins, but only one has a WC. Breakfast only is served, but there are several eating-establishments within walking distance. This is a popular venue for business people, as well as tourists.

OWNERS: Peter and Lesley Norton OPEN: all year exc Christmas ROOMS: 2 double, 3 twin; all rooms with shower (but only 1 with WC); tea/coffee and TV in all bedrooms

TERMS: single occupancy £22–£25, twin/double £35–£40; babies free, children's reductions by arrangement; deposit: £20 for advance bookings CARDS: none DETAILS: children welcome; dogs welcome; smoking in bedrooms only; car park

IRONBRIDGE Shropshire **map 5**

Wharfage Cottage

NEW ENTRY

17 The Wharfage, Ironbridge TF8 7AW TEL: (01952) 432721
on B4373 Telford to Bridgnorth road

Wharfage Cottage was formerly two cottages, one above the other, built about 300 years ago and it was once a sweet factory and a blacksmith's workshop. Now fully restored, it provides immaculate bed-and-breakfast accommodation, with small cottage-style bedrooms decorated with floral, pastel wallpapers. Maxine Roberts is a friendly, outgoing lady who extends a very warm welcome – tea or coffee is usually offered on arrival – and plenty of advice on what to see in the area. One bedroom is on the ground floor, but there are several steps up to the front of the house. Wharfage Cottage overlooks the River Severn and the Iron Bridge, and the Museum of the River is just a few minutes' walk away.

OWNER: Maxine Roberts OPEN: all year ROOMS: 2 double, both with shower; 1 twin, with private bathroom; 1 family, with shower; tea/coffee and TV in all bedrooms TERMS: single occupancy £30, twin/double £40–£44, family room £55–£65; deposit: £20 per room CARDS: Amex, Delta, MasterCard, Switch, Visa DETAILS: children welcome; no dogs; no smoking; car park; garden

IVEGILL Cumbria **map 10**

Streethead Farmhouse

NEW ENTRY

Ivegill CA4 0NG TEL: (01697) 473327
from M6 junction 41 take B5305 and turn right at Hutton Hall; continue 5m; farm at top of hill

This lovely old Grade II-listed farmhouse was built on the site of a Roman dwelling, and is part of a busy dairy farm that is also inhabited by rare breeds of poultry. Some original features remain, such as flagstone floors, bacon hooks, old fireplaces and exposed beams. The two guest bedrooms are very spacious; one has a double plus a single bed, and both have *en suite* shower facilities, and good views over the farm's orchard and ornamental duck pond to the fells beyond. Mrs Wilson when possible greets new arrivals with home-baking and tea, and also provides a complimentary light supper with cakes at 9.30pm. Substantial breakfasts also feature home-made items – scones, bread and jams, for example – as well as traditional cooked items. The cosy TV lounge has a wood-burning stove. The house is occasionally closed during the day after breakfast if farm duties demand. There are three pubs within five miles that serve evening meals.

OWNER: Mrs J. Wilson OPEN: Mar to Nov ROOMS: 1 double, 1 twin; both rooms with shower and tea/coffee; lounge with TV TERMS: single occupancy £20, twin/double £40; deposit: £10 per booking CARDS: none DETAILS: no children under 7; no dogs; smoking in lounge only; car park; garden

JACOBSTOWE Devon map 1

Higher Cadham Farm

Jacobstowe EX20 3RB TEL: (01837) 851647 FAX: (01837) 851410
off B3072 towards Hatherleigh, 6m NW of Okehampton

Originally a Devon longhouse, Higher Cadham Farm has been altered substantially over the years. Approached down a long lane, it is a sixteenth-century oak-beamed building making up one side of the farmyard. It has reputedly been owned by only two families throughout its history, and it was acquired by the Kings in 1910; the present owners are the third generation to live here. The 140-acre farm supports beef and sheep, and is set in attractive countryside with a stream at the bottom of the fields. The Tarka Trail country walk crosses the farm. There are now nine well-equipped bedrooms, all prettily furnished, some in a renovated cow shed. Good home-cooked food is served by arrangement in the dining-room. There is a lounge bar and two other lounges, one of which is for smokers.

OWNERS: John and Jenny King OPEN: all year exc Christmas ROOMS: 1 single, with wash-basin; 2 double, 1 with bath/shower, 1 with wash-basin; 3 twin, 2 with bath/shower, 1 with wash-basin; 1 four-poster, with bath/shower; 2 family, 1 with bath/shower, 1 with wash-basin; tea/coffee in all bedrooms; TV in some bedrooms; 2 lounges, 1 with TV TERMS: single/single occupancy £17–£23, twin/double £34–£46, four-poster £46, family room £51–£69; children's reductions according to age; dinner £10; deposit: credit card details CARDS: MasterCard, Switch, Visa DETAILS: no babies; small dogs welcome; no smoking in public rooms; car park; garden

KEMPLEY Gloucestershire map 5

The Granary

Kempley GL18 2BS TEL/FAX: (01531) 890301
off A449 / B4024 / B4215, 6m NE of Ross-on-Wye

The Granary, formerly known as Lower House Farm, dates from the sixteenth century. The farm supports a dairy herd on its 130 acres, and is in a superb location ideal for outdoor-lovers, with 1,300 acres of Forestry Commission-routed nature walks. The accommodation is in a modernised wing of the farmhouse, and the bedrooms are furnished with some antique pieces and some old-fashioned furniture. There is a separate sitting-room and a cosy lounge. Gill Bennett is an excellent cook who provides good-value home-cooked three-course dinners, using home-reared meat and -grown vegetables. Children's helpings and vegetarian dishes can be requested, and guests may bring their own wine. An 18-hole golf course, a falconry centre and two family-run vineyards are within a two-mile radius. A self-catering unit sleeping six people is also available.

OWNERS: Gill and Glyn Bennett OPEN: all year exc Christmas ROOMS: 1 double, 2 twin; all rooms with bath/shower, tea/coffee and TV; lounge with TV TERMS: single occupancy £20, twin/double £36–£50; half-price for children under 12; dinner £10; deposit: £10 CARDS: none DETAILS: children welcome; dogs welcome; car park; garden

KENDAL Cumbria — map 8

Holmfield

41 Kendal Green, Kendal LA9 5PP TEL/FAX: (01539) 720790

This blue and white Edwardian cottage is set in an elevated position on the edge of town. The three rooms are thoughtfully decorated and overlook the well-nurtured garden, which contains a heated swimming-pool and croquet-lawn. As we were going to press there were plans to convert the three existing bedrooms into two rooms, both with private bathroom. The sun terraces provide an ideal place for relaxation on a sunny day, and offer a very pretty panoramic view over the countryside. Breakfasts are served in a dining-room, and the cosy lounge has a TV. Holmfield is within walking distance of the shops and restaurants in the town centre, and is ideally based for exploring the Lake District.

OWNERS: Brian and Eileen Kettle OPEN: all year ROOMS: 1 double, 1 twin, 1 four-poster; tea/coffee and TV in all bedrooms; lounge with TV TERMS: single occupancy £25–£30, twin/double £42–£45, four-poster £44–£50; deposit: £20 CARDS: none DETAILS: no children under 12; no dogs; car park; garden; swimming-pool

KENILWORTH Warwickshire — map 5

Ferndale

45 Priory Road, Kenilworth CV8 1LL
TEL: (01926) 853214 FAX: (01926) 858336

This pleasant modernised Victorian house is bedecked with an award-winning floral display of hanging baskets and tubs. The house is well maintained and spotlessly clean, with double-glazing to ensure a peaceful night's sleep. All the bedrooms are decorated in Victorian style with flowered wallpapers and fabrics. Breakfast is served in the mock-Tudor dining-room, but there are several eating-places for evening meals close by. Ferndale is licensed, and guests can enjoy a drink in the lounge.

OWNER: Joan Wilson OPEN: all year exc Christmas ROOMS: 1 single, 2 double, 3 twin, 2 family; all rooms with bath/shower, tea/coffee and TV; lounge with TV TERMS: single £22, single occupancy £23–£25, twin/double £38, family room £46; children under 5 free if sharing family room with parents CARDS: MasterCard, Switch, Visa DETAILS: children welcome; no dogs; no smoking; car park

Victoria Lodge Hotel

180 Warwick Road, Kenilworth CV8 1HU
TEL: (01926) 512020 FAX: (01926) 858703

Chris and Trevor Woolcock took over this Victorian house with its pretty hanging baskets and climbers in summer 1997 and have been busy upgrading the property. The well-appointed bedrooms have new white furniture and each is individually co-ordinated with pinks, blues and floral patterns; two are on the ground floor and three have shuttered french windows that open out on to a balcony. One room has a four-poster bed with a lace canopy, and a private patio. As we went to press, there were plans to add two more *en suite* double bedrooms. Among items of interest in the house are a monk's table in the reception area and an unusual sideboard made by Chris's father. Victoria Lodge has a licensed bar, and evening meals are available by arrangement.

OWNERS: Chris and Trevor Woolcock OPEN: all year ROOMS: 1 single, 4 double, 1 twin, 1 four-poster; all rooms with bath/shower, tea/coffee and TV; lounge TERMS: single £37.50, single occupancy £42.50, twin/double/four-poster £52.50; dinner £15 CARDS: Amex, Delta, Diners, MasterCard, Switch, Visa DETAILS: no children under 10; no dogs; no smoking; car park; garden

KENTISBURY Devon **map 1**

Bridwick Farm

Kentisbury EX31 4NN TEL: (01598) 763416
on A39, 9m NE of Barnstaple and ½m W of Blackmoor Gate crossroads

Bridwick Farm is a 370-acre sheep and beef farm on the edge of Exmoor, and was built in the 1850s. Marilyn Purchase makes her guests feel very welcome. Breakfast times are flexible, the washing machine and tumble-dryer can be used, the dining-room is available for eating food or picnics brought in, and babysitting can be arranged. The large, well-furnished bedrooms are spotlessly clean. An open fire warms the comfortable lounge on cool evenings, and plenty of books and tourist information are available for guests' use; there is also a conservatory/sun-lounge at the front of the house. The Purchases have a couple of ponies and can arrange riding nearby; guests are welcome to walk round the farm with prior notice.

OWNERS: Marilyn and Derek Purchase OPEN: all year ROOMS: 1 double, with bath; 1 twin, 1 family, both with private bathroom; tea/coffee and TV in all bedrooms; lounge with TV TERMS: twin/double £32–£40, family room £40–£64; children's reductions according to age; deposit: 1 night's charge CARDS: none DETAILS: children welcome; no dogs; no smoking in bedrooms; car park; garden

---

'Lounge' in the details at the bottoms of entries refers to a room (or rooms) in which guests can relax, watch TV, read or chat, and may vary from a large, elegantly furnished drawing-room exclusively for guests' use to a cosy sitting-room shared with the owners.

KERSEY Suffolk **map 6**

Fair View

NEW ENTRY

Priory Hill, Kersey IP7 6DU TEL: (01473) 828606
from Hadleigh take A1141 to Bildeston, then left turn to Kersey, past church, through village and water-splash

Fair View is a tastefully modernised seventeenth-century house situated in an elevated position in the pretty village of Kersey, where the ducks have the right of way. Guests are assured of personal attention here as Ruth only has one letting room. The luxurious bedroom has peony design curtains, a king-sized bed, armchairs, TV and radio alarm, and *en suite* bathroom with a corner bath and power-shower. The view from the bedroom takes in the village, the surrounding countryside and fourteenth-century St Mary's church, which is floodlit at night. Breakfasts are served in the dining-room, which has an inglenook fireplace with a wood-burning stove. There are several places for evening meals close by, including a pub in the village which serves good food.

OWNER: Ruth Worsley OPEN: all year ROOMS: 1 double, with bath/shower, tea/coffee and TV; lounge with TV TERMS: single occupancy £24–£28, double £36–£44; deposit: £10 per night CARDS: none DETAILS: no children; no dogs; no smoking; car park; garden

KESWICK Cumbria **map 10**

Abacourt Guest House

26 Stanger Street, Keswick CA12 5JU TEL: (017687) 72967

Close to the centre of this bustling Lakeland tourist town, Abacourt is situated in a quiet cul-de-sac and is fully double-glazed, ensuring visitors of a tranquil night's sleep. The house dates from Victorian times, and after sympathetic renovation in the early 1990s retains features such as pitch pine doors and cast-iron fireplaces. Five double rooms, all with *en suite* showers and TVs, are offered, and are prettily decorated in pastels. Keswick's bus station is just 250 yards away, and the town provides plenty of choice for evening meals.

OWNERS: Bill and Sheila Newman OPEN: all year ROOMS: 5 double; all rooms with shower, tea/coffee and TV TERMS: double £42; deposit: 1 night's charge CARDS: none DETAILS: no children; no dogs; no smoking; car park

Berkeley Guest House

NEW ENTRY

The Heads, Keswick CA12 5ER TEL: (017687) 74222

This turn-of-the-century terraced property sits on a quiet road, with stunning views of the mountains, valley and golf course. All the bedrooms have views and are decorated with bright floral wallpapers and co-ordinated fabrics; two have *en suite* facilities, and all have TVs. The top-floor rooms with their sloping ceilings are very popular. Barbara Crompton is an informal lady, with a good sense of humour, who takes excellent care of her guests. Breakfast is served at individual tables in the dining-room, and there is a separate guest lounge, and a sunny terrace for sitting out in summer. Menus from local restaurants are available for guests' perusal for evening meals.

OWNERS: Dennis and Barbara Crompton OPEN: Feb to Dec exc Christmas ROOMS: 1 single, with wash-basin; 2 double, 1 with bath/shower, 1 with wash-basin; 1 twin, 1 family, both with bath/shower; tea/coffee and TV in all bedrooms; lounge TERMS: single £20, twin/double £32–£44, family room £44; children's reductions according to age; deposit: £10 per person CARDS: none DETAILS: no children under 3; no dogs; no smoking; garden

Claremont House

Chestnut Hill, Keswick CA12 4LT TEL: (01768) 772089
on A591, 1m S of Keswick

Built in the mid-nineteenth century as a lodge for nearby Fieldside Manor, Claremont House stands in nearly an acre of peaceful mature gardens, and provides first-class accommodation. Some bedrooms are named after local beauty spots, and all have good views. One bedroom has a brass bed, and all rooms except one have double-glazing to keep out traffic noise. Breakfast includes home-made bread and locally cured bacon. Dinner is also served, with a choice between light meals or a substantial five courses. There are always vegetarian options available, and the house is licensed. The guests' lounge has a pretty window seat and is stocked with books on the area. The bus to Keswick stops outside the house.

OWNERS: Geoff and Hilda Mackerness OPEN: all year exc Christmas ROOMS: 3 double, 2 twin; all rooms with bath/shower, tea/coffee and TV; lounge with TV TERMS: single occupancy £35–£50, twin/double £50–£80; dinner £18.50; deposit: £10 per person CARDS: none DETAILS: children welcome; no dogs; smoking in lounge only; car park; garden

KETTLEBURGH Suffolk — map 6

Church Farm — NEW ENTRY

Kettleburgh IP13 7L TEL: (01728) 723532
off B1116, 2m SW of Framlingham

This 300-year-old farmhouse stands next to the village church in a large garden with ponds inhabited by ducks and geese, and has delightful views of the Debden Valley. Guests have their own entrance, and the TV lounge has a log fire, plus a piano and an organ, which the musically inclined are welcome to take advantage of. Excellent breakfasts feature home-made marmalades and a generous cooked platter, and are served in the dining-room, which is warmed by a wood-burning stove. Evening meals can be provided if pre-booked, with children's portions and vegetarian options available. Bedrooms are bright and comfortable, and the double room is on the ground floor. A child's cot and high chair are available. Historical Framlingham, two miles away, is worth a visit – be sure to pick up the detailed 'town trail' map.

OWNER: Anne Bater OPEN: all year ROOMS: 1 double, with shower; 2 twin, both with private bathroom; tea/coffee in all bedrooms; lounge with TV TERMS: single occupancy £17–£18, twin/double £34–£36; babies free, half-price for children under 8; dinner £12; deposit required CARDS: none DETAILS: children welcome; no dogs upstairs; no smoking in dining-room and bedrooms; car park; garden

KETTLEWELL North Yorkshire **map 8**

The Elms

Kettlewell BD23 5QX TEL: (01756) 760224 FAX: (01756) 760380

This attractive stone house, built in 1872, stands in secluded gardens on the edge of the village of Kettlewell, in the Yorkshire Dales. The three attractive bedrooms are decorated in dainty floral patterns, have matching fabrics and pine furniture. The comfortable, well-furnished lounge has satellite TV and is warmed by an open fire on chilly days. Breakfast is served family-style in the pleasant dining-room, which has the original coving and a piano. Packed lunches can be provided by arrangement, and there are several venues nearby for evening meals. The area is popular with walkers, and picturesque Malham Cove is only a few miles away.

OWNERS: Ian and Jennifer Cuthbert OPEN: all year exc Christmas ROOMS: 2 double, 1 twin; all rooms with bath/shower, tea/coffee and TV; lounge with TV TERMS: single occupancy £28.50–£32, twin/double £42–£48; deposit: minimum £10 CARDS: none DETAILS: no children; no dogs; no smoking; car park; garden

KILMINGTON Devon **map 2**

White Hall

Kilmington EX13 7SB TEL: (01297) 32067
just off A35, S of Axminster

Standing in four acres of pleasant grounds and gardens just off the main road, this small Georgian farmhouse enjoys fine views of the Devon countryside from all the rooms. The peaceful house has a relaxed feel, and a most charming owner. The two bedrooms share two bathrooms, and guests have use of a sitting-room and a quiet library. Breakfast features home-made bread and free-range eggs, and is served in the dining-room. The property's own spring water is available for drinking. Kilmington is a convenient location for exploring the Devon coastline, only six miles away. Evening meals are available in the fourteenth-century thatched inn close to the village.

OWNER: Micheal Keenes OPEN: all year exc Christmas ROOMS: 2 double, both with wash-basin, tea/coffee and TV; lounge with TV TERMS: single occupancy £20–£30, twin/double £36–£40; deposit: £10 CARDS: none DETAILS: no children under 10; no dogs; no smoking; car park; garden

KILVE Somerset **map 2**

Old Mill

NEW ENTRY

Kilve TA5 1EB TEL: (01278) 741571
on A39 between Bridgwater and Minehead

This listed watermill has been beautifully restored and adapted to provide very comfortable accommodation, while retaining the workings of the mill. The Lloyds are warm and friendly hosts and do everything possible to make people's stays comfortable and relaxing. The house has been beautifully furnished with antiques, and has a lovely large lounge and dining-room on the first floor, where breakfast and evening meals (if arranged in advance) are served. All the rooms have original beams, with the entrance to the double bedroom being particularly low. Guests can also enjoy the attractive garden and pond. The Old Mill lies on the edge of the Quantocks, in an area of outstanding natural beauty, half a mile from the sea. It is well placed for coastal and hill walks and for exploring Exmoor.

OWNERS: Dorothy and Graham Lloyd OPEN: all year ROOMS: 2 single; 1 double, with bath/shower; lounge with TV TERMS: single/single occupancy £22, twin/double £44; children's reductions; dinner £12.50; deposit: £10 per person CARDS: none DETAILS: no children under 4; no dogs; no smoking; car park; garden

KIMBOLTON Hereford & Worcester **map 5**

Lower Bache House

Kimbolton HR6 0ER TEL: (01568) 750304
2m NE of Leominster; house signposted at top of hill on A4112 Leysters road ('unsuitable for vehicles' sign on approach road does not apply to access to Lower Bache House)

Character, quiet, comfort and excellent food all serve to make a stay at this seventeenth-century stone farmhouse in the heart of rural Herefordshire an exceptional experience. The once-derelict house has been sensitively restored by Rose and Leslie Wiles, and old beams and many other original features have been retained. Guest accommodation is in the granary annexe – in the form of three charming suites consisting of a bedroom, sitting-room and *en suite* bath or shower-room – and in the converted stables across the courtyard, where there is a self-contained ground-floor luxury suite. Period furniture, old maps and prints and low ceilings add to the atmosphere. Superb breakfasts, as well as imaginative and varied evening meals by arrangement, are served in the barnlike and fascinating dining-room, once the farm's cider-making area and still featuring the original cider mill. A smokehouse on the property and a kitchen garden source some of the quality ingredients used at meals. A wine list hand-selected by the Wileses is also provided. Outside are 14 acres of grounds: among them you will find a croquet lawn and some panoramic views.

OWNERS: Rose and Leslie Wiles OPEN: all year ROOMS: 3 double, 1 twin; all rooms with bath/shower, tea/coffee and TV; 1 room suitable for wheelchair-users; lounge with TV TERMS: single occupancy £31.50, twin/double £53; dinner £12.50–£18.50; deposit: £10 per person CARDS: none DETAILS: no children under 8; no dogs; no smoking; car park; garden

KINGSAND Cornwall **map 1**

Cliff House

Devonpoint Hill, Kingsand, nr Torpoint PL10 1NJ
TEL: (01752) 823110 FAX: (01752) 822595
turn off B3247 to Kingsand 1m S of Millbrook

As its name suggests, this Grade II-listed seventeenth-century house is at the top of a very steep and narrow lane, although in the centre of Kingsand. The large first-floor double drawing-room, with open log fire, grand piano, and French windows leading out to a balcony, has impressive views over Plymouth Sound. The three spacious bedrooms are comfortable and have *en suite* facilities. Home-cooked, wholefood evening meals are available, and include home-baked bread, soups, pâtés, mousses and ice-cream yoghurt. Cliff House is almost next to the Rising Sun pub, Mount Edgcumbe Country Park, and is only a few yards from the South Cornwall Coastal footpath and the sea.

OWNER: Ann Heasman OPEN: all year ROOMS: 3 double; all rooms with bath/shower and tea/coffee; lounge with TV TERMS: single occupancy £25–£35, double £40–£48; dinner £20; deposit: 33% of cost or 1 night's charge CARDS: none DETAILS: no dogs; no smoking; car park; garden

KINGSBRIDGE Devon **map 1**

Galleons Reach

Embankment Road, Kingsbridge TQ7 1JZ TEL: (01548) 853419

A beautiful view over its own attractive garden down to the estuary with its passing boats is a plus at this modern, comfortable bungalow. Nearly at the water's edge, it is on a private service road just a ten-minute walk to the town centre. The welcome here is warm and friendly. Two double rooms are offered, plus a TV lounge, and a dining-room where breakfast is served at separate tables and which overlooks the water.

OWNER: Mrs S. Bell OPEN: Easter to Oct ROOMS: 2 double, 1 with private bathroom, 1 with wash-basin; tea/coffee in both bedrooms; lounge with TV TERMS: single occupancy £20–£22, double £32–£40; deposit: £8 per person CARDS: none DETAILS: no children under 10; no dogs; smoking in lounge only; car park; garden

---

If a B&B offers off-street car parking, we note 'car park' at the end of the entry. If nearby on-street parking must be used, in most cases we give details in the descriptive text.

KINGSDOWN Wiltshire **map 2**

Owl House

NEW ENTRY

Lower Kingsdown Road, Kingsdown, nr Box SN13 8BB
TEL: (01225) 743883 FAX: (01225) 744450
off A4 between Bath and Corsham

Set on the side of a valley, Owl House stands in an attractive sloping garden, enjoying lovely views towards Bath, a few miles away. It is a compact stone-built house with a warm, relaxed atmosphere. The comfortable sitting-room and the dining-room share the best views and lead out to the garden. The double and twin-bedded rooms have *en suite* facilities and can be converted into three-bedded rooms, and the single has a private bathroom. There is a golf course nearby, and Bath is easily accessible.

OWNER: Anne Venus OPEN: all year ROOMS: 1 single, with private bathroom; 1 double, with bath/shower; 1 twin, with bath/shower; tea/coffee and TV in all bedrooms; lounge with TV TERMS: single £25–£35, single occupancy £30–£40, twin/double £40–£50; deposit: 50% or credit card details CARDS: Diners, MasterCard, Visa DETAILS: children welcome; no dogs; no smoking; car park; garden

KINGSEY Buckinghamshire **map 2**

Foxhill

Risborough Road, Kingsey HP17 8LZ TEL: (01844) 291650
from Thame take A4129 to Kingsey; Foxhill is last house on right

This Grade II-listed seventeenth-century farmhouse with its oak beams, creaky floors and sloping ceilings is set peacefully in a large secluded garden with a duck pond. There are wonderful views to the Chiltern Hills from the rear of the house and from the garden, which also has a heated swimming-pool available for use during the summer. Indoors is a lounge/breakfast room which has a TV, plus a separate sitting-area in the hall with plenty of books to browse through. The large bedrooms are warm and comfortable, and all have TVs. The amiable owners are happy to advise visitors on local restaurants for evening meals.

OWNERS: Mary-Joyce and Nick Hooper OPEN: Mar to Nov ROOMS: 1 double, with shower (not WC); 2 twin, 1 with shower (not WC), 1 with wash-basin; all rooms with tea/coffee and TV; lounge with TV TERMS: single occupancy £22–£24, twin/double £40–£42 CARDS: none DETAILS: no children under 5; no dogs; no smoking; car park; garden; swimming-pool

---

Breakfast at B&Bs tends to mean a cooked breakfast of bacon, eggs, toast and so on, although many establishments also offer a good choice of cereals, yoghurts, fruit and other options. If you have special dietary requirements, it is best to discuss these when you make a booking.

KING'S LYNN Norfolk — map 6

Fairlight Lodge — NEW ENTRY

79 Goodwins Road, King's Lynn PE30 5PE
TEL: (01553) 762234 FAX: (01553) 770280

This pleasant Victorian house, with an attractive garden, is only a ten-minute walk from the town centre, bus and railway station. Penny Rowe runs her warm and welcoming home with flair, and it is tastefully decorated and has traditional furniture. Four of the bedrooms are on the ground floor, overlooking the garden, and have *en suite* showers. A portfolio of local information, including a listing of local restaurants, is available for guests' use. Excellent breakfasts are served at individual tables in the breakfast room. Pebbles the Pekinese dog is placid.

OWNER: Mrs P.A. Rowe OPEN: all year exc Christmas ROOMS: 2 single, 1 with shower, 1 with wash-basin; 2 double, both with shower; 3 twin, 1 with bath/shower, 1 with wash-basin; tea/coffee and TV in all bedrooms TERMS: single £18–£25, single occupancy £20–£25, twin/double £34–£40; half-price for children under 10 sharing with parents CARDS: none DETAILS: children welcome; dogs welcome; no smoking in breakfast room and some bedrooms; car park; garden

KING'S SOMBORNE Hampshire — map 2

How Park Farm — NEW ENTRY

King's Somborne SO20 6QG TEL: (01794) 388716
from Stockbridge take A3057 2m S to King's Somborne; in village take first right up Cowdrove Hill; at top turn left on the ridge; How Park Farm on right, through black gate

Set in peaceful countryside above the River Test and with lovely views across the Downs to the south, How Park Farm is built on the site of John of Gaunt's hunting-lodge. It dates from 1680 and is surrounded by seven acres of grounds, including gardens with a croquet lawn. Caroline Halse is a very welcoming host and animal lover, and has peacocks, cats and a dog. She is also a trained cook and offers excellent evening meals, if arranged in advance. The house is beautifully and elegantly furnished, and guests have use of a drawing-room with grand piano, as well as a sitting-room and conservatory. Meals are served in the dining-room. How Park lies on the Test and Clarendon Ways.

OWNER: Caroline Halse OPEN: all year ROOMS: 1 single; 1 double, with bath/shower; 1 twin, with private bathroom; TV in all bedrooms and lounge TERMS: single £27, single occupancy £40–£50, twin/double £60–£70; dinner £25; deposit: letter of confirmation CARDS: none DETAILS: no children; no dogs; no smoking; car park; garden

If there are any bedrooms with TV, or with tea / coffee-making facilities, we mention this in the details at the end of an entry.

KINNERSLEY Hereford & Worcester map 5

Upper Newton Farmhouse

Kinnersley HR3 6QB TEL/FAX: (01544) 327727
take A438 for 13m NW from Hereford, turn right on to A4112 for 2m, then left 200yds

This black and white property dates from the seventeenth century, and is approached up a private drive bordered by fields and rolling countryside dotted with sheep. It stands in a well-tended garden with orchards, and is part of a 270-acre mixed farm. The atmosphere is welcoming and friendly. One of the well-equipped bedrooms is in the main house, and the other two (one with a four-poster bed) are in adjoining cottages, each of which has its own kitchen, lounge and dining-room; all have private bathrooms. Breakfast can be taken either in the cottages or in the main dining-room in the house. Staying here is also ideal for business people, as word processing, desk-top publishing and secretarial services are available. Dinners are no longer served, but menus from local restaurants are available for perusal.

OWNERS: Pearl and Jon Taylor OPEN: all year ROOMS: 1 double, 1 twin, 1 four-poster; all rooms with private bathroom, tea/coffee and TV; lounge with TV TERMS: single occupancy £25, twin/double/four-poster £40; half-price for children; deposit: 25% CARDS: none DETAILS: children welcome; no dogs; no smoking; car park; garden

KIRKBY STEPHEN Cumbria map 10

Fletcher House

Fletcher Hill, Kirkby Stephen CA17 4QQ TEL/FAX: (017683) 71013

Creepers and flowers at the front further prettify this handsome Georgian house, set behind iron railings in the centre of Kirkby Stephen. Original features, including the entrance-hall archway, have been sensitively restored, while the guest accommodation provides modern comforts. Bedrooms are spacious and decorated in soft pastels; two rooms have *en suite* facilities, while one has a half-tester bed, and one is on the ground floor. The guest lounge, with its beautiful chandelier and marble fireplace, has a TV plus a good selection of books. A nice touch at breakfast is home-baked bread. Beau and Nell, the Lancashire Heelers, are friendly. A self-catering flat sleeping two is also available.

OWNER: Dorothy Bradwell OPEN: Easter to Oct ROOMS: 1 single; 3 double, 1 with bath/shower, 2 with wash-basin; 3 twin, 1 with bath/shower, 2 with wash-basin; lounge with TV TERMS: single £17.50, single occupancy £25, twin/double £36–£45; half-price for children under 11; deposit: £5 CARDS: none DETAILS: children welcome; no dogs; no smoking; car park

---

The end details for each entry state whether or not dogs are allowed, but it is always best to check when booking.

KIRKBY THORE Cumbria **map 10**

Bridge End Farm

Kirkby Thore CA10 1UZ TEL: (017683) 61362
on A66, 8m SE of Penrith

This eighteenth-century farmhouse is part of a pedigree Holstein dairy farm in the Eden Valley overlooking the Pennine Hills. The spacious bedrooms have some antique furniture; the patchwork quilts on the beds are made by Yvonne Dent, a cheerful lady who is interested in crafts and cooking. Two bedrooms are *en suite* and the third has its own bathroom. Home-cooked meals are served, if arranged in advance, and feature lots of fresh vegetables, and delicious desserts, such as Yvonne's speciality – sticky toffee pudding. Children's portions and vegetarian options are available with advance notice, and guests may bring their own wine to dinner as Bridge End is unlicensed. Fishing can be arranged, and keen gardeners may wish to visit the Acorn Herb Garden, which is just a few minutes away.

OWNER: Yvonne Dent OPEN: all year exc Christmas ROOMS: 2 double, 1 with bath/shower, 1 with private bathroom; 1 twin, with bath/shower; tea/coffee and TV in all bedrooms; lounge with TV TERMS: single occupancy £21, twin/double £40; half-price for children under 12; dinner £9; deposit: £10 CARDS: none DETAILS: children welcome; dogs by arrangement; no smoking; car park; garden

KIRKHARLE Northumberland **map 11**

Shieldhall

Wallington, by Kirkharle NE61 4AQ TEL/FAX: (01830) 540387
on B6342 ¼m E of junction with A696

This impressive eighteenth-century house has been restored to a high standard, and combined with later farm buildings to form a courtyard. The east part of the house incorporates a large workshop in which Stephen Gay makes and restores furniture, many examples of which can be found in the house. The small bedrooms are individually decorated, and named after the various kinds of timber featured in them. The oak room has a four-poster bed, copied by Stephen from the seventeenth-century original in Lindisfarne Castle. There is a lounge with TV, and a library which has a secret door into a small bar. Both rooms have french windows which lead out to a landscaped garden that includes a croquet lawn. Shieldhall overlooks Wallington Hall, with its extensive parks and gardens.

OWNERS: Stephen and Celia Gay OPEN: Mar to Nov ROOMS: 1 single; 2 double, 1 with bath/shower; 2 twin; 1 four-poster, with bath/shower; tea/coffee and TV in all bedrooms; lounge with TV TERMS: single/single occupancy £30, twin/double £44–£50, four-poster £48, family room £30–£68; dinner £15; deposit: 1 night's charge CARDS: MasterCard, Visa DETAILS: children welcome; no dogs; no smoking; car park; garden

KIRKWHELPINGTON Northumberland map 10

Cornhills Farmhouse

Cornhills, Kirkwhelpington NE19 2RE TEL: (01830) 540232
turn W off A696 1m N of Kirkwhelpington, and continue for 1½m

This impressive nineteenth-century stone house is part of a large stock-rearing farm, situated close to the Northumberland National Park. There is a large landscaped garden in which guests can sit on warm days. The house has an informal, friendly atmosphere, and children are most welcome. Plenty of original features remain, including a marble fireplace in the lounge, a mosaic tiled hallway and a Canadian-pine staircase. The large bedrooms have new beds and are tastefully decorated and colour co-ordinated. Breakfast is cooked on the Aga, and a pub a short drive away serves evening meals. A three-bedroomed self-catering cottage is also available.

OWNER: Lorna Thornton OPEN: all year exc April ROOMS: 2 double, 1 with bath/shower; 1 twin; tea/coffee in all bedrooms; TV in 1 bedroom and lounge TERMS: single occupancy £25, twin/double £35–£40; children under 2 free, £12 for ages 2–12 CARDS: none DETAILS: children welcome; no dogs; no smoking; car park; garden

KNARESBOROUGH North Yorkshire map 9

Balaka

Wetherby Road, Knaresborough HG5 8LQ TEL: (01423) 864598

Look for the zig-zag lines painted on Wetherby Road, for they signal the start of a private lane leading to this immaculate detached family house. The name derives from an Aboriginal word for 'house of content', and contentment is just what visitors find when they get here: the house is secluded and quiet, with a pretty garden chocked full of garden furniture plus a summer-house which guests may use. Within, new carpets have been installed in the entrance way, stairs and double bedroom, and all three bedrooms are well appointed and have garden views. Residents have a sitting-room with TV and a separate dining-room where breakfast is served. A warm and welcoming atmosphere prevails. The centre of Knaresborough is a ten-minute walk away.

OWNERS: Ron and Margaret Williams OPEN: Easter to Oct ROOMS: 1 single, with private bathroom; 1 double, 1 twin, both with bath/shower; tea/coffee and TV in all bedrooms; lounge with TV TERMS: single £20–£22, single occupancy £27–£30, twin/double £44–£50; deposit: £10 per person CARDS: none DETAILS: no children under 10; no dogs; no smoking; car park; garden

Grove House

14 Boroughbridge Road, Knaresborough HG5 0NG TEL: (01423) 868857

This interesting house dates from two eras, the oldest part from the sixteenth century, the newer half being Georgian, and the two sections are divided by a staircase. It is a friendly, welcoming place, and has a large, comfortable lounge with leather furniture. Bedrooms are pleasantly decorated, and the ground-floor annexe is ideal for families or a group of friends. Only breakfast is served, but there are plenty of eating-establishments within walking distance in the town centre. Knaresborough is a good base for exploring the Dales.

OWNER: Joan Davy OPEN: all year exc Christmas ROOMS: 2 double, both with bath/shower; 2 twin, both with wash-basin; tea/coffee and TV in all bedrooms; lounge with TV TERMS: single occupancy £25, twin/double £36 CARDS: none DETAILS: children welcome; no dogs; no smoking; car park; garden

KNOCKIN Shropshire **map 5**

Top Farmhouse

NEW ENTRY

Knockin SY10 8HN TEL: (01691) 682582

from A5 5m S of Oswestry, take B4396 Knockin road for 3m, house last on left

Situated in a small, peaceful village, Top Farmhouse is a sixteenth-century listed half-timbered building with an unusually decorated gable on the front of the house. Many original features remain, such as leaded windows, casement shutters and fireplaces. The spacious bedrooms are decorated with floral fabrics, and the main bathroom has a sauna and jacuzzi. The oak-beamed drawing-room has a snooker table and a piano. Excellent breakfasts are served in the dining-room, including yoghurts and fresh fruit juice, with a full English breakfast also on offer. Pam Morrissey offers guests a hot drink and home-baked cakes on arrival, and the atmosphere is informal and welcoming. A portfolio of local attractions and menus from local restaurants is available.

OWNERS: Pam and Peter Morrissey OPEN: all year ROOMS: 1 double, 1 twin, 1 family; all rooms with bath/shower, tea/coffee and TV; lounge TERMS: single occupancy £25, twin/double £39–£42, family room £48.50–£58.50 CARDS: none DETAILS: children welcome; dogs welcome; car park; garden

LADOCK Cornwall **map 1**

Bissick Old Mill

Ladock TR2 4PG TEL: (01726) 882557 FAX: (01726) 884057

on B3275, 7m NE of Truro

Bissick Old Mill is a most attractive stone-built house in the centre of the small village of Ladock, and until 25 years ago was a working mill. The house is just off the main road, and has an outside patio with tables and chairs for sitting out. It operates as a tea-room-cum-restaurant during the day, offering meals and delicious home-made cakes and pastries. Elizabeth is a trained chef and prepares imaginative evening meals, with the emphasis on French cooking, using fresh local produce. Light suppers are also available. The Hendersons have completely refurbished the first floor, creating three pretty, comfortable bedrooms, all with TV, mini-bar and hair-dryers. There is a very comfortable lounge with open fireplace, and a self-catering cottage which is ideal for families is also available.

OWNERS: Elizabeth and Keith Henderson OPEN: all year exc Christmas ROOMS: 1 single, 2 double, 1 twin; all rooms with shower, tea/coffee and TV; lounge TERMS: single £35.50–£40, single occupancy £40, twin/double £54.50–£62.50; dinner £13.50–£17.50; deposit: £15 per person CARDS: Delta, MasterCard, Switch, Visa DETAILS: no children under 10; dogs by arrangement; smoking in lounge only; car park; garden

LAMBOURN WOODLANDS Berkshire map 2

Lodge Down

Lambourn Woodlands RG17 7BJ TEL/FAX: (01672) 540304

from M4 junction 14 follow signs to Wantage for 300yds, then turn left at sign for Baydon and continue for 4m

This large attractive country house was built about 50 years ago and stands in 75 acres of garden and woodlands close to the village of Lambourn, which is one of the most famous racehorse-training centres in the country, and whose gallops are visible from the house. The large, parquet-floored drawing-room has a warm, inviting atmosphere, an open fire, a piano and a display of old family photographs. The spacious bedrooms are traditionally furnished and all have *en suite* facilities. The house is full of interest, and the remains of a prisoner-of-war camp can be seen along the drive. John Cook is happy to take interested guests on a tour of the horse-training centre, and for a modest charge can arrange a stable visit. The Cooks are a charming couple who serve breakfast only, but can recommend places in the area for dinner. A separate self-catering flat has a double and a single bedroom.

OWNERS: John and Sally Cook OPEN: all year ROOMS: 1 double, 1 twin, 1 family; all rooms with bath/shower and tea/coffee; lounge with TV TERMS: single occupancy £25–£30, twin/double £45, family room £55; deposit CARDS: none DETAILS: children welcome; no dogs; car park; garden

LANCASTER Lancashire map 8

Edenbreck House

Sunnyside Lane, Lancaster LA1 5ED TEL: (01524) 32464

Set in a large, secluded garden, this impressive Victorian-style house is just ten minutes' walk from the town centre. The house is tastefully decorated with a mixture of contemporary and traditional furnishings, and has a galleried lounge. Each bedroom has its own theme: one has a four-poster bed and a pink jacuzzi, another takes you to a bygone era, while the garden suite has wonderful views of Lancaster's most famous folly. Breakfast is served in the attractive dining-room; there is a help-yourself buffet for starters, followed by a traditional cooked platter. Several places for evening meals are within walking distance.

OWNERS: Mr and Mrs Houghton OPEN: all year exc Christmas ROOMS: 3 double, 2 twin; all rooms with bath/shower, tea/coffee and TV; lounge with TV TERMS: single occupancy £30, twin/double £40; deposit: £10 CARDS: none DETAILS: children welcome; dogs welcome; car park; garden

Elsinore House

76 Scotforth Road, Lancaster LA1 4SF TEL: (01524) 65088

This immaculately kept detached house, close to the university, has a fine display of colourful window boxes in summer. Linda and David Moorhouse continue to maintain excellent standards and offer good-value accommodation. The two bedrooms are a decent size and well furnished, and an excellent breakfast is served in the dining-room; several venues for eating out are nearby. There is also a TV lounge for guests' use. Linda and David are both keen walkers and are happy to share their knowledge of the area with their guests.

OWNER: Linda Moorhouse OPEN: all year exc Christmas ROOMS: 2 double; both rooms with bath/shower, tea/coffee and TV; lounge with TV TERMS: double £38; deposit: £10 CARDS: none DETAILS: no children; no dogs; no smoking; car park; garden

LANDFORD Wiltshire map 2

Landsbrook Farm

Landford Wood, Landford SP5 2ES TEL/FAX: (01794) 390220
turn off A36, 6m W of Romsey signposted Landfordwood, then ½m

This old mellow-stone farmhouse stands just off a busy road and is a comfortable and welcoming place. It may be a little difficult to find, so it is advisable to ask for directions. Mrs O'Brien is a charming lady who is a garden lover, teaches tennis to children and is happy to assist guests with their itineraries for visits to local houses and gardens. The house is beautifully furnished, with a lovely sitting-room, and both breakfast and dinner are served in the dining-room. The house is convenient for visiting Salisbury and the New Forest.

OWNER: Mrs P. O'Brien OPEN: all year ROOMS: 1 single; 2 double, 1 with private bathroom, 1 with wash-basin; 1 twin, with bath/shower; tea/coffee in all bedrooms; lounge with TV TERMS: single £20, twin/double £50–£60; dinner £10–£20; deposit required CARDS: none DETAILS: no children under 13; no dogs; no smoking; car park; garden

'Bath / shower' in the details under each entry means that the rooms have en suite *facilities. 'Private bathroom' signifies that a room has a bathroom for its exclusive use. The B&B may have other, shared bathroom facilities as well. We list 'wash-basins' for rooms that have them but do not have* en suite *or private facilities.*

LANGTON MATRAVERS Dorset map 2

Maycroft

Old Malthouse Lane, Langton Matravers BH19 3HH
TEL/FAX: (01929) 424305
off B3069 Swanage to Kingston road, turn into Old Malthouse School at top of village; house on left past school car park and buildings

This attractive Victorian detached house is in the middle of the lovely village of Langton Matravers, and enjoys wonderful views across farmland to the sea at Swanage. The house is in a quiet spot at the top of the village, surrounded by a pretty garden, and is reached through the grounds of the Old Malthouse School. It is a comfortably furnished place with a cheerful atmosphere, and the Björkstrands offer a warm welcome. Maycroft is well placed for coastal paths and beaches.

OWNERS: Janet and Erik Björkstrand OPEN: Mar to Nov ROOMS: 1 double, 1 twin; both rooms with wash-basin, tea/coffee and TV TERMS: single occupancy £20–£25, twin/double £32–£35 CARDS: none DETAILS: no children; no dogs; smoking downstairs only; car park; garden

LANGWITH Derbyshire map 9

Blue Barn Farm

Langwith NG20 9JD TEL/FAX: (01623) 742248
on A616 heading towards Newark, 6m E of junction 30 on M1

This 450-acre working arable farm is approached up a three-quarter-mile private track in the middle of rolling hills on the Welbeck Estate, on the edge of Sherwood Forest. The house is comfortably furnished, and the twin bedroom has an *en suite* shower. One room is suitable for families and a cot can be provided for those with babies. June Ibbotson is an extremely helpful and accommodating host; she is a Blue Badge Tourist Guide and, with notice, is happy to offer tours of the area and assist guests with itineraries. The lounge is warmed by an open fire, and a generous farm breakfast is served. Self-catering accommodation is also available in a cottage next to the house.

OWNER: June Ibbotson OPEN: all year exc Christmas ROOMS: 1 double, with wash-basin; 1 twin, with shower; 1 family, with wash-basin; tea/coffee and TV in all bedrooms; lounge with TV TERMS: single occupancy £18, twin/double £40, family room from £36; children's reductions according to age; deposit: £5 per person CARDS: none DETAILS: children welcome; no dogs; no smoking in bedrooms; car park; garden

---

If a B&B accepts credit cards, we list them in the details at the end of an entry – or specify no cards are accepted if that is so. There may be a surcharge if you pay by credit card. It is always best to check when booking whether the card you want to use will be accepted.

LAVENHAM Suffolk **map 6**

Meathe House

Hill Green, Lavenham CO10 9LS TEL: (01787) 247809
just E of A1141, 1m N of Lavenham

Standing in an acre of well-maintained gardens and lawns, this modern yet traditionally styled red-brick house has fine views of the rolling Suffolk countryside. The guest accommodation is at one end of the house, with the owners occupying the opposite end, though they are available to assist and advise when needed. Residents have the use of a large lounge with a TV plus plenty of books to dip into. Breakfast is served in the spacious dining-room. The three bedrooms are individually decorated and share a bathroom; all have wash-basins.

OWNERS: Ken and Margaret Yates OPEN: Easter to Oct ROOMS: 1 single, 1 double, 1 twin; all rooms with wash-basin and tea/coffee; lounge with TV TERMS: single £25, single occupancy £35, twin/double £45; deposit by arrangement CARDS: none DETAILS: no children; no dogs; no smoking; car park; garden

LEA Wiltshire **map 2**

Winkworth Farm NEW ENTRY

Lea SN16 9NH TEL: (01666) 823267
off B4042, 3m SE of Malmesbury; opposite village school

Visitors speak highly of the warmth of welcome and friendliness they receive at this seventeenth-century Cotswold-stone farmhouse standing in a lovely walled garden. Mrs Harwood is a charming hostess, who has a good reputation for her food, which can be sampled at dinner if arranged in advance. The house is beautifully furnished, and offers guests two large, comfortable bedrooms, one *en suite* and the other with its own bathroom – although said to be 'a long walk away'. The beamed dining-room is furnished with antiques, and the comfortable drawing-room has an open fire, and overlooks the garden at one end and the patio at the other. Winkworth Farm, which is a working beef farm, is in a peaceful position about a mile off the main road, and within easy reach of Westonbirt Arboretum, Bath, Cirencester and Cheltenham.

OWNERS: Doi Harwood and Anthony Newman OPEN: all year exc Christmas ROOMS: 2 double, 1 with bath/shower, 1 with private bathroom; tea/coffee and TV in both bedrooms; lounge with TV TERMS: double £40; dinner £12.50; deposit: £10 per room CARDS: none DETAILS: children welcome; no dogs; no smoking; car park; garden

Many B&Bs are in remote places, and although in many cases we provide directions, it is always advisable to ask for clear instructions when booking.

LEEDS West Yorkshire **map 9**

118 Grovehall Drive

118 Grovehall Drive, Beeston, Leeds LS11 7ET TEL/FAX: (0113) 270 4445

Friendliness, good humour and good value continue to be extended to visitors at this semi-detached family home about three miles from the city centre. Bus service into Leeds is frequent, and the house is within easy reach of the M1 and M62 motorways – and just a ten-minute walk from Leeds United football ground. The Sabines do all they can to ensure guests feel at home, sharing their lounge (which has a TV and video), happily assisting with itineraries, and providing excellent breakfasts with plenty of choice. The three bedrooms are spotlessly maintained, and two have sloping ceilings. On-street parking is unrestricted.

OWNERS: Rod and Ann Sabine OPEN: all year exc Christmas ROOMS: 2 double, 1 twin; lounge with TV TERMS: single occupancy £16–£18, twin/double £27–£30; £10 for children 10–15 CARDS: none DETAILS: no children under 10; no dogs; no smoking; garden

LEGBOURNE Lincolnshire **map 9**

Gordon House

Station Road, Legbourne LN11 8LH
TEL: (01507) 607568 FAX: (01507) 609323

A cheerful welcome, good food and attractive, comfortable accommodation are what draw visitors to this red-brick country house on the fringe of the Lincolnshire Wolds. The house is on the main road through Legbourne and backs on to the grounds of the village church. Both bedrooms have stripped pine doors and sloping floors, TVs and wash-basins, and share a bathroom. Local sausages and Lincolnshire plum bread feature at breakfast, and home-cooked evening meals, which focus on healthy eating, can be pre-booked. Guests are welcome to relax in the TV lounge, which has a piano, or to sit out in the large garden, which has a fish pond.

OWNERS: Keith and Elizabeth Norman OPEN: all year ROOMS: 1 double, 1 twin; both rooms with wash-basin, tea/coffee and TV; lounge TERMS: single occupancy £20.50, twin/double £36; £5 for children under 5; dinner £8.50; deposit: 10% CARDS: none DETAILS: children welcome; dogs welcome with own bedding; no smoking; car park; garden

---

To find an entry in the Guide, *go to the maps at the back of the book. Entries are plotted on the maps under their closest village, hamlet or city, except in London, where they are listed by name of B&B. After choosing your localities, go to the relevant section of the book (England, Scotland, Wales etc.), where localities are listed in alphabetical order (by B&B name order in London). There is also an index at the back of the book.*

LEYSTERS Hereford & Worcester **map 5**

Hills Farm

NEW ENTRY

Leysters, nr Leominster HR6 0HP TEL: (01568) 750205
just off A4112, off A49, 5m NE of Leominster

This fifteenth-century farmhouse, on a 120-acre arable farm, is in an elevated position with splendid views of rural Herefordshire. Original features of the building remain, such as flagstone floors, oak beams and fireplaces. Two of the bedrooms are in the main building, while the others are in individually converted barns, each with its own front door. In the sitting-room are guide books and maps of the area. Breakfast and, by arrangement, excellent evening meals are served in the dining-room, which was formerly the dairy. The farm is not licensed but guests are welcome to bring their own wine to dinner. Note that at bank holiday weekends the minimum booking is two nights.

OWNERS: Peter and Jane Conolly OPEN: Mar to Oct ROOMS: 3 double, 2 with bath/shower, 1 with private bathroom; 2 twin, both with bath/shower; tea/coffee and TV in all bedrooms; lounge TERMS: single occupancy £33–£35, twin/double £46–£50; dinner £16; deposit: 20% CARDS: Delta, MasterCard, Switch, Visa DETAILS: no children; no dogs in dining-room or sitting-room; no smoking; car park; garden

LESBURY Northumberland **map 10**

Hawkhill Farmhouse

NEW ENTRY

Lesbury NE66 3PG TEL/FAX: (01665) 830380
on A1068, 2½m E of Alnwick

Approached by a private lane, this impressive stone farmhouse built in 1860 stands in a secluded position, with extensive views of the surrounding countryside. It is a working arable farm extending to 630 acres, and is part of the Duke of Northumberland's estate. Margery Vickers decided to do B&B after the children had left, and has been enjoying her venture since 1996. The spacious bedrooms are well appointed, have soft pastel colours, traditional furniture and comfortable high beds. All the rooms have *en suite* shower-rooms and TVs. The quiet lounge has a coral décor, an antique davenport and window seats. Guests can come and go as they please, and there is a free-and-easy atmosphere, but the Vickers are always available if required.

OWNER: Margery Vickers OPEN: Apr to end Oct ROOMS: 1 double, 2 twin; all rooms with shower, tea/coffee and TV; lounge TERMS: single occupancy £28, twin/double £40 CARDS: none DETAILS: no children under 12; no dogs; smoking in 1 bedroom only; car park; garden

---

If you are forced to turn up later than planned, please telephone to warn the proprietor. It is always best to book a room in advance, even in winter. B&Bs with few rooms may close at short notice for periods not specified in the details.

LEWES East Sussex **map 3**

Millers

134 High Street, Lewes BN7 1XS
TEL: (01273) 475631 FAX: (01273) 486226

Millers is a delightful place, full of character and charm, and is on the main street of the historic town of Lewes. The front room of this sixteenth-century timber-framed building was used by millers for their business, and they also operated the only known six-sail post-mill in the country. One of the grinding stones survived, and can now be seen in the rear walled garden. The cosy dining-room has a fire and sitting-area, and a table where breakfast is served. One of the large and unusual bedrooms was used as a studio by members of the Bloomsbury Group, and has an impressive array of exposed beams; both bedrooms have four-posters. The house has lots of panelling and natural wood, and is decorated and furnished in keeping with its period.

OWNERS: Teré and Tony Tammar OPEN: all year exc Christmas, 4 and 5 Nov ROOMS: 2 four-poster; both rooms with bath/shower, tea/coffee and TV TERMS: single occupancy £45, four-poster £50 CARDS: none DETAILS: no children; no dogs; no smoking; garden

LEYBOURNE Kent **map 3**

Woodgate NEW ENTRY

Birling Road, Leybourne ME19 5HT TEL: (01732) 843201
from M20 junction 4 go towards Tonbridge, then first right and first left

Woodgate has been converted to a house from a pair of seventeenth-century woodcutters' cottages, and is down a quiet country lane in a beautiful four-acre natural woodland garden that is a bird-watchers' paradise. The Ludlows are a very interesting, well-travelled couple who offer their guests a warm welcome, and have collected their furnishings from all over the world. They are also very interested in birds and have their own bantams. The large, well-furnished and comfortable sitting-room has a wood-burning stove, and leads into a conservatory overlooking the garden. Breakfast and, by arrangement, dinner are served here. The bedrooms are small, two have *en suite* facilities (separated from the rest of the room by a curtain); one room is on the ground floor and suitable for the infirm. Leybourne is a ten-minute walk away.

OWNERS: Ken and Judy Ludlow OPEN: all year exc Christmas ROOMS: 1 single, with wash-basin; 2 double, 1 with bath/shower, 1 with wash-basin; 1 twin, with bath/shower; tea/coffee and TV in all bedrooms; lounge with TV TERMS: single/single occupancy £20–£25, twin/double £44–£50; babies free, children's reductions according to age; dinner £16 CARDS: none DETAILS: children welcome; dogs welcome; no smoking; car park; garden

LEYBURN North Yorkshire **map 9**

Secret Garden House

Grove Square, Leyburn DL8 5AE TEL: (01969) 623589

This elegant stone house, dating from 1720, is right in the middle of the market town of Leyburn, but appears to be more secluded, because it stands in a large walled garden. Inside, it is filled with antiques and curios, including a display of patchwork quilts. Breakfasts and traditional three-course dinners are served in the licensed dining-room. There is a 200-year-old summer-house in the garden, and the converted coach-house loft provides self-catering for four to six people.

OWNERS: Dermot and Norma Digges OPEN: all year exc Christmas ROOMS: 1 single, with wash-basin; 3 double, all with private bathroom; 2 twin, both with private bathroom; tea/coffee and TV in all bedrooms; lounge with TV TERMS: single/single occupancy £22–£27, twin/double £44–£54; dinner £25; deposit: £10 per room CARDS: MasterCard, Visa DETAILS: no children under 12; no smoking in dining-room; car park; garden

LICHFIELD Staffordshire **map 5**

Gaialands

9 Gaiafields Road, Lichfield WS13 7LT TEL: (01543) 263764

Jean White has been offering bed and breakfast at this attractive late-Victorian house for around a quarter of a century. It is set in a beautiful garden on a quiet residential street near the cathedral, and Jean has created a home-from-home ambience. The spacious, bright bedrooms are tastefully decorated and have comfortable beds. Guests also have use of a well-furnished lounge with TV. Generous breakfasts are served, and there are several eating-establishments within walking distance. Gaialands is popular with business people and tourists alike, so early booking is advised.

OWNERS: Mr and Mrs R. White OPEN: all year ROOMS: 2 single; 1 double, with bath/shower; 1 twin, with bath/shower; TV in all bedrooms and lounge TERMS: single £23–£26, single occupancy £27–£30, twin/double £45–£47; children's reductions by arrangement CARDS: none DETAILS: children welcome; no dogs; no smoking; car park; garden

LIMPLEY STOKE Wiltshire **map 2**

Avonside

Winsley Hill, Limpley Stoke BA3 6EX TEL/FAX: (01225) 722547
from A36 S of Bath, take B3108 Bradford-on-Avon road

Aptly named, Avonside stands on the banks of the River Avon. Built of Bath stone in the eighteenth century, it is a comfortable family home with a large and quiet garden with a hard tennis court available for guests' use. The house is stylishly decorated and furnished with antiques, and the bedrooms are large. A conservatory has been added to the dining-room, where evening meals are served by arrangement. A local restaurant with a good reputation is just two minutes' walk away.

OWNERS: Peter and Ursula Challen OPEN: all year exc Christmas ROOMS: 1 double, 1 twin, both rooms with wash-basin and tea/coffee TERMS: single occupancy £20–£22, twin/double £40–£44; dinner £15; deposit required CARDS: none DETAILS: no children under 10; no dogs; no smoking in bedrooms; car park; garden; tennis

LINCOLN Lincolnshire **map 9**

Carline Guest House

1–3 Carline Road, Lincoln LN1 1HL TEL/FAX: (01522) 530422

This smart Edwardian house offers high-class accommodation. The well-appointed bedrooms have attractive wallpaper and stripped pine doors; all are now *en suite* and three are on the ground floor. An annexe across the road has three additional bedrooms, and a sitting-room. Excellent breakfasts feature speciality sausages and free-range eggs, and the Pritchards are happy to recommend eating-establishments for evening meals. The pleasant dining-room overlooks the patio. The house is an ideal base from which to explore the city, and is only five minutes' uphill walk from the cathedral. Garage parking is available for a modest charge.

OWNERS: Gillian and John Pritchard OPEN: all year exc Christmas ROOMS: 8 double, 2 twin, 2 family; all rooms with bath/shower, tea/coffee and TV TERMS: twin/double £40, family room £50–£55; children's reductions if sharing with parents; deposit: 50% of first night's charge CARDS: none DETAILS: children welcome, no babies; no dogs; no smoking; car park; garden

Lindum View Guest House

3 Upper Lindum Street, Lincoln LN2 5RN TEL: (01522) 548894

Jaki and Bruce Low continue their enthusiastic approach to the bed and breakfast business, maintaining their spotlessly clean house in good decorative order. Built in 1873, this solid brick building in a conservation area of the city has the distinction of being the closest guesthouse to the cathedral. Bedrooms are spacious and all have *en suite* facilities and TVs; one room has a four-poster bed and can also be used as a family room. Guests have the use of a cosy sitting-room which is also part of the reception area. Breakfasts offering a good choice are served in the dining-room.

OWNERS: Jaki and Bruce Low OPEN: all year exc Christmas ROOMS: 2 double, 2 twin, 1 four-poster, 1 family; all rooms with bath/shower, tea/coffee and TV; lounge TERMS: single occupancy £25, twin/double £40, four-poster £50, family room £60; children under 5 free CARDS: none DETAILS: children welcome; no dogs; car park

Any smoking restrictions that we know of are given in the details at the end of the entry.

LINTON Kent

map 3

Hill Place

NEW ENTRY

Linton ME17 4AL TEL: (01622) 743834
on A229, 4m S of Maidstone

Although the entrance to Hill Place is just off the main road, it is a tranquil place set in a mature two-acre garden. The substantial house is a listed building dating from the seventeenth century, with panoramic views over the Weald of Kent. The spacious interior is tastefully decorated and furnished with some antique pieces. Two of the three large bedrooms have *en suite* showers. Breakfast is taken at one end of the kitchen. The grounds include a tennis court and, in summer, a heated swimming-pool, which may be used on request. A pub within walking distance serves evening meals. Leeds Castle is nearby.

OWNERS: Ross and Elizabeth Johnston OPEN: all year exc Christmas ROOMS: 1 double, with wash-basin; 1 twin, 1 four-poster, both rooms with shower; tea/coffee and TV in all bedrooms TERMS: single occupancy £19–£25, twin/double £38–£46, four-poster £50; children under 2 free, £10 for ages 2–12 sharing with parents; deposit: 20% CARDS: none DETAILS: children welcome; dogs by arrangement; no smoking; car park; garden; swimming-pool; tennis

White Lodge

Loddington Lane, Linton ME17 4AG TEL/FAX: (01622) 743129
just N of Linton village; from M20 junction 8 take B2163 S through Leeds village, turn left after Boughton Monchelsea into Loddington Lane before Linton crossroads

A beautiful setting and a welcoming, accommodating host help make a stay at this classical-looking white country house memorable. Standing in lovely, secluded grounds, with a small lake in front, the house has an elegance that belies the fact that it once served as the laundry to Linton Park, the former home of Lord Cornwallis. Inside, the atmosphere is informal: 'The friendliness of our host was a treat,' said one visitor, who was glad to have found such a refuge after a long and tiring journey. Five of the six bedrooms have wash-basins and one has *en suite* facilities; all have TVs. A maximum of six guests are accepted at any one time. Residents have a lounge to relax in, and the kitchen – or the dining-room on weekends – is where they can tuck into a 'wonderful breakfast'. Merrilyn Boorman is pleased to share her considerable knowledge about the area with her visitors.

OWNER: Merrilyn Boorman OPEN: all year ROOMS: 2 single, 2 double, 2 twin; all rooms with wash-basin exc 1 double with bath/shower; tea/coffee and TV in all bedrooms; lounge TERMS: single £22, single occupancy £22–£35, twin/double £44–£60; deposit: 33% CARDS: none DETAILS: children welcome; dogs by arrangement; no smoking; car park; garden

LITTLE LANGFORD Wiltshire **map 2**

Little Langford Farmhouse

Little Langford SP3 4NR TEL: (01722) 790205 FAX: (01722) 790086
off A36 Salisbury to Bath road, 5m NW of Wilton

This unusual house, built in 1858, is part of the Earl of Pembroke's estate. It is set on a 1,400-acre arable and dairy farm in a quiet valley on the beautiful Wiltshire downs, the peace only disturbed by the occasional sound of a passing train. Families are welcome and guests can walk round the farm and watch the milking of the cows or feeding of the calves. It is a spacious house with an old-fashioned, comfortable feel. All the rooms are either *en suite* or have private bathrooms; one has a Victorian brass bed in the main room, which has a small double bunk room off it for children. Breakfast is served at one big table in the dining-room, and guests also have the use of a games room with a billiard table.

OWNER: Patricia Helyer OPEN: all year exc Christmas ROOMS: 2 twin, 1 with shower, 1 with private bathroom; 1 family, with private bathroom; tea/coffee in all bedrooms; lounge with TV TERMS: single occupancy £25–£30, twin £42–£48, family room £60–£70; reductions for children sharing with parents; deposit: 20% CARDS: none DETAILS: children welcome; dogs by arrangement; no smoking; car park; games room; garden

LITTLE LONGSTONE Derbyshire **map 9**

The Hollow

NEW ENTRY

Little Longstone DE45 1NN TEL: (01629) 640746
off B6465, 4m N of Bakewell

This peaceful old Derbyshire farmhouse in the middle of the Peak District has fine views and stands in a lovely garden with several old saddle-stones. Although comfortably appointed, the house retains lots of old-world charm; original features include an oak staircase and fireplaces. Both of the two bedrooms have their own good-sized bathroom, are tastefully decorated in pastels, have some antique furnishings and overlook the very pleasant and colourful garden. Imaginative breakfasts featuring (among other things) poached fruit, muffins, fresh fish-cakes, yoghurts, home-baked bread and home-made preserves are served in the dining-room with its impressive Welsh dresser and display of pretty china. A pub nearby is a convenient place for evening meals. Chatsworth House and Haddon Hall are within ten minutes' drive away, and there are plenty of challenges for serious walkers in the vicinity, including the Dark Peak.

OWNERS: Dr and Mrs Chadwick OPEN: all year exc Christmas ROOMS: 1 double, 1 twin; both rooms with private bathroom, tea/coffee and TV TERMS: twin/double £40; deposit: 10% for advanced bookings CARDS: none DETAILS: no children under 12; dogs by arrangement; no smoking; car park; garden

LITTLE PETHERICK Cornwall map 1

Molesworth Manor NEW ENTRY

Little Petherick, nr Padstow PL27 7QT TEL: (01841) 540292
on A389 between Wadebridge and Padstow

This has to be one of the largest and grandest former rectories now doing B&B. The impressive stone-built house dates from the early seventeenth century and is set in an attractive garden. It was the home of Sir Hugh Molesworth in the mid-nineteenth century, and of the eighth Viscount Molesworth later on. The present owners bought the house when it was in disrepair, and have spent many years renovating it, while retaining many original features such as the tall windows incorporating the Molesworth coat-of-arms and the row of servants' bells in the hall. There are several spacious rooms for guests to use, including the drawing-room, library, morning-room and breakfast-room. A dining-room is also available for those wishing to bring in their own food in the evening. The large bedrooms are arranged on the first and second floors, and even the room once belonging to the cook would be considered palatial in many other houses. A footpath runs from the Manor to the church, and continues on to the pretty fishing port of Padstow with its sandy beaches, two miles away.

OWNERS: Peter Pearce and Heather Clarke OPEN: Jan to end Oct ROOMS: 1 single, with private bathroom; 5 double, all with bath/shower; 1 twin, with private bathroom; 2 four-poster, 2 family, all with bath/shower; lounge with TV TERMS: single £22, single occupancy £28–£44, twin/double £40–£50, four-poster £60–£65, family room £59–£70; children's reductions according to age CARDS: none DETAILS: children welcome; no dogs; no smoking; car park; garden

LITTLE WITLEY Hereford & Worcester map 5

Ribston House

Little Witley WR6 6LS TEL: (01886) 888750 FAX: (01886) 888925
on A443, 8m NW of Worcester

Parts of this handsome, modernised house date back as far as the sixteenth century. The property is surrounded by peaceful countryside, and the historic city of Worcester is only a short drive away. There are three tastefully furnished bedrooms, all of which are *en suite*; the spacious family room has a half-tester bed. Some rooms have views of Witley Court, a stately home that is now an impressive ruin; its baroque chapel is still used as the parish church for the nearby village of Great Witley. A cosy lounge, complete with log fire and TV, is available to guests; and breakfasts and evening meals, which include home-grown vegetables, are served in the licensed dining-room. Three Llamas – Pandora, Ely and Sybil – are kept in an adjacent field, and the Wellses are willing to meet visitors at Worcester, or – if given good notice – at Heathrow or Birmingham airports.

OWNERS: Richard and Sarah Wells OPEN: all year exc Christmas ROOMS: 1 single, 1 twin, 1 family; all rooms with bath/shower and tea/coffee; lounge with TV TERMS: single/single occupancy £25–£30, twin/double £50–£60, family room £50–£90; half-price for children under 12; dinner £18; deposit: £20 CARDS: none DETAILS: children welcome; dogs by arrangement; car park; garden

LITTON North Yorkshire **map 8**

Park Bottom

NEW ENTRY

Litton BD23 5QJ TEL: (01756) 770235

off B6160 West Burton to Threshfield road, signposted Arncliffe, then 6m; house 50yds on left past Queens Arms pub

Set in beautiful scenery in the heart of the Yorkshire Dales National Park, this is a new house built in the traditional style with stones from old miners' cottages. Lyn and Bryan Morgan are a warm and hospitable couple. Excellent breakfasts are served in the dining-room, which overlooks a large flagstoned terrace with splendid views, and the sitting-area provides magazines and local information; there is no TV. All the bedrooms have *en suite* facilities and pine furniture. Laundry facilities are available, and packed lunches can be provided. Various inns are nearby for evening meals.

OWNERS: Bryan and Lyn Morgan OPEN: all year exc Christmas ROOMS: 2 double, 1 twin, 1 family; all rooms with bath/shower and tea/coffee TERMS: single occupancy £22–£30, twin/double £44, family room £40–£44; dinner £10–£15; deposit: £15 minimum CARDS: none DETAILS: children welcome; dogs in family room only; no smoking in bedrooms; car park; garden

LIVERPOOL Merseyside **map 7**

Blenheim Guest House

NEW ENTRY

37 Aigburth Drive, Sefton Park, Liverpool L17 4JE
TEL: (0151) 727 7380 FAX: (0151) 727 5833

This restored Victorian villa is on a tree-lined street overlooking the lake at Sefton Park. It is one of the original large detached homes that formerly belonged to Liverpool's wealthy merchants and traders. The atmosphere is friendly, and guests are greeted with a hot drink on arrival. Room sizes vary, with the largest family rooms taking up to six people. Some of the double rooms are really 'triples' and can be let as twins; eight rooms have *en suite* showers. Breakfasts and good-value evening meals are served in the separate dining-room, and there is a residents' bar/lounge where snacks can be ordered at any time of the day. Liverpool city centre is a ten-minute bus ride away, and the airport a ten-minute drive.

OWNER: Mr S. Easton OPEN: all year ROOMS: 2 single, both with wash-basin; 11 double, 5 with shower, 6 with wash-basin; 4 family, 3 with shower, 1 with wash-basin; tea/coffee and TV in all bedrooms; lounge with TV TERMS: single £19.50, single occupancy £29, twin/double £33–£39, family room £33–£70; children under 2 free, £8 for ages 3–12; dinner £6; deposit required CARDS: Delta, MasterCard, Visa (3.5% surcharge on credit cards) DETAILS: children welcome; no dogs; car park; garden

LIZARD Cornwall map 1

Lizard Hotel

Penmenner Road, Lizard TR12 7NP TEL: (01326) 290305
take B3083 from Helston to Lizard village, turn right into Penmenner road after village green, then up drive signposted Lizard Hotel

This detached Victorian building set in a large garden can be found at the end of Lizard Point, down a private road. Previously called Mounts Bay House, the property was taken over last year by Tess and John Barlow, who are continuing to run the hotel on the same lines. The house has some original stained-glass windows, and there is a cosy bar and a dining-room with sea views where evening meals can be served by arrangement. The accommodation is simple and most rooms have shower units. Within easy reach are clifftop walks, sandy beaches and fishing harbours.

OWNERS: Tess and John Barlow OPEN: all year ROOMS: 1 single, 4 double, 1 twin, 1 family; all rooms with shower (2 with no WC); lounge with TV TERMS: single £17.50–£26, single occupancy £26.50–£35, twin/double £35–£52, family room £39–£56; dinner £13.50; deposit: £10 minimum CARDS: MasterCard, Visa DETAILS: children welcome; no dogs; smoking in bar only; car park; garden

LLANWARNE Hereford & Worcester map 5

The Lawns

Llanwarne HR2 8EN TEL: (01981) 540351 FAX: (01981) 540273
on A466, 8m S of Hereford

Features of this beautiful seventeenth-century house include a deep well, which was discovered during renovation. It is in an idyllic spot at the end of a private lane, in 25 acres of grass and woodland – ideal for an away-from-it-all holiday. Elizabeth and Ralph Howard are friendly hosts, and invite guests to join them in the drawing-room in the evening, and to use the patio on fine days. Bedrooms are comfortable, and lavishly decorated. Breakfast sometimes includes duck eggs. The Forest of Dean and the Wye Valley are within easy driving distance.

OWNERS: Ralph and Elizabeth Howard OPEN: mid-Jan to Nov ROOMS: 1 double, with bath/shower; 2 twin, 1 with bath/shower, 1 with wash-basin; tea/coffee and TV in all bedrooms; lounge with TV TERMS: single occupancy £28–£35, twin/double £44–£50; deposit: £10 CARDS: none DETAILS: no children; no dogs; no smoking; car park; garden

---

If you intend to spend several days at a B&B, it is worth asking whether there are reduced rates, particularly if the period is midweek or off-season. It is always best to check prices, especially for single occupancy, when booking. If we know of any particular payment stipulations, we mention them in the details at the end of the entry. We asked the proprietors to estimate their 1998 prices in the autumn of 1997, so the rates may have changed since publication. If a deposit is required for an advance booking, this is stated in the details.

LLANYMYNECH Shropshire **map 5**

Hospitality

Vyrnwy Bank, Llanymynech SY22 6LG TEL: (01691) 830427
on B4398, ¼m from village centre

Hospitality is an eighteenth-century building almost in Wales, with rural views and a homely, comfortable atmosphere. The house is impeccably maintained and improvements are ongoing. All the bedrooms have either *en suite* facilities or a private bathroom, and are decorated with floral fabrics. The guest lounge has period furnishings, and guests can relax around a log fire on cool evenings. Carol Fahey trained as a caterer, and offers excellent breakfasts, as well as modestly priced evening meals by arrangement, including vegetarian choices if ordered in advance. Hospitality provides a good base for walking, golf and fishing.

OWNERS: Mr and Mrs B.J. Fahey OPEN: all year exc Christmas and Feb ROOMS: 2 double, 1 with bath/shower, 1 with private bathroom; 1 twin, with private bathroom; tea/coffee and TV in all bedrooms; lounge with TV TERMS: single occupancy £17, twin/double £34–£40; children's reductions; dinner £9 CARDS: none DETAILS: children welcome; smoking in lounge only; car park; garden

LONG COMPTON Warwickshire **map 5**

Butler's Road Farm

Long Compton CV36 5JZ TEL/FAX: (01608) 684262

Visitors to this down-to-earth eighteenth-century farmhouse are greeted with a warm welcome from owner Eileen Whittaker, and a hot drink served in the cosy sitting-room. Guests are free to explore the 120-acre dairy farm, and there is a large collection of wellington boots of all sizes, should conditions require them. Several original features of the house remain, including flagstone floors, oak beams, stone walls and an inglenook fireplace. The comfortable, good-sized bedrooms share a large bathroom which has a power-shower, and there is an additional WC. Substantial breakfasts start the day, and evening meals can be taken in one of the pubs in the village.

OWNERS: Eileen and Peter Whittaker OPEN: all year ROOMS: 1 twin/family, 1 double/family; both rooms with wash-basin; lounge with TV TERMS: single occupancy £18, twin/double £34, family room £38–£55; children's reductions CARDS: none DETAILS: children welcome; no smoking upstairs; car park; games room

---

Please do not rely on an out-of-date Guide. Although some B&Bs in the current edition have steadfastly retained their high standards and have featured in every edition since the first, a great many others have faded from the scene. In addition, many new, superb B&Bs have been added. Relying on an old Guide will limit your choices and may lead to disappointment.

LONG MELFORD Suffolk map 6

1 Westropps

1 Westropps, Long Melford CO10 9HW TEL/FAX: (01787) 373660
on B1064, just N of Sudbury

A warm welcome awaits visitors at this comfortable modern house situated at the edge of the village. Audrey Fisher maintains the house to a very high standard, and the traditionally furnished rooms are spotlessly clean. The double bedroom is *en suite*, and the other two have their own WCs but share a shower. There is a separate sitting-room, and a dining-room where freshly cooked breakfasts are served. The patio gives a pleasant view of the garden, which has a fish pond stocked with carp. Audrey was born in nearby Lavenham, and is happy to share her knowledge of the area with guests.

OWNER: Audrey Fisher OPEN: all year exc Christmas ROOMS: 1 single, with wash-basin; 1 double, with bath/shower; 1 twin, with wash-basin; tea/coffee and TV in all bedrooms; lounge with TV TERMS: single £22–£24, single occupancy £25, twin/double £42–£44; £10 for children under 12, £15 for ages 12–15 CARDS: none DETAILS: children welcome; no smoking; car park; garden

LOOE Cornwall map 1

Marwinthy Guest House

East Cliff, Looe PL13 1DE TEL: (01503) 264382
from Fore Street, turn left at Ship Inn signposted coast path; house 140yds up hill just beyond crossroads

This small, friendly family-run place is in a quiet location right in the centre of Looe, up a steep narrow lane with a wonderful outlook over the town, harbour and beach. The Mawbys are happy to share their sitting-room with guests: it has a balcony with a telescope for enjoying the marvellous view – which is shared by most of the bedrooms. Marwinthy is located on the coastal footpath, and packed lunches for intrepid walkers can be provided. Evening meals are no longer served, but there are plenty of places for them in the area.

OWNERS: Eddie and Geraldine Mawby OPEN: all year exc mid-Nov to mid-Dec ROOMS: 3 double, 2 with shower, 1 with wash-basin; 1 twin, 1 family, both with wash-basin; tea/coffee in all bedrooms; TV in some bedrooms and lounge TERMS: single occupancy £17–£36, twin/double £34–£44, family room from £43; £9 for children sharing with parents; deposit: 1 night's charge CARDS: none DETAILS: children welcome; dogs welcome; no smoking in dining-room or toilets

B&B rates specified in the details at the end of each entry are given (as applicable) for a single room, for single occupancy of a double room, and then per room in the case of two people sharing a double or twin-bedded room, or for a family room. Because double rooms with four-poster beds often cost more, those are listed separately.

LOUGHBOROUGH Leicestershire **map 5**

Charnwood Lodge

136 Leicester Road, Loughborough LE11 2AQ TEL: (01509) 211120

Formerly known as Garenden Lodge, this B&B has been taken over by Liz and Klaus Charwat, who are maintaining the high standards set by their predecessor. The house is set back from the main road, at the end of a conifer-lined drive. The six bedrooms are well equipped and all have *en suite* facilities and satellite TV. There is no lounge, but guests have use of the conservatory and garden. Breakfast is served in the pleasant dining-room, and evening meals can be taken at the Charwats' hotel, two minutes' walk away. Alternatively, there are several pubs and restaurants in the vicinity.

OWNERS: Elizabeth and Klaus Charwat OPEN: all year ROOMS: 2 single, both with shower; 4 double, 3 with shower, 1 with private bathroom; 2 twin, both with shower; 1 family, with shower; tea/coffee and TV in all bedrooms TERMS: single £22–£26, twin/double £34–£36, family room £36–£52; dinner £6; deposit: £10 per room or credit card details CARDS: Delta, MasterCard, Switch, Visa DETAILS: children welcome; dogs welcome; car park; garden

Highbury Guest House

146 Leicester Road, Loughborough LE11 2AQ
TEL: (01509) 230545 FAX: (01509) 233086

This centrally positioned, immaculately kept guesthouse offers 11 traditionally furnished, comfortable guest bedrooms. All but one of the rooms has an *en suite* shower, although two of the *en suite* rooms do not have their own WCs. Double-glazing throughout keeps external noise down. The conservatory/lounge is spacious and bright, and has satellite TV. Of special interest are a leaded stained-glass window in the hall and a collection of antique plates. Good-value simple evening meals are available if pre-arranged, and the guesthouse has an alcohol licence; alternatively, a number of eating-establishments are within walking distance. Visitors might want to have a look at the steam railway that runs behind the house.

OWNERS: John and Sadie Cunningham OPEN: all year ROOMS: 4 single, 4 double, 3 twin/family; all rooms with shower exc 1 single with wash-basin (no WC in 2 rooms); 1 room suitable for wheelchair-users; tea/coffee and TV in all bedrooms; lounge with TV TERMS: single £20–£24, single occupancy £25, twin/double £34–£37, family room £34–£45; children's reductions according to age if sharing with parents; dinner £6 CARDS: Delta, MasterCard, Switch, Visa DETAILS: children welcome; small dogs welcome; car park; garden

In the details listed at the bottom of each entry, the following information is set out: owners' names; months when open; room details; prices per room, children's reductions and prices of evening meals if available; credit and debit cards accepted; any restrictions on children, dogs and smoking; whether there's a car park, plus amenities for guests such as a garden they can use, games room, tennis court and swimming-pool.

LOVESOME HILL North Yorkshire map 9

Lovesome Hill Farm

Lovesome Hill DL6 2PB TEL: (01609) 772311
on A167, 4m N of Northallerton

This 165-acre working farm, situated between the Yorkshire Dales and the North York Moors, offers warm and homely accommodation. The modified granary contains four comfortable bedrooms, including a double room suitable for wheelchair-users. There is a further double in the farmhouse; all the rooms are *en suite* and have TVs. As we were going to press, plans were in progress for the 'Gate Cottage', a self-contained building which will include a half-tester bed, kitchen, sitting-area and bathroom. Guests are welcome to explore the farm; the garden has slides for children to play on.

OWNERS: Mary and John Pearson OPEN: Mar to Nov ROOMS: 1 single, 2 double, 1 twin, 1 family; all rooms with bath/shower, tea/coffee and TV; 1 room suitable for wheelchair-users; lounge with TV TERMS: single £19–£25, single occupancy £25–£30, twin/double £38–£60, family room from £38; dinner £11; deposit: required CARDS: none DETAILS: children welcome; no dogs; smoking in lounge only; car park; garden

LOWDHAM Nottinghamshire map 5

Old School Mews NEW ENTRY

64A Main Street, Lowdham NG14 7BE TEL: (0115) 966 4838
on A612, 7m NE of Nottingham

Formerly a Victorian school house, Old School Mews has been cleverly converted to provide comfortable accommodation in a convenient location. There is a bus and train service to Nottingham every 20 minutes, with a bus stop just outside the door. The attractive bedrooms have beams and sloping ceilings; one has pink coronets and another a chintzy décor, and all have TVs. Breakfasts are served in the huge family kitchen, which has an interesting plate collection, or on the secluded patio in fine weather. Joy McLaughlin is a friendly lady with a good sense of humour. This good-value guesthouse is a convenient base for exploring Sherwood Forest and visiting Belvoir Castle.

OWNER: Joy McLaughlin OPEN: all year exc Christmas ROOMS: 1 double, with bath/shower; 2 twin, both with private bathroom; tea/coffee and TV in all bedrooms TERMS: single occupancy £20–£30, twin/double £36–£40 CARDS: none DETAILS: children welcome; no dogs; car park; garden

---

We welcome your feedback about B&Bs you have stayed in. Please make use of the report forms at the end of the book – or use your own stationery if you prefer – and mail your report to: The Editors, The Good Bed and Breakfast Guide, *FREEPOST, 2 Marylebone Road, London NW1 1YN. (No stamps are needed if mailed within the UK.) Recommendations for B&Bs for our next edition are very welcome. Please let us know if you need more report forms and we will send you a fresh supply.*

LOWESTOFT Suffolk **map 6**

Coventry House

8 Kirkley Cliff, Lowestoft NR33 0BY TEL: (01502) 573865

Coventry House is part of a Victorian terrace on Lowestoft seafront, overlooking the sandy south beaches, near the public gardens. The atmosphere is friendly and informal and the B&B is well placed for the beach and shops. Bedrooms are immaculate and some have *en suite* facilities – one twin-bedded room is on the ground floor. Double-glazing helps keep out traffic noise. Evening meals are served every day except Friday, and guests may bring their own wine to dinner.

OWNER: Gill Alden OPEN: all year exc Christmas ROOMS: 2 single, both with wash-basin; 4 double, 2 with bath/shower, 1 with wash-basin; 1 twin, with bath/shower; 2 family, both with bath/shower; tea/coffee and TV in all bedrooms; lounge with TV TERMS: single £18–£24, single occupancy £20, twin/double £32–£40, family room from £32; half-price for children under 12; dinner £6.50; deposit: 10% CARDS: none DETAILS: children welcome; small, well-behaved dogs only; no smoking in dining-room; car park

Longshore Guest House

7 Wellington Esplanade, Lowestoft NR33 0QQ
TEL: (01502) 565037 FAX: (01502) 582032

Longshore Guest House is a listed building facing the sea and offering six well-equipped bedrooms, most of them with sea views. Although the house is located on the promenade, double-glazing helps minimise the traffic noise. The bedrooms either have *en suite* showers or private bathrooms, and all have TVs. The varied breakfast menu includes smoked haddock and kippers plus a traditional cooked platter, and is served in the mock-Tudor dining-room. The Nolans are an accommodating couple who extend a warm welcome to their guests.

OWNERS: Frank and Sandra Nolan OPEN: all year ROOMS: 2 single, both with private bathroom; 4 double, all with shower; tea/coffee and TV in all bedrooms TERMS: single £18–£20, twin/double £40–£42; deposit: £20 per person CARDS: Amex, Delta, Diners, MasterCard, Visa DETAILS: children welcome; dogs welcome; car park

LOXLEY Warwickshire **map 5**

Loxley Farm

Loxley CV35 9JN TEL/FAX: (01789) 840265
off A429/A422, 4m SE of Stratford-upon-Avon

This attractive fourteenth-century thatched and half-timbered cruck-frame house has used naturally curved wood to form the arch supporting the wall ends, and stands in one and a half acres of pretty, secluded gardens. Within, there are antiques, polished wooden floors, and old equestrian drawings on the walls. The two *en suite* bedrooms, decorated with flowery fabrics, are in a barn conversion, and have their own sitting-rooms, fridges and TVs. Breakfast, cooked on the Aga, is served in the traditional dining-room.

OWNERS: Mr and Mrs R. Horton OPEN: all year exc Christmas ROOMS: 2 double; both rooms with bath/shower, tea/coffee and TV; lounge with TV TERMS: single occupancy £36, double £55; children's reductions by arrangement; deposit: £25 CARDS: none DETAILS: children welcome; no dogs; no smoking; car park; garden

LUDLOW Shropshire **map 5**

Number Twenty Eight

28 Lower Broad Street, Ludlow SY8 1PQ
TEL: (01584) 876996 FAX: (01584) 876860

High standards continue to be maintained at this listed, half-timbered Georgian house, situated close to the town centre, not far from the ancient bridge over the River Teme. Four of the six elegantly furnished bedrooms are in two nearby renovated properties: Broadgate Mews (formerly two Tudor cottages) and Westview (part of a Victorian terrace, built with the first recorded internal water closet in Ludlow). Both of these properties are furnished in keeping with their own character and have a sitting-room, garden and patio. Breakfast is served in the main house. Ludlow Castle is the venue for an annual Shakespearian Festival, and the church is the largest in Shropshire. There is no car park, but street parking is unrestricted. No one-night bookings are taken at weekends.

OWNERS: Patricia and Philip Ross OPEN: all year ROOMS: 4 double, 2 twin; all rooms with bath/shower, tea/coffee and TV; lounge with TV TERMS: single occupancy £35–£65, twin/double £55–£65; deposit: £25 per room CARDS: Amex, MasterCard, Visa DETAILS: children welcome; dogs welcome in Broadgate Mews only; no smoking; garden

LUTON Bedfordshire **map 3**

Belzayne Guest House

70 Lalleford Road, Luton LU2 9JH TEL: (01582) 736591

Guests continue to enjoy the down-to-earth welcome from the delightful owners, Andy and Elsie Bell, who often join their guests in the lounge in the evening for a chat and a cup of tea or coffee. There are no fancy frills here, just old-fashioned hospitality in a well-maintained small modern house in a residential street. The three bedrooms share two bathrooms. Modestly priced, tasty home-cooked dinners, which may include home-made pies, soups and desserts, are available by arrangement. Belzayne is only a five-minute drive from the airport.

OWNERS: Andy and Elsie Bell OPEN: all year exc Christmas ROOMS: 1 single, 1 double, 1 twin; tea/coffee in all bedrooms; lounge with TV TERMS: single £18, single occupancy £18–£22, twin/double £44; children's reductions; dinner £10; deposit: £5 CARDS: none DETAILS: no children under 6; no dogs; smoking in lounge only; car park; garden

LYDLINCH Dorset **map 2**

Holebrook Farm

Lydlinch DT10 2JB TEL: (01258) 817348 FAX: (01258) 817747
from Lydlinch take lane signposted 'Lydlinch Church and Holebrook only' for 1½m

Holebrook Farm is set in peaceful countryside just south of the small village of Lydlinch. Bedrooms, all of which are now *en suite*, are either in the pretty farmhouse or in individual converted stables, and some can be used as family rooms. Guests also have use of a sitting-room and conservatory; other facilities include a small outdoor swimming-pool, a mini-gym and a games room with pool table, table tennis and darts. Clay-pigeon shooting can also be arranged. Good home-cooked evening meals are available by arrangement, and breakfast is served in the farmhouse kitchen. Guests are free to come and go as they please and to look round this working farm, which has rare Middle White pigs, and is an ideal spot for peace and quiet. The accommodation also includes four self-catering cottages. It is advisable to phone in advance for directions.

OWNERS: Charles Wingate-Saul OPEN: all year ROOMS: 3 double, 5 twin; all rooms with bath/shower; lounge with TV TERMS: single occupancy £34, twin/double £42–£46, family room from £36; dinner £13.50; deposit: £10 per person CARDS: none DETAILS: children welcome; no dogs; car park; games room; garden; swimming-pool

LYME REGIS Dorset **map 2**

Rashwood Lodge

Clappentail Lane, Lyme Regis DT7 3LZ TEL: (01297) 445700

Rashwood Lodge is an unusual octagonal white-painted house set in its own grounds in a peaceful position on the edge of town. One bedroom has views over the lovely garden and a private bathroom, while the other has *en suite* shower. As well as the two main double bedrooms, there is an additional twin-bedded room which is let only to extra family members travelling together, and shares the bathroom with one of the double rooms. There is an attractive breakfast room, and guests are welcome to enjoy the garden, with its sloping lawn and seating-area. Mrs Lake is a cheerful and hospitable hostess.

OWNERS: Diana and Mike Lake OPEN: Feb to Nov ROOMS: 2 double, 1 with shower, 1 with private bathroom; tea/coffee and TV in both bedrooms TERMS: single occupancy £25–£28, twin/double £40–£48; deposit: £20 CARDS: none DETAILS: no children under 5; dogs by arrangement; no smoking; car park; garden

The Red House

Sidmouth Road, Lyme Regis DT7 3ES TEL/FAX: (01297) 442055

This substantial 1920s-built, tile-hung house is set above Lyme Regis in a large garden, close to open countryside and with fine views of the coast. It is within walking distance of the town centre and harbour. A balcony runs around the front of the house, with tables and chairs for sitting out on warm days. The three large, comfortable bedrooms have attic-type sloping ceilings, and all have *en suite* facilities and TVs. Mrs Norman has a studio in the garden where she makes dolls.

OWNERS: Tony and Vicky Norman OPEN: mid-Mar to mid-Nov ROOMS: 2 twin, 1 double/family; all rooms with bath/shower, tea/coffee and TV TERMS: single occupancy £30–£37.50, twin/double £40–£50, family room £50–£82; reductions for children sharing with parents; deposit: 1 night's charge CARDS: MasterCard, Visa DETAILS: no children under 8; no dogs; no smoking; car park; garden

---

Willow Cottage

Ware Lane, Lyme Regis DT7 3EL TEL: (01297) 443199

from town-centre take A3052 towards Exeter, after ⅓m turn left into Ware Lane; house 50yds on left

Willow Cottage stands on a quiet country lane, just outside Lyme Regis, and has lovely views over fields sloping down to the sea. Guest accommodation is in a self-contained annexe of the house with its own front door and a private breakfast room. There is one *en suite* double room with a balcony to take advantage of the view, plus an adjoining single room available to a third member of a party. The Griffins are very friendly people, and guests are made to feel very welcome.

OWNERS: Geoffrey and Elizabeth Griffin OPEN: Mar to Nov ROOMS: 1 single; 1 double, with shower, tea/coffee and TV TERMS: single £21–£22, double £46–£52 CARDS: none DETAILS: no children under 8; dogs welcome by arrangement; car park; garden

LYMINGTON Hampshire **map 2**

Wheatsheaf House

25 Gosport Street, Lymington SO41 9BG TEL: (01590) 679208

This attractive, listed seventeenth-century house was originally a coaching-inn and is in the heart of Lymington. It has a warm and friendly atmosphere, and is furnished as a family home with ornaments and antique furniture. The entrance to the house leads into the unusual sitting-room, which has a fireplace on each side, beams, brick pillars and a wooden floor. Double-glazing in the front of the house helps to minimise any noise from the street. There is space for two cars in the courtyard. Wheatsheaf House is an ideal place to explore this delightful old market town, and is handy for ferries to the Isle of Wight.

OWNERS: Jennifer and Peter Cutmore OPEN: all year exc Christmas ROOMS: 3 double, 2 with bath/shower, 1 with private bathroom; 1 twin/family, with bath/shower; lounge with TV TERMS: single occupancy £30–£36, twin/double £50–£64, family room from £50; deposit: 1 night's charge CARDS: none DETAILS: children welcome; dogs by arrangement; no smoking; car park

LYNTON Devon **map 1**

Fernleigh

15 Park Street, Lynton EX35 6BY TEL/FAX: (01598) 753575

Built in the mid-1980s and standing on a quiet side street, Fernleigh was taken over in late 1996 by the McDonnells, who offer a friendly and cheerful welcome to guests. Most rooms have country views, and the shops and harbour are within easy walking distance. The house has a comfortable and warm atmosphere, and is immaculately clean. The dining-room, which overlooks the garden, is where both breakfast and evening meals are served at individual tables. All the bedrooms have *en suite* facilities, and one is on the ground floor. The McDonnells are happy to arrange walks for guests and provide local information.

OWNERS: Anne and Hugh McDonnell OPEN: Feb to end Oct ROOMS: 4 double, 2 twin, 1 family; all rooms with bath/shower; tea/coffee and TV in most bedrooms; lounge with TV TERMS: single occupancy £26–£28, twin/double £32–£40, family room £48–£58; dinner £10; deposit: £10 per person CARDS: none DETAILS: no children under 12; dogs welcome in 1 bedroom only; no smoking; car park; garden

Valley House

NEW ENTRY

Lynbridge Road, Lynton EX35 6BD TEL: (01598) 752285
on B3234 Lynmouth to Barnstaple road at top of Lynton Hill

This 1840s-built house has a wonderful position, tucked into the rocks on the side of a steep valley above the West Lyn River. The old road, just above the house, is now a footpath leading to the village. For those arriving by car, there is a steep driveway up from the main road way below; once safely in the car park, you will need to follow a narrow footpath through dense foliage to the house. Within, the atmosphere is relaxed and welcoming. Some of the bedrooms have balconies, and every room in the house has a view – some quite spectacular, over the steep, wooded slopes of Summerhouse Hill to the Bristol Channel. The lounge, shared with the Herberts, has a good assortment of books and maps, and the small terraced lawn is an appealing place for sitting out on fine days. Slap-up three-course evening meals are offered, or you can opt for just a main course and pudding; portions are generous, and vegetarians have plenty to choose from. Alternatively, Lynton town centre, a five-minute walk away, offers a number of eating-places. Valley House is licensed, and has a cosy bar.

OWNERS: Russell and Joan Herbert OPEN: Feb to Oct ROOMS: 4 double, 1 twin, 1 family; all rooms with bath/shower, tea/coffee and TV; lounge with TV TERMS: single occupancy £22–£24, twin/double £44–£52, family room £66–£78; half-price for children sharing with parents; dinner £11–£16; deposit: £10 per person CARDS: Amex, Delta, MasterCard, Switch, Visa DETAILS: no children under 12; dogs by arrangement. no smoking; car park; garden

MACCLESFIELD Cheshire map 8

Chadwick House

55 Beech Lane, Macclesfield SK10 2DS
TEL: (01625) 615558 FAX: (01625) 610265

This pleasant Victorian house near the town centre is efficiently run and is very popular with both tourists and business people. Most of the colour-co-ordinated rooms have *en suite* facilities, and the luxury suite has a four-poster bed with a white lace canopy. The house is licensed, and guests have the use of two lounges, one with a bar and the other with a TV, plus a sauna and exercise room. Dinner is served at 7pm, and vegetarians can be catered for with advance notice. The Dansons are a musical couple – William has a band which plays '60s music, and he also performs duets with Karen.

OWNERS: William and Karen Danson OPEN: all year exc Christmas ROOMS: 4 single, 2 with bath/shower, 2 with private bathroom; 7 double, 1 twin, 1 four-poster; all with bath/shower; tea/coffee and TV in all bedrooms; lounge with TV TERMS: single £25–£35, single occupancy £40, twin/double/four-poster £55–£65; children's reductions by arrangement; dinner £9; deposit: credit card details CARDS: Amex, Diners, MasterCard, Visa DETAILS: children welcome; no dogs; smoking in lounge only; car park

MACCLESFIELD FOREST Cheshire map 8

Hardingland Farm

Macclesfield Forest SK11 0ND TEL: (01625) 425759
heading out of Macclesfield on A537, turn right opposite millstone 100yds after Setter Dog pub and follow B&B signs

Part of a 17-acre working sheep farm, this recently refurbished Georgian house is ideally based for the Peak District. New carpets have been fitted upstairs, and all the bedrooms have private facilities; one has an antique French bed and two can be converted into twins. The spacious lounge is a comfortable place to relax in, and its log-burning fire is lit at the first sign of chill. Anne Read serves appetising dinners, which might feature mouth-waterers like filo parcels with salmon and prawns, and brandy-snap baskets with home-made sorbet. Hardingland Farm enjoys some spectacular views across the countryside.

OWNER: Anne Read OPEN: Mar to Nov ROOMS: 3 double/twin, 2 with bath/shower, 1 with private bathroom; tea/coffee in all bedrooms; lounge with TV TERMS: single occupancy £35–£40, twin/double £38–£44; dinner £13; deposit: £20 CARDS: none DETAILS: no children; no dogs; no smoking; car park

MAIDENCOMBE Devon map 1

The Beehive

NEW ENTRY

Steep Hill, Maidencombe TQ1 4TS TEL: (01803) 314647
just off A379, 4½m N of Torquay

The Beehive stands in a wonderful position up a steep hill just off the Torquay to Teignmouth road, and enjoys fine views across Babbacombe Bay. It was designed by Norman Sibthorp, whose wife runs the B&B, and offers comfortable, immaculate accommodation. One of the three bedrooms has *en suite* facilities. Breakfast is served in the dining-room, which has doors out to the terrace and lovely garden. An inn a little way down the hill serves good meals, and just beyond is a sandy cove and the coastal footpath to Teignmouth.

OWNER: Mrs D. Sibthorp OPEN: all year exc Christmas ROOMS: 2 double, 1 with bath/shower; 1 twin, with private bathroom; tea/coffee in all bedrooms; TV in most bedrooms TERMS: twin/double £35–£40; deposit CARDS: none DETAILS: no children; no dogs; no smoking; car park; garden

MAIDENHEAD Berkshire map 3

Beehive Manor

Cox Green Lane, Maidenhead SL6 3ET
TEL: (01628) 620980 FAX: (01628) 621840
off M4 at junction 8/9, then A404(M) until left turn for Cox Green

This beautiful medieval manor is on a quiet residential street with a large, peaceful garden, and is delightful in every way. The house has a simple elegance, with antique furniture and many original features, including thick stone walls, oak panelled doors, fireplaces and latticed windows. The beamed drawing-room has a TV, and there is an additional sitting-area on the landing where visitors can browse through the books provided and help themselves to a hot drink and biscuits. The spacious bedrooms are tastefully decorated and have *en suite* facilities. Breakfasts are served at one large table in the dining-room. For evening meals, a selection of local restaurant menus is available. Beehive Manor is very convenient for the Thames Valley, Windsor Castle, Henley and Ascot, and Heathrow Airport is only 15 minutes' away.

OWNERS: Barbara Barbour and Sue Lemin OPEN: all year exc Christmas ROOMS: 2 double, with bath/shower; 1 twin, with private bathroom; lounge with TV TERMS: single occupancy £38, twin/double £58 CARDS: none DETAILS: no children under 12; no dogs; no smoking; car park; garden

B&Bs are selected for the Guide for their warm welcome, cleanliness, a friendly atmosphere and, wherever possible, an attractive location or a building that is itself of some historical or architectural interest.

MAIDSTONE Kent map 3

Willington Court

Willington Street, Maidstone ME15 8JW
TEL: (01622) 738885 FAX: (01622) 631790

Willington Court is a listed tudor-style building and stands on a grassy bank above the Ashford road only a mile and a half east of the town centre. It has a carved oak staircase and an inglenook fireplace in the dining-room. The comfortable bedrooms are well equipped and have double-glazing to keep out the traffic noise; the one with a four-poster bed has been extended and refurbished. There are two lounges for guests' use, one of which is for smokers, and breakfast is served at one table in the dining-room. Leeds Castle and Mote Park are nearby. Willington Court is popular with business people.

OWNERS: David and Mandy Waterman OPEN: all year ROOMS: 2 double, both with bath/shower; 1 twin, with private bathroom; tea/coffee and TV in all bedrooms; lounge with TV TERMS: single occupancy £27–£35, twin/double £42–£46, four-poster £50; deposit: £10 per person CARDS: Amex, Delta, Diners, MasterCard, Visa DETAILS: no children; no dogs; smoking in 1 lounge only; car park; garden

MALPAS Cheshire map 7

Laurel Farm

Chorlton Lane, Malpas SY14 7ES TEL/FAX: (01948) 860291
on B5069 1m W of Malpas, turn at sign for Chorlton, then turn right after 1m

Dating from the seventeenth century, this large red-brick farmhouse stands in nine and a half acres which include a duck pond stocked with well-established rare breeds. The house has period furniture throughout, and the oldest part is the entrance hall, which has a Welsh quarry-tiled floor. Anthea Few is friendly and creates a free-and-easy atmosphere which makes guests feel welcome; they have the use of a sun lounge with TV. Breakfast and light snacks are cooked on the Aga, and dinner for parties of four or more can be pre-booked; light suppers are also on offer, and are served in guests' bedrooms. There is a suite available, comprising a double and a twin room plus a sitting-room, which is ideal for a family or friends travelling together; all the bedrooms have *en suite* facilities. A newly opened golf course is close by, and the village is only two miles away with an excellent range of pubs and restaurants for evening meals. Horses can also be accommodated at the farm.

OWNER: Anthea Few OPEN: all year ROOMS: 1 single, 1 double, 2 twin, 1 family; all rooms with bath/shower, tea/coffee and TV; lounge with TV TERMS: single £36–£42, single occupancy £40–£45, twin/double £55–£65, family room £70–£80; dinner £10–£20; deposit: 25% of first night's booking CARDS: none DETAILS: no children under 12; no dogs; no smoking; car park; garden

MALPAS Cornwall **map 1**

Woodbury

Malpas TR1 1SQ TEL: (01872) 271466
2m SE of Truro

This large house stands in its own garden at the entrance to the village, just above a narrow dead-end road. The sitting-room leads through to a spacious sun porch/conservatory that overlooks the Truro river and is where breakfast and dinner are served. The three small bedrooms are simply furnished and share a large bathroom; all have river views. A pub in the village, only a few minutes' walk away, is also handy for evening meals. Limited parking is available opposite the house.

OWNER: Marion Colwill OPEN: all year exc Christmas ROOMS: 1 single; 2 double, 1 with wash-basin; lounge with TV TERMS: single £15, single occupancy £19.50, double £35; dinner £10; deposit CARDS: none DETAILS: no children; no dogs; no smoking in bedrooms; car park; garden

MALVERN WELLS Hereford & Worcester **map 5**

Mellbreak

177 Malvern Road, Malvern Wells WR14 4HE TEL: (01684) 561287
on A449 road to Great Malvern

Mellbreak is a Grade II-listed building dating from the 1830s, on the main road just beyond the Three Counties Agricultural Showground (double-glazing keeps traffic noise to a minimum). It was once the home of the headmaster of Wells House School. The house is surrounded by a terraced garden, and has views over the Severn and Avon valleys. Within is a varied selection of furniture, paintings and ornaments, and the comfortable bedrooms are attractively decorated; all have *en suite* showers and TVs. Guests can relax in the lounge with its TV, books and a log fire in winter. Many visitors return here for the excellent dinners prepared by Mrs Cheeseman from traditional recipes, and enjoy home-made rolls, fresh vegetables in season, and delicious desserts. The house has a comprehensive cellar of 300 wines from around the world.

OWNER: Mrs R.A. Cheeseman OPEN: all year ROOMS: 1 single, 2 double, 1 twin; all rooms with shower, tea/coffee and TV; lounge with TV TERMS: single £21, twin/double £42; babies free, half-price for children under 8; dinner £15; deposit: 50% CARDS: none DETAILS: children welcome; no dogs; smoking in lounge only; car park; garden

---

Old Vicarage

Hanley Road, Malvern Wells WR14 4PH TEL/FAX: (01684) 572585

This Victorian house stands in a quiet street, in an acre of gardens, on the slopes of the Malvern Hills overlooking the Severn Vale. It is in excellent decorative order and furnished in keeping with its character. The spacious bedrooms are warm and comfortable and have *en suite* facilities and TVs. The large sitting-room has lots of books to browse through. Breakfast and dinner (if pre-arranged) are served in the traditional dining-room. The house is within walking distance of the Three Counties Agricultural Showground.

OWNER: Michael Gorvin OPEN: all year ROOMS: 2 double, 2 twin, 1 family; all rooms with bath/shower; 1 room suitable for wheelchair-users; tea/coffee and TV in all bedrooms; lounge TERMS: single occupancy £28–£34, twin/double £44–£48, family room £50–£55; children's reductions by arrangement; dinner £14.50 CARDS: none DETAILS: children welcome; no dogs in dining-room and lounge; no smoking in dining-room; car park; garden

MARAZION Cornwall — map 1

Castle Gayer

Leys Lane, Marazion TR17 0AQ TEL: (01736) 711548
off A30, 2m E of Penzance

With uninterrupted sea views, Castle Gayer stands on a peninsula, at the end of a narrow lane leading to the village. It is a whitewashed Victorian property, formerly a sea captain's house, standing on the edge of a cliff, looking out to St Michael's Mount. What seems to be the top of a lighthouse at the bottom of the garden is a small listed folly. Directly beneath the house is the National Trust harbour, from where boats go over to the island. The two comfortable bedrooms are reached by means of a narrow staircase off the dining-room, where breakfast is served. Residents have the use of a lounge with a log fire and baby grand piano. Brian Ivory is chiropodist and John Trewhella is a psychologist, and both run their practices from the house.

OWNERS: Brian Ivory and John Trewhella OPEN: all year exc Christmas ROOMS: 1 double, 1 twin; both rooms with bath/shower, tea/coffee and TV; lounge with TV TERMS: single occupancy £30, twin/double £50; deposit: £20 for 1 night, £40 for 2 or more nights CARDS: none DETAILS: no children; no dogs; no smoking; car park; garden

MARDEN Kent — map 3

Merzie Meadows

Hunton Road, Chainhurst, Marden TN12 9SL TEL: (01622) 820500
from A229 Maidstone to Hastings road take B2079 to Marden; then first right (Pattendane Lane) for 2m; after Chainhurst sign turn right into drive

This stone and boarded single-storey house in a large garden is surrounded by peaceful countryside. Mrs Mumford is a charming host, and the house is beautifully furnished and decorated. The guest accommodation is in one wing of the house, on the ground floor, with doors out to the garden and swimming-pool. Breakfast is served in the garden room which also overlooks the pool. Merzie Meadows is near Leeds and Sissinghurst Castles and Rye. No one-night bookings are taken at weekends.

OWNERS: Rodney and Pamela Mumford OPEN: all year exc Christmas ROOMS: 2 double; both rooms with bath/shower and TV; lounge with TV TERMS: single occupancy £40, double £40–£45, family room £54–£60; deposit: £5 per person CARDS: none DETAILS: no children under 14; no dogs; no smoking; car park; garden; swimming-pool

MARGARET RODING Essex map 3

Greys

Ongar Road, Margaret Roding CM6 1QR TEL: (01245) 231509
by A1060 in village

Greys stands in an acre of gardens, surrounded by its own farmland. It used to be two 200-year old beamed cottages, but has been well converted to provide its present accommodation. There are three simply appointed, bright and fresh bedrooms, plus a lounge/dining-room with a TV and a separate quiet sitting-room. Breakfast is served, but there are several eating-places nearby for evening meals. Geoffrey and Joyce Matthews are a retired couple, and work together to provide a warm welcome to their home.

OWNER: Joyce Matthews OPEN: all year exc Christmas ROOMS: 2 double, 1 with wash-basin; 1 twin, with wash-basin; 2 lounges, 1 with TV TERMS: single occupancy £20, twin/double £38; deposit required CARDS: none DETAILS: no children under 10; no dogs; no smoking; car park; garden

MARLBOROUGH Wiltshire map 2

Clench Farmhouse NEW ENTRY

Clench, Marlborough SN8 4NT TEL/FAX: (01672) 810264

In an idyllic situation, this eighteenth-century brick and stone farmhouse stands in a lovely garden complete with tennis court, swimming-pool and croquet. The farmland itself was sold off some 40 years ago except for a couple of fields. The Roes are charming, welcoming people, and have an interesting family tree, a record of which hangs on the landing wall, dating back to 1280. The pretty bedrooms are comfortable, and guests have use of a drawing-room with an open fire. Breakfast and, by arrangement, evening meals are served in the elegant dining-room. Mrs Roe is happy to take people walking, and Clench Farmhouse is within easy reach of Salisbury, Bath and Oxford.

OWNER: Clarissa Roe OPEN: all year ROOMS: 2 double, 1 with private bathroom; 1 twin; tea/coffee in all bedrooms; TV in most bedrooms and lounge TERMS: single occupancy £25–£30, twin/double £42–£48; dinner £16.50–£20 CARDS: none DETAILS: children welcome; dogs by arrangement; no smoking in bedrooms; car park; garden; swimming-pool; tennis

MARNHULL Dorset map 2

Lovells Court NEW ENTRY

Marnhull DT10 1JJ TEL: (01258) 820652 FAX: (01258) 820487
take B3092 N from Sturminster Newton for 3m; at village church take Church Hill for ¾m

This large, rambling 100-year-old house occupies a quiet position at the end of an avenue of chestnut trees, and enjoys fine views over Blackmoor Vale. It has an air of relaxed comfort, and the Newson-Smiths are welcoming hosts. Bedrooms are large, comfortable and well equipped, and there is a lovely, bright sitting-area on the first-floor landing, overlooking the garden. Guests also have use of the patio and three acres of garden. 'Blue Vinny' cottage, a wing of the main house named after the famous cheese made in the area, offers self-catering accommodation. Two pubs in the village serve evening meals.

OWNERS: Peter and Mary-Ann Newson-Smith OPEN: all year ROOMS: 2 double, 1 with bath/shower, 1 with private bathroom; 1 twin, with bath/shower; tea/coffee and TV in all bedrooms; lounge TERMS: single occupancy £26, twin/double £46 CARDS: none DETAILS: no children under 12; no dogs; no smoking; car park; garden

---

Old Bank NEW ENTRY

Burton Street, Marnhull DT10 1PH TEL/FAX: (01258) 821019
take A30 W from Shaftesbury, then B3092 S at East Stour for 4m

This eighteenth-century stone-built house is in the centre of the village, next to the shops and post office. The Hoods are very welcoming, and the house has an informal atmosphere, with guests treated as friends. The lovely drawing-room is shared by residents and owners. Breakfast is served in the kitchen, and there is also an attractive courtyard to sit in. The Hoods are keen gardeners, and Mr Hood is an agricultural journalist. The bedrooms, one of which is a charming attic room, share an upstairs bathroom and a downstairs shower-room. A pub, only 100 yards away, serves evening meals.

OWNERS: Sarah and Robin Hood OPEN: all year exc Christmas ROOMS: 1 double, 1 twin, 1 family; all rooms with bath/shower and tea/coffee; lounge with TV TERMS: single occupancy £18, twin/double £36, family room £36; half-price for children under 14; deposit CARDS: none DETAILS: children welcome; no dogs; no smoking; car park; garden

---

Old Lamb House

Walton Elm, Marnhull DT10 1QG
TEL: (01258) 820491 FAX: (01258) 821464
on B3092 at Walton Elm crossroads, ½m S of Marnhull and 2½m N of Sturminster Newton

This lovely Georgian house is set in peaceful countryside with views across the Blackmoor Vale to Cranborne Chase. Lying on a quiet country road, it was formerly a coaching-inn reputed to be 'Rollivers' in Hardy's *Tess of the d'Urbervilles*. The interior has been beautifully decorated and furnished, and has spacious rooms. Both attractive bedrooms have armchairs and TVs, and share a bathroom. Guests can relax in the conservatory, and are welcome to use the walled garden. Breakfast can either be taken in the dining-room overlooking the garden, or in the bedrooms. Several pubs serving good food are within a couple of miles' radius, and Shaftesbury, Sherborne and Blandford Forum are all an easy drive away.

OWNERS: Jenny and Ben Chilcott OPEN: all year exc Christmas ROOMS: 1 double, 1 family; tea/coffee and TV in both bedrooms TERMS: single occupancy £20, twin/double £40, family room £20; children under 3 free, £13 for ages 3–10; deposit: 33% CARDS: none DETAILS: children welcome; no dogs; no smoking; car park; garden

MARTOCK Somerset — map 2

Wychwood

7 Bearley Road, Martock TA12 6PG TEL/FAX: (01935) 825601
just off A303, 6m NW of Yeovil

Wychwood is a small house on a modern development. Mrs Turton is friendly and knowledgeable, and does everything possible to make sure her guests have an interesting stay. The bedrooms are clean and well equipped, and the comfortable TV lounge has plenty of videos of the area, featuring interesting gardens and houses, such as Montacute House and Barrington Court. A recent addition to the house is the conservatory, which leads off the lounge. A full English breakfast is served in the dining-room.

OWNER: Helen Turton OPEN: all year exc Christmas and New Year ROOMS: 2 double, both with shower; 1 twin, with private bathroom; tea/coffee and TV in all bedrooms; lounge with TV TERMS: single occupancy £28–£32, twin/double £38–£42; deposit: £5 per person per night CARDS: MasterCard, Visa DETAILS: no children; no dogs; no smoking; car park; garden

MATLOCK Derbyshire — map 5

Bradvilla

26 Chesterfield Road, Matlock DE4 3DQ TEL: (01629) 57147

Good-value accommodation is offered in this well-maintained Victorian house standing in its own grounds. There are several steps up to the house and a ten-minute walk back from town, so it is essential that visitors coming to stay are fairly fit. One of the two double bedrooms has its own adjacent bathroom and small sitting-room. An additional single room is now available, and the second double can be used as a family room; a new patio has been built for guests' use. Jean Saunders is a friendly host who provides a welcoming atmosphere.

OWNER: Jean Saunders OPEN: all year exc Christmas ROOMS: 1 single, with wash-basin; 2 double, 1 with private bathroom, 1 with wash-basin; tea/coffee in some bedrooms; TV in all bedrooms TERMS: single £16–£17.50, double/family £32–£35; children's reductions by arrangement; deposit: £10 CARDS: none DETAILS: children welcome; no dogs; smoking in conservatory only; car park; garden

Kensington Villa

84 Dale Road, Matlock DE4 3LU TEL: (01629) 57627

This Victorian guesthouse is as warm and friendly as ever. The Gormans are a relaxed couple who have created a homely atmosphere in this town-centre property, with its bright, freshly decorated rooms, which now have new carpets. The approach to the house has several steps, making it unsuitable for infirm people. All the bedrooms have wash-basins, and a cot can be provided if required. Generous breakfasts are served in the dining-room overlooking the small patio garden, where guests may relax on sunny days.

OWNERS: Bill and Val Gorman OPEN: all year exc Christmas ROOMS: 2 double, 1 twin; all rooms with wash-basin, tea/coffee and TV TERMS: single occupancy £18–£19, twin/double £36–£38; children under 3 free, half-price for ages 3–11 CARDS: none DETAILS: children welcome; no dogs; no smoking; garden

Sunnybank

37 Clifton Road, Matlock DE4 3PW TEL: (01629) 584621

Graham and Marguerite Ward took over the running of Sunnybank in August 1997, and although they are new to the B&B business, they previously ran a teashop and are excited about their new venture. Built in 1883, the house is situated in a secluded cul-de-sac with views of Wild Cat Tor and Cromford Moor. It is full of character, and has a most attractive ceiling rose and coving in the lounge, where log fires burn on chilly days. The well-appointed bedrooms are tastefully furnished, and the rooms at the back have garden views. Excellent breakfasts, and dinners (by arrangement) are served in the sunny dining-room. Parking is available on the street outside.

OWNERS: Mr and Mrs G.J. Ward OPEN: all year exc Christmas ROOMS: 1 single, 2 double, 1 twin, 1 family; all rooms with bath/shower exc 1 single with private shower-room; tea/coffee and TV in all bedrooms; lounge TERMS: single £20–£23, single occupancy £23–£30, twin/double £44– £52, family room £44–£69; babies free, children's reductions in family room; dinner £13.50; deposit: £10 per person CARDS: Amex, Delta, MasterCard, Switch, Visa DETAILS: children welcome; no dogs; no smoking; garden

The descriptive part of entries usually includes some facts about setting, the house itself, décor and furnishings, the atmosphere, any special features, and whether evening meals are offered. If the B&B has no car park, we give wherever possible some indication of where guests may find a place to park. If one-night bookings are not accepted at certain times of the week or year, that is mentioned.

MAXSTOKE Warwickshire **map 5**

Old Rectory

NEW ENTRY

Church Lane, Maxstoke B46 2QW
TEL: (01675) 462248 FAX: (01675) 481615
10m E of Birmingham

This Victorian sandstone rectory stands in five acres of secluded, walled gardens, with interesting historical monastic remains in the grounds, and many unusual trees, including a tulip and a dawn redwood. The Pages are a charming, unpretentious couple who are slowly refurbishing the house, and who have created an informal and peaceful ambience. The two bedrooms have *en suite* facilities, and the double room also has a single bed, so it can be used as a family room. The Old Rectory, although in the heart of the country, is just ten minutes by car from the N.E.C. and Birmingham Airport, and convenient for the National Motorcycle Museum.

OWNER: Judy Page OPEN: all year exc Christmas ROOMS: 1 double/family, 1 twin; both rooms with bath/shower, tea/coffee and TV; lounge TERMS: single occupancy £32, twin/double £48, family room £66; deposit: £10 per person for bookings of more than 1 night CARDS: none DETAILS: children welcome; no dogs; smoking in lounge only; car park; garden

MAYFIELD Staffordshire **map 5**

Lichfield House

Bridge View, Mayfield DE6 2HN TEL/FAX: (01335) 344422
off A52 Ashbourne to Leek road; take Mayfield road 1½m from Ashbourne, then 300yds up hill to first house on left

This beautifully maintained Georgian house is set in two acres of landscaped gardens, in an elevated position with magnificent views of the bridge and River Dove below. The bedrooms are decorated in light pastel florals; all have TVs and easy chairs, and two rooms have *en suite* facilities. Breakfasts are served in the dining-room, which has antique pine furniture and lovely views. The lounge has a green and pink décor. The short walk to the village is along the river bank. Packed lunches can be provided, and self-catering accommodation is also available.

OWNERS: Mr and Mrs K. Mellor OPEN: all year exc Christmas ROOMS: 1 single, with wash-basin; 1 double, with shower; 1 twin, with wash-basin; 1 family, with shower; tea/coffee and TV in all bedrooms; lounge with TV TERMS: single £20, single occupancy £25–£30, twin/double £38–£44, family room £40–£44; deposit required CARDS: none DETAILS: children welcome; no dogs; no smoking; car park; garden

---

We state at the end of an entry whether children are welcome, and explain any age restrictions. If there are reduced rates for children, this is mentioned; if no reductions are specified, assume you will have to pay full rates for children.

MENDHAM **Norfolk** **map 6**

Weston House Farm

Mendham IP20 0PB TEL: (01986) 782206 FAX: (01986) 782414
on A143 Harleston bypass turn at sign for Mendham, then follow signs for farm from the village

This seventeenth-century listed farmhouse, with Dutch-style gable ends, has an acre of garden and is on a 300-acre mixed farm, with views over the Waveney Valley. June Holden extends a warm welcome to her guests and keeps the *en suite* bedrooms spotlessly clean; the family bedroom and lounge have recently been redecorated. Breakfasts, and pre-booked dinners are served in the attractive dining-room, and there is a separate lounge with TV. This is a wonderful spot for nature lovers, with fishing available on the River Waveney two miles away, and the Norfolk Broads within easy driving distance.

OWNER: June Holden OPEN: Mar to Nov ROOMS: 1 double, 1 twin, 1 family; all rooms with shower and tea/coffee; lounge with TV TERMS: single occupancy £20–£22, twin/double £34–£38, family room £50–£60; children's reductions by arrangement; dinner £11; deposit: 30% CARDS: Amex DETAILS: children welcome; dogs by arrangement; no smoking; car park; garden

MENDLESHAM GREEN **Suffolk** **map 6**

Cherry Tree Farm

Mendlesham Green IP14 5RQ TEL: (01449) 766376
off A140 Needham Market to Norwich road

Set in a peaceful hamlet, this restored pink-washed Suffolk farmhouse has a large garden with an orchard and duck pond. The immaculate house is tastefully decorated, and there are several pieces of antique furniture. One of the three bedrooms has a beamed sloping roof and oak furniture, and overlooks the garden. The cosy guest lounge has new furnishings and is warmed by a wood-burning fire in winter. Exposed beams and a huge stone fireplace add to the character of the dining-room, where meals are served around a large refectory table. Freshly cooked dinners making good use of vegetables from the garden are a highlight here, and breakfasts include home-baked bread, free-range eggs and home-made jams.

OWNERS: Martin and Diana Ridsdale OPEN: all year exc Christmas ROOMS: 3 double; all rooms with bath/shower; lounge with TV TERMS: single occupancy £35–£40, double £44–£48; dinner £17.50; deposit: £30 CARDS: none DETAILS: no children; no dogs; smoking in lounge only; car park; garden

---

If we know a B&B has an alcohol licence, we say so. Most unlicensed B&Bs that offer evening meals allow guests to bring their own wine to dinner. If you wish to do this, ask the B&B when you book.

MERE Wiltshire **map 2**

Chetcombe House

NEW ENTRY

Chetcombe Road, Mere BA12 6AZ
TEL: (01747) 860219 FAX: (01747) 860111

Chetcombe House lies just off the A303, on the outskirts of Mere, and is a traditional 1930s country house set in an acre of gardens. It has lovely views to Shaftesbury and the Blackmoor Vale. Colin and Susan Ross are very friendly, caring hosts and provide comfortable, immaculate accommodation. The five bedrooms are furnished in pine or rattan and all have *en suite* facilities; one double can also be used as a family room. The lounge has a log-burning stove and doors out to the garden. Home-grown or locally produced ingredients are used by Susan Ross for her evening meals; packed lunches can be provided.

OWNERS: Colin and Susan Ross OPEN: all year ROOMS: 1 single, 2 double, 2 twin; all rooms with bath/shower, tea/coffee and TV; lounge TERMS: single £29, single occupancy £33, twin/double £50, family room £66; dinner £14.50; deposit: £15 per room CARDS: Amex, MasterCard, Visa DETAILS: children welcome; dogs welcome exc in public areas; no smoking; car park; garden

MEVAGISSEY Cornwall **map 1**

Southcliffe

Polkirt Hill, Mevagissey PL26 6UX TEL: (01726) 842505
just off B3273, 6m S of St Austell

Lovely sea views and a friendly atmosphere add to the enjoyment of a stay at this guesthouse perched on the cliff road just outside the pretty town of Mevagissey. The simple, tidy bedrooms overlook St Austell Bay and the headland at Chapel Point. The large lounge and the dining-room also enjoy sea views, and both have direct access to the attractive terraced garden. There is a self-catering flat in part of the building, with its own entrance and sitting-room, but at the time of going to press the owners were planning to convert this to a further double bedroom, and to add *en suite* facilities to another room. Evening meals are served if required. Portmellon beach is only a five-minute walk away.

OWNERS: Ronald Haskins and David Templeton OPEN: all year exc Christmas ROOMS: 2 double, 1 twin; all rooms with wash-basin and TV; lounge TERMS: single occupancy £21.50, twin/double £33; dinner £12; deposit: £10 CARDS: none DETAILS: no children; no dogs; car park; garden

---

Some B&Bs try to 'solicit' recommendations; they may even photocopy our report forms and hand them out to guests. We can spot these easily, and give them no credence. But genuine reports from readers, prompted only by a desire to share details of a stay at a B&B, are given our full attention.

MEYSEY HAMPTON Gloucestershire map 2

Old Rectory

Meysey Hampton GL7 5JX TEL: (01285) 851200 FAX: (01285) 850452
off A417 Cirencester to Lechlade road

This elegant listed seventeenth-century rectory stands in six acres of attractive grounds in a quiet Cotswold village. The house is beautifully maintained, and Caroline Carne ensures her guests are warmly welcomed and comfortable. The two well-appointed bedrooms are tastefully decorated and have *en suite* facilities; each can take an extra bed to make them family rooms. Freshly prepared breakfasts are served in the dining-room/lounge, which has comfortable chairs and a TV. For evening meals, there is a pub serving good food within walking distance. Guests are welcome to use the garden and swimming-pool on summer days. This is a very tranquil spot from which to explore this lovely area.

OWNERS: Mr and Mrs R.E. Carne OPEN: Feb to Nov ROOMS: 1 double, 1 twin; both rooms with bath/shower and tea/coffee; lounge with TV TERMS: single occupancy £35, twin/double £50, family room £60; children's reductions by arrangement; deposit: £20 CARDS: none DETAILS: children welcome; no dogs; no smoking; car park; garden; swimming-pool

MIDDLE CHINNOCK Somerset map 2

Chinnock House NEW ENTRY

Middle Chinnock TA18 7PN TEL/FAX: (01935) 881229
off A30, 5m SW of Yeovil

This stone-built Georgian manor-house is in the charming hamlet of Middle Chinnock, in a beautiful two-acre walled garden, with a swimming-pool at the back. Elegance and spaciousness characterise the interior, and the large, well-appointed bedrooms have *en suite* facilities or a private bathroom. A copy of the Venus de Milo stands at the foot of the stairs, and there is an eighteenth-century baby's crib in one of the bedrooms. Another bedroom is in the coach-house, which has a small kitchen where guests can make breakfast if they wish. Evening meals, if arranged in advance, are served in the dining-room and feature vegetables and fruit from the garden. Guest also have the use of an attractive drawing-room.

OWNERS: Guy and Charmian Smith OPEN: all year exc Christmas ROOMS: 3 double/twin; 2 rooms with bath/shower, 1 with private bathroom; lounge TERMS: single occupancy £35, twin/double £55; babies free; dinner £22; deposit: £25 CARDS: none DETAILS: children welcome; no dogs; no smoking in bedrooms; car park; garden; swimming-pool

---

If a B&B offers off-street car parking, we note 'car park' at the end of the entry. If nearby on-street parking must be used, in most cases we give details in the descriptive text.

MIDDLE WINTERSLOW Wiltshire **map 2**

Beadles

NEW ENTRY

Middleton, Middle Winterslow SP5 1QS TEL/FAX: (01980) 862922
take A30 and 7m E of Salisbury turn right at Pheasant pub, then right to West Winterslow, then first right and right again after 'Trevano'

Built in the Georgian style in 1994, Beadles stands right in the middle of the quiet village of Middle Winterslow, just off the road in an attractive garden with views on a clear day to Salisbury Cathedral. The Yuille-Baddeleys strive to provide everything a visitor could possibly want; one guest writes that 'the hospitality was superb'. The food has a good reputation as Anne Yuille-Baddeley was previously a caterer with her own outside catering business. The comfortable and tastefully furnished sitting-room has a grand piano, no TV and lots of books. Meals are served either in the lovely conservatory or in the elegant dining-room with a complimentary glass of sherry offered before dinner (available by prior arrangement), as well as a glass of wine with the meal. Visitors can be met at the station or airports by arrangement.

OWNERS: David and Anne-Marie Yuille-Baddeley OPEN: all year ROOMS: 1 double, 2 twin; all rooms with bath/shower, tea/coffee and TV; lounge TERMS: single occupancy £27.50–£35, twin/double £48–£52; half-price for children; dinner £17.50; deposit: credit card details CARDS: Delta, MasterCard, Visa DETAILS: no children under 6; no dogs; no smoking; car park; garden

MILFORD ON SEA Hampshire **map 2**

Seawinds

Westminster Road, Milford on Sea SO41 0WU TEL: (01590) 644548
off B3058, 1m W of village

A warm and hospitable welcome greets visitors to this spick-and-span modern house just a few yards from the clifftop and beach. The Crunkhorns offer two comfortable *en suite* rooms, and although there is no TV lounge for guests, the bedrooms themselves have TVs as well as tea/coffee-making facilities. The twin room has a double and a single bed. Breakfasts are served in the dining-room overlooking the garden. Milford on Sea is about a mile away, and the attractive town and sailing centre of Lymington is nearby.

OWNERS: Eric and Joy Crunkhorn OPEN: all year exc Christmas ROOMS: 1 double, with bath; 1 twin, with shower; tea/coffee and TV in both bedrooms TERMS: single occupancy £28; twin/double £40–£42; children's reductions by arrangement CARDS: none DETAILS: children welcome; no dogs; no smoking; car park; garden

The end details for each entry state whether or not dogs are allowed, but it is always best to check when booking.

MILLOM Cumbria map 8

Buckman Brow House

Thwaites, Millom LA18 5HX TEL: (01229) 716541
on A595, 2m SW of Broughton-in-Furness

This Victorian neo-Gothic house has marvellous views of the Duddon valley and estuary, and was once a girls' boarding school. It now provides comfortable accommodation in a peaceful setting. The bedrooms are tastefully furnished and decorated, and the ground-floor room is suitable for wheelchair-users; originally the school chapel, this room still has part of the altar and the original ceiling. The large dining-room/lounge is where guests can enjoy breakfast and excellent five-course dinners; vegetarians can be catered for by prior arrangement. The house is unlicensed, but guests may bring their own wine to dinner. The Dunns always make their guests feel very welcome.

OWNER: Gwen Dunn OPEN: all year exc Christmas ROOMS: 1 double, with shower; 1 twin, with private bathroom; 1 family, with shower; 1 room suitable for wheelchair-users; tea/coffee and TV in all bedrooms; lounge TERMS: single occupancy £30, twin/double/family room £45; children under 3 free, half-price for ages 3–10; dinner £18 CARDS: none DETAILS: children welcome; dogs in bedrooms only; no smoking; car park; garden

MINCHINHAMPTON Gloucestershire map 2

Hunters Lodge

Dr Brown's Road, Minchinhampton GL6 9BT
TEL: (01453) 883588 FAX: (01453) 731449
off A419/A46, 3m SE of Stroud

Built in the early 1900s, this Cotswold-stone house is in a large garden that adjoins 600 acres of National Trust land and a golf course. The warm and inviting house is elegantly appointed, and refurbishments are ongoing. The sitting-room, which has a TV, leads to a conservatory with two stone fireplaces. The three large bedrooms, one of which has a super-king-sized bed, are decorated in soft pastels. One has *en suite* facilities, while the other two have their own private bathrooms. Superb breakfasts are served at a refectory table overlooking the garden. The Helms are welcoming hosts, and Peter is happy to assist with information on places to visit in the area, and on local restaurants for evening meals.

OWNERS: Margaret and Peter Helm OPEN: all year exc Christmas ROOMS: 1 double, with bath/shower; 1 twin, with private bathroom; 1 family, with private bathroom; tea/coffee and TV in all bedrooms; lounge with TV TERMS: single occupancy £26–£30, twin/double £40–£46, family room £54–£56; deposit: £10 per night CARDS: none DETAILS: children welcome; no dogs; no smoking; car park; garden

---

Any smoking restrictions that we know of are given in the details at the end of the entry.

MINEHEAD **Somerset** **map 1**

Hindon Farm

Minehead TA24 8SH TEL/FAX: (01643) 705244
from Alcombe take A39 E approx 1m; turn right into small lane signposted Bratton; over stream, left at junction signposted Hindon Farm

This busy 500-acre farm with its full assortment of sheep, pigs, goats, horses, cows, free-roaming poultry, dogs and cats has the benefit of an idyllic setting. It is tucked away in a tranquil valley behind the cliffs of the Somerset coast, in the midst of wonderful walking and riding country: you can even bring your own horse (stabling is available). There is plenty for families to do: croquet, badminton, table tennis in the barn, swimming in the small, above-ground outdoor pool, or just sitting by the stream watching the ducks. The house dates from the early eighteenth century and, within, presents attractive accommodation in a friendly and very informal atmosphere. Two pretty bedrooms share a bathroom and WC, and guests have the use of the family lounge with its TV and games. Slap-up farmhouse breakfasts, which feature the farm's own honey, free-range eggs and 'proper' sausages, are served in the dining-room with its dark-wood flooring and open fireplace, as are evening meals if pre-arranged. Self-catering accommodation is also available.

OWNER: Penny Webber OPEN: all year exc Christmas ROOMS: 1 double, 1 twin; both rooms with wash-basin and tea/coffee; lounge with TV TERMS: double/twin £40–£44; dinner £15; deposit: 25% DETAILS: children welcome; well-behaved dogs welcome; no smoking; car park; garden; games room (in barn); swimming-pool

MISTERTON **Somerset** **map 2**

Dryclose

Newbery Lane, Misterton, nr Crewkerne TA18 8NE TEL: (01460) 73160
off A356 Crewkerne to Dorchester road, 1½m SE of Crewkerne, turn into Silver Street, then after 200yds turn left into Newbery Lane; house is at bottom of hill

This creeper-clad sixteenth-century former farmhouse, named after the field in which it was built, is in a peaceful location on the edge of Misterton. Sally Gregory is a friendly and welcoming host and the house has a homely atmosphere. The bedrooms are very comfortable, and the twin-bedded room has a particularly nice private bathroom. There is a small upstairs sitting-room and another lounge with log fire on the ground floor. The house has two acres of gardens with an outdoor swimming-pool. The gardens also supply fruit and vegetables for light suppers, available by arrangement. There are many lovely walks in the area, including the Liberty Trail, which passes close by the house.

OWNERS: John and Sally Gregory OPEN: all year exc Christmas ROOMS: 1 single; 2 twin, 1 with shower; tea/coffee in all bedrooms; lounge with TV TERMS: single

£18.50–£21, single occupancy £21–£27, twin/double £36–£46; light supper £10 CARDS: none DETAILS: no children under 8; no dogs; no smoking; car park; garden; swimming-pool

MITCHELDEAN Gloucestershire **map 5**

Gunn Mill House

Lower Spout Lane, Mitcheldean GL17 0EA TEL/FAX: (01594) 827577
from A48 6m SW of Gloucester turn at sign for Mitcheldean, then after approx 2½m straight over Y-junction and up unmade road

Gunn Mill is an elegant Georgian house in five acres of grounds with a meadow and stream, and just by an old mill. David Anderson's association with the film industry is why the bedrooms are named after famous actors: you can stay in the 'Connery Suite', for example, or perhaps the 'Chevalier'. Some rooms are in tastefully converted outbuildings, and all are elegantly furnished, with large, old-fashioned bathrooms. Ornaments, paintings and furniture from different parts of the world are displayed around the house. The Andersons are keen cooks, and offer dinner-party type evening meals in the dining-part of the large galleried sitting-room. Comfortable seating is available around the large fireplace at the other end of the room, which has a log fire in winter, and there are plenty of books and magazines to browse through. Gunn Mill is licensed, and vegetarian meals are available on request.

OWNERS: David and Caroline Anderson OPEN: all year ROOMS: 2 double, 2 twin, 1 family; all rooms with bath/shower; tea/coffee and TV; lounge TERMS: single occupancy £29.50–£32.5, twin/double £40–£50, family room £50–£74; £10 for children under 12; dinner £18; deposit required for weekend stays CARDS: none DETAILS: children welcome; dogs welcome; no smoking; car park; garden

MOBBERLEY Cheshire **map 8**

Laburnum Cottage Guest House

Knutsford Road, Mobberley WA16 7PU TELL/FAX: (01565) 872464
on B5085, 1½m NE of Knutsford

This 1930s cottage is decorated with hanging baskets and has won no less than seven tourism awards for its beautiful, landscaped country garden, in which guests are welcome to wander or play croquet. Within, the atmosphere is cosy and relaxed, with visitors treated as friends. The house is luxuriously furnished, with each bedroom decorated in co-ordinating fabrics; three have *en suite* facilities, and the other two share a bathroom. There are plenty of books to read, and a log fire to keep the lounge warm in winter. Breakfasts include home-made jams and plenty of fresh fruit.

OWNERS: Shirley Foxwell and Malcolm Collinge OPEN: all year ROOMS: 2 single, 1 with bath/shower, 1 with wash-basin; 1 double, with shower; 2 twin, 1 with shower, 1 with wash-basin; tea/coffee and TV in all bedrooms; lounge with TV TERMS: single

£35–£39, single occupancy £38–£42, twin/double £45–£50; children's reductions by arrangement; deposit: £10 CARDS: none DETAILS: children by arrangement; no dogs; no smoking; car park; garden

MONKTON COMBE Bath & N.E. Somerset **map 2**

Dundas Lock Cottage

Monkton Combe, nr Bath BA2 7BN TEL: (01225) 723890
just off A36, 5m E of Bath

Dundas Lock is a charming cottage, covered in roses and honeysuckle, in an idyllic spot. It was built of Bath stone in 1801 by the Somerset Coal Canal Company for the lock-keeper and his family. The Wheeldons are great enthusiasts for the waterways, and restored the stretch of the canal that passes through their own garden. They also hire out boats to guests, and two of the three bedrooms have views of the canals. The Dundas Aqueduct starts just outside the garden. Breakfast is served in the beamed sitting-room, which has a log fire for winter evenings.

OWNERS: Tim and Wendy Wheeldon OPEN: all year exc Christmas ROOMS: 1 single, with wash-basin; 1 double, with private bathroom; 1 twin/double, with private bathroom; tea/coffee in all bedrooms; lounge with TV TERMS: single £22.50–£25, single occupancy £35, twin/double £45–£50; deposit: minimum £10 CARDS: none DETAILS: children welcome; no dogs; no smoking; car park; garden

MONKTON FARLEIGH Wiltshire **map 2**

Fern Cottage

Monkton Farleigh BA15 2QJ TEL: (01225) 859412 FAX: (01225) 859018
1m off A363, midway between Bath and Bradford-on-Avon

The Valentines extend a warm welcome at their rose and creeper-covered stone-built listed cottage in the main street of the peaceful village of Monkton Farleigh. The interior is more spacious than you would at first expect, and is warm and comfortable. Two of the bedrooms are in the main house, and the third is above the garage. All are well equipped, two having *en suite* facilities and the third the use of a private bathroom. Breakfast is served at one table in the charming dining-room, graced by family portraits on the walls. Guests have a lounge to relax in, and can also make use of the small, secluded back garden. The pub almost opposite the house is handy for evening meals.

OWNERS: Christopher and Jenny Valentine OPEN: all year ROOMS: 3 double, 2 with bath/shower, 1 with private bathroom; tea/coffee and TV in all bedrooms; lounge TERMS: single occupancy £30–£36, double £48–£58; reductions for children by arrangement; deposit: £25 CARDS: none DETAILS: children welcome; no dogs; no smoking; car park; garden

MORECAMBE Lancashire **map 8**

Yacht Bay View

359 Marine Road East, Morecambe LA4 5AQ TEL: (01524) 414481

For over a decade Derek and Beryl Woods have been inviting B&B guests to their pleasant and friendly Victorian house, situated right on the promenade. They were in the B&B business previously too, and are dab hands at looking after guests well. The modestly furnished bedrooms have *en suite* shower facilities; all have TVs and six rooms have sea views. Breakfast and pre-booked home-cooked dinners are available, and guests may bring their own wine to dinner. There is also a lounge with an open fire.

OWNERS: Beryl and Derek Woods OPEN: all year exc Christmas ROOMS: 4 double, 2 twin, 3 family; all rooms with shower, tea/coffee and TV; lounge with TV TERMS: single occupancy £16–£17, twin/double £32–£34, family room from £32; half-price for children sharing with parents; dinner £5; deposit: £20 per room CARDS: none DETAILS: children welcome; no dogs in public rooms; no smoking in dining-room

MORETON Dorset **map 2**

Vartrees House

Moreton DT2 8BE TEL: (01305) 852704
on B3390, 5m E of Dorchester and ½m S of Moreton station

Vartrees is a pleasant turn-of-the-century country house in a three-acre woodland garden, reached down a rhododendron-lined drive. Mrs Haggett is a most welcoming lady, and guests enjoy the peaceful atmosphere and large garden. The bedrooms are simply furnished, and the one with an *en suite* shower can be used as a family room. Breakfast is served in the dining-room overlooking the garden, and there is a small sitting-room with TV for guests' use. A local pub serves good food for evening meals, and Vartrees is a convenient place from which to explore Thomas Hardy country.

OWNER: Mrs D.M. Haggett OPEN: all year exc Christmas ROOMS: 2 double, both with wash-basin; 1 twin/family, with shower; tea/coffee in all bedrooms; lounge with TV TERMS: single occupancy £25, twin/double £36–£46, family room £41–£56; deposit required for bank holiday bookings CARDS: none DETAILS: no children under 10; no dogs in dining-room; no smoking in bedrooms or dining-room; car park; garden

MORWENSTOW Cornwall **map 1**

Old Vicarage

Morwenstow EX23 9SR TEL: (01288) 331369 FAX: (01288) 356077
7m N of Bude; in Morwenstow follow signs for church; turn right down public footpath (suitable for car) just before church

The Old Vicarage stands in a peaceful position on the north Cornish coast in the tiny village of Morwenstow, and is surrounded by unspoilt National Trust and church land. It is an unusual stone house built in the 1830s by the eccentric Rev R.S. Hawker. Each of the chimneys is different: one is a life-sized replica of his mother's coffin. Running through the grounds is a link footpath of the coastal path, with its dramatic sea views. It was along this footpath that the Rev Hawker built – from wood collected from shipwrecks – a small hut where he wrote poetry. The house has a comfortable and informal atmosphere, and the Wellbys are welcoming hosts. Dinner is served in the dining-room by prior arrangement, though not on Mondays, Tuesdays and Wednesdays. The house is licensed, and there is a billiard room with a bar, plus a study with a large selection of books and a TV. Guests are invited to make use of the garden in summer.

OWNERS: Richard and Jill Wellby OPEN: all year exc Christmas ROOMS: 1 single, with bath/shower; 1 double, with bath/shower; 1 twin, with private bathroom; tea/coffee in all bedrooms; lounge with TV TERMS: single £20, twin/double £40; half-price for children under 12; dinner £17; deposit: £10 per person CARDS: none DETAILS: children welcome; no dogs; smoking in billiard room and study only; car park; games (billiard) room; garden

MOTTISTONE Isle of Wight — map 2

Mottistone Manor Farm — NEW ENTRY

Mottistone PO30 4ED TEL: (01983) 740232
on B3399, 1m W of Brighstone

Parts of this attractive house, on a 460-acre arable farm, date back to the beginning of the seventeenth century. It is set in pleasant countryside on the south side of the island, approximately two miles from the coast. Two of the spacious bedrooms and the lounge/dining-room enjoy lovely sea views, and there is a fridge on the landing for guests' use. Mottistone Manor, a quarter of a mile away, holds open-air jazz concerts in August.

OWNER: Anne Humphrey OPEN: all year exc Christmas ROOMS: 2 double, both with bath/shower; 1 twin, with private bathroom; tea/coffee in all bedrooms; lounge with TV TERMS: single occupancy £25–£30, twin/double £36–£40; deposit: £10–£50 CARDS: none DETAILS: no children under 12; no dogs; no smoking; car park; garden

MOUNT Cornwall — map 1

Mount Pleasant — NEW ENTRY

Mount, nr Bodmin PL30 4EX TEL: (01208) 821342 FAX: (01208) 821417
off A38 between Bodmin and Liskeard, signposted Mount; continue for 2m through village, hotel on right

Set in unspoilt, peaceful countryside, Mount Pleasant was originally a farmhouse dating from the seventeenth century, but has been added to over the years. The Cappers have been running the small hotel since the mid-1980s, and are acclaimed for their friendly welcome, good home-cooking, the comfort of the house and its relaxed atmosphere. Guests have use of a heated outdoor swimming-pool, a sun-lounge filled with plants (including a vine with grapes), a licensed bar, a TV lounge and a dining-room, where both evening meals and breakfasts are served. Dinner may end with home-made ice-creams. The bedrooms are spacious, have double-glazing, and most are *en suite*. Mount Pleasant is a good base for exploring Cornwall – both the north and south coasts are accessible, and it is right on the edge of Bodmin Moor.

OWNERS: Mr and Mrs J. Capper OPEN: Easter to Sept ROOMS: 1 single, with private bathroom; 3 double, all with shower; 1 twin, with shower; 2 family, both with shower; tea/coffee in all bedrooms; 2 lounges, 1 with TV TERMS: single £21–£26, single occupancy £26–£36, twin/double £42–£52, family room from £42; children sharing with parents half-price; dinner £12; deposit: £40 per person per week CARDS: Delta, MasterCard, Switch, Visa DETAILS: no children under 5; no dogs; smoking in 1 lounge and bar only; car park; garden; swimming-pool

MUCH WENLOCK Shropshire map 5

Walton House NEW ENTRY

35 Barrow Street, Much Wenlock TF13 6EP TEL: (01952) 727139
on A4169, S of Telford

This red-brick house is located in the fascinating medieval town of Much Wenlock. Owner Gladys Sivertsen has lived in the house for 50 years and it has been regularly modernised during this time, but still retains its original beams and three large cellars. The three bedrooms are spotlessly clean, with a bathroom and two WCs exclusively for guests' use. Excellent breakfasts are served in the small dining-area, and there is a guest lounge with TV. This good-value B&B is an excellent base from which to explore the surrounding area and, using the guided-tour leaflet, to see the well-preserved buildings in Much Wenlock itself.

OWNER: Mrs M. Sivertsen OPEN: Apr to Oct ROOMS: 1 single; 2 twin, 1 with wash-basin; tea/coffee in all bedrooms; lounge with TV TERMS: single £15, single occupancy £20, twin £30; deposit: £10 CARDS: none DETAILS: no children under 5; no dogs; no smoking; car park; garden

MUNDFORD Norfolk map 6

Colveston Manor

Mundford IP26 5HU TEL: (01842) 878218 FAX: (01842) 879218
from Mundford take A1065 to Swaffham for ½m, house signposted on left

Colveston Manor is a beautiful red-brick Georgian-style house set in extensive grounds and surrounded by farmland. The spacious rooms are elegantly furnished, with original fireplaces and a collection of prints, and the lounge has a log fire in winter. The single room is on the ground floor and has a bathroom nearby, two of the upstairs bedrooms share a bathroom and the four-poster room is *en suite*. Wendy Allingham is a charming hostess who enjoys sharing her home with visitors, and prepares excellent meals on the Aga. As there is no licence, guests may bring their own wine to dinner, and vegetarian choices can be requested. Wendy and her husband usually join their guests for dinner, and in summer barbecues are sometimes held in the garden. There are three friendly dogs.

OWNER: Wendy Allingham OPEN: all year ROOMS: 1 single; 1 double, with wash-basin; 1 twin, with wash-basin; 1 four-poster, with bath/shower; tea/coffee in all bedrooms; TV in some bedrooms and lounge TERMS: single £20, single occupancy £25, twin/double £40, four-poster £50; dinner £15; deposit required CARDS: none DETAILS: no children under 12; no dogs; no smoking; car park; garden

MURSLEY Buckinghamshire **map 3**

Richmond Lodge

Mursley MK17 0LE TEL: (01296) 720275
on B4032, 3m E of Winslow

Originally built as a shooting-lodge in the early 1900s, Richmond Lodge is approached up a tree-lined drive, and stands high up in three acres of grounds which include gardens, an orchard, paddocks, a grass tennis court and a croquet lawn. The Abbeys are very welcoming hosts and ensure their guests are well looked after. The three bedrooms have colour-co-ordinated fabrics, and either private bathrooms or *en suite* facilities as well as TVs. Guests have the use of a comfortable lounge with a TV. Evening meals,which must be booked in advance, are served on the patio when the weather permits, and breakfasts feature home-made jams.

OWNERS: Christine and Peter Abbey OPEN: all year exc Christmas ROOMS: 1 double, with private bathroom; 2 twin, 1 with bath/shower, 1 with private bathroom; tea/coffee and TV in all bedrooms; lounge with TV TERMS: single occupancy £25–£28, twin/double £42–£48; dinner £12.50; deposit: £10 per booking CARDS: none DETAILS: children welcome; no dogs; no smoking; car park; garden; tennis

NAILSEA N.W. Somerset **map 2**

Highdale Guest House

82 Silver Street, Nailsea BS19 2DS
TEL: (01275) 858004 FAX: (01275) 810175

Highdale Guest House is a detached Victorian house in an acre of grounds, with an immaculate lawn and colourful flowerbeds. It offers a warm and friendly welcome and a high standard of accommodation. The bedrooms are spacious and tastefully furnished, and a generous breakfast is served; free newspapers add to the comfort factor. The facilities are particularly suited to business guests, including message-taking, photocopying and fax services; the guests' lounge is available as a venue for daytime business meetings, and a 24-hour chauffeur service is provided. There are several nearby pubs and restaurants for meals, and Nailsea is only seven miles from Bristol.

OWNER: Fran Davey OPEN: all year ROOMS: 2 double, 1 twin; all rooms with wash-basin, tea/coffee and TV; lounge TERMS: twin/double £42 CARDS: none DETAILS: no children; dogs welcome; car park

NANTWICH Cheshire map 7

Stoke Grange Farm

Chester Road, Nantwich CW5 6BT TEL/FAX: (01270) 625525
E of A51, 3m N of Nantwich

This attractive farmhouse, dating from 1883, is part of a working dairy farm which backs on to the Shropshire Union Canal. The farm has geese and a pony, and guests are welcome to enjoy the garden, where a sailing dinghy has been converted into an unusual plant container. A sitting-room and a conservatory are available where visitors can relax and watch the boats pass by. One of the large, comfortable bedrooms has a balcony overlooking the canal. Substantial breakfasts are on offer and can include vegetarian options. A stroll along the towpath can be combined with an evening meal at one of the local pubs. Georgina West is a congenial host who is happy to assist guests with information about the area. A self-catering unit is also available on the farm.

OWNER: Georgina West OPEN: all year ROOMS: 1 double, 2 twin, 1 four-poster; all rooms with bath/shower, tea/coffee and TV; lounge with TV TERMS: single occupancy £25–£30, twin/double £40–£45, four-poster £50–£55; children's reductions if sharing with parents; deposit: £10 per person CARDS: none DETAILS: children welcome; no dogs; smoking in some bedrooms only; car park; garden

NEAR SAWREY Cumbria map 8

Buckle Yeat

Near Sawrey LA22 0LF
TEL: (01539) 436446/436538 FAX: (01539) 436446
on B5285, 2m S of Hawkshead

Drawings of this beautifully restored 200-year old whitewashed cottage, in the heart of the Lake District, appear in Beatrix Potter's *The Tale of Tom Kitten*. Original features such as the low oak beams and the flagstone floors in the well-proportioned lounge – plus log fires on cool days – add to the atmosphere. The well-appointed bedrooms are decorated in a chintzy style and have a mix of traditional and antique furniture; one bedroom is on the ground floor. Breakfast is served in the pleasant dining-room which has a cast-iron range. An old barn has been converted to a teashop and serves home-made cakes and light snacks. For evening meals there is a pub in the village about 100 yards away.

OWNERS: Robert and Helen Kirby OPEN: all year ROOMS: 1 single, 4 double, 2 twin, 1 family; all rooms with bath/shower exc single with private bathroom; tea/coffee and TV in all bedrooms; lounge with TV TERMS: single £22.50–£25, single occupancy £35–£40, twin/double £45–£50, family room £55–£65; half-price for children sharing with parents; deposit: £30 CARDS: Amex, Delta, Diners, MasterCard, Switch, Visa DETAILS: children welcome; dogs welcome exc in public rooms; smoking in lounge only; car park; garden

NEATISHEAD Norfolk map 6

Regency Guest House

The Street, Neatishead NR12 8AD TEL: (01692) 630233

In the heart of the Norfolk Broads, and only a few miles from sandy beaches, is this seventeenth-century house with beamed ceilings. The bedrooms are spotlessly clean and have been decorated and refurbished where needed; some have views of the garden and all have TVs. The patio has been extended and garden furniture added, providing a peaceful spot in which to relax and enjoy the lovely garden on warm days. 'Enormous, delicious' breakfasts are served at locally made oak tables in the sunny breakfast-room. A sitting-room is also available for guests' use. Sue Wrigley can provide a wealth of information on local attractions and eating-places. Light suppers are served by arrangement.

OWNERS: Alan and Sue Wrigley OPEN: all year ROOMS: 2 double, 1 with bath/shower, 1 with wash-basin; 3 twin, 1 with bath/shower, 2 with wash-basin; 1 family, with bath/shower; tea/coffee and TV in all bedrooms; lounge with TV TERMS: single occupancy £20–£30, twin/double £40–£48, family room from £50; children's reductions according to age; dinner £5; deposit required CARDS: Diners DETAILS: children welcome; dogs welcome; no smoking in public areas; car park; garden

NETHERBURY Dorset map 2

Heritage

Bridge Street, Netherbury DT6 5LS TEL: (01308) 488268
off A3066 Beaminster to Bridport road, 1½m S of Beaminster

Heritage is a 1940s Tudor-style house with a lovely large garden enclosed by a yew hedge. It stands in a peaceful location on the edge of the pretty village of Netherbury and is run by Mrs Seymour, a friendly French lady. The pretty bedrooms are small and share one bathroom between them, which has both bath and shower. The garden and patio can be reached through the small, comfortable lounge, next door to which is the separate dining-room, where breakfast is served.

OWNER: M.G. Seymour OPEN: all year exc Christmas ROOMS: 1 single, 1 double, 1 twin; all rooms with private bathroom; lounge with TV TERMS: single £20, single occupancy £35, twin/double £40; dinner £10; deposit: 20% CARDS: none DETAILS: no children; no dogs; no smoking; car park; garden

---

Breakfast at B&Bs tends to mean a cooked breakfast of bacon, eggs, toast and so on, although many establishments also offer a good choice of cereals, yoghurts, fruit and other options. If you have special dietary requirements, it is best to discuss these when you make a booking.

NETHER WALLOP Hampshire **map 2**

The Great Barn **NEW ENTRY**

Five Bells Lane, Nether Wallop SO20 8EN TEL: (01264) 782142
on A343 going W turn left after Middle Wallop Army Museum at crossroads by Q8 garage and George pub; after 1m turn right; Great Barn is the third house after Five Bells pub

The Great Barn is a listed building dating from the sixteenth century and was converted to a private house in 1990. It has a lovely garden and is in the centre of the picturesque village of Nether Wallop, famous as the setting for Agatha Christie's *Miss Marple* stories. Mrs Quaife is an extremely welcoming and friendly lady who offers two comfortably appointed, small *en suite* bedrooms on the ground floor in a separate wing of the house. Each has its own entrance, settee and fridge. Breakfast is provided in the lounge/dining-room, and evening meals are available in a nearby pub. Nether Wallop is halfway between Winchester and Salisbury, and not far from Stonehenge.

OWNER: Mrs R. Quaife OPEN: all year exc Christmas ROOMS: 1 double, 1 twin; both rooms with bath/shower, tea/coffee and TV; lounge TERMS: single occupancy £26, twin/double £38; children's reductions; deposit: 30% for bookings of 2 nights and over CARDS: none DETAILS: children welcome; no dogs; no smoking; car park; garden

NEWLYN EAST Cornwall **map 1**

Degembris Farmhouse

Newlyn East TR8 5HY TEL: (01872) 510555 FAX: (01872) 510230
just off A3058 Truro to Newquay road; after Summercourt village take third left signposted Newlyn East, then second lane on left

This neat, slate-tile-faced, listed eighteenth-century farmhouse is part of a 165-acre working arable farm. Built on the site of an old manor, it is set to one side of the farmyard, and has a well-kept, small front garden.The house is in an elevated position, with beautiful views over a peaceful wooded valley. Guests receive a warm welcome, and the house is bright and cheerful. The bedrooms are immaculately clean, with most having lovely views. Residents have use of a lounge with a TV, books and games, and are served breakfast and optional four-course dinners at separate tables in the small dining-room. A country trail leads from the farm. Over bank-holiday weekends, bookings must be for a minimum of three nights.

OWNER: Kathy Woodley OPEN: all year exc Christmas ROOMS: 1 single, 1 double, both with wash-basin; 1 twin, 2 family, all with bath/shower; tea/coffee and TV in all bedrooms; lounge with TV TERMS: single £18–£20, twin/double £40–£44, family room from £50; half-price for children under 10 sharing family room with parents; dinner £12; deposit: 25% CARDS: Delta, MasterCard, Switch, Visa DETAILS: children welcome; no dogs; no smoking; car park; garden

Trewerry Mill

Trerice, Newlyn East TR8 5HS TEL: (01872) 510345
off A3058, 3m S of Newquay

Reached down a series of narrow lanes, this seventeenth-century converted watermill is in a peaceful part of north Cornwall, only a few miles from the coast. The mill once ground corn for the Elizabethan country house of Trerice about half a mile away, now owned by the National Trust and open to the public. Five acres of beautifully kept gardens and uncultivated areas of wild flowers, rich in wildlife, surround the mill, and there is a terrace for sitting out. The guests' lounge has a large stone fireplace and a view of the mill wheel. The B&B was taken over in 1996 by the Clarks, who have added *en suite* facilities to three bedrooms. The guests' lounge has a large stone fireplace and a view of the mill wheel. The Clarks also run the adjacent tea room, which is open from 10.30 to 5.30, serving coffee, light snacks, cream teas and ice-creams.

OWNERS: Terri and Dave Clark OPEN: Mar to Nov ROOMS: 2 single, both with wash-basin; 2 double, 1 with shower, 1 with wash-basin; 1 twin, with shower; 1 family, with shower; tea/coffee in all bedrooms; lounge with TV TERMS: single £15–£21, single occupancy £15–£30, twin/double £30–£48, family room £37.50–£60; half-price for children under 12 sharing with parents; dinner £8; deposit: 1 night's charge CARDS: none DETAILS: no children under 7; no dogs; no smoking; car park; garden

NEWNEY GREEN Essex **map 3**

Moor Hall

Newney Green CM1 3SE TEL/FAX: (01245) 420814
heading W from Chelmsford on A1060, turn left at Hare & Hounds pub, first left, and left again at T-junction, then right 200 metres after Duck pub

This large fourteenth-century timber-framed medieval farmhouse is in open countryside, surrounded by 500 acres of arable farmland, and two acres of garden. A moat goes halfway round the house. The property also has a lake, where two black East Indian ducks are in residence, and where rods can be provided for fishing. The house has been beautifully restored and retains a wealth of oak beams, panelling and inglenook fireplaces, and is elegantly furnished. The two bedrooms are large and suitable for families. Breakfast and dinner are served at a refectory table in the oak-panelled dining-room. The Gemmills also hire out a horse-drawn carriage. A nearby pub is also handy for evening meals.

OWNERS: Sue and Will Gemmill OPEN: all year exc Christmas ROOMS: 2 family; tea/coffee in both bedrooms; lounge with TV TERMS: single occupancy £23–£25, family room £40–£43, children's reductions according to age; dinner from £8 CARDS: none DETAILS: children welcome; no dogs; no smoking; car park; garden

NORTHAMPTON Northamptonshire **map 5**

St Georges Private Hotel

128 St Georges Avenue, Northampton NN2 6JF TEL: (01604) 792755

Opposite a park, this large Victorian house is just a mile and a half from the town centre. It has a pleasant atmosphere, and the good-sized, comfortable bedrooms have floral bedspreads and pine furniture, and most have *en suite* facilities. Four have their original fireplaces and two are on the ground floor. The house retains some of its original features, such as the brass and wrought-iron surround in the large lounge and the mosaic tiles in the hall. Breakfast is served at individual tables in the bright basement dining-room, and light snacks are also available.

OWNER: T. Goodwin OPEN: all year exc Christmas ROOMS: 2 single, with wash-basin; 2 double, both with bath/shower; 2 twin, 1 with bath/shower; 2 family, both with bath/shower; lounge with TV TERMS: single £22.50–£27.50, single occupancy £27.50, twin/double £42.50, family room £50–£65; reductions for children sharing with parents; deposit: letter of confirmation CARDS: MasterCard, Visa DETAILS: children welcome; dogs by arrangement; car park

NORTH BOVEY Devon **map 1**

Gate House

North Bovey TQ13 8RB TEL/FAX: (01647) 440479

This picturesque, whitewashed thatched house stands in the middle of an unspoilt little village. Dating from the mid-fifteenth century, the Gate House is next to the village pub, which is an even earlier building constructed to house the workmen who built the church. There are lovely countryside views from the pretty cottage-style garden, which also has an unheated swimming-pool. Inside, beams feature in nearly every room, and the cosy sitting-room boasts a massive granite fireplace and bread oven. The bright bedrooms are tastefully decorated, and all have *en suite* facilities. Both breakfast and candelit dinners are served in the small dining-room, which is warmed by the Aga in winter. The Williams are a friendly couple willing to help with the planning of tours and walks, and they have a good selection of maps and travel books for guests' use. Dartmoor is within striking distance.

OWNERS: John and Sheila Williams OPEN: all year ROOMS: 3 double, all rooms with bath/shower, tea/coffee and TV; lounge TERMS: single occupancy £32, double £50; dinner £14 CARDS: none DETAILS: no children under 12; well-behaved dogs welcome exc in dining-room; no smoking; car park; garden; swimming-pool

---

'Lounge' in the details at the bottoms of entries refers to a room (or rooms) in which guests can relax, watch TV, read or chat, and may vary from a large, elegantly furnished drawing-room exclusively for guests' use to a cosy sitting-room shared with the owners.

NORTHLEACH Gloucestershire map 5

Market House

Market Square, Northleach GL54 3EJ TEL: (01451) 860557
just by intersection of A40 and A429

Once the covered sheep-fleece market, this converted house is over 400 years old and is in the centre of the pretty village of Northleach. It became a dwelling in 1950, but retained some original features, such as the flagstone floors and oak beams. Breakfasts are served in the bright dining/sitting-room, which has plenty of books and a good supply of brochures describing local places of interest. The four bedrooms, one of which has *en suite* facilities, have exposed stone walls and original fireplaces.

OWNERS: Theresa and Mike Eastman OPEN: all year exc Christmas ROOMS: 2 single, both with wash-basin; 1 double, with shower; 1 twin, with wash-basin; lounge with TV TERMS: single £22, single occupancy £25, twin/double £38–£40; deposit: 1 night's charge CARDS: none DETAILS: no children under 12; no dogs; no smoking; garden

NORTHLEIGH Devon map 2

The Pantiles NEW ENTRY

Thorn Cottage, Northleigh EX13 6BN TEL: (01404) 871553
from Honiton railway station follow signs to Northleigh; continue past golf club, then take right fork and continue for 2m; entering village, house is first property on right

Previously owners of the Old Vicarage in Cardigan, Wales, the Goveys moved to Northleigh during 1997, bringing with them the enthusiasm and level of hospitality they earned a reputation for there. Thorn Cottage, originally two flint cottages built in the nineteenth century, is on the outskirts of the tiny, remote village of Northleigh, and enjoys lovely views of the surrounding hills and fields. Guest accommodation comprises the Pantiles, a small studio in the grounds, with double bedroom, sitting-room, bathroom and kitchen, plus a double bedroom with private bathroom in the main house. Breakfast is served in the dining-room in the main house.

OWNERS: Anthony and Peggy Govey OPEN: all year exc Christmas ROOMS: 2 double, 1 with bath/shower, 1 with private bathroom; tea/coffee in both bedrooms; TV in 1 bedroom and lounge TERMS: single occupancy £30–£35, double £40–£48; deposit: £10 per person CARDS: none DETAILS: no children; no dogs; no smoking; car park; garden

If you are forced to turn up later than planned, please telephone to warn the proprietor. It is always best to book a room in advance, even in winter. B&Bs with few rooms may close at short notice for periods not specified in the details.

NORWICH Norfolk **map 6**

Linden House

557 Earlham Road, Norwich NR4 7HW
TEL: (01603) 451303 FAX: (01603) 250641

This detached 1920s house is a comfortable place to stay, and is conveniently situated for visiting the city as the bus stops right outside. The Peters are a friendly, much-travelled couple, and they combine high standards with an informal atmosphere. The well-furnished bedrooms are immaculately kept and all have *en suite* facilities and TVs. Home-cooked evening meals can be provided by arrangement, and vegetarians can be catered for. Linden House is popular both with tourists and with business travellers, who have fax, photocopying and secretarial services at their disposal.

OWNERS: Carol and Don Peters OPEN: all year exc Christmas ROOMS: 1 double, 2 twin; all rooms with bath/shower, tea/coffee and TV; lounge with TV TERMS: single occupancy £27–£30, twin/double £39–£42; children's reductions if sharing parents' room; dinner £10–£15; deposit: £10 or credit card number CARDS: MasterCard, Visa DETAILS: children welcome; dogs welcome; smoking in bedrooms only; car park; garden

OAKAMOOR Staffordshire **map 5**

Bank House

Farley Lane, Oakamoor ST10 3BD TEL/FAX: (01538) 702810
on B5417, 2½m N of Alton Towers

This large country house stands in six acres of gardens and woodlands that are full of wildlife and which guests may wander through. The house is on the edge of the Peak National Park in the Staffordshire Moorlands. The Egerton-Ormes are a charming couple who have created a country-house-party ambience in their elegant home, and have furnished it with old family pieces. Two of the immaculate bedrooms have luxury *en suite* bathrooms, one with a jacuzzi, and two adjacent rooms can be used as a family suite. As only three rooms are let at any one time, there is always a private bathroom available for the third bedroom. Guests have the use of an enormous drawing-room with a log fire and a library. The dining-room opens on to a terrace, where breakfast can be taken in warm weather. Evening meals can be booked, and are likely to feature locally grown vegetables, home-made desserts and ice-creams. The owners often join their guests at dinner, or for drinks beforehand; wine can be chosen from the well-stocked wine cellar.

OWNER: Mrs M. Egerton-Orme OPEN: all year exc Christmas ROOMS: 1 single, with private bathroom; 1 double; 2 twin, 1 with bath/shower, 1 with private bathroom; 1 four-poster, with bath/shower; tea/coffee and TV in all bedrooms; lounge with TV TERMS: single £39, single occupancy £39–£47, twin/double £54–£74, four-poster £64; reductions for children sharing with parents; dinner £20–£30; deposit: £10 per adult per night CARDS: MasterCard, Visa DETAILS: children welcome; dogs by prior arrangement; no smoking upstairs and in dining-room; car park; garden

OAKFORD Devon

map 1

Newhouse Farm

Oakford, nr Tiverton EX16 9JE TEL: (01398) 351347
on B3227, 5m W of Bampton

Dating from around 1600, this traditional working farm is reached down a long rutted track. It is in glorious countryside on the southern fringes of Exmoor National Park, and has a pretty sheltered garden which follows the valley down to a trout stream and small pond. Sturdy oak beams, an inglenook fireplace, and a bread oven give a clue to the house's origins and add to its character. The welcome here by Anne Boldry and her family is warm and friendly. Two comfortable and attractively decorated *en suite* bedrooms are offered, and there is a small guests' kitchen for making drinks and picnic lunches. Evening meals can be arranged, and focus on fresh, local supplies. At breakfast look out for a big choice of home-made marmalades and jams.

OWNER: Anne Boldry OPEN: all year exc Christmas, Feb and Mar ROOMS: 1 double, 1 twin/double/family; both rooms with bath/shower, tea/coffee and TV; lounge TERMS: twin/double/family £34–£40; dinner £11; deposit: 20% CARDS: none DETAILS: no children under 10; no dogs; no smoking in dining-room; car park; garden

ODIHAM Hampshire

map 2

Poland Mill

Poland Lane, Odiham RG29 1JL TEL: (01256) 702251
from M3 junction 5 take A287 signposted Farnham, at first roundabout continue straight on, then take first left signed Winchfield, then first left again into Poland Lane

Poland Mill's interesting history means that it has parts dating from the fifteenth, sixteenth and eighteenth centuries, and it is even mentioned in the Domesday Book. It is in a quiet position at the end of a lane and surrounded by fields. Janice Cole is a charming, hospitable and welcoming lady, and has furnished her house to a high standard of comfort and elegance. There is a lovely dining-room for breakfast and a pleasant sitting-room with TV. Two bedrooms have four-poster beds, and all have *en suite* facilities, except the small four-poster and single, which share a bathroom. A most attractive garden with a pond surrounds the house. Poland Mill is a comfortable, relaxing place to stay, the only disturbance being the noisy peacocks.

OWNERS: Brian and Janice Cole OPEN: all year ROOMS: 1 single; 1 twin, with shower; 2 four-poster, 1 with shower; tea/coffee in all bedrooms; TV in some bedrooms and lounge TERMS: single £27.50, single occupancy £30–£35, twin £55, four-poster £55–£65; reductions for children sharing with parents CARDS: none DETAILS: children welcome; no dogs; no smoking; car park; garden

OLD Northamptonshire map 5

Wold Farm

Old NN6 9RJ TEL: (01604) 781258
6m SW of Kettering between A43 and A508

Clad in wistaria and 300 years old, this venerable farmhouse is part of a working sheep and cattle farm. It offers six comfortable bedrooms, all with either *en suite* facilities or private bathrooms. Three are in the main house and three in the restored granary at the bottom of the garden; one bedroom is on the ground floor. Both buildings have a TV lounge. Breakfast and optional four-course dinners are served in the dining-room in the main house, which has oak beams, an old dresser and an enormous fireplace. Alternatively, a pub just 80 yards away serves food. Lamport Hall, Brixworth church (dating from the seventh century) and Pitsford Water trout fishing and nature reserve are all within easy reach.

OWNER: Anne Engler OPEN: all year ROOMS: 2 single, both with bath/shower; 3 double, 2 with bath/shower, 1 with private bathroom; 1 twin, with private bathroom; tea/coffee in all bedrooms; TV in some bedrooms and lounges TERMS: single £22–£25, twin/double £44–£50; half-price for children under 14; dinner £18 CARDS: none DETAILS: children welcome; dogs by arrangement; no smoking; car park; garden

OLDFIELD West Yorkshire map 8

Far Two Laws Farm NEW ENTRY

Two Laws, Oldfield BD22 0JN TEL: (01535) 643376
3m W of Haworth on the Colne road

This seventeenth-century stone-built farmhouse lies in picturesque countryside, very close to the Pennine hills. Although it is no longer a working farm, there are some animals about, and guests enjoy watching Gyp the border collie round up the ducks. The B&B is rich in character, with a warm, relaxed atmosphere. Sarah Schofield is outgoing and friendly, and her children also enjoy chatting to guests. Evening meals are a speciality: almost everything is home-made, including the bread and ice-cream, and the water comes from their own spring. The lounge has a wood-stove and a piano, and it adjoins the dining-room. A self-catering cottage is next to the main building.

OWNER: Sarah Schofield OPEN: all year exc Christmas ROOMS: 1 twin, with shower, tea/coffee and TV; lounge TERMS: single occupancy £20; twin £40; dinner £7–£12; deposit: 20% CARDS: none DETAILS: no children under 10; no dogs; no smoking; car park; garden

---

If a B&B accepts credit cards, we list them in the details at the end of an entry – or specify no cards are accepted if that is so. There may be a surcharge if you pay by credit card. It is always best to check when booking whether the card you want to use will be accepted.

OMBERSLEY Hereford & Worcester map 5

Eden Farm

Ombersley WR9 0JX TEL: (01905) 620244
just W of A449, 5m W of Droitwich

This Grade II-listed seventeenth-century farmhouse is on a 200-acre mixed farm set in beautiful countryside a mile from the unspoilt village of Ombersley, and guests are assured of a personal level of service from the Yardleys. The house has old-fashioned furniture and the two spacious bedrooms have *en suite* showers. Substantial breakfasts are taken in the pleasant dining-room/lounge. Packed lunches can be provided, and there are several places for evening meals in the village. The Wychavon Way passes close by, and Ombersley golf course is only half a mile away.

OWNERS: W.D. and M.A. Yardley OPEN: all year exc Christmas ROOMS: 1 twin, 1 family; both rooms with bath/shower and tea/coffee; lounge with TV TERMS: single/single occupancy £22, twin/double £40, family room from £40; children's reductions according to age; deposit: £5–£10 CARDS: none DETAILS: children welcome; no dogs; no smoking; car park; garden

OTLEY Suffolk map 6

Bowerfield House NEW ENTRY

Otley IP6 9NR TEL: (01473) 890742 FAX: (01473) 890059
on B1079, 6m E of Woodbridge in centre of village

Bowerfield House is reached up a long drive and is peacefully set in two acres of gardens complete with terracing, Chinese fountain, and a large natural pond stocked with Koi carp and Golden Orfe. The charming seventeenth-century stable/barn conversion has been beautifully decorated, with some interesting antique pieces and furniture about. A billiards table can be found in the games room, which adjoins the elegant lounge area with its open fire and grand piano. Two of the well-appointed bedrooms are housed in the adjacent carriage house with its wonderful exposed beams; one of these, a double room which can be converted into a twin, has a small connecting kitchen with a microwave and fridge. Michael Hall and Lise Hilton are extremely accommodating hosts. A full-sized croquet lawn is also available for guests.

OWNERS: Michael Hall and Lise Hilton OPEN: end Mar to Oct ROOMS: 1 single, 1 double, 1 double/twin, 1 four-poster; all rooms with bath/shower exc 1 double with private bathroom; tea/coffee and TV in all bedrooms; lounge with TV TERMS: single £34, single occupancy £36, twin/double £46, four-poster £46; dinner £18.50; deposit: £40 CARDS: none DETAILS: no children under 12; no dogs; no smoking; car park; garden; games room

---

'NEW ENTRY' indicates that a B&B was not in the previous edition (although its owners may have been, at a different address).

OXFORD Oxfordshire **map 2**

Chestnuts

NEW ENTRY

45 Davenant Road, Oxford OX2 8BU TEL/FAX: (01865) 553375

This modern red-brick house is situated in North Oxford, just two miles from the town centre, and is surrounded by a colourful display of flowering tubs and baskets. The house is luxuriously furnished, and the elegant *en suite* bedrooms are decorated in soft pastel florals and have quality pine furnishings. Breakfasts are a speciality here and include fresh fruit, yoghurts, prunes, cereals and fruit juice, followed by a traditional cooked breakfast. The conservatory-style dining-room overlooks a patio which has flowers and a fountain. The snug lounge which leads on to the patio has lots of books, magazines and information on what to see and do in the area. Guests are well advised to leave their car here and take the bus into town.

OWNERS: Tony and Ann O'Connor OPEN: all year exc Christmas ROOMS: 1 single, 3 double, 1 twin; all rooms with shower, tea/coffee and TV; lounge TERMS: single £35–£38, single occupancy £50–£58, twin/double £55–£65; deposit: £25 CARDS: none DETAILS: no children under 10; no dogs; no smoking; car park; garden

---

Cotswold House

363 Banbury Road, Oxford OX2 7PL TEL: (01865) 310558

Jim and Anne O'Kane continue to maintain and improve this homely property situated in a leafy part of Oxford, two miles from the city centre. The house is beautifully kept and the entrance hall has oriental rugs and flower arrangements. There is a small sitting-room, and a separate dining-room where excellent breakfasts are served. The bedrooms all have floral colour-schemes, *en suite* shower-rooms and TVs.

OWNERS: Jim and Anne O'Kane OPEN: all year exc Christmas ROOMS: 2 single, 2 double, 2 twin, 1 family; all rooms with shower, tea/coffee and TV; lounge TERMS: single £42, single occupancy £50–£60, twin/double £64, family room £76; children's reductions by arrangement CARDS: none DETAILS: no children under 5; no dogs; no smoking; car park

---

The Gables

6 Cumnor Hill, Oxford OX2 9HA
TEL: (01865) 862153 FAX: (01865) 864054
from M40 to A34 south, turn off at roundabout, right a T-junction

This white guesthouse, set off prettily with hanging baskets and tubs of flowers in summer, is just about a mile and a half from the centre of Oxford, and not far from bus and rail stations. It occupies a corner site on one of the main roads into the city. The house is impeccably maintained, and the owners were winners in the Oxford in Bloom contest in 1997. Five of the bedrooms have either *en suite* shower or bath, and the sixth – the family room – has a private bathroom. All have satellite TV and direct-dial telephones. Guests also have the use of a small lounge, plus a new conservatory which overlooks the garden, and breakfasts are served in a separate dining-room.

OWNERS: Sally and Tony Tompkins OPEN: all year exc Christmas ROOMS: 2 single, 2 double, 1 twin, 1 family; all rooms with bath or shower exc 1 family with private bathroom; tea/coffee and TV in all bedrooms; lounge with TV TERMS: single £22–£28, single occupancy £30–£40, twin/double £40–£48, family room £45–£60; children reductions according to age if sharing with parents; deposit: 33% of 1 night's charge CARDS: MasterCard, Visa DETAILS: children welcome; no dogs; no smoking; car park; garden

Norham Guesthouse

16 Norham Road, Oxford OX2 6SF
TEL: (01865) 515352 FAX: (01865) 793162

Only a 15-minute walk from the town centre, this late-Victorian three-storeyed house is in a conservation area near the beautiful University parks. Rosemary and Peter Welham continue to maintain their high standards, and the house is in excellent decorative order. The bedrooms are a good size, and all but one has an *en suite* shower. Generous cooked breakfasts are served in the bright dining-room, which overlooks the garden.

OWNERS: Rosemary and Peter Welham OPEN: all year exc Christmas ROOMS: 2 single, 3 double, 2 twin, 1 family; all rooms with shower exc 1 twin with private bathroom; tea/coffee and TV in all bedrooms; lounge with TV TERMS: single £32–£35, single occupancy £40–£48, twin/double £46–£55, family room £62–£65; deposit required CARDS: none DETAILS: no children under 5; no dogs; no smoking; car park

PADSTOW Cornwall — map 1

Dower House

Fentonluna Lane, Padstow PL28 8BA
TEL: (01841) 532317 FAX: (01841) 532667

Dating from the nineteenth century, this attractive listed house stands on the edge of Padstow in a quiet position high above the town, with views down to the sea. The house has undergone a lot of refurbishment recently. The large, bright bedrooms are smartly decorated, well furnished and have *en suite* facilities. There is a comfortable lounge, small bar and dining-room with mullioned windows. The breakfast menu has plenty of choice, and on Mondays in summer Paul Brocklebank offers a barbecue on the terrace (at an additional cost of £20 a head); lunch, supper and afternoon tea are available – except on Wednesday – and fish and chips can be brought in twice a week. The house has a welcoming and friendly atmosphere, and is a good place to stay for those looking for quiet and comfortable accommodation within easy reach of this popular seaside town.

OWNERS: Paul and Patricia Brocklebank OPEN: Mar to Nov ROOMS: 4 double, 2 twin; all rooms with bath/shower, tea/coffee and TV; lounge with TV TERMS: single occupancy £38–£48, twin/double £50–£74; reductions for children under 13; deposit: £30 per person CARDS: Delta, MasterCard, Switch, Visa DETAILS: children welcome; dogs welcome (not on beds); no smoking; car park; garden

Khandalla

Sarahs Lane, Padstow PL28 8EL TEL: (01841) 532961

Khandalla is an Edwardian semi-detached house in a quiet residential area on a hillside enjoying excellent views over the Camel estuary and surrounding countryside. Padstow harbour and town centre are less than ten minutes' walk away, though the uphill walk back may take longer. Bedrooms are large, very comfortable and well equipped, and Lisa Hair makes her guests feel at home. Breakfasts are good, with a choice between full English or continental.

OWNER: Lisa Hair OPEN: all year ROOMS: 1 single, 1 double, 1 family; all rooms with bath/shower, tea/coffee and TV; lounge with TV TERMS: single £20–£25, single occupancy £35, twin/double £35–£45, family room £45–£55; half-price for children sharing with parents; deposit: £10 per room CARDS: none DETAILS: children welcome; no smoking; car park; garden

PATELEY BRIDGE North Yorkshire map 9

Bruce House Farm

Top Wath Road, Pateley Bridge HG3 5PG
TEL: (01423) 711813 FAX: (01423) 712843
off B6265, 11m NW of Harrogate

This handsome stone-built Victorian farmhouse is entered via a flagstone courtyard, and stands in six acres of secluded land overlooking Nidderdale. The house has a lived-in ambience, and guests can expect a warm welcome from the friendly owner. Tasty cooked breakfasts, and pre-arranged evening meals are served. The elegant dining-room opens out to the conservatory, which enjoys good views over the valley and Pateley Bridge. The surrounding countryside is excellent walking territory, and Brimham Rocks, Stump Cross Caverns and Fountains Abbey are nearby.

OWNER: Mrs M. Treble OPEN: Easter to late Oct ROOMS: 2 double, 1 with shower, 1 with private bathroom; 1 twin, with private bathroom; tea/coffee in all bedrooms; lounge with TV TERMS: single occupancy £21–£25, twin/double £38–£40; children's reductions; dinner £10–£14; deposit: £20 CARDS: none DETAILS: children welcome; no dogs; no smoking; car park; garden

B&B rates specified in the details at the end of each entry are given (as applicable) for a single room, for single occupancy of a double room, and then per room in the case of two people sharing a double or twin-bedded room, or for a family room. Because double rooms with four-poster beds often cost more, those are listed separately.

PELYNT Cornwall map 1

Trenderway Farm

Pelynt PL13 2LY TEL: (01503) 272214 FAX: (01503) 272991
off B3359, 1m S of Pelynt

This delightful farmhouse, tucked away down a quiet country lane halfway between Looe and Polperro, dates from the sixteenth century, although the 400-acre farm is much older, and was recorded in the Domesday Book. Two of the bedrooms are in a converted barn, and one room has a four-poster bed; all are spacious and furnished with easy chairs, and have *en suite* bath and shower. The house is simply but prettily decorated, and the relaxing sitting-room has an open fire. It leads through to the conservatory, where breakfast, which includes the farm's own free-range eggs and sausages from the local butcher, is served. Eating-places in the area include the local sixteenth-century inn. Note that the minimum booking taken at weekends is two nights.

OWNERS: Lynne and Anthony Tuckett OPEN: all year exc Christmas and New Year ROOMS: 2 double, 1 twin, 1 four-poster; all rooms with bath and shower, tea/coffee and TV; lounge TERMS: single occupancy £30–£45, twin/double £56–£60, four-poster £60–£70; deposit: £30 per person CARDS: none DETAILS: no children; no dogs; no smoking; car park; garden

PENISTONE South Yorkshire map 9

Aldermans Head Manor NEW ENTRY

Hartcliffe Hill Road, Penistone S36 9FS TEL/FAX: (01226) 766209
from A616 take road to Penistone; at crossroads turn left into Mossley Rd, after 1m turn left; B&B is up a ⅔m drive

This attractive manor house, the oldest part of which dates from the seventeenth century, enjoys spectacular views across the Langsett and Midhope reservoirs, and the Peak District National Park. It is part of a 50-acre working sheep farm, which also includes a small fold of pedigree Highland cattle. There are four luxury bedrooms, including the enormous Alderman's Suite, which has a sunken double bath and a king-sized bed; the other three also have special features. Breakfasts are cooked on the Aga, and served in either the conservatory or the oak-beamed dining-room. Evening meals are served by arrangement, and a small selection of wines is available. Aldermans Head Manor is in a remote but accessible location, only ten minutes from the M1 motorway.

OWNERS: Phil and Ann Unitt OPEN: all year exc Christmas ROOMS: 1 double, 2 twin, 1 four-poster; all rooms with bath/shower exc 1 twin with private bathroom; tea/coffee and TV in all bedrooms; lounge with TV TERMS: single occupancy £30–£45, twin/double £45–£65, four-poster £50–£55; dinner £17.50; deposit: 1 night's charge or credit card details CARDS: Delta, MasterCard, Visa DETAILS: no children under 12; dogs by arrangement; no smoking; car park; garden

PENRITH Cumbria map 10

Barco House

Carleton Road, Penrith CA11 8LR TEL: (01768) 863176

The Stockdales offer good-value accommodation in an informal atmosphere at their Victorian house, just half a mile from the centre of Penrith. Bedrooms are clean and comfortable, a decent size and two have their own shower. Breakfast and, by prior arrangement, dinner are served in the dining-room at separate tables, which has an adjacent small licensed bar/lounge. Guests may also bring their own wine to dinner.

OWNERS: Christine and Colin Stockdale OPEN: all year ROOMS: 1 twin, with wash-basin; 2 family, both with bath/shower; tea/coffee and TV in all bedrooms TERMS: single occupancy £25–£38, twin £38–£40, family room £44–£50; children's reductions by arrangement; dinner £18 CARDS: none DETAILS: children welcome; dogs by arrangement; no smoking in dining-room; car park; garden

PENRYN Cornwall map 1

Clare House

20 Broad Street, Penryn TR10 8JH TEL: (01326) 373294

Clare House, a seventeenth-century listed building in the heart of Penryn, is easily spotted with its bright white exterior, window box and hanging baskets. It also has a pretty back garden, reached through a narrow conservatory where an ancient Black Hamburg vine grows. Jean and Jack Hewitt are 'the perfect hosts', in the view of one reader, and welcome guests with a hot drink and home-made scones. Three spacious, comfortable bedrooms share a bathroom and shower-room, and the large drawing-room is stocked with books and magazines. Morning papers come with breakfast, which includes home-made bread and preserves, and hot drinks are always available in the 'refreshment room'. There are many beaches and coves to explore in the area, and the coastal path makes a pleasant walk.

OWNERS: Jean and Jack Hewitt OPEN: all year exc Christmas and New Year ROOMS: 3 twin, 1 with bath/shower, 2 with private bathroom; tea/coffee and TV in all bedrooms; lounge TERMS: single occupancy £30, twin £40–£50; deposit: 20% CARDS: none DETAILS: older children welcome by arrangement; no dogs; no smoking; car park; garden

---

We welcome your feedback about B&Bs you have stayed in. Please make use of the report forms at the end of the book – or use your own stationery if you prefer – and mail your report to: The Editors, The Good Bed and Breakfast Guide, *FREEPOST, 2 Marylebone Road, London NW1 1YN. (No stamps are needed if mailed within the UK.) Recommendations for B&Bs for our next edition are very welcome. Please let us know if you need more report forms and we will send you a fresh supply.*

PENSHURST Kent

map 3

Swale Cottage

Poundsbridge Lane, Penshurst TN11 8AH TEL: (01892) 870738
off B2176, ¾m SE of Penshurst Place, turn into Poundsbridge Lane, then first on right

Set in a peaceful location with wonderful views over the hilly woodlands of the Medway Valley, Swale Cottage is a Grade II-listed barn, dating from the eighteenth-century and sympathetically converted to retain its character. Of the three attractive bedrooms, one has a four-poster bed, another a pretty Victorian bed, and the third has canopied beds. There is an elegant sitting-room with TV, and breakfast is served at an antique refectory table in the dining-room. Owner Cynthia Dakin is an artist and her paintings are displayed throughout the house. Historical Penshurst Place with its Tudor gardens is nearby. It is advisable to phone for directions to Swale Cottage.

OWNER: Cynthia Dakin OPEN: all year ROOMS: 1 double, with bath/shower; 1 twin, with private bathroom; 1 four-poster, with bath/shower; tea/coffee and TV in all bedrooms; lounge with TV TERMS: single occupancy £36–£46, twin/double £56–£66, four-poster £60–£66; deposit required CARDS: none DETAILS: no children under 10; no dogs in public rooms; no smoking; car park; garden

PENTEWAN Cornwall

map 1

Polrudden Farm

Pentewan PL26 6BJ TEL/FAX: (01726) 842051
off B3273, 3m S of St Austell

This modern bungalow stands on the site of the ancient manor of Sir John Polrudden, in a spectacular clifftop position looking out to sea. It is at the top of a very steep hill at the end of a long driveway leading from the village square. The 74-acre sheep and beef farm extends to the shore, and there is a path that leads to the small private beach, five minutes' walk away. A terrace furnished with tables and chairs runs along the front of the house. Accommodation is simple and the welcome warm, and the atmosphere is serene and pleasant. Traditional English breakfast is served, and evening meals are available by arrangement. Note that the minimum booking taken is for two nights.

OWNERS: Andrew and Johanna Jackson OPEN: all year exc Christmas ROOMS: 1 double, with bath/shower; 2 twin, 1 with bath/shower, 1 with private bathroom; tea/coffee and TV in all bedrooms; lounge with TV TERMS: single occupancy £27, twin/double £40; deposit: £40 CARDS: none DETAILS: no children; no dogs; no smoking; car park; garden

If there are any bedrooms with TV, or with tea / coffee-making facilities, we mention this in the details at the end of an entry.

PENZANCE Cornwall map 1

Lombard House

16 Regent Terrace, Penzance TR18 4DW TEL/FAX: (01736) 364897

This cheerful pink house in a Regency terrace is only one street away from the seafront and very close to the town centre, and is run by the 'friendly, welcoming and efficient' Rita and Tom Kruge. Bedrooms at the front are large and have good views, though the single room at the back is quite small. Some of the ground-floor rooms still have the original fireplaces. Five rooms are suitable for families, but may be let as twin rooms. The combined dining-room/lounge also has a licensed bar and TV, and leads through to the front garden, where guests can sit and enjoy the sea views. Evening meals are available by arrangement, and parking facilities can be provided while guests visit the Scilly Isles.

OWNERS: Tom and Rita Kruge OPEN: all year ROOMS: 1 single, with wash-basin; 3 double, 1 with bath/shower, 2 with wash-basin; 5 twin/family, all with bath/shower; tea/coffee and TV in all bedrooms; lounge TERMS: single £17.50–£25, single occupancy £25–£30, twin/double £40–£50, family room from £40; 25% reduction for children under 12; dinner £10.50–£12.50; deposit: £20 CARDS: MasterCard, Visa DETAILS: children welcome; no dogs; no smoking in lounge/dining- room; car park; garden

PERRANPORTH Cornwall map 1

Morgans of Perranporth

3 Grannys Lane, Perranporth TR6 0HB
TEL: (01872) 573904 FAX: (01872) 572425

Charles and Yvonne Morgan's guesthouse is a compact modern house in a quiet residential area overlooking the town of Perranporth and five minutes' walk from the beach and shops. Two of the small bedrooms have sea views and there is a combined lounge and dining-room, which also overlooks the beach. The Morgans are a friendly and welcoming couple who make their guests feel at home. Full English or continental breakfast is served, but note that dinner is no longer available. On fine days, guests can relax on the patio and enjoy sunsets over the water.

OWNERS: Charles and Yvonne Morgan OPEN: all year exc Christmas ROOMS: 1 single; 2 double, 1 with shower; 2 double/twin/family, both with shower; tea/coffee and TV in all bedrooms; lounge with TV TERMS: single £22–£25, single occupancy £25, twin/double £37–£44, family room £50–£60; reductions for children sharing with parents; deposit CARDS: none DETAILS: children welcome; smoking in lounge only; car park; garden

---

B&Bs are selected for the Guide for their warm welcome, cleanliness, a friendly atmosphere and, wherever possible, an attractive location or a building that is itself of some historical or architectural interest.

PERRANUTHNOE Cornwall **map 1**

Ednovean Farm

Perranuthnoe TR20 9LZ TEL: (01736) 711883
from Penzance take A394 Helston road beyond Marazion, turn right at Dynasty restaurant; farm drive on left by postbox

This granite barn with lovely views over the bay to St Michael's Mount was probably built in the seventeenth century, and definitely converted by the Taylors in the late twentieth century. It is comfortable and has an informal atmosphere, and the pretty bedrooms, each with its own colour scheme, are all on the ground floor, two with their own entrance off the courtyard. An open-plan living-room/dining-room/kitchen occupies the first floor, though at the time of going to press the Taylors were planning to create a separate lounge. There is also a 'garden room' extension which opens on to the patio. Perranuthnoe, where there is a pub serving food and an unspoilt sandy beach, is only a few minutes' walk away across the fields.

OWNERS: Christine and Charles Taylor OPEN: all year exc Christmas ROOMS: 3 double; all rooms with bath/shower, tea/coffee and TV TERMS: double £40–£60; deposit: £20 CARDS: none DETAILS: no children; no dogs in bedrooms; no smoking; car park; garden

PERSHORE Hereford & Worcester **map 5**

The Barn NEW ENTRY

Pensham Hill House, Pensham, Pershore WR10 3HA TEL: (01386) 555270
just of A44 Worcester to Evesham road, 1m SW of Pershore

This tastefully converted farm building with its exposed beams and wonderful sloping ceilings dates back to the nineteenth century. The three luxurious bedrooms are decorated in soft pinks and greens; one has a jacuzzi. A hot drink, delicious malt bread, and other home-baked items are just part of the warm greeting. In the summer months guests can make use of the unheated above-ground swimming-pool, and a sauna and carpet-covered tennis court are also available. The spacious sitting-area opens out to a terrace where delightful views of sheep-dotted fields and the nearby town of Pershore can be enjoyed. The River Avon and the local Norman Abbey, which is floodlit at night, can also be seen from the building.

OWNER: Gina Horton OPEN: all year ROOMS: 2 double, 1 twin; all rooms with bath/shower, tea/coffee and TV; lounge with TV TERMS: single occupancy £29–£35, twin/double £43–£55; children's reductions by arrangement; deposit sometimes required CARDS: none DETAILS: children welcome; no dogs; no smoking; car park; garden; swimming-pool; tennis

---

Any smoking restrictions that we know of are given in the details at the end of the entry.

PETER TAVY Devon — map 1

The Barn

Higher Churchtown Farm, Peter Tavy PL19 9NR TEL: (01822) 810337
1m off A386, 3m NE of Tavistock

The Barn has a large garden with picnic tables and is peacefully situated on the edge of the village, which is a good base for exploring Dartmoor. The three smallish bedrooms are in an annexe and can be used in any combination – as single, double, twin or family rooms – and share a shower-room. Breakfast is served in the spacious sitting-room, which has pleasant views over the garden. The Burdens are very friendly, welcoming people, and the Barn offers good-value accommodation.

OWNER: Jane Burden OPEN: all year exc Christmas ROOMS: 3 single/double/twin/family; lounge TERMS: single/single occupancy £15–£18, twin/double £30–£36, family room from £45; deposit: £5 per person CARDS: none DETAILS: children welcome; guide dogs by arrangement; no smoking; car park; garden

---

Churchtown

Peter Tavy PL19 9NN TEL: (01822) 810477
1m off A386, 2m N of Tavistock

Standing in an attractive garden close to the edge of Dartmoor, this substantial late-Victorian house is a comfortable, friendly place, particularly suited to those interested in country pursuits. The Lanes used to keep horses that were in training for three-day events, and can provide stabling for guests who bring their own horses. Two of the comfortable bedrooms are *en suite*, and all have TVs. A pub serving evening meals is a five-minute walk away.

OWNERS: Major and Mrs W.L.S. Lane OPEN: all year exc Christmas ROOMS: 2 single, both with wash-basin; 2 double, 1 with bath, 1 with shower; tea/coffee and TV in all bedrooms TERMS: single £15–£18, single occupancy £15–£30, double £30–£36; deposit required CARDS: none DETAILS: no children under 10; no dogs; car park; garden

PETWORTH West Sussex — map 3

Old Railway Station NEW ENTRY

Coultershaw Bridge, Petworth GU28 OJF TEL/FAX: (01798) 342346
on A285, 1m S of Petworth

Petworth's former railway station, a Grade II-listed building dating from 1894, has been most attractively converted to provide accommodation in an unusual setting. The platform is now a terrace where guests can take breakfast on fine days, and there is a lawn where the rails used to run. Beyond is a beguiling steep bank, with steps and benches, and covered in wild flowers and trees. The Rapleys are welcoming and friendly, and provide an 'outstanding' breakfast, according to one reader. Both double bedrooms are spacious and well equipped, with *en suite* bath and shower, and one is reached by a spiral staircase. The large lounge incorporates the dining-area and was once the station's waiting-room. Petworth House is the nearest attraction, but Goodwood, Parham, Uppark, Arundel and Chichester are all within easy reach.

OWNERS: Mr and Mrs Rapley OPEN: all year ROOMS: 2 double; both rooms with bath/shower, tea/coffee and TV; 1 room suitable for wheelchair users; lounge with TV TERMS: single occupancy £35–£45, double £58–£65; deposit: £10 per night CARDS: none DETAILS: no children under 10; no dogs; smoking in public areas only; car park; garden

PICKERING North Yorkshire — map 9

Bramwood Guest House

19 Hallgarth, Pickering YO18 7AW TEL: (01751) 474066
off A169 heading out of Pickering centre towards Whitby

Bramwood, a Grade II-listed terraced house with walled gardens, built in 1734, was taken over by Steve and Georgina Hackett late in 1996. Bedrooms have been refurbished and redecorated, and all rooms now have *en suite* facilities. Breakfast and pre-arranged dinners are served in a separate dining-room, where a fine collection of blue dishes is on display. The comfortable lounge has satellite TV and a fire to keep it warm on cooler evenings. Pickering makes a good base for exploring the North York Moors and the coast.

OWNERS: Steve and Georgina Hackett OPEN: all year exc Christmas ROOMS: 2 single, 3 double, 1 family; all rooms with bath/shower and tea/coffee; lounge with TV TERMS: single occupancy £25–£28, twin/double £40–£46, family room £50–£56; half-price for ages 5–11; dinner £12; deposit: £15 CARDS: Switch, Visa DETAILS: no children under 5; no dogs; no smoking; car park; garden

PICKET HILL Hampshire — map 2

Picket Hill House

Picket Hill BH24 3HH TEL: (01425) 476173 FAX: (01425) 470022
heading W on A31, 1m before Ringwood take exit marked Hightown and Crow and then first driveway on left

'Delightful in every way' was one reporter's verdict on this family home on the edge of the New Forest, just outside the small market town of Ringwood. It is set in a lovely garden with well-kept lawns and shrubs, and surrounded by a seven-foot-high fence to keep out wandering deer. Mrs Pocock is a welcoming and friendly host, and provides comfortable accommodation in pleasant *en suite* bedrooms and a large lounge with TV, books and games. Evening meals are not usually provided as there are many restaurants and pubs nearby, but breakfast is very good. The Pococks keep horses, as well as a cat and a dog, and can accommodate guests' horses by arrangement. Beaches and ferries to the Isle of Wight are only a few miles away.

OWNERS: Audrey and Norman Pocock OPEN: all year exc Christmas ROOMS: 2 double, 1 twin; all rooms with bath/shower and tea/coffee; lounge with TV TERMS: single occupancy £25–£44, twin/double £36–£44; deposit required CARDS: Delta, MasterCard, Switch, Visa DETAILS: no children under 12; no dogs; smoking in 1 lounge only; car park; games room; garden

PLAXTOL Kent **map 3**

Jordans

Sheet Hill, Plaxtol TN15 0PU TEL: (01732) 810379
from M25, take A25 to Ightham, then join A227 for 2m; Plaxtol on left

Leaded windows, inglenook fireplaces, oak beams and a friendly atmosphere all add to the charm of this fifteenth-century Tudor house. Set in an acre of well-maintained gardens (which guests may explore), it lies on a quiet country lane amid orchards and woodland, half a mile from the centre of Plaxtol. Jo Lindsay is a painter and gardener, and a Blue Badge local guide. The single room adjoins the double and they can be let together for families. Residents can relax in the attractively furnished sitting-room, which has a TV. Continental breakfast is normally served, but a cooked breakfast is available for an extra charge.

OWNER: Jo Lindsay OPEN: mid-Jan to mid-Dec ROOMS: 1 single; 2 double/family, both with bath; TV in double bedrooms TERMS: single/single occupancy £38–£40, double £58–£62, family room £87–£93; deposit: 50% CARDS: none DETAILS: no children under 12; no dogs; no smoking; car park; garden

PLYMOUTH Devon **map 1**

Park View

13 Radford Road, West Hoe, Plymouth PL1 3BY TEL: (01752) 260669

Park View is an attractively creeper-covered Victorian terraced guesthouse in a side street close to the centre of Plymouth. It is also only a short walk from the sea front, citadel and Hoe. Accommodation is simple, clean and comfortable, and the atmosphere is friendly and welcoming. The four bedrooms have shower cubicles and share two WCs and a shower-room. Breakfast is served in the lounge/dining-room, which overlooks the square across the road. Although the house has no garden of its own, there is a garden and tennis court in the square.

OWNER: Beryl Mavin OPEN: all year ROOMS: 2 single, 2 double; all rooms with shower (no WC), tea/coffee and TV; lounge with TV TERMS: single/single occupancy £16, double £31; half-price for children under 10 CARDS: none DETAILS: children welcome; dogs welcome

Rosaland Hotel

32 Houndiscombe Road, Mutley, Plymouth PL4 6HQ
TEL: (01752) 664749 FAX: (01752) 256984

This well-maintained and attractively decorated large Victorian terraced house was built in 1888, and is in a quiet residential street near the railway station and university. The bedrooms are quite small and furnished in pine, and all have telephones and satellite TV. Breakfast and evening meals are served in the pine-furnished dining-room, and there is a residents' dining-room with leather armchairs, a large fireplace and rich red carpet, and also a licensed bar. The Hoe and Barbican are only 15 minutes' walk away.

OWNERS: Peter and Heather Shaw OPEN: all year ROOMS: 3 single, 2 with shower, 1 with wash-basin; 3 double, with shower; 1 twin; 1 family, with shower; tea/coffee and TV in all bedrooms; lounge with TV TERMS: single/single occupancy £17–£26, twin/double £32– £38, family room £45–£50; dinner £10; deposit required CARDS: Amex, Diners, MasterCard, Visa DETAILS: children by arrangement; no dogs; smoking in bedrooms only; car park

POINTON Lincolnshire map 6

Greenoaks

NEW ENTRY

Pinfold Lane, Pointon NG34 0NB
TEL: (01529) 240193 FAX: (01529) 240612
off B117 in centre of Pointon

Greenoaks is a red-brick Georgian house surrounded by three acres of pleasant gardens and paddocks. The name is taken from the two unusual Ilex oak trees which stand at the entrance to the property. Many of the house's original features remain, including casement shutters, oak beams and a huge fireplace in the lounge, and there is a wonderful old-fashioned lived-in ambience. The spacious bedrooms are adorned with antiques and decorated in rich colours; one has an *en suite* shower. Ann Firth is a friendly, outgoing lady, and is a keen horse rider. This establishment is well situated for attending the Stamford Shakespeare season, and local village pubs serve evening meals.

OWNERS: Anthony and Ann Firth OPEN: all year exc Christmas and New Year ROOMS: 1 single; 2 twin, 1 with shower; tea/coffee in all bedrooms; lounge with TV TERMS: single £20, single occupancy £22–£25, twin £40–£45; deposit required CARDS: none DETAILS: no children under 10; no dogs; no smoking; car park; garden

'Bath / shower' in the details under each entry means that the rooms have en suite *facilities. 'Private bathroom' signifies that a room has a bathroom for its exclusive use. The B&B may have other, shared bathroom facilities as well. We list 'wash-basins' for rooms that have them but do not have* en suite *or private facilities.*

POOLE Dorset map 2

ITP Lodge

NEW ENTRY

53 Branksea Avenue, Poole BH15 4DP
TEL: (01202) 673419 FAX: (01202) 667260

Renate Wadham offers not only bed-and-breakfast, but English lessons, sailing and golf lessons, and helps with antique hunting. Originally from Germany, Renate is a delightful lady who loves having guests and doing whatever she can to ensure they have a good time. The modern whitewashed house stands at the end of a quiet road with views of green fields and the yachting harbour. The double room has a balcony overlooking the harbour and Brownsea Island. Bedrooms are comfortable and well equipped, and a free glass of sherry is offered to arriving guests. Breakfast is served either on the lovely first-floor landing, the combined breakfast/sitting-room overlooking the garden, or – weather permitting – on the patio.

OWNER: Renate Wadham OPEN: all year ROOMS: 1 double, 1 twin; both rooms with bath/shower, tea/coffee and TV TERMS: single occupancy £25–£30, twin/double £45–£50 CARDS: none DETAILS: children welcome; no dogs; no smoking; car park

PORT ISAAC Cornwall map 1

Archer Farm

Trewetha, Port Isaac PL29 3RU TEL: (01208) 880522
off B3267, 5m N of Wadebridge

Archer Farm has the appearance of a modern house, both from the outside and the inside, but it was once an almost derelict rambling farmhouse. Vicki and David Welton converted the house and extended it to provide comfortable accommodation. The simply furnished bedrooms vary in size, with one room on the ground floor and two having balconies. There is a relaxing lounge/bar, a spacious and bright dining-room, a small TV lounge, and drinks can be taken on one of the outside patios. Archer Farm is set in peaceful, unspoilt countryside just 15 minutes' walk from the charming fishing village of Port Isaac, and is close to sandy beaches, coves and cliff walks.

OWNER: Victoria Welton OPEN: Apr to Oct ROOMS: 4 double, 3 with bath/shower, 1 with private bathroom; 1 family, with bath/shower; tea/coffee and TV in all bedrooms; lounge with TV TERMS: single occupancy £21, double £42–£60, family room £54–£60; children's reductions by arrangement; deposit: 10% CARDS: none DETAILS: no children under 3; no dogs in public rooms; smoking in lounge/bar only; bedrooms by arrangement; car park; garden

---

Many B&Bs are in remote places, and although in many cases we provide directions, it is always advisable to ask for clear instructions when booking.

PORTLOE Cornwall

map 1

Tregain

NEW ENTRY

Portloe TR2 5QU TEL/FAX: (01872) 501252

Tregain combines the roles of tea-room, licensed restaurant, souvenir shop and bed and breakfast, and is even the village post office. It is run single-handedly by Clare Holdsworth, who – in spite of all her hard work – still has time for a good conversation. Unsurprisingly, she knows everything there is to know about the unspoilt fishing village of Portloe. Accommodation is very simple, the twin and single sharing a downstairs bathroom. Very steep stairs lead up to the bedrooms, so Tregain is not ideal for the infirm. The restaurant is very popular and the food has an excellent reputation – Clare's crab soup is particularly recommended. There is a patio at the back for residents, overlooking a stream and green hills.

OWNER: Clare Holdsworth OPEN: Apr to Oct ROOMS: 1 single, 1 twin TERMS: single £20, single occupancy £30, twin/double £40; dinner £25; deposit: £5 per person per night CARDS: MasterCard, Switch, Visa DETAILS: children welcome; dogs welcome but not to be left alone in bedrooms; no smoking *(The Good Food Guide)*

PORTSMOUTH Hampshire

map 2

Fortitude Cottage

51 Broad Street, Old Portsmouth PO1 2JD TEL/FAX: (01705) 823748

Fortitude Cottage, named after an old ship, is a narrow terraced house with bow windows in the heart of Old Portsmouth. It overlooks the harbour towards the Isle of Wight, and is a stone's throw from the ferry terminal and the quay for the waterbus to HMS Victory and the Mary Rose. Carol Harbeck is a friendly and enthusiastic host and has lived in the cottage – built at the end of the World War II by her parents – for most of her life. Bedrooms are tiny but prettily decorated, warm and cosy, and two are *en suite*. The breakfast room overlooks the fishing boats and ferries. There are no parking facilities, although there is a public car park, charging £2 per day, across the street. Carol Harbeck's mother, who lives in a house to the rear of the cottage, also offers B&B. She has two double rooms, both with wonderful views.

OWNER: Carol Harbeck OPEN: all year exc Christmas ROOMS: 1 double, with bath/shower; 2 twin, 1 with bath/shower, 1 with private bathroom; tea/coffee and TV in all bedrooms TERMS: single occupancy £24–£30, twin/double £40–£46; deposit required CARDS: Amex, MasterCard, Switch, Visa DETAILS: no children under 12; no dogs; no smoking

If we know a B&B has an alcohol licence, we say so. Most unlicensed B&Bs that offer evening meals allow guests to bring their own wine to dinner. If you wish to do this, ask the B&B when you book.

POULSHOT Wiltshire map 2

Middle Green Farm

The Green, Poulshot SN10 1RT
TEL: (01380) 828413 FAX: (01380) 828826
3m SW of Devizes, 1m off A361 Devizes to Trowbridge road

Middle Green Farm is in the centre of the quiet and picturesque village of Poulshot. This Georgian house is on the edge of the village green, surrounded by an attractive garden, and has a welcoming atmosphere. Three of the bedrooms are in main the house and share a bathroom, and one double room is in a garden annexe with its own bathroom and small kitchenette. Guests have use of a drawing-room with TV, and evening meals are served in the nearby Raven Inn.

OWNERS: Angela and Derek Bullen OPEN: all year exc Christmas and New Year ROOMS: 1 single; 2 double, 1 with bath/shower, 1 with wash-basin; 1 twin; tea/coffee in all bedrooms; TV in 1 double bedroom and lounge TERMS: single £19–£25, single occupancy £25, twin/double £38–£41; reductions for children sharing with parents; deposit: £10 per room CARDS: none DETAILS: children welcome; no dogs; no smoking; car park; garden

PRINCETOWN Devon map 1

Duchy House

Tavistock Road, Princetown PL20 6QF TEL: (01822) 890552
off B3357, 7m E of Tavistock

This semi-detached Victorian house, right in the middle of Dartmoor, is both a guesthouse and licensed café, and is a relaxing place to stay. It stands almost opposite the primary school, and the High Moorland Visitors' Centre and the world-famous Dartmoor Prison are both nearby. Although the Trimbles have been running Duchy House only since 1994, they are very knowledgeable about the area and happy to advise on walking, bird-watching, pony-trekking and golfing. The house has been simply furnished and has spacious rooms. The upstairs lounge has a TV, video and lots of games and books, and overlooks the moor. The café, which serves home-made cakes and scones, is open for food most of the day. Breakfast and evening meals are served in the residents' dining-room.

OWNERS: Ernie and Hilary Trimble OPEN: all year exc Nov ROOMS: 2 double, 1 with bath/shower, 1 with wash-basin; 1 twin, with wash-basin; tea/coffee in all bedrooms; lounge with TV TERMS: single occupancy £17–£25, twin/double £34–£40; £5 for children under 10 sharing with parents; dinner £10; deposit: £10 per room CARDS: none DETAILS: children welcome; well-behaved dogs welcome; no smoking; car park; garden

B&Bs are selected for the Guide for their warm welcome, cleanliness, a friendly atmosphere and, wherever possible, an attractive location or a building that is itself of some historical or architectural interest.

PULHAM MARKET Norfolk **map 6**

Old Bakery

NEW ENTRY

Church Walk, Pulham Market, Diss IP21 4SJ TEL/FAX: (01379) 676492
1½m from A140, on B1134 Harleston road

The Old Bakery is a listed 400-year old oak-framed and studded building, situated in the centre of this conservation village, surrounded by old thatched houses. The pretty garden has a pond, and a summer house with an interesting mural on the back wall created by Martin Croft's brother, who is an artist. Full of old-world charm, the spacious interior of the house is furnished with antiques, has heavy lined curtains, and retains its old timbers, fireplaces and spiral staircases. There are three large bedrooms, all of which have their own *en suite* facilities, armchairs and TV. Martin is a talented chef – superb meals are served in the dining-room – as well as being an accomplished cellist, and is happy to play duets with any piano-playing guests. Mulled wine is served around the log fire in the lounge on cool evenings, and guests also have the use of a garden room. The ambience is relaxed and informal in this comfortable house, and Martin and Jean are wonderful hosts who have compiled a wealth of information on places of interest in the area. As a recent report says, 'This guesthouse is one of those little treasured finds which stand out as rather special.' Diss and an Elizabethan church at nearby Tivetshall are both worth a visit.

OWNERS: Martin and Jean Croft OPEN: all year exc Christmas ROOMS: 1 double, 2 twin; all rooms with bath/shower and TV; lounge TERMS: single occupancy £35–£38, twin/double £40–£46; dinner £15; deposit: £20–£40 CARDS: none DETAILS: no children; no dogs; smoking in garden room only; car park; garden

READING Berkshire **map 2**

Rainbow Lodge

152 Caversham Road, Reading RG1 8AZ
TEL: (01734) 588140 FAX: (01734) 586500

Rainbow Lodge offers good-value accommodation within half a mile of the town centre. There are eight modestly sized, well-appointed *en suite* rooms, all with cable TV. Breakfast (at an extra charge) is taken in the hotel restaurant 100 yards away. It is licensed and vegetarian meals are always on offer; snacks and sandwiches are also available on request. The Lodge is well maintained, and information on the area is provided. Bedrooms facing the street are subject to noise, so light sleepers should ask for a bedroom at the back. Cots and highchairs are available, and there is car parking.

OWNER: Mr D. Staples OPEN: all year exc sometimes Christmas ROOMS: 3 single, 1 double, 4 twin; all rooms with bath/shower, tea/coffee and TV; lounge with TV (in hotel) TERMS: room only: single £30–£38, single occupancy £40–£44, twin/double £40–£44; babies free; dinner £13; deposit: credit card details CARDS: Amex, Delta, Diners, MasterCard, Switch, Visa DETAILS: children welcome; no dogs; car park

REDFORD West Sussex map 3

Redford Cottage NEW ENTRY

Redford, Midhurst GU29 0QF TEL/FAX: (01428) 741242
off A3 at Liphook, then 3m S

Redford Cottage is a creeper-covered house dating from around 1640, set in a lovely garden in the peaceful hamlet of Redford, which is three miles from Midhurst. The Angelas give a warm welcome to their guests and have furnished the house with antiques in keeping with its original character. The bedrooms are comfortable, with the two upstairs ones sharing a bathroom. The third bedroom, which is more like a suite, is on the ground floor and has its own beamed sitting-room with open fire, private shower-room, and access to the garden. The large drawing-room has a round corner table where breakfast, cooked on the Aga, is served.

OWNER: Caroline Angela OPEN: all year exc Christmas and New Year ROOMS: 2 double, 1 with shower, 1 with private bathroom; 1 twin, with private bathroom; tea/coffee and TV in all bedrooms; lounge with TV TERMS: single occupancy £28–£34, twin/double £48–£56; children under 5 free, half-price for ages 5–15; deposit: £10 per room per night CARDS: none DETAILS: children welcome; dogs by arrangement; smoking in certain areas only; car park; garden

REDLYNCH Wiltshire map 2

Templemans Old Farmhouse

Redlynch SP5 2JS TEL: (01725) 510331
from Salisbury take A338 S for 5m, turn left at Downton traffic lights, first left after sign for Redlynch, then first right, fork left and follow to end of lane

This spacious seventeenth-century farmhouse was part of the Trafalgar Estate presented to Lord Nelson's family by a grateful nation. It stands in a secluded hilltop position with panoramic views over the New Forest. The Dabells are a friendly couple, and the house has a pleasant family atmosphere. There is an elegant drawing-room, and breakfasts are served in the dining-room. All three bedrooms are large, and the double has lovely New Forest views. The grounds extend to ten acres of gardens, paddocks with sheep, croquet lawn and a hard tennis court. It is advisable to ask for directions to the house, as it is somewhat difficult to find.

OWNERS: June and Peter Dabell OPEN: Apr to Oct ROOMS: 1 single, 1 double, 1 twin; all rooms with wash-basin; lounge with TV TERMS: single £18–£20, twin/double £36–£40; children's reductions by arrangement; deposit: 50% CARDS: none DETAILS: children welcome; no dogs; no smoking in bedrooms or dining-room; car park; garden; tennis

---

If a B&B offers off-street car parking, we note 'car park' at the end of the entry. If nearby on-street parking must be used, in most cases we give details in the descriptive text.

RICHMOND North Yorkshire **map 9**

The Old Brewery

29 The Green, Richmond DL10 4RG
TEL: (01748) 822460 FAX: (01748) 825561

Tucked away in a quiet part of the town, with picturesque views of the castle ruins, is this charming nineteenth-century building. Within, the rooms are furnished in elegant Victorian style, and the attractive lounge has books, games, puzzles and a TV to occupy guests. One of the bedrooms has a hand-made four-poster, and some of the beds are adorned with richly patterned coverlets. The beautiful garden, alive with flowers and plant life in the summer, is the perfect place to unwind. Pre-arranged three-course dinners are served at separate tables in the dining-room. Free car-parking is available around the adjacent green.

OWNER: Yvonne Mears OPEN: Feb to Nov ROOMS: 3 double, 1 twin, 1 four-poster; all rooms with bath/shower exc 1 double with private bathroom; tea/coffee and TV in all bedrooms; lounge with TV TERMS: single occupancy £30, twin/double £40, four-poster £42; dinner £13; deposit sometimes required CARDS: Delta, MasterCard, Switch, Visa DETAILS: no children under 8; no dogs; garden

---

West End

45 Reeth Road, Richmond DL10 4EX TEL: (01748) 824783

West End, on the outskirts of Richmond, very close to the river and open countryside, is an interesting and slightly unusual Victorian guesthouse. It is run by a charming couple, Kath and Trevor Teeley, who have provided everything possible to ensure their guests' comfort. Bedrooms are decorated in pastel colours and are pine furnished. Residents also have use of a large lounge, decorated in a blue and pink design, and a small sitting-area on the first floor. Three-course dinners are served in the licensed dining-room. There are four cottages in the grounds, available for self-catering. The Forbidden Corner in the nearby Tupgill Park Estate is worth a visit.

OWNERS: Kath and Trevor Teeley OPEN: all year exc Christmas ROOMS: 1 single, 2 double, 1 twin, 1 family; all rooms with bath/shower exc single with private bathroom; tea/coffee and TV in all bedrooms; lounge TERMS: single £21, single occupancy £30, twin/double £42, family room £49; dinner £12.50; deposit: £10 CARDS: none DETAILS: children welcome; dogs welcome; smoking in lounge only; car park; garden

---

If you intend to spend several days at a B&B, it is worth asking whether there are reduced rates, particularly if the period is midweek or off-season. It is always best to check prices, especially for single occupancy, when booking. If we know of any particular payment stipulations, we mention them in the details at the end of the entry. We asked the proprietors to estimate their 1998 prices in the autumn of 1997, so the rates may have changed since publication. If a deposit is required for an advance booking, this is stated in the details.

RINGMORE Devon map 1

Ayrmer House

Ringmore TQ7 4HL TEL: (01548) 810391
from A379 2m E of Modbury take B3392 towards Bigbury-on-Sea then follow signs to Ringmore from St Ann's Chapel

Ayrmer House occupies a wonderful position overlooking a pretty village near the south coast of Devon. Inside, it is bright and has large windows plus a wide balcony, accessible from some of the bedrooms, to take full advantage of the magnificent views down the valley to the sea. Bedrooms are spacious and comfortably furnished, and there is also a suite (suitable for families with older children) comprising a twin-bedded room, a double room and a bathroom. The comfortable lounge has a dining-area at one end, and leads out on to a terrace, which makes a pleasant place to sit on fine days. Evening meals are available by arrangement. A track leads down to the relatively unspoilt beach.

OWNER: Isabella Dodds OPEN: all year exc Christmas ROOMS: 1 double, 1 twin, 1 family; all rooms with private bathroom, tea/coffee and TV; lounge with TV TERMS: single occupancy £26, twin/double £40–£48, family room from £40; deposit: 20% CARDS: none DETAILS: no children under 10; no dogs; no smoking; car park; garden

RINGWOOD Hampshire map 2

Little Forest Lodge

Poulner Hill, Ringwood BH24 3HS
TEL: (01425) 478848 FAX: (01425) 473564
just off A31 Ringwood to Cadnam road

High standards continue at this large country house, which is now run by Judith Harrison, who extends to guests a very warm and friendly welcome. Set in two acres of landscaped gardens, the house is elegantly furnished and very comfortable. Breakfast and home-cooked dinners are served in the oak-panelled dining-room overlooking the garden. Drinks can be enjoyed in the bar, and on chilly evenings a log fire burns in the elegant lounge. All the attractive bedrooms have *en suite* facilities and are well appointed; a new addition is the 'garden room', which is also available on a self-catering basis. Little Forest Lodge is an ideal base from which to explore the New Forest and surrounding area.

OWNER: Judith Harrison OPEN: all year ROOMS: 5 double, 1 family; all rooms with bath/shower, tea/coffee and TV; lounge TERMS: single occupancy £25–£40, double £45–£75, family room £45–£80; children under 2 free, £8 for ages 2–12; dinner £14.50; deposit: £25 CARDS: MasterCard, Visa DETAILS: children welcome; no dogs in public rooms; smoking in lounge only; car park; garden

If there are any bedrooms with TV, or with tea / coffee-making facilities, we mention this in the details at the end of an entry.

Moortown Lodge

244 Christchurch Road, Ringwood BH24 3AS
TEL: (01425) 471404 FAX: (01425) 476052
on B3347, 1½m S of Ringwood

This Georgian house lies on the edge of the New Forest about a mile and a half from the town centre. It was formerly a fishing lodge on the Moortown Estate, which was once owned by William Gladstone. The small bedrooms have floral wallpapers and are all *en suite* except for the single; one has a four-poster bed. Guests can relax in the cosy lounge, or enjoy a drink in the bar. Jilly Burrows-Jones has earned quite a reputation for her cooking, preparing freshly cooked food from locally produced ingredients, and the restaurant is also open to non-residents.

OWNERS: Jilly and Bob Burrows-Jones OPEN: all year exc Christmas to mid-Jan ROOMS: 1 single, 2 double, 2 twin, 1 four-poster, 1 family; all rooms exc single with bath/shower; tea/coffee and TV in all bedrooms; lounge TERMS: single £30–£32, single occupancy £38–£45, twin/double £50–£70, four-poster/family room £60–£80; dinner £18.50; deposit required CARDS: Amex, MasterCard, Visa DETAILS: children welcome; no dogs; no smoking in dining-room and some bedrooms; car park

RIPON North Yorkshire

map 9

Bishopton Grove House

NEW ENTRY

Bishopton, Ripon HG4 2QL TEL: (01765) 600888

Built in 1795, this Georgian house stands in a peaceful, secluded garden. It has a free and easy atmosphere, and owner Suzi Wimpress is a friendly, chatty lady who treats her guests as friends, allowing them to come and go as they please. Original fireplaces remain, and the house is warm and comfortable. The three good-sized bedrooms have either *en suite* or private bathrooms. Breakfast, with choices including kedgeree, kippers, croissants or a full cooked breakfast, is served in the dining-room, which has a sitting-area. The town centre is a short walk away, and Fountains Abbey is among the many nearby attractions.

OWNER: Susi Wimpress OPEN: all year ROOMS: 1 double, with shower; 1 twin, with wash-basin; 1 family, with wash-basin; tea/coffee in all bedrooms; lounge with TV TERMS: single occupancy £20–£25, twin/double £35–£40, family room from £35; dinner £10 CARDS: none DETAILS: children welcome; dogs welcome; car park; garden

---

To find an entry in the Guide, *go to the maps at the back of the book. Entries are plotted on the maps under their closest village, hamlet or city, except in London, where they are listed by name of B&B. After choosing your localities, go to the relevant section of the book (England, Scotland, Wales etc.), where localities are listed in alphabetical order (by B&B name order in London). There is also an index at the back of the book.*

ROADWATER Somerset map 1

Wood Advent Farm

Roadwater TA23 0RR TEL/FAX: (01984) 640920
from M5 junction 23 take A39 to Washford; turn at sign to Roadwater; in village turn left at post office

Wood Advent Farm stands at the foot of the Brendon Hills within the Exmoor National Park. The farmhouse is a spacious listed building dating from the early 1800s (although the Brewer family has been farming the site since the 1700s), and is part of a 340-acre working farm. John and Diana Brewer are welcoming hosts who go out of their way to ensure visitors are well looked after. The four well-appointed bedrooms have *en suite* facilities and TVs, are individually decorated and have fine views of the grounds. Guests have the use of two lounges: one is supplied with leaflets on local places of interest, board games and a TV; while the drawing-room, filled with books, provides a quieter place to relax in. Diana Brewer takes great pride in her cooking, which includes fresh produce from the farm; and pre-arranged evening meals and Sunday lunches are served at separate tables in the dining-room with its big open fireplace. A wine list complements the food nicely; alternatively, there is the farm's own spring water. The large garden includes a small heated swimming-pool and informal grass tennis court. Well-marked footpaths run across the farm, and the Brewers will happily supply maps.

OWNERS: John and Diana Brewer OPEN: all year exc Christmas ROOMS: 2 double, 2 twin; all rooms with bath/shower, tea/coffee and TV; lounge TERMS: single occupancy £25–£40, twin/double £38–£50; dinner £14; deposit: 10% CARDS: MasterCard, Switch, Visa DETAILS: no children under 10; dogs in kennels only; smoking in 1 lounge only; car park; games room; garden; swimming-pool; tennis

ROBIN HOOD'S BAY North Yorkshire map 9

Devon House

Station Road, Robin Hood's Bay YO22 4RL TEL: (01947) 880197

It is easy to find this modest Victorian house in the town centre, especially in summer: look for the house with the wonderful array of colourful hanging baskets and potted plants. Within, everything is spick and span and in excellent decorative order. Lace and dried-flower arrangements made by Daphne Duncalfe's mother help prettify the house, and the bedrooms are fresh and bright. The double and family rooms have *en suite* facilities and all have TVs; the other two rooms share a bathroom, a shower-room with WC and a separate WC. Breakfast is served in the dining-room. Guests are charged a nominal £1 per stay for parking their cars in the public car park across the street.

OWNER: Mrs D.H. Duncalfe OPEN: all year exc Christmas ROOMS: 1 double, with shower; 1 twin, with wash-basin; 1 family, with shower; tea/coffee and TV in all bedrooms TERMS: twin/double £32–£36, family room £48–£54; half-price for children sharing with parents; deposit: £10 CARDS: none DETAILS: children welcome; no dogs; no smoking; garden

ROCKBOURNE Hampshire map 2

Shearings

Rockbourne SP6 3NA TEL: (01725) 518256 FAX: (01725) 518255
take Rockbourne turning off A354, 1m S of Coombe Bissett

Shearings, a beautiful sixteenth-century thatched cottage, overlooks a stream in the middle of Rockbourne, on the edge of the New Forest. Visitors to the pretty village will no doubt be charmed by its thirteenth-century church, Roman villa and picturesque old pub. The house is full of old-world charm, with uneven floors, oak beams and inglenook fireplaces, and is set in a lovely, well-maintained garden of lawns and shrubs, with a summerhouse, croquet lawn and a sunny patio. Guests are treated as friends by owner Brigadier Colin Watts. Bedrooms are comfortable and well equipped, and there is a small sitting-room with TV, games, books and brochures.

OWNER: Colin Watts OPEN: mid-Feb to mid-Dec ROOMS: 1 single, with private bathroom; 1 double, with shower; 1 twin, with private bathroom; 1 family, with shower; tea/coffee in all bedrooms; lounge with TV TERMS: single £24–£25, single occupancy £30, twin/double £48–£50, family room £50–£60; deposit: 10% CARDS: none DETAILS: no children under 12; no dogs; no smoking; car park; garden

RODE Somerset map 2

Irondale House NEW ENTRY

67 High Street, Rode BA3 6PB TEL/FAX: (01373) 830730
off A36, 10m S of Bath

This late eighteenth-century house is located in the main street of a quiet Somerset village, with a lovely walled garden with northerly views. The house has a warm and friendly atmosphere, and has been comfortably refurbished to a high standard. The two bedrooms are designed to be either doubles or twins, one of which is *en suite*, complete with bidet. Guests are free to make tea or coffee at any time in the family kitchen, and have use of a large, elegant drawing-room, the garden, and a dining-room off the kitchen where breakfast is served. Irondale House is a good base for visiting Bath, Glastonbury, Longleat House and Stourhead Gardens.

OWNERS: Mr and Mrs Holder OPEN: all year exc Christmas ROOMS: 2 double/twin, 1 with bath/shower, 1 with private bathroom; tea/coffee and TV in both bedrooms; lounge with TV TERMS: single occupancy £45–£55, twin/double £58–£60; deposit: credit card details CARDS: Delta, MasterCard, Visa DETAILS: children welcome; no dogs; no smoking upstairs or in bedrooms; car park; garden

ROGATE West Sussex map 3

Cumbers House

Rogate GU31 5EJ TEL: (01730) 821401
on A272, 1½m E of Rogate

A large (three-and-a-half acre) woodland garden adds to the appeal of Cumbers House, which lies down a quiet rhododendron-lined driveway and enjoys pleasant views over open countryside. A walk around the garden may allow you glimpses of deer, rabbits and other wild things. The 1930s-built house is spacious and comfortable, furnished in part with antiques. The Asletts ensure that guests receive a warm welcome, and maintain a friendly, informal atmosphere. Open fires burn on chilly days in both the drawing-room, which has a TV, and the dining-room. The two twin-bedded guest rooms share a bathroom. Home-baked bread and eggs from their hens feature at breakfast.

OWNERS: Major and Mrs Jon Aslett OPEN: all year exc Christmas and Jan ROOMS: 2 twin, both with wash-basin; tea/coffee in both bedrooms; lounge with TV TERMS: single occupancy £22–£23, twin £44–£46 CARDS: none DETAILS: no children; no dogs; no smoking; car park; garden

---

Mizzards Farm

Rogate GU31 5HS TEL: (01730) 821656 FAX: (01730) 821655
from A272 at Rogate turn S at crossroads; after ½m cross river and first right after 300yds

Mizzards Farm is set in 13 acres of pleasant gardens and fields bordering the River Rother. It is a sixteenth-century mellow brick and stone building on the edge of the village, in a designated area of outstanding beauty. The entrance hall with its old flagstone floors has a splendid wooden staircase leading to a galleried landing. Breakfasts are served in the dining-room, with its large stone fireplace, vaulted ceiling, lovely old furniture and interesting pictures. Guests may relax in the large elegant drawing-room, which has a grand piano and lots of family antiques. All the bedrooms are well appointed; one – reflecting a former pop star owner's taste – boasts an impressive four-poster bed on a raised hexagonal platform and an *en suite* ornate marble bathroom full of mirrors and a double-sized bath. The gardens include a croquet lawn, plus an enchanting woodland area complete with deer and badgers and a lake with waterfowl. A covered swimming-pool is available for guests' use from May through September. A minimum of two nights must be booked at weekends.

OWNERS: Mr and Mrs J.C. Francis OPEN: all year exc Christmas ROOMS: 1 double, 1 twin, 1 four-poster; 2 rooms with bath, 1 with bath and shower; tea/coffee and TV in all bedrooms; lounge TERMS: single occupancy £32–£38, twin/double £52–£54, four-poster £60; deposit: 1 night's charge CARDS: none DETAILS: no children under 7; no dogs; no smoking; car park; garden; swimming-pool

ROMSEY Hampshire map 2

Spursholt House NEW ENTRY

Salisbury Road, Romsey SO51 6DJ
TEL: (01794) 512229 FAX: (01794) 523142
take A27 NW from Romsey; house is ¾m on right-hand side

Spursholt House is an impressive seventeenth-century manor set back from the main road at the end of a long drive. It is surrounded by a large garden with paved terraces, lawns (including croquet), topiary, a parterre and lily pond. The house was originally built for one of Cromwell's generals, and at one time belonged to the Palmerston family. Mrs Hughes is a most welcoming lady who takes great pride in her home, and treats visitors as part of the family. The house has been furnished in keeping with its age and style, with a charming drawing-room. One of the bedrooms is oak panelled, and all have extra large beds, sofas and garden views. Breakfasts and excellent home-cooked evening meals (available by arrangement from Monday to Thursday), are served in the dining-room. For those eating out there is a good selection of places in Romsey. No one-night bookings are taken at weekends.

OWNERS: Anthea and Bill Hughes OPEN: all year exc Christmas ROOMS: 1 single, with private bathroom; 3 double, 1 with bath/shower, 2 with private bathroom; tea/coffee in all bedrooms; lounge with TV TERMS: single/single occupancy £25–£35, twin/double £44–£48, £10 for children sharing with parents; dinner £15; deposit: £10 CARDS: none DETAILS: children welcome; dogs on lead only in house; no smoking; car park; garden

ROSS-ON-WYE Hereford & Worcester map 5

The Arches NEW ENTRY

Walford Road, Ross-on-Wye HR9 5PT TEL: (01989) 563348

The Arches is a Georgian-style house set in half an acre of secluded gardens. The seven well-appointed bedrooms have good-quality furniture, are individually decorated and have views of the garden. The various pieces of antique furniture in the house include a grandfather clock, and there is a teapot and cup collection on display in the Victorian-style conservatory, where guests can relax. This tranquil spot makes an ideal base for visiting the many places of interest, including several castles, in the area. Evening meals can be pre-booked, or there is a pub within walking distance that serves food.

OWNER: Jean Jones OPEN: all year ROOMS: 1 single, 4 double, 2 twin; 1 room suitable for wheelchair-users; tea/coffee and TV in all bedrooms TERMS: single £21–£25, twin/double £38–£46; dinner £11; deposit required CARDS: none DETAILS: children welcome; dogs by arrangement; no smoking; car park; garden

---

The end details for each entry state whether or not dogs are allowed, but it is always best to check when booking.

Benhall Farm

NEW ENTRY

Wilton, Ross-on-Wye HR9 6AG   TEL: (01989) 563900

This comfortable B&B is approached up a tree-lined drive, and is part of a 235-acre working farm. The Georgian farmhouse which houses the three bedrooms, is well positioned for spectacular countryside views over the Wye Valley. The large bedrooms are comfortably appointed with solid old-fashioned furniture; one has an *en suite* shower. Eileen Brewer is an accommodating host, who greets guests on arrival with a mug of tea. A self-catering cottage is also available. It is best to ask for directions when booking.

OWNER: Eileen Brewer   OPEN: Easter to 31 Oct   ROOMS: 2 double, 1 with shower, 1 with wash-basin; 1 twin, with wash-basin; lounge with TV   TERMS: single occupancy £15.50–£18, twin/double £31; children's reductions according to age   CARDS: none   DETAILS: children welcome; no dogs; no smoking; car park; garden

Lumleys Guest House

NEW ENTRY

Kerne Bridge, Bishopswood, nr Ross-on-Wye HR9 5QT
TEL: (01600) 890040
on B4234, 3½m S of Ross-on-Wye

This impressive Victorian double-fronted house stands in an area of outstanding natural beauty on the banks of the River Wye. The *en suite* bedrooms have pine furniture, and are individually decorated in soft and soothing colours; the four-poster room leads out to a private balcony. The two friendly owners extend a warm welcome, and have a good sense of humour. Breakfasts include free-range eggs, courtesy of the chickens kept in the garden, and evening meals are served by prior arrangement. All the front-facing rooms have a delightful view of the gently flowing river. Lumleys is an ideal base for exploring the wonderful walks of the Wye Valley.

OWNERS: Helen Mattis and Judith Hayworth   OPEN: all year exc Christmas and Jan   ROOMS: 2 double, 1 twin, 1 four-poster; all rooms with bath, tea/coffee and TV; lounge   TERMS: single occupancy £30, twin/double £40, four-poster £50; dinner £12; deposit: £20   CARDS: none   DETAILS: no children under 10; dogs welcome; no smoking in bedrooms or dining-room; car park; garden

ROTHBURY   Northumberland   **map 10**

Silverton Lodge

NEW ENTRY

Silverton Lane, Rothbury NE65 7RJ   TEL/FAX: (01669) 620144
from village take B6342 ½m S, turn right into Silverton Lane

Built in 1902, this stone and slate building operated as the village school until the 1960s, when it became derelict. In 1988 the Hewisons came to its rescue, converted it utterly (including replacing original panelling), and the result is a charming, inviting home. The two large bedrooms have colour-co-ordinated fabrics and good-sized bathrooms (one *en suite* and one adjoining). The lounge/dining-room has comfortable sofas plus an open fire for chilly days, and can be used any time of the day (guests are given their own key to the house). Traditional-style evening meals can be booked, and feature tasty home-made puddings. The Hewisons are attentive hosts, who are happy to advise on local places of interest. Laundry services, ironing facilities and even shoe-cleaning kits, are provided on request. A self-catering two-bedroom cottage is also available.

OWNER: Jeanette Hewison OPEN: Mar to Nov ROOMS: 1 double, with bath; 1 twin, with private bathroom; tea/coffee in both bedrooms; lounge with TV TERMS: single occupancy £36–£38, twin/double £36–£38; dinner £13; deposit: 50% CARDS: none DETAILS: no children under 10; no dogs; no smoking; car park; garden

ROWLAND Derbyshire map 8

Holly Cottage

Rowland DE45 1NR TEL: (01629) 640624
from B6001 at Hassop turn at sign for Rowland, then take first right

Holly Cottage is situated within the Peak District National Park, three miles from Bakewell, on a dead-end road leading directly to the hills. The stone-built cottage dates from the eighteenth century and is set among landscaped gardens, with a stone patio. It is in ideal walking country and well placed for visiting the stately homes of Chatsworth House, Haddon Hall and Hardwick Hall. The two bedrooms share a bathroom with shower and a separate WC. Mary Everard was once English Ladies' Golf Champion and provides guests with information about the nearby golf courses. The large lounge is comfortable, and an open fire burns in the hall when the weather gets cold. Excellent breakfasts are cooked on the Aga, and include home-baked rolls and home-made marmalades. Three night bookings are required over bank holiday weekends.

OWNER: Mrs D.M. Everard OPEN: Jan to Oct ROOMS: 1 double, with wash-basin; 1 twin; tea/coffee in both bedrooms; lounge with TV TERMS: single occupancy £24, twin/double £40–£42; reductions for children; dinner £12; deposit: £10 CARDS: none DETAILS: children welcome; no dogs; no smoking; car park; garden

RUDGEWAY South Gloucestershire map 2

Friezecroft

Rudgeway BS12 2SF TEL/FAX: (01454) 412276
off A38, 2m N of M4 / M5 junction

Guests are well looked after at this seventeenth-century cottage not far from the Severn Estuary. Outside, the setting is rural, and the house is approached down a private lane. Within, old-world charm rules: there are beams and thick stone walls, and log fires burn in an inglenook fireplace on chilly days. Visitors have appreciated the 'pleasantness and helpfulness' of the owners, who extend a warm welcome to their guests and are always happy to provide information on local places of interest. Two of the well-appointed bedrooms have their own private bathrooms, while one has *en suite* facilities.

Breakfasts are served in the lounge-cum-dining-room, which has a TV. Friezecroft is well placed for visits to Thornbury and Berkeley castles, and is handy for the M4 and M5 motorways.

OWNERS: Richard and Melodie Morris OPEN: all year exc Christmas ROOMS: 2 single, both with private bathroom; 1 double, with bath/shower; tea/coffee in all bedrooms; TV in two bedrooms and lounge TERMS: single £25, double £45; children's reductions by arrangement CARDS: none DETAILS: children welcome; no dogs; smoking in lounge only; car park; garden

RYARSH Kent map 3

Heavers

Chapel Street, Ryarsh ME19 5JU TEL/FAX: (01732) 842074
from M20 junction 4 take A228 to Leybourne, then right on A20 towards Wrotham Heath and turn right to cross motorway

Heavers is a typical smallholding, supporting sheep, geese, chickens and bees (honey from the bees is for sale). The seventeenth-century house, with its clematis-covered porch, can be found at the top of a hill on a dead-end country lane leading up from the tiny village of Ryarsh. The house is comfortable, with small rooms and low ceilings, and guests are treated as members of the family, with all the facilities of the house available to them. Mrs Edwards is a friendly, cheerful lady who provides home-cooked evening meals by arrangement, using home-grown produce.

OWNERS: James and Jean Edwards OPEN: all year exc Christmas ROOMS: 1 double, with wash-basin; 2 twin, both with wash-basin; tea/coffee in all bedrooms; lounge with TV TERMS: single occupancy £20–£22, twin/double £32–£38; half-price for children under 10; dinner £14 CARDS: none DETAILS: children welcome; dogs by arrangement; no smoking; car park; garden

RYE East Sussex map 3

Cadborough Farm NEW ENTRY

Udimore Road, Rye TN31 6AA TEL: (01797) 255426 FAX: (01797) 224097
on B2089, 1m from Rye

Cadborough Farm is a fifteen-minute walk from the centre of Rye. A Georgian building, it is a former farmhouse set in 24 acres, with superb views of Camber Castle and out to sea. Chickens and sheep are kept in the grounds. Jane Apperly is a welcoming host who ensures her guests feel at home. The lovely drawing-room has a grand piano which residents can use and breakfasts are served in the attractive dining-room. Three of the spacious, comfortable bedrooms are in the main house, and the other two are in the converted stables; some have fridges, and all have *en suite* facilities or private bathroom.

OWNER: Jane Apperly OPEN: all year exc Christmas ROOMS: 5 double, 4 with bath/shower, 1 with private bathroom; tea/coffee and TV in all bedrooms; lounge TERMS:

twin/double £45–£55, family room £70; reduction for children sharing with parents CARDS: MasterCard, Visa DETAILS: no children under 8; dogs by arrangement; smoking in lounge only; car park; garden

Half House

Military Road, Rye TN31 7NY TEL: (01797) 223404

Built at the turn of the century, Half House is set back a little off the road, with a very colourful front garden. It offers comfortable, good-value accommodation just ten minutes' walk from the centre of Rye. Bedrooms are fresh and bright, and attractively decorated, and there is a pretty breakfast-room. Bicycles can be provided for guests' use.

OWNERS: Norman and Agnes Bennett OPEN: all year ROOMS: 2 double, both with wash-basin; 1 twin, with bath/shower; tea/coffee and TV in all bedrooms TERMS: single occupancy £25–£40, twin/double £36–£44; children's reductions; deposit: one night's charge CARDS: none DETAILS: children welcome; no dogs; no smoking

Jeake's House

Mermaid Street, Rye TN31 7ET TEL: (01797) 222828 FAX: (01797) 222623

Right in the middle of Rye, approached up a steep, cobbled street, this listed building was originally used as a storehouse and was built in 1689 by Samuel Jeake, a wool merchant. It was later used as a Baptist school and in 1924 became the home of the American author Conrad Aiken, whose visitors included writers and artists such as T.S. Eliot, E.F. Benson, Paul Nash and Malcolm Lowry. Jenny Hadfield is an extremely friendly and professional host and is responsible for the décor and furnishings, which have been done with great taste in keeping with the period of the house. The beautifully appointed bedrooms, with direct-dial telephones, overlook the rooftops of the town or face south across the marsh to the sea. Breakfast is served in the eighteenth-century dining-room, which was once used as a Quaker meeting place. There is also a licensed bar. Car parking is available at the bottom of the street at a cost of £2.50 a day.

OWNERS: Francis and Jenny Hadfield OPEN: all year ROOMS: 1 single, with wash-basin; 7 double, 6 with bath/shower, 1 with wash-basin; 1 twin, 1 four-poster, 2 family, all with bath/shower; tea/coffee and TV in all bedrooms; lounge TERMS: single £24.50, single occupancy £40–£58, twin/double £45–£63, four-poster £87, family room £82.50–£126; deposit: £25 or credit card details CARDS: MasterCard, Visa DETAILS: children welcome; no dogs in dining-room; no smoking in dining-room

Little Orchard House

West Street, Rye TN31 7ES TEL/FAX: (01797) 223831

Little Orchard House, a stone building dating from around 1750, is hidden away down a cobbled lane in the centre of the old town. It looks small and unassuming from the outside, but behind the bright red front door, it is spacious and elegant, with an abundance of

Georgian panelling and period furniture. Owner Sara Brinkhurst is a very friendly and welcoming host who looks after visitors well. There are three individually styled guest rooms, one of which has just a curtain separating the bedroom from the *en suite* bathroom. Guests are welcome to use the family sitting-room and the attractive, hilly garden. The Rare Breeds and Waterfowl Park is nearby as are beaches, a golf course and botanic garden. Note that the minimum booking taken over bank holiday weekends is three nights.

OWNERS: Sara Brinkhurst and Robert Bird OPEN: all year ROOMS: 1 twin, 2 four-poster; all rooms with bath/shower, tea/coffee and TV; lounge TERMS: single occupancy £45–£65, twin/four-poster £64–£84; deposit or credit card details required CARDS: Delta, MasterCard, Visa DETAILS: no children under 12; no dogs; no smoking in four-poster rooms; car park; garden

Old Vicarage

66 Church Square, Rye TN31 7HF
TEL: (01797) 222119 FAX: (01797) 227466

The Old Vicarage dates originally from the time of the Reformation, and remained a vicarage until 1889. Today this listed, pink-washed house in a delightful cobbled setting by the ancient church of St Mary's offers elegant, comfortable guest accommodation. Among its famous owners have been John Fletcher, dramatist and collaborator with Shakespeare, and Henry James. The two sitting-rooms (one with TV) and the dining-room, with their exposed beams, overlook the pretty walled garden, and the small, well-appointed bedrooms have bottled water, fudge and biscuits; most have views over the rooftops of Rye and across the churchyard to the sea. Two rooms have four-posters and one a coronet bed, and one room on the second floor has its own small sitting-area. Breakfast includes home-baked scones and bread. A glass of sherry is offered on arrival, and a newspaper provided daily.

OWNERS: Julia and Paul Masters OPEN: all year exc Christmas ROOMS: 1 double, 1 twin, 2 four-poster, 1 family; all rooms with bath/shower, tea/coffee and TV; lounge with TV TERMS: single occupancy £35–£55, twin/double £44–£59, four-poster £50–£60; family room from £60; deposit required CARDS: none DETAILS: no children under 8; no dogs; smoking in both lounges only; car park; garden

Playden Cottage

Military Road, Rye TN31 7NY TEL: (01797) 222234
1m N of Rye; from Rye take A268 N; after crossing bridge over railway line turn right into Military Rd; house on left at town boundary

Playden is a Domesday village on the edge of Rye, and Playden Cottage is said to be the house called Grebe in E.F. Benson's *Mapp and Lucia* novels. It is a large, striking, whitewashed building tucked into the side of a hill, overlooking the River Rother and Romney Marsh. The atmosphere in the house is relaxed and friendly. The three spacious and well-appointed *en suite* bedrooms – named 'Wysteria', 'Hornbeam' and 'Badger' – have lovely views. There is also an additional bathroom and a WC for the exclusive use of residents. The 'long sitting-room' has a TV, books and games, and the 'writing-room' leads to a small patio in a quiet part of the large and rather spectacular garden. On the patio is a barbecue that guests may use for a small fee. Sheelagh Fox prepares cooked breakfasts to order (there is also a continental option), and offers straightforward evening meals if pre-arranged; alternatively, Rye has a wealth of eating-establishments.

OWNER: Sheelagh Fox OPEN: all year ROOMS: 1 double, 2 twin; all rooms with shower and tea/coffee; lounge with TV TERMS: single occupancy £37.50–£64, twin/double £50–£64; dinner £12; deposit: £20 or credit card details CARDS: MasterCard, Visa DETAILS: no children under 12; no dogs; no smoking in dining-room; car park; garden

ST AGNES Isles of Scilly **map 1**

Coastguards

St Agnes TR22 0PL TEL: (01720) 422373 FAX: (01720) 423326

Danny and Wendy Hick reckon that their former coastguard station, now a friendly family home, must be the most south-westerly guest house in Britain. It stands on one of the highest points of St Agnes, with views over the sea towards Bishop Rock Lighthouse. Guests and family share the facilities, and accommodation is in two of the three adjoining cottages, which, thanks to an architect's error, were built back-to-front. All bedrooms have private bath or shower, plus toilet. The comfortable sitting-room is stocked with books, games and jigsaws, and both breakfast and dinner are served (room prices include evening meals). St Agnes is a beautiful island and its small population welcomes visitors who come to relax and enjoy the peace and quiet, the mild climate, the wealth of flora and fauna, and excellent bird-watching opportunities.

OWNERS: Danny and Wendy Hick OPEN: all year exc Christmas ROOMS: 2 double, 1 twin; all rooms with private bathroom and tea/coffee; lounge TERMS: D,B&B single occupancy £27.50–£30.50, twin/double £45–£61; children's reductions by arrangement; deposit: 25% CARDS: none DETAILS: no children under 7; no dogs in lounge or dining-room; no smoking; garden

Covean Cottage

St Agnes TR22 0PL TEL: (01720) 422620

This small stone house is a few minutes' walk from the quay and only a little farther from the sandy bay at Covean. It is run by the Sewells, a friendly couple, who offer B&B accommodation in both the main house and a small cottage in the grounds (self-catering is available in the cottage during the winter). All the well-appointed bedrooms are *en suite* and have sea views. There is a comfortable lounge, and meals, featuring when available fresh seafood and local farm produce, are served in the dining-room or in the conservatory. The island has its own boatman who runs daily trips to the other islands.

OWNERS: Mr and Mrs P. Sewell OPEN: Mar to Dec ROOMS: 3 double, all with bath/shower; 1 twin, with wash-basin; tea/coffee and TV in all bedrooms; lounge with TV TERMS: single occupancy £32–£36, twin/double £64–£70; dinner £13.20; deposit: £10 CARDS: none DETAILS: no children under 9; small, well-behaved dogs welcome; no smoking in dining-room; garden

ST ALBANS Hertfordshire map 3

Care Inns

29 Alma Road, St Albans AL1 3AT TEL: (01727) 867310

This Victorian house lies in a quiet part of St Albans, within a six-minute walk of the town centre. The amiable Karin Arscott is multilingual, and provides comfortable B&B in a warm and friendly environment. Each of the three bedrooms has an *en suite* bath or shower, TV and mini-fridge. If warned in advance, Karin is willing to arrange free transport from the local station for arriving guests. As we were going to press, an extension incorporating self-catering accommodation was in the process of being added to the house.

OWNER: Karin Arscott OPEN: all year ROOMS: 1 single, 1 double, 1 twin; all rooms with bath/shower, tea/coffee and TV; lounge TERMS: single £25, single occupancy £30, twin/double £40; half-price for children under 12 CARDS: none DETAILS: children welcome; dogs by arrangement; no smoking in 1 bedroom and dining-room; car park

ST BEES Cumbria map 8

Tomlin Guest House NEW ENTRY

Beach Road, St Bees CA27 0EN
TEL: (01946) 822284 FAX: (01946) 824243

Tomlin Guest House is situated close to the start of the coast-to-coast walk, just 500 yards from the sea. The spotlessly clean bedrooms are traditionally decorated with pine furniture, and the two twin rooms have *en suite* showers. Irene Whitehead is a helpful host, and provides good-value B&B. Free parking is available in the opposite field; alternatively, a lock-up garage with space enough for a single car can be used for a small fee. There are several eating-establishments that serve evening meals in the nearby village.

OWNER: Irene Whitehead OPEN: all year exc Christmas ROOMS: 1 double; 2 twin, both with shower; 1 family, with wash-basin; tea/coffee and TV in all bedrooms; lounge with TV TERMS: single occupancy £16, twin/double £28–£32, family room from £28; children's reductions according to age; deposit: £5 per room CARDS: none DETAILS: children welcome; dogs welcome; no smoking; garden

---

If you are forced to turn up later than planned, please telephone to warn the proprietor. It is always best to book a room in advance, even in winter. B&Bs with few rooms may close at short notice for periods not specified in the details.

ST BRIAVELS Gloucestershire map 2

Cinderhill House

St Briavels GL15 6RH TEL: (01594) 530393 FAX: (01594) 530098
take A46 from Chepstow towards Monmouth, go over Bigsweir Bridge, follow sign for St Briavels and then turn left

Parts of this characterful whitewashed house date from the fourteenth century. It has been lovingly restored, and the elegant rooms feature exposed beams and flagstone floors. Gillie Peacock keeps things informal, and serves freshly made evening meals that include home-grown ingredients; a wide range of breakfast options are also available. There are four well-appointed bedrooms in the main house; a king-sized bed and a canopied bed feature in the two double rooms. The four-poster room comes as part of a suite known as the Bothy, and adjoins one of three self-catering cottages on the property. All the bedrooms are *en suite* and have TVs and electric blankets. The peaceful village of St Briavels with its 135 footpaths is ideal for walkers. Cinderhill House has some spectacular views over the Wye Valley to Sugar Loaf Mountain.

OWNER: Gillie Peacock OPEN: all year exc Christmas ROOMS: 2 double, 1 twin, 1 four-poster, 1 family; all rooms with bath/shower and tea/coffee; 1 room suitable for wheelchair-users; TV in four-poster and lounge TERMS: single occupancy £36–£40, twin/double £56–60, four-poster from £70, family room from £56; children's reductions by arrangement; dinner £13–£19; deposit: £10 per room CARDS: none DETAILS: children welcome; no dogs; no smoking; car park; games room; garden

ST HILARY Cornwall map 1

Ennys

St Hilary TR20 9BZ TEL/FAX: (01736) 740262
signposted on B3280, 2m E of Marazion

Surrounded by its 50-acre farm bordering the River Hayle, this seventeenth-century, creeper-clad stone manor-house is set in wooded countryside. Good food in a relaxed atmosphere is a feature of a stay at Ennys. Meals are served by candlelight at separate tables, and include locally caught fish, vegetables and herbs from the garden, and home-baked bread. When weather permits, breakfast can be served on the patio, which overlooks the walled garden. Three of the bedrooms are in the main house, and a converted barn contains the two family rooms. All the bedrooms are *en suite* and have patchwork quilts, paintings and prints. On chillier evenings guests gather in front of the log fire in the comfortable sitting-room before dinner is served, and in winter the Whites offer gourmet weekend breaks. The grounds include a grass tennis court and a heated swimming-pool. No one-night bookings are taken in high season.

OWNERS: Sue and John White OPEN: all year exc Christmas ROOMS: 1 twin, 2 four-poster, 2 family; all rooms with bath/shower and TV; lounge with TV TERMS: single occupancy £40–£45, twin £55–£60, four-poster £60, family room £90–£95; dinner £17.50–£19; deposit: £50 per booking CARDS: MasterCard, Visa DETAILS: children welcome; no dogs; no smoking; car park; games room; garden; swimming-pool; tennis

ST IVES Cornwall — map 1

The Count House

Trenwith Square, St Ives TR26 1DJ TEL: (01736) 795369
exit A30 Hayle bypass at roundabout for St Ives; at second mini-roundabout turn left following signs for St Ives via Halsetown; at junction with B3306 continue approx ½m towards St Ives, turn right at mini-roundabout, pass school; Trenwith Sq on right

Attractive bedrooms and a great deal of charm make this interesting old granite house a pleasant place to stay. The Count House derives its name from the days when wages for the workers at a nearby tin mine (now closed) were counted here. Built in 1825, it stands in a quiet square about a five-to-ten-minute walk from the centre of St Ives; visitors can also make use of the nearby park-and-ride scheme. All the bedrooms have either *en suite* or private bath/shower facilities, and one room has a four-poster bed, a jacuzzi and TV. From most of the rooms are fine views of the town, harbour and bay. Guests can have a drink in the cosy bar, or read, watch TV or have a chat in the lounge, where an open fire is lit on chilly days. Kenneth Canning is a decorator by trade, and has produced some imaginative paint details throughout the house. Evening meals, complemented by a good selection of wines, can be pre-arranged, and Cheryl Canning is happy to cater for special dietary requirements with enough advance notice.

OWNERS: Kenneth and Cheryl Canning OPEN: all year ROOMS: 2 single, 5 double, 1 twin, 1 four-poster; all rooms with bath/shower, exc 1 single with private bathroom; tea/coffee in all bedrooms; TV in four-poster room and lounge TERMS: single £27–£28, twin/double £42–£45, four-poster £60–£64; dinner £10.50; deposit: £40 per person per week CARDS: Delta, MasterCard, Switch, Visa DETAILS: no children; no dogs; no smoking; car park

Sunrise Guest House

22 The Warren, St Ives TR26 2EA TEL: (01736) 795407
50 metres from railway station, off Station Approach

A central location and good value are pluses at this terraced guesthouse in one of the oldest, narrowest streets of St Ives, close to the harbour. On the lower-street level are a cosy TV lounge and a pretty dining-room with lacy tablecloths and fresh flowers. A wide choice is offered at breakfast, including fresh fruit, a cooked vegetarian spread, pancakes and bacon, as well as traditional full English and more. A flight of steep, narrow stairs leads up to three of the bedrooms, which are small and pleasantly decorated. At the rear of the property are more stairs up to four more bedrooms, and two small patio areas for sitting out. These top-floor rooms are all either *en suite* or have a private bathroom, and two have brilliant views of the town and the sea front. Parking is limited, with some spaces reservable at the railway station for a fee of £2.50 a day.

OWNERS: Audrey Adams, and Diana and Derek Mason OPEN: open all year exc Oct ROOMS: 1 single; 3 double, 2 with bath/shower, 1 with private bathroom; 2 twin, 1 with shower; 1 family, with bath/shower; tea/coffee and TV in all bedrooms; lounge with TV TERMS: single £18–£22, single occupancy £19–£25, twin/double/family £32–£44 plus children's charge; children's reductions according to age; deposit: £20 per person CARDS: MasterCard, Switch, Visa DETAILS: children welcome; no dogs; no smoking in dining-room; garden

ST JUST Cornwall — map 1

Penrose House

NEW ENTRY

Nancherrow, St Just TR19 7PP TEL/FAX: (01736) 787218
on B3306, 300yds N of St Just towards St Ives

Penrose House is a granite-mine captain's house, built in 1854, and is set in two acres of mature gardens in the Nancherrow Valley. Beth Holman gives her guests a warm welcome, and the house has a comfortable, family atmosphere. Bedrooms are spacious and share two bathrooms, and there is a cosy lounge. Bird-watching is a very popular activity in the area, and there are lovely walks over clifftops, beaches and moors. Children are very welcome here. Packed lunches can be provided. The bus to Penzance, Land's End and St Ives stops right outside the house.

OWNER: Beth Holman OPEN: all year ROOMS: 1 single, with wash-basin; 2 double, 1 with shower, 1 with private bathroom; 1 twin, with shower; tea/coffee and TV in all bedrooms; lounge TERMS: single £15–£25, single occupancy £20–£27, twin/double £30–£40; deposit: £10 CARDS: none DETAILS: children welcome; dogs by arrangement; car park; garden

ST LAWRENCE Isle of Wight — map 2

Lisle Combe

Undercliff Drive, St Lawrence PO38 1UW TEL: (01983) 852582
off A3055 W of Ventnor, next to Rare Breeds Park

Lisle Combe is a listed Elizabethan-style farmhouse, with wonderful views overlooking the Channel. It is surrounded by large, attractive grounds which include the Rare Breeds and Waterfowl Park, which is also owned by the Noyes and to which guests have free entry. The house was once the home of the poet and author Alfred Noyes, whose family have turned it into a guesthouse, and is in an area of outstanding natural beauty. Mrs Noyes is an enthusiastic host who goes out of her way to make guests feel welcome. The spacious rooms are furnished with antiques, and guests have use of a TV room. Small beaches and coves are nearby, and Lisle Combe is a good place for children, with many interesting things to see.

OWNERS: Hugh and Judy Noyes OPEN: all year exc Christmas ROOMS: 1 single, 1 double, 1 twin/family; all rooms with wash-basin and tea/coffee; lounge with TV TERMS: single/single occupancy £18.50–£19, twin/double/ family room £37–£38; deposit: £10 CARDS: none DETAILS: children welcome; no dogs; no smoking in bedrooms; car park; garden

ST MARGARET'S AT CLIFFE Kent — map 3

Merzenich Guest House

Station Road, St Margaret's at Cliffe CT15 6AY TEL/FAX: (01304) 852260

The Claringboulds have been here since 1971, and continue to extend a friendly welcome to visitors at their modern guesthouse in the quiet village of St Margaret's at Cliffe. The house, which has been recently redecorated, presents clean and comfortable accommodation. Breakfast is served in the dining-room or, in summer, the conservatory. Although there is no guest lounge, all the bedrooms have TVs and tea/coffee-making facilities. One bedroom is in the attic, and all have *en suite* facilities. Rob Claringbould used to be a fireman: look for his collection of fire-engine cartoons decorating the staircase. Nearby are clifftop walks with views to the French coast, and the house is a five-to-six-minute drive to the Dover ferry docks and half an hour to the Channel Tunnel.

OWNER: Mrs D.H. Claringbould OPEN: all year ROOMS: 3 double, 1 twin; all rooms with bath/shower, tea/coffee and TV TERMS: single occupancy £23, twin/double £36; children's reductions; deposit: £5 per person CARDS: none DETAILS: children welcome by arrangement; no dogs; car park; garden

ST MARTIN'S Isles of Scilly — map 1

Glenmoor Cottage

Higher Town, St Martin's TR25 0QL TEL: (01720) 422816

This cottage on the sparsely populated island of St Martin's has been extended and modernised, and adjoins a gift shop also run by Barbara Clarke. It stands in Higher Town and has fine views over the attractive garden to the sandy beach and islands beyond. One of the three small bedrooms has an *en suite* shower and the other two have wash-basins. There is a large lounge with TV, and a conservatory in the extension with sea views. Breakfasts and home-cooked evening meals (dinner is included in the price), using locally grown vegetables and locally caught fish, are served in the dining-room. Glenmoor is close to excellent beaches, one of which is only a few minutes' walk away, and it is a good centre for scuba-diving and sailing.

OWNER: Barbara Clarke OPEN: all year exc Christmas ROOMS: 1 single, with wash-basin; 1 double, with wash-basin; 1 family, with shower; tea/coffee in all bedrooms; lounge with TV TERMS: D,B&B single/single occupancy £31, twin/double £62, family room £31; half-price for children under 12; deposit: £20 per person CARDS: none DETAILS: no children under 5; dogs welcome; smoking in lounge only; garden

Polreath

Higher Town, St Martin's TR25 0QL TEL: (01720) 422046

Originally built for a local farmer, this attractive granite Victorian house is in the centre of the island, only a few minutes from the quay. Geoff and Elaine Watt offer six guest bedrooms, and also operate a separate tea-room with a garden, where a selection of home-made food is available all day (evening-meal prices are included in room rates). The house is fresh and bright, and some of the bedrooms have good views. Unspoilt beaches, fine coastal and country walks, and pretty farmland dotted with fields of narcissi are not far away.

OWNERS: Geoff and Elaine Watt OPEN: all year exc Christmas ROOMS: 1 single, with wash-basin; 3 double, 1 with bath/shower, 2 with wash-basin; 2 twin, 1 with bath/shower, 1 with wash-basin; lounge with TV TERMS: D,B&B single/single occupancy £24.50–£41, twin/double £49–£82; reductions for children aged 5–10; deposit: 20% CARDS: none DETAILS: no children under 5; no dogs; smoking in lounge only; garden

ST MARY'S Isles of Scilly **map 1**

The Boathouse

St Mary's TR21 0LN TEL: (01720) 422688

Visitors to this small guesthouse right on the sea front will find the atmosphere serene and the views magnificent. Bedrooms are simply furnished but comfortable, and three have sea views. The first-floor lounge, with facilities for making hot drinks, leads out on to a small terrace. Breakfasts, and home-cooked evening meals using fresh produce from the vegetable garden, are served in the dining-room. The Boathouse is close to the town centre.

OWNER: Maureen Stuttaford OPEN: Easter to end Oct ROOMS: 3 double, 2 twin; all rooms with wash-basin; lounge TERMS: single occupancy £23, twin/double £46; half-price for children sharing with parents; dinner £13.50; deposit: £50 per room CARDS: none DETAILS: no children under 8; dogs welcome; no smoking in dining-room; garden

ST MAWES Cornwall **map 1**

Braganza

St Mawes TR2 5BJ TEL: (01326) 270281

This imposing Georgian country-house has a wonderful position in the centre of St Mawes, with views over the picturesque fishing village and across the water towards Falmouth. The tradition of hospitality carries on at Braganza – the house has been in the Moseley family for 50 years, and continues to exude a feel of space and tranquillity. The bathrooms still have their pre-war fittings, and fresh flowers are a thoughtful touch in the bedrooms. Guests can watch TV in the upstairs sitting-room, and tuck into breakfast at one table in the separate dining-room. A large garden surrounds the house, which is off a steep lane leading down to the harbour. Trelissick and Heligan gardens are within easy reach.

OWNER: Mrs Moseley-Kergorlay OPEN: mid-Mar to Oct ROOMS: 1 single, with wash-basin; 3 twin, 2 with bath, 1 with wash-basin; tea/coffee in all bedrooms; lounge with TV TERMS: single £19–£22, single occupancy £30–£33, twin £40–£50; deposit required for long bookings CARDS: none DETAILS: no young children; dogs by arrangement; no smoking in dining-room; car park; garden

ST MEWAN Cornwall map 1

Poltarrow Farm

St Mewan PL26 7DR TEL/FAX: (01726) 67111
off A390 St Austell to Truro road, turn right 1m after St Austell, continue ¼m

Poltarrow Farm is in a peaceful spot, just outside the small village of St Mewan, surrounded by spacious grounds and a 45-acre farmyard supporting cows, sheep, geese and ducks. It is a stone-built, whitewashed farmhouse with a welcoming and relaxed atmosphere, and is a wonderful place for children. The accommodation is comfortable, and there is a pleasant sitting-room and dining-room, plus a games room with pool, table-tennis and darts. The old ports of Mevagissey, Fowey and St Mawes are all within easy reach, as are the Lost Gardens of Heligan, old tin mines and coastal paths. Self-catering accommodation is also available.

OWNER: Judith Nancarrow OPEN: all year exc Christmas ROOMS: 1 single, with private bathroom; 3 double, all with bath/shower; 1 twin, with private bathroom; 1 family, with bath/shower; tea/coffee and TV in most bedrooms; lounge with TV TERMS: single £22–£25, twin/double £40–£44, family room from £65 CARDS: MasterCard, Visa DETAILS: children welcome; no dogs; smoking in lounge only; car park; games room; garden

SALCOMBE Devon map 1

Sunningdale

Main Road, Salcombe TQ8 8JW TEL: (01548) 843513

This large, 1930s house stands in elevated terraced grounds, ten minutes' walk from the centre of picturesque Salcombe, and enjoys wonderful views over the sea towards Bolt Head from large bay windows at each corner. It also has a beautifully maintained garden, with a sunny patio where tables and chairs are set in summer. Two of the large, bright and comfortably furnished bedrooms are on the ground floor and share a bathroom, and there is one twin bedroom with *en suite* shower on the first floor. The dining-room, where breakfast is served, has a bay window facing south-west. There is also a self-catering flat with its own entrance from the garden.

OWNERS: Michael and Erica Poynter OPEN: all year exc Christmas ROOMS: 1 double, with wash-basin; 2 twin, 1 with shower, 1 with wash-basin; tea/coffee in all bedrooms; TV in 2 bedrooms TERMS: single occupancy £22.50, twin/double £45 CARDS: none DETAILS: children over 8 welcome by arrangement; dogs by arrangement; no smoking; car park; garden

SALE Greater Manchester

map 8

Brooklands Luxury Lodge

208 Marsland Road, Sale M33 3NE
TEL: (0161) 973 3283 FAX: (0161) 282 0524
on A6144, 1½m W of M63 junction 8

Standing in attractive private gardens and set back from the main road is this mid-nineteenth-century Austrian-style lodge offering nine guest bedrooms. The interior has been well-maintained, and the comfortable good-sized rooms have breakfast bars, mini fridges and TVs; five have *en suite* showers. 'Complimentary breakfasts', which include cereal, yoghurt and fruit juice, and evening meals are taken in the bedrooms; pre-arranged continental and cooked breakfasts are available for an additional fee. Guests have access to a jacuzzi and sun-bed. The tram-line into Manchester is only 200 yards away.

OWNERS: Les and Ann Bowker OPEN: all year ROOMS: 5 single, 1 with shower, 4 with wash-basin; 1 twin, with shower; 1 four-poster, with shower; 2 family, both with shower; tea/coffee and TV in all bedrooms; lounge with TV TERMS: single £27–£32, single occupancy £34–£39, twin/double £44–£54, four-poster £36–£56, family room £54–£69; children's reductions by arrangement; dinner £10; deposit: £20 per room CARDS: Amex, Delta, MasterCard, Switch, Visa DETAILS: children welcome; no dogs; smoking in some bedrooms; car park; garden

Cornerstones

230 Washway Road, Sale M33 4RA TEL/FAX: (0161) 283 6909
on A56 between M63 and M56

This Victorian building is conveniently situated on a main road into Manchester, and is only a five-minute walk from the tram. Most of the elegant bedrooms are *en suite*, and all have telephones; a fax service is also available. Anthony and Dorothy Casey make sure the tastefully restored interior is well maintained. Evening meals are served in the dining-room, which has a table licence; two of the double bedrooms can be converted into family rooms. Manchester city centre is about a 15-minute drive away.

OWNERS: Anthony and Dorothy Casey OPEN: all year exc Christmas ROOMS: 3 single, 3 double, 3 twin; all rooms with shower exc 2 single with wash-basin; tea/coffee and TV in all bedrooms; lounge TERMS: single £23–£35, single occupancy £25–£35, twin/double £46–£54, family room £50; children under 5 free, reductions for ages 5–15 by arrangement; dinner £15; deposit: credit card details CARDS: Delta, MasterCard, Visa DETAILS: children welcome; no dogs; no smoking; car park; garden

SALISBURY Wiltshire

map 2

Farthings

9 Swaynes Close, Salisbury SP1 3AE TEL/FAX: (01722) 330749

Farthings is a Victorian house in the north of the town, about ten minutes' walk from the centre and all the attractions it has to offer. Bedrooms are tastefully decorated, and a collection of black and white photographs decorates the sitting-room and dining-room. There is a good choice for breakfast, and many restaurants nearby for dinner. Gill Rodwell is a charming lady who goes out of her way to be helpful and informative.

OWNER: Gill Rodwell OPEN: all year exc Christmas ROOMS: 2 single, both with wash-basin; 1 double, with bath/shower; 1 twin, with bath/shower; tea/coffee in all bedrooms; lounge with TV TERMS: single £18–£20, single occupancy £27–£30, twin/double £36–£40; deposit: £15 for first-time guests CARDS: none DETAILS: no children; no dogs; no smoking; car park; garden

---

Hayburn Wyke

72 Castle Road, Salisbury SP1 3RL TEL/FAX: (01722) 412627
on A345 Amesbury road, 1m N of city centre

This detached late-Victorian house is named after a village in North Yorkshire, birthplace of its original occupant, a man who came to Salisbury to work in the cathedral. The B&B can be found on the main road to Amesbury, close to Victoria Park. The city centre, old town and cathedral are easily reached by a pleasant half-mile walk along the banks of the River Avon. The simple, immaculate bedrooms are small and bright; two are up a narrow staircase on the second floor. Breakfast is served in the dining-room, which also has a TV.

OWNERS: Dawn and Alan Curnow OPEN: all year ROOMS: 3 double, 1 with shower, 2 with wash-basin; 2 twin, both with wash-basin; 2 family, 1 with shower, 1 with wash-basin; tea/coffee and TV in all bedrooms; lounge with TV TERMS: single occupancy £25–£37, twin/double £36–£42, family room from £48; children's reductions according to age CARDS: Delta, MasterCard, Switch, Visa DETAILS: children welcome; guide dogs only; no smoking in dining-room; car park; garden

---

Old Bakery

35 Bedwin Street, Salisbury SP1 3UT TEL: (01722) 320100

This charming sixteenth-century listed building, with a double bow fronted window, was a bakery until 1971. It is constructed of old ships' timbers and is in the centre of Salisbury. Although the house is on a busy street, the noise is minimal because of double-glazing. Guests have the use of a large, homely TV lounge/breakfast-room. There are four small and quite simple bedrooms, up narrow staircases under low beams; two have showers (one has no WC), and the other two share a shower-room, and one can take an extra bed and be used as a family room.

OWNERS: Peter and Evelyn Bunce OPEN: all year exc Christmas ROOMS: 1 single, with wash-basin; 2 double/family, 1 with shower (no WC); 1 twin, with shower; tea/coffee and TV in all bedrooms; lounge with TV TERMS: single £18–£22, single occupancy £24–£30, twin/double £34–£44, family room £50–£60 CARDS: none DETAILS: no children under 10; no dogs; no smoking in dining-room; garden

Stratford Lodge

4 Park Lane, Castle Road, Salisbury SP1 3NP
TEL: (01722) 325177 FAX: (01722) 412699

Although Stratford Lodge changed hands in 1997, reporters have confirmed that Ian and Jacqueline Lawrence are continuing to maintain the high standards set by the previous owner. The Victorian house is on a quiet lane, off the Salisbury to Amesbury Road, and overlooks Victoria Park. Bedrooms are comfortably furnished and all have *en suite* facilities, and guests have use of a lovely big sitting-room, music room, breakfast room and attractive dining-room. The centre of Salisbury can be reached by a pleasant and peaceful 15-minute walk along the river.

OWNERS: Ian and Jacqueline Lawrence OPEN: all year exc Christmas ROOMS: 8 double, 3 twin, 2 family; all rooms with bath/shower and TV; 1 room suitable for wheelchair-users; lounge with TV TERMS: single occupancy £38.50–£40.50, twin/double £56.50–£58.50, family room £74–£90; dinner £18.50 CARDS: Delta, Diners, MasterCard, Switch, Visa DETAILS: children welcome; no dogs; no smoking; car park; garden

SANDFORD ORCAS Dorset **map 2**

The Alders

Sandford Orcas DT9 4SB TEL: (01963) 220666 FAX: (01963) 220106
from Sherborne take B3148 N, after 2½m turn right signposted Sandford Orcas; at village T-junction turn left

The Alders is tucked away from the main road in the pretty conservation village of Sandford Orcas. It is an attractive old stone house in a lovely walled garden, and overlooks a Tudor manor-house, which is open to the public, and a medieval church. The house has been cleverly converted by its architect owner, who works from home. It is tastefully furnished, with a fire in the comfortable lounge, and with two smartly decorated bedrooms equipped to a high standard; both have *en suite* facilities. Breakfast only is served, but the village pub is handy for evening meals.

OWNERS: John and Sue Ferdinando OPEN: all year ROOMS: 1 double, 1 twin; both rooms with bath/shower, tea/coffee and TV; lounge with TV TERMS: single occupancy £30–£40, twin/double £40–£45; reductions for children under 14 sharing with parents CARDS: none DETAILS: children welcome; no dogs; no smoking; car park; garden

SARACEN'S HEAD Lincolnshire **map 6**

Pipwell Manor

Washway Road, Saracen's Head, nr Holbeach PE12 8AL
TEL: (01406) 423119
just off A17, 1½m NW of Holbeach

Guests are welcomed with tea and cakes on arrival at this listed Georgian manor-house in the tiny village of Saracen's Head. The house was built around 1730 on the site of a Cistercian grange, an outpost of Pipwell Abbey in Northamptonshire, from which it derives its name. It is set in an acre of beautiful flower gardens, which also boasts a model railway, which guests have been known to ride. Within, rooms are elegantly, even luxuriously, furnished in keeping with the house's origins, with many antiques in evidence. The sitting-room with its open fire is a good place to come back to after a day exploring the fens, and there is also a conservatory. Traditional cooked breakfasts, featuring eggs from the Manor's own hens and home-made preserves, are served in the gracious dining-room. The comfortable bedrooms all have either *en suite* facilities or private bathrooms. Free cycles can be provided, and there is also secure storage for those who bring their own.

OWNER: Lesley Honnor OPEN: all year exc Christmas ROOMS: 3 double, 1 with bath/shower, 2 with private bathroom; 1 twin, with bath/shower; tea/coffee in all bedrooms; lounge with TV TERMS: single occupancy £30, twin/double £40; reductions for children sharing with parents CARDS: none DETAILS: children welcome; no dogs; no smoking; car park; garden

SAXLINGHAM THORPE Norfolk **map 6**

The Lodge

NEW ENTRY

Cargate Lane, Saxlingham Thorpe NR15 1TU
TEL: (01508) 471422 FAX: (01508) 471682
off A140 Norwich to Ipswich road, 7m S of Norwich

The Lodge is a fine listed house standing in three acres of grounds, with a wide variety of plants, mature trees and herbaceous borders. The main part of the building dates back to Regency times, with tasteful alterations and additions completed in the Victorian era to blend in sympathetically with its character. The Dixons are a charming couple, and Sally is a Cordon Bleu-trained cook who prepares imaginative candlelit dinners featuring fresh local produce and herbs from the garden; vegetarian and special diets can be catered for with advance notice. A sitting-room, and beautifully furnished drawing-room with interesting old family portraits, as well as a restored Edwardian conservatory, are all available to guests. Badminton and croquet can be played in the garden.

OWNERS: Roger and Sally Dixon OPEN: all year exc Christmas ROOMS: 1 single, with bath/shower; 2 double/twin, 1 with bath/shower, 1 with private bathroom; tea/coffee in all bedrooms; lounge with TV TERMS: single £35, twin/double £58–£60; dinner £18.50; deposit: £5 per person per night CARDS: none DETAILS: no children under 12; no dogs; smoking in lounge and conservatory only; car park; garden

Please do not rely on an out-of-date Guide. Although some B&Bs in the current edition have steadfastly retained their high standards and have featured in every edition since the first, a great many others have faded from the scene. In addition, many new, superb B&Bs have been added. Relying on an old Guide will limit your choices and may lead to disappointment.

SCARBOROUGH North Yorkshire map 9

Lyncris Manor

45 Northstead Manor Drive, Scarborough YO12 6AF TEL: (01723) 361052

This small, family-run hotel sparkles and shines, offering comfortable, well-maintained accommodation underpinned by a warm and friendly ambience. The red-brick double-fronted house stands in its own grounds and overlooks a park and mini golf course. The roomy bedrooms have pretty duvets and modern furniture; as we went to press there were plans to add more *en suite* facilities. Guests have a TV lounge to relax in, and there is a separate bar/lounge for drinks and snacks. Good-value evening meals can also be arranged, and are served in the separate dining-room at individual tables. Private parking is limited to four spaces, but on-street parking near the hotel is unrestricted. The town centre is a 15-minute walk away.

OWNERS: John and Patricia Cass OPEN: all year ROOMS: 2 double, both with private bathroom; 4 family, 1 with bath, 3 with shower; tea/coffee and TV in all bedrooms; lounge with TV TERMS: single occupancy £21, double £42, family room from £32 plus children's charge; children's reductions by arrangement; dinner £5; deposit: £20 per person CARDS: none DETAILS: children welcome; no dogs; smoking in bar only; car park; garden

SEDBERGH Cumbria map 8

Holmecroft NEW ENTRY

Station Road, Sedbergh LA10 5DW TEL: (015396) 20754

Situated on the edge of town, this attractive Westmorland-stone house is set back from the main road behind a long front garden. The bedrooms are furnished in pine, and have views over the Howgill Fells. Susan Sharrocks keeps the place spotlessly clean, and serves complimentary hot drinks on arrival and before retiring, in the comfortable television lounge. Sedbergh lies within the Yorkshire Dales National Park, and there are many beautiful walks in the area; the town centre is just a six- or seven-minute walk away.

OWNERS: John and Susan Sharrocks OPEN: all year exc Christmas ROOMS: 2 double, both with wash-basin; 1 twin, with wash-basin; lounge with TV TERMS: single occupancy £20, twin/double £34; deposit: £10 per room CARDS: none DETAILS: children welcome; dogs by arrangement; no smoking; car park; garden

Marshall House

Main Street, Sedbergh LA10 5BL TEL: (015396) 21053

According to recently discovered deeds, this listed house, which is located in the town centre, dates from the sixteenth century. Many of its original features remain, including flagstone floors, coved ceilings and an old vaulted cellar. The house has recently been refurbished, and is beautifully maintained. All the *en suite* rooms have TVs, and the panelled lounge has an open fire. Evening meals can be prearranged, and vegetarians can be catered for.

OWNERS: Mr and Mrs David Kerry OPEN: all year exc Christmas ROOMS: 1 double, 2 twin; all rooms with bath/shower, tea/coffee and TV; 1 room suitable for wheelchair-users; lounge TERMS: single occupancy £35–£44, twin/double £44–£54; dinner £15.50–£19.50; deposit: £7.50 per person CARDS: none DETAILS: no children under 12; no dogs; no smoking in 1 bedroom; car park; garden

SELLING Kent — map 3

Owens Court Farm

Selling ME13 9QN TEL/FAX: (01227) 752247
off A2 S of Faversham, turn right at Shell Garage signposted Selling

This whitewashed Georgian farmhouse, covered with an old climbing rose, stands in quiet countryside and is part of a traditional hop and fruit farm. Many original features have been retained, and the house has well-proportioned rooms. The Higgses are a hospitable couple and provide a warm and friendly atmosphere. The spacious, comfortable bedrooms are pleasantly furnished, there is a first-floor lounge with TV, and tea and coffee-making facilities are available on the landing. Breakfast is served in the dining-room, which has a piano. Owens Court Farm is within easy reach of Canterbury and is a good place for country walks. Evening meals can be taken at the village pub.

OWNER: Mrs E. Higgs OPEN: all year exc Christmas ROOMS: 1 single, 1 double, 1 twin; all rooms with wash-basin and TV; lounge with TV TERMS: single £18, single occupancy £25, twin/double £36; half-price for children under 12; deposit: £10 CARDS: none DETAILS: children welcome; no dogs; smoking in guests' lounge only; car park; garden

SETTLE North Yorkshire — map 8

Whitefriars — NEW ENTRY

Church Street, Settle BD24 9JD TEL: (01729) 823753

This seventeenth-century family home stands in three-quarters of an acre of secluded gardens, 50 yards from the market place in the centre of town. Bedrooms are quite large and furnished with traditional and antique furniture. There are two lounges with original beams and marble fireplaces, and a chaise longue and a grandfather clock in the reception area. Breakfast and dinner, available every day except Monday, are served in the licensed dining-room. The town is famous for the Settle to Carlisle steam railway, and is well-placed for exploring the Pennines. Note that the minimum booking taken over bank holiday weekends is three nights.

OWNERS: Susan and Mary Wall, Janet Mackintosh and Helen Thompson OPEN: all year exc Christmas ROOMS: 4 double, 2 with shower, 2 with wash-basin; 3 twin, 1 with shower, 1 with private bathroom, 1 with wash-basin; 2 family, both with shower; tea/

coffee and TV in all bedrooms; lounge with TV TERMS: single occupancy £17.50–£39, twin/double £35–£44, family room £35–£62; dinner £10.50 CARDS: none DETAILS: children welcome; no dogs; no smoking; car park; garden

SHALDON Devon **map 1**

Virginia Cottage

Brook Lane, Shaldon, Teignmouth TQ14 0HL TEL/FAX: (01626) 872634
off B3199, just S of Teignmouth

Virginia Cottage, dating from the early seventeenth century, enjoys a peaceful setting in secluded gardens on a quiet lane just a few minutes' walk from the River Teign and the village of Shaldon. The elaborately carved front door is set in a porch built with decorated timbers from South Africa and is shaded by a superb magnolia. The three bedrooms are attractively furnished and decorated, and there is also a sitting-room, and a dining-room where breakfast is served. In the garden to the rear of the cottage is a small heated swimming-pool. The village has several pubs and restaurants, and Torquay and Exeter are within easy driving distance.

OWNERS: Jennifer and Michael Britton OPEN: Mar to Dec ROOMS: 1 double, with bath/shower; 1 twin, with private bathroom; 1 family, with bath/shower; tea/coffee in all bedrooms; lounge with TV TERMS: single occupancy £29, twin/double £46, family room £65; deposit: £20 CARDS: none DETAILS: no children under 12; no dogs; no smoking; car park; garden; swimming-pool

SHALFLEET Isle of Wight **map 2**

Orchard Cottage

2 Mill Road, Shalfleet PO30 4NE TEL: (01983) 531589
4m from Yarmouth off B3054; in Shalfleet turn into Mill Rd at traffic lights at New Inn pub

Excellent breakfasts, a very welcoming atmosphere and attractive, comfortable accommodation all add to the appeal of a stay at Orchard Cottage. It is a pretty cream-painted building set in a large, lovely garden with a stream. The twin and double bedrooms share a bathroom, while the family room has an *en suite* shower; all are well appointed, with fresh flowers, biscuits and tea/coffee, plus TVs. Guests also have the use of a lounge, garden room and the garden itself. Breakfasts are served in the dining-room. Evening meals are available at the New Inn, opposite, and June Thompson will be happy to reserve a table, as the pub is often a popular place in high season. Baby-listening, too, can be arranged while parents are out to dinner. Single-night bookings are not preferred, though are accepted occasionally. Shalfleet Quay is within walking distance.

OWNERS: June Thompson and Roy Silvester OPEN: all year exc Christmas ROOMS: 1 double, 1 twin, both with wash-basin; 1 family, with shower; tea/coffee and TV in all bedrooms; lounge TERMS: single occupancy £20–£25, twin/double £36–£50, family room £40–£50 plus children's charge; babies free, reductions for older children according to age; deposit required CARDS: none DETAILS: children welcome; no dogs; no smoking; car park; garden

Shalfleet House

Shalfleet PO30 4NS TEL/FAX: (01983) 531280
400yds W of village

Shalfleet House was built in Victorian times as the vicarage, and lies in its own extensive gardens just outside the village. It is a substantial house, sheltered from the road by trees, offering three large, well-furnished guest bedrooms. One of the twin rooms has three single beds, plus a cot if required, and is suitable for families, while the downstairs twin room has access to the garden. This room can be let out as a self-catering unit along with a sitting-room/kitchen above it. Upstairs are the other two bedrooms, a large double and a twin which share a bathroom. Breakfast is served in the dining-room, which has a piano that the musically inclined may use, and a fine old fireplace. A hard tennis court is on the grounds, and bird-watchers will be happy to know that the house overlooks the Newtown Estuary Nature Reserve and Bird Sanctuary.

OWNERS: Lt Col and Mrs J.R.E. Laird OPEN: all year exc Easter, Christmas and New Year ROOMS: 1 double, with wash-basin; 1 twin, with shower; 1 family, with wash-basin TERMS: single occupancy £20–£25, twin/double/family £36 plus children's charge; children under 3 free, reductions for older children; deposit: £10 per night CARDS: none DETAILS: children welcome; dogs in welcome in 1 room only; no smoking; car park; garden; tennis

SHEARSBY Leicestershire **map 5**

Knaptoft House Farm/The Greenway

Bruntingthorpe Road, Bruntingthorpe, Shearsby, LE17 6PR
TEL/FAX: (0116) 247 8388
leave A5199 at Bruntingthorpe/Saddington crossroads, and continue 1m towards Bruntingthorpe

This B&B is set in lovely countryside, only a short drive from Leicester. The main farmhouse contains three bedrooms with *en suite* showers, and a sun lounge with some wonderful views. The Greenway is a modern bungalow with three ground-floor bedrooms, two of them *en suite*. Fridges stocked with fresh milk and cold drinks are available to guests, and breakfasts are served in the farmhouse dining-room. This establishment is part of a working mixed farm, which includes a cobbled stableyard where horses are kept. Coarse-fishing is available by arrangement, on the series of restored medieval fish ponds situated on the property.

OWNER: Mrs A.T. Hutchinson OPEN: all year exc Christmas ROOMS: 3 double, all with shower; 3 twin, 2 with shower, 1 with wash-basin; tea/coffee and TV in all bedrooms;

lounge TERMS: single occupancy £24, twin/double £38–£43; children's reductions by arrangement; deposit required CARDS: Delta, MasterCard, Switch, Visa DETAILS: no children under 6; no dogs; smoking in some bedrooms only; car park; garden

SHEEPWASH Devon **map 1**

Half Moon Inn

Sheepwash EX21 5NE TEL: (01409) 231376 FAX: (01409) 231673
1m N of A3072 between Hatherleigh and Holsworthy

The Half Moon has been the village inn for over 200 years, and it forms one side of the picturesque village square. It is a 400-year old building with a large garden, and has been run by the Inniss family since 1958. Benjie's Bar is a popular meeting place for locals and visitors alike. Dinner is served in the attractive dining-room, and residents have use of a small lounge with TV. The bedrooms are well equipped with direct-dial telephones, and three are on the ground floor. There are excellent facilities for fishermen, with a large rod room, excellent drying facilities, a small shop stocking the basic requirements for fishing, and tackle for hire; tuition and advice are also available if required. For non-fishermen, the inn is a relaxing place to stay, and an ideal base from which to explore the area; packed lunches can be provided. The Dartington glass factory and the recently opened Rosemoor Gardens are nearby.

OWNERS: Benjamin and Charles Inniss OPEN: all year exc Christmas ROOMS: 2 single, 5 double, 9 twin, 2 family; all rooms with bath/shower exc both singles with private bathroom; tea/coffee and TV in all bedrooms TERMS: single £35–£45, single occupancy £40–£50, twin/double £65–£75, family room £75–£90; dinner £19 CARDS: MasterCard, Switch, Visa DETAILS: children welcome; car park; games room; garden

SHEFFIELD South Yorkshire **map 9**

Holme Lane Farm

38 Halifax Road, Grenoside, Sheffield S35 8PB TEL/FAX: (0114) 246 8858

This seventeenth-century former farmhouse, renovated to a high standard by the Hills, is in a secluded location in the quiet suburb of Grenoside, on the outskirts of Sheffield, not far from the M1. Three of the six bedrooms are on the ground floor in the main house, and the others are in the converted barn, which is ideal for those wanting a little extra privacy. Breakfast, a choice of continental or cooked, is served in the pleasant dining-room, overlooking green fields. Guests have use of a lounge with a minstrel's gallery. Meadowhall, the largest shopping mall in Europe, is only ten minutes' drive away. Several pubs in the village serve food, and self-catering is also available on the farm.

OWNERS: Keith and Sheila Hill OPEN: all year ROOMS: 4 single, 1 double, 2 twin; all rooms with bath/shower, tea/coffee and TV; 1 room suitable for wheelchair-users; lounge with TV TERMS: single/single occupancy £26, twin/double £45; reductions for children under 8 sharing with parents; deposit: £10 CARDS: MasterCard, Visa DETAILS: children welcome; no dogs; no smoking in lounge, dining-room or hallway; car park; garden

SHENINGTON Oxfordshire map 5

Sugarswell Farm

Shenington OX15 6HW TEL: (01295) 680512 FAX: (01295) 688149
leave A422 3m W of Banbury at sign for Shenington, continue through village, turn right at T-junction then right at crossroads

This large, modern Cotswold-stone-built farmhouse, set in its own ample gardens surrounded by flat, open countryside – once the site of Civil War battles – offers a splendidly warm welcome. Bedrooms are very well maintained and stylishly furnished: look for ivory brocade armchairs, 'magnificent bathrooms' and colour-themed décor. The front bedroom is the largest and allows one to keep an eye on farm activities, while the two at the back overlook the garden and open fields. Rosemary Nunneley's cooking is proving more popular than ever, and she has now produced a second edition of her recipe book; dinners are served in the formal dining-room. Breakfasts, too, are excellent, and even cooked lunches can be arranged. The blue-toned lounge with its TV, books and chubby sofas is the perfect place to relax in. The farm is named after the sweet-mineral-water well in its gardens.

OWNER: Rosemary Nunneley OPEN: all year ROOMS: 1 double, 2 twin; all rooms with bath and tea/coffee; lounge with TV TERMS: single occupancy £35–£45, twin/double £40–£60; dinner £19; deposit: £20 CARDS: none DETAILS: no children under 12; no dogs; no smoking; car park; garden

SHEPHERDSWELL Kent map 3

Sunshine Cottage

The Green, Mill Lane, Shepherdswell CT15 7LQ
TEL: (01304) 831359 and 831218
1m off A2, 6m NW of Dover

Sunshine Cottage, a listed building dating from 1635, overlooks the village green in the pretty village of Shepherdswell. It is on the North Downs Way, between the port of Dover and historic Canterbury. A ground-floor extension at the front of the house was formerly an antique shop, but it is now a large, simply furnished lounge. The cottage retains many of its original features, including beams and an inglenook fireplace in the lounge, and the rustic dining-room has antique pine furniture and stickback chairs. Some of the comfortable bedrooms have antique bedsteads. Two are on the ground floor, and one of these is suitable for wheelchair access. Breakfast features home-made preserves, which are also available for sale to guests.

OWNERS: Barry and Lyn Popple OPEN: all year ROOMS: 5 double, 2 with bath/shower, 3 with wash-basin; 1 twin, with wash-basin; 1 room suitable for wheelchair-users; tea/

coffee in all bedrooms; 2 lounges, 1 with TV TERMS: single occupancy £25–£35, twin/double £40–£44, family room from £42; dinner £15 CARDS: MasterCard, Switch, Visa DETAILS: children welcome; no dogs; no smoking; car park; garden

SHEPTON MALLET Somerset map 2

Bowlish House NEW ENTRY

Wells Road, Shepton Mallet BA4 5JD TEL/FAX: (01749) 342022
on A371 to Wells, ¼m from town centre, opposite Horseshoe Inn

This elegant eighteenth-century house can be found on the outskirts of Shepton Mallet. It is primarily a restaurant with an excellent reputation, offering classical dishes making use of local produce. The three bedrooms have cream panelling and floral bedspreads and curtains, as well as spacious *en suite* bathrooms, one of which has an interesting arrangement of doors at both ends of the room. A bar is just off the spacious flagstoned entrance hall, which has a large table with a mass of literature about places to visit. There is a large, comfortable drawing-room decorated in period style, and continental breakfast is taken in the pleasant dining-room; a cooked breakfast is available for a supplement. The market town of Shepton Mallet lies on the edge of the Mendip Hills, ten minutes from the cathedral city of Wells.

OWNERS: Bob and Linda Morley OPEN: all year exc 1 week spring and autumn ROOMS: 2 double, 1 twin; all rooms with bath/shower, tea/coffee and TV; lounge TERMS: single occupancy £48, twin/double £58; dinner £24.50; deposit: letter of confirmation CARDS: Amex, MasterCard, Visa DETAILS: children welcome; no dogs in public rooms; car park; garden *(The Good Food Guide)*

SHERIFF HUTTON North Yorkshire map 9

Hall Farm NEW ENTRY

High Stittenham, Sheriff Hutton YO6 7TW TEL: (01347) 878461
off A64, 5m NE of York, signposted Flaxton and High Stittenham

This charming brick-built house is part of a working sheep and cattle farm, and offers good-value B&B. Elaine Hemingway is a warm and friendly host, who offers tea and home-baked cakes to arriving guests. The large room in the main house can accommodate up to four people, and *en suite* facilities were being installed as the *Guide* went to press. There is also self-catering accommodation in a separate wing of the house. Hall Farm is ideally placed for walkers, with the Ebor Way and the Centenary Way running right past the farm. Mrs Hemingway will provide evening meals for guests without their own transport; otherwise there are several pubs serving food nearby.

OWNERS: Mr and Mrs T.W. Hemingway OPEN: all year ROOMS: 1 double/family, with tea/coffee and TV; lounge with TV TERMS: single occupancy £15, double/family from £30; children's reductions according to age CARDS: none DETAILS: children welcome; no dogs; car park; garden

SHERINGHAM Norfolk map 6

Fairlawns

26 Hooks Hill Road, Sheringham NR26 8NL TEL/FAX: (01263) 824717

Fairlawns has new owners since the last edition, Danny and Barbara Rowe, a sociable couple who enjoy looking after their guests. The house is a large Victorian building, half a mile from the centre of the small coastal town of Sheringham, set in beautiful gardens with a croquet lawn. The four bedrooms all have *en suite* facilities, and overlooking the garden is a pleasant lounge with satellite TV, games, books and music. Breakfast and dinner are served in the fully licensed dining-room, and Fairlawns is the recipient of a healthy eating award.

OWNERS: Danny and Barbara Rowe OPEN: Feb to Nov ROOMS: 2 double, 2 twin, 1 family; all rooms with bath/shower, tea/coffee and TV; lounge with TV TERMS: single occupancy £33–£35, twin/double £42–£46, family room £47–£51; dinner £12.50 CARDS: none DETAILS: children welcome; guide dogs only; no smoking in bedrooms or dining-room; car park; garden

Oak Lodge

2 Morris Street, Sheringham NR26 8JX TEL: (01263) 823158

Oak Lodge, an Edwardian house located right in the centre of Sheringham, is run by easy-going Mary and Charles Hall, who offer good-value, comfortable accommodation. It is spotlessly clean and tastefully decorated, and the bedrooms are all very large and have TVs. Substantial breakfasts are served and there are several places for evening meals in the town. Sheringham's attractions include the steam railway which runs to Cromer.

OWNERS: Charles and Mary Hall OPEN: Easter to Oct ROOMS: 1 single, 2 double, 1 twin; all rooms with wash-basin, tea/coffee and TV TERMS: single £20, twin/double £40; deposit: £20 CARDS: none DETAILS: no young children or babies; strictly controlled dogs welcome; no smoking in public rooms; garden

SHIPTON BELLINGER Hampshire map 2

Parsonage Farm

High Street, Shipton Bellinger SP9 7UF TEL/FAX: (01980) 842404
1m N of A338 between Andover and Amesbury

The oldest part of this brick-and-flint building dates from the sixteenth century and is now the dining-room, which has a beamed ceiling and is where breakfast is served at separate tables. Parsonage Farm is in the centre of a quiet village on the edge of Salisbury Plain, and opposite a pub which serves evening meals. It is very much a family home, where guests are treated as friends, and have the use of a large lounge/dining-room, and a pretty walled garden, where there are tables and chairs for sitting out on warm days. This is a wonderful area for walking and riding, with access to Salisbury Plain, and the owners keep horses themselves. Salisbury, Marlborough and Stonehenge are all within easy reach.

OWNERS: Col and Mrs B.R. Peecock OPEN: all year exc Christmas ROOMS: 2 twin, both with wash-basin; 1 family, with private bathroom; tea/coffee and TV in all bedrooms; lounge with TV TERMS: single occupancy £20–£30, twin £35, family room £40–£50; deposit: £10 per night CARDS: none DETAILS: no children under 10; no dogs; no smoking; car park; garden

SHOTTLE Derbyshire map 5

Dannah Farm

Bowmans Lane, Shottle, nr Belper DE56 2DR
TEL: (01773) 550273 FAX: (01773) 550590
from A517 2m W of Belper turn at sign for Shottle, go straight over crossroads then next right

This lovingly restored eighteenth-century house, and its accompanying converted farm buildings, lies in tranquil countryside. All of the luxuriously furnished bedrooms have private facilities and TVs, including three suites which also incorporate sitting-rooms. One of the suites has a medieval theme, and features a cast-iron bed and massive exposed beams. Guests can relax with a drink in the main lounge, which has a licensed bar. Breakfasts and dinners are served in the 'Mixing Place', a restaurant housed in one of the farm buildings; it is open to non-residents only on Saturday evenings. Dannah farm is home to a colourful collection of animals, including calves, ducks, hens, lambs and Vietnamese pot-bellied pigs.

OWNERS: Martin and Joan Slack OPEN: all year exc Christmas ROOMS: 4 double, 2 twin, 1 four-poster, 1 family; all with bath/shower exc 1 twin with private bathroom; tea/coffee and TV in all bedrooms; lounge TERMS: single £38.50–£41, single occupancy £41–£45, twin/double £60–£70, four-poster £70–£79, family room from £60; £13.50 for children sharing with parents; dinner £17; deposit: £20 per person CARDS: Delta, MasterCard, Switch, Visa DETAILS: children welcome; no dogs; smoking in lounge only; car park; garden

Shottle Hall

Shottle, nr Belper DE5 2EB TEL: (01773) 550203 FAX: (01773) 550276
on B5023, 200yds N of A517

This impressive mid-nineteenth-century building stands in three acres of private gardens in the scenic Ecclesbourne Valley. An early Singer sewing machine and an old spinning-wheel are among a number of antiques on display about the house; a few small items are for sale. Most of the well-furnished bedrooms are *en suite*; some have TVs. One of the two guest lounges has an adjoining bar, and evening meals are served in either of the two licensed dining-rooms; guests may also bring their own wine. The Derbyshire tradition of well-dressing, which dates from the time of the Plague, can be observed in several of the nearby villages during the summertime.

OWNERS: Philip and Phyllis Matthews OPEN: all year exc Nov and Christmas ROOMS: 2 single, both with bath/shower; 3 double, 2 with bath/shower, 1 with private bathroom; 2 twin, 1 with bath/shower, 1 with private bathroom; 2 family, both with bath/shower; tea/coffee in all bedrooms; TV in some bedrooms and lounge TERMS: single/single occupancy £27–£37, twin/double £50–£65, family room from £50; children's reductions according to age; dinner £13.50 CARDS: none DETAILS: children welcome; dogs in bedrooms only; no smoking in bedrooms; car park; games room; garden

SHREWSBURY Shropshire map 5

Anton Guest House NEW ENTRY

1 Canon Street, Monkmoor, Shrewsbury SY2 5HG TEL: (01743) 359275

This family-run Victorian-built guesthouse with its pretty front garden is on the corner of Canon Street and Monkmoor Road, about ten-minutes' walk to the centre of Shrewsbury. Anne Sandford enjoys chatting to her guests, and treats them as friends in her immaculately kept house. The bedrooms are good-sized, bright and fresh; they are colour-co-ordinated with matching fabrics, are furnished in pine, and share two bathrooms. All have TVs and tea/coffee-making facilities, and visitors also have the use of a sitting-room with a TV. Double-glazing keeps traffic noise at bay.

OWNERS: Anne and Tony Sandford OPEN: all year exc Christmas ROOMS: 2 double, 1 twin, 1 family; all rooms with wash-basin, tea/coffee and TV; lounge with TV TERMS: single occupancy £20–£22, twin/double £35, family room £48–£50 CARDS: none DETAILS: children welcome; no dogs; no smoking; car park

Fieldside

38 London Road, Shrewsbury SY2 6NX
TEL: (01743) 353143 FAX: (01743) 358645

Fieldside is an elegant Victorian house set in a lovely garden, one and a half miles from the town centre. It is easy to find – look for the large statue of lions at the end of the road. Inside, it is beautifully kept and adorned throughout with pictures, and brass, copper and china artefacts. Bedrooms are decorated in soft colours and some have half-tester beds. Generous breakfasts include a help-yourself buffet, and are served in the stylish dining-room, which opens out on to the patio and gardens.

OWNERS: Ian and Pat Fraser OPEN: all year exc 2 weeks Oct ROOMS: 4 double, 1 twin; all rooms with shower, tea/coffee and TV TERMS: single occupancy £28–£30, twin/double £42–£44; deposit: £10 per room CARDS: Delta, MasterCard, Visa DETAILS: no children under 9; no dogs; no smoking; car park; garden

---

'NEW ENTRY' indicates that a B&B was not in the previous edition (although its owners may have been, at a different address).

SIDMOUTH Devon **map 2**

Old Farmhouse

Hillside Road, Sidmouth EX10 8JG TEL: (01395) 512284

Said to be one of the oldest buildings in Sidmouth, dating from 1569, this attractive thatched house is down a quiet lane close to the town centre. The house retains many original features, and the furnishings and décor are tasteful and comfortable. Most of the traditionally decorated bedrooms have *en suite* facilities, and some are housed in an adjoining cottage, which was once the local cider mill. There is a patio for sitting outside, as well as an award-winning garden. Evening meals are available by arrangement, and the cosy Inglenook bar is open in the evenings.

OWNER: Susan Rignall OPEN: Feb to Oct ROOMS: 1 single, 5 double, 1 twin, 1 family; all rooms with bath/shower exc 1 single with private bathroom; tea/coffee in all bedrooms; TV in some bedrooms and lounge TERMS: single £21–£25, single occupancy £25–£30, twin/double/family £42–£50; reductions for children according to age; dinner £10; deposit: £20 per person CARDS: MasterCard, Visa DETAILS: children welcome; dogs welcome in the cottage only; no smoking; car park; garden

SILVERDALE Lancashire **map 8**

Limes Village Guest House

23 Stankelt Road, Silverdale LA5 0TF TEL/FAX: (01524) 701454

This converted Victorian house is set in extensive landscaped gardens, enclosed by thick woodland. Silverdale is known for its beautiful countryside, and holds particular allure for ornithologists, with the Leighton Moss RSPB sanctuary nearby. The three sizeable bedrooms all have private facilities and TVs. Both of the twins can be used as family rooms; one is in the attic, and has access to a Victorian sunken bathroom. Guests have a choice between a five-course dinner or a lighter meal which is served earlier in the evening. Breakfast includes local marmalades and Colombian coffee. Two self-catering units are also available.

OWNERS: Noel and Andree Livesey OPEN: all year ROOMS: 1 double, with shower; 2 twin/family, both with private bathroom; tea/coffee and TV in all bedrooms; lounge TERMS: single occupancy £24.50, twin/family from £35; half-price for children sharing with parents; dinner £5.50–£12.50; deposit: from £15 CARDS: none DETAILS: children welcome; no dogs; no smoking; car park; garden

We welcome your feedback about B&Bs you have stayed in. Please make use of the report forms at the end of the book – or use your own stationery if you prefer – and mail your report to: The Editors, The Good Bed and Breakfast Guide, *FREEPOST, 2 Marylebone Road, London NW1 1YN. (No stamps are needed if mailed within the UK.) Recommendations for B&Bs for our next edition are very welcome. Please let us know if you need more report forms and we will send you a fresh supply.*

SINNINGTON North Yorkshire map 9

Riverside Farm

Sinnington YO6 6RY TEL/FAX: (01751) 431764
off A170, 4m W of Pickering

This handsome stone-built house offers friendly B&B. There are three comfortable bedrooms, one of which has an *en suite* shower; the single and twin share a bathroom, but are never let separately. The two acres of delightful gardens are a plus, and under the National Garden Scheme they are open to the public once or twice a year. Varied breakfasts are served in the traditionally furnished dining-room, and the sitting-room has a TV. A nearby pub is handy for evening meals. Riverside Farm is situated in the unspoilt village of Sinnington, and has views over the River Seven.

OWNERS: William and Jane Baldwin OPEN: Apr to end Oct ROOMS: 1 single, with wash-basin; 1 double, with shower; 1 twin; tea/coffee in all bedrooms; lounge with TV TERMS: single £20–£22, single occupancy £25, twin/double £40–£44; deposit: £10 per room CARDS: none DETAILS: no children under 9; no dogs; no smoking; car park; garden

SISSINGHURST Kent map 3

Camden Lodge NEW ENTRY

Sissinghurst TN17 2HW
TEL: (01580) 713999/713323 FAX: (01580) 713309
on the A262 just N of Sissinghurst

Camden Lodge has been lovingly converted out of a former stable block into, in the words of one reporter, 'a house full of character'. It is in a peaceful setting just a few hundred yards from the village of Sissinghurst, and stands in a beautiful garden complete with fish pond. The Thomsons offer a warm, attentive welcome, and Patrick is very helpful in advising on local places of interest. Both of the 'tranquil' bedrooms are comfortably furnished and have private bathrooms. Sissinghurst Gardens, Great Dixter and Scotney Castle are all close by. One-night bookings are not available on weekends.

OWNERS: Sally and Patrick Thomson OPEN: all year exc Christmas ROOMS: 1 double, 1 twin; both rooms with private bathroom, tea/coffee and TV TERMS: single occupancy £25–£30, twin/double £42–£48; deposit: £10 per person CARDS: none DETAILS: no children under 12; no dogs; no smoking; car park; garden

---

'Lounge' in the details at the bottoms of entries refers to a room (or rooms) in which guests can relax, watch TV, read or chat, and may vary from a large, elegantly furnished drawing-room exclusively for guests' use to a cosy sitting-room shared with the owners.

SITTINGBOURNE Kent **map 3**

The Beaumont

74 London Road, Sittingbourne ME10 1NS
TEL: (01795) 472536 FAX: (01795) 425921

Dating from the seventeenth century, this attractive, rambling former farmhouse has a weatherboarded Victorian extension with high ceilings and large windows. In the original part, features such as oak beams, sloping floors and an inglenook fireplace have been retained. The Beaumont is a warm and inviting house and is pleasantly furnished and immaculately kept. Hand-painted murals and door panels depict climbing plants and flowers with butterflies, with a different style for each room. The bedrooms are very well equipped, now mostly *en suite*, with direct-dial telephones and dressing-gowns. There is a large farmhouse-style dining-room/lounge with TV, which is where excellent breakfasts, with a large choice of various teas and coffees, are served. Guests may sit in the charming garden in summer. The Beaumont is on the main A2, and is well placed for the motorways and the major ports.

OWNER: Marcia Brennand OPEN: all year ROOMS: 3 single, 2 with shower (1 no WC), 1 with wash-basin; 3 double, all with shower (1 no WC); 1 twin, with shower; 1 four-poster, with shower; 1 family, with shower; 2 rooms suitable for wheelchair-users; tea/coffee and TV in all bedrooms; lounge with TV TERMS: single £24–£38, single occupancy £32–£38, twin/double £40–£42, four-poster £45–£50, family room £42–£60 (all prices exclusive of VAT); children's reductions according to age; dinner £8.50–£10 CARDS: Amex, Delta, Diners, MasterCard, Switch, Visa DETAILS: children welcome; dogs by arrangement in 1 room only; smoking in lounge only; car park; garden

SKIPTON North Yorkshire **map 8**

Low Skibeden Farm House

Skibeden Road, Skipton BD23 6AB
TEL: (01756) 793849 FAX: (01756) 793804
1½m E of Skipton just by junction of A65 and A59

Lying on the edge of the Yorkshire Dales, only a short distance from the market town of Skipton, is this hospitable B&B. A warm welcome can be expected from the friendly owners, and hot drinks and other refreshments are offered on arrival, and late in the evening. The sixteenth-century farmhouse has five spacious bedrooms; there is an original, intricately designed 17-foot-high window on the north side of the building. The cosy lounge contains lots of books and other information on the area. Guests are welcome to relax in the large, well-kept garden; outdoor furniture is provided on warm days. Low Skibeden Farm also incorporates a smallholding with sheep and Charolais cattle. A self-catering cottage adjoins the house.

OWNERS: Bill and Heather Simpson OPEN: all year exc Christmas ROOMS: 1 double, with wash-basin; 1 twin, with wash-basin and WC; 3 family, 2 with shower, 1 with wash-basin; tea/coffee in all bedrooms;

lounge with TV TERMS: single occupancy £28–£36, twin/double £32–£40, family room from £35; reductions for children 10–15; deposit: £20 CARDS: none DETAILS: no children under 10; no dogs; no smoking; car park; garden

SLAD Gloucestershire **map 2**

Chessed

Slad GL6 7QD TEL: (01452) 812253 FAX: (01452) 813473
on B4070 Stroud to Birdlip road

Chessed is situated in an elevated position, with views over the village, to the beautiful countryside beyond. Wendy Wood makes sure guests are welcomed with a hot drink, and the house has a comfortable lived-in feel. The *en suite* family room has an antique brass bed. A swimming-pool is available to residents, and the conservatory proves a pleasant place to relax in. Evening meals are served at several eating-establishments in the village. The property is colourfully adorned with flowers and plants, and looks splendid in the summer months.

OWNER: Wendy Wood OPEN: all year ROOMS: 1 double, with wash-basin; 1 twin; 1 family, with bath/shower; tea/coffee and TV in all bedrooms TERMS: single occupancy £30–£35, twin/double £50–£60; children's reductions according to age; deposit: £10 CARDS: none DETAILS: children welcome; no dogs; car park; garden; swimming-pool

SLAIDBURN Lancashire **map 8**

Pages Farm

Woodhouse Lane, Slaidburn BB7 3AH TEL: (01200) 446205
off B6478; at Slaidburn go W past the Hark to Bounty Inn, farm is ½m on left

This seventeenth-century farmhouse is set in the beautiful Forest of Bowland, in the Ribble Valley, less than half a mile from the village of Slaidburn. Mary Cowking greets guests with a warm welcome, a hot drink and home-made biscuits. There are three bedrooms, all with *en suite* facilities, and guests can relax in the oak-beamed TV lounge, warmed by a log fire on chilly days. Breakfasts feature free-range eggs from the farm, and evening meals can be provided by arrangement, with vegetarian options available. Alternatively, the nearby pub also serves food. Drying facilities are also available. The area provides excellent walks.

OWNERS: Peter and Mary Cowking OPEN: all year exc Christmas ROOMS: 2 double, 1 twin; all rooms with bath/shower and tea/coffee; lounge with TV TERMS: single occupancy £17–£18, twin/double £34; children under 3 free, half-price for ages 3–11; dinner £11; deposit: £10 per room CARDS: none DETAILS: children welcome; no dogs; no smoking in bedrooms; car park; garden

SLALEY Northumberland **map 10**

Rye Hill Farm

NEW ENTRY

Slaley NE47 0AH TEL: (01434) 673259 FAX: (01434) 673608
take B6306 4½m S from Hexham, take first turning right after Travellers' Rest pub, then first farm track right

This 300-year-old stone farmhouse is part of a small working farm set in rural Tynedale, complete with pigs and ponies, poultry and sheep. Guest accommodation is in comfortably converted, self-contained farm buildings and is decorated daintily; the well-appointed bedrooms vary in size, are all *en suite* and have TVs. Breakfasts and, if pre-booked, evening meals are served in the licensed lounge/dining-room with its open fire, with menus focusing on traditional dishes using fresh ingredients. A games room with a pool table is shared with visitors staying at the farm's self-catering accommodation. The farm is in good walking country, and within striking distance of Hadrian's Wall and Durham.

OWNER: Elizabeth Courage OPEN: all year ROOMS: 3 double, 1 twin, 2 family; all rooms with bath/shower, tea/coffee and TV; lounge TERMS: single occupancy £24, twin/double £40, family room £40–£60; children under 2 free; dinner £10 (less for children); deposit: £5 per person per night CARDS: Delta, MasterCard, Switch, Visa DETAILS: children welcome; £1 per night for dogs; no smoking in bedrooms and dining-room; car park; games room; garden

SLEIGHTS North Yorkshire **map 9**

Dalegarths

NEW ENTRY

Iburndale, Sleights, nr Whitby YO22 5DS TEL: (01947) 810788
off A169, 5m SW of Whitby

This elegant Victorian house lies in its own gardens and orchards, in the unspoilt hamlet of Iburndale, near the village of Sleights. The roomy bedrooms are tastefully furnished in oak and pine; the twin is *en suite*, and has a TV. There is a television lounge where a complimentary hot drink is offered before bedtime. Wholesome breakfasts are served in a separate dining-room, and evening meals are on offer at several local pubs. There are some good walks in the area, including the Cleveland Way; Whitby is a short drive away.

OWNERS: Tony and Jacqueline Roberts OPEN: Apr to Oct ROOMS: 2 double, 1 with private bathroom, 1 with wash-basin; 1 twin, with shower; tea/coffee in all bedrooms; TV in twin room and lounge TERMS: single occupancy £20, twin/double £34–£42; deposit: £20 CARDS: none DETAILS: no children under 12; no dogs; no smoking; car park; garden

---

Some B&Bs try to 'solicit' recommendations; they may even photocopy our report forms and hand them out to guests. We can spot these easily, and give them no credence. But genuine reports from readers, prompted only by a desire to share details of a stay at a B&B, are given our full attention.

SLINGSBY North Yorkshire map 9

The Hall

Slingsby YO6 7AL TEL: (01653) 628375
just off B1257, 6m W of Malton

This attractive, creeper-covered Regency house is situated in the charming of Slingsby, close to the North Yorkshire moors. The tastefully furnished interior includes six spacious bedrooms with *en suite* facilities. Freshly prepared dinners are taken at separate tables in the licensed dining-room; full English breakfasts are also served. The spacious sitting-room, complete with log fire, looks out on the five-acre garden. Horse stabling, cycle hire and croquet can be arranged. York and Castle Howard are within striking distance.

OWNERS: Peter and Cynthia Fell OPEN: Easter to mid-Oct ROOMS: 3 double, 2 twin, 1 family; all rooms with bath/shower, tea/coffee and TV; lounge with TV TERMS: single occupancy £22–£24, twin/double £40–£44, family room from £40; babies free, reductions for older children according to age; dinner £9.50; deposit: £15 per person CARDS: none DETAILS: children welcome; dogs by arrangement; smoking in bedrooms only; car park; garden

SNAPE Suffolk map 6

Flemings Lodge NEW ENTRY

Gromford Lane, Snape IP17 1RG TEL: (01728) 688502
from A1094 take B1069 to Snape; on entering village take first right at crossroads; Flemings Lodge is 150yds on right

This creeper-clad modern bungalow stands in a delightful garden, filled with statues and carvings concealed amongst the foliage. The two comfortable bedrooms have cotton sheets, quality bedding and armchairs, and they share a large bathroom with a corner bath. Freshly prepared breakfasts are served in the bright dining-room, and there is an adjacent TV lounge. Ilse Edwards has made a hobby out of decorating her house, and the immaculate rooms sparkle and shine with her efforts. The Edwardses are an engaging couple who are happy to provide information and advice on visiting Aldeburgh and the surrounding area. Flemings Lodge is ideally based for visiting the Snape Maltings.

OWNER: Ilse Edwards OPEN: all year exc Christmas ROOMS: 1 double, 1 twin; both rooms with wash-basin and tea/coffee; lounge with TV TERMS: single occupancy £24–£26, twin/double £36–£40; deposit: £10 CARDS: none DETAILS: no children; no dogs; no smoking; car park; garden

---

B&B rates specified in the details at the end of each entry are given (as applicable) for a single room, for single occupancy of a double room, and then per room in the case of two people sharing a double or twin-bedded room, or for a family room. Because double rooms with four-poster beds often cost more, those are listed separately.

SOMERTON Somerset — map 2

The Lynch NEW ENTRY

4 Behind Berry, Somerton TA11 7PD
TEL: (01458) 272316 FAX: (01458) 272590

This Grade II-listed Georgian house, built in 1812, is on the edge of the unspoilt market town of Somerton, which has seventh-century origins. The house has been restored and furnished with antiques, and there is a lovely breakfast room overlooking gardens and a lake, which is home to black swans and numerous exotic ducks. Bedrooms are very comfortable, mostly with good *en suite* bathrooms, and one has a magnificent Georgian four-poster bed. Each has been individually decorated and all have direct-dial telephone. The Lynch is well placed for visiting Glastonbury, Wells and Cheddar.

OWNER: Roy Copeland OPEN: all year exc Christmas ROOMS: 2 double, both with bath/shower; 1 twin, with bath/shower; 1 four-poster, with bath/shower; 1 family, with private bathroom; tea/coffee and TV in all bedrooms; lounge TERMS: single occupancy £45–£53, twin/double £65, four-poster £65–£75, family room £49–£69; deposit or credit card details required CARDS: Amex, MasterCard, Visa DETAILS: no children under 8; no dogs; no smoking; car park; garden

---

Still Cottage NEW ENTRY

North Street, Somerton TA11 7NY TEL: (01458) 272323

Built in 1729 as two cottages and later converted into one building, Still Cottage is at the end of the main street. Mrs Bearne is a friendly and outgoing lady, and the house is comfortable and elegantly furnished. Guests have the use of a sitting-room and a breakfast room, with french windows to the charming garden, where breakfast or evening meals (by prior arrangement) can be served on fine days. The bedrooms are simple, but tastefully furnished, and have easy chairs, good bedside reading lights and bottled water. They share a bathroom and have no TVs. Somerton is a good base for visiting Bath and Wells.

OWNER: Diane Bearne OPEN: all year exc Christmas ROOMS: 1 single, 1 double, 1 twin; all rooms with wash-basin and tea/coffee; lounge with TV TERMS: single/single occupancy £25–£28, twin/double £40–£46; dinner £15; deposit: £10 CARDS: none DETAILS: no children under 12; no dogs; no smoking; garden

SOUTHBOROUGH Kent — map 3

Number Ten

10 Modest Corner, Southborough TN4 0LS TEL: (01892) 522450

This small brick-built terraced house is reputed to have been used as lodgings for Queen Victoria's servants during her visits to nearby Tunbridge Wells. It is situated in a quiet cul-de-sac with lovely wooded views to front and rear, seemingly miles from anywhere, though a busy main road is only half a mile away. Anneke Leemhuis is a friendly and helpful host, and treats guests as part of the family. Breakfast is taken at the kitchen table or, on fine days, outdoors on the patio, and evening meals are available by arrangement. The double room with *en suite* shower is upstairs, while the two simply furnished twin-bedded rooms are on the ground floor and share a bathroom with a power-shower. Modest Corner is on the Weald Way walk.

OWNER: Anneke Leemhuis OPEN: all year ROOMS: 1 double, with shower; 2 twin, both with private bathroom; tea/coffee and TV in all bedrooms TERMS: single occupancy £25–£30, twin/double £38–£42; reductions for children under 4; dinner £10–£12 CARDS: none DETAILS: children welcome; dogs by arrangement; smoking in some areas only; car park; garden

SOUTHEND-ON-SEA Essex map 3

Pebbles Guest House

190 Eastern Esplanade, Thorpe Bay, Southend-on-Sea SS1 3AA
TEL/FAX: (01702) 582329

Edna Christian's floral displays, which have merited much success in the Southend in Bloom contest, make for a colourful approach to this seafront Edwardian guesthouse. Visitors are treated to a high standard of accommodation, the bedrooms have *en suite* tiled shower-rooms and TVs. The seated roof-top garden has an assortment of plants, and is a pleasant place in which to soak up the sunshine. Three-course evening meals, including vegetarian options, are served with prior notice. There is a public car park nearby and free on-street parking on the esplanade.

OWNERS: Colin and Edna Christian OPEN: all year ROOMS: 1 single, 3 double, 1 twin; all rooms with shower, tea/coffee and TV TERMS: single £25, single occupancy £25–£40, twin/double £40; £10 for children under 6 sharing with parents; deposit: 10%; dinner £12.50 CARDS: MasterCard, Visa DETAILS: children welcome; no dogs; smoking in bedrooms only

SOUTH KILVINGTON North Yorkshire map 9

Thornborough House Farm

South Kilvington YO7 2NP TEL/FAX: (01845) 522103
N from Thirsk follow signs for Teesside, through S. Kilvington to roundabout; straight across, entrance 100yds on left

Situated about one and a half miles north of Thirsk, this 200-year-old farmhouse is part of a large sheep and arable farm. A friendly and informal atmosphere rules here, and the owners are very welcoming hosts. Tess Williamson grew up on the farm and is happy to provide information on the area. The prettily decorated bedrooms have either *en suite* or private facilities; all have TVs and sturdy old-fashioned furniture. Three-course home-cooked evening meals are available by arrangement and, along with breakfast, are served in the dining-room. After a day's traipse around the farm, the lounge with its open fire is a good place to relax in. Families with small children will be happy to note that a high chair and cot are available.

OWNERS: D. and T.H. Williamson OPEN: all year ROOMS: 1 double, with shower; 1 twin, with private bathroom; 1 family, with shower; tea/coffee and TV in all bedrooms; lounge with TV TERMS: single occupancy £15–£18, twin/double/family £30–£36 plus children's charge; children's reductions by arrangement; dinner £9.50; deposit: £5 for advance bookings CARDS: MasterCard, Visa DETAILS: children welcome; dogs by arrangement; smoking in lounge only; car park; garden

SOUTHWOLD Suffolk — map 6

Acton Lodge

18 South Green, Southwold IP18 6HB TEL: (01502) 723217

This impressive-looking Italianate/Gothic red-brick Victorian building is set on Southwold's South Green, which is 50 yards from the sea and surrounded by Georgian mansions, fishermen's cottages plus the town's oldest pub. Once the house of a wealthy merchant, the Lodge has been modernised sympathetically, retaining lofty ceilings, marble fireplaces and a turret offering views over the town, sea and marshes. Plush Victorian style characterises the décor, and the bedrooms are all *en suite* and beautifully appointed. A sitting-room with TV and plenty of books is available for guests, and breakfasts feature locally caught kippers and smoked haddock, as well as traditional full English fare and home-made bread and jams. Residents are given their own keys, and will find that the town centre, Gun Hill and many of Southwold's excellent pubs and restaurants are only a short stroll away. Unrestricted on-street parking is available nearby.

OWNER: Brenda Smith OPEN: all year ROOMS: 2 double, 1 with private bathroom; 1 twin, with shower; tea/coffee and TV in all bedrooms; lounge with TV TERMS: single £20–£25, single occupancy £30–£40, twin/double £40–£54; reductions for children sharing with parents; deposit: £25 CARDS: none DETAILS: no children under 6; no dogs; no smoking

SOWERBY BRIDGE West Yorkshire — map 9

Park Villa Guesthouse

141 Park Villas, Bolton Brow, Sowerby Bridge HX6 2BE
TEL: (01422) 832179

This Victorian house was originally a Presbytery to the adjacent St Patrick's church, and now offers comfortable good-value accommodation. Leaded stained-glass windows and Lincustra frieze moulding are some of the period features. Each of the bedrooms has a wash-basin and TV, and Marion Lane is an accommodating host who serves teas in the guest lounge at almost any hour. There is private parking for up to three vehicles, as well as free on-street parking. Evening meals are available at several nearby establishments.

OWNERS: Marion and Ron Lane OPEN: all year ROOMS: 3 twin, 1 family; all rooms with wash-basin, tea/coffee and TV; lounge with TV TERMS: single occupancy £15.50, twin £31, family room from £30; children's reductions according to age; deposit: 10% CARDS: none DETAILS: children welcome; dogs welcome; smoking in conservatory only; car park; garden

SPALDING Lincolnshire — map 6

Bedford Court

10 London Road, Spalding PE11 2TA TEL/FAX: (01775) 722377

Records date this impressive-looking house back to 1711, though it has been much extended and modified since then. However, several original features remain, such as the bevelled glass in the dining-room, and coving, some of which came from Hampton Court. The house occupies a peaceful location at the end of a private drive, close to the River Welland, and it is impeccably maintained by owners Russell and Pamela Herd. The spacious and comfortable bedrooms have desks, armchairs, and *en suite* facilities. One reader found breakfasts to be 'excellent and enormous'; they are served in the elegant dining-room overlooking the garden. The Herds are happy to direct guests to the nearby pub for evening meals.

OWNERS: Russell and Pamela Herd OPEN: all year exc Christmas ROOMS: 1 single, with private bathroom; 1 double, with bath and shower; 2 twin, 1 with bath and shower; tea/coffee and TV in all bedrooms TERMS: single/single occupancy £25, twin/double £40; deposit: £10 CARDS: none DETAILS: no children; no dogs; no smoking; car park; garden

SPAXTON Somerset — map 2

Gatesmoor

Hawkridge, Spaxton TA5 1AL TEL: (01278) 671353

take Spaxton turning off A39 Bridgwater to Nether Stowey road; house is on right, ¼m from village

Gatesmoor is an attractive whitewashed cottage in a peaceful and secluded setting bordering a reservoir on the edge of the Quantock Hills, and its large, colourful garden has lawns sloping down to the water. Peter and Rachel Harvey are a charming couple whose attitude is that nothing is too much trouble. The house is elegantly furnished and the sitting-room has an inglenook fireplace. The two bedrooms, one of which is very large, are both upstairs and share a bathroom on the ground floor. Breakfast is served in the sun-room, with wonderful views over the reservoir and up the valley to the hills. The area is wonderful for walking, bird-watching and riding.

OWNERS: Peter and Rachel Harvey OPEN: Mar to Oct ROOMS: 1 double, 1 twin; both rooms with private bathroom and tea/coffee; lounge with TV TERMS: twin/double £34–£40; deposit required CARDS: none DETAILS: no children under 10; no dogs; no smoking; car park; garden

SPORLE Norfolk map 6

Corfield House

Sporle PE32 2EA TEL: (01760) 723636
½m N of A47, 3m E of Swaffham

This attractive red-brick country house, dating from the early nineteenth century and extended in the 1950s, enjoys a quiet location in the peaceful village of Sporle, not far from the attractive market town of Swaffham. The well-equipped and tastefully decorated bedrooms are in the old part of the house; one is on the ground floor and can accommodate wheelchair-users. There is a sunny lounge, and a licensed dining-room, where breakfast and dinner are served. In summer, guests can appreciate the lovely lavender and rose bushes in the well-maintained garden. Martin Hickey runs the local tourist information centre and can provide a comprehensive fact file on the many things to see and do in north Norfolk.

OWNERS: Linda and Martin Hickey OPEN: end Mar to mid-Dec ROOMS: 2 double, 2 twin; all rooms with bath/shower, tea/coffee and TV; 1 room suitable for wheelchair-users; lounge TERMS: single occupancy £29–£40, twin/double £37–£43; children's reductions by arrangement; dinner £12.50; deposit: £20–£40 CARDS: MasterCard, Visa DETAILS: children welcome; dogs in ground-floor room only; no smoking; car park; garden

STAINDROP Co Durham map 10

Fawn Lea

10 Winston Road, Staindrop DL2 3NN TEL/FAX: (01833) 660356
just of A688, 5m NE of Barnard Castle

This homely, well-maintained establishment is within a few minutes' drive of Barnard Castle. The three snug bedrooms are *en suite*, and are attractively decorated in floral patterns. A warm welcome, including biscuits for arriving visitors, can be expected from hospitable Joy Robson. Joy's husband, Les, trains horses for harness-racing, and the fruits of his success are on display about the house. The seated patio area, which overlooks a small garden, is a perfect place in which to soak up the sunshine in the summer. Guests can also make use of the conservatory and TV lounge.

OWNER: Joy Robson OPEN: all year ROOMS: 2 double, 1 twin; all rooms with bath/shower, tea/coffee and TV; lounge with TV TERMS: single occupancy £24, twin/double £36; children under 3 free, half-price for ages 3 and over CARDS: none DETAILS: children welcome; dogs welcome; smoking in lounge only; car park

STAMFORD Lincolnshire — map 6

Martins

20 St Martins, Stamford PE9 2LF
TEL: (01780) 752106 FAX: (01780) 482691

Marie Martin's cooking is a popular feature of this beautifully maintained B&B. She uses fresh vegetables and herbs from the garden, makes her own bread, and conjures up delicious desserts at dinner. Hearty breakfasts with an abundance of choice, are also served. Hidden behind a wall-panel in the dining-room is a beautiful medieval painting, which Marie is easily persuaded to display to guests. The spacious bedrooms are furnished with antiques and colourful fabrics; the double rooms can also be used as twins. Residents can relax in the downstairs drawing-room, which is warmed by a log fire, and enjoy the large walled garden and croquet lawn in the summer. Martins is a listed Georgian house which takes its name from the adjacent church. The property stands within walking distance of Burleigh House and Stamford train station. There is on-street car parking; house-parties can be arranged for the weekends.

OWNER: Marie Martin OPEN: all year exc Christmas ROOMS: 3 double/twin, 1 with private bathroom; 1 family, with private shower-room; tea/coffee in all bedrooms; lounge with TV TERMS: single occupancy £35, twin/double £50, family room £80; dinner £17.50; deposit: £10 per room CARDS: none DETAILS: children welcome; dogs by arrangement; no smoking in dining-room; garden

STAPLEHAY Somerset — map 2

West Amberd Cottage

Amberd Lane, Staplehay TA3 7AA TEL: (01823) 270765
2½m S of Taunton on minor road off A38

This semi-detached cottage was built around 1912, most probably as the gardener's lodgings for West Amberd House. It is on a quiet road in the village of Staplehay, overlooking the Quantock Hills, and surrounded by mature trees. Joan Oliver is a very friendly, welcoming lady, and as there is only one comfortable twin-bedded room, guests can be assured of personal attention. Both the house and small, pretty garden are immaculately kept. There is a large sitting-room and a garden room at the back of the house, which is ideal to relax in on sunny days. Taunton is under three miles away.

OWNER: Joan Oliver OPEN: all year exc Christmas ROOMS: 1 twin, with bath and shower, tea/coffee and TV; lounge with TV TERMS: single occupancy £19, twin £36; children's reductions by arrangement CARDS: none DETAILS: children welcome; no dogs; no smoking; car park; garden

---

Any smoking restrictions that we know of are given in the details at the end of the entry.

STARBOTTON North Yorkshire **map 8**

Bushey Lodge Farm

NEW ENTRY

Starbotton BD23 5HY TEL: (01756) 760424
heading N on B6160 from Shipton, turn left just beyond pub by bridge, just S of village

This tastefully renovated seventeenth-century lodge is part of a 2,000-acre working stock farm. It has an ideal setting, in the heart of the Dales, and there are plenty of good walks from the farm. The good-sized bedrooms are attractively decorated with pastel floral fabrics and matching duvets; both rooms have *en suite* facilities and TVs. Breakfasts are substantial, and include fresh fish and fruit as well as traditional fare. The dining-room has some interesting pieces, including an old marble washstand. A pub that serves evening meals is less than 100 yards away.

OWNER: Rosie Lister ROOMS: 1 double, 1 twin; both rooms with bath/shower, tea/coffee and TV, lounge TERMS: single occupancy £30, twin/double £40–£44 CARDS: none DETAILS: no children; no dogs; no smoking; car park; garden

STARCROSS Devon **map 1**

The Old Vicarage

Starcross EX6 8PX TEL/FAX: (01626) 890206
on A379, 5m S of Exeter, at S end of village

Maggie and Mervyn Hayes are a charming and welcoming couple, and have created an informal, comfortable atmosphere at this cob-stone house with thick walls, standing in three acres of grounds overlooking the Exe Estuary, famous for its bird life. The Old Vicarage is now well over three hundred years old and has been a guesthouse since 1991, having formerly been a church property and before that a farmhouse. It is simply furnished, the three bedrooms being individually decorated, and the 'Woodbury' suite has a small room with bunk beds off the main bedroom and a large *en suite* bathroom. The lounge has a piano and games. Dawlish Warren nature reserve is only three miles away.

OWNERS: Maggie and Mervyn Hayes OPEN: all year ROOMS: 2 double, 1 with bath/shower, 1 with wash-basin; 2 twin, 1 with bath/shower, 1 with wash-basin; 1 family, with bath/shower; tea/coffee in all bedrooms; TV in most bedrooms and lounge TERMS: single occupancy £18–£25, twin/double £32–£36, family room £40–£70; children under 2 free, 50% reduction for ages 2–11, 25% reduction for ages 12–14; deposit: 1 night's charge CARDS: none DETAILS: children welcome; no dogs; car park; garden

B&Bs are selected for the Guide for their warm welcome, cleanliness, a friendly atmosphere and, wherever possible, an attractive location or a building that is itself of some historical or architectural interest.

STARSTON Norfolk **map 6**

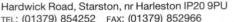

Starston Hall

NEW ENTRY

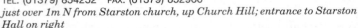

Hardwick Road, Starston, nr Harleston IP20 9PU
TEL: (01379) 854252 FAX: (01379) 852966
just over 1m N from Starston church, up Church Hill; entrance to Starston Hall on right

This handsome listed house of Elizabethan origins stands in four acres of beautiful grounds and is surrounded partly by the original moat. After recent extensive but sensitive renovation, the interior retains a great deal of character, and has been furnished to a high standard with antiques, plush carpets and rich curtains. The unusual wall paintings are by the artistic owner, Mrs Baxter. Just about everything has been thought of in the luxurious bedrooms, from filled bookcases, cosy bathrobes, a desk and armchairs, plus complimentary mineral water and fruit. The double rooms are in the main house, and the twin-bedded room, which is suitable for wheelchair-users, is in the barn; all have either *en suite* facilities or a private bathroom. Superb candlelit dinners, with complimentary wine, take place by arrangement in the elegant dining-room. Breakfast is a more casual affair, served in the breakfast room, and includes free-range eggs – duck or bantam when available – as part of a large cooked platter; guests staying in the main house may opt instead for a continental breakfast served in their room. Residents also have the use of a large drawing-room with its beamed ceiling and log fire.

OWNERS: Mr and Mrs Baxter OPEN: all year exc Christmas ROOMS: 2 double, 1 with bath/shower, 1 with private bathroom; 1 twin, with bath/shower; 1 room suitable for wheelchair-users; TV in all bedrooms; lounge TERMS: single occupancy £37.50–£42.50; twin/double £60–£70; dinner £25; deposit: £10 per person per night CARDS: none DETAILS: children welcome; no dogs; no smoking; car park; garden

STAUNTON Gloucestershire **map 5**

Mayfield Cottage

Moat Lane, Staunton GL19 3QA TEL: (01452) 840673
from Gloucester, take A417 Ledbury road; on approaching Staunton keep left at mini-roundabout, then Moat Lane is first turning on right; or from M50 junction 2 take A417 to Staunton in Gloucester direction

Mayfield is a seventeenth-century former crofter's cottage, in a peaceful rural area, and has been tastefully renovated while retaining its old-world charm and many period details. John and Jennifer Clayton are a friendly couple and make guests feel very much at home, offering a hot drink on arrival. The immaculately kept bedrooms are decorated with dainty fabrics and wallpapers. Breakfast and, by arrangement, dinner make good use of local produce; both are served in the beamed dining-room. Guests can also use the sitting-room, which still has the original bread oven in the fireplace, and the beautiful landscaped garden, still with the original water pump. Jennifer Clayton belongs to the local rambling club and is happy to give information on local walks.

OWNERS: John and Jennifer Clayton OPEN: all year exc Christmas and New Year ROOMS: 1 single, with private bathroom; 1 double, with bath/shower; 1 twin, with bath/shower; tea/coffee and TV in all bedrooms; lounge with TV TERMS: single £16–£18, single occupancy £20, twin/double £32–£36; dinner £10; deposit: £10 per person CARDS: none DETAILS: children welcome; dogs by arrangement; no smoking; car park; garden

STEEPLE BUMPSTEAD Essex map 6

Yew Tree House

15 Chapel Street, Steeple Bumpstead CB9 7DQ TEL/FAX: (01440) 730364
off B1054, 3m S of Haverhill

Set in the village of Steeple Bumpstead with its old church, former tiny 'lock-up' and sixteenth-century Moot Hall, Yew Tree House is a red-brick Victorian house offering two comfortable *en suite* bedrooms. Each has a floral-themed décor, one has a marble antique dressing-table and the other an original fireplace; both have TVs. Guests have the use of a lounge with TV, a real fire on chilly days, board games and a good selection of local information. Breakfast is served at times to suit, and offers a choice of 'light' cooked items as well as cereals and juices, or, for £1.50 extra, a full cooked platter. Evening meals, too, can be booked, and guests are most welcome to bring their own wine. The village is served by a twice-daily bus service to Cambridge and London.

OWNER: Mrs S.J. Stirling OPEN: all year exc Christmas ROOMS: 1 double, 1 twin; both rooms with shower, tea/coffee and TV; lounge with TV TERMS: single occupancy £25–£28, twin/double £36–£39; reductions for children sharing with parents; dinner £10; deposit: 25% CARDS: none DETAILS: children by arrangement; no dogs; no smoking in bedrooms; car park

STERT Wiltshire map 2

Spout Cottage NEW ENTRY

Stert SN10 3JD TEL: (01380) 724336
just off A342, 2m E of Devizes

Spout Cottage takes its name from the numerous springs around the house – so no water shortage here. It is a delightful thatched cottage dating from 1850, reached down a very steep drive, in the peaceful village of Stert. The two bedrooms, with wash-basins, share a bathroom, and both rooms have been beautifully furnished with antiques. The sitting-room is cosy with an inglenook fireplace and original beams, and both breakfast and evening meals, by arrangement, are served here, or in the Victorian conservatory. The charming garden has a paved patio, with tables and chairs for sitting outside, and there are lovely rural views which include two fishing lakes. Spout Cottage is very comfortable, and has a welcoming and hospitable atmosphere.

OWNERS: David and Beryl Porter OPEN: all year exc Christmas ROOMS: 1 single, 1 twin; both rooms with wash-basin and tea/coffee; lounge with TV TERMS: single £18–£20, single occupancy £28–£30, twin £32–£36; dinner £14.50–£18; deposit: 20% CARDS: none DETAILS: no children under 12; no dogs; smoking in conservatory only; car park; garden

STOCKLAND Devon map 2

Kings Arms Inn

Stockland EX14 9BS TEL: (01404) 881361 FAX: (01404) 881732
signposted from A30 Chard to Honiton road; or from A35 take Shute garage exit W of Axminster

Set in pretty Devon countryside in the centre of the picturesque village of Stockland, this ancient thatched inn has an unspoilt rustic charm, even though it has been extended and now includes a skittle alley as well as a very busy restaurant. A couple of the bars have been rebuilt and one now has a flagstone floor. The dining-room is in the oldest part of the building and has stone walls and an enormous fireplace. Excellent food is served to a wide clientele at lunch-time (though not on Sunday) and in the evening. Bar games such as skittles and darts keep things spirited, and live music fills the pub on Sunday nights. The three *en suite* bedrooms all have telephones and TVs, and one has its own patio. The Kings Arms has plenty of character and a friendly atmosphere, and best suits those who are seeking a sociable and lively stay.

OWNERS: Paul Diviani, Heinz Kiefer and John O'Leary OPEN: all year exc Christmas and New Year ROOMS: 2 double, 1 twin; all rooms with bath, tea/coffee and TV; lounge with TV TERMS: single occupancy £25, twin/double £40; dinner £15; deposit: 1 night's charge CARDS: Delta, MasterCard, Switch, Visa DETAILS: children welcome; dogs welcome; car park *(The Good Food Guide)*

STOKE GABRIEL Devon map 1

Red Slipper

Stoke Gabriel TQ9 6RU TEL/FAX: (01803) 782315
off A385 Totnes to Paignton road, opposite post office in centre of village

The Red Slipper is in the centre of the picturesque village of Stoke Gabriel, which is by the River Dart and surrounded by lovely countryside. As well as B&B, meals are offered in licensed tea-rooms, open to residents and non-residents alike. The Watts are a friendly and hospitable couple who go out of their way to take care of their guests' needs. Bedrooms are attractively furnished and well provided with extras, such as fresh flowers and fruit, and hair-dryers. A single room, which can accommodate two children, can be let in conjunction with one of the double rooms for families. There is one lounge upstairs and another on the ground floor for smokers. Bookings for bank holiday weekends must be for a minimum of two nights.

OWNERS: John and Elizabeth Watts OPEN: mid-Mar to late Oct ROOMS: 1 double, 3 twin; all rooms with shower, tea/coffee and TV; lounge with TV TERMS: single £20–£21, single occupancy £31–£32, twin/double £45–£53; children under 2 free, reductions for older children according to age; dinner £15; deposit: £10 per person CARDS: none DETAILS: children welcome; dogs welcome; smoking in 1 lounge only; car park; garden

STOKE-ON-TRENT Staffordshire **map 5**

Corrie Guesthouse

13 Newton Street, Basford, Stoke-on-Trent ST4 6JN TEL: (01782) 614838
200yds S of A53/A500 junction

Situated in a quiet cul-de-sac, this Victorian house is fairly close to the town centre. The owners live in the house next door, but are always available to help guests. The small bedrooms are spick and span and prettily decorated; four have *en suite* showers, and as we went to press there were plans to turn the two single rooms into an *en suite* double. Plenty of information is on hand for guests intending to visit the potteries, and the Burtons are pleased to offer advice for local tours. There is a residents' lounge with TV. Those venturing into town will probably benefit by leaving their car and taking the bus.

OWNERS: R.W. and A.M. Burton OPEN: all year exc Christmas ROOMS: 2 single; 2 double, both with shower; 2 twin, 1 with shower; 2 family, 1 with shower; lounge with TV TERMS: single/single occupancy £19–£28, twin/double £36–£40, family room £42–£46; children's reductions by arrangement; deposit usually required CARDS: none DETAILS: children welcome; no dogs; smoking in lounge only; car park; garden

Westfield House

312 Princes Road, Penkhull, Stoke-on-Trent ST4 7JP TEL: (01782) 844582

A warm and congenial ambience is a plus at this good-value B&B, which lies within two miles of the main shopping district. Mrs White treats her guests as friends, and keeps the place in good order. The cosy, refurbished TV lounge has a recently fitted carpet, and new furniture. Westfield House is a charming Victorian residence, situated in Penkhull, which is the oldest part of the city.

OWNERS: Norma and John White OPEN: all year exc Christmas ROOMS: 1 double, 1 twin; tea/coffee in both bedrooms; TV in double room and lounge TERMS: single occupancy £20, twin/double £40; children's reductions by arrangement CARDS: none DETAILS: children welcome; no dogs; no smoking in bedrooms; car park

If you are forced to turn up later than planned, please telephone to warn the proprietor. It is always best to book a room in advance, even in winter. B&Bs with few rooms may close at short notice for periods not specified in the details.

STOKE ST GREGORY Somerset **map 2**

Slough Court

Stoke St Gregory TA3 6JQ TEL/FAX: (01823) 490311
just S of A361, 8m E of Taunton

There aren't many fourteenth-century moated farmhouses around these days, but Slough Court is a lovely example, set in peaceful countryside. The farmyard is approached through a stone archway and across an attractive terrace with an oval heated swimming-pool. The house, complete with oak beams, mullioned windows and open fires, is part of a working farm run by Sally's husband, and has been in the Gothard family for many generations. There are three attractive and tastefully decorated bedrooms, all with *en suite* facilities, plus a spacious sitting-room with open fireplace, and a family dining-room where breakfast is served. The lawned garden includes a grass tennis court and croquet lawn. Bicycles can be hired.

OWNER: Sally Gothard OPEN: Jan to Oct ROOMS: 2 double, 1 twin; all rooms with bath/shower, tea/coffee and TV; lounge with TV TERMS: single occupancy £28, twin/double £46–£52; deposit: £10 CARDS: none DETAILS: no children under 12; no dogs; no smoking in public rooms; car park; garden; swimming-pool; tennis

STOW-ON-THE-WOLD Gloucestershire **map 5**

Tall Trees NEW ENTRY

Oddington Road, Stow-on-the-Wold GL54 1AL TEL: (01451) 831296

This charming Cotswold-stone house stands in four acres of private gardens, with lovely views of the surrounding countryside. Several farmyard animals are kept in the grounds, including two ponies and some chickens which provide the fresh eggs for breakfast. The bedrooms are on two floors in a separate wing of the house. Both floors have a large bathroom, and there is a kitchen in which guests can prepare light snacks and picnic lunches. The lounge-cum-dining-room comes complete with TV and wood-burning stove, and leads out on to the garden terrace. Mrs Scarsbrook is an unobtrusive host, but is always happy to offer advice on local restaurants and places of interest.

OWNER: J.C. Scarsbrook OPEN: all year exc Christmas ROOMS: 2 double; 1 family, with private bathroom; tea/coffee and TV in all bedrooms; lounge with TV TERMS: single occupancy £25–£30, double £40–£50, family room £60–£70; children's reductions according to age CARDS: none DETAILS: children welcome; no dogs; no smoking in bedrooms; car park; garden

Wyck Hill Lodge

Wyck Hill, Stow-on-the-Wold GL54 1HT TEL: (01451) 830141
off A424 Burford to Stow-on-the-Wold road

Gloria and Eddie Holbrook took charge of this listed Victorian house in August 1996, and the high standard of accommodation continues under the new owners. The tastefully-furnished interior includes a lounge-cum-dining-room which has a log-fire, and an additional sitting-area with a good supply of books to dip into. Of the three attractive *en suite* bedrooms, two are on the ground floor and are suitable for the partially mobile; all have TVs and rich-coloured duvets. Wyck Hill Lodge stands in private grounds overlooking the Vale of Burton; the quiet wooded lane that leads off the property is a good spot for an early-morning stroll.

OWNERS: Gloria and Eddie Holbrook OPEN: 1 Mar to 30 Nov ROOMS: 2 double, 1 twin; all rooms with bath/shower, tea/coffee and TV TERMS: single occupancy £30, twin/double £42–£46; deposit: £20 per room CARDS: none DETAILS: no children; no dogs; no smoking; car park; garden

STRATFORD-UPON-AVON Warwickshire **map 5**

32 College Street

NEW ENTRY

32 College Street, Stratford-upon-Avon CV37 6BW TEL: (01789) 266784

This 1930s cottage-style semi-detached house is situated on a quiet street just five minutes' walk from the Royal Shakespeare Theatre and town centre. Mr and Mrs Kenton (whose family has lived in the Stratford area for over four generations) are gracious and welcoming hosts. Both are actors, and obtaining theatre tickets and assisting guests with information on the area are all part of the excellent service extended here. The well-appointed *en suite* bedrooms are bright and light, and have comfortable beds. A generous cooked or continental breakfast is served in the elegant dining-room or, on warm days, on the patio in the well-tended garden. There is also a drawing-room for guests' use. Off-street parking is limited and so should be arranged when booking.

OWNER: Mary Kenton OPEN: all year ROOMS: 1 single, 1 twin; both rooms with bath/shower; lounge TERMS: single/single occupancy £25, twin £50 CARDS: none DETAILS: no children under 10; no dogs; garden

Victoria Spa Lodge

Bishopton Lane, Stratford-upon-Avon CV37 9QY
TEL: (01789) 207985 FAX: (01789) 204728

1½m N of Stratford, where A3400 and A46 intersect, take first left at roundabout; hotel on right

This charming Grade II-listed building, built in 1837, stands in its own grounds about a mile and a half north of Stratford. It overlooks the canal, where the towpath leads to the town centre. The Lodge was originally built as a spa – Queen Victoria gave her name to the hotel, and her coat of arms still resides in the gables. The roomy and airy bedrooms, all with *en suite* showers and TVs, are decorated in a variety of styles, and have good views over either the garden or the canal. One attic room affords additional privacy and has the most extensive views. Breakfast is cooked by Paul Tozer and served by

Dreen from a sideboard in the huge lounge/dining-room. The room has lots to interest the eye – ornate decanters in antique cases, cherubs playing musical instruments, some lovely paintings – as well as comfortable sofas and a CD player.

OWNERS: Paul and Dreen Tozer OPEN: all year ROOMS: 3 double, 1 twin, 3 family; all rooms with shower, tea/coffee and TV; lounge TERMS: single occupancy £38–£45, twin/double £50–£55, family room £68; deposit or credit card details required CARDS: MasterCard, Visa DETAILS: children welcome; no dogs; no smoking; car park; garden

Woodstock

30 Grove Road, Stratford-upon-Avon CV37 6PB TEL: (01789) 299881

This beautifully decorated and impeccably maintained family-run guesthouse is only five minutes' walk from the town centre, the river, the theatre and Shakespeare's house. There are five attractive, good-sized, well-appointed bedrooms, decorated with pretty fabrics, lace coronets and traditional furnishings. One room is on the ground floor and has *en suite* facilities, and is suitable for the partially disabled. Breakfast is served in the attractive dining-room.

OWNER: Maisie Haufe OPEN: all year exc Christmas ROOMS: 1 single, 2 double, 1 twin, 1 family; all rooms with shower exc single with private bathroom; tea/coffee and TV in all bedrooms TERMS: single £20–£26, single occupancy £30–£40, twin/double £40–£52, family room £60–£70; reductions for children according to age; deposit: 1 night's charge CARDS: none DETAILS: no children under 3; no dogs; no smoking; car park

STREFFORD Shropshire **map 5**

Strefford Hall

Strefford SY7 8DE TEL/FAX: (01588) 672383
¼m off A49, 2m N of Craven Arms

This handsome stone-built farmhouse is part of a 360-acre working farm, and lies in pretty Shropshire countryside not far from Wenlock Edge. Serious walkers will be pleased to know that a track from the farm connects with the Shropshire Way. Within the house, a sense of old-fashioned solidity and space prevails: rooms are large, there's a quarry tile entrance way and Victorian pine stairway, and you may hear the ticking of a grandfather clock. None the less, the atmosphere is informal and friendly, and the three *en suite* bedrooms are well appointed and comfortable, with good views across the fields to the hills. Guests have a sitting-room, and can tuck into a full English breakfast in the dining-room. Evening meals, too, can be arranged; alternatively, pubs and restaurants are not far off. As we went to press, central heating was being installed.

OWNERS: Caroline and John Morgan OPEN: Feb to Nov ROOMS: 2 double, both with shower; 1 twin, with bath; all rooms with tea/coffee and TV; lounge TERMS: single occupancy £20–£25, twin/double £38–£40; children under 2 free, reductions for older children by arrangement; dinner £11; deposit required for long-term bookings CARDS: none DETAILS: children welcome; no dogs; no smoking; car park; garden

STURMINSTER NEWTON Dorset map 2

Stourcastle Lodge

Goughs Lodge, Sturminster Newton DT10 1BU
TEL: (01258) 472320 FAX: (01258) 473381

Stourcastle Lodge dates from 1600 and was originally a farmhouse, but it burnt down in the 'Great Fire of Sturminster' in 1729, and was rebuilt as a family home a few years later. It is in a quiet position down a narrow lane from the centre of the small town of Sturminster Newton. The comfortable bedrooms all have *en suite* facilities and are furnished mostly in pine. Jill Hookham-Bassett is a cheerful host, and prepares meals on the Aga using herbs and vegetables from the garden. Breakfast and dinner are served at separate tables in the dining-room, which is decorated with husband Ken's collection of antique kitchenalia. Pictures by local artists hang all around the house. Guests can sit out in the garden on warm days and look for the interesting sculptures.

OWNERS: Jill and Ken Hookham-Bassett OPEN: all year ROOMS: 4 double, 1 twin; all rooms with bath/shower, tea/coffee and TV; lounge TERMS: single occupancy £33–£42, twin/double £53–£68; half-price for children sharing with parents; dinner £16; deposit: £20 per room or credit card details CARDS: MasterCard, Visa DETAILS: children welcome; no dogs; smoking in lounge only; car park; garden

STURTON BY STOW Lincolnshire map 9

Gallows Dale Farm

Stow Park Road, Sturton by Stow LN1 2AH TEL: (01427) 788387
on A1500, 1m W of Sturton by Stow; half-way between Lincoln and Gainsborough

This listed farmhouse is run by the amiable Brenda Williams, and offers comfortable, good-value accommodation. One of the four-poster rooms has an *en suite* shower, and the family room, which features a cast-iron bed, is sometimes let as a twin. Brenda keeps her house well, and does much of the upholstering herself. Hearty breakfasts are served in the beamed dining-room at individual tables, and there is a cosy TV lounge. The main building is set a little way back off the main road, and is part of a 32-acre working cattle farm.

OWNER: Brenda Williams OPEN: all year ROOMS: 1 single; 2 four-poster, 1 with shower, 1 with wash-basin; 1 family, with wash-basin and WC; tea/coffee in all bedrooms; TV in most bedrooms and lounge TERMS: single/single occupancy £20–£25, four-poster £38–£40, family from £34; children's reductions according to age CARDS: none DETAILS: children welcome; dogs by arrangement; no smoking; car park; garden

SUDBURY Suffolk map 6

St Faiths Villa NEW ENTRY

90 Queens Road, Sudbury CO10 6PG TEL: (01787) 374627
from town centre follow sign for Bury St Edmunds; just after zebra-crossing, at junction with St Johns Met. Church, turn right into York Rd and then left into Queens Rd

This good-value, immaculately kept establishment is five minutes' walk from the town centre and stands in a terraced garden with two ponds stocked with a variety of fish. It is a detached Victorian house with stripped pine woodwork throughout, and offers three *en suite* bedrooms, all comfortably appointed and with TVs. Breakfasts are served in the dining-room/lounge, which has satellite TV, a video and lots of information on the local area. Rosalind Edwards is very happy to assist guests in every way. Thomas Gainsborough was born in Sudbury in 1727, and his home is open to the public at certain times.

OWNER: Mrs R.A. Edwards OPEN: all year exc Christmas ROOMS: 1 single, 2 double; all rooms with bath/shower, tea/coffee and TV; lounge with TV TERMS: single £25/ single occupancy £25, double £35; deposit: £10–£15 CARDS: none DETAILS: no children under 10; no dogs; smoking in lounge only; car park; garden

SUMMER BRIDGE North Yorkshire map 9

Clough House Farm

Summerbridge, Summer Bridge HG3 4JR TEL: (01423) 780823
leave A61 6m S of Ripon and follow B6165 towards Pateley Bridge for 6m

In the middle of grand walking country, Clough House is a renovated seventeenth-century farmhouse offering seven comfortable, well-appointed *en suite* bedrooms. Three of the rooms are on the ground floor and suitable for wheelchair-users. In summer, old stone troughs are filled with colourful flowers, and all around are pleasant views of the countryside. Traditional home-cooked evening meals can be arranged, and are served in the dining-room. Guests also have use of a TV lounge. Self-catering accommodation is available on the property, which also has a riding-school.

OWNERS: Kenneth and Brenda Walmsley OPEN: all year ROOMS: 2 double, 3 twin, 2 family; all rooms with bath/shower; 3 rooms suitable for wheelchair-users; tea/coffee in all bedrooms; lounge with TV TERMS: single occupancy £30, twin/double £45, family room £50; dinner £10.50; deposit required CARDS: none DETAILS: children welcome; no dogs; no smoking in some bedrooms; car park; garden

---

Breakfast at B&Bs tends to mean a cooked breakfast of bacon, eggs, toast and so on, although many establishments also offer a good choice of cereals, yoghurts, fruit and other options. If you have special dietary requirements, it is best to discuss these when you make a booking.

SUNDERLAND Tyne & Wear **map 10**

Mayfield Hotel

Sea Lane, Seaburn, Sunderland SR6 8EE TEL: (0191) 529 3345

This pleasant, spick-and-span turn-of-the-century house is approximately one mile from the centre of Sunderland and not far from Roker and Seaburn beaches. Local bus services stop just outside. The bedrooms are well maintained; one has a four-poster bed, seven have *en suite* showers, four are on the ground floor, all have TVs and some have sea views. Hearty, cooked-to-order breakfasts are served in the no-smoking dining-room.

OWNERS: Vincent and Judith Richardson OPEN: all year exc Christmas ROOMS: 1 single, with wash-basin; 4 double, 3 with shower, 1 with wash-basin; 5 twin, 3 with shower, 2 with wash-basin; 1 four-poster, with shower; 2 family, both with private bathroom; tea/coffee and TV in all bedrooms TERMS: single £17.50–£28, single occupancy £28, twin/double £38, four-poster £40, family room from £33; children under 5 free, reductions for older children according to age CARDS: none DETAILS: children welcome; no dogs; no smoking in dining-room; car park; garden

SWAFFHAM BULBECK Cambridgeshire **map 6**

The Old Rectory

Swaffham Bulbeck CB5 0LX TEL/FAX: (01223) 811986
off B1102 in village, 5m NE of Cambridge

Just behind the old village church, up a long drive, stands this handsome Georgian residence. The well-maintained house with its stone entrance way, antique furniture and marble fireplace exudes old-world charm, and Jenny Few-Mackay keeps things informal. A mill stream runs through the three-and-a-half acre gardens, which are open to the public under the National Gardens Scheme. Guests can make use of a heated outdoor swimming-pool in the summer. Bedrooms are well proportioned and comfortable; one has *en suite* facilities. A pub within walking distance is convenient for evening meals. Newmarket with its famous race-course is five miles away.

OWNER: Jenny Few-Mackay OPEN: all year exc Christmas ROOMS: 2 double, 1 with bath/shower; 1 twin; tea/coffee and TV in all bedrooms; lounge TERMS: single occupancy £30, twin/double £45–£60; deposit required CARDS: none DETAILS: no children under 12; dogs welcome; no smoking; car park; games room; garden; swimming-pool

---

Please do not rely on an out-of-date Guide. Although some B&Bs in the current edition have steadfastly retained their high standards and have featured in every edition since the first, a great many others have faded from the scene. In addition, many new, superb B&Bs have been added. Relying on an old Guide will limit your choices and may lead to disappointment.

SWAY Hampshire — map 2

Kingfishers

Coombe Lane, Sway SO41 6BP
TEL: (01590) 682414 FAX: (01590) 683460
off B3055, 3m SW of Brockenhurst

Kingfishers is a modern house on the outskirts of the small, peaceful village of Sway, on the edge of the New Forest, and was designed by the present owners. Lesley Smith settles her guests in with tea and cake, and was described by one reader as 'an exceptional hostess'. Children are more than welcome; both bedrooms are large and ideal for a family, and have well-appointed *en suite* facilities. The conservatory overlooks the beautiful garden, and there is a stable block behind the house. Sway is convenient for Lymington, with its marinas and ferry to the Isle of Wight, and for riding.

OWNER: Lesley Smith OPEN: all year exc Christmas ROOMS: 2 double, both with shower; lounge with TV TERMS: single occupancy £30, double £45; deposit required CARDS: none DETAILS: children welcome; no dogs; no smoking; car park; garden

SWINHOPE Lincolnshire — map 9

Hoe Hill

Swinhope LN8 6HX TEL: (01472) 398206
on B1203, 1m N of Binbrook

Surrounded by lovely Lincolnshire countryside, and only a short drive from the coast, this late-eighteenth-century farmhouse is a peaceful rural retreat. One of the bedrooms overlooks the pretty garden, and has an *en suite* luxury bathroom. There are two other smaller but equally comfortable bedrooms, which share a bathroom. Erica Curd is well known locally for her imaginative cooking, and her pre-arranged evening-meals, served with a complimentary glass of wine or sherry, are excellent value. There is no table licence, but guests may bring their own wine; evening meals are not available during Christmas.

OWNERS: Ian and Erica Curd OPEN: Feb to Dec ROOMS: 2 double, 1 with bath/shower, 1 with wash-basin; 1 twin, with wash-basin; tea/coffee in all bedrooms; lounge with TV TERMS: single occupancy £20–£30, twin/double £36–£40; children's reductions according to age; dinner £14; deposit required for bookings of 3 nights or over CARDS: none DETAILS: no children under 5; no dogs; smoking in lounge only; car park; garden

---

The descriptive part of entries usually includes some facts about setting, the house itself, décor and furnishings, the atmosphere, any special features, and whether evening meals are offered. If the B&B has no car park, we give wherever possible some indication of where guests may find a place to park. If one-night bookings are not accepted at certain times of the week or year, that is mentioned.

TALKIN Cumbria **map 10**

Hullerbank

Talkin CA8 1LB TEL/FAX: (016977) 46668
off B6413, 3m SE of Brampton, take road signposted Talkin, then take Hallbankgate Road and follow signs to Hullerbank

Hullerbank is a charming Georgian farmhouse set in pretty gardens with an orchard, next to 14 acres of pasture with a small flock of sheep. It is surrounded by unspoilt countryside, on the edge of the Pennines and, within, a warm welcome is extended by Brian and Sheila Stobbart. Breakfast and dinner are served, and the Stobbarts' cooking, using home-grown and local produce, is commended by a reporter. The speciality is their own lamb. The house is unlicensed but guests may bring their own wine to dinner. Talkin Town Country Park, with lovely walks, sailing and fishing, is close by, and Brampton golf course is just a mile away.

OWNERS: Brian and Sheila Stobbart OPEN: all year exc Christmas ROOMS: 1 double, with private bathroom; 2 twin, both with shower; tea/coffee in all bedrooms; lounge with TV TERMS: single occupancy £25–£26, twin/double £40–£42; dinner £12–£13; deposit: £10 per room CARDS: Delta, MasterCard, Visa DETAILS: no children under 12; no dogs; no smoking; car park; garden

TALLINGTON Lincolnshire **map 6**

The Old Mill

Mill Lane, Tallington PE9 4RR TEL: (01780) 740815 FAX: (01780) 740280
just off A16, 4m E of Stamford

This unique building, converted out of an mill dating from 1682, has been in the Olver family for three generations. Low ceilings, wooden floors and exposed beams give the place a wonderful old-world feel. Pre-arranged dinners are served in the dining-room, which retains some of the original mill workings. All six of the elegantly furnished bedrooms have *en suite* facilities; residents can make use of the fridge on the landing. The Olvers own some 550 acres of farmland, which guests are welcome to explore, and also a nearby seven-acre coarse-fishing lake; fishing is also available on the river by the house. The Old Mill lies on a quiet country lane, only 300 yards from the village.

OWNERS: Sue and John Olver OPEN: all year ROOMS: 2 double, 4 family; all rooms with bath/shower, tea/coffee and TV TERMS: single occupancy £30–£45, double £45–£60, family room £50–£65; reductions for children sharing with parents; dinner £12 CARDS: none DETAILS: children welcome; dogs welcome; no smoking; car park; tennis

---

Many B&Bs are in remote places, and although in many cases we provide directions, it is always advisable to ask for clear instructions when booking.

TANSLEY Derbyshire map 5

Packhorse Farm

Tansley DE4 5LF TEL/FAX: (01629) 580950

This 200-year-old farmhouse is in the village of Tansley, in a remote spot on the edge of the Peak District, and close to Matlock. It is set in a large garden on a 40-acre working farm with sheep, pigs, rare-breed hens and turkeys. The Hayneses have created a warm, informal home-from-home atmosphere, and guests find it easy to relax here. Two of the bedrooms have antique pine furniture and *en suite* facilities, and the beamed guest lounge is warmed by an open fire. Substantial breakfasts are served in the sunny dining-room. The garden incorporates a putting green, badminton court and a mini-nature reserve.

OWNERS: Byron and Susan Haynes OPEN: all year exc Christmas ROOMS: 1 single, with wash-basin; 2 double, both with bath/shower; 1 twin, with private bathroom; 1 family, with private bathroom; tea/coffee and TV in all bedrooms; lounge with TV TERMS: single/single occupancy £25, twin/double £40–£60, family room £50–£60; children's reductions; deposit: 25% CARDS: none DETAILS: children welcome; no dogs; no smoking in bedrooms; car park; garden

TARVIN Cheshire map 7

Grove House

Holme Street, Tarvin CH3 8EQ TEL: (01829) 740893 FAX: (01829) 741769
on A54 near junction with A51, 5m E of Chester

Guests continue to enjoy this family-run Victorian house, set on the outskirts of a peaceful village, within a short drive of Chester. The Spiegelbergs are an interesting and friendly family, and their beautifully maintained home has been tastefully furnished with antiques. All of the bedrooms now have *en suite* or private facilities; the double room has a king-sized bed. A one-acre walled garden, complete with listed trees and a croquet lawn, surrounds the property. The cosy guest lounge has satellite TV. Grove House is within a two-to-three minute walk of the village shop, and a nearby Chinese restaurant serves evening meals.

OWNER: Mrs H. Spiegelberg OPEN: all year exc Christmas and New Year ROOMS: 1 single, with private bathroom; 1 double, with bath/shower; 1 twin, with shower; tea/coffee and TV in all bedrooms; lounge with TV TERMS: single £23, single occupancy £25–£35, twin/double £50–£56; deposit: £10 per person CARDS: none DETAILS: no children under 12; no dogs; smoking in lounge only; car park; garden

---

'Bath / shower' in the details under each entry means that the rooms have en suite *facilities. 'Private bathroom' signifies that a room has a bathroom for its exclusive use. The B&B may have other, shared bathroom facilities as well. We list 'wash-basins' for rooms that have them but do not have* en suite *or private facilities.*

TAUNTON Somerset **map 2**

Forde House

9 Upper High Street, Taunton TA1 3PX TEL/FAX: (01823) 279042

Forde House is a charming, elegant period house with spacious rooms. It stands on a main road almost opposite the Guildhall, and two hundred yards from Vivary Park. The house has been sensitively renovated, and in the attractive drawing-room with its grand piano and open fireplace are french windows leading to the large walled garden. A sheltered, creeper-covered patio is a pleasant place to sit in the summer. The comfortable bedrooms are tastefully decorated, and all have TVs and *en suite* showers except the single. A substantial breakfast is served in the characterful dining-room, which has an old slate floor, pine dresser, inglenook fireplace and beams, and was probably the house's original kitchen. This is an ideal spot for exploring the Quantock, Blackdown and Mendip Hills.

OWNERS: Peter and Sheila Naylor OPEN: all year exc Christmas ROOMS: 1 single, 2 double, 2 twin; all rooms with shower exc single with private bathroom; tea/coffee and TV in all bedrooms; lounge TERMS: single £27, single occupancy £30, twin/double £50 CARDS: none DETAILS: no children under 10; no dogs; car park; garden

---

Huntersmead

Hele, Taunton TA4 1AJ TEL: (01823) 461315
off A38, just SW of Taunton

Huntersmead is located in the tiny village of Hele, which is surrounded by fields and not featured on all maps: so it is best to ask for precise directions when booking. The B&B is actually two adjoining houses dating from different periods, one a long, pretty whitewashed building and the other a charming stone cottage. It is in a peaceful spot, with a lovely garden, and offers two tastefully decorated bedrooms. Guests also have the use of a comfortable TV lounge, and the Amors provide three-course, home-cooked evening meals by arrangement.

OWNERS: Mr and Mrs Keith Amor OPEN: all year exc Christmas ROOMS: 1 double, 1 twin; both rooms with wash-basin and TV; lounge with TV TERMS: single occupancy £22–£25, twin/double £40–£44; reductions for children sharing with parents; dinner £14 CARDS: none DETAILS: children welcome; no dogs; no smoking; car park; garden

---

Orchard House

NEW ENTRY

Fons George, Middleway, Taunton TA1 3JS
TEL: (01823) 351783 FAX: (01823) 351785

This grand Georgian house, built in 1814, stands on a main road on the edge of Taunton, about ten minutes' walk from the town centre. It has been a B&B since 1992, but Pauline and Chris Young took over only in the summer of 1997. They are a charming couple who love what they do. Breakfast is served in the cheerful, light breakfast room and the sitting-room is equipped with office facilities. Bedrooms are spacious and spotlessly clean; all have *en suite* facilities.

OWNER: Pauline Young OPEN: all year ROOMS: 1 double, 5 twin; all rooms with bath/shower; lounge with TV TERMS: single occupancy £35, twin/double £50; deposit: 10% CARDS: Delta, MasterCard, Switch, Visa DETAILS: no children under 11; no dogs; no smoking; car park; garden

TAVERHAM Norfolk map 6

Foxwood

Fakenham Road, Taverham NR8 6HR TEL: (01603) 868474
on A1067, 5m N of Norwich

Built in 1930, Foxwood is set in 18 acres of well-maintained park-like grounds and woodland, inhabited by peacocks. Several outdoor seating areas are provided, and in summer barbecues are often organised. There are some interesting pieces of furniture in the house, including a chaise longue and a carved chest in the entrance hall. The three bedrooms are all a decent size, and two have an *en suite* shower-room. As well as breakfast, modestly priced evening meals are available in the licensed dining-room/lounge, which is shared with owner Yvonne Todd.

OWNER: Yvonne Todd OPEN: all year exc Christmas ROOMS: 1 double, with shower; 2 twin, 1 with shower, 1 with private bathroom; lounge with TV TERMS: single occupancy £20–£25, twin/double £40–£50; dinner £10; deposit: £10 CARDS: none DETAILS: children welcome; no dogs; no smoking; car park; games room; garden

TAVISTOCK Devon map 1

April Cottage

Mount Tavy Road, Tavistock PL19 9JB TEL: (01822) 613280

Standing on the banks of the River Tavy, April Cottage is only a few minutes' walk to the centre of the interesting market town of Tavistock. It is a very pretty stone-built, Victorian semi-detached cottage, with a well-kept colourful garden. A friendly welcome from Rose and Norman Bacon awaits guests, and a cosy ambience pervades. Three *en suite* bedrooms, all with TVs, are offered; one overlooks the river. Residents have a comfortable TV lounge, and are served breakfast at individual tables in the dining-room. Tavistock is a good base for visiting Dartmoor.

OWNERS: Rose and Norman Bacon OPEN: all year exc Christmas ROOMS: 2 double, 1 twin; all rooms with shower, tea/coffee and TV; lounge with TV TERMS: single occupancy £22–£30, twin/double £32–£38; half-price for children under 10; deposit: £10 CARDS: none DETAILS: children welcome; dogs by arrangement; no smoking; car park; garden

TAYNTON Oxfordshire **map 2**

Coombe Brook Lodge

Taynton OX18 4UH TEL: (01993) 823616
take A424 N from Burford; at bottom of hill turn left at roundabout signposted Stow-on-the-Wold; keep straight on when main road turns right, then after 1m turn left; house adjacent to church

This old farm building has been lovingly converted by the Floreys, and provides well-appointed, comfortable guest accommodation. The Lodge is set in large gardens in a tranquil corner of the small Cotswold hamlet of Taynton, in the Windrush Valley. Both bedrooms have fine countryside views. The double, with its king-sized bed, is especially roomy and has an *en suite* bath with shower attachment, while the twin has an *en suite* shower; both have TVs and are decorated in pastels and matching fabrics. Guests may relax in the lounge, and are served hearty breakfasts in the big country kitchen or – weather permitting – on the patio. Visitors are welcome to enjoy the gardens, which lead down to a stream.

OWNER: Janet Florey OPEN: all year exc Christmas ROOMS: 1 double, with bath/shower; 1 twin, with shower; tea/coffee and TV in both bedrooms; lounge with TV TERMS: single occupancy £25–£30, twin/double £50 CARDS: none DETAILS: no children under 8; no dogs; car park; garden

TENTERDEN Kent **map 3**

Brattle House

NEW ENTRY

Watermill Bridge, Tenterden TN30 6UL TEL: (01580) 763565
from Tenterden on A28 towards Hastings turn right at Cranbrook Rd (signposted); house on left ½m down hill

A listed building dating from the seventeenth century with eighteenth-century additions, Brattle House sits in a pretty garden surrounded by 11 acres of ancient woodland and meadows. Three bedrooms have *en suite* showers and are large and beautifully equipped, while the single has a private bathroom. The long sitting-room overlooks the garden, beyond which is the conservatory, where breakfast is taken. Candlelit evening meals are served by arrangement in the dining-room and might feature twice-baked goats'-cheese soufflé. No one-night bookings are taken at weekends or between March and October.

OWNERS: Maureen and Alan Rawlinson OPEN: all year exc Christmas ROOMS: 1 single, with private bathroom; 2 double, both with shower; 1 twin, with shower; tea/coffee in all bedrooms; lounge with TV TERMS: single £30–£36, single occupancy £40–£45, twin/double £60; dinner £20; deposit: 20% CARDS: none DETAILS: no children; no dogs; no smoking; car park; garden

---

'NEW ENTRY' indicates that a B&B was not in the previous edition (although its owners may have been, at a different address).

TESTON Kent — map 3

Court Lodge Farm

The Street, Teston M18 5AQ TEL: (01622) 812570 FAX: (01622) 814200
off A26, 4m W of Maidstone

This sixteenth-century farmhouse is next to the church at one end of the small village of Teston, in an elevated position with fine views over the Medway Valley and fruit and hop fields. It is a particularly attractive place at apple blossom time. Guests have use of a large, comfortably furnished, high-ceilinged beamed sitting-room, with an open fireplace containing a wood-burning stove; the room has diamond-shaped leaded windows which look out over the attractive garden. Three guest bedrooms are offered, two with *en suite* facilities, the third with a private bathroom. Breakfast is served at one large table in the dining-hall. Mr Bannock is knowledgeable on local places of historic interest.

OWNER: Rosemarie Ann Bannock OPEN: all year exc Christmas ROOMS: 1 double, with bath/shower; 2 twin, 1 with bath/shower, 1 with private bathroom; tea/coffee and TV in 1 bedroom; lounge with TV TERMS: single occupancy £28–£34, twin/double £38–£50; deposit: £20–£50 or credit card details CARDS: Visa DETAILS: no children under 12; no dogs; no smoking; car park; garden

TEWKESBURY Gloucestershire — map 5

Two Back of Avon — NEW ENTRY

Riverside Walk, Tewkesbury GL20 5BA TEL: (01684) 298935

This red-bricked Queen Anne house, situated on a quiet side-street near the town centre, overlooks the River Avon. It offers four comfortable bedrooms; one has *en suite* facilities, and all have TVs. The house looks lovely when it is adorned with hanging baskets and flowering tubs in the summer. Guests can take boat trips on the river, and there are many pleasant walks nearby; Tewkesbury has a Norman Abbey.

OWNERS: Eric and Jean Leach OPEN: all year ROOMS: 1 single, with wash-basin; 1 double, with bath/shower; 1 twin, with private bathroom; 1 family, with private bathroom; tea/coffee and TV in all bedrooms; lounge with TV TERMS: single £18–£20, single occupancy £20–£22, twin/double £32–£36; family room by arrangement; dinner £7; deposit: £10 per person CARDS: none DETAILS: children welcome; dogs by arrangement; no smoking

THAXTED Essex — map 6

Folly House

Watling Lane, Thaxted CM6 2QY TEL: (01371) 830618

This modern house is in a quiet location overlooking open countryside in the centre of the ancient, unspoilt village of Thaxted, which pre-dates the Domesday Book. The good-sized bedrooms are well appointed, all with satellite TV, and comfortably furnished, and guests can help themselves to tea and coffee, always available in the dining-room. Jackie and Gerald King have many years of experience in the catering trade and provide excellent breakfasts, and, by arrangement, lunch and dinner. Alternatively, there are several eating-establishments in the village. Guests arriving at or departing from nearby Stansted Airport can arrange to be transported to and fro for a modest charge. The fourteenth-century church and guildhall in the village should not be missed.

OWNER: Jacqueline King OPEN: all year exc Christmas ROOMS: 2 double, both with shower; 1 twin, with wash-basin; tea/coffee and TV in all bedrooms; lounge with TV TERMS: single occupancy £35, twin/double £50; babies free, children's reductions by arrangement CARDS: none DETAILS: children welcome; no dogs; no smoking; car park; garden

THELNETHAM Norfolk — map 6

Lodge Farmhouse

High Street, Thelnetham IP22 1LJ TEL/FAX: (01379) 898203
on B1111 follow signs to Hopton; 2m past Hopton turn right after White Horse pub

This seventeenth-century thatched and timber-framed house is set in 15 acres of meadowland with its own lake, where free trout and carp fishing can be arranged for guests. Old beams, an inglenook fireplace and a quarry-tiled floor add to the air of venerability inside the house. The richly decorated bedrooms have *en suite* baths and are comfortably appointed. The sitting-room overlooks the walled garden, which now has a furnished patio for guests' use. Home-cooked dinners are available if booked 24 hours in advance, and guests may purchase wine from Lodge Farmhouse's own vineyard to complement their food. Alternatively, a pub close by serves meals. Blossom and Lulu, two grey shire horses, live here.

OWNERS: Michael and Christine Palmer OPEN: all year exc Christmas ROOMS: 1 double, 2 twin; all rooms bath and tea/coffee; TV in 1 bedroom and lounge TERMS: single occupancy £25, twin/double £36–£44; dinner £13; deposit required bank holidays only CARDS: none DETAILS: no children under 10; no dogs; smoking in lounge only if other guests agree; car park; garden

THIRLMERE Cumbria — map 10

Brackenrigg

Thirlmere CA12 4TF TEL: (017687) 72258
on A591, 3m S of Keswick

Situated in the heart of the Lake District, this beautiful Victorian house is set in two acres of gardens with a summer-house, croquet lawn and beautiful views. The bedrooms are well proportioned and appointed, and are named after local lakes: Ullswater and Grasmere, for example. Most have *en suite* showers, one has its own bathroom.

All the rooms except the single have TVs. Guests can unwind around the open fire in the TV-free lounge with its comfortable chairs. Evening meals, available most nights, can be pre-arranged and are served in the attractive beamed dining-room; guests are welcome to bring their own wine, as the house is unlicensed. Self-catering apartments in a skilfully converted barn on the property are let all through the year, and self-catering guests may choose to dine and use other amenities in the main house.

OWNERS: Anne and Roy Wilson OPEN: Easter to Oct ROOMS: 1 single, with wash-basin; 3 double, 1 twin, all with shower; 1 family, with private bathroom; tea/coffee and TV in most bedrooms; lounge TERMS: single £24, single occupancy £34–£36, twin/double £48–£52, family room from £48; half-price for children sharing with parents; dinner £16; deposit: £20 per person CARDS: none DETAILS: no children under 10; no dogs; no smoking in dining-room; car park; garden

THOMPSON Norfolk — map 6

Thatched House

Pockthorpe Corner, Thompson IP24 1PJ TEL: (01953) 483577
off A1075, 3m S of Watton

This pretty sixteenth-century whitewashed cottage is in a quiet location in the unspoilt village of Thompson. The three bedrooms have original beams and lots of character; two are on the ground floor and suitable for wheelchair-users – one has an old stable door leading out into the garden, while the other has french windows opening on to a patio. The upstairs room has sloping ceilings and is reached by a steep, narrow staircase. Breakfast and dinner are served in the dining-room, and guests are welcome to join the owner in the family lounge. Visitors should be sure to investigate the pingos – dome-shaped mounds formed by glaciers – which are a pleasant walk away.

OWNER: Brenda Mills OPEN: all year ROOMS: 1 double, with private bathroom; 2 twin, both with private bathroom; 2 rooms suitable for wheelchair-users; tea/coffee and TV in all bedrooms; lounge with TV TERMS: single occupancy £20–£25, twin/double £36–£40; dinner £7.50 CARDS: none DETAILS: no children under 10; well-behaved dogs welcome; no smoking; car park; garden

THORALBY North Yorkshire — map 8

Low Green House

Thoralby DL8 3SZ TEL: (01969) 663623
on minor road off A684, 1m S of Aysgarth

This homely nineteenth-century stone house offers comfortable accommodation. The good-sized bedrooms are decorated in soft pastels, and all have private facilities and TVs. Residents can put their feet up in the spacious, comfortably furnished dining-room-cum-lounge, with its log fire and antique pine sideboard; there is also a window seat where guests can admire the lovely countryside views at their leisure. Free-range eggs, courtesy of the Philpots' own hens, feature at breakfast, and home-made evening-meals, available Friday to Wednesday, use local produce. A collection of leaflets, maps and books on the Yorkshire Dales is available, and Tony Philpot is full of useful information about interesting things to see and do. Low Green House is peacefully set in the tiny village of Thoralby; Aysgarth Falls is just a mile and a half away.

OWNERS: Tony and Marilyn Philpot OPEN: all year exc Christmas ROOMS: 2 double, 1 with shower, 1 with private bathroom; 1 twin, with shower; tea/coffee and TV in all bedrooms; lounge TERMS: single occupancy £36, twin/double £45; reductions for children sharing with parents; dinner £14; deposit: £10 per room CARDS: none DETAILS: no children under 10; small dogs by arrangement; no smoking; car park; garden

THRANDESTON Norfolk — map 6

Abbey Farm — NEW ENTRY

Great Green, Thrandeston IP21 4BN TEL: (01379) 783422
between A143 and A140, 2m S of Diss

This restored Elizabethan farmhouse stands in three acres of wooded grounds with three natural ponds inhabited by moorhens. It is a delightful place for families and has an unpretentious and friendly atmosphere. Jean breeds Dalmatians (she has three of her own) and keeps Shetland ponies, which children can be taken for a ride on. The house still has many of the original features, such as the mullioned windows which were uncovered during renovation. Bedrooms have solid old-fashioned furniture; the double is quite large and can be adapted to take an extra person, and the single is small. The former cheese loft is now an attic bathroom. Breakfast only is served, but there are several places for evening meals close by.

OWNER: Jean Carlisle OPEN: all year ROOMS: 1 single, with private bathroom; 1 double, with shower; tea/coffee and TV in both bedrooms; lounge with TV TERMS: single £20–£25, single occupancy £30–£35, twin/double £40–£45; half-price for children CARDS: none DETAILS: children welcome; no smoking in dining-room; car park; garden

THRELKELD Cumbria — map 10

Blease Farm

Threlkeld CA12 4SF TEL/FAX: (017687) 79087
turn off A66 4m E of Keswick into Threlkeld, then right into Blease Rd; Blease Farm is after ⅓m

This eighteenth-century stone farmhouse lies on the slopes of Blencathra, in 40 acres of beautiful countryside, inhabited by sheep, horses and chickens. On cool days a log fire warms the sitting-room, which has a baby grand piano, video library and a good selection of books. Detailed maps of the Lakes are available for perusal in the sun lounge, and guests can make use of the library of laminated route maps. The well-appointed bedrooms have pine furniture and power-showers; satellite TV is available in the lounge and all the bedrooms. Pre-arranged evening meals are served in the licensed dining-room; the farm chickens provide the free-range eggs at breakfast. The décor is warm and traditional, and all of the rooms enjoy breathtaking views. Easter and Bank Holiday weekend bookings must be for a minimum of three nights, and carry a £4 surcharge.

OWNERS: John and Ruth Knowles OPEN: all year exc Christmas ROOMS: 2 double, 1 twin; all rooms with bath/shower, tea/coffee and TV; lounge with TV TERMS: single occupancy £29, twin/double £50; dinner £17; deposit: 1 night's charge CARDS: none DETAILS: no children under 12; no dogs; no smoking; car park; garden

THROPTON Northumberland — map 10

Thropton Demesne Farmhouse

Thropton NE65 7LT TEL/FAX: (01669) 620196
off B6341 at west end of village

This Victorian farmhouse is set on a working farm with views across rolling countryside and the River Coquet to the Simonside Hills. It has been sensitively modernised and furnished in keeping with its origins, and guests will be able to spot some original features such as fireplaces and doors. The three good-sized bedrooms have either an *en suite* bath or a private bathroom, are decorated in rich colours and have TVs. Breakfasts feature home-made bread and are served in the dining-room. A separate lounge, without a TV, is a quiet place to unwind in, and guests are welcome to enjoy the walled garden and explore the farmland as far as the River Coquet, known for its salmon and trout fishing. For the more energetic, there are fine walks across the moors, valleys and farmlands of Croquetdale. Two pubs in Thropton are handy for evening meals.

OWNERS: Tim and Alison Giles OPEN: all year exc Christmas ROOMS: 2 double, both with bath; 1 twin, with private bathroom; tea/coffee and TV in all bedrooms; lounge TERMS: single occupancy £25–£30, twin/double £38–£42; children's reductions by arrangement; deposit: £10 per booking CARDS: none DETAILS: children welcome; no dogs; no smoking; car park; garden

THURSBY Cumbria — map 10

How End Farm

Thursby CA5 6PX TEL: (016973) 42487 FAX: (016973) 49239
on A595, 7m W of Carlisle

How End Farm offers good-value accommodation in a warm and friendly environment. The 250-year-old building is kept spotlessly clean, and the comfortable bedrooms are traditionally furnished and both have views over the Lakeland Fells. The walking sticks in the entrance way are the family's own work. The guest lounge has a TV, and breakfast is served in a separate dining-room. The local village pub serves evening meals.

OWNER: Margaret Swainson OPEN: all year exc Christmas ROOMS: 1 twin, 1 family; tea/coffee in both bedrooms; lounge with TV TERMS: single occupancy £16–£18, twin/family from £32; children's reductions according to age CARDS: none DETAILS: children welcome; no dogs; smoking in lounge only; car park; garden

TILSTON Cheshire map 7

Tilston Lodge

Tilston SY14 7DR TEL/FAX: (01829) 250223
from Whitchurch take A41 N for 1½m, turn left at Horse and Jockey pub on to B5395, continue through Malpas and for further 3m, Tilston Lodge on left

This charming Victorian lodge is situated on the edge of an unspoilt village, close to the scenic sandstone trail running through the Bickerton Hills. The property encompasses 16 acres of landscaped gardens, in which guests will find the Ritchies' collection of rare farm animals, including Hebridean and Manx Loghtan ewes, and Khaki Campbell ducks. Antiques, such as an elegant grandfather clock and a chaise longue, adorn the impeccably maintained interior. The large *en suite* bedrooms are well appointed, with some nice touches like the shoe-cleaning kits.

OWNERS: Neil and Kathie Ritchie OPEN: all year ROOMS: 1 twin, 2 four-poster; all rooms with bath/shower, tea/coffee and TV; lounge with TV TERMS: single occupancy £35–£40, twin £58, four-poster £60–£65; half-price for children under 14 CARDS: none DETAILS: children welcome; no dogs; no smoking; car park; garden

TINTAGEL Cornwall map 1

Ferny Park NEW ENTRY

Bossiney Hill, Tintagel PL34 0BB TEL: (01840) 770523
on B3263, off A39 Bude to Wadebridge road

This simple, small whitewashed cottage is set a little back from a minor road, with beautiful colourful gardens to front and rear. Owner Penelope Mendoza is a charming lady who loves to paint and garden, and she offers guests a warm, hospitable welcome. The house is comfortably furnished, and breakfast is served in the sun alcove of the small lounge/dining-room, which has a TV and a piano. The two bedrooms share a bathroom, and can be used as a family suite. This is a good spot for walking, bird-watching, surfing and riding, and studio space is available for painters.

OWNER: Penelope Mendoza OPEN: all year exc Christmas ROOMS: 1 single, 1 double/twin/family; both rooms with wash-basin and tea/coffee; lounge with TV TERMS: single/single occupancy £20, twin/double £32–£34, family room £48–£50; children under 5 free, half-price for ages 5–10; deposit CARDS: none DETAILS: children welcome; no dogs; no smoking; car park; garden

Ye Olde Malthouse

Fore Street, Tintagel PL34 0DA TEL/FAX: (01840) 770461
in village, 50 yds from castle entrance

This restaurant-with-rooms offers good value for money in one of Cornwall's most popular tourist towns. It is a charmingly picturesque fourteenth-century building right in the centre of Tintagel, just a few yards from a track to the castle. Ye Olde Malthouse is popular with tourists both at lunch-time and in the evening, and offers good-value accommodation. It was taken over at the beginning of 1997 by the Haddows, who are experienced hoteliers, and who have upgraded the property considerably. Most of the bedrooms now have either *en suite* or private facilities, and are very well equipped and attractively decorated. There is a small, cosy guests' lounge and bar.

OWNERS: Paul and Deborah Haddow OPEN: all year ROOMS: 1 single, with wash-basin; 5 double, 4 with shower, 1 with wash-basin; 2 twin, 1 with bath/shower, 1 with private bathroom; tea/coffee and TV in all bedrooms; lounge TERMS: single £18.50–£20, single occupancy £25–£35, twin/double £37–£40; dinner £10–£15; deposit: 1 night's charge CARDS: Delta, MasterCard, Switch, Visa DETAILS: children welcome; no dogs; no cigars/pipes in bedrooms; car park

TIVERTON Devon **map 1**

Hornhill

Exeter Hill, Tiverton EX16 4PL TEL/FAX: (01884) 253352
from M5 junction 27 follow A361 to Tiverton, exit at signs to Gornhay Cross, then follow signs to Grand Western Canal; at Canal Hill take first right into Exeter Hill

Set on top of a steep hill just a few minutes from Tiverton, Hornhill stands in an acre of gardens and has very fine views over the Exe Valley. It was built as a coaching-inn in the eighteenth century, and has been in the Pugsley family for over 100 years. One of the three bedrooms has a Victorian four-poster bed and private bathroom, and another *en suite* room is on the ground floor and is suitable for the partially disabled. Breakfasts are served at one long table in the dining-room, the hall has armchairs, and the comfortable drawing-room, which overlooks the garden, has an open fire and plenty of books. The Pugsleys are friendly and hospitable, and guests enjoy the quiet, peaceful setting.

OWNER: Barbara Pugsley OPEN: all year ROOMS: 1 double, with shower; 1 twin, with private bathroom; 1 four-poster, with private bathroom; tea/coffee and TV in all bedrooms; lounge TERMS: single occupancy £21.50, twin/double £39–£40, four-poster £39–£42 CARDS: none DETAILS: no children; no dogs; no smoking; car park; garden

---

The end details for each entry state whether or not dogs are allowed, but it is always best to check when booking.

TOPPESFIELD Essex **map 6**

Ollivers Farm

NEW ENTRY

Toppesfield CO9 4LS TEL: (01787) 237642 FAX: (01787) 237602
from A1017 (formerly A604) in Gt Yeldham turn to Toppesfield, continue 1½m past Toppesfield Hall on right; next drive on left to farm

This seventeenth-century timber-framed farmhouse stands in two acres of beautiful, secluded gardens which include a vineyard. This characterful house retains a wealth of oak beams and original fireplaces, and is in an idyllic spot – perfect for people wanting to get away from it all. The beautifully furnished lounge has a piano, plenty of books and roaring log fires in winter. In summer the splendid garden, maintained by Mrs Blackie, is the place to unwind. The two bedrooms, attractively furnished with antiques, have good views over the garden. One reader was particularly impressed with the cooked breakfasts, which feature home-made jam with fruit from the garden and freshly baked bread.

OWNERS: Mr and Mrs J.G. Blackie OPEN: all year exc 23 Dec to 2 Jan ROOMS: 1 double, with private bathroom; 1 twin, with shower; tea/coffee in both bedrooms; lounge TERMS: single occupancy £25–£27.50, twin/double £45–£50; deposit required CARDS: none DETAILS: no children under 10; no dogs; no smoking; car park; garden

TORMARTON South Gloucestershire **map 2**

Chestnut Farm

Tormarton GL9 1HS TEL: (01454) 218563
just off M4 at junction 18, 3m SE of Chipping Sodbury

This modern stone-built farmhouse is on a small farm in the village of Tormarton, which lies just off the M4, only a few miles from both Bath and Bristol. The house has a relaxed atmosphere, and the owners are friendly and chatty. Guest bedrooms are in a separate building, and breakfast is served in the conservatory in the main house, and competitively priced two- or three-course evening meals are available by arrangement. The interesting village church is worth a visit.

OWNERS: Mr and Mrs R. Cadei OPEN: all year ROOMS: 3 double, 2 twin; all rooms with shower, tea/coffee and TV TERMS: single occupancy £30, twin/double £40; reductions for children sharing with parents; dinner £9–£10.50; deposit required CARDS: none DETAILS: children welcome; dogs welcome; car park; garden

TORQUAY Devon **map 1**

Fairmount House Hotel

Herbert Road, Chelston, Torquay TQ2 6RW TEL/FAX: (01803) 605446

Each of the eight bedrooms here has been given a name from *Lord of the Rings* – an appropriate touch, given that the owners are called Tolkien – and all have *en suite* facilities, are comfortably furnished, and most are south-facing. Two bedrooms open directly on to the garden and are suitable for disabled visitors. Fairmount House was built in 1900 as a family residence and – having survived a period when it was turned into flats – is now a homely and welcoming small hotel standing in a quiet residential area a mile from the harbour. It has a small, pretty rear garden and views over Chelston to Brixham. Guests have use of a TV lounge, which has a sunny balcony as well as a small library that includes maps and guidebooks, and of a bar in a small conservatory overlooking the garden. Meals are served in the pretty dining-room, and bar snacks at lunch-time are available.

OWNERS: Mr and Mrs N.A. Tolkien OPEN: early Mar to early Nov ROOMS: 2 single, 4 double, 2 family; all rooms with bath/shower, tea/coffee and TV; 2 rooms suitable for wheelchair-users; lounge with TV TERMS: single £28–£32, single occupancy £28–£55, double £56–£64, family room £56–£96; reductions for children according to age; dinner £12.50; deposit: £5 per person per night CARDS: Amex, MasterCard, Visa DETAILS: children welcome; dogs by arrangement; no smoking in bedrooms; car park; garden

---

Mulberry House

NEW ENTRY

1 Scarborough Road, Torquay TQ2 5UJ TEL: (01803) 213639

Mulberry House is a small restaurant with three inviting bedrooms. It is an end-of-terrace Victorian building, only five minutes' walk from the town centre and sea. Lesley Cooper is a charming host and a talented cook. Breakfast, lunch and dinner are available, and are served in the cheerful dining-room. There is a small gallery sitting-area upstairs, supplied with tea/coffee-making facilities. Bedrooms are decorated with some individual touches, such as the Victorian sofa in one, and two are south-facing and catch the sun. Lesley also runs demonstration cooking mornings followed by a three-course lunch with wine. There is no car park, but on-street parking is unrestricted.

OWNER: Lesley Cooper OPEN: all year ROOMS: 2 double, 1 with bath/shower, 1 with private bathroom; 1 twin, with bath/shower; tea/coffee in all bedrooms; TV in all bedrooms TERMS: single occupancy £25–£35, twin/double £42–£50; dinner £15–£20; deposit: 10% CARDS: none DETAILS: children welcome; no dogs; no smoking (*The Good Food Guide*)

Walnut House

7 Walnut Road, Chelston, Torquay TQ2 6HP TEL: (01803) 606854

Marie Landau, a former teacher, has been offering excellent-value bed and breakfast in a warm and friendly atmosphere at this Victorian sandstone house since 1987. It is in the village of Chelston on the southern outskirts of Torquay, close to the seafront, shops and railway station. The front garden is a blaze of colour, and there is a patio for sitting outside on fine days. The house is comfortable and clean, and the bedrooms, one of which is on the ground floor, are well equipped. Only breakfast is available, but the pub next door serves good food. Walnut House is near historic Torre Abbey and only 15 minutes' walk from the picturesque village of Cockington, with its thatched cobstone cottages, working watermill and blacksmith's forge.

OWNER: Marie Landau OPEN: all year ROOMS: 1 single, with private bathroom; 2 double, both with shower (no WC); 1 twin, with shower (no WC); tea/coffee and TV in all bedrooms; lounge with TV TERMS: single £14–£15, single occupancy £20, twin/double £28–£30; deposit: 1 night's charge CARDS: none DETAILS: children under 10 by arrangement; no dogs; no smoking; car park; garden

TOSSIDE North Yorkshire

map 8

Sandy Laithe

NEW ENTRY

Tosside BD23 4SE TEL: (01729) 840482
on B6478, 4m W of Long Preston

This converted stone barn stands in nearly 2 acres of landscaped gardens, surrounded by unspoilt countryside. It is just off a quiet country road in the hamlet of Tosside, which straddles the Yorkshire-Lancashire border. Rosalind and Martin provide excellent-value accommodation and offer welcoming tea and home-made scones to guests on arrival. A galleried landing leads to an enormous open-plan oak-beamed lounge, with exposed stone walls and an open fire. Generous breakfasts are served in the sunny dining-room, warmed by a wood-burning stove on chilly mornings. Bedrooms are well appointed and spacious; one double is on the ground floor, and the twin room on the first floor has an adjacent single room, making it ideal for a small family. A nearby pub serves evening meals.

OWNERS: Rosalind and Martin Davey OPEN: all year exc Christmas ROOMS: 2 double, 1 twin; all rooms with bath/shower, tea/coffee and TV; lounge with TV TERMS: single occupancy £21–£25, twin/double £38; deposit: £10 per room CARDS: none DETAILS: children welcome; no dogs; no smoking; car park; garden

TOTNES Devon

map 1

Old Forge

Seymour Place, Totnes TQ9 5AY
TEL: (01803) 862174 FAX: (01803) 865385

The 600-year-old Old Forge, complete with wheelwright's workshop, coach-houses and stables, was restored from a semi-derelict state and converted into comfortable, well-appointed accommodation by owners Jeannie and Peter Allnutt. It has a warm, friendly atmosphere, and the bedrooms are pleasantly furnished and have *en suite* facilities. Two rooms have microwaves and fridges, and two are on the ground floor and suitable for the partially disabled. Breakfast is served in the Tudor-style dining-room, and cream teas and snacks are available during the summer. The Old Forge has a large walled garden that includes a patio where drinks are served. Totnes is an interesting old town with an excellent choice of restaurants and pubs for evening meals.

OWNER: Jeannie Allnutt OPEN: all year exc Christmas ROOMS: 1 single, 2 double, 2 twin, 5 family; all rooms with bath/shower, tea/coffee and TV; lounge with TV TERMS: single/single occupancy £40–£50, twin/double £50–£58, family room £64–£100; reductions for children sharing with parents; deposit: 1 night's charge CARDS: Delta, MasterCard, Visa DETAILS: children welcome; guide dogs only; no smoking; car park; garden

TOY'S HILL Kent **map 3**

Corner Cottage

Toy's Hill TN16 1PY TEL: (01732) 750362 FAX: (01959) 561911
take A25 to Brasted, turn left at King's Arms, then 3m to Puddledock Lane, turn right; first house on left

This is a long, low building, at the top of a hill just two miles from Westerham, with fine views over the Weald of Kent. It is a delightful, fifteenth-century cottage set in a garden with terraces and lawns, and is full of character: there are old beams and antiques, including an old green mangle in the entrance hall. With just one guest bedroom on offer, guests are assured of individual attention, and Mrs Olszowska is a hospitable and attentive host. The spacious bedroom has a brass bed and private shower-room, and is above the garage block, giving complete privacy. Breakfast is taken in the dining-room, which also enjoys the spectacular view, but there are several pubs nearby for evening meals. There is playing equipment in the garden which children are welcome to use under their parents' supervision.

OWNER: Kerstin Olszowska OPEN: all year ROOMS: 1 family, with shower and tea/coffee; lounge TERMS: single occupancy £25–£30, family room £40–£80; deposit: £10 CARDS: none DETAILS: children welcome; no dogs; no smoking; car park; garden

Heath House NEW ENTRY

Scords Lane, Toy's Hill TN16 1QE TEL: (01732) 750631
2m from A25 Sevenoaks to Westerham road

Dating from the eighteenth century, this attractive creeper-covered house can be found down a quiet lane, surrounded by a lovely garden, sheep farms and fields. Heath House stands on the edge of National Trust woodland with fine views across the Weald of Kent. The house has a welcoming, relaxed atmosphere, and offers three well-appointed bedrooms. The pleasant dining-room has a sitting-area, with further seating on the terrace. Chartwell, Hever Castle and Knole House are nearby.

OWNER: Patricia Murkin OPEN: all year ROOMS: 3 double, 1 with bath/shower, 1 with private bathroom; tea/coffee and TV in most bedrooms; lounge with TV TERMS: single £25–£30, single occupancy £25–£30, double £37–£40 CARDS: none DETAILS: children welcome; no dogs; no smoking; car park; garden

TREFONEN Shropshire map 5

The Pentre NEW ENTRY

Trefonen SY10 9EE TEL: (01691) 653952
from A5 in Oswestry take left turn to Trefonen, after 2m turn right signposted Pentre Issa, then 1m

Pentre House is a listed sixteenth-century house in an elevated remote location, with spectacular views. The Gilberts have owned the farmhouse for many years, and spent weekends and holidays here while restoring the property. The house is full of old-world charm, and features thick stone walls, original doors, an inglenook fireplace and a Jacobean staircase. The *en suite* bedroom has solid old-fashioned furnishings and comfortable beds. A warm welcome is extended by the Gilberts and their two delightful daughters. Pre-arranged evening meals are served, often featuring home-grown produce; vegetarians can be catered for with advance notice. Snooker, pool and table-tennis are available. A pick-up and put-down service can be provided for walkers. A few ducks and pet sheep inhabit the grounds, and Ruby the dog is friendly.

OWNERS: Stephen and Helen Gilbert OPEN: all year ROOMS: 1 double/family room, with bath/shower, tea/coffee and TV; lounge with TV TERMS: single occupancy £20, double £37–£40, family room from £45; dinner £10–£12; deposit CARDS: none DETAILS: children welcome; well-behaved dogs welcome; no smoking in bedrooms; car park; games room; garden

TRESILLIAN Cornwall map 1

Manor Cottage

Tresillian TR1 4BN TEL: (01872) 520212
2½m from Truro on A39 towards St Austell

Enthusiasm and a welcoming atmosphere prevail in this small restaurant-with-rooms, an attractive 200-year-old building set back from the main road. Carlton Moyle cooks imaginative meals which are served in a small conservatory-style room off the front of the house; the restaurant is also open to non-residents in the evening from Thursday to Saturday. The five bedrooms are small, and extra *en suite* facilities were being added as we went to press. No one-night bookings are accepted in August.

OWNERS: Gillian Jackson and Carlton Moyle OPEN: all year exc Christmas ROOMS: 1 single, with wash-basin; 2 double, 1 with bath/shower, 1 with private bathroom; 1 twin, with wash-basin; 1 family, with bath/shower; tea/coffee and TV in all bedrooms; lounge TERMS: single £18–£22, single occupancy £22–£36, twin/double £34–£50, family room £44–£60; reductions for children sharing with parents; dinner £21; deposit: 1 night's charge CARDS: Delta, MasterCard, Switch, Visa DETAILS: children welcome; no dogs; no smoking in eating-areas; car park

Polsue Manor Farm

Tresillian TR2 4BP TEL: (01872) 520234 FAX: (01872) 520616
up driveway N of A39, on W edge of Tresillian

Parts of this spacious, unpretentious farmhouse date from the sixteenth century, with the front area having been added 150 years ago. It stands above and well away from the noise of the main road into Truro, up a long, well-maintained track, and is part of a 190-acre mixed farm. The house has lovely views, and overlooks the tidal Tresillian River. Four of the five simply furnished and decorated bedrooms share a bathroom, shower-room and WC; one family room is *en suite* and one is on the ground floor. There is a sitting-room with TV, and a pleasant dining-room where breakfast and evening meals are served.

OWNER: Geraldine Holliday OPEN: all year exc Christmas ROOMS: 1 double, 1 twin, both with wash-basin; 3 family, 1 with shower, 2 with wash-basin; tea/coffee in all bedrooms; lounge with TV TERMS: single occupancy £18–£25, twin/double £34–£40, family room £50–£60; babies free, half-price for children under 10 sharing with parents; dinner £9.50; deposit: 10% CARDS: none DETAILS: children welcome; dogs by arrangement; car park; garden

TROTTON West Sussex — map 3

Trotton Farm

Trotton GU31 5EN TEL: (01730) 813618 FAX: (01730) 816093
just off A272 Midhurst to Petersfield road, 3m W of Midhurst

Trotton Farm is in the tiny hamlet of Trotton, with its fifteenth-century bridge spanning the River Rother. Mr Baigent runs the farm while Mrs Baigent looks after the bed-and-breakfast side of the business. Guests are accommodated in an old converted barn adjoining the house. On the ground floor is a large games room/lounge with table tennis, TV and french windows leading out to a patio. One of the twin-bedded rooms is also on the ground-floor. Breakfast is served in the farmhouse and there are plenty of pubs nearby for evening meals.

OWNERS: Mrs J.E. Baigent OPEN: all year ROOMS: 1 double, 2 twin; all rooms with bath/shower; tea/coffee in all bedrooms; lounge with TV TERMS: single occupancy £25–£30, twin/double £40–£45 CARDS: none DETAILS: children welcome; dogs welcome; no smoking; car park; games room; garden

TROUTBECK Cumbria — map 8

Yew Grove

Troutbeck LA23 1PG TEL: (015394) 33304

This sturdy stone-built house in the peaceful village of Troutbeck is run by Derek and Angela Pratt, who extend a warm welcome and offer good-value accommodation. The main building, which dates back to the early eighteenth century, has been rennovated and added to over the years. It now houses three modestly furnished but comfortable bedrooms, some of which retain their original fireplaces; one double has an *en suite* shower. Evening meals are served at a local village pub.

OWNERS: Derek and Angela Pratt OPEN: all year exc Christmas ROOMS: 3 double, 1 with shower, 2 with wash-basin; 1 twin, with wash-basin; tea/coffee in all bedrooms; lounge with TV TERMS: single occupancy £21–£22, twin/double £36–£44; reductions for children under 12 sharing with parents; deposit: £10 per room CARDS: none DETAILS: children welcome; no dogs; no smoking; car park; garden

TUNBRIDGE WELLS Kent — map 3

Danehurst House Hotel

41 Lower Green Road, Rusthall, Tunbridge Wells TN4 8TW
TEL: (01892) 527739 FAX: (01892) 514804
on A264, 1½m W of Tunbridge Wells

This large Victorian house can be found in Rusthall, on the outskirts of historic Tunbridge Wells. It is professionally run with a welcoming atmosphere created by the charming and attentive Godbolds. Bedrooms are well equipped and decorated in pastel colours. Breakfast is served in the pretty conservatory. The drawing-room has a grand piano, comfortable seating and lots of magazines and books. Drinks from the bar can be enjoyed on the front terrace.

OWNERS: Michael and Angela Godbold OPEN: all year exc Christmas and last week in Aug ROOMS: 1 single, with wash-basin; 2 double, both with bath/shower; 3 twin, 2 with bath/shower, 1 with wash-basin; tea/coffee and TV in all bedrooms; lounge with TV TERMS: single £35–£45, single occupancy £39.50–£45, twin/double £49.50–£65; deposit: £20 or credit card details CARDS: Amex, MasterCard, Visa DETAILS: no children under 8; no dogs; no smoking; car park; garden

TWEEDMOUTH Northumberland — map 11

Old Vicarage

Church Road, Tweedmouth, Berwick TD15 2AN TEL: (01289) 306909
on old A1 (not bypass) approaching Berwick-upon-Tweed from S, turn right at Queen's Head

Across the river from Berwick-upon-Tweed, this large Victorian guesthouse with its rather fascinating windows continues to offer a high standard of accommodation. There are seven well-kept bedrooms, four with *en suite* showers and all with TVs. The larger rooms have their own fireplaces and are given their own extra dash of comfort with solid old-fashioned furniture. Many original features remain, and attractive stencilling can be seen in the entrance way and stairwell. In the guest lounge, which is available to residents at all times, are plenty of books, games and information on the local area. Full, traditional breakfasts also feature Craster kippers. The centre of Berwick is just a 20-minute walk away.

OWNER: Tina Richardson OPEN: all year exc Christmas ROOMS: 1 single, with wash-basin; 4 double, 2 with shower, 2 with wash-basin; 1 twin, with shower; 1 family, with shower; tea/coffee and TV in all bedrooms; lounge TERMS: single £16–£18, single occupancy £16–£40, twin/double £32–£50, family room £40–£55; children's reductions; deposit: £20 CARDS: none DETAILS: children welcome; dogs welcome; car park; garden

TWYFORD Berkshire map 3

The Hermitage

63 London Road, Twyford RG10 9EJ TEL/FAX: (0118) 934 0004

Set back from the main road that runs through the town centre is this well-maintained double-fronted early-Georgian house. The charming bedrooms have antique and stripped-pine furnishings, and are decorated in soft and soothing colours; two are housed in the adjacent converted stables. Breakfasts are served in a separate dining-room in the main building. The mock-Georgian extension at the back of the house, completed in 1851, elegantly complements the original structure, and overlooks the large landscaped garden. There is a good selection of local eating-establishments, and Twyford has a direct rail link with London.

OWNER: Carel Barker OPEN: all year exc Christmas ROOMS: 2 double, 1 with bath/shower, 1 with wash-basin; 3 twin, 2 with bath/shower, 1 with wash-basin; tea/coffee and TV in all bedrooms TERMS: single occupancy £29–£40, twin/double £42–£60; deposit: £10 per room CARDS: none DETAILS: no children; no dogs; no smoking; car park; garden

UPPER CLATFORD Hampshire map 2

Malt Cottage

Upper Clatford, nr Andover SP11 7QL
TEL: (01264) 323469 FAX: (01264) 334100
off A303; take A3057 towards Stockbridge, then first right, first left, right at T-junction, right turn opposite Crook & Shears pub; house is at bottom of lane

Malt Cottage is more than 250 years old and was formerly used as a malting barn by the village brewer. It has been converted and modernised, and has six acres of beautiful gardens – Richard Mason is a landscape gardener – which lead down to a lake and stream. The house is spacious and decorated to a high standard, and the Masons are welcoming and knowledgeable about the area. The large, well-equipped bedrooms have garden views, and guests have use of a beamed sitting-room, which has a wood-burning stove for chilly evenings. Breakfast only is served, but other meals can be obtained at the pub only 100 yards up the lane.

OWNERS: Richard and Patsy Mason OPEN: all year exc Christmas ROOMS: 2 double, both with shower; 1 twin, with private bathroom; tea/coffee and TV in all bedrooms; lounge with TV TERMS: single occupancy £30, twin/double £50–£55 CARDS: none DETAILS: children welcome; no dogs; smoking in lounge only; car park; garden

UPPER MINETY Wiltshire **map 2**

Flisteridge Cottage

Flisteridge Road, Upper Minety SN16 9PS TEL: (01666) 860343
take A429 Cirencester to Malmesbury road, turn left at Crudwell by Plough Inn, signposted Oaksey / Eastcourt, after 1½m over crossroads signposted Minety, then after 1½m cottage down concealed drive on right

This small whitewashed cottage set in a pretty cottage-style garden is in beautiful countryside, only seven miles from Malmesbury, and reached down a long drive. The house is comfortable and clean, and Mrs Toop-Rose is a delightful person who offers guests a welcoming pot of tea and home-baked cakes on arrival. Evening meals are available by arrangement, but there are plenty of pubs and restaurants in the area. Flisteridge Cottage makes a peaceful base for exploring Bath and the Cotswolds, and there are lovely walks nearby, including an area of very old woodland going back to Saxon days. Plenty of reference books and maps are available for guests' use.

OWNER: Fay Toop-Rose OPEN: all year ROOMS: 2 double, 1 with private bathroom; 1 twin; tea/coffee in all bedrooms; lounge with TV TERMS: single occupancy £18–£22, twin/double £33–£40; dinner £10– £15; deposit: £10–£20 CARDS: none DETAILS: no children under 11; no dogs; no smoking; car park; garden

UPPER ODDINGTON Gloucestershire **map 5**

Orchard Cottage

Back Lane, Upper Oddington GL56 0XL TEL: (01451) 830785
off A436, 2m E of Stow-on-the-Wold

Guests continue to enjoy this homely Cotswold cottage, peacefully set in the secluded hamlet of Upper Oddington. The local fourteenth-century church with its contemporary wall-paintings makes for an interesting visit. The two small but comfortable bedrooms are well maintained; one has an *en suite* shower, the other has a private bathroom. Jane Beynon's delicious home-made dinners might feature herb pancakes with smoked trout and cucumber stuffing, or pineapple cheesecake. A pretty garden and a television lounge with a log fire are available to visitors. Stow-on-the-Wold is just a short drive away.

OWNER: Jane Beynon OPEN: Mar to Nov ROOMS: 1 double, with private bathroom; 1 twin, with shower; tea/coffee in both bedrooms; lounge with TV TERMS: single occupancy £22–£25, twin/double £38–£44; half-price for children sharing with parents; dinner £13–£15; deposit: £10 CARDS: none DETAILS: no children under 5; dogs by arrangement; no smoking; car park; garden

---

If we know a B&B has an alcohol licence, we say so. Most unlicensed B&Bs that offer evening meals allow guests to bring their own wine to dinner. If you wish to do this, ask the B&B when you book.

UPPER QUINTON Warwickshire map 5

Winton House

The Green, Upper Quinton CV37 8SX TEL: (01789) 720500
off B4632, 6m S of Stratford-upon-Avon

Standing behind a low brick wall, in the heart of the secluded village of Upper Quinton, stands this charming creeper-clad farmhouse. Dating from 1856, the Victorian building retains its period feel. Two of the three comfortably furnished bedrooms have four-poster beds and *en suite* facilities, while the family room has a private bathroom. Breakfasts include home-made jams and freshly picked fruit; the 'Winton House Special', perhaps an unusual dish like date, oatmeal, honey and banana bake, is also offered. Residents can relax in the comfortable lounge with its log fire and TV, and on warm days in the well-tended garden. Winton House is on the edge of Cotswold country, which means an abundance of cycle paths and walks; a bike-hire service is available.

OWNER: Mrs G. Lyon OPEN: all year ROOMS: 2 four-poster, both with bath/shower; 1 family, with private bathroom; tea/coffee and TV in all bedrooms; lounge with TV TERMS: single occupancy £35, four-poster £48, family room £65; deposit required CARDS: none DETAILS: children welcome; no dogs; no smoking; car park; garden

UPPINGHAM Rutland map 5

Rutland House NEW ENTRY

High Street East, Uppingham LE15 9PY TEL/FAX: (01572) 822497

This attractive Victorian house is situated near the centre of the small market town of Uppingham. The airy *en suite* bedrooms are decorated in pastel shades of blue, cream, pink and green, and two of the rooms have retained their period fireplaces. Full English or continental breakfasts are served at separate tables in the bay-windowed dining-room. There are plenty of places that serve evening meals within walking distance.

OWNER: Jenny Hitchen OPEN: all year ROOMS: 1 single, 2 double, 1 twin, 1 family; all rooms with bath/shower, tea/coffee and TV; 1 room suitable for wheelchair-users TERMS: single £30, single occupancy £30, twin/double £40, family room £50–£54; deposit: £10; children's reductions according to age CARDS: MasterCard, Visa DETAILS: no children under 5; dogs welcome; no smoking in some bedrooms and dining-room; car park

---

If any bedrooms are suitable for wheelchair-users, we mention this in the details at the end of the entry.

If a B&B accepts credit cards, we list them in the details at the end of an entry – or specify no cards are accepted if that is so. There may be a surcharge if you pay by credit card. It is always best to check when booking whether the card you want to use will be accepted.

UPTON SNODSBURY Hereford & Worcester **map 5**

Upton House

Upton Snodsbury WR7 4NR TEL: (01905) 381226 FAX: (01905) 381775
on A422, 6m E of Worcester

Standing in its own grounds in the peaceful village of Upton Snodsbury is this comfortable and elegant twelfth-century manor-house. Guest accommodation comprises two luxuriously decorated bedrooms, each with TV and *en suite* bathroom. Residents can relax and socialise in the sitting-room, and on warm days make use of the outdoor swimming-pool and croquet lawn. A gate in the front garden leads to the adjacent Norman church. The Jeffersons are happy to provide maps for exploring the Elgar Trail, and the lesser-known Cotswold villages. One-night bookings are not available at weekends; suppers and five-course evening meals are provided by arrangement.

OWNERS: Hugh and Angela Jefferson OPEN: all year exc Christmas and Easter ROOMS: 1 double, 1 twin; both rooms with bath, tea/coffee and TV; lounge TERMS: twin/double £68; dinner £15-£25; deposit: £10 per person CARDS: none DETAILS: no children; no dogs; no smoking; car park; garden; swimming-pool

VELLOW Somerset **map 2**

Curdon Mill **NEW ENTRY**

Lower Vellow TA4 4LS TEL: (01984) 656522 FAX: (01984) 656197
on A358, B&B is on left after 1m

A small river still runs past this creeper-clad former mill. The property stands in a blissfully peaceful spot, with some lovely views across hilly fields towards the Quantocks. Individually styled around the shape of the old watermill, the *en suite* bedrooms have easy chairs, flowers, fruit and lots of other extras. The wheel shaft runs through the licensed restaurant, where evening meals, largely consisting of decent English home-cooked food, are served. Richard and Daphne Criddle offer a warm welcome, and enjoy sharing their family home. A heated swimming-pool is situated in the well-tended gardens. The house is also licensed for weddings.

OWNERS: Richard and Daphne Criddle OPEN: all year ROOMS: 3 double, 3 twin; all rooms with bath/shower, tea/coffee and TV; lounge TERMS: single occupancy £40–£55, twin/double £60–£80; dinner £22.50; deposit required CARDS: Delta, MasterCard, Switch, Visa DETAILS: no children under 10; dogs in outside kennels only; smoking in lounge only; car park; garden; swimming-pool

---

Some B&Bs try to 'solicit' recommendations; they may even photocopy our report forms and hand them out to guests. We can spot these easily, and give them no credence. But genuine reports from readers, prompted only by a desire to share details of a stay at a B&B, are given our full attention.

VERYAN Cornwall **map 1**

Broom Parc

Camels, Veryan TR2 5PJ TEL: (01872) 501803 FAX: (01872) 501109
off A3078, 5m SE of Truro

Keith and Lindsay Righton offer cheerful and simple accommodation at their rendered Victorian villa, which is owned by the National Trust and was used in the television adaptation of Mary Wesley's novel *The Camomile Lawn*. It occupies a superb clifftop position, with panoramic coastal views, and is a good stopping-off place for those walking the paths of the Roseland peninsula. There are three bedrooms, two with *en suite* facilities, the other with a private bathroom, and guests also have use of a lounge with TV and the attractive sloping garden bordered by shrubs. Evening meals are available by arrangement. The nearby Lost Gardens of Heligan are worth a visit.

OWNERS: Keith and Lindsay Righton OPEN: all year exc Christmas and New Year ROOMS: 1 double, with private bathroom; 2 twin, both with bath/shower; tea/coffee in all bedrooms; lounge with TV TERMS: twin/double £42–£55; dinner £13.50 CARDS: none DETAILS: no children; dogs welcome; car park; garden

WADSWICK Wiltshire **map 2**

Manor Farm

NEW ENTRY

Wadswick SN13 8JB TEL: (01225) 810700 FAX: (01225) 810307
just off B3109 Corsham to Bradford-on-Avon road

Set in peaceful Wiltshire countryside, Manor Farm dates partly from the seventeenth century and partly from the Edwardian era. The property is a working farm, and the house stands in a lovely garden, set apart from a complex of beautifully maintained farm buildings. These have been converted to include a country clothing shop selling riding clothes, harnesses, saddles and gift items. All the rooms are spacious, and the bedrooms are very comfortable with plenty of easy chairs. Both the enormous drawing-room and dining-room are beautifully furnished with antiques. Breakfast only is served. Manor Farm is located six miles east of Bath, and is close to the villages of Lacock and Castle Combe.

OWNER: Carolyn Barton OPEN: Mar to Oct ROOMS: 1 double, 2 twin; all rooms with shower, tea/coffee and TV TERMS: single occupancy £25–£30, twin/double £45–£50; deposit: £10 per night CARDS: Delta, MasterCard, Switch, Visa DETAILS: no children under 5; no dogs; no smoking; car park; garden

If a B&B offers off-street car parking, we note 'car park' at the end of the entry. If nearby on-street parking must be used, in most cases we give details in the descriptive text.

WALBERTON West Sussex **map 3**

Berrycroft

Tye Lane, Walberton BN18 0LU TEL/FAX: (01243) 551323
just off A27 between Arundel and Chichester

Offering one well-appointed guest bedroom with its own private bathroom, Berrycroft is just the place for those wanting to get away from it all. It is set in its own one-and-a-half-acre grounds on the edge of the village. Mrs Hayward provides a friendly welcome, and ensures her guests are well looked after. The twin-bedded room can also be used as a family room – although more than one child would be a bit of a squeeze. Breakfast is served in the dining-room, and there is an attractively furnished drawing-room with satellite TV. Outside in summer, the energetic may wish to take a dip in the (unheated) swimming-pool.

OWNERS: Mr and Mrs G. Hayward OPEN: all year exc Christmas ROOMS: 1 twin/family, with private bathroom, tea/coffee and TV; lounge with TV TERMS: single occupancy £25, twin/family £40–£44; reductions for children; deposit: £10 per person in high season CARDS: none DETAILS: children welcome; no dogs; no smoking in bedroom; car park; garden; swimming-pool

WALTON HIGHWAY Norfolk **map 6**

Maple Lodge

NEW ENTRY

Lynn Road, Walton Highway PE14 7DE TEL: (01945) 461430
off A47, 2m NE of Wisbech

Visitors receive a warm welcome at this modern brick-built house, situated on the outskirts of a small village on the Cambridgeshire/Norfolk border. Generous breakfasts are served in the bright dining-room, and home-cooked dinners are available by arrangement. The three bedrooms share a bathroom, and the twin has views over open countryside. Books, board-games and toys are provided in the lounge, and in the summer guests can use the heated swimming-pool in the large garden.

OWNERS: Alan and Thelma Etherington OPEN: all year ROOMS: 1 single, 1 double, 1 twin; tea/coffee and TV in all bedrooms; lounge with TV TERMS: single/single occupancy £16, twin/double £32; babies free, £10 for ages 2–5; dinner £5.50–£7; deposit: £5 per person CARDS: none DETAILS: children welcome; no dogs; no smoking; car park; garden; swimming-pool

Stratton Farm

West Drove North, Walton Highway PE14 7DP TEL: (01945) 880162
from B198 follow signs to Walton Highway; go through village, turn left ½m past Highwayman pub into West Drove North; farm is on left after ½m

Stratton Farm with its herd of prize-winning shorthorn cattle extends to 22 acres, surrounded by open Norfolk countryside. The modern ranch-style farmhouse is approached by a private drive and is set in landscaped gardens with a small lake, where guests may fish for carp, and a heated swimming-pool, which is open in summer. Accommodation consists of three very large bedrooms, each with *en suite* facilities and comfortable sitting-areas with easy chairs. As the house is a bungalow, all rooms are on the ground floor, and one room has been designed with wheelchair-users in mind. Breakfast features home-made marmalade and preserves, and several pubs in the area serve evening meals.

OWNERS: Derek and Sue King OPEN: all year ROOMS: 2 double, 1 twin; all rooms with bath/shower, tea/coffee and TV; 1 room suitable for wheelchair-users; lounge TERMS: single occupancy £23, twin/double £46; £14.50 for children 7–12; deposit: £10–£30 CARDS: none DETAILS: no children under 7; no dogs; no smoking; car park; garden; swimming-pool

WANGFORD Suffolk map 6

Hill House NEW ENTRY

Hill Road, Wangford NR34 8AR TEL: (01502) 578588
turn off A12 on to B1126, signposted Wangford, take Hill Road on right at left bend, Hill House is 100 yards on right

This attractive, modern, half-timbered house stands in a large garden on the edge of the unspoilt village of Wangford, a couple of miles from the coastal town of Southwold. Ann Yeats Brown greets her guests with tea and home-made cakes, and is a very helpful host. One couple setting off at 4.30am for bird-watching at nearby Minsmere RSPB Reserve were impressed by the 'service beyond normal expectations': Ann was up even earlier to prepare a breakfast that included freshly squeezed orange juice and freshly brewed coffee. The two bedrooms are comfortably furnished, with floral bedspreads and curtains made by Ann; several paintings by her daughter are on display around the house. Laundry facilities are available for guests staying a while. There is a small supplement for one-night bookings.

OWNER: Ann Yeats Brown OPEN: all year exc Christmas and New Year ROOMS: 1 single; 1 twin/double, with shower; lounge with TV TERMS: single £20–£22, single occupancy £34–£37.50, twin/double £45–£50; dinner £12.50–£15; deposit: 10% CARDS: none DETAILS: no children under 8; dogs by arrangement; no smoking in bedrooms; car park; garden

Poplar Hall

Frostenden Corner, Frostenden, nr Wangford NR34 7JA
TEL: (01502) 578549
off A12 between Wangford and Wrentham, take turning signposted Frostenden and South Cove; house is on left just past green

Poplar Hall is an early-sixteenth-century thatched house set in over an acre of lovely gardens in the hamlet of Frostenden Corner, which is surrounded by open countryside and only three and a half miles from the seaside town of Southwold. The house is full of character, with thick stone walls and oak beams, one of which is carved with a 'hag' mark to ward off witches. Bedrooms are a good size and one has a half-tester bed, another an Egyptian theme. There is a roof garden decorated with hanging baskets, and guests have two sitting-areas, one with an open fireplace. 'Excellent' breakfasts are served in the elegant dining-room. There are also two self-catering cottages in the grounds.

OWNERS: John and Anna Garwood OPEN: all year exc Christmas ROOMS: 1 single, with private bathroom; 2 double, 1 with bath, 1 with private bathroom; tea/coffee and TV in all bedrooms TERMS: single £20–£25, single occupancy £32–£36, double £38–£44; deposit: £20 per room CARDS: none DETAILS: children welcome; no dogs; no smoking; car park; garden

WANSFORD Cambridgeshire map 6

Stoneacre

Elton Road, Wansford PE8 6JT TEL/FAX: (01780) 783283
on A6118 (formerly B671) between Elton and Wansford

This luxurious, modern ranch-style house is set in an acre of secluded grounds with views across the Nene Valley. Owners Ann and Peter Wilkinson are a charming couple who have considered all their guests' needs and provided more besides, including a five-hole pitch-and-putt golf course, and a large summer-house equipped with music system, gas fire, sink, kettle and WC, plus a covered barbecue for guests' use. Most bedrooms are on the ground floor and open on to the patio, while the residents' lounge is on the first floor, and has a balcony; there is also a kitchen stocked with help-yourself drinks. Buffet breakfast is served in the dining-room, which has been extended. Burghley House and Sibson Airfield are two nearby places worth visiting, and Peterborough is a short drive away.

OWNERS: Ann and Peter Wilkinson OPEN: all year ROOMS: 4 double, 1 with bath/shower, 3 with private bathroom; 1 twin/double, with shower; 1 family, with shower; lounge with TV TERMS: single occupancy £24–£40, twin/double £30–£52, family room £50–£60; deposit: £20 per room CARDS: none DETAILS: no children under 5; well-behaved dogs welcome; smoking in lounge and summer-house only; car park; garden

WARGRAVE Berkshire map 3

Windy Brow

204 Victoria Road, Wargrave RG10 8AJ
TEL: (0118) 940 3336 FAX: (0118) 940 1260
from Maidenhead take A4 towards Reading; after 3m turn right towards Upper Wargrave, continue for 1m; Windy Brow is second house on left after Wargrave village sign

Windy Brow, an attractive red-brick house, stands on the edge of Wargrave in a peaceful situation surrounded by open countryside. All of the comfortably furnished bedrooms have a TV, and two of the rooms can be used as either a twin or double. The *en suite* ground-floor room has a separate entrance, and is suitable for wheelchair-users. Breakfasts are cooked on the Aga, and are served in the small conservatory which overlooks the well-tended garden. Several nearby establishments serve evening meals.

OWNERS: Heather and Michael Carver OPEN: all year exc Christmas ROOMS: 2 single; 2 double/twin, 1 with shower, 1 with wash-basin; 1 room suitable for wheelchair-users; tea/coffee and TV in all bedrooms TERMS: single £25–£35, single occupancy £30–£35, double £45–£55; half-price for children 8–14; deposit required CARDS: none DETAILS: no children under 8; no dogs; no smoking; car park; garden

WARK Northumberland **map 11**

Low Stead NEW ENTRY

Wark NE48 3DP TEL: (01434) 230352

from B6320 in centre of Wark take Stonehaugh road for 2½m; take sharp left bend before Hetherington Farm; turn right through gate, follow to bottom of hill, then turn first left (marked No Through Road); fork left into Low Stead

A truly spectacular setting will greet guests arriving at this idyllic 400-year-old stone farmhouse: it is set in five acres of beautiful grounds with a stream running through. Sheep graze on the fellside, wildlife abounds, and a stretch of the Pennine Way is just a stone's throw from the front door. Both of the well-equipped *en suite* bedrooms are in converted farm buildings and have their own private entrances; one is on the ground floor, one up a flight of stone stairs. Sally Peel is an excellent cook who believes in using fresh, local supplies and, by arrangement, elegantly presents four-course meals in the beamed dining-room.

OWNERS: David and Sally Peel OPEN: Mar to Oct ROOMS: 1 double, 1 twin; both rooms with shower, tea/coffee and TV; lounge TERMS: single occupancy £29.50, twin/double £49; dinner £14.50 CARDS: none DETAILS: no children under 9; no dogs; no smoking; car park; garden

WARNHAM West Sussex **map 3**

Glebe End NEW ENTRY

Warnham, nr Horsham RH12 3QW

TEL: (01403) 261711 FAX: (01403) 257572

150yds S of church

Right in the centre of the attractive, sleepy village of Warnham, Glebe End is a delightful 500-year-old house in a walled garden full of old-fashioned roses and herbs. It has an interesting history and retains many of its original features including ships' timbers in the kitchen and Tudor flagstones in the dining-room. Mrs Cox is very welcoming, and the comfortable house is homely and full of fresh flowers. The bedrooms are furnished with antiques, and two are adjoining and share a staircase, making them ideal for families. There is an elegant, comfortable drawing-room with french windows to the garden, and evening meals are available (for four or more people), if arranged in advance. Warnham is Shelley's birthplace, and the gardens at Leonardslee, Nymans and Wakehurst are within half-an-hour's drive.

OWNERS: Elizabeth and Christopher Cox OPEN: all year ROOMS: 1 single, with private bathroom; 1 double, with bath/shower; 1 twin, with bath/shower; 1 family, with bath/shower; tea/coffee and TV in all bedrooms; lounge with TV TERMS: single £24, single occupancy £30, twin/double £48, family room from £48; babies free, half-price for children under 10; dinner £12–£14; deposit required CARDS: none DETAILS: children welcome; no smoking; car park; garden

WARTON Lancashire

map 8

Cotestones Farm

Sand Lane, Warton LA5 9NH TEL: (01524) 732418

This charming farmhouse is part of a 120-acre dairy farm, and offers good-value B&B. Gill Close extends a warm welcome, and offers a hot drink to arriving guests. The bedrooms all have wash-basins, and share a bathroom and shower-room. Generous breakfasts are served in the lounge-cum-dining-room, and may feature kippers and omelettes. The surrounding countryside is excellent walking territory, and Leighton Moss bird reserve is nearby.

OWNER: Gill Close OPEN: all year exc Christmas ROOMS: 1 single, 1 double, 1 twin, 1 family; all rooms with wash-basin and tea/coffee; TV in most bedrooms and lounge TERMS: single/single occupancy £16, twin/double £30, family room £30–£45; half-price for children in family room CARDS: none DETAILS: children welcome; dogs welcome; car park; garden

WARWICK Warwickshire

map 5

Avon Guest House

7 Emscote Road, Warwick CV34 4PH TEL/FAX: (01926) 491367

This Victorian house, offering simple, clean and comfortable accommodation, is within easy reach of the castle and the centre of Warwick, and owner Lyn Bolton is a friendly, outgoing lady. All bedrooms have their own *en suite* showers but three do not have WCs. Guests can relax and enjoy a drink (the house is licensed) in the comfortable sitting-room, or have a stroll around the walled garden. Breakfast and three-course evening meals are served. The bus and railway stations are also nearby, and secure parking facilities are provided.

OWNERS: Lyn and Nobby Bolton OPEN: all year ROOMS: 3 single, 2 double, 2 twin, 2 family; all rooms with shower (3 no WC) and tea/coffee; lounge with TV TERMS: single £18–£20, twin/double £34–£36, family room £60; half-price for children under 10; dinner £8 CARDS: none DETAILS: children welcome; no dogs; smoking in lounge only; car park; garden

Forth House

44 High Street, Warwick CV34 3AX
TEL: (01926) 401512 FAX: (01926) 490809

Forth House, a beautifully maintained property with a Georgian facade, enjoys a very central location, but the two guest suites are at the rear of the house, away from the street noise. The larger ground-floor suite has its own door to the garden and is particularly suitable for families. Breakfast is served in the bedroom or – weather permitting – in the garden. Evening meals are no longer offered, but Elizabeth Draisey is happy to recommend places to eat out in town. Long-staying guests have use of a small kitchen for self-catering. Forth House is just a couple of minutes' drive from the castle.

OWNER: Elizabeth Draisey OPEN: all year ROOMS: 2 double/twin/family; both rooms with bath/shower; 1 room suitable for wheelchair-users; lounge with TV TERMS: single occupancy £40, twin/double £46–£56, family room £50–£70; deposit: £20 CARDS: none DETAILS: children welcome; dogs in ground-floor suite only; no smoking; car park; garden

WATERBEACH Cambridgeshire **map 6**

Berry House

High Street, Waterbeach CB5 9JU
TEL: (01223) 860702 FAX: (01223) 570588
just of A10, 5m NE of Cambridge

Set in the historical village of Waterbeach, this eighteenth-century former coach-house offers comfortable accommodation in an informal atmosphere. The two traditionally furnished bedrooms are in what was the back wing of the house, and have *en suite* showers; one has a king-sized bed. The large garden has a new summer-house and a sunken terrace, where guests can sit and even have breakfast in summer, and croquet is also available. Phil Myburgh, who is South African, is a keen golfer, and is preparing a small putting green, which guests will be welcome to use when the surface has matured. There is a large guest lounge complete with cable TV, log fire and a baby grand piano which may be used by experienced players. Guests have their own access to the bedrooms through french windows and they are provided with keys. Hearty breakfasts and evening meals (by arrangement when the Myburghs' other commitments permit) are served in the dining-room.

OWNERS: Phil and Sally Myburgh OPEN: all year ROOMS: 2 double; both with shower and tea/coffee; lounge with TV TERMS: single occupancy £40, double £50–£60; dinner £20 CARDS: none DETAILS: children welcome; no dogs; car park; garden

---

'Lounge' in the details at the bottoms of entries refers to a room (or rooms) in which guests can relax, watch TV, read or chat, and may vary from a large, elegantly furnished drawing-room exclusively for guests' use to a cosy sitting-room shared with the owners.

WATERDEN Norfolk

map 6

The Old Rectory

NEW ENTRY

Waterden NR22 6AT TEL: (01328) 823298
off B1355 Fakenham to Burnham Market road, 4m NW of Fakenham

This red-brick Victorian rectory is set in unspoilt countryside, only six miles from the Norfolk coast. Rosemary Pile welcomes guests with a hot drink on arrival, and the house has a warm and friendly atmosphere. Bedrooms are of a good size and all have *en suite* bathrooms. One double bedroom is in a ground-floor annexe and can easily be converted into a family room as it has a sofa bed. The guest lounge is warmed by a log fire in winter. Breakfast only is available, but Rosemary is happy to recommend one of the several excellent pubs and restaurants in the area. The Old Rectory is owned by Holkham Hall, which is well worth a visit, as is the nearby Saxon church, which is mentioned in the Domesday Book.

OWNER: Rosemary Pile OPEN: all year ROOMS: 2 double, 1 twin; all rooms with bath/shower; 1 room suitable for wheelchair-users; lounge with TV TERMS: single occupancy £25–£30, twin/double £40–£42; deposit: £10 CARDS: none DETAILS: children welcome; dogs welcome in one downstairs room only; no smoking; car park; garden

WATERROW Somerset

map 2

Pare Mill

NEW ENTRY

Waterrow TA4 2AS TEL: (01984) 623865
on B3227, 3m SW of Wiveliscombe

Dating from the fourteenth century, this former mill enjoys a peaceful and beautiful setting on the edge of Exmoor and the Brendon Hills, and the River Tone flows along one side of the property. The Sargents are a charming couple; Dick takes care of the sheep farm, while Hazel is a professional cook, producing excellent, imaginative meals using local produce, including vegetables and lamb from the farm. Accommodation is comfortable and the rooms are tastefully decorated and furnished. The three bedrooms share a bathroom and a shower-room between them. The pine-furnished dining-room and elegant drawing-room are both warmed by a wood-burning stove.

OWNERS: Hazel and Dick Sargent OPEN: all year exc Christmas ROOMS: 1 single, 1 double, 1 twin; tea/coffee in all bedrooms; lounge with TV TERMS: single £15, single occupancy £30, twin/double £30; £5 for children under 5, £10 for ages 5–15; dinner £8.50–£14.50; deposit: 10% CARDS: none DETAILS: children welcome; dogs by arrangement; no smoking in bedrooms; car park; garden

---

Any smoking restrictions that we know of are given in the details at the end of the entry.

WEARE GIFFARD Devon map 1

Burnards

Weare Giffard EX39 4QR TEL: (01237) 473809
off A386 between Bideford and Torrington; in Weare Giffard 50yds from Cyder Presse pub

This eighteenth-century cottage with its low ceilings and cosy atmosphere is set in a peaceful position in the pretty village of Weare Giffard overlooking the River Torridge. On fine days guests can sit out on the patio in the colourful small garden with its rambling roses and enjoy the peaceful views over the river to the hills. Mrs Carter, who loves cooking, will prepare evening meals by arrangement. Alternatively, the pub nearby offers food in the evenings. The two attractive guest bedrooms are upstairs and share a bathroom, and there is a comfortable sitting-room with a TV. Rosemoor Gardens are three miles away.

OWNER: Mrs J. Carter OPEN: Mar to Sept ROOMS: 1 double, 1 twin; both rooms with wash-basin and tea/coffee; lounge with TV TERMS: single occupancy £17, twin/double £33; half-price for children under 12; dinner £9 CARDS: none DETAILS: children welcome; no dogs; no smoking upstairs or in dining-room; car park; garden

WEAVERHAM Cheshire map 7

Beechwood House

206 Wallerscote Road, Weaverham CW8 3LZ TEL: (01606) 852123
on B5153, just W of Northwich

Since the last edition, Janet Kuypers retired, but missed having guests so much that she is now back in business. Her comfortable farmhouse occupies a peaceful position on an 18-acre livestock farm, also inhabited by over 60 varieties of bird life. Guest accommodation is in a separate wing of the house, but Janet is easy to reach if needed. There is a pleasant lounge, and a separate dining-room where breakfast is served. One of the single rooms is on the ground floor. Janet will happily arrange to pick guests up from the railway station. An energetic stroll up the bank will be rewarded with lovely views, and nearby is a rare Anderton lift, used to carry boats between the upper and lower levels of the canal.

OWNER: Janet Kuypers OPEN: all year exc Christmas ROOMS: 2 single, both with wash-basin; 1 twin, with bath/shower; tea/coffee in all bedrooms; lounge with TV TERMS: single £16.50, single occupancy £20, twin £38; deposit required CARDS: none DETAILS: no children; no dogs; no smoking; car park

---

B&B rates specified in the details at the end of each entry are given (as applicable) for a single room, for single occupancy of a double room, and then per room in the case of two people sharing a double or twin-bedded room, or for a family room. Because double rooms with four-poster beds often cost more, those are listed separately.

WELLS Somerset **map 2**

Infield House

36 Portway, Wells BA5 2BN TEL: (01749) 670989 FAX: (01749) 670093

Infield House, a spacious Victorian town house, was taken over by Richard and Heather Betton-Foster during the summer of 1997. It backs on to a wooded conservation area, and is only five minutes' walk from the centre of the historic town of Wells. Each of the bedrooms has its original fireplace, and the bathrooms have automatic lights. Breakfast is served at separate tables in the attractive dining-room, which has an Adam-style fireplace. Guests can relax in the comfortable lounge and peruse the collection of local guide books and information. There is a small rear garden and parking area.

OWNERS: Richard and Heather Betton-Foster OPEN: all year ROOMS: 2 double, 1 with bath/shower, 1 with private bathroom; 1 twin, with bath/shower; tea/coffee and TV in all bedrooms; lounge TERMS: single occupancy £31–£34.50, twin/double £42–£45; deposit: 1 night's charge or credit card details CARDS: Delta, MasterCard, Visa DETAILS: no children under 15; no dogs; no smoking; car park; garden

WELLS-NEXT-THE-SEA Norfolk **map 6**

The Normans NEW ENTRY

Invaders Court, Standard Road, Wells-next-the-Sea NR23 1JW
TEL: (01328) 710657 FAX: (01328) 710468

Carol Macdonald and Trevor Francis enjoy welcoming guests to their lovely home, a listed Georgian building, only 100 yards from the quay. Bedrooms are spacious, tastefully furnished and decorated in keeping with the character of the house. Some have views over the salt marshes towards the sea, and one double room has an *en suite* dressing-room. The large TV lounge has a log fire, and is stocked with games, and books on local walks, and the landing look-out window is supplied with a pair of binoculars. A substantial breakfast is served and there are several pubs and restaurants within easy walking distance. The area is ideal for nature lovers, with plenty of sandy beaches and nature reserves. There are also two narrow-gauge railways nearby.

OWNERS: Carol Macdonald and Trevor Francis OPEN: all year exc Christmas ROOMS: 6 double, 1 twin; all rooms with bath/shower, tea/coffee and TV; lounge with TV TERMS: single occupancy £28–£30, twin/double £40–£55; deposit: £20 per room CARDS: none DETAILS: no children under 10; no dogs in dining-room; no smoking; car park

---

If you are forced to turn up later than planned, please telephone to warn the proprietor. It is always best to book a room in advance, even in winter. B&Bs with few rooms may close at short notice for periods not specified in the details.

The Warren

NEW ENTRY

Warham Road, Wells-next-the-Sea NR23 1NE TEL: (01328) 710273
on B1105, heading S out of Wells-next-the-Sea

This modern bungalow, run by David and Jean Wickens, a warm and friendly couple, stands in a pretty garden with a pond, and is just ten minutes' walk from the town centre. Both bedrooms are of a good size and attractively decorated with matching floral curtains and duvets. Breakfast is served in the large conservatory, and there is a separate lounge with a log fire. The Wickenses are natives of the area – David knows the history of the town and can supply guests with information on walks and the local attractions, which include an Iron Age fort.

OWNER: Jean Wickens OPEN: all year exc Christmas ROOMS: 1 double, 1 twin; both rooms with bath/shower (no WC in twin), tea/coffee and TV; lounge TERMS: single occupancy £20, twin/double £36; deposit: 1 night's charge CARDS: none DETAILS: no children; dogs welcome; no smoking; car park; garden

WEM Shropshire **map 5**

Foxleigh House

NEW ENTRY

Foxleigh Drive, Wem SY4 5BP TEL/FAX: (01939) 233528
heading out of Wem on B5476 Whitchurch road, take second turning on right after Hawkestone pub, then immediately left into Foxleigh Drive

This impressive part-Victorian, part-Georgian house is hidden away in a large, well-tended garden, which includes a croquet lawn. Many original features remain, including a large ceiling rose, interesting coving and working casement shutters. A gallery of ancestral portraits is on display in the hall. Bedrooms are spacious and have elegant antique furniture; one has its own bathroom while the other two share. Breakfast and, by arrangement, dinner are served at a large round table constructed from a single piece of wood, and the big sitting-room is warmed by a log fire. Ted and Barbara are a gracious couple who go out of their way to ensure the comfort of their guests. Shrewsbury is only nine miles away, and nearby is Hodnet Hall with its not-to-be-missed gardens.

OWNERS: Ted and Barbara Barnes OPEN: all year exc Christmas ROOMS: 2 twin, 1 with private bathroom; 1 family; tea/coffee and TV in all bedrooms; lounge TERMS: single occupancy £24, twin £38–£44, family room from £34; dinner £11; deposit: £10 per person CARDS: none DETAILS: no children under 10; no dogs; no smoking; car park; garden

In the details listed at the bottom of each entry, the following information is set out: owners' names; months when open; room details; prices per room, children's reductions and prices of evening meals if available; credit and debit cards accepted; any restrictions on children, dogs and smoking; whether there's a car park, plus amenities for guests such as a garden they can use, games room, tennis court and swimming-pool.

WEST BRIDGFORD Nottinghamshire map 5

Gallery Hotel

8–10 Radcliffe Road, West Bridgford NG2 5FW
TEL: (01159) 813651 FAX: (01159) 813732

Gallery Hotel is in the town of West Bridgford, one mile from the centre of Nottingham, and right next door to Trent Bridge cricket ground. It is run by Don and Brenda Masson, a friendly, welcoming couple. Bedrooms are comfortable and decorated in rich colours, and all have *en suite* facilities and TV; two of the rooms are suitable for wheelchair-users. Guests also have use of a lounge with satellite TV, and a small licensed bar with a pool table. Note that dinner is no longer served.

OWNERS: Don and Brenda Masson OPEN: all year ROOMS: 3 single, 5 double, 6 twin, 4 family; all rooms with bath/shower, tea/coffee and TV; 2 rooms suitable for wheelchair-users; lounge with TV TERMS: single £26–£29, single occupancy £29, twin/double £38–£40, family room from £38; children under 5 free, under 10 half-price; deposit: 10% or credit card details CARDS: Delta, MasterCard, Switch, Visa DETAILS: children welcome; no dogs; smoking in bar and 2 bedrooms only; car park; games room; garden

WEST BUCKLAND Devon map 1

Huxtable Farm

West Buckland EX32 0SR TEL/FAX: (01598) 760254
leave A361 5m E of Barnstaple at signs for West and East Buckland; continue 2m; farm entrance opposite school between the two villages

This lovely old 80-acre farm, supporting mostly sheep, dates back to the fourteenth century and was originally part of the Fortescue Estate, which still owns most of the adjoining land. The renovated barn, roundhouse and medieval longhouse are all listed buildings, and the farmhouse itself, built in 1520, retains many original features. There are bread ovens, open fireplaces, uneven flagstone floors and beams galore, with décor and furnishings in keeping with the house's age and style. The guest accommodation, however, offers every comfort: the well-appointed bedrooms are all *en suite* except one with a private bathroom, are kitted out with all sorts of toiletries and have TVs. The two family rooms are in the outbuildings, and cots, high chairs and baby alarms are available. Imaginative candlelit dinners, beginning with a complimentary glass of home-made wine, are served in the attractive, 'medieval' dining-room. Guests also have the use of a drawing-room, small library, fitness room, sauna, and games room with darts and table tennis; outside, there's a tennis court and, for children, a play area with swings, sandpit and wendy house. Children are also invited to help feed the lambs in spring, and to meet the tame rabbits, pygmy goats and chickens, and the farm's two friendly dogs.

OWNERS: Jackie and Antony Payne OPEN: all year exc Christmas ROOMS: 3 double, 1 twin, 2 family; all rooms with bath/shower exc 1 double with private bathroom; tea/coffee and TV in all bedrooms; lounge TERMS: single occupancy £27, twin/double/

family £46–£48 plus children's charge; £10 for children sharing with parents; dinner £14; deposit usually required CARDS: none DETAILS: children welcome; no dogs; no smoking in dining-room or bedrooms; car park; games room; garden; tennis

WEST BURTON North Yorkshire — Map 8

The Grange

NEW ENTRY

West Burton DL8 4JR TEL/FAX: (01969) 663348
just off the B6160, 8m E of Hawes

This elegant ivy-covered country house stands in park-like grounds, overlooking the dales and waterfalls of the River Walden. The Grange is located on the edge of the unspoilt village of West Burton, with its ancient market cross. Its spacious bedrooms are beautifully decorated, and the house has antique furnishings. There is also an inviting drawing-room, where guests can relax by a log fire on cold evenings. Breakfasts and pre-arranged dinners are served in the dining-room; special diets, including vegetarian, can be catered for. Private fishing can be arranged; two self-catering cottages are also available.

OWNERS: Mr and Mrs P. Ashford OPEN: all year ROOMS: 2 double, with bath/shower; 1 twin, with private bathroom; all rooms with tea/coffee and TV; lounge with TV TERMS: single occupancy £30, twin/double £50–£55; children's reductions according to age; dinner £15 CARDS: MasterCard, Visa DETAILS: children welcome; dogs welcome; no smoking in bedrooms; car park; games room; garden

WEST CHILTINGTON West Sussex — map 3

New House Farm

Broadford Bridge Road, West Chiltington RH20 2LA TEL: (01798) 812215
take B2133 from A29, after 2m turn right signposted West Chiltington and Golf Course; farmhouse is on left

New House Farm is a delightful fifteenth-century farmhouse in the centre of the village of West Chiltington. Although Mr Steele has retired from farming, he still keeps a few sheep on the 50 acres. The immaculately clean house has a pleasant atmosphere and is decorated inside in white with black woodwork. The bedrooms have flowered wallpapers and are comfortably furnished; one is exceptionally large, and the tiny double room in the garden annexe is particularly popular with those who cannot cope with stairs. Breakfast is served in an attractive dining-room/sitting-area with open fire, and there is a separate sitting-room for summer use.

OWNER: Alma Steele OPEN: all year exc Christmas ROOMS: 1 double, with private bathroom; 2 twin, both with shower; tea/coffee and TV in all bedrooms; lounge with TV TERMS: single occupancy £25–£35, twin/double £44–£50; deposit: 25% CARDS: none DETAILS: no children under 10; no dogs; no smoking; car park; garden

WEST CLANDON Surrey

map 3

Ways Cottage

Lime Grove, West Clandon GU4 7UT TEL: (01483) 222454
just off A247, 5m NE of Guildford

This 1930s brick house is a good location for those wishing to explore the Surrey countryside, or to stay within easy reach of London. It is in a lime tree-lined, wide road and has a pleasant garden. There is a large, comfortably furnished sitting-room and a lovely dining-room where continental breakfast is served; cooked breakfast is available for a modest extra charge, and dinner can be provided if arranged in advance. One bedroom is *en suite* and the other has the use of a private bathroom. The Hugheses are a friendly and welcoming couple.

OWNERS: Mr and Mrs Christopher Hughes OPEN: all year ROOMS: 2 twin, 1 with bath/shower, 1 with private bathroom; tea/coffee and TV in both bedrooms; lounge with TV TERMS: single occupancy £19–£21, twin/double £32–£35; babies free, half-price for children 5–10; dinner £10; deposit: £10 per room CARDS: none DETAILS: children welcome; no dogs; no smoking; car park; garden

WESTDEAN East Sussex

map 3

Old Parsonage

Westdean, nr Seaford BN25 4AL TEL: (01323) 870432
off A259 at Exceat, just E of Seaford

This beautiful medieval house is next to the even more ancient church in the quiet hamlet of Westdean, a designated conservation area. Dating from 1280, it was built from local flint and chalk by monks, and an extension was added in the Victorian era. The sitting-room, where breakfast is also served, is in the original part, as are two of the bedrooms, which can be reached by very narrow circular stairways; the third is in the more modern side. Angela and Raymond Woodhams are a delightful couple and love sharing their unique house with guests. A reader's comment captures the atmosphere of this unusual place: 'Catching sight of Raymond dashing across the churchyard in his cassock just in time to preach at the Sunday morning service after cooking us a superb breakfast will not easily be forgotten. His timing, like everything else at the Old Parsonage, was judged to perfection.' The Long Man of Wilmington, the Seven Sisters and Beachy Head are all within walking distance.

OWNERS: Angela and Raymond Woodhams OPEN: all year exc Christmas ROOMS: 1 double, 1 twin, 1 four-poster; all rooms with private bathroom and tea/coffee; lounge with TV TERMS: single occupancy £37.50–£45, twin/double £55–£65, four-poster £70 CARDS: none DETAILS: no children under 12; no dogs; no smoking; car park; garden

WEST GRAFTON Wiltshire map 2

Rosegarth

West Grafton SN8 3BY TEL: (01672) 810288
from M4 junction 14, take A338 S for 12m

Rosegarth is an attractive thatched, whitewashed cottage dating from 1580, in three acres of gardens with pleasant farmland views. It was originally a terrace of four cottages for servants of the Crown, and was converted into one house about 40 years ago. The guest accommodation is at one end of the house, and consists of a large sitting-room with TV, comfortable chairs and sofas plus two bedrooms reached up a narrow, steep staircase; their private bathrooms are on the ground floor off the sitting-room. Breakfast is served in the dining-room. Rosegarth is convenient for Stonehenge, Savernake Forest and Lacock Abbey among other places.

OWNERS: Rick and Anne Ruddock-Brown OPEN: all year exc Christmas ROOMS: 1 twin, 1 family; both rooms with private bathroom; lounge with TV TERMS: single occupancy £22–£23, twin £36–£37, family room £48–£50; deposit required CARDS: none DETAILS: no babies or toddlers; no dogs; no smoking; car park; garden

WEST HOATHLY West Sussex map 3

Coneybury NEW ENTRY

Hook Lane, West Hoathly RH19 4PX
TEL: (01342) 810200 FAX: (01342) 810887

Coneybury is in a very peaceful spot, surrounded by fields and a lovely six-acre garden, and has glorious views towards the south coast. It was built of cedarwood in 1937, and the Days almost totally gutted it when they bought it in 1970. They are a very pleasant, welcoming couple; Mr Day looks after the farm while wife Jill runs the B&B side. The two comfortable bedrooms share a bathroom, although it is possible to have private use of a bathroom, and breakfast is served in the pleasant dining-room. Coneybury is one mile from both Ardingly and West Hoathly. Deer stalking, pheasant shooting and hunting can all be arranged. The minimum booking taken at weekends is two nights.

OWNER: Jill Day OPEN: all year exc Christmas ROOMS: 1 double, 1 twin; both rooms with wash-basin, tea/coffee and TV; lounge TERMS: single occupancy £35–£45, twin/double £40–£50; deposit: 1 night's charge CARDS: none DETAILS: no children under 10; dogs welcome in kennel only; no smoking; car park; garden

B&Bs are selected for the Guide for their warm welcome, cleanliness, a friendly atmosphere and, wherever possible, an attractive location or a building that is itself of some historical or architectural interest.

WEST MALLING Kent map 3

Scott House

37 High Street, West Malling ME19 6QH
TEL: (01732) 841380 FAX: (01732) 870025
½m from M20 junction 4

Scott House is a handsome Grade II-listed family home in the centre of the small town of West Malling. The facade was added in 1815, but the building has Tudor origins, given away by old beams, and the only entrance is through the shop. As well as offering bed and breakfast, the Smiths, who are a charming, welcoming couple, also run an antique business, so naturally the house is furnished with beautiful things. The bedrooms are very well appointed, and there is an enormous first-floor drawing-room. Breakfast is served in the large, elegant dining-room, and in good weather, guests can take advantage of the pleasant paved courtyard, which has a grapevine.

OWNER: Ernest Smith OPEN: all year exc Christmas ROOMS: 2 double, 1 twin; all rooms with bath/shower, tea/coffee and TV; lounge TERMS: single occupancy £45, twin/double £55; deposit: credit card details CARDS: Amex, Delta, Diners, MasterCard, Switch, Visa DETAILS: no children; no dogs; no smoking

WEST MEON Hampshire map 2

Home Paddocks

West Meon GU32 1NA TEL: (01730) 829241 FAX: (01730) 829577
just off A32, 10m SW of Alton; from village take East Meon road for ½m

Home Paddocks lies on the outskirts of the village of West Meon in a three-acre garden, with tennis court and croquet lawn. It was at one time the home of Thomas Lord (of cricketing fame), and started life as cottages in the 1560s, with later extensions. Mrs Ward is a charming host, and the attractively decorated, comfortable family house is furnished with antiques. Most meals, including dinner if arranged in advance, are taken in the delightful Victorian conservatory, and there is also a drawing-room and dining-room.

OWNERS: the Ward family OPEN: all year exc Christmas and Easter ROOMS: 2 twin, 1 with bath/shower, 1 with private bathroom; tea/coffee and TV in both bedrooms; lounge with TV TERMS: single occupancy £30–£35, twin/double £42–£45; dinner £15; deposit: 25% CARDS: none DETAILS: children welcome; no dogs; no smoking upstairs; car park; garden; tennis

---

We welcome your feedback about B&Bs you have stayed in. Please make use of the report forms at the end of the book – or use your own stationery if you prefer – and mail your report to: The Editors, The Good Bed and Breakfast Guide, *FREEPOST, 2 Marylebone Road, London NW1 1YN. (No stamps are needed if mailed within the UK.) Recommendations for B&Bs for our next edition are very welcome. Please let us know if you need more report forms and we will send you a fresh supply.*

WEST PORLOCK Somerset map 1

Bales Mead

West Porlock TA24 8NX TEL: (01643) 862565
off A39, on B3225 halfway between Porlock and Porlock Weir

This small Edwardian house occupies a lovely position on the edge of the hamlet of West Porlock, not far from the harbour village of Porlock Weir, and has wonderful views across the bay to Hurlstone Point. In the other direction the view is of the steep wooded hills of Exmoor. The house was restored by owners Stephen Blue and Peter Clover; it stands in a pretty garden filled with specimen plants from all over the world, planted here in the '50s when a well-known horticulturist owned the house. Two of the beautifully furnished bedrooms have sea views, and the stencilling here and in one of the bathrooms was done by Peter, who also drew the illustrations in the humorous 'rule' book found in each bedroom. The baby grand piano in the elegant and comfortable sitting-room reflects Stephen's musical interests. Breakfast only is served in the small dining-room.

OWNERS: Stephen Blue and Peter Clover OPEN: all year exc Christmas ROOMS: 3 double; all rooms with bath/shower, tea/coffee and TV TERMS: single occupancy £34–£44, twin/double £54; deposit: £25; per person CARDS: none DETAILS: no children; no dogs; no smoking; car park; garden

---

West Porlock House

West Porlock TA24 8NX TEL: (01643) 862880
follow sign for Porlock Weir from A39 at Porlock; house is $^{3}/_{4}$m along road on left

Formerly the local manor-house, this large stone building occupies a quiet and peaceful position in four acres of woodland gardens with lovely views of the sea and countryside. It is comfortable with a homely atmosphere and spacious rooms. There are five bedrooms with either *en suite* facilities or private bathrooms, a tastefully decorated lounge and the dining-room, which overlooks the garden, as well as a sitting-area in the hall and a licensed bar. West Porlock House is a short walk from the harbour and the beach. A gate in the grounds offers direct access to footpaths to the woods and Exmoor.

OWNERS: H. and M. Dyer OPEN: Feb to Nov ROOMS: 2 double, both with shower; 2 twin, both with private bathroom; 1 family, with private bathroom; tea/coffee and TV in all bedrooms; lounge with TV TERMS: single occupancy £28, twin/double £48–£52, family room from £48; children over 8 half-price CARDS: none DETAILS: no children under 8; no dogs; no smoking; car park; garden

---

'Bath / shower' in the details under each entry means that the rooms have en suite *facilities. 'Private bathroom' signifies that a room has a bathroom for its exclusive use. The B&B may have other, shared bathroom facilities as well. We list 'wash-basins' for rooms that have them but do not have* en suite *or private facilities.*

WEST WITTON North Yorkshire map 8

Ivy Dene

West Witton DL8 4LP TEL: (01969) 622785
on A684 in village, between Leyburn and Aysgarth

Situated in the centre of a charming historical village, with some lovely views of Wensleydale, this seventeenth-century country house is well placed for touring the Dales. Most of the attractively decorated bedrooms are *en suite* with bath or shower; extra touches are provided by floral coronets, lace canopies and brass bedsteads. Home-cooked dinners are served in the licensed dining-room. The ancient church in the village is worth a visit, and the stunning Aysgarth Falls are only four miles away. A self-catering cottage for two people is also available.

OWNERS: Bob and June Dickinson OPEN: all year exc Christmas ROOMS: 3 double, 2 with bath/shower, 1 with private bathroom; 1 four-poster, with shower; 1 family, with shower; tea/coffee in all bedrooms; TV in most bedrooms and lounge TERMS: double £46–£48, four-poster £48–£50, family room from £48; children's reductions by arrangement; dinner £13.50; deposit: £25 CARDS: none DETAILS: no children under 5; no dogs; no smoking; car park

WHEDDON CROSS Somerset map 1

Raleigh Manor

Wheddon Cross TA24 7BB TEL: (01643) 841484
off B3224, just W of A396, 6m SW of Minehead

Raleigh Manor stands in a peaceful secluded spot, in one and a half acres of woods and gardens at the end of a half-mile drive, with terrific views across Exmoor. The attractive tile-hung house was built in 1889 as the manor-house of the Cutcombe Estate. It is a relaxing place, with a log fire in the comfortable lounge, a small library well stocked with books and magazines, and there is also a small conservatory. The dining-room has wonderful views, as do most of the pleasantly decorated bedrooms. The Squire's Room is particularly large and has a half-tester bed. A footpath leads through the grounds to Dunkery Beacon, the highest point on Exmoor.

OWNERS: Mahmoud and Dorothy Sahlool OPEN: Mar to Nov ROOMS: 1 single, 3 double, 2 twin, 1 four-poster; all rooms with bath/shower, tea/coffee and TV; lounge with TV TERMS: single £26–£30, single occupancy £36–£40, twin/double £52–£60, four-poster £64–£71; children's reductions by arrangement; dinner £14.50; deposit: £20 per person CARDS: MasterCard, Visa DETAILS: no children under 5; no dogs; no smoking; car park; garden

---

If there are any bedrooms with TV, or with tea / coffee-making facilities, we mention this in the details at the end of an entry.

WHIMPLE Devon map 2

Down House

Woodhayes Lane, Whimple EX5 2QR TEL: (01404) 822860
just off A30 between Exeter and Honiton

This large Edwardian house is surrounded by five acres of garden, paddock and orchard, in a secluded position up a narrow lane about a mile from Whimple, with views to the Tiverton hills and, on clear days, to Dartmoor. Mike and Joanne Sanders are a charming couple who have made a lot of improvements to the house. The spacious lounge has an unusual fireplace and there is a second sitting-area on the large landing. Most of the well-equipped bedrooms have *en suite* facilities. Killerton House and Garden is nearby and there are plenty of footpaths for walkers.

OWNERS: Mike and Joanne Sanders OPEN: all year exc Christmas ROOMS: 1 single, with private bathroom; 3 double, 2 with bath/shower, 1 with private bathroom; 2 twin, both with bath/shower; 1 family, with bath/shower; 1 room suitable for wheelchair-users; tea/coffee and TV in all bedrooms; lounge with TV TERMS: single £18–£28, single occupancy £24–£30, twin/double £42–£46, family room £50; children's reductions by arrangement; deposit: £10 per person CARDS: none DETAILS: children welcome; dogs welcome by arrangement; no smoking; car park; games room; garden

WHITBY North Yorkshire map 9

Grantley House NEW ENTRY

26 Hudson Street, Whitby YO21 3EP TEL: (01947) 600895

This Victorian terraced house is situated on Whitby's West Cliff, only a short walk from the beach and town centre. The modestly furnished bedrooms all have *en suite* showers, floral duvets, easy chairs and TVs. The bright and airy top-floor bedrooms, though quite a climb, prove popular with guests. The sitting-room has a Victorian fireplace, and is a good spot in which to relax and chat after a busy day. Home-cooked dinners are served by arrangement.

OWNERS: Carol and Kevin Cox OPEN: Feb to Nov ROOMS: 2 double, 1 twin, 3 family; all rooms with shower, tea/coffee and TV TERMS: single occupancy £30, twin/double £38, family room from £38; three-quarters reduction for children under 4, half-price for ages 5–14; dinner £8; deposit: £20 per room CARDS: none DETAILS: children welcome; no dogs; no smoking in dining-room

---

Grove Hotel

36 Bagdale, Whitby YO21 1QL TEL: (01947) 603551

This imposing red-brick hotel is set back from the main road, only a short walk from the centre of town and harbour. The pine staircase dates back to Victorian times, and the tastefully furnished bedrooms have easy chairs and TVs. Guests can relax and socialise in the comfortable lounge, or at the bar. Traditional breakfasts and five-course evening meals are served at separate tables in the licensed dining-room. A self-catering flat is also available.

OWNER: Mrs M. Jackson OPEN: all year exc Christmas ROOMS: 6 double, 5 with shower, 1 with wash-basin; 2 twin, 1 with shower, 1 with wash-basin; tea/coffee and TV in all bedrooms; lounge TERMS: twin/double £33–£39; children's reductions by arrangement; dinner £9.50; deposit sometimes required CARDS: MasterCard, Switch, Visa DETAILS: no children under 3; no dogs; no smoking in dining-room; car park; garden

Lansbury Guest House

29 Hudson Street, Whitby YO21 3EP TEL/FAX: (01947) 604821

This tastefully decorated Victorian guesthouse has a welcoming ambience, and is only 300 yards from the seafront. Most of the well-maintained bedrooms have *en suite* facilities, and there is a spacious family room on the top floor. Watercolours depicting local beauty spots are hung throughout the house. Visitors can relax in the comfortable TV lounge, complete with video, parlour games and an open fire. Evening meals are served Sunday to Friday only.

OWNERS: Tom and Anne Wheeler OPEN: all year exc Christmas ROOMS: 2 single, both with wash-basin; 4 double, all with shower; 1 twin, with shower; 1 family, with shower; tea/coffee and TV in all bedrooms; lounge with TV TERMS: single £18, single occupancy £30, twin/double £37, family room £43–£57; children under 5 free, half-price for ages 5–12; dinner £9.50; deposit: £10 per person CARDS: none DETAILS: children welcome; no dogs; no smoking in dining-room or lounge

WHITCHURCH Shropshire **map 5**

Dearnford Hall NEW ENTRY

Whitchurch SY13 3JJ TEL: (01948) 662319 FAX: (01948) 666670
on B5476, 1m S of Whitchurch

This imposing building dates from 1690, and stands in one acre of well-tended grounds. It is elegantly decorated and furnished with some interesting antiques. The two spacious *en suite* bedrooms overlook the gardens, and beds have floral duvets. Superb breakfasts are served in a separate dining-room, and a comfortable lounge, warmed by an open fire, is available to guests. Musical visitors are welcome to make use of the grand piano in the entrance hall. Adjacent to the house is the Bebbingtons' 15-acre trout fishery. All the restaurants and amenities of Whitchurch are within a short distance.

OWNERS: Charles and Jane Bebbington OPEN: all year exc Christmas ROOMS: 2 double, with bath/shower, tea/coffee and TV; lounge with TV TERMS: single occupancy £40, double £60–£70; deposit: £15 CARDS: none DETAILS: no children; no dogs; no smoking; car park; garden

WHITSTABLE Kent map 3

Windyridge

Wraik Hill, Whitstable CT5 3BY TEL: (01227) 263506 FAX: (01227) 771191

The house is built of a mixture of stone and bricks and has lovely views across the estuary to the Isle of Sheppey. It is up a quiet lane, off the A299, in peaceful countryside and stands in a large garden. The house has been furnished and decorated with imagination; the lounge is enormous, the dining-room has a wooden terrace around it with steps into the garden, and the bedrooms are well equipped. Evening meals are available by arrangement, but only for a minimum of four people. There are good sailing opportunities nearby.

OWNERS: Colin and Elizabeth Dyke OPEN: all year ROOMS: 3 single, 3 double, 1 four-poster, 2 family; all rooms with shower, tea/coffee and TV; lounge TERMS: single £25–£30, single occupancy £30–£50, double £45–£50, four-poster £50–£60, family room £50–£60; dinner £12 CARDS: Amex, Delta, Diners, MasterCard, Switch, Visa DETAILS: children welcome; dogs welcome; no smoking in dining-room; car park; garden

WIDECOMBE IN THE MOOR Devon map 1

Rutherford House NEW ENTRY

Widecombe in the Moor TQ13 7TB TEL: (01364) 621264
on B3387, 5m NW of Ashburton

Located on the edge of the Dartmoor village of Widecombe in the Moor, this former police house, built in 1933, is run with warmth and friendliness by Pauline and Ian Boyes. They previously worked for the Dartmoor National Park Authority and so are experts on the area and happy to help guests find places to visit, and to plan interesting walking routes. Accommodation is clean and comfortable, with three small bedrooms, and a cosy sitting-room provided with drinks-making facilities. Only breakfast is available, but the nearby pub serves food.

OWNERS: Pauline and Ian Boyes OPEN: all year exc Christmas ROOMS: 2 double, 1 twin; all rooms with wash-basin; lounge with TV TERMS: single occupancy £20–£23, twin/double £30–£34; deposit: £5 per person per night CARDS: none DETAILS: no children under 10; no dogs; no smoking; car park; garden

WIDEGATES Cornwall map 1

Coombe Farm

Widegates PL13 1QN TEL: (01503) 240223
on B3253, just S of village

Coombe Farm was originally part of a large estate, and the house was built in the 1920s in the style of an Indian hill-station bungalow. Many of the rooms contain interesting heirlooms and antiques. The house is just outside the village, surrounded by several acres of gardens, woodland and fields, with glimpses of the sea. Alexander and Sally Low are enthusiastic hosts, and are improving the property continually. The TV lounge has a log fire, and the dining-room extends into a glassed-in verandah overlooking the garden. Families are welcome here, and several of the *en suite* bedrooms are designed for three or more people. Of the nine bedrooms, five are on the ground floor, with three being suitable for wheelchair-users, and three rooms are in a separate cottage. Four-course dinners are available by arrangement. There is plenty to do at Coombe Farm, with a heated outdoor swimming-pool, croquet lawn, and a games room with snooker and table-tennis tables.

OWNERS: Alexander and Sally Low OPEN: March to end October ROOMS: 3 double, 3 twin, 3 family; all rooms with shower; 5 rooms suitable for wheelchair-users; tea/coffee and TV in all bedrooms; lounge with TV TERMS: twin/double £52–£72; reductions for children 12–16 sharing with parents; dinner £16; deposit: £20 per person CARDS: Amex, Delta, Diners, MasterCard, Switch, Visa DETAILS: no children under 12; no dogs; no smoking; car park; games room; garden; swimming-pool

WIGMORE Hereford & Worcester — map 5

Queen's House

Wigmore HR6 9UN TEL: (01568) 770451
on A4110, 7m NW of Leominster

Margaret and John Hook took over Queen's House, in the centre of the village of Wigmore, at the end of 1996, and have established a relaxed and informal atmosphere. The building, originally two cottages, dates from the late fifteenth century, and its age shows in the flagstone floors, oak beams, thick stone walls and inglenook fireplaces. Accommodation is simple, comprising three bedrooms sharing a bathroom, plus a lounge with TV. Guests can also use the garden. Breakfast only is served, and the house is no longer licensed, but there are several venues for evening meals within walking distance.

OWNERS: Margaret and John Hook OPEN: all year exc Christmas ROOMS: 2 double, 1 twin; all rooms with wash-basin and tea/coffee; lounge with TV TERMS: single occupancy £15, twin/double £30; children's reductions CARDS: none DETAILS: children welcome; no dogs; no smoking; car park; garden

WILLINGTON Cheshire — map 7

Roughlow Farm

Chapel Lane, Willington CW6 0PG TEL/FAX: (01829) 751199
leave A54 at Kelsall, head up Waste Lane then Chapel Lane to Willington Corner

This former farmhouse, built around 1800, is set in four and a half acres of land in beautiful countryside, with views over the Cheshire plains towards Shropshire and Wales. Improvements are ongoing, and bedrooms are frequently redecorated; all are spacious and luxurious, and the top-floor suite comprises double and twin bedrooms, a sitting-room and bathroom, and has its own private entrance. A galleried oak-beamed drawing-room has a brick-built log-burning fireplace, and guests also have use of an attractive garden, cobbled courtyard, and tennis court. Breakfast is cooked on the Aga, and there are plenty of eating-establishments close by for dinner. Chester is a short drive away.

OWNERS: Mr and Mrs Peter Sutcliffe OPEN: all year ROOMS: 3 double/twin; all rooms with bath/shower and tea/coffee; lounge with TV TERMS: single occupancy £30–£35, twin/double £50–£70; deposit: £10 per person CARDS: none DETAILS: no children under 6; no dogs; no smoking; car park; garden; tennis

WIMBORNE MINSTER Dorset map 2

Acacia House

2 Oakley Road, Wimborne Minster BH21 1QJ
TEL: (01202) 883958 FAX: (01202) 881943
from A31 just S of Wimborne, take A349 heading S towards Poole; after 100yds turn left then take second right

The Stimpsons welcome guests to their warm and inviting home with tea and home-made fruitcake. The solid red-brick house, dating from the 1930s, is just off the main road, a mile or so from the small town of Wimborne Minster. Bedrooms are pretty and comfortably furnished and have TVs. Guests are welcome to sit in the conservatory, and breakfast is served in the dining-room. A pub almost next door serves evening meals. The Stimpsons are more than happy to offer advice on what to see and do in the area. Kingston Lacy House, with its park and gardens, is nearby.

OWNER: Eveline Stimpson OPEN: all year exc Christmas ROOMS: 1 single, with wash-basin; 1 double, with shower; 1 twin, with private bathroom; 1 family, with shower; tea/coffee and TV in all bedrooms; lounge TERMS: single £18.50, single occupancy £21–£25, twin/double £38–£44, family room £40–£55; £5 reduction for children; deposit: £10 per night CARDS: Delta, MasterCard, Switch, Visa DETAILS: no children under 3; no dogs; no smoking; car park; garden

---

Ashton Lodge

10 Oakley Hill, Wimborne Minster BH21 1QH
TEL: (01202) 883423 FAX: (01202) 886180

Set back from the main road, this detached 1930s family home with bow windows stands on the edge of Wimborne; and a long hill leads to the town centre and the minster. There is an attractive rear garden and all four bedrooms are cheerfully decorated and have TVs. They are either *en suite* or have private bathrooms, except for the singles, which have wash-basins. Breakfast only is available, but a nearby pub serves food.

OWNER: Margaret Gregory OPEN: all year ROOMS: 2 single, both with wash-basin; 1 double, with bath/shower; 1 twin, with private bathroom; 1 family, with bath/shower;

tea/coffee and TV in all bedrooms; lounge with TV TERMS: single £20–£22, single occupancy £25, twin/double £40–£44, family room £44–£50; deposit required CARDS: Visa DETAILS: children welcome; no dogs; no smoking; car park; garden

WINCHCOMBE Gloucestershire map 5

Gower House

16 North Street, Winchcombe GL54 5LH TEL: (01242) 602616
just off B4632 Cheltenham to Broadway road

This extremely hospitable B&B is in the heart of Winchcombe village, and is well placed for exploring the Cotswolds. The seventeenth-century stone house is maintained to a high standard; there are three attractive bedrooms with wicker, pine and antique furniture, and a collection of copper and pewter mugs is on display in the dining-room. The large garden, tucked away at the back of the property, is a soothing place in which to relax. A ghost reputedly haunts the nearby Corner Cupboard Inn.

OWNERS: Mr and Mrs Simmonds OPEN: all year exc Christmas ROOMS: 1 double, with wash-basin; 2 twin, 1 with private bathroom, 1 with wash-basin; tea/coffee and TV in all bedrooms; lounge with TV TERMS: single occupancy £22–£34, twin/double £36–£42; reductions for children sharing with parents CARDS: none DETAILS: children welcome; no dogs; no smoking in dining-room or lounge; car park; garden

The Homestead

Footbridge, Broadway Road, Winchcombe GL54 5JG TEL: (01242) 602536
just off B4632 at edge of village

A warm welcome is extended at this friendly Cotswold-stone cottage, which dates from the mid-eighteenth century. One of the attractive, good-sized bedrooms has an *en suite* shower; the other two share a bathroom. With its exposed beams, inglenook fireplaces and bare stone walls the building retains an old-world flavour. Walkers will be happy to know that The Homestead is situated on the Cotswold Way. A selection of pubs and restaurants serving evening meals is available in the village, just a four-minute walk away across the footbridge.

OWNERS: Allan and Maureen Brooker OPEN: all year exc Christmas ROOMS: 2 double, 1 with shower; 1 twin; tea/coffee and TV in all bedrooms TERMS: single occupancy £25–£30, twin/double £40–£45; deposit: £10 per room CARDS: none DETAILS: children welcome; dogs welcome; no smoking; car park; garden

Breakfast at B&Bs tends to mean a cooked breakfast of bacon, eggs, toast and so on, although many establishments also offer a good choice of cereals, yoghurts, fruit and other options. If you have special dietary requirements, it is best to discuss these when you make a booking.

WINCHELSEA East Sussex map 3

Cleveland House

Winchelsea TN36 4EE TEL/FAX: (01797) 226256

Situated in the centre of this unspoilt small Cinque Port town, Cleveland House is a listed eighteenth-century building. It has an immaculately kept one-and-a-half-acre walled garden which includes a heated swimming-pool, open from mid-May to mid-September, and games room. The comfortable house is stylishly furnished and a peaceful place to stay. Breakfast is served in the dining-room. The double room has a sea view, and the *en suite* twin overlooks the rose garden. No one-night bookings are taken at weekends in high season.

OWNERS: Sarah and Jonathan Jempson OPEN: all year exc Christmas ROOMS: 1 double, with private bathroom; 1 twin, with shower; tea/coffee and TV in both bedrooms TERMS: single occupancy £35–£55, twin/double £55–£65 CARDS: MasterCard, Visa DETAILS: children welcome; small dogs welcome; no smoking; garden; swimming-pool

St Anthony's House NEW ENTRY

Castle Street, Winchelsea TN36 4EL TEL: (01797) 226255

St Anthony's is a very elegant small house, set in an attractive garden with a patio, in the centre of historic Winchelsea, facing the Armoury. Most of the house is eighteenth century but parts of it date back to the thirteenth, including an arch in the beamed dining-room. There is one guest bedroom, which has a double bed and *en suite* bathroom, and is furnished with comfortable chairs and TV. Breakfast only is served, but St Anthony's is within walking distance of the local pub, where lunch and dinner are available.

OWNER: Mrs A.E. Mansfield OPEN: all year exc Christmas ROOMS: 1 double, with bath and shower, tea/coffee and TV TERMS: double £45 CARDS: none DETAILS: no children; no dogs; no smoking; garden

WINCHESTER Hampshire map 2

Brymer House NEW ENTRY

29–30 St Faiths Road, St Cross, Winchester SO23 9QD
TEL: (01962) 867428 FAX: (01962) 868624

Brymer House is a Victorian double-fronted building in a lovely garden on a quiet road in the St Cross area, only a ten-minute walk to the centre of Winchester. The Warrens are delightful hosts who took over the business in 1996, and they live in one wing of the house, with the guest accommodation in the other. The two palatial *en suite* bedrooms are light and comfortably furnished; there is also a cosy sitting-room with open fire, TV and video, and a pleasant breakfast room where guests can choose from an extensive menu. An honesty bar is available for drinks. Permits are provided for on-street parking.

OWNERS: Guy and Fizzy Warren OPEN: all year exc Christmas ROOMS: 1 double, 1 twin; both rooms with bath/shower; tea/coffee and TV in both bedrooms; lounge with TV TERMS: single occupancy £30–£35, twin/double £45–£50; deposit: £10 per person CARDS: none DETAILS: no children under 6; no dogs; smoking in lounge only; garden

Dellbrook

Hubert Road, St Cross, Winchester SO23 9RG TEL/FAX: (01962) 865093
1m S of city centre

Dellbrook, an Edwardian building on the outskirts of historical Winchester, is an attractive and highly individual family home – also home to more than 30 doves – with a warm atmosphere. Christine Leonard is a friendly and enthusiastic host, and offers guests tea on arrival. This can be taken on the terrace while you enjoy the views over the garden towards the eleventh-century church and twelfth-century St Cross Hospital, both of which are well worth a visit. Beyond that lies the Hampshire countryside. Bedrooms are large, bright, and simply decorated and furnished. Dinner (by arrangement only, and not always available) is served in the annexe of the large kitchen. A pleasant walk through water meadows leads to the cathedral, only a mile away.

OWNERS: John and Christine Leonard OPEN: all year ROOMS: 1 twin; 2 family, both with bath/shower; tea/coffee and TV in all bedrooms; lounge with TV TERMS: single occupancy £29–£36, twin/double £40–£44, family room £56–£65; children under 3 free, reductions for ages 4–12; dinner £13; deposit: 20% CARDS: MasterCard, Visa DETAILS: children welcome; dogs by arrangement; smoking in bedrooms only; car park; garden

East View

16 Clifton Hill, Winchester SO22 5BL TEL/FAX: (01962) 862986

East View is a comfortable, beautifully maintained house with a welcoming atmosphere, and is about a ten-minute walk from the cathedral and city centre. The large Victorian semi-detached town house is reached up a steep flight of stairs from the street, and is in a fairly quiet position with views over the city to the surrounding hills. It has an attractive sitting-room with TV, and breakfast is served in the dining-room, or the conservatory overlooking the garden in summer. Two of the three well-equipped bedrooms are *en suite*, and one twin room has space for an extra bed.

OWNERS: John and Judy Parker OPEN: all year exc Christmas ROOMS: 1 double, with private bathroom; 2 twin, both with bath/shower; tea/coffee and TV in all bedrooms; lounge with TV TERMS: single occupancy £35, twin/double £45–£48; £10 per night for children sharing with parents; deposit: £10 or credit card details CARDS: MasterCard, Visa DETAILS: no children under 5; no dogs; no smoking; car park; garden

54 St Cross Road

54 St Cross Road, Winchester SO23 9PS TEL/FAX: (01962) 852073

Although St Cross Road is a busy main thoroughfare, only one of the bedrooms in this large, handsome Victorian house, faces the front, and this has double-glazing that almost totally eliminates traffic noise. The house is set in a small garden, and is comfortable, tastefully decorated and has a welcoming atmosphere and friendly owner. The three bedrooms share a bathroom; the single faces the garden and the twin is on the side of the house. The cathedral is a little over ten minutes' walk away.

OWNER: Mrs R.A. Blockley OPEN: all year exc Christmas ROOMS: 1 single; 1 double; 1 twin, with wash-basin; tea/coffee and TV in all bedrooms TERMS: single £20–£21, single occupancy £25–£30, twin/double £38–£40; children's reductions CARDS: none DETAILS: preferably no children under 3; no dogs; no smoking; car park; garden

---

Florum House Hotel

47 St Cross Road, Winchester SO23 9PS
TEL: (01962) 840427 FAX: (01962) 862287

Built in 1887, this small, neat Victorian brick house is just off a main road between the centre of Winchester and St Cross Hospital. The small bedrooms are *en suite* and have telephones, and a few are in the new extension. A pleasant sitting-room leads out to the patio, beyond which is the rear garden, where guests can sit on warmer days. Florum House has a small bar, and breakfast and simple, home-cooked evening meals (by arrangement only) are served in the small, pretty dining-room. The centre of town is easily accessible and there is a parking area in front of the house.

OWNERS: Frank and Joy Hollick OPEN: all year exc Christmas ROOMS: 2 single, 3 double, 3 twin, 1 family; all rooms with bath/shower, tea/coffee and TV lounge TERMS: single £42–£44, single occupancy £48–£49, twin/double £53–£59; family room from £60; dinner £13 CARDS: MasterCard, Visa DETAILS: children welcome; dogs welcome; smoking in lounge only; car park; garden

WINDERMERE Cumbria **map 8**

The Archway

13 College Road, Windermere LA23 1BU TEL: (01539) 445613

Aurea Greenhalgh's cooking often takes centre stage at this small, stone-built guest house. The characterful interior features a Welsh pine dresser full of pink china, and there are four cosy *en suite* bedrooms with TVs and telephones. The breakfast menu presents a good choice: grilled kippers, home-made American pancakes, and the full English fare, which involves spicy Cumberland sausage and free-range eggs. Just as tempting are the gourmet dinners, with dishes such as monkfish with lime and garlic, and frangipane tart with fresh apricots as possible options. Vegetarian choices are served by arrangement, and a wine list is also available. The Archway is situated on a quiet side street near the town centre. There is free on-street parking nearby, and the B&B has a limited number of private spaces.

OWNERS: Anthony and Aurea Greenhalgh OPEN: all year, exc 4 weeks in winter (phone to check) ROOMS: 2 double, 2 twin; all rooms with bath/shower, tea/coffee and TV; lounge TERMS: single occupancy £36–£44, twin/double £40–£54; dinner £12.50; deposit: £20 CARDS: Visa DETAILS: no children under 10; no dogs; no smoking; car park

Boston House

NEW ENTRY

The Terrace, Windermere LA23 1AJ TEL/FAX: (01539) 443654
off A591 on a private drive, just before main junction to Windermere

This stone-built Victorian house stands on the edge of town, overlooking the lake and fells. Sandra Garside enjoys spending time with her guests, and has created an informal and relaxed atmosphere. A pitch-pine staircase leads to the elegantly furnished bedrooms, two of which have four-poster beds; the double has a dark-oak half-tester. A sitting-room, complete with chaise longue and music cupboard, is available to guests. Home-cooked three-course dinners are served by prior arrangement. Sandra is happy to supply maps and other information on the many beautiful walks in the area. Note that one-night bookings are not accepted in high season.

OWNER: Sandra Garside OPEN: all year exc Christmas ROOMS: 1 double, 1 twin, 2 four-poster, 1 family; all rooms with shower, tea/coffee and TV; lounge with TV TERMS: single occupancy £25–£40, double/twin £42–£52, four-poster £42–£55, family room £50–£65; children's reductions by arrangement; dinner £11.50; deposit: 1 night's charge CARDS: MasterCard, Visa DETAILS: children welcome; no dogs; no smoking; car park

Kirkwood Guest House

Princes Road, Windermere LA23 2DD
TEL: (01539) 443907 FAX: (01539) 443904

Kirkwood Guest House stands in a stone-walled garden in a quiet residential area, between Windermere and Bowness. Carol and Neil are congenial hosts, who have tastefully furnished their house to a high standard. Four of the bedrooms have four-poster beds; one has a corner bath. Breakfast includes a buffet starter, followed by a filling cooked course.

OWNERS: Neil and Carol Cox OPEN: all year exc Christmas ROOMS: 1 double, 1 twin, 4 four-poster, 1 family; all rooms with bath/shower, tea/coffee and TV; lounge TERMS: single occupancy £30, twin/double £44, four-poster £48, famiiy room from £44; deposit: £20 per person CARDS: MasterCard, Switch, Visa DETAILS: children welcome; dogs by arrangement; no smoking; garden

'NEW ENTRY' indicates that a B&B was not in the previous edition (although its owners may have been, at a different address).

Villa Lodge

Cross Street, Windermere LA23 1AE TEL/FAX: (01539) 443318

Villa Lodge is a traditional nineteenth-century Lakeland house situated in a quiet cul-de-sac, only a few minutes' walk from the town centre. Owners John and Liz Christopherson are a friendly couple and have created a warm and relaxed atmosphere, with dried-flower arrangements and paintings depicting Beatrix Potter scenes. Bedrooms are decorated with attractive floral wallpapers; most have *en suite* shower-rooms, and two have four-poster beds. There is also a comfortable lounge and a sunny conservatory for guests to relax in, and in summer the Christophersons organise barbecues in the garden.

OWNERS: John and Liz Christopherson OPEN: all year exc Christmas ROOMS: 4 double, all with shower; 2 twin, both with private bathroom; 2 four-poster, both with shower; tea/coffee and TV in all bedrooms TERMS: single occupancy £25–£36, twin/double £38–£44, four-poster £40–£50, family room from £36; half-price for children sharing with parents CARDS: Delta, MasterCard, Visa DETAILS: children welcome; no dogs; no smoking in dining-room; car park; games room; garden

WINDSOR Berkshire **map 3**

Beaumont Lodge

NEW ENTRY

1 Beaumont Road, Windsor SL4 1HY TEL/FAX: (01753) 863436

This turn-of-the-century house is situated in a quiet residential area, just a few minutes' walk from the town centre and castle. Guest bedrooms are furnished in pine and decorated to a high standard. All are *en suite* and well equipped, having hair-dryer, trouser press, TV and video (there is also a small library of tapes). The main double bedroom has a spa bath, and can be converted into a family room. There is also a comfortable lounge and a garden with a patio for guests' use.

OWNER: Brenda Hamshere OPEN: all year ROOMS: 1 double, 2 twin, 1 family; all rooms with bath and shower, tea/coffee and TV; lounge with TV TERMS: single occupancy £45–£50, twin/double £52–£56, family room £65–£70; deposit required CARDS: none DETAILS: children welcome; no dogs; garden

Langton House

46 Alma Road, Windsor SL4 3HA TEL: (01753) 858299

Set in a quiet residential part of Windsor, is this attractive Victorian building. Its good-sized immaculately kept bedrooms are furnished in keeping with the character of the house. Recent developments include two more rooms with *en suite* showers; one double and the family room still share a bathroom. A good supply of tourist information is available, and Marjorie Fogg is very helpful when it comes to deciding which places to visit. Generous breakfasts are served at individual tables. There is a self-catering flat at the top of the house. The town centre and castle are within a five-minute walk.

OWNER: Marjorie Fogg OPEN: all year exc Christmas ROOMS: 2 double, 1 with shower, 1 with wash-basin; 1 twin, with shower; 1 family; TV in all bedrooms TERMS: twin/double/family room £40–£55; deposit: 10% CARDS: none DETAILS: children welcome; no dogs; no smoking

WINEHAM West Sussex — map 3

Frylands

Frylands Lane, Wineham BN5 9BP
TEL: (01403) 710214 FAX: (01403) 711449
from A23 follow A272 1½m W, then left into Wineham Lane and right at red telephone box

Frylands is a half-timbered Tudor farmhouse built around 1570 and has been the Fowler family's home almost continuously since 1622. The house is at the end of a quiet country lane, three miles north-east of Henfield, and has an acre of landscaped gardens, surrounded by 250 acres of farmland. Many original features have been retained, such as the leaded windows, oak beams, flagstone floors and thick stone walls. One of the three bedrooms has an *en suite* shower and the other two share a bathroom; all have TV. Mr Fowler is a swimming-pool consultant, and guests are welcome to use the pool (heated in summer). Mrs Fowler is very knowledgeable about the area and can help guests with information on places to visit. Coarse-fishing can be arranged, and there is a self-catering cottage for rental which sleeps five people.

OWNER: Sylvia Fowler OPEN: all year exc Christmas ROOMS: 1 double, with private bathroom; 1 twin, with wash-basin; 1 family, with wash-basin; tea/coffee and TV in all bedrooms TERMS: single occupancy £20, twin/double £38–£40, family room £47.50–£57; reductions for children sharing with parents CARDS: none DETAILS: children welcome; no dogs; car park; garden; swimming-pool

WINFRITH NEWBURGH Dorset — map 2

Manor House

High Street, Winfrith Newburgh DT2 8JR
TEL: (01305) 852988 FAX: (01305) 854988
¾m off A352, 3m S of Wool

The Manor House dates from the sixteenth century but has a Georgian appearance due to later renovation. It is on a quiet country road in the picturesque village of Winfrith Newburgh, next to the church. Charles and Jennie Smith are extremely friendly, welcoming people who enjoy working on the house and maintaining the large walled garden. Fresh flowers fill the rooms and excellent breakfasts are served. This is a wonderful area for walks and for visiting the beaches along the Dorset coast; Lulworth Cove and Corfe Castle are nearby. Note that one-night bookings are not taken.

OWNERS: Charles and Jennie Smith OPEN: all year exc Christmas ROOMS: 1 double, with bath; 1 twin, with private bathroom; tea/coffee and TV in both bedrooms TERMS: single occupancy £32–£34, twin/double £44–£48; deposit: £20 CARDS: none DETAILS: children welcome; no dogs; no smoking; garden

WINTERTON-ON-SEA Norfolk map 6

Tower Cottage

Black Street, Winterton-on-Sea NR29 4AP TEL: (01493) 394053

Standing opposite the thirteenth-century church in the unspoilt and peaceful village of Winterton, this 200-year-old brick and flint cottage has old beams, exposed walls, lots of charm and a friendly atmosphere. Two of the bedrooms are in the main house and share a bathroom, while the other is in a converted barn with its own entrance, sitting-room and shower-room. A superb breakfast is served in the dining-room or among the grapevines in the conservatory, which overlooks the sheltered garden with its wooden benches and picnic tables. Dinner is not available, but a pub in the village serves food, and Great Yarmouth, eight miles away, offers further options.

OWNERS: Alan and Muriel Webster OPEN: all year exc Christmas ROOMS: 2 double, 1 with shower, 1 with wash-basin; 1 twin, with wash-basin; tea/coffee and TV in all bedrooms TERMS: single occupancy £20–£25, twin/double £34–£38; children's reductions by arrangement CARDS: none DETAILS: no children under 8; dogs welcome in barn suite; smoking in barn suite only; car park; garden

WISSENDEN Kent map 3

Old Stables NEW ENTRY

Wissenden, nr Bethersden TN26 3EL TEL/FAX: (01233) 820597

take A28 to Bethersden, turn into village, then take Wissenden Lane (next to village school); take left fork after 1½m, house is fourth on right, opposite oasthouse

This former stable block, dating from the eighteenth century, was tastefully converted in the 1970s. It is set in a lovely big garden with a croquet lawn, in the heart of the Weald of Kent, not far from Ashford. Two of the comfortable bedrooms share a bathroom, and there is a double *en suite* room. Penny Gillespie is a charming host and prepares evening meals by arrangement, using home-grown vegetables, meat from a local butcher and free-range eggs. Dinner is served in the elegant dining-room, which has a piano, or, weather permitting, in the garden. The Old Stables is within easy reach of Sissinghurst, and Leeds and Bodiam castles.

OWNERS: John and Penny Gillespie OPEN: all year ROOMS: 2 double, 1 with bath, 1 with private bathroom; 1 twin, with private bathroom; tea/coffee and TV in all bedrooms; lounge TERMS: single occupancy £30–£40, twin/double £45–£55; dinner £15; deposit: minimum £20 per room CARDS: none DETAILS: children welcome; no dogs; no smoking in bedrooms; car park; garden

WITCHFORD Cambridgeshire **map 6**

Clare Farm House

86 Main Street, Witchford CB6 2HQ TEL: (01353) 664135
off A142, 2m W of Ely

This cheerful B&B is peacefully located in the centre of a small village, overlooking acres of farmland. Each of the comfortable bedrooms has a TV and its own sitting-area; the family room is particularly spacious. Rita Seymour keeps the house spick and span, and there is a bright and airy feel to the place. Guests can relax in the large garden. Clare Farm House is ideally situated for walks in the Wicken Fen Nature reserve; Ely and the Nene Valley Railway are nearby.

OWNERS: Peter and Rita Seymour OPEN: all year ROOMS: 1 single; 1 double, with bath/shower; 1 twin, with private bathroom; 1 family, with bath/shower; tea/coffee and TV in all bedrooms TERMS: single £16, single occupancy £16–£25, twin/double £32–£40, family room £40–£60; children's reductions according to age; deposit: £10 CARDS: none DETAILS: children welcome; no dogs; car park; garden

WIVELISCOMBE Somerset **map 2**

Alpine House

10 West Road, Wiveliscombe TA4 2TF TEL: (01984) 623526
on B3227 at W edge of town

Alpine House, a large detached Victorian building, can be found on the edge of the small town of Wiveliscombe. One of its features is the wonderful terraced garden, which has been lovingly landscaped and stocked with some unusual plants by Nevill and Indrani, both keen gardeners; Indrani is also an excellent photographer. Alpine House is very comfortable and well furnished, and most rooms still have their original Victorian fireplaces. Bedrooms have cane chairs specially made by a local craftsman. The dining-room overlooks the cricket and rugby ground, and there are views of the Brendon and Blackdown Hills – wonderful areas for walking – from the garden.

OWNERS: Nevill and Indrani Hewitt OPEN: all year ROOMS: 3 double, 2 with bath, 1 with shower; 1 twin, with private bathroom; tea/coffee and TV in all bedrooms; lounge with TV TERMS: single occupancy £30, twin/double £50; deposit: £10 per person per night CARDS: MasterCard, Visa DETAILS: no children; no dogs; no smoking; garden

The descriptive part of entries usually includes some facts about setting, the house itself, décor and furnishings, the atmosphere, any special features, and whether evening meals are offered. If the B&B has no car park, we give wherever possible some indication of where guests may find a place to park. If one-night bookings are not accepted at certain times of the week or year, that is mentioned.

WOKING Surrey map 3

Knap Hill Manor

Carthouse Lane, Woking GU21 4XT
TEL: (01276) 857962 FAX: (01276) 855503
1m S of Chobham, off road to Knaphill

This rambling late-eighteenth-century brick-built house has been added to over the years. It is in a very rural setting, in pleasant countryside, with six acres of garden. The comfortable, traditionally decorated *en suite* bedrooms have garden views. The large drawing-room has a wood-burning stove, and breakfast and dinner (by arrangement) are served in the pleasant family dining-room which also has the view. There is a terrace and garden with chairs for sitting out, and a croquet lawn, hard tennis court and lily pond with fountains.

OWNERS: Teresa and Kevin Leeper OPEN: all year exc Christmas ROOMS: 2 double, 1 twin; all rooms with bath/shower, tea/coffee and TV; lounge with TV TERMS: single occupancy £42.50, twin/double £65; children's reductions by arrangement; deposit: credit card details CARDS: MasterCard, Visa DETAILS: no children under 8; no dogs; smoking in limited areas only; car park; garden; tennis

WOLLASTON Northamptonshire map 5

Duckmire

1 Duck End, Wollaston NN29 7SH TEL/FAX: (01933) 664249
from Wellingborough take A509 to Wollaston, turn left at Cuckoo pub, left again by church, follow lane to no-entry sign, and then to last house on left

With its creaky floors, slab-stone entrance way and old fireplaces, this eighteenth-century house, built from local limestone, is full of character and charm. As there are only two bedrooms, a single and a twin, guests are assured of a high level of personal attention from Mrs Woodrow, who is also happy to help arrange touring itineraries. Both rooms are a good size and have private bathrooms. Breakfast and dinner are served at one large table in the dining-room; the house is not licensed, but guests may bring their own wine to dinner. They also have use of the acre of beautiful gardens.

OWNER: Mrs S.M. Woodrow OPEN: all year exc Christmas ROOMS: 1 single, 1 twin; both rooms with private bathroom and tea/coffee; TV in twin bedroom and lounge TERMS: single £18, single occupancy £20, twin £36; reductions for children sharing with parents; dinner £15; deposit sometimes required CARDS: none DETAILS: no children under 5; no dogs; no smoking; car park; garden; tennis

---

Many B&Bs are in remote places, and although in many cases we provide directions, it is always advisable to ask for clear instructions when booking.

WOODCHESTER Gloucestershire map 2

Southfield House

Woodchester GL5 5PA TEL: (01453) 873437 FAX: (01453) 872049
just off B4066, 2m S of Stroud

This family-run sixteenth-century Cotswold house is set in six acres of private gardens and paddocks. The Richardsons maintain a friendly and informal ambience, ensuring an enjoyable and comfortable stay for their guests. The single and the *en suite* twin bedrooms can be let out as a family suite; the other twin has a private bathroom. Southfield House is an ideal base for scenic walks and cycling; three nearby pubs serve evening meals. The races at Cheltenham, and several charming unspoilt villages, are within striking distance.

OWNERS: Mr and Mrs A. Richardson OPEN: all year exc Christmas ROOMS: 1 single; 2 twin, 1 with bath/shower, 1 with private bathroom; tea/coffee in all bedrooms; TV in 1 bedroom TERMS: single £25, single occupancy £30, twin £45; deposit: 10% CARDS: none DETAILS: no children; no dogs; smoking in dining-room only; car park; garden; swimming-pool

WOODMANCOTE West Sussex map 3

Eaton Thorne House

Woodmancote BN5 9BH TEL: (01273) 492591
on B2116, between Henfield and Albourne, W of A23

Standing in open countryside not far from Brighton, this attractive small house is a comfortable family home with a relaxed, informal atmosphere. It dates from around 1500 and has all the character one would expect in a building of this period, with low beamed ceilings and little nooks and crannies everywhere. Breakfast is served in the attractive dining-room, and a pub within walking distance serves evening meals. Transport from Gatwick Airport and local car hire can be arranged. The Langhornes are a friendly couple and great animal lovers. They keep 14 horses in a stable block in the grounds, and their daughter, a qualified riding instructor, is happy to give lessons to guests.

OWNER: Nan Langhorne OPEN: all year exc Christmas ROOMS: 1 double, 1 twin, 1 family; all rooms with wash-basin, tea/coffee and TV TERMS: single occupancy £20, twin/double £35, family room £50; children under 5 free; deposit required CARDS: none DETAILS: children welcome; no dogs; smoking in bedrooms only; car park; garden

---

Tithe Barn

Brighton Road, Woodmancote BN5 9ST TEL/FAX: (01273) 492986
on A481 between Henfield and Pyecombe

Christine Warren took over this old converted flint tithe barn in the village of Woodmancote in 1996. The main alteration work was done in the 1920s and the old character of the place has been well preserved. The bedrooms are comfortably furnished and some have splendid views across the garden to the South Downs. Breakfast is served in the conservatory or beamed dining-room, and guests are welcome to use the two-acre garden.

OWNER: Christine Warren OPEN: all year ROOMS: 1 single, 2 twin; all rooms with wash-basin and TV TERMS: single £18, twin £36; reductions for children CARDS: none DETAILS: children welcome; well-behaved dogs welcome; no smoking; car park; garden

WOODSTOCK Oxfordshire map 2

Holmwood

NEW ENTRY

6 High Street, Woodstock OX20 1TF
TEL: (01993) 812266 FAX: (01993) 813233

This listed Queen Anne house, built in 1710, is on the main street in the centre of Woodstock, in a conservation area. It had stood empty for a year when Roberto and Christina Gramellini bought the property with a view to restoring it to its original splendour. The original oak staircase, beams and panelling, casement shutters and fireplaces are now enhanced by a range of modern comforts. The two guest suites have their own sitting-rooms and large, well-equipped *en suite* bathrooms; one has a king-sized bed. The Gramellinis enjoy sharing their lovely home, and guests are assured of a warm welcome.

OWNERS: Roberto and Christina Gramellini OPEN: Feb to Dec ROOMS: 1 double, 1 double/twin; both rooms with bath/shower, tea/coffee and TV; lounge with TV TERMS: single occupancy £50–£60, double £65–£75; deposit: £30 CARDS: none DETAILS: no children under 12; no dogs; no smoking; garden

Pine Trees

44 Green Lane, Woodstock OX20 1JS TEL: (01993) 813300
leave A34 in Woodstock just S of river and turn into Lower Brook Hill; Green Lane is on right

A friendly, informal atmosphere reigns at this attractive house in a quiet residential area, just a few minutes' walk from the town centre. The spacious beamed lounge has a log fire burning in winter. A spiral staircase leads up to the bedrooms: two large *en suite* double rooms, which can be let to families, plus a twin bedroom with its own bathroom. Additional accommodation is offered in 'Wishing Well Cottage', just next to the main house, which sleeps four people and has its own bathroom, microwave oven and a small patio. The B&B is set in large gardens, complete with a thatched summer-house and ponds stocked with carp and goldfish. Blenheim Palace is very near by, and well worth a visit.

OWNER: Malcolm Snell OPEN: all year ROOMS: 2 double/family, both with shower; 1 twin, with private bathroom, 1 family, with bath/shower; lounge with TV TERMS: twin £46, double/family from £48, family room from £50; children's reductions according to age CARDS: none DETAILS: children welcome; no dogs; no smoking; car park; garden

WOOL Dorset map 2

East Burton House

East Burton, Wool, nr Wareham BH20 6HE
TEL: (01929) 463857 FAX: (01929) 463026
from Wareham take A352 to Wool and turn right just before level crossing, then ¾m on right

Originally a farmhouse, this part-seventeenth-century, part-Victorian village house is set in an acre of peaceful gardens. Sonia and Mike Francis are a friendly, but not intrusive, couple who take great pride in giving the best possible attention and service to their guests. The comfortable TV lounge is shared with the family, and the bedrooms, with antique brass beds, are attractively decorated. The only meal served is breakfast, but this is quite a feast, with home-made dishes and locally produced ingredients, such as Dorset smoked bacon and free-range eggs. Bicycles can be borrowed, and lovely beaches and the coastal footpath are within easy reach.

OWNERS: Sonia and Mike Francis OPEN: all year ROOMS: 2 double, both with wash-basin; 1 twin, with wash-basin; tea/coffee in most bedrooms; lounge with TV TERMS: single occupancy £25–£35, twin/double £40–£44, family room £48–£60; children's reductions by arrangement; deposit required CARDS: none DETAILS: children welcome; no dogs; no smoking; car park; garden

WOOTTON BRIDGE Isle of Wight map 2

Bridge House

Kite Hill, Wootton Bridge PO33 4LA TEL: (01983) 884163
on A3054 next to bridge

In summer at high tide the views from the pretty front garden of this handsome Georgian listed house are splendid. Although the house sits on the main road to Ryde, double-glazing keeps traffic noise down. Two of the fresh and bright bedrooms now have *en suite* facilities, and the third has its own bathroom, which has an old claw-foot bath and a Victorian blue and white porcelain WC. Breakfast is served at one table in the dining-room, and guests have use of a small sitting-area in the entrance hall. Just next to Bridge House is a public slipway for boats, and a couple of large pubs that serve food are an easy stroll away.

OWNER: Denise Blackman OPEN: all year exc Christmas ROOMS: 2 double, 1 with shower, 1 with private bathroom; 1 twin, with shower; tea/coffee and TV in all bedrooms; lounge TERMS: single occupancy £18–£36; twin/double £36; deposit: 1 night's charge CARDS: none DETAILS: no children under 14; no dogs; no smoking; car park

Oakenshore

New Road, Wootton Bridge PO33 4HY TEL: (01983) 884117
on A3054 next to bridge

Oakenshore stands in a garden in a pleasant location, overlooking a wide creek, about a quarter of a mile from Wootton High Street. The Duncans took over the B&B from the Minns in June 1997. The accommodation is very spacious and clean. Both bedrooms are on the ground floor and have *en suite* facilities; the twin is furnished as a bedroom/lounge and has views of the creek. Breakfast is served in the upstairs dining-room, which is in the owners' private area, and guests also have the use of a kitchen for making tea or coffee.

OWNERS: Valerie and Stewart Duncan OPEN: all year exc Christmas ROOMS: 1 double, 1 twin; both rooms with bath/shower, tea/coffee and TV TERMS: single occupancy £25–£27, twin/double £38–£42; deposit: 10% CARDS: none DETAILS: no children; no dogs; no smoking; car park; garden

WOOTTON FITZPAINE Dorset map 2

Rowan House

Wootton Fitzpaine, Charmouth DT6 6NE TEL/FAX: (01297) 560574
just off A35 Axminster to Bridport road

Rowan House lies in a peaceful location on the edge of the village and has beautiful country views. The attractive sitting-room has a built-on conservatory, which overlooks the garden and is where breakfast and evening meals are served. The bedrooms are small but prettily decorated and furnished; some have *en suite* facilities and the rest private bathrooms. The patio is a pleasant place to sit and contemplate the views, and there is a footpath running from the back of the garden through fields to the coastal village of Charmouth.

OWNER: Linda Dedman OPEN: all year ROOMS: 1 single, with private bathroom; 2 double, 1 with bath/shower, 1 with private bathroom; 2 twin, 1 with bath/shower, 1 with private bathroom; lounge with TV TERMS: single £20, single occupancy £24, twin/double £38–£39, family room £49; one-quarter reduction for children under 10 and half-price if sharing with parents; dinner £11; deposit: 20% CARDS: none DETAILS: children welcome; no dogs; no smoking; car park; garden

WORCESTER Hereford & Worcester map 5

Burgage House

4 College Precincts, Worcester WR1 2LG TEL/FAX: (01905) 25396

This handsome brick-built Georgian house is in a peaceful setting, with views over the cathedral grounds. Two of the bedrooms have *en suite* showers, and one has a Jacobean bed. The hearty breakfasts are served in the dining-room, and feature free-range eggs and home-made marmalade. There is a guest lounge and another sitting-area with an inglenook fireplace. Burgage House is within walking distance of the Royal Gloucester Porcelain factory, and is ideally placed for visiting the beautiful surrounding countryside.

OWNER: Janette Ratcliffe OPEN: all year exc Christmas ROOMS: 2 single, 1 with private bathroom, 1 with wash-basin; 1 double, with shower; 1 twin; 1 family, with shower; tea/coffee and TV in all bedrooms; lounge TERMS: single £28–£30, single occupancy £32–£34, twin/double £40–£48, family room from £48; half-price for children sharing with parents CARDS: none DETAILS: children welcome; no dogs; smoking in lounge only

40 Britannia Square

40 Britannia Square, Worcester WR1 3DN
TEL: (01905) 611920 FAX: (01905) 27152

This nineteenth-century detached house is set in a quiet part of Worcester, close to the city centre. The freshly furnished bedrooms come with an *en suite* bath or shower, and feature hand-stencilled décor and matching fabrics. The first-floor luxury double room has been recently refurbished, and has a king-sized bed. Breakfasts are served on a large table in the comfortable dining-room, which has an open fire. During the warm months guests can sit and enjoy the sunshine in the pleasant, well-maintained garden. A self-catering cottage for two people adjoins the house. Free on-street parking is available at all times.

OWNER: Val Lloyd OPEN: all year ROOMS: 1 double, 2 twin; all rooms with bath/shower, tea/coffee and TV; lounge TERMS: single occupancy £45–£50, twin/double £50–£60 CARDS: Amex, MasterCard, Visa DETAILS: children welcome; no dogs; no smoking; garden

WORMSHILL Kent **map 3**

Saywell Farm House

Bedmonton, Wormshill ME9 0EH TEL/FAX: (01622) 884444
off old B2163 Hollingbourne to Sittingbourne road, 3m N of Harrietsham

This attractive white-painted former farmhouse stands in secluded farmland at the end of a quiet lane on the North Downs. The oldest parts of the building date as far back as the thirteenth century, though most of it was added in the seventeenth century, and a beam over the fireplace in the dining-room is inscribed with the date 1611. The house has been cleverly updated, with many old features retained, including some wattle and daub walls. The comfortable bedrooms are attractively decorated, and two have *en suite* bathrooms, one of which is shared with the third room when that is let. Evening meals are available; the house is unlicensed, but guests may bring their own wine to dinner. Saywell may be difficult to find, so it is advisable to ask for directions.

OWNER: Yvonne Carter OPEN: all year exc Christmas ROOMS: 1 double, with bath/shower; 2 twin, 1 with bath/shower; tea/coffee and TV in all bedrooms; lounge TERMS:

single occupancy £30–£50, twin/double £50–£55; dinner £18.50; deposit: £20 per room per night CARDS: none DETAILS: no children under 12; no dogs; no smoking; car park; garden

WORTHING West Sussex map 3

Delmar Hotel

1–2 New Parade, Worthing BN11 2BQ
TEL: (01903) 211834 FAX: (01903) 219052

This well-situated, attractive seafront hotel has only a narrow quiet road and grass separating it from the beach. The Elms are a cheerful, welcoming couple, for whom nothing is too much trouble. The well-equipped bedrooms are very comfortable, with fridges, TVs, videos and hair-dryers, and some have balconies. There is a roof garden, where weekly barbecues are held, a bar and TV lounge. Mr and Mrs Elms now offer morning coffee, lunch and tea to non-residents. The Delmar is about half a mile east of the pier and next to the leisure centre.

OWNERS: Mr and Mrs N. Elms OPEN: all year ROOMS: 5 single, 2 double, 1 twin, 2 four-poster, 2 family; all rooms with bath/shower; 1 room suitable for wheelchair-users; tea/coffee and TV in all bedrooms; lounge with TV TERMS: single £32, single occupancy £40, twin/double £60, four-poster £70–£80, family room £60–£90; children under 3 free, half-price for ages 3–12; dinner £17.50; deposit: £25 per person CARDS: Amex, Delta, Diners, MasterCard, Switch, Visa DETAILS: children welcome; dogs welcome; no smoking in dining-room and bedrooms; car park; garden

WRABNESS Essex map 6

Dimbols Farm NEW ENTRY

Station Road, Wrabness CO11 2TH TEL/FAX: (01255) 880328
off A120 Colchester to Harwich road

This Georgian farmhouse stands in a well-tended garden, and is part of a 650-acre arable farm overlooking the River Stour. A warm and welcoming atmosphere has been created by Mrs Macaulay in her comfortable home, which is beautifully kept and traditionally furnished. A freshly prepared farm breakfast is served in the dining-room, which overlooks the river, and evening meals can be taken at a nearby pub. The two bedrooms share a bathroom, and there is an additional WC. A separate lounge has an abundance of books to suit all tastes, and there are many interesting items around the house including a Thai brass rubbing, and various paintings and pictures. Dimbols Farm is adjacent to the Essex Way.

OWNERS: Mr and Mrs Macaulay OPEN: all year exc Christmas ROOMS: 1 double, 1 family; tea/coffee and TV in both bedrooms; lounge with TV TERMS: single occupancy £21, double £30, family room £30–£55; children's reductions according to age CARDS: none DETAILS: children welcome; no dogs; no smoking upstairs; car park; garden

WROXHAM Norfolk **map 6**

Garden Cottage

96 Norwich Road, Wroxham NR12 8RY
TEL: (01603) 784376 FAX: (01603) 783734

Boaters passing through the Norfolk Broads town of Wroxham could do worse than stop over at this converted eighteenth-century barn and stable; in addition, boats can be hired for the day from a number of places nearby. The three bedrooms are furnished in pine and have *en suite* bathrooms; the ground-floor twin-bedded room is suitable for wheelchair-users. Guests are welcome to enjoy the gardens and patio, and the snug sitting-room. Both breakfast and dinner are served in the licensed dining-room, and in summer there are barbecues in the garden.

OWNERS: Tim and Maureen Hyde OPEN: all year exc Christmas ROOMS: 2 double, 2 twin; all rooms with bath/shower, tea/coffee and TV; 1 room suitable for wheelchair-users; lounge TERMS: single occupancy £30–£40, twin/double £45–£55; dinner £11; deposit: 1 night's charge or credit card details CARDS: Amex, Delta, MasterCard, Switch, Visa DETAILS: children welcome; dogs welcome with own bedding; smoking in lounge only; car park; garden

WYE Kent **map 3**

Wife of Bath NEW ENTRY

4 Upper Bridge Street, Wye TN25 5AW
TEL: (01233) 812540 FAX: (01233) 813630
just off A28, Ashford to Canterbury road

The Wife of Bath, primarily a restaurant-with-rooms, is a delightful timber-framed house dating from 1760, and stands in Wye's historic main street. Medieval pilgrims on their way to Canterbury would have passed nearby; now twentieth-century pilgrims flock here for the food. Dishes might include rack of lamb with ratatouille or local duckling with limes and redcurrants. The house has a welcoming atmosphere, and each of the individually furnished and beautifully appointed rooms is named after one of the pilgrims from Chaucer's *Canterbury Tales*. Two of these are in the converted stables, and share a small kitchen with everything needed for continental breakfast; alternatively, breakfast with cooked or continental options is available in the main house. Wye is a good base for visiting Canterbury, the many castles and gardens in the area, and is close to Dover and Folkestone.

OWNER: John Morgan OPEN: all year ROOMS: 2 double, both with bath/shower; 2 twin, 1 with bath/shower, 1 with private bathroom; 1 four-poster, with bath/shower; 1 family, with bath/shower; tea/coffee and TV in all bedrooms TERMS: single occupancy £40, twin/double £50–£55, four-poster £80, family room £60; dinner £23 CARDS: Delta, Diners, MasterCard, Switch, Visa DETAILS: children welcome; no dogs; smoking in 2 bedrooms only; car park; garden *(The Good Food Guide)*

YELVERTON Devon — map 1

Cider House

Buckland Abbey, nr Yelverton PL20 6EZ
TEL: (01822) 853285 FAX: (01822) 853626
off A386, 5m S of Tavistock; from Yelverton follow signs to Buckland Abbey, just before Abbey entrance at crossroads take Buckland turn, then first left signposted 'Abbey deliveries private'

An informal and friendly atmosphere prevails at this beautiful fourteenth-century stone house with mullioned windows. It started out as the refectory for Buckland Abbey and was a cider barn in Elizabethan times, and occupies a peaceful and tranquil setting, with lovely views, in 15 acres of landscaped gardens (open under the National Gardens Scheme). Mrs Stone is a first-class cook and wonderful host, who likes to ensure her guests are comfortable. The two large, well-appointed bedrooms share a bathroom, although as the *Guide* was going to press there were plans to install another bathroom. There is a breakfast room where generous breakfasts are served, and a separate dining-room where evening meals or lighter suppers are available by arrangement. Also in the grounds are a hard tennis court and two self-catering cottages.

OWNER: Mrs M.J. Stone OPEN: all year exc Christmas ROOMS: 1 double; 1 twin, with wash-basin; tea/coffee in both bedrooms; TV in 1 bedroom and lounge TERMS: single occupancy £30, twin/double £45–£50; half-price for children under 12; dinner £18; deposit required CARDS: none DETAILS: children welcome; dogs welcome; no smoking; car park; garden; tennis

YEOVIL Somerset — map 2

Sunnymede

26 Lower Wraxhill Road, Yeovil BA20 2JU TEL: (01935) 425786

Sunnymede is a 1920s house, standing in a large terraced garden, set in a quiet position in a side street on the edge of Yeovil, about 20 minutes' walk from the town centre. Margaret Lock is a very friendly lady who enjoys meeting her guests, and has decorated the house in keeping with its period. The twin and double bedrooms have *en suite* facilities and the single room has its own bathroom; the double can also be used as a family room. Breakfast is served in the dining-room/lounge, and guests are welcome to use the microwave in there and the fridge on the landing. Montacute House is nearby and T.S. Eliot is buried in East Coker church about a mile away.

OWNER: Margaret Lock OPEN: all year ROOMS: 1 single, with private bathroom; 1 double/family, with bath/shower; 1 twin, with bath/shower; tea/coffee and TV in all bedrooms; lounge with TV TERMS: single £16–£18, single occupancy £18–£20, twin/double £32–£34, family room £38–£42; children's reductions by arrangement; deposit: 25% CARDS: none DETAILS: children welcome; no dogs; no smoking; car park; garden

YETMINSTER Dorset

map 2

Manor Farmhouse

High Street, Yetminster DT9 6LF TEL/FAX: (01935) 872247
from Yeovil take A37 towards Dorchester, after 4m turn left, then after 2m house is on left

This seventeenth-century farmhouse is part of a mixed working farm, with the land and livestock set apart from the house, in the historic village of Yetminster, known for its attractive stone-built houses. Although the house retains many original features, it has been modernised to a high standard. The spacious bedrooms are comfortable, and guests have lots of books and guidebooks to browse through in the sitting-room. Evening meals can be pre-booked, and focus on traditional home-cooking, where good use is made of meat and vegetables produced on the farm. Ann Partridge is a very friendly lady and is a mine of information about local history and architecture.

OWNERS: Ann and Jack Partridge OPEN: all year ROOMS: 1 single, 1 double, 2 twin; all rooms with bath/shower; 1 room suitable for wheelchair-users; tea/coffee and TV in all bedrooms; lounge TERMS: single/single occupancy £30, twin/double £55; dinner £15; deposit: £25 CARDS: Delta, MasterCard, Switch, Visa DETAILS: no children; no dogs; no smoking; car park; garden

YORK North Yorkshire

map 9

Abbeyfields

19 Bootham Terrace, York YO3 7DH TEL/FAX: (01904) 636471

A stroll along the river or through the museum gardens takes you from this immaculately kept Victorian house to the attractions of the city centre. Almost all of the comfortable bedrooms are *en suite*; one single has a private bathroom. The particularly pleasant attic rooms have skylights and wonderful sloping ceilings. Tasty breakfasts are served in a separate dining-room, and the lounge with its marble fireplace is a good place in which to relax and socialise. One-night bookings are subject to availability, and are not accepted at Christmas.

OWNERS: Richard Martin and Gwen Derrett OPEN: all year ROOMS: 3 single, 5 double, 1 twin, all rooms with shower exc 1 single with private bathroom; tea/coffee and TV in all bedrooms; lounge TERMS: single £20–£28, single occupancy £28–£38, twin/double £40–£48; deposit: £20 CARDS: none DETAILS: no children under 12; no dogs; no smoking; car park

Burton Villa

NEW ENTRY

22 Haxby Road, York YO3 7JX TEL/FAX: (01904) 626364

This Victorian house is situated in a quiet residential part of town, just opposite Clarence Gardens. The place is kept spotlessly clean, and the bedrooms feature a mixture of pine furnishings, colourful burnt-orange duvets and dainty wallpapers; two have fireplaces. Tasty breakfasts are served at individual tables in the dining-room. Burton Villa is within walking distance of York Minster and the city centre.

OWNER: Mike Buss OPEN: all year exc Christmas ROOMS: 1 single, with wash-basin; 6 double, 4 with bath/shower, 2 with wash-basin; 2 twin, 1 with bath/shower, 1 with wash-basin; 3 family, all with bath/shower; tea/coffee and TV in all bedrooms TERMS: single £15–£21, single occupancy £15–£30, twin/double £35–£50; family room from £35; £5 for babies in cots, half-price for children sharing with parents; deposit: £20 CARDS: Delta, MasterCard, Visa DETAILS: children welcome; dogs welcome; smoking in bedrooms only; car park

---

Curzon Lodge & Stable Cottages

23 Tadcaster Road, Dringhouses, York YO2 2QG TEL: (01904) 703157

Built in the seventeenth century, this charming house lies in a quiet location, one mile from the city walls. Former residents include the Terrys, one of York's most renowned 'chocolate families'. Also on the property are Stable Cottages, a converted former coach-house and stables, which are well suited to residents who value their privacy. All the buildings have been beautifully restored, and some of the rooms feature exposed beams, quarry-tiled floors, antique pine furnishings and Victorian brass bedsteads. The ten bedrooms are all *en suite* with baths or showers, and have TVs. Guests are greeted in the elegant drawing-room with a complimentary glass of sherry. There is a lovely landscaped garden to relax in, and the property overlooks the racecourse. One-night bookings are not available on Friday or Saturday.

OWNERS: Richard and Wendy Wood OPEN: all year exc Christmas ROOMS: 1 single, 3 double, 3 twin, 2 four-poster, 1 family; all rooms with bath/shower, tea/coffee and TV; lounge TERMS: single £30–£42, single occupancy £40–£55, twin/double £49–£63, four-poster £55–£69, family room £60–£90; half-price for children sharing with parents; deposit: 1 night's charge or credit card details CARDS: Delta, MasterCard, Switch, Visa DETAILS: no children under 8; no dogs; no smoking; car park; garden

---

Dairy Guesthouse

3 Scarcroft Road, York YO2 1ND TEL: (01904) 639367

This elegant terraced house dates back to 1890, and stands in a central part of town, 200 yards from the city walls. Several original features, including stained-glass windows, pine doors and Victorian fireplaces, have been retained. The bedrooms have floral duvets, and have been modestly but attractively furnished in soft colours; the hot drinks selection includes herbal teas. Wholesome breakfasts are served, with vegetarians well catered for. The property is built around a peaceful courtyard adorned with ivy and flowers.

OWNER: Keith Jackman OPEN: all year exc Christmas and Jan ROOMS: 2 double, 1 with bath/shower, 1 with wash-basin; 1 twin, with wash-basin; 1 four-poster, with wash-basin; 1 family, with bath/shower; tea/coffee and TV in all bedrooms TERMS: single occupancy £26–£36, twin/double £34–£44, four-poster £38; children under 3 free, half-price for ages 3–14 if sharing with parents CARDS: none DETAILS: children welcome; dogs welcome; no smoking; car park

Holgate Bridge Hotel

NEW ENTRY

106 Holgate Road, York YO2 4BB
TEL: (01904) 647288 FAX: (01904) 670049

This early-Victorian terraced house, built in 1848, is just a short walk from Micklegate Bar, and within easy reach of the town centre. The pretty bedrooms vary in size, and are decorated with co-ordinated floral fabrics. All are well appointed, with direct-dial telephones and TVs, and most have *en suite* facilities or a private bathroom. The five family rooms can also be let as twin bedrooms. Breakfast and, by arrangement, dinner are served in the licensed dining-room, and there is a good selection of wines to choose from. Guests have the use of a conservatory lounge overlooking the garden, plus a separate bar lounge which has a TV. There is a private car park, and the bus into the town centre stops very close by.

OWNERS: Mr and Mrs F.H. Hind OPEN: all year exc Christmas ROOMS: 2 single, 1 with bath/shower, 1 with wash-basin; 2 double, 1 with bath/shower, 1 with wash-basin; 2 twin, 1 with private bathroom, 1 with wash-basin; 3 four-poster, all with bath/shower; 5 family, all with bath/shower; tea/coffee and TV in all bedrooms; lounge TERMS: single £22–£40, single occupancy £30–£40, twin/double £36–£58, four-poster £64–£70, family room £56–£70; children's reductions according to age; dinner £7; deposit required CARDS: Amex, Delta, MasterCard, Visa DETAILS: children welcome; no dogs in public areas; car park; garden

---

Holmwood House

114 Holgate Road, York YO2 4BB
TEL: (01904) 626183 FAX: (01904) 670899

Rosie Blanksby and Bill Pitts took charge of this nineteenth-century building in February 1996, and have enthusiastically taken to the job of maintaining and improving on the high standards established by their predecessors. Most of the elegantly furnished bedrooms have queen- or king-sized beds, and all have *en suite* facilities, telephones and TVs. Several rooms can be used as either twins or doubles; one of these has a luxury six-foot-ten bed and a spa bath. The house is licensed, and drinks are usually served in the spacious lounge or in the bedrooms; plans for an honesty bar were in progress as we were going to press. Holmwood is a beautifully restored listed building, originally built as two separate houses. Guests with babies or small children are advised to bring a travel cot. One-night bookings are not available during weekends, bank holidays, Christmas and Easter.

OWNERS: Rosie Blanksby and Bill Pitts OPEN: all year ROOMS: 5 double, 3 twin/double, 2 four-poster, 1 family; all rooms with bath/shower, tea/coffee and TV; lounge TERMS: single occupancy £45–£55, twin/double £55–£70, family room £60–£90; reductions for children sharing with parents; deposit: £25 CARDS: Amex, Delta, MasterCard, Switch, Visa DETAILS: children welcome; no dogs; no smoking; car park; garden

23 St Mary's

NEW ENTRY

23 St Mary's, Bootham, York YO3 7DD
TEL: (01904) 622738 FAX: (01904) 628802

This Victorian terrace house is beautifully maintained, and only five minutes' walk from the city centre. The well-appointed bedrooms have floral fabrics, and a mixture of hand-painted and antique furniture. All have *en suite* facilities, TVs and direct-dial telephones. At breakfast a sideboard is laid out with cereals, fruit, yoghurts and so on for guests to help themselves, after which cooked dishes are served. The elegant sitting-room is furnished with antiques and has a marble fireplace; there is also a small sitting-area upstairs which overlooks the garden. Guests are provided with a helpful information pack on arrival. Free on-street parking is available with a permit provided by Mrs Hudson.

OWNER: Greta Hudson OPEN: all year exc Christmas and New Year ROOMS: 2 single, 6 double, 1 twin; all rooms with bath/shower, tea/coffee and TV; lounge TERMS: single £28–£32, single occupancy £44–£54, twin/double £54–£64; deposit: £30 CARDS: none DETAILS: children welcome; no dogs; no smoking in bedrooms or dining-room; car park; garden

ZEALS Wiltshire — map 2

Stag Cottage

Fantley Lane, Zeals BA12 6NX TEL/FAX: (01747) 840458
just off A303, 5m NE of Wincanton

Stag Cottage is a pretty seventeenth-century thatched house, originally three separate cottages, and is full of character, with its beamed ceilings, inglenook fireplace, and cottage-style furnishings; bedrooms are very small and also charmingly decorated. There is a TV in the tea-room/sitting-room – afternoon cream tea with home-made scones and cakes is served here or, on fine summer afternoons, on the lawn opposite the house. The cottage is on the main road through the village, which is a lot quieter since the bypass was built. The Boxalls are happy to arrange to pick up guests from Gillingham station. Stourhead Gardens, a short walk away, is worth a visit.

OWNERS: Marie and Peter Boxall OPEN: all year ROOMS: 2 double, 1 with bath/shower, 1 with private bathroom; 1 twin, with bath/shower; tea/coffee and TV in all bedrooms TERMS: single occupancy £18–£22, twin/double £30–£40; £1.50 for babies in cots, half-price for children under 12; deposit: £5 per person CARDS: none DETAILS: children welcome; no smoking; car park; garden

---

Please do not rely on an out-of-date Guide. Although some B&Bs in the current edition have steadfastly retained their high standards and have featured in every edition since the first, a great many others have faded from the scene. In addition, many new, superb B&Bs have been added. Relying on an old Guide will limit your choices and may lead to disappointment.

ZENNOR Cornwall **map 1**

Tregeraint House

Zennor TR26 3DB TEL/FAX: (01736) 797061
¼m SW of Zennor on B3306

Tregeraint House stands above the road on the outskirts of Zennor in a remote, wild location with sea views across the fields. It is a simply constructed granite farmhouse with many original features, and has a pretty back and side garden. Inside, the atmosphere is one of warmth and cosiness, with guests sharing the dining-room, which has a large stone fireplace, with the owners. Besides looking after their B&B business, the Wilsons also run a publishing business from the house. The simply furnished bedrooms have wash-basins built into old washstands, and share a shower-room and WC. St Ives is just six miles away, and Land's End fifteen.

OWNERS: Sue and John Wilson OPEN: all year exc Christmas ROOMS: 2 double, 1 twin, 1 family; all rooms with wash-basin and tea/coffee TERMS: single occupancy £19, twin/double/family room £34 plus children's charge; half-price for children 7–14; deposit: £5 CARDS: none DETAILS: no children under 7; no dogs; no smoking; car park; garden

Scotland

STRUAN HALL, ABOYNE

ABERDEEN Aberdeen **map 11**

Aberdeen Springdale Guest House

404 Great Western Road, Aberdeen AB1 6NR
TEL: (01224) 316561 FAX: (01224) 210773

This Victorian terraced guesthouse is located on one of the main roads into Aberdeen among many houses offering accommodation. It has warm, comfortable and spacious rooms, some with ornate ceilings. The two family bedrooms have *en suite* facilities, and there is a shared bathroom on the first floor and a shower-room on the ground floor. The guests' lounge has a TV, and breakfast is served in the dining-room. All bedrooms have cable TV.

OWNERS: Mr and Mrs Stirling OPEN: all year exc Christmas ROOMS: 1 single, 2 double, 1 twin, all with wash-basin; 2 family, both with bath/shower; tea/coffee and TV in all bedrooms; lounge with TV TERMS: single £21, single occupancy £25–£34, twin/double £34–£36, family room £44–£60; children's reductions according to age CARDS: none DETAILS: children welcome; no smoking in dining-room; car park

Ewood House

NEW ENTRY

12 Kings Gate, Aberdeen AB15 4EJ TEL/FAX: (01224) 648408

Ewood House is an exceptionally friendly and comfortable establishment in a pleasant residential area of Aberdeen, conveniently located for the centre. The Hawkeys are a cheerful, down-to-earth English couple, who opened the bed and breakfast in 1993. It is a large stone-built house with spacious rooms. There is a grand piano in the lounge, and the attractive dining-room has tartan tablecloths. Breakfast is served at separate tables, and comprises cooked options plus a large buffet of cereals, fruits and yoghurts. The bedrooms are beautifully appointed, with fresh flowers, fruit and a lavish hospitality tray. Breakfast timing is flexible, and a good selection of newspapers is provided.

OWNER: Sheila Hawkey OPEN: all year ROOMS: 4 double, 1 twin, 1 four-poster; all rooms with bath and shower, tea/coffee and TV; 1 room suitable for wheelchair-users; lounge with TV TERMS: single occupancy £42–£46, twin/double £60–£66, four-poster £60–£66; deposit required CARDS: MasterCard, Visa DETAILS: children welcome; guide dogs only; no smoking; car park; garden

ABERDOUR Fife **map 11**

Hawkcraig House

Hawkcraig Point, Aberdour KY3 0TZ TEL: (01383) 860335

To reach Hawkcraig Point from the village, one must go through an enormous car park and down an extremely steep, rough track. The journey is worth it: standing at the foot of cliffs, this whitewashed house overlooks the myriad jetties on the banks of the Firth of Forth and, across the water, the skyline of Edinburgh. The two simple bedrooms both have *en suite* facilities; the twin has the better views.

Afternoon tea and after-dinner coffee are available in the conservatory and an upstairs lounge, which also enjoy the stunning outlook. Guests may also relax in a cosy ground-floor sitting-room with an open fire and TV. Dinner, served in a small, elegant dining-room, is based on fresh, local ingredients; for dessert, try Mrs Barrie's much-praised clootie dumpling. A 15-minute walk along a shoreline footpath leads to Aberdour Station, from where Edinburgh is a half-hour ride away.

OWNER: Elma Barrie OPEN: Apr to Oct ROOMS: 1 double, with shower; 1 twin, with bath; TV in both bedrooms and lounge TERMS: single occupancy £32–£34, twin/double £48–£50; reductions for children sharing with parents; dinner £21 CARDS: none DETAILS: no children under 10; guide dogs only; no smoking; car park; garden

ABERLEMNO Angus **map 11**

Wood of Auldbar

Aberlemno DD9 6SZ TEL: (01307) 830218
from Brechin take A90 south for 1½m to B9134 (signposted to Aberlemno); follow B9134 for ¼m, turn left on to Pitkennedy Road and continue for 3m

Wood of Auldbar is a working family farm covering 187 acres. The Victorian stone-built farmhouse is set in a small front garden next to an orchard and offers simple and clean accommodation in a warm and welcoming atmosphere. There is a comfortable sitting-room with a TV, and a sun-room where breakfast and dinner are served. There is no licence but guests may bring their own wine to dinner. Packed lunches can also be provided. The Angus Glens, Royal Deeside, Balmoral and Glamis Castle are all within easy reach.

OWNER: Jean Stewart OPEN: all year ROOMS: 1 single, 1 twin, 1 family; tea/coffee in all bedrooms; lounge with TV TERMS: single £17, single occupancy £18, twin £30, family room £56; dinner £10, children's helpings CARDS: none DETAILS: children welcome; dogs welcome; no smoking; car park; garden

ABINGTON South Lanarkshire **map 11**

Craighead Farm

Crawfordjohn Road, Abington ML12 6SQ TEL: (01864) 502356
leave M74 at junction 13 and follow signs for Crawfordjohn

The stone-built, whitewashed farmhouse in the heart of the Southern Uplands dates from the fourteenth century and has lovely views of the nearby river. It is on a 600-acre mixed farm, set in peaceful, rolling countryside, and offers simple accommodation with two comfortable bedrooms. Breakfasts and evening meals (by prior arrangement) are served in the dining-room at one large table. Fishing can also be arranged. Despite its seemingly remote location, Craighead Farm is only one and a half miles off the main Glasgow to Carlisle road.

OWNER: Mary Hodge OPEN: May to Oct ROOMS: 1 double, 1 twin; both rooms with private bathroom and tea/coffee; lounge with TV TERMS: single occupancy £16–£17, twin/double £32–£34; children under 5 free, reductions for ages 5–12; dinner £10 (less for children); deposit: £5 CARDS: none DETAILS: children welcome; no dogs; car park; garden

ABOYNE Aberdeenshire **map 11**

Hazlehurst Lodge

Ballater Road, Aboyne AB34 5HY
TEL: (01339) 886921 FAX: (01339) 886660
on A93, 10m E of Ballater

Hazlehurst is a small, old rose-granite house built in 1880 as the coachman's lodge to Aboyne Castle, and was at one time home of Robert Milne, photographer to Queen Victoria. It stands in an attractive wooded garden close to the centre of town. The house is furnished and decorated in a variety of mostly contemporary styles, with lighting designed by a Belgian architect and furniture made by students at the Mackintosh School of Architecture in Glasgow. Anne Strachan prides herself on the preparation of carefully selected meals featuring the best of Scottish ingredients. There is an immaculate small dining-room at the front of the house and another at the back next to the kitchen; Hazlehurst is licensed. Guests have the use of two comfortable sitting-rooms, and are welcome to visit the gallery/studio in the garden where exhibitions are staged from time to time. Three bedrooms are in the main house, and there is a two-room family suite above the gallery. Salmon fishing on the River Dee and other sporting activities can be arranged.

OWNER: Anne Strachan OPEN: all year ROOMS: 3 double, 2 with bath/shower, 1 with shower; 1 family, with bath/shower; tea/coffee in all bedrooms; TV in family room; lounge with TV TERMS: single occupancy £35–£80, twin/double £60–£80, family room £75–£90; half-price for children; dinner £27; deposit: credit card details CARDS: Amex, Diners, MasterCard, Visa DETAILS: children welcome; no dogs; no smoking; car park; garden

Struan Hall

Ballater Road, Aboyne AB34 5HY TEL/FAX: (01339) 887241
at junction of A93 and B9094, ½m W of Aboyne

This spacious granite-built house stands in two acres of grounds just off the main road and half a mile from the village centre. It was originally built about five miles east of Aboyne, where it was known as Tillydrine House, and in 1904 was moved stone by stone to its present site. The Inghams are warm and welcoming hosts, and their care and attention shows in the renovation of the house, which they took over in 1990, having previously owned a hotel elsewhere in Scotland. The rooms are spacious, light and tastefully decorated, and an attractive tartan-style carpet has been laid throughout the hallways and stairs. Aboyne is close to Balmoral Castle, as well as a number of National Trust properties.

OWNERS: Phyllis and Michael Ingham OPEN: Mar to Oct ROOMS: 1 double, 2 twin; all rooms with shower and tea/coffee; lounge with TV TERMS: single occupancy £30, twin/double £48; deposit: £20 per person CARDS: MasterCard, Visa DETAILS: no children under 7; no dogs; no smoking; car park; garden

ACHARACLE Highland — map 11

Ardshealach Lodge — NEW ENTRY

Acharacle, Ardnamurchan PH36 4JL TEL: (01967) 431301
on A861, 2m N of Salen

This whitewashed Victorian lodge is set in a lovely position overlooking Loch Shiel – its grounds extend right down to the water – in the small village of Acharacle. The Smiths are a very welcoming couple, and have furnished the house comfortably and tastefully; all three bedrooms have *en suite* showers and TV, and guests can relax in the lounge with its open fire. Families can be given adjoining rooms with a private bathroom. Dinners are served in a separate dining-room, and might include dishes such as salmon steaks with a cream and chive sauce, or casserole of venison, and then sticky toffee pudding or fresh strawberry meringues to follow. Acharacle is an ideal base for hill-walkers; ironing and drying facilities are available at the B&B.

OWNER: Norma Smith OPEN: Apr to Oct ROOMS: 2 double, 1 twin; all rooms with shower, tea/coffee and TV; lounge with TV TERMS: single occupancy £24–£28; twin/double £40–£48; children under 5 free, half-price for ages 5–12 CARDS: none DETAILS: children welcome; dogs welcome; no smoking; car park; garden

ACHMORE Western Isles — map 11

Cleascro Guest House — NEW ENTRY

Achmore, Isle of Lewis HS2 9DU TEL/FAX: (01851) 860302
on A858, 8m W of Stornoway

This comfortable, modern house is in a quiet rural position enjoying southerly views over the Harris and Uig hills. It has a comfortable, warm atmosphere and well-equipped *en suite* bedrooms. Guests have use of a comfortable TV lounge and library, as well as the dining-room, where breakfast and good Scottish evening meals, using mainly home-grown vegetables and local produce, are served. Cleascro is in a very central position, well placed for exploring both Lewis and Harris, and not far from the Callanish Standing Stones.

OWNER: Donna Murray OPEN: all year exc Christmas ROOMS: 1 double, 2 twin; all rooms with shower, tea/coffee and TV; lounge with TV TERMS: single occupancy £36–£40, twin/double £46; half-price for children under 12; dinner £17 CARDS: none DETAILS: children welcome; dogs welcome with own bedding; no smoking in dining-room; car park; garden

AIRDRIE North Lanarkshire map 11

Easter Glentore Farm NEW ENTRY

Slamannan Road, Greengairs, Airdrie ML6 7TJ TEL/FAX: (01236) 830243
on B803, midway between Greengairs and Slamannan

Easter Glentore Farm is a 245-acre stock-rearing farm set in unspoilt countryside enjoying views of the Trossach hills, and is well placed for both Glasgow and Edinburgh and many tourist attractions. Built in 1705, the house has been extensively modernised and offers comfortable, simple accommodation. The three double bedrooms, one of which has an *en suite* shower-room, are all on the ground floor, and are supplied with tea- and coffee-making facilities and home-made shortbread, and home-baking is offered in the lounge in the evening. A wide range of choice is offered for breakfast, including haggis.

OWNERS: Alastair and Elsie Hunter OPEN: all year exc Christmas ROOMS: 3 double, 1 with shower, 2 with wash-basin; tea/coffee in all bedrooms; lounge with TV TERMS: single occupancy £22–£27, twin/double £36–£44; children's reductions according to age; deposit: £10 CARDS: MasterCard, Visa DETAILS: children welcome; no dogs; no smoking; car park; garden

ANCRUM Borders map 11

Ancrum Craig Guest House

Ancrum TD8 6UN TEL: (01835) 830280 FAX: (01835) 830259
turn W off A68 3½m N of Jedburgh, on to B6400 to Ancrum; take first fork left (signposted Denholm), drive 1¾m, turn right (signposted Lillesleaf), drive uphill ¾m, turn left

Sitting in its own extensive grounds at the end of a long driveway, this handsome Victorian country house has grand views of the hills. It is about two miles from the small village of Ancrum, where the owners also run a shop and the post office. Evening meals by prior arrangement are served in the elegant dining-room, and guests also have use of a drawing-room, a games room with table tennis and darts, and the garden. The house has many of its original features, and is spacious and comfortable. All three bedrooms are *en suite*; two are in the front of the house overlooking the hills.

OWNER: Jill Hensens OPEN: all year exc Christmas ROOMS: 2 double, 1 twin; all rooms with bath/shower, tea/coffee and TV; lounge TERMS: single occupancy £29–£36, twin/double £38–£48; dinner £10 CARDS: none DETAILS: children welcome; dogs welcome; no smoking in public rooms; car park; garden

---

Breakfast at B&Bs tends to mean a cooked breakfast of bacon, eggs, toast and so on, although many establishments also offer a good choice of cereals, yoghurts, fruit and other options. If you have special dietary requirements, it is best to discuss these when you make a booking.

ANSTRUTHER Fife — map 11

The Hermitage

NEW ENTRY

Ladywalk, Anstruther KY10 3EX
TEL: (01333) 310909 FAX: (01333) 311505

The Hermitage is an interesting old house set in a beautiful walled garden in the pretty little fishing village of Anstruther. The oldest part of the building, which used to be various farm outbuildings, dates from the sixteenth century, and the adjoining three-storey house was built in 1817 by the local doctor. The present owners have created extremely comfortable and well-thought-out spacious accommodation for guests. Two suites each comprise two twin/double bedrooms, a bathroom and a large, well-equipped lounge. These were designed to be let for parties of four, but rooms can be let to individuals or couples. The bedrooms are all south-facing and have lovely views; from the second-floor rooms the harbour and coastline is visible, while the first-floor rooms have garden views and a glimpse of the sea. The dining-room has pretty, separate tables, and there is a small sitting-room with plenty of tourist books and brochures. The harbour, Fisheries Museum and shops are all within three minutes' walk of the house.

OWNERS: Margaret McDonald and Eric Hammond OPEN: Easter to Oct ROOMS: 3 double, all with wash-basin; 1 twin, with wash-basin; tea/coffee in all bedrooms; lounge with TV TERMS: single occupancy £25–£35, twin/double £40–£50; children's reductions; deposit: 10% CARDS: Amex, MasterCard, Visa DETAILS: children welcome; no dogs; no smoking; car park; garden

ARBROATH Angus — map 11

Farmhouse Kitchen

Grange of Conon, Arbroath DD11 3SD
TEL: (01241) 860202 FAX: (01241) 860424
from Arbroath take A933 for 1m, turn left at Redford sign, after 2m take private signposted drive

Set in a garden in its own undulating farmland, Farmhouse Kitchen is a roomy, comfortable family home, with many amenities for guests. They include satellite TV and refrigerators in bedrooms, all of which are either *en suite* or have a private bathroom. Two bedrooms are on the first floor, and the third, ground-floor room – which is suitable for the disabled – has been refurbished since the last edition of the *Guide*. There is also a games room with a full-sized snooker table, and a sun lounge overlooking the garden. Full-monty Scottish breakfasts are served in the large kitchen. This mixed arable farm, reached by a long private roadway, extends to over 560 acres, and from the house are lovely views to the hills and a glimpse of the sea.

OWNER: Sandra Caldwell OPEN: all year exc Christmas ROOMS: 1 double, with shower; 2 twin, 1 with shower, 1 with private bathroom; tea/coffee and TV in all bedrooms; 1 room suitable for wheelchair-users TERMS: single occupancy £42.50; twin/double £70–£85; deposit: 20% CARDS: none DETAILS: children welcome; guide dogs only; no smoking in bedrooms; car park; games room; garden

ARDINDREAN Highland map 11

Taigh Na Mara

The Shore, Ardindrean, Loch Broom IV23 2SE
TEL: (01854) 655282 FAX: (01854) 655292
off A835, 8m S of Ullapool

Classy vegetarian food is a main draw of this small whitewashed house, approached by foot down a 200-yard steep and sometimes muddy slope from the road. It lies on the west shore of Loch Broom, and was once the village store. It is now a charming guesthouse, with one wing offering a long, comfortable sitting/dining-room with a wood-burning stove and – up a spiral staircase – two tiny bedrooms and bathroom with skylights and views over the loch. The third bedroom, the 'honeymoon suite', is in the old boat shed and has *en suite* facilities. There is a utility room with drying facilities. Jackie and Tony serve enormous breakfasts and, for dinner (which is included in the room price), offer dishes such as onions stuffed with vegetarian haggis; pancakes with oyster mushrooms, leeks and pine-nuts; an enormous selection of vegetarian and vegan cheeses; plus much more. Boats, kayaks and bikes can be arranged for guests.

OWNERS: Tony Weston and Jackie Redding OPEN: all year ROOMS: 2 double, 1 with bath, 1 with wash-basin; 1 twin; tea/coffee in 2 bedrooms; lounge TERMS: D,B&B twin/double £70–£80; reductions for children by arrangement; deposit: 25%, or £25 minimum CARDS: Delta, MasterCard, Switch, Visa DETAILS: children welcome; dogs welcome in 1 bedroom only; no smoking; garden

ARDNADAM Argyll & Bute map 11

Lochside

Fir Brae, Ardnadam, Sandbank PA23 8QD TEL: (01369) 706327
on A815 between Dunoon and Sandbank village

This whitewashed, immaculately kept Edwardian villa, about two miles from Dunoon, enjoys wonderful views over Holy Loch to the wooded slopes of Strone and Blairmore. The fresh, bright bedrooms are decorated with floral wallpapers. Breakfast is served in the pretty dining-room at one table in the window. Packed lunches can also be provided. The Younger Botanical Gardens are nearby.

OWNER: Rosemary Brooks OPEN: Mar to Oct ROOMS: 1 double, with shower; 1 twin, with private bathroom; tea/coffee and TV in both bedrooms TERMS: single occupancy £18–£20, twin/double £30–£40; half-price for children under 10 sharing with parents; deposit: £10 CARDS: none DETAILS: children welcome; no dogs; no smoking in dining-room; car park; garden

ARINAGOUR Argyll & Bute map 11

Garden House NEW ENTRY

Arinagour, Isle of Coll PA78 6TB TEL/FAX: (01879) 230374
at western end of island, 5m from Arinagour

Garden House is in one of the remotest parts of the island, surrounded by the RSPB reserve. The small, 24-acre farm has hens, ducks, geese, sheep, goats and dogs, and an old walled garden built around 1750 for the nearby New Castle. Mrs Graham, who works for the ferry company, knows almost everything there is to know about Coll; if in doubt she has a small reference library in the cosy sitting-room. On Thursday evenings she takes guests on a guided walk to watch otters and other wildlife. Two bedrooms are available for guests, and both breakfast and evening meals (by arrangement) are served in the owner's dining-room. Garden House is an extremely informal place, and suited to those who enjoy country living. Two Breachacha castles are within a short walking distance.

OWNER: Mrs P. Graham OPEN: all year ROOMS: 1 double, 1 twin; tea/coffee in both bedrooms TERMS: single occupancy £20, twin/double £34; 20% reduction for children under 12; dinner £11; deposit: £20 per person CARDS: none DETAILS: no children under 5; no dogs; smoking in lounge only; car park; garden

Taigh Solas NEW ENTRY

Arinagour, Isle of Coll PA78 6SY TEL: (01879) 230333
on main road from ferry port, opposite Arinagour post office

Roy and Elaine Barrie built this small house in 1995, in the village of Arinagour, a mile from the ferry terminal. Guests without cars can arrange to be picked up from the ferry, and can take advantage of the Barries' bicycle rental business. The house is comfortable and well equipped, and the two bedrooms share a bathroom (with both bath and shower); the double room can be adapted to accommodate families. Lunch and dinner are available by arrangement, as are packed lunches. Most visitors to Coll come for walking and the wildlife. Seals, otters and many varieties of seabird can be seen all around the shoreline, and the southern end of the island is an RSPB reserve.

OWNERS: Elaine and Roy Barrie OPEN: all year ROOMS: 1 double, 1 twin; tea/coffee in both bedrooms; lounge with TV TERMS: single occupancy £20, twin/double £34; children's reductions according to age; dinner £9; deposit: £10 CARDS: none DETAILS: children welcome; no dogs; no smoking; car park; garden

Any smoking restrictions that we know of are given in the details at the end of the entry.

Many B&Bs are in remote places, and although in many cases we provide directions, it is always advisable to ask for clear instructions when booking.

ARISAIG Highland

map 11

Old Library Lodge

Arisaig PH39 4NH TEL: (01687) 450651 FAX: (01687) 450219

'Excellent, delightful, pretty, good firm beds, delicious food' is how one reader summed up her stay at this restaurant-with-rooms located in the middle of the small village of Arisaig. It is a converted stone stable with panoramic views over Loch Nan Ceall to the islands of the Inner Hebrides – although coaches in summer may sometimes obscure the outlook. There are two sea-facing bedrooms in the main house, and a further four in an extension at the back. The older rooms may have more character, but the newer ones have the benefit of small, private patios overlooking the pretty garden. Lunches and imaginative dinners are served daily in the licensed restaurant, and dishes might include scallop and artichoke soup, grilled duck breast in honey and soy, and crème brûlée. Ferries link Arisaig with the Isles of Rhum, Eigg, Muck and Skye. Parking is available in the public car park across the street.

OWNERS: Alan and Angela Broadhurst OPEN: Easter to end Oct ROOMS: 5 double, 1 twin, 4 rooms with bath, 2 with shower; tea/coffee and TV in all bedrooms; lounge TERMS: single occupancy £42–£45, twin/double £68; children's reductions; dinner £22.50; deposit: £20 CARDS: Amex, Delta, MasterCard, Switch, Visa DETAILS: children welcome; no dogs; garden

ASCOG Argyll & Bute

map 11

Ascog Farm

Ascog, nr Rothesay, Isle of Bute PA20 9LL TEL: (01700) 503372

Ascog Farm lies in pretty countryside just south of Rothesay. The attractive, old whitewashed main building forms one side of a courtyard, and the sea can be glimpsed from the upper floor. The Watsons keep some of their 159 acres aside for sheep, ducks, peacocks and hens, and guests are free to explore the land. There is also a small, pretty walled garden. Irene Watson is friendly and energetic, and a mine of information on the island's attractions. Guests may even be invited to join her exercise class in Rothesay. Most bedrooms have their own sitting-room – the one on the top floor is particularly large – and the house has been stylishly furnished and decorated. Breakfast may include home-produced eggs and tomatoes in season.

OWNER: Irene Watson OPEN: all year exc Christmas ROOMS: 3 single, 1 double; tea/coffee in all bedrooms; TV in some bedrooms; lounge with TV TERMS: single/single occupancy £15, double £30; children under 5 free, half-price for ages 6–15; deposit: £10 CARDS: none DETAILS: children welcome; smoking in lounge only; car park; garden

---

If any bedrooms are suitable for wheelchair-users, we mention this in the details at the end of the entry.

AUCHTERMUCHTY Fife map 11

Ardchoille Farm

Dunshalt, Auchtermuchty KY14 7EY TEL/FAX: (01337) 828414
from Auchtermuchty take B936 S to Dunshalt, then over bridge, first right

This neat white and stone house is located on the edge of the tiny village of Dunshalt, 20 miles from St Andrews. It was built when Donald and Isobel Steven got married in 1956. Donald has now retired from the farm, which has been in his family since the early part of the century, and helps Isobel with the guesthouse. The three small and comfortable, south-facing bedrooms have views to the Lomond Hills. There are all kinds of extras in the rooms, as well as a supply of Isobel's home-made shortbread. She loves cooking and makes good use of home-grown vegetables and seasonal supplies; the four-course evening meals (which must be pre-booked) are one of the highlights of a stay here. Guests enjoy the friendly atmosphere and getting to know each other at meal times, when they are seated together at one table in the dining-room. Ardchoille is unlicensed, but visitors may bring their own wine.

OWNERS: Donald and Isobel Steven OPEN: all year exc Christmas and New Year ROOMS: 3 twin, 2 with shower, 1 with private bathroom; TV in all bedrooms and lounge TERMS: twin £50–£70; dinner £20; deposit: £20 CARDS: Amex, Delta, MasterCard, Visa DETAILS: no children under 12; guide dogs only; no smoking; car park; garden

AYR South Ayrshire map 11

The Crescent

NEW ENTRY

26 Bellevue Crescent, Ayr KA7 2DR
TEL: (01292) 287329 FAX: (01292) 286779

Set in a pleasant, quiet residential street within a few minutes walk of the main shopping area of Ayr and the beach, the Crescent is a small, luxury guesthouse. It was built in 1898, one of many attractive terraced houses in the street, with an immaculately kept small front garden. One of the bedrooms has a four-poster bed, and another is on the ground floor with French doors opening on to the garden. The small dining-room, furnished in pine, where visitors eat at individual tables, is full of trinkets, dried flowers and an impressive amount of matching china. The Crescent is close to Robert Burns's cottage and Heritage Centre, and Culzean Castle, one of Scotland's biggest tourist attractions, is about a half-hour's drive down the coast.

OWNERS: Iain and Caroline Macdonald OPEN: 5 Jan to mid-Nov ROOMS: 1 double, 2 twin, 1 four-poster; all rooms with bath/shower; lounge TERMS: single occupancy £25–£30, twin/double £40–£46, four-poster £48–£52; reductions for children sharing with parents; deposit: £20 CARDS: MasterCard, Visa DETAILS: no children under 5; no dogs; no smoking; car park

Windsor Hotel

6 Alloway Place, Ayr KA7 2AA TEL: (01292) 264689

Set on a busy but pleasant residential street, this Victorian end-of-terrace hotel is just a few minutes' walk from the main shopping street, and only a two-minute walk from the sea. Sea views can be enjoyed from the back bedrooms and the first-floor lounge. The hotel offers simple accommodation, with three bedrooms on the ground floor. The dining-room has a splendid old ceiling and original fireplace, and the big, solid chairs come from an old passenger liner. Breakfast and dinner (with vegetarian options and children's portions on request) are served here; there is no licence, but guests may bring their own wine. Packed lunches can also be provided. Golfers are especially welcome, as are parties coming for the race meetings.

OWNERS: Mike and Anne Hamilton OPEN: all year exc Christmas ROOMS: 2 single, both with wash-basin; 3 double, 2 with bath/shower, 1 with private bathroom; 1 twin, with bath/shower; 4 family, all with bath/shower; 1 room suitable for wheelchair-users; lounge with TV TERMS: single £20, single occupancy £25, twin/double £44, family room £50; dinner £10; deposit: 10% CARDS: MasterCard, Visa DETAILS: children welcome; dogs welcome; no smoking in dining-room

BALEPHETRISH Argyll & Bute map 11

Sandy Cove NEW ENTRY

26 Balephetrish, Isle of Tiree PA77 6LY TEL: (01879) 220334

This simple whitewashed house, just 50 yards from a lovely beach, is a wonderful place for the friendliness and hospitality of the Campbells, and the warm welcome extended to visitors even applies to their black labrador, Monty. Guests have their own little wing of the house with a bathroom and a small twin-bedded room, and are invited to share the owners' lounge. There are magnificent views to the Outer Hebrides and the small isles.

OWNERS: Bill and Pat Campbell OPEN: all year exc Christmas ROOMS: 1 twin, with private bathroom, tea/coffee and TV; lounge with TV TERMS: single occupancy £15–£17, twin/double £30–£34; deposit: £10 CARDS: none DETAILS: children welcome; no dogs; no smoking; car park; garden

BALLACHULISH Highland map 11

Home Farm

Ballachulish PA39 4JX TEL: (01855) 811792
on A82, on S shore of Loch Leven

At the end of a long driveway off the main road close to the Ballachulish Bridge, this modern farmhouse (it was built in the early 1990s) has fine views over fields to Loch Leven and to the Ben Vair mountain range. Mrs McLauchlan writes that guests are welcome to walk anywhere on the farm, and local pony trekking, fishing, walking and climbing attract the visitors. The three *en suite* rooms are exceptionally spacious and very comfortably furnished. There is a large, television-free lounge for guests, and a dining-room where breakfast is served.

OWNERS: Joan and Ronnie McLauchlan OPEN: Mar to Oct ROOMS: 2 double, 1 twin, all with shower, tea/coffee and TV; lounge TERMS: single occupancy £30–£35, twin/double £45–£50; deposit: 20% CARDS: none DETAILS: no children; no dogs; no smoking; car park; garden

Lyn-Leven Guest House

West Laroch, Ballachulish PA39 4JP
TEL: (01855) 811392 FAX: (01855) 811600

This large, modern, well-cared-for bungalow is on the main road facing Loch Leven, just outside the village. There is a large guests' lounge and a spacious, semi-circular-shaped dining-room with impressive views over the loch. The B&B is licensed and vegetarians are catered for. All eight bedrooms have *en suite* showers, three of them also have a bath, and two are suitable for families. Hill-walking, skiing and fishing are available nearby at Glencoe, site of the massacre of 1692.

OWNERS: John and Priscilla Macleod OPEN: all year exc Christmas ROOMS: 4 double, 2 twin, 2 family; all rooms with bath/shower, tea/coffee and TV; lounge with TV TERMS: single/single occupancy £26, twin/double £40–£44, family room £55–£60; reductions for children under 12; dinner £9; deposit: £20 per person CARDS: MasterCard, Visa DETAILS: children welcome; dogs welcome in bedrooms only; car park; garden

BALLYGRANT Argyll & Bute **map 11**

Kilmeny Farmhouse

Ballygrant, Isle of Islay PA45 7QW TEL/FAX: (01496) 840668
just off A846, 4m W of Port Askaig

This whitewashed farmhouse stands a little way up the hillside, overlooking an ancient graveyard, and is not far from Finlaggan, seat of the Lords of the Islands for almost 400 years. Kilmeny is a working 300-acre beef farm, and the Rozgas work in co-operation with Scottish Natural Heritage to ensure geese are not disturbed while feeding on their land. Many visitors return for the comfort, friendly ambience and Margaret Rozga's superb, imaginative cooking, which makes good use of local produce. Dinner is included in the price, and is served in the charming dining-room around a large old Irish dining-table; the house is unlicensed but guests may bring their own wine. Bedrooms are spacious and beautifully furnished, and each has its own colour scheme. The pink and yellow rooms, both on the ground floor, have access to the small garden through French windows, while the apricot room on the first floor enjoys uninterrupted views of the countryside; all have *en suite* bathrooms, and are well equipped with ironing and shoe-cleaning facilities.

OWNERS: Margaret and Blair Rozga OPEN: all year exc Christmas ROOMS: 2 double, 1 twin; all rooms with bath and shower and tea/coffee; lounge with TV TERMS: D,B&B twin/double £104; deposit: £10 per person CARDS: none DETAILS: children welcome; dogs welcome by arrangement only; no smoking; car park; garden

BALQUHIDDER Stirling **map 11**

Calea Sona

Balquhidder FK19 8NY TEL/FAX: (01877) 384260
off A84, 4m SW of Lochearnhead

Rod Blain built Calea Sona using stones from the ruins of an old homestead. It is an attractive house standing in its own grounds in the tranquil village and has fine views over the valley to the hills beyond. The interior is simply furnished, clean and comfortable. Guests have breakfast at a table by the front window of the Blains' barn-shaped sitting-room with its high ceiling. The double room, with private bathroom, is on the ground floor, and upstairs is the twin-bedded room with *en suite* shower, as well as a large sitting-area for guests. Rod and Lesley extend a warm welcome to visitors.

OWNERS: Rod and Lesley Blain OPEN: all year exc Christmas ROOMS: 1 double, with private bathroom; 1 twin, with shower; lounge with TV TERMS: single occupancy £26, twin/double £42; children's reductions by arrangement CARDS: none DETAILS: no babies; no dogs; guests requested not to smoke in bedrooms; car park; garden

Monachyle Mhor

Balquhidder FK19 8PQ TEL: (01877) 384622 FAX: (01877) 384305
off A84 at Kingshouse, continue for 6m; Monachyle Mhor is 4m W of Balquhidder

This charming small farmhouse hotel on a 2,000-acre estate is reached down a rough single-track road which snakes along the banks of Loch Voil. Antique furniture and old sporting prints and pictures decorate the walls. A bar and a comfortable lounge are available for guests, and good, imaginative Scottish food is served to residents and non-residents either in the intimate dining-room with its single old refectory-style table, or in the adjoining, long, narrow conservatory which has excellent loch views. There are five bedrooms in the main building, and across the courtyard in the old stable block is a mixture of *en suite* bedrooms, including a large room with its own sitting-area, often used as a honeymoon suite, and attractive self-catering flats. The Lewis family provide salmon and trout fishing, stalking and shooting. Rob Roy's grave is nearby.

OWNERS: Jean, Rob and Tom Lewis OPEN: all year exc 2 weeks end Jan ROOMS: 8 double, 2 twin, all rooms with bath/shower and tea/coffee; TV in most bedrooms and lounge TERMS: single occupancy £42.50–£50, twin/double £65–£80; dinner £25, children's helpings; deposit: £20 CARDS: Delta, MasterCard, Switch, Visa DETAILS: no children under 10; no dogs; no smoking in bedrooms or dining-room; car park; garden *(The Good Food Guide)*

BANCHORY Aberdeenshire map 11

The Old West Manse NEW ENTRY

71 Station Road, Banchory AB31 5UD TEL/FAX: (01330) 822202

This attractive and beautifully maintained building was a manse until the early 1980s. It stands above the main road on the eastern end of Banchory in mature gardens, and has views across the Dee Valley. The Taylors are warm, informal people, and guests immediately feel at home here. The bedrooms are in what used to be the servants quarters at garden level, and are comfortably and unfussily furnished to a high standard. The main part of the house, above, is where an elegant sitting-room overlooking the valley is available for guests, and there is a pretty dining-room with individual tables, with white linen and lace tablecloths and napkins. Dinner is available by arrangement. The Manse is a 'fisher friendly' house, providing freezer, drying-room and secure rod storage facilities.

OWNERS: John and Jayne Taylor OPEN: all year ROOMS: 1 double, with shower; 2 twin, 1 with bath/shower, 1 with private bathroom; tea/coffee and TV in all bedrooms; lounge TERMS: single occupancy £32, twin/double £48; £5 for children sharing with parents; dinner £16; deposit: £20 per room CARDS: Delta, MasterCard, Visa DETAILS: children welcome; no dogs in dining-room; no smoking in bedrooms and dining-room; car park; garden

BANFF Aberdeenshire map 11

Eden House

by Banff AB45 3NT TEL: (01261) 821282 FAX: (01261) 821283
off A947 Turiff to Banff road, take turning 3m S of Banff, signposted Scatterty and Dunlugas, then ½m to Eden House

Eden House is approached up a long wooded driveway and stands in a spectacular position with views over the Deveron Valley. The oldest part of the Grade II-listed house dates from 1725, while the classical façade with porticoed entrance was added in 1825. It is a spacious house, with well-proportioned rooms, tastefully decorated and elegantly furnished, offering comfort in a warm, friendly, relaxed atmosphere. There is a large drawing-room, hung with hand-painted nineteenth-century wallpaper, as well as a smaller, cosier sitting-room, a billiard room and a basement games room. The Sharps often dine with their guests in the elegant dining-room, and can arrange fishing on some of the best beats of the River Deveron, as well as shooting for pheasant, duck and grouse on nearby estates. Eden House is unlicensed but guests may bring their own wine to dinner. There is also a self-catering lodge for up to six people in the grounds.

OWNERS: Antony and Di Sharp OPEN: all year exc Christmas ROOMS: 1 single, with private bathroom; 2 double, 1 with bath/shower, 1 with private bathroom; 3 twin, 2 with bath/shower, 1 with private bathroom; tea/coffee in all bedrooms; lounge with TV TERMS: single £34–£36, single occupancy £36, twin/double £68–£72; dinner £20; deposit: £10 per night CARDS: none DETAILS: no children under 12; no dogs in bedrooms; smoking in 1 room only; car park; games room; garden; tennis

BLAIR ATHOLL Perthshire & Kinross **map 11**

Woodlands

St Andrews Crescent, Blair Atholl, nr Pitlochry PH18 5SX
TEL: (01796) 481403

This little house in its own garden is in a peaceful spot on the edge of Blair Atholl and has views of the hills. Dolina Maclennan has made her mark in the charming and imaginative decoration and furnishing. Her time is split between the bed-and-breakfast business and an acting career, mostly in Gaelic-language television, and Woodlands closes when she has filming commitments. She is also a keen cook, and guests can be assured of excellent Highland hospitality. Vegetarians and children are catered for, and although the B&B is unlicensed, guests may bring their own wine to dinner.

OWNER: Dolina Maclennan OPEN: variable depending on owner's commitments ROOMS: 2 double, 1 with shower, 1 with wash-basin; 1 twin with wash-basin; lounge with TV TERMS: single occupancy £25, twin/double £40; dinner £17.50; deposit required CARDS: none DETAILS: children welcome; dogs welcome; smoking in lounge only; car park; garden

BOAT OF GARTEN Highland **map 11**

Heathbank

Boat of Garten PH24 3BD TEL: (01479) 831234

Heathbank dates from the turn of the century and is subtitled 'The Victorian House' – appropriately, since the Burges have refurbished it with care and with attention to period detail. Imagination and flair have gone into the decorating of the seven bedrooms. Two of the rooms have four-poster beds. The top floor is let out as a suite, and there is one room on the ground floor. Graham Burge trained as a chef, and he and Lindsay previously ran a traditional Scottish restaurant in Inverness. They serve breakfast and dinner in the conservatory-style licensed dining-room, which is inspired by Charles Rennie Mackintosh. From the house there are views to the golf course and the Abernethy Forest RSPB Reserve, and beyond to the Cairngorms.

OWNERS: Lindsay and Graham Burge OPEN: Mar to Oct and New Year ROOMS: 3 double, 2 twin, 2 four-poster; all rooms with bath/shower and tea/coffee; 2 lounges, 1 with TV TERMS: single occupancy from £30, twin/double £50–£70, four-poster £64–£80; half-price for children sharing with parents; dinner £20–£27; deposit: £25 per person CARDS: none DETAILS: no children under 10; guide dogs only; no smoking; car park; garden

Old Ferryman's House

Boat of Garten PH24 3BY TEL/FAX: (01479) 831370

The Old Ferryman's House, just across the river from the village, is a simple stone-built house surrounded by a small garden, which has tables and chairs for use in fine weather. Visitors enjoy the informal, relaxed atmosphere and good home-cooked meals, served at one table in the dining-room, which is shared with the owner's office. The bedrooms are simply but attractively decorated and furnished, and have single beds which can be zipped together. There is one bathroom and one WC, and no TV. The cosy sitting-room has a wood-burning stove, lots of books and cane furniture, made specially to order in India. The house is close to an RSPB reserve, and there are river walks to Nethy Bridge. Most guests come to bird-watch, fish, canoe, walk, or take part in some other outdoor activity. Additionally, there are mountain bikes for hire.

OWNER: Elizabeth Matthews OPEN: all year ROOMS: 2 single, 1 double, 1 twin; tea/coffee in all bedrooms TERMS: single/single occupancy £18, twin/double £36; reductions for children; dinner £12.50; deposit: 1 night's charge CARDS: none DETAILS: children welcome; dogs welcome by arrangement; no smoking; car park; garden

BREASCLETE Western Isles **map 11**

Eshcol Guest House

Breasclete, Isle of Lewis HS2 9ED TEL/FAX: (01851) 621357
off A858, 16m W of Stornoway

Set in a quiet position in this small weaving village, this long, white, neat-looking house has good views over Loch Roag to the island of Great Bernera, with the hills of Harris and Uig visible in the distance. It offers three comfortable bedrooms with either private or *en suite* facilities, both a tastefully decorated guest lounge and a sun lounge (the only room where smoking is allowed), a play area for children and a separate dining-room where Scottish breakfasts (try Neil's porridge) and home-cooked evening meals are served. Dinner often features fresh produce from the MacArthurs' own vegetable garden. The house is unlicensed, but guests may bring their own wine, and packed lunches are also available. The Stones of Callanish are a brisk walk away.

OWNERS: Isobel and Neil MacArthur OPEN: Mar to Oct ROOMS: 1 double, with private bathroom; 2 twin, one with bath, 1 with shower; tea/coffee and TV in all bedrooms; lounge TERMS: single occupancy £23, twin/double £46; half-price for children from 5–12; deposit: £20 per person CARDS: none DETAILS: no children under 5; small dogs welcome with own bedding; smoking allowed in 1 area only; car park; garden

BRECHIN Angus **map 11**

Doniford NEW ENTRY

26 Airlie Street, Brechin DD9 6JX TEL: (01356) 622361

The Stewarts used to own Blibberhill Farmhouse just outside Brechin, and after selling the farm in late 1995 they moved to this spacious Victorian house, where they continue to provide a hospitable welcome to visitors. Doniford is a substantial stone building standing in a large secluded garden in a quiet residential area a few minutes' walk from the centre of town. The two bedrooms are large and comfortable, and both have *en suite* facilities and TV. Guests can relax in the roomy lounge, and breakfast is served at one table in an eating-area just off the kitchen. From this area are doors out to a large patio and the back garden. Brechin is a good base for touring the Angus glens and coast.

OWNER: Margaret Stewart OPEN: all year exc Christmas ROOMS: 1 double, 1 twin; both rooms with bath/shower, tea/coffee and TV; lounge TERMS: single occupancy £25, twin/double £37–£39; dinner from £10; deposit required CARDS: none DETAILS: no children; no dogs; no smoking; car park; garden

BROADFORD Highland — map 11

Corry Lodge

NEW ENTRY

Liveras, Broadford, Isle of Skye IV49 9AA
TEL: (01471) 822235 FAX: (01471) 822318

Corry Lodge is a delightful, mostly eighteenth-century house at the end of a quiet lane leading from Broadford. Originally a much larger estate, it now comprises about 45 acres of pasture, mature woodland and a walled garden, and is bordered on two sides by the sea. When the Wilckens bought the property in the early '90s it was in a decrepit state, but the result of their renovation is superb. The house has been decorated with flair and elegance and the spacious rooms are furnished largely with antiques. The drawing-room houses a grand piano, and the cosy sitting-room at the back of the house has plenty of books. Guests sit at one table in the elegant dining-room, where excellent home-cooked dinners are served. The house has a warm, relaxed air, and Jane Wilcken is a cheerful and gracious host. Broadford is located towards the southern end of Skye, and is well placed for walking, hill-climbing and fishing.

OWNERS: Jane and Anthony Wilcken OPEN: Mar to Oct ROOMS: 2 double, 1 twin, 1 four-poster; all rooms with bath/shower, tea/coffee and TV; lounge TERMS: single occupancy £45–£50, twin/double £50–£60, four-poster £50–£60; children's reductions exc in June and Aug; dinner £17.50; deposit required CARDS: MasterCard, Visa DETAILS: children welcome; no dogs in bedrooms; no smoking in bedrooms and 1 lounge; car park; garden

BRODICK North Ayrshire — map 11

Glencloy Farmhouse

Glencloy, Brodick, Isle of Arran KA27 8DA TEL: (01770) 302351
just N of Brodick, 1½m from Brodick Pier

Set in a pretty, peaceful glen down a narrow track on the outskirts of Brodick, Glencloy is a 100-year-old sandstone farmhouse. Vicki Padfield is an expert at making dolls' houses and doing embroidery, and sometimes holds embroidery courses at the house. The spacious rooms have been interestingly and attractively decorated, and have views of rolling hills and the sea. Mark is an enthusiastic chef, and meals, served in the elegant dining-room, feature home-grown vegetables, free-range eggs, locally produced fish and meat, and home-baked bread. Card and board games can be played in the large, comfortable lounge, with its good selection of local guides and an open fire. Brodick Castle and Gardens are nearby, and Arran has plenty to offer for walkers, golfers and wildlife-watchers.

OWNERS: Mark and Vicki Padfield OPEN: Mar to mid-Nov ROOMS: 1 single, with wash-basin; 2 double, 1 with shower, 1 with wash-basin; 2 twin, 1 with shower, 1 with wash-basin; tea/coffee and TV in all bedrooms; lounge TERMS: single £21–£25, single occupancy £30–£50, twin/double £42–£50; reductions for children under 11; dinner £14.50; deposit: £20 per person CARDS: Delta, MasterCard, Visa DETAILS: children welcome; small dogs welcome; car park; garden

BRORA Highland — map 11

Inverbrora Farm — NEW ENTRY

Inverbrora, Brora KW9 6NJ TEL: (01408) 621208
1½m S of Brora

Just to the south of Brora up a long driveway from the main road, Inverbrora is an attractive old stone-built farmhouse. Sally McCall, who is a bright, cheerful person, has decorated the house in a pretty, unfussy way. The rooms are light and simply furnished; the double and family rooms share a bathroom, and the twin is *en suite*. Guests have use of a lounge with TV, and are served breakfast in the dining-room. This is a mixed farm, with cattle, sheep and arable land; the farm buildings lie behind the house.

OWNERS: Malcolm and Sally McCall OPEN: May to Sept ROOMS: 1 double, with wash-basin; 1 twin, with private bathroom; 1 family, with wash-basin; tea/coffee in all bedrooms; lounge with TV TERMS: single occupancy £18, twin/double £32, family room from £32; reductions for children under 12 CARDS: none DETAILS: children welcome; dogs welcome; car park; garden

Lynwood

Golf Road, Brora KW9 6QS TEL/FAX: (01408) 621226
on A9 Inverness to Wick road; in Brora turn right from S, or left from N, into Golf Road; house 250yds on left

Lynwood is a comfortable Victorian period house set in a large, pretty garden not very far from a golf course. The four bedrooms, all with either *en suite* facilities or private bathroom, are generously sized; one is reached through the garden and is suitable for wheelchair-users. Guests have use of a pleasant lounge, and meals – including dinner, if pre-arranged – are served in the conservatory overlooking the garden. Mrs Cooper extends a warm welcome, and takes care to ensure guests feel at home. Lynwood is convenient for beaches and Dunrobin Castle, and Brora's attractions include the woollen mill and Clynelish distillery.

OWNER: Mary Cooper OPEN: all year exc Christmas ROOMS: 2 double, both with bath/shower; 2 twin, 1 with bath/shower, 1 with private bathroom; 1 room suitable for wheelchair-users; tea/coffee and TV in all bedrooms; lounge with TV TERMS: single occupancy £24–£27, twin/double £38–£44; half-price for children under 12 sharing with parents; dinner £12; deposit: minimum £10 CARDS: MasterCard, Visa DETAILS: children welcome; no dogs; no smoking in bedrooms; car park; garden

Tigh Fada

Golf Road, Brora KW9 6QS TEL/FAX: (01408) 621332
off A9 Inverness to Wick road, just N of bridge over River Brora on sea side; on Golf Road, take second left and continue approx 300 metres

John and Ishbel Clarkson describe their B&B on the edge of town as a non-smokers' haven. It enjoys fine, uninterrupted views of the hills and sea, and the solar panels on the roof make good use of nature to heat the water. The garden has a pitch and putt course and a croquet lawn. Through the garden gate is a path leading down to the golf course and the sandy beach. Two bedrooms have a private bathroom, and one *en suite* bedroom has its own sitting-area with views of the sea and golf course. TV is available on request. The lounge has a large bay window with a good view of the sea, a peat fire for cold days, and a sun porch for fine weather. Breakfast is served in the dining-room, and complimentary tea and home-baking are offered each evening. The Clarksons can arrange hire of golf and fishing equipment and scenic tours.

OWNERS: John and Ishbel Clarkson OPEN: all year exc Christmas (Nov to Mar by arrangement only) ROOMS: 1 double, with private bathroom; 2 twin, 1 with shower, 1 with private bathroom; lounge TERMS: single occupancy £19.50, twin/double £35–£42; children's reductions; deposit: £10 per person per week CARDS: none DETAILS: children welcome (no toddlers); no dogs; no smoking; car park; garden

CALGARY Argyll & Bute **map 11**

Calgary Farmhouse Hotel

Calgary, by Dervaig, Isle of Mull PA75 6QW TEL/FAX: (01688) 400256
on B8073, 12m W of Tobermory

Just above the lovely Calgary beach – considered to be one of Mull's finest beaches – these imaginatively converted old stone farm buildings have been run as a B&B since 1989. Meals are served in the charming licensed Dovecote restaurant, which is also open to non-residents, and the menu features much local produce. The adjoining Carthouse Gallery displays works of local artists for sale, including some interesting wooden pieces created by owner Matthew Reade. The Gallery also serves snacks and meals during the day. There are nine comfortable bedrooms, all with *en suite* bath or shower, and three bedrooms are on the ground floor. Residents have use of a cosy lounge with wood-burning stove and a small TV room. Packed lunches can be provided.

OWNERS: Matthew and Julia Reade OPEN: Apr to Oct ROOMS: 1 single, 4 double, 2 twin, 2 family; all rooms with bath/shower and tea/coffee; TV in some bedrooms and lounge TERMS: single £30, single occupancy £37.50–£60, twin/double £60, family room £30; children under 3 free, £7.50–£12.50 for ages 3–14; dinner £16; children's menu available; deposit: 1 night's charge CARDS: MasterCard, Switch, Visa DETAILS: children welcome; dogs welcome; no smoking in dining-room while others eat; car park; garden

CALLANDER Stirling — map 11

Leny House

Leny Estate, Callander FK17 8HA TEL/FAX: (01877) 331078
on A84, 1m N of Callander

Dating originally from the early 1500s, Leny House is part of local history: home to the Buchanan family, it was used as a weapons' cache and for surreptitious meetings during the Jacobite Rebellion. Still visible in the grounds is Gallows Hill, once infamous for executions when it was known as the 'Knoll of Justice'. The building was enlarged over the centuries and is now an imposing grey-stone country mansion that, as well as being a family home, provides friendly and spacious B&B accommodation from spring to autumn; most rooms have lovely views. One guest thought 'it was like being in our own little stately home'. Baby-sitting can be arranged, and packed lunches provided. There is partial central heating. The grounds are extensive, with a waterfall, river and a 'wild glen' with its deer and other wildlife for guests to explore. Within walking distance too is the Lade Inn, also owned by the Roebucks, at which bar and restaurant meals are available. The estate also offers self-catering accommodation in the form of six spruce lodges.

OWNERS: Mr and Mrs A.F. Roebuck OPEN: Easter to Oct ROOMS: 1 double; 1 twin, with private bath; 1 family, with shower; tea/coffee in all bedrooms; lounge with TV TERMS: twin/double £44–£48; reductions for children under 12; deposit or credit card details required CARDS: MasterCard, Switch, Visa DETAILS: children welcome; dogs welcome; no smoking; car park; garden

The Priory — NEW ENTRY

Bracklinn Road, Callander FK17 8EH TEL/FAX: (01877) 330001

This former Church of Scotland manse is a substantial, well-cared-for stone building, set in an acre of lovely walled gardens with views to the hills. The house is very comfortable, well appointed and efficiently run; one ground-floor room is suitable for mobility-impaired guests, and one of the double rooms has a king-sized bed. Buffet breakfasts offer a big variety, and the aim is to create a New England-type inn. Excellent home-cooked dinners (available Thursday to Monday) making good use of Scottish produce are served in the licensed dining-room, and newspapers, books and magazines can be enjoyed in the comfortable lounge. There is a golf course almost next door, and this is a lovely area for walking.

OWNERS: Karen Warren and Ian Wylie OPEN: Easter to Oct ROOMS: 1 single, 4 double, 2 twin, 1 family; all rooms with bath/shower, tea/coffee and TV; lounge TERMS: single £27, single occupancy £35–£37, twin/double £50–£54, family room £50–£54; children's reductions; dinner £15; deposit: £25 per person CARDS: none DETAILS: children welcome; no dogs; no smoking; car park

CAMPBELTOWN Argyll & Bute **map 11**

Balegreggan Country House

Balegreggan Road, Campbeltown PA28 6NN TEL/FAX: (01586) 552062
approaching Campbeltown from N on A83, take second left after 30mph signs

Built in 1861, Balegreggan Country House stands in a fine position up a half-mile rough track on the outskirts of town, with views of hills and sea. Refurbishment since the last edition of the *Guide* has added further to the already high standard here. One of the doubles – the 'master bedroom' – has a king-sized bed and an enormous luxury *en suite* bathroom. Rooms are well proportioned, and all have *en suite* facilities, as well as heated towel rails, hair dryers and TV. The front rooms have the best views. Halfway up the stairs is an enormous stained-glass window depicting a peacock in a grove of trees. Good Scottish home-cooked evening meals are served in the dining-room, and guests also have use of a comfortable lounge.

OWNERS: Bruce and Sarah Urquhart OPEN: all year ROOMS: 3 double, 1 twin; 3 rooms with shower, 1 with bath/shower; tea/coffee and TV in all bedrooms; lounge TERMS: single occupancy £40–£45, twin/double £70–£90; dinner £25; deposit: £25 per person CARDS: MasterCard, Switch, Visa DETAILS: no children; well-behaved dogs welcome; no smoking; car park; garden

Sandiway

Fort Argyll Road, Campbeltown PA28 6SN TEL: (01586) 552280

Sandiway is in a quiet residential area on the edge of Campbeltown. The modern bungalow is surrounded by a pretty rose garden and has a patio at the back. The Bells are a musical family, and there is a piano in the lounge. One of the two twin bedrooms has *en suite* facilities, while the other has use of a private bathroom. Home-cooked evening meals and packed lunches are available by arrangement. Sandiway is unlicensed, but guests may bring their own wine to dinner. There are three golf courses in the area.

OWNERS: Dorothy and Graham Bell OPEN: all year exc Christmas ROOMS: 2 twin, 1 with shower, 1 with private bathroom; tea/coffee and TV in both bedrooms; lounge with TV TERMS: single occupancy £22–£25, twin £36–£40; dinner £9; deposit: £10 per room. CARDS: none DETAILS: children welcome; no dogs; no smoking; car park; garden

B&Bs are selected for the Guide for their warm welcome, cleanliness, a friendly atmosphere and, wherever possible, an attractive location or a building that is itself of some historical or architectural interest.

CARDROSS Argyll & Bute map 11

Kirkton House

Darleith Road, Cardross G82 5EZ
TEL: (01389) 841951 FAX: (01389) 841868

Kirkton House, a late-eighteenth-century farmstead with modern alterations, commands a panoramic view of the Firth of Clyde from its position above the village of Cardross. The attractive courtyard is furnished with tables and chairs, and decorated with flowers. Two of the bedrooms are on the ground floor, and the two attic-type rooms on the second floor have skylights. All rooms have individually controllable heating. Home-cooked meals are served in the large dining-room/lounge, which has stone walls and old fireplaces. There is a large garden with a play area for children, and horses can be accommodated in the stables and paddock. The twelfth-century Kirkton Chapel is nearby, and Charles Rennie Mackintosh's Hill House is only four miles away.

OWNERS: Stewart and Gillian Macdonald OPEN: Feb to Nov ROOMS: 4 double/family, 2 twin; all rooms with bath/shower, tea/coffee and TV TERMS: single occupancy £38.50, twin/double £57–£62, family room £67–£77; dinner £19.50; deposit: £20 per person CARDS: Amex, Delta, MasterCard, Visa DETAILS: children welcome; dogs welcome; no smoking in dining-room; car park; garden

CARRADALE Argyll & Bute map 11

Dunvalanree Guest House

Port Righ Bay, Carradale PA28 6SE
TEL: (01583) 431226 FAX: (01583) 431339

This substantial stone guesthouse built in 1938 stands in a lovely position at the end of the village of Carradale. Its pretty, sheltered front garden has tables and chairs for sitting out on warm days. There are marvellous views across Kilbrannan Sound to the Isle of Arran to the front, and of Carradale Bay to the rear of the property, so almost every room has a sea view. Stained-glass windows are an original feature, and there is a comfortable lounge. The Pryors are friendly, hospitable hosts, and serve evening meals and lunch by arrangement. The property is adjacent to a nature reserve and a golf course, and there are wonderful shore and cliff walks and the ruins of Saddell Castle nearby.

OWNERS: John and Sue Pryor OPEN: Easter to end Sept ROOMS: 3 single, 4 double, 2 twin, 3 family; all rooms with wash-basin and tea/coffee; lounge with TV TERMS: single £20, twin/double £40, family room from £40; children's reductions according to age; dinner £12; deposit: 10% CARDS: none DETAILS: children welcome; no dogs in lounge or dining-room; no smoking in dining-room; car park; garden

---

The end details for each entry state whether or not dogs are allowed, but it is always best to check when booking.

CARRBRIDGE Highland

map 11

Féith Mho'r Country House

Station Road, Carrbridge PH23 3AP TEL: (01479) 841621
1¼m from village centre

This small nineteenth-century country house is in a quiet and peaceful setting, surrounded by well-maintained gardens and views of mountains and hills on all sides. It has a large dining-room and a pleasant lounge with a log fire, and the bedrooms, one of which is on the ground floor, are comfortably appointed. Penny Rawson is an artist, and some of the pictures displayed in the house are for sale. Evening meals are no longer provided, though bookings at a local restaurant can be arranged. Féith Mho'r is approached down a quiet road from Carrbridge, which is a good location for walking, skiing and bird-watching.

OWNERS: Peter and Penny Rawson OPEN: all year exc Christmas ROOMS: 2 double, 3 twin, 1 family; all rooms with bath/shower, tea/coffee and TV; lounge TERMS: single occupancy £25–£26, twin/double £50–£52; family room from £50; reductions for children sharing with parents; deposit: £20 CARDS: none DETAILS: no children under 12; no dogs in public rooms; no smoking in public rooms; car park; garden

CASTLEBAY Western Isles

map 11

Ceol Mara

NEW ENTRY

Nasg, Castlebay, Isle of Barra HS9 5XN TEL: (01871) 810294
from ferry turn at third left; Ceol Mara is tenth house on hillside

Although Mary Sarah takes the name MacNeil from her husband, she was a MacNeil before marrying, so the specially made MacNeil tartan carpet which covers the living areas of the house seems particularly appropriate. They built Ceol Mara as a family home, and recently extended it to accommodate guests. There is a large lounge, and a conservatory where meals are served, and the *en suite* bedrooms are spacious and comfortable. The house stands above the road, just outside Castlebay, and has wonderful views over the bay.

OWNER: Mary Sarah MacNeil OPEN: all year ROOMS: 1 double, 2 twin; all rooms with shower, tea/coffee and TV; lounge with TV TERMS: single occupancy £27, twin/double £40–£44; deposit: £10 CARDS: none DETAILS: children welcome; dogs welcome; no smoking; car park; garden

Terra Nova

Nasg, Castlebay, Isle of Barra HS9 5XN TEL: (01871) 810458

The Galbraiths, Barra natives and a friendly couple, built Terra Nova themselves almost 20 years ago. It is right on the shoreline and enjoys fine views of the bay, particularly from the conservatory, which has a small sitting-area. This room is also where breakfast and, by arrangement, evening meals are served. The large main lounge, facing the water, is also available to guests. The three bedrooms, two of which overlook the sea, now have small *en suite* facilities. Terra Nova is a comfortable, homely place in a convenient location for exploring Barra.

OWNER: Katie Galbraith OPEN: all year exc Christmas ROOMS: 1 double, 2 twin; all rooms with shower, tea/coffee and TV; lounge with TV TERMS: single occupancy £19–£20, twin/double £38–£40; children under 14 free CARDS: none DETAILS: children welcome by arrangement; dogs by arrangement; no smoking; car park; games room; garden

---

Tigh-na-Mara

Castlebay, Isle of Barra H59 5XD TEL/FAX: (01871) 810304

turn left from top of road at ferry terminal; house is across road on right

This attractive, old stone building is just a couple of minutes from the ferry terminal, and overlooks the bay towards the old castle, which stands on a rock and can be visited in summer. There is a small lounge and both breakfast and evening meals are provided. Most of the rooms have *en suite* facilities, and two of them face the bay. Barra can be reached by air from Glasgow and by ferry from Oban, and now with extended services and an Island Rover Ticket the Outer Hebridean Islands can easily be visited.

OWNER: Linda Maclean OPEN: Apr to Oct ROOMS: 2 single, both with wash-basin and shower but not WC; 1 double and 2 twin, all with shower; tea/coffee and TV in all bedrooms; lounge with TV TERMS: single £20, single occupancy £25, twin/double £40; half-price for children under 12 CARDS: none DETAILS: children welcome; smoking in lounge only; car park; garden

CLADDACH KIRKIBOST Western Isles map 11

Sealladh Traigh

Claddach Kirkibost, North Uist HS6 5EP

TEL: (01876) 580248 FAX: (01876) 510360

200yds off Clachan to Bayhead road, 2m N of Clachan

Not far from sandy beaches, Sealladh Traigh is a modern house with fine views to Kirkibost Island. As we went to press, refurbishment was planned to make all the bedrooms *en suite* and to add a lounge. Evening meals are available and are served from 7 to 9pm at one table in the lounge. Bird-watching, trout-fishing and boating are activities within easy reach, and the Quarms are friendly, local people happy to give helpful tips. They used to own the pub next door and run a hotel, and now they run the Bayhead shop.

OWNERS: Mr and Mrs W.J. Quarm OPEN: all year ROOMS: 2 single, 2 double, 1 twin; all rooms with wash-basin, tea/coffee and TV; 1 room suitable for wheelchair-users; lounge TERMS: single/single occupancy £18–£20, twin/double £36–£40; children under 3 free, half-price for ages 4–14; dinner £10–£12 CARDS: Delta, MasterCard, Visa DETAILS: children welcome; dogs welcome; car park; garden

CLEATON Orkney **map 11**

Cleaton House Hotel

NEW ENTRY

Cleaton, Westray KW17 2DB TEL: (01857) 677508 FAX: (01857) 677442

This attractive Victorian country-house was built for the Laird of Cleat, and is set in peaceful countryside on the island of Westray and has sea views. It has been converted into comfortable accommodation, retaining much of its original character, and its young owner, Malcolm Stout, is a congenial, welcoming host, as well as being a talented chef. Dinner is served in the dining-room, with menus featuring local produce, such as Westray fish and beef, while bar meals are served in the lounge, which also has a pool table and dartboard. The five individual bedrooms, all *en suite*, are comfortable and well appointed. Westray has a thriving fishing community, cottage industries such as knitwear and the making of the traditional Orkney straw-backed chairs, the impressive ruins of a fifteenth-century castle, seals galore and wonderful birdlife.

OWNER: Malcolm Stout OPEN: all year ROOMS: 1 single, 1 double, 2 twin, 1 family; all rooms with bath/shower, tea/coffee and TV; lounge TERMS: single/single occupancy £32, twin/double £58, family room £70; dinner £25 CARDS: Delta, MasterCard, Visa DETAILS: children welcome; dogs welcome; no smoking in restaurant; car park; garden

CONNEL Argyll & Bute **map 11**

Dunfuinary

NEW ENTRY

Connel, by Oban PA37 1PG TEL: (01631) 710300
on A85, 4m N of Oban

The Deans acquired this substantial nineteenth-century stone-built house at the beginning of 1997, having retired from London. At the time of going to press there are three bedrooms available for guests, and more accommodation will be available when another wing of the house has been renovated. The house occupies a small rocky outcrop above Loch Etive, there are views from three sides, and every room overlooks the water. The drawing-room and one bedroom have sitting-room annexes in the tower, and all bedrooms are spacious and well furnished. Dunfuinary is surrounded by two acres of gardens, which run down to the lochside, and there is a boathouse at one end of the property. This is a truly spectacular location, and the house is easily visible from the Connel Bridge a mile away.

OWNERS: Judith and William Dean OPEN: Easter to Oct ROOMS: 1 single, 1 double, 1 twin; all rooms with bath/shower, tea/coffee and TV; lounge with TV TERMS: single £17.50–£20, twin/double £40–£50 CARDS: none DETAILS: children welcome; dogs welcome; no smoking; car park; garden

---

If you are forced to turn up later than planned, please telephone to warn the proprietor. It is always best to book a room in advance, even in winter. B&Bs with few rooms may close at short notice for periods not specified in the details.

Ronebhal Guest House

Connel, by Oban PA37 1PJ TEL/FAX: (01631) 710310
on A85 Glasgow to Oban road, 5m NE of Oban

This well-kept Victorian house is set back from the main road on the edge of Connel overlooking the mouth of Loch Etive and the Morvern hills beyond. It has a warm and friendly atmosphere, and the Strachans are a lively couple offering excellent service to their guests. The rooms are spacious and well furnished, and all have their own bathrooms or are *en suite*. The twin room is on the ground floor. Both the comfortable lounge and dining-room with individual tables enjoy the view. Packed lunches are available by arrangement. The local area is good for walks and a Rare Breeds Park and Sea Life Centre are nearby.

OWNERS: Robert and Shirley Strachan OPEN: Easter to Oct ROOMS: 1 single, with private bathroom; 3 double, 2 with shower, 1 with private bathroom; 1 twin, with shower; 1 family, with shower; tea/coffee and TV in all bedrooms; lounge TERMS: single £18–£23, single occupancy £25–£50, twin/double £36–£55, family room £45–£67; deposit: £10 CARDS: Delta, MasterCard, Visa DETAILS: no children under 5; no dogs; no smoking; car park; garden

CRAIGNURE Argyll & Bute **map 11**

Inverlussa

by Craignure, Isle of Mull PA65 6BD TEL/FAX: (01680) 812436
on A849, 6m S of Craignure ferry

Inverlussa is an attractive house standing beside a stream in peaceful countryside with lovely views. The Wilsons built Inverlussa in 1989 both as their family home and for bed-and-breakfast guests. Helen Wilson is a most welcoming and hospitable host, and the house has a warm and friendly atmosphere. The comfortable bedrooms are simply decorated, and the lounge has a warming fire for chilly days. An excellent breakfast is served and packed lunches can be arranged.

OWNER: Helen Wilson OPEN: Apr to Oct ROOMS: 1 double with shower; 1 twin; 1 family; lounge with TV TERMS: single occupancy £18–£20, twin/double £36–£40, family room £36–£40; half-price for children under 10 CARDS: none DETAILS: children welcome; dogs welcome by arrangement; car park; garden

CRAIL Fife **map 11**

Selcraig House

47 Nethergate, Crail KY10 3TX TEL: (01333) 450697 FAX: (01333) 451113

Selcraig House, a charming 200-year-old stone building, stands right in the middle of the village, close to the picturesque harbour and beaches. It has a warm and relaxing atmosphere, and has been thoughtfully furnished and decorated in an Edwardian style by owner Margaret Carstairs. Breakfast and dinner are served in the attractive ground-floor dining-room, which extends into the conservatory. On the first floor are a comfortable sitting-room and two spacious bedrooms. All rooms are well equipped, and although the top-floor rooms are very small, two have a sea view. There are three bathrooms, one on each floor; one has a bath and two have showers. At the back of the house is a neatly kept small garden with an area for sitting out on fine days. Although off-street parking space is limited, there is unrestricted free parking on the road outside.

OWNER: Margaret Carstairs OPEN: all year ROOMS: 1 single, 1 double, 2 twin, 1 four-poster, 1 family; all rooms with wash-basin, tea/coffee and TV; lounge with TV TERMS: single £18–£20, single occupancy £23–£25, twin/double £36– £40, four-poster £40–£45, family room £45–£54; children under 2 free, half-price for children 2–10; dinner £15; deposit: £10 CARDS: none DETAILS: children welcome; dogs welcome; no smoking; garden

CRAOBH HAVEN Argyll & Bute map 11

Buidhe Lodge

Craobh Haven, by Lochgilphead PA31 8UA TEL/FAX: (01852) 500291
take A816 for 17m N from Lochgilphead or 20m S of Oban, turn at signpost for Craobh Haven

Buidhe Lodge, which takes its name from the Gaelic word for 'yellow', is a modern wooden building set at the water's edge in a sheltered bay on the small island of Eilean Buidhe in Loch Shuna. It is linked to Craobh Haven on the mainland by a short causeway. All six bedrooms are on the ground floor and are small, simply furnished in pine and *en suite*. Guests have the use of a large open-plan room with a sitting-area at one end and a dining-room at the other; a balcony running the length of the room provides splendid views of the water and surrounding hills. Imaginative evening meals, prepared by Simone Twinn, might include items such as potted salmon with lemon and walnuts to start, then chicken breast in sherry and tarragon sauce, and banana and mint meringue ice-cream cake to finish. Buidhe Lodge is licensed and there is a 'trust bar' in the lounge. The property has its own slipway and mooring, and the atmosphere is happy and relaxed. This is a good place for sailing, and boat trips to the uninhabited islands in the area can be booked at the marina nearby.

OWNERS: Nick and Simone Twinn OPEN: all year exc Christmas ROOMS: 2 double, 4 twin; all rooms with bath/shower, tea/coffee and TV; lounge with TV TERMS: single occupancy £33–£36, twin/double £46–£52; dinner £14; deposit: 33% of total CARDS: MasterCard, Visa DETAILS: children welcome; dogs welcome with own bedding but not to be left alone in bedrooms; car park; garden

---

B&B rates specified in the details at the end of each entry are given (as applicable) for a single room, for single occupancy of a double room, and then per room in the case of two people sharing a double or twin-bedded room, or for a family room. Because double rooms with four-poster beds often cost more, those are listed separately.

CRIANLARICH **Stirling** map 11

Ewich House

Strathfillan, Crianlarich FK20 8RU TEL: (01838) 300300
off A82, 2m N of Crianlarich

Ian and Jean Walker have improved the appearance of this long, stone-built house and its grounds considerably since the last edition of the *Guide*. Originally an old farmhouse dating from the early 1800s, the building had its living area in the middle and barns for the animals at each end. It lies just off the main Crianlarich to Tyndrum road in an isolated position, with lovely mountain views. In fact, the mountains are close enough to walk to from the house, and the West Highland Way runs along the opposite side of the road. All the plainly decorated bedrooms are *en suite* and on the first floor. The lounge has an open fire and is the only room where smoking is permitted. The house is licensed, and three-course evening meals are served at 7.30pm in the dining-room.

OWNERS: Ian and Jean Walker OPEN: all year ROOMS: 1 single, 2 double, 2 twin; all rooms with shower, tea/coffee and TV; lounge TERMS: single/single occupancy £20–£30, twin/double £40–£60; reductions for children sharing with parents; dinner £15; deposit: 20% CARDS: MasterCard, Visa DETAILS: children welcome; no dogs; smoking in lounge only; car park; garden

DALBEATTIE **Dumfries & Galloway** map 11

Briardale House

17 Haugh Road, Dalbeattie DG5 4AR TEL: (01556) 611468
on B794 on outskirts of Dalbeattie

Briardale House, a solid, granite-built Victorian building, has retained many original features, such as decorative cornices and tiled fireplaces. It stands in its own garden on the edge of town with views of the countryside. The three bedrooms are spacious, comfortably furnished and well equipped. John and Verna have been professional chefs for many years and enjoy preparing meals for their guests. Breakfast and, by arrangement, dinner are served at separate tables in the dining-room, off which is a large conservatory with comfortable chairs and with garden views. There is also a pleasant lounge with open fire and, outside, a patio area. Dalbeattie's attractions include a small museum relating the history of granite quarrying and life in the area.

OWNER: Verna Woodworth OPEN: Jan to Oct ROOMS: 2 double, 1 twin; all rooms with bath/shower and TV; lounge TERMS: single occupancy £42, twin/double £42; half-price for children sharing with parents; dinner £12; deposit: £20 per person CARDS: none DETAILS: children welcome; no dogs; no smoking; car park; garden

---

If any bedrooms are suitable for wheelchair-users, we mention this in the details at the end of the entry.

DALMALLY Argyll & Bute

map 11

Orchy Bank

Orchy Bank, Dalmally PA33 1AS TEL: (01838) 200370
on B8077, just N of junction with A85

Orchy Bank provides unpretentious, comfortable accommodation enhanced by a very pleasant informal atmosphere. Set in a quiet position on the banks of the River Orchy and beside an eighteenth-century stone bridge, it is an attractive building with a garden that reaches down to the river. Though not centrally heated, the house has a very large, comfortable lounge kept cosy on cool days by a wood-burning stove; there is also a piano which guests are welcome to play. Every bedroom except one has a view of the river, and one of the bathrooms has an enormous old bath. This is an ideal setting for fishing, golf, hill-walking and bird-watching.

OWNERS: Jinty and John Burke OPEN: all year exc New Year ROOMS: 2 single, 2 double, 2 twin, 2 family; all rooms with wash-basin and tea/coffee; lounge with TV TERMS: single £16–£19, single occupancy £24–£26, twin/double £32–£38, family room from £32; half-price for children under 11; deposit: £10 CARDS: none DETAILS: children welcome; dogs welcome; smoking in lounge only; car park; garden

DARNICK Borders

map 11

The Gables

NEW ENTRY

Darnick, Melrose TD6 9AL TEL/FAX: (01896) 822479
in Melrose take left fork off B6374 towards Galashiels; house is ½m on left

This very pretty small house stands in the attractive village of Darnick, which is just outside and away from the tourist bustle of Melrose. It is easily accessible by bus, with a bus stop nearly outside the front door. Dating from 1825, the house has a small, neatly kept front garden and offers simple accommodation. The Aitkens are very welcoming people, and Mr Aitken upon occasion enjoys conducting breakfast-time quizzes for guests. One reader was impressed with the good value and friendliness, and enjoyed the breakfasts too.

OWNER: Margaret Aitken OPEN: all year ROOMS: 1 single, 1 double, 1 twin; all rooms with wash-basin, tea/coffee and TV; lounge TERMS: single £20, single occupancy £25, twin/double £34; £10 per night for children sharing with parents CARDS: none DETAILS: children welcome; well-behaved dogs welcome with own bedding; no smoking; garden

---

We welcome your feedback about B&Bs you have stayed in. Please make use of the report forms at the end of the book – or use your own stationery if you prefer – and mail your report to: The Editors, The Good Bed and Breakfast Guide, *FREEPOST, 2 Marylebone Road, London NW1 1YN. (No stamps are needed if mailed within the UK.) Recommendations for B&Bs for our next edition are very welcome. Please let us know if you need more report forms and we will send you a fresh supply.*

DENNY Falkirk — map 11

Lochend Farm

Carronbridge, Denny FK6 5JJ TEL: (01324) 822778
off B818, 5m W of Denny

Although it is located only a few miles from the motorway, it is advisable to phone for directions to this low, stone-built eighteenth-century farmhouse. The attractive farm sits on top of a small rise with marvellous views in all directions over 650 acres of hills and moorland (populated only by grazing sheep) and across Loch Coulter. The house and other farm buildings form a courtyard which surrounds a very colourful, slightly sunken garden. The two comfortable first-floor bedrooms share a bathroom, and downstairs is a pleasant TV lounge. One enthusiastic guest commended the 'wonderful hospitality' and 'just delicious' home-baking.

OWNER: Jean Morton OPEN: Easter to Oct, or by arrangement ROOMS: 1 double, 1 twin; both rooms with wash-basin, tea/coffee and TV; lounge with TV TERMS: twin/double £35–£37; deposit: £10 CARDS: none DETAILS: no children under 3; no dogs; no smoking in dining-room or bedrooms; car park; garden

DERVAIG Argyll & Bute — map 11

Ardrioch Farm Guest House

Dervaig, Isle of Mull PA75 6QR TEL/FAX: (01688) 400264
1m W of Dervaig on Calgary road

Ardrioch Farm, a mile from Dervaig, extends to 70 acres, supporting Cheviot sheep, a pony, collies and cats. The approach to the simple cedar bungalow gives no impression of the charm of the interior, which is warm and cosy. The comfortable, wood-panelled sitting-room is well supplied with books, maps, games and a TV, and attractive antique furniture and pictures, and the small bedrooms are furnished in pine. Apart from running the farm and guesthouse, Jeremy and Jenny Matthew organise boat trips around smaller islands in their Shetland skiff and Orkney ketch, which are kept nearby at the natural harbour of Croig. Jeremy is also a folk musician, playing banjo and mandolin in a local band, and Jenny, an imaginative cook, prepares evening meals using local produce.

OWNERS: Jenny and Jeremy Matthew OPEN: Apr to Oct ROOMS: 1 single, with wash-basin; 2 double, 1 with bath, 1 with wash-basin; 2 twin, 1 with bath, 1 with wash-basin; tea/coffee in all bedrooms; lounge with TV TERMS: single £18.50, single occupancy £21–£23.50, twin/double £37–£42; dinner £15; deposit: £10 CARDS: MasterCard, Visa DETAILS: no children under 5; no dogs; no smoking; car park; garden

---

Many B&Bs are in remote places, and although in many cases we provide directions, it is always advisable to ask for clear instructions when booking.

Balmacara

NEW ENTRY

Kilmore, Dervaig, Isle of Mull PA75 6QN TEL/FAX: (01688) 400363
take B8073 from Dervaig towards Tobermory, signposted down private road on left just outside village

Anne and Andrew Arnold owned and ran the Ballachroy Hotel in Dervaig for 11 years, before building their dream house, on a hillside overlooking the village, with panoramic views across Glen Bellart to Loch Cuin and the hills beyond. Andrew designed the house, and built it with help from friends and former employees. It looks small from the outside, but it is a substantial building on four levels. Guests have use of a comfortably furnished sitting-room, off which there is a small conservatory where breakfast and dinner are served; both rooms take full advantage of the view. A small sitting-area upstairs overlooks the conservatory. There are three beautifully appointed bedrooms, two with zip-link beds which can be made up as double or twin, and one with a four-poster bed. The Arnolds prepare wonderful food, specialising in local produce, and there are also several good restaurants nearby.

OWNERS: Anne and Andrew Arnold OPEN: all year exc Christmas ROOMS: 2 double/ twin, 1 with bath and shower, 1 with private bathroom; 1 four-poster, with bath and shower; all rooms with tea/coffee and TV; lounge with TV TERMS: single occupancy £30, twin/double £51–£54, four-poster £51–£54; dinner £13.50; deposit: £20 CARDS: none DETAILS: no children under 11; no dogs; no smoking in bedrooms; car park; garden

DORNOCH Highland — map 11

Trevose Guest House

Cathedral Square, Dornoch IV25 3SD TEL: (01862) 810269

In a conservation area in the centre of Dornoch, close to the cathedral and overlooking the tree-lined green, stands the Trevose Guest House. It is an attractive, sandstone building constructed in 1830 and is set in a pretty, colourful small garden. The Mackenzies are a friendly, hospitable couple and the house is warm and comfortable. There is a pleasant lounge, and a cosy dining-room. The local area is rich with castles and golf courses.

OWNERS: Donald and Jean Mackenzie OPEN: Mar to Sept ROOMS: 1 single with wash-basin; 1 double, with wash-basin; 1 twin, with shower; 2 family, both with shower; tea/coffee in all bedrooms; TV in some bedrooms; lounge with TV TERMS: single £16–£18, single occupancy £25–£30, twin/double £36–£38, family room £45–£48; children under 5 free, half-price for older children sharing with parents; deposit: £15 per room CARDS: none DETAILS: children welcome; dogs welcome but must not be left unattended in bedrooms; smoking in lounge only; car park

---

If a B&B accepts credit cards, we list them in the details at the end of an entry – or specify no cards are accepted if that is so. There may be a surcharge if you pay by credit card. It is always best to check when booking whether the card you want to use will be accepted.

DRUMNADROCHIT Highland map 11

Glenkirk

Drumnadrochit IV3 6TZ TEL/FAX: (01456) 450802
from A82 Inverness to Fort William road take the A831 Cannick road in Drumnadrochit; B&B is 500 metres on right

Once a chapel, this distinctive and attractive building stands on the quiet main street of Drumnadrochit. The four bright, small, first-floor bedrooms are simply furnished, mostly in pine, have skylights and share a bathroom and shower-room. The guests' lounge, which unusually is at mezzanine level and has the original large chapel window, has a TV plus plenty of board games and books. The breakfast room is located on the ground floor, and in the hallway leaflets are laid out on an old pew for guests to browse through. Drumnadrochit is one mile west of Loch Ness.

OWNERS: Fiona and Ross Urquhart OPEN: all year exc mid-Jan to Mar ROOMS: 2 double, 1 twin, 1 family; all rooms with wash-basin; lounge with TV TERMS: single occupancy £16–£24, twin/double £32–£32, family room £48; children under 2 free, half-price for ages 3–14 sharing with parents CARDS: none DETAILS: children welcome; no dogs; no smoking; car park; garden

DRYMEN Stirling map 11

Dunleen

Milton of Buchanan, Drymen G63 0JE TEL: (01360) 870274
from Drymen take B837 towards Balmaha

This well-kept modern bungalow is in a very attractive setting beside a pretty stream, only about a mile from Loch Lomond and a mile and a half from the West Highland Way. There is a large, colourful garden, which Mr Macfadyen has been improving since the house was built. The large lounge incorporates the breakfast room and has windows all round which overlook the stream and fields of sheep. The bedrooms are comfortably furnished and spotlessly clean.

OWNERS: Mr and Mrs D. Macfadyen OPEN: May to Oct ROOMS: 1 double, 1 twin, both with wash-basin and tea/coffee; lounge with TV TERMS: single occupancy £20–£22, twin/double £34–£38; babies free, half-price for children sharing with parents; deposit: £5 CARDS: none DETAILS: children welcome; no dogs; no smoking; car park; garden

DUNOON Argyll & Bute map 11

Abbot's Brae NEW ENTRY

West Bay, Dunoon PA23 7QJ TEL/FAX: (01369) 705021
on A815, 1m S of Dunoon

Built as a holiday home in the Victorian era, Abbot's Brae sits high up above the road. It is reached by a long, curved driveway that climbs steeply through an area of trees and shrubs, known as Morag's Fairy Glen. The house and garden enjoy spectacular views, and the rooms are spacious and comfortably furnished; all bedrooms have TV and telephones. Helen and Gavin Dick, both experienced hoteliers, took over the house in early 1997. Gavin cooks excellent Scottish dinners, which are served in the dining-room overlooking the Clyde. Abbot's Brae is licensed.

OWNERS: Gavin and Helen Dick OPEN: all year ROOMS: 4 double, 1 four-poster, 2 family; all rooms with bath/shower, tea/coffee and TV; lounge TERMS: single occupancy £34.50, twin/double £49, four-poster £69; family room £59; reductions for children sharing with parents; dinner £14.50 CARDS: Delta, MasterCard, Visa DETAILS: children welcome; well-behaved dogs welcome; smoking in lounge only; car park; garden

DUNSYRE South Lanarkshire **map 11**

Dunsyre Mains

Dunsyre, nr Carnwath ML11 8NQ TEL: (01899) 810251
off A702 Biggar to Edinburgh road, signposted from Dolphinton

This attractive, early-eighteenth-century stone building is set in beautiful, unspoilt countryside, just above the tiny village of Dunsyre. The farmhouse has a friendly atmosphere and offers simple, comfortable accommodation. There are three large bedrooms, a lounge and a dining-room. Evening meals are available by arrangement. It is part of a 400-acre beef and sheep farm and has a colourful, pretty farmyard. Dunsyre Mains is within easy reach of Edinburgh and the Borders.

OWNER: Mrs Armstrong OPEN: all year ROOMS: 2 double, 1 family; all rooms with wash-basin and tea/coffee; lounge with TV TERMS: single occupancy £18, twin/double £33–£52, family from £33; children's reductions according to age; dinner £9; deposit: 10% CARDS: none DETAILS: children welcome; dogs by arrangement; no smoking in bedrooms or dining-room; car park; garden

EDINBURGH Edinburgh **map 11**

Ashlyn Guest House NEW ENTRY

42 Inverleith Row, Edinburgh EH3 5PY TEL/FAX: (0131) 552 2954

This listed early-nineteenth-century terraced house retains many of its original features, and is beautifully maintained by the unobtrusive but welcoming Macintoshes. Bedrooms are spacious and tastefully furnished, and some are *en suite*, while others have been left as they were so as not to spoil their shape and size. There is an attractive sitting-room, and a pretty breakfast room, where guests sit at individual tables. Home-made bread and scones feature at breakfast. Ashlyn Guest House is immaculate and efficiently run, and is on a main road next to the Botanical Gardens, and only a mile from Princes Street. 'Absolutely value for money,' reckoned one correspondent. Parking is on-street only.

OWNERS: Mr and Mrs L.E. Macintosh OPEN: all year ROOMS: 2 single, both with wash-basin; 3 double, all with bath/shower; 2 twin, both with bath/shower; tea/coffee and TV in all bedrooms; lounge with TV TERMS: single £22–£30, single occupancy £30–£70, twin/double £46–£70, family room £30–£44; deposit required CARDS: none DETAILS: no children under 7; no dogs; no smoking; garden

Bonnington Guest House

202 Ferry Road, Edinburgh EH6 4NW TEL: (0131) 554 7610

The Watts have offered B&B at this listed Victorian house on the north side of the city (not far from the docks) since 1990. Set back a little from the main road, it can be reached from the city centre in ten minutes by bus. Almost all the rooms are either *en suite* or have private facilities, and are comfortably furnished. The lounge has a piano, games and books for guests' use and breakfast is served in the basement dining-room at separate tables.

OWNERS: Eileen and David Watt OPEN: all year ROOMS: 3 double, 1 with bath/shower, 1 with private bathroom, 1 with wash-basin; 3 family, 2 with bath/shower, 1 with wash-basin; tea/coffee and TV in all bedrooms; lounge with TV TERMS: single occupancy £23–£30; double £46–£60, family room £60–£75; children under 3 free, half-price for older children; deposit required CARDS: none DETAILS: children welcome; dogs welcome; smoking in lounge only; car park

Classic House

50 Mayfield Road, Edinburgh EH9 2NH
TEL: (0131) 667 5847 FAX: (0131) 662 1016

This comfortable and professionally run small guesthouse lies on a main road and bus route with easy access to the city centre. It is a smart terraced Victorian house offering a high standard of accommodation. The breakfast room is now housed in the conservatory, reached through the small guests' lounge. The four second-floor rooms are of a reasonable size, but the staircase to reach them is narrow and steep. Parking is on-street only.

OWNER: Emad Ismail OPEN: all year exc Christmas ROOMS: 1 single, 2 double, 1 twin, 2 family; all rooms with shower, tea/coffee and TV; lounge with TV TERMS: single £20, single occupancy £25–£50, twin/double £40–£60, family room £60–£120; children's reductions; deposit required CARDS: Delta, Diners, MasterCard, Visa DETAILS: children welcome; no dogs; no smoking; garden

Gloria's Place

20 London Street, Edinburgh EH3 6NA
TEL: (0131) 557 0216 FAX: (0131) 556 6445

Gloria Stuart has changed the name of her Georgian town house from 'Twenty London Street', and continues to maintain very high standards. There are three well-equipped and tastefully decorated bedrooms, all with small *en suite* shower or bath. The two double rooms have king-sized beds and overlook the small back garden. Guests have a comfortable, warm-coloured large sitting-room, where breakfast is served at one table. Gloria's Place is in Edinburgh's New

Town, and is handily positioned for Princes Street. On-street free parking is unrestricted, though demand for spaces may be high; there is also a 'pay and display' parking directly outside.

OWNER: Gloria Stuart OPEN: all year exc Christmas ROOMS: 2 double, 1 twin; all rooms with bath/shower, tea/coffee and TV; lounge TERMS: single occupancy £60–£80, twin/double £70–£80; deposit: 1 night's charge CARDS: MasterCard, Switch, Visa DETAILS: children welcome; no dogs; no smoking; garden

Hopetoun Guest House

15 Mayfield Road, Edinburgh EH9 2NG
TEL: (0131) 667 7691 FAX: (0131) 466 1691

This small, terraced Victorian guesthouse with its neat blue door is conveniently located in a pleasant residential area served by frequent bus routes into the city; for the energetic the Castle and Royal Mile are a mere 25-minutes' walk away. Visitors also come here for the friendly atmosphere, excellent breakfasts and strict no-smoking policy. The bedrooms are spacious and comfortable; one is *en suite* and one has a private shower-room. The breakfast room is at the rear of the house. Although off-street parking is limited, streets nearby allow unrestricted parking.

OWNER: Rhoda Mitchell OPEN: all year exc Christmas ROOMS: 1 double, with wash-basin; 2 family, 1 with shower, 1 with private shower-room; tea/coffee and TV in all bedrooms TERMS: single occupancy £25–£35; double £36–£56, family room £60–£80; reductions for children under 12; deposit: 1 night's charge CARDS: MasterCard, Visa DETAILS: children welcome; no dogs; no smoking; car park

17 Abercromby Place

17 Abercromby Place, Edinburgh EH3 6LB
TEL: (0131) 557 8036 FAX: (0131) 558 3453

This charming and elegantly comfortable listed Georgian house was formerly the home of William Playfair, a renowned local architect. It is conveniently situated in the heart of the New Town, close to George Street and Princes Street, and only a few minutes' walk from Waverley station. Most of the bedrooms are on the lower level, but two of the most popular (a double and a twin, both *en suite*) are on the upper floor of the old mews house, reached from the back of the main building. They are all attractively decorated, well equipped and have good-sized bathrooms. Breakfast is served in an elegant dining-room, there is also a small cosy sitting-room with a fax machine for guests' use, and off-street parking for seven cars at the rear of the property. Eirlys Lloyd is a relaxed but very professional host.

OWNER: Eirlys Lloyd OPEN: all year ROOMS: 6 double, 2 twin, 1 family; all rooms with bath/shower, tea/coffee and TV; lounge TERMS: single occupancy £45–£70, twin/double £70–£90, four-poster £90–£120; reductions for children sharing with parents; dinner £25; deposit required CARDS: Delta, MasterCard, Switch, Visa DETAILS: children welcome; no dogs; no smoking; car park

Sibbet House

26 Northumberland Street, Edinburgh EH3 6LS
TEL: (0131) 556 1078 FAX: (0131) 557 9445

Previously at Cuilmore Cottage, Kinloch Rannoch, Jens and Anita Steffen have taken over the running of Sibbet House on the retirement of the Sibbets, and continue its very high standard. The beautifully decorated and furnished, elegant Georgian terraced house, built in 1809, is in the heart of Edinburgh's New Town, only ten minutes' walk from Princes Street. The large, well-appointed bedrooms, one of which has a four-poster bed, are reached by a unique hanging staircase crowned by a cupola. There is a formal drawing-room, and breakfast is taken at separate tables in the large dining-room. The Steffens also have three self-catering flats, and continue their culinary arts (Cuilmore Cottage was featured in *The Good Food Guide*) in catering for small parties and groups at the house.

OWNERS: Aurora Sibbet and Jens and Anita Steffen OPEN: all year ROOMS: 1 double, 1 twin, 1 four-poster, 1 family; all with bath/shower, tea/coffee and TV; lounge with TV TERMS: single occupancy £60–£75, twin/double £90–£100, four-poster £90–£100, family room £100–£110; deposit: credit card details CARDS: MasterCard, Switch, Visa DETAILS: no children under 8; no dogs; no smoking; car park

Sonas Guest House

3 East Mayfield, Edinburgh EH9 1SD
TEL: (0131) 667 2781 FAX: (0131) 667 0454

Guests can be assured of a warm welcome at this small guesthouse; 'Sonas' is Gaelic for happiness. Built in 1876 for a railway director, it is in a quiet residential street a mile from the Royal Mile and Princes Street. The breakfast/sitting-room is on the ground floor, and the small bedrooms are pretty and bright, and regularly redecorated and refurnished. There is a small car park where guests can leave their cars and take the bus to town. The Royal Scottish Museum and University are close by.

OWNERS: Dennis and Irene Robins OPEN: all year exc Christmas ROOMS: 1 single, 3 double, 2 twin, 2 family; all rooms with bath/shower, tea/coffee and TV; lounge with TV TERMS: single £25–£40, single occupancy £25–£50, twin/double £38–£70, family room £40–£80; deposit required CARDS: none DETAILS: children welcome; no dogs; no smoking in dining-room and some bedrooms; car park

The Town House

65 Gilmore Place, Edinburgh EH3 9NU TEL: (0131) 229 1985

A fairly central location – just a 10- or 15-minute walk to Princes Street – is a plus for this three-storey B&B, built in 1876 as the manse for the adjoining church. Five *en suite* bedrooms are offered, all but one on the second floor, and the attractively decorated house retains a number of its original architectural features. Only breakfast is provided, but an abundance of pubs, cafés and restaurants for evening meals are nearby. The car park is at the rear of the house, and guests are asked to check in and off-load luggage at the front when they arrive.

OWNER: Susan Virtue OPEN: all year exc Christmas ROOMS: 1 single, 2 double, 1 twin, 1 family; all rooms with bath/shower, tea/coffee and TV; lounge with TV TERMS: single £28–£33, single occupancy £35–£45, twin/double £56– £66, family room from £56; half-price for children sharing with parents; deposit: 1 night's charge CARDS: none DETAILS: no children under 10; no dogs; no smoking; car park

Turret Guest House

8 Kilmaurs Terrace, Edinburgh EH16 5DR
TEL: (0131) 667 6704 FAX: (0131) 668 1368

Located in a quiet residential area about a five minutes' drive or bus journey away from the city centre, this mid-terrace Victorian guesthouse offers immaculately clean and comfortable rooms, plus a friendly atmosphere. One visitor was pleased with the many 'personal touches' provided by Mrs Cameron. The house has a wide wooden staircase with a minstrels' gallery, and the original cornices. The bedrooms come in a variety of sizes and those with *en suite* showers are on the smallish side. The lounge/dining-room is where superb breakfasts are served, including waffles and a wide choice of teas and coffees. Mrs Cameron has extended smoking restrictions, and smoking is now only allowed in one single bedroom and one double. One-night bookings may not be accepted during the Edinburgh Festival and bank holidays. Parking is on-street only.

OWNERS: Jackie and Ian Cameron OPEN: all year exc Christmas ROOMS: 2 single, 1 with private bathroom, 1 with wash-basin; 1 double, with shower; 2 twin, 1 with bath/shower, 1 with wash-basin; 1 four-poster, with bath/shower; 1 family, with bath/shower; tea/coffee and TV in all bedrooms; lounge TERMS: single £18–£29, twin/double £40–£56, four-poster £46–£58, family room £46–£78; half-price for children under 12 CARDS: Visa DETAILS: children welcome (under-2s in family room only); no dogs; smoking allowed in 2 bedrooms only

ELGIN Moray

map 11

The Croft

NEW ENTRY

10 Institution Hill, Elgin IV30 1XQ TEL: (01343) 546004

The Croft is an elegant, stone-built house with a pillared entrance, in a peaceful residential area, only a short walk from the town centre. It was built in 1848, has a large, partly walled rear garden, and has been restored to include modern comforts while retaining its original character. There are three spacious bedrooms, two with *en suite* shower, and a guest lounge. Breakfast only is served, but there are many places to eat nearby. Ann Cartmell is a friendly, welcoming lady. Elgin is a good centre for visiting whisky distilleries, the beaches and fishing villages of the Moray Firth, and for fishing and walking.

OWNER: Ann Cartmell OPEN: all year ROOMS: 2 double, 1 with shower, 1 with private bathroom; 1 family, with shower; tea/coffee and TV in all bedrooms; lounge with TV TERMS: single occupancy £25–£30, twin/double £44–£46, family room £42–£62; children's reductions; deposit required CARDS: none DETAILS: children welcome; no dogs; no smoking; car park; garden

ERBUSAIG Highland — map 11

Old Schoolhouse

NEW ENTRY

Tigh Fasgaidh, Erbusaig IV40 8BB TEL/FAX: (01599) 5343698

2½m from Kyle of Lochalsh towards Plockton, on outskirts of Erbusaig

Erbusaig is an attractive hamlet just a couple of miles outside Kyle of Lochalsh. The Old Schoolhouse combines bed and breakfast accommodation with a popular licensed restaurant, serving dinner to residents and non-residents, with a menu specialising in local ingredients. There are four attractive, spacious bedrooms, all with *en suite* shower-rooms, and a resident's lounge. As the name implies, it was originally the village school combined with the teacher's house. This is a delightful place to stay, in a quiet spot and very close to the bridge linking the mainland to the Isle of Skye.

OWNERS: Calum and Joanne Cumine OPEN: Easter to Oct ROOMS: 2 double, 1 twin; all rooms with shower, tea/coffee and TV; lounge TERMS: single occupancy £30–£35, twin/double £38–£52; children's reductions; dinner £20 to £25; children's menu; deposit: minimum £10 CARDS: Amex, Delta, MasterCard, Switch, Visa DETAILS: children welcome; dogs welcome; no smoking in dining-room; car park; garden

FALA Midlothian — map 11

Fala Hall Farm

Fala EH37 5SZ TEL/FAX: (01875) 833249

just N of A68, 4m SE of Pathhead, ½m from Fala Village

Approach this sixteenth-century stone house – part of a 285-acre farm – down a half-mile rough track from the tiny hamlet of Fala, which is on the A68 trunk road to Edinburgh. An attractive garden at the front of the house is bounded on two sides by the backs of the stone farm buildings, creating a partly walled effect; the countryside all around is peaceful and pretty. The two simple but large bedrooms share a bathroom, and breakfast featuring eggs cooked any way you like them is served in the TV lounge/dining-room at the back of the house.

OWNER: Helen Lothian OPEN: all year exc Christmas ROOMS: 1 double, 1 family; lounge with TV TERMS: single occupancy £20–£22, double £32–£40, family room from £32; half-price reductions for children under 12 sharing with parents CARDS: none DETAILS: children welcome; dogs welcome, car park; garden

FESHIEBRIDGE Highland map 11

Balcraggan House NEW ENTRY

Feshiebridge, Kincraig PH21 1NG TEL: (01540) 651488
going N on A9 take B9152 to Kincraig; through village to B970, then turn left and house is ½m on right

Jim and Helen Gillies, who used to operate a bed and breakfast from Alvie Manse just a few miles away, built this attractive house and moved in during the summer of 1996. It stands in a lovely rural position above the B970 close to Loch Insh, and on the edge of the Cairngorm Mountains. The ski slopes are a short distance away, and this area is good for walking and bird-watching. There are two very spacious *en suite* bedrooms, furnished with antiques, and guests have use of the drawing-room. Mrs Gillies is very knowledgeable about local attractions and activities, and likes to welcome guests with afternoon tea on arrival. Evening meals are provided by prior arrangement and served at a time to suit guests.

OWNERS: Jim and Helen Gillies OPEN: all year exc Christmas ROOMS: 1 double, 1 twin; both rooms with bath, tea/coffee and TV; lounge TERMS: single occupancy £25–£40, twin/double £50; dinner £15; deposit £10 per person CARDS: none DETAILS: no children under 10; no dogs; no smoking; car park; garden

FIONNPHORT Argyll & Bute map 11

Achaban House

Fionnphort, Isle of Mull PA66 6BL
TEL: (01681) 700205 FAX: (01681) 700649

Visitors who arrived on a nippy autumn day were delighted with the warm welcome they received from the Baigents – and their quickness to put on the central heating. Originally an old manse, built around 1840, Achaban House stands in its own grounds overlooking Loch Poit na h-l, locally known as Loch Pottee. It is about a mile from the village of Fionnphort, from where the ferry runs to the island of Iona, and there is also a daily service to Staffa. The house is largely unaltered since its manse days; consequently the bedrooms are of a good size, and are simply furnished in pine. The two ground-floor rooms are suitable for wheelchair-users; the lounge too is on the ground floor, along with the attractive dining-room (formerly the kitchen), where both breakfast and evening meals by arrangement are served. Washing and drying facilities are available.

OWNERS: Camilla and Chris Baigent OPEN: all year ROOMS: 1 single, with wash-basin; 2 double, 1 with private bathroom, 1 with wash-basin; 3 twin, all with wash-basin; 1 family, with bath/shower; 2 rooms suitable for wheelchair-users; tea/coffee in 1 bedroom; 2 lounges, 1 with TV TERMS: single £18, twin/double £32–£44, family room £50–£60; children's reductions; dinner £10; deposit usually required CARDS: none DETAILS: children welcome; dogs welcome; smoking in 1 room only; car park; garden

Dungrianach

NEW ENTRY

Fionnphort, Isle of Mull PA66 6BL TEL: (01681) 700417

This small whitewashed house overlooks the bay and beach of Fionnphort, set apart from the village, and has lovely views over the sound to the island of Iona. Alison Rimell is a cheerful, welcoming lady, offering two simple *en suite* bedrooms, and serving breakfast at one end of the family lounge. Other meals can be obtained in the village. Weather permitting, boats leave from Fionnphort every morning for Staffa, site of Fingal's Cave (made famous by Mendelssohn), and every half-hour or so the Caledonian MacBrayne ferry leaves for Iona.

OWNER: Alison Rimell OPEN: all year exc Christmas ROOMS: 2 twin, both with shower, tea/coffee and TV TERMS: single occupancy £20–£23, twin/double £34–£38 CARDS: none DETAILS: no children; no dogs; no smoking; car park; garden

FORD Argyll & Bute — map 11

Tigh an Lodan

Ford, by Lochgilphead PA31 8RH TEL/FAX: (01546) 810287
at southern end of Loch Awe, just off B840

Tigh an Lodan, a wooden chalet-style building, dating from the 1970s, lies just outside the tiny village of Ford in a quiet glen at the foot of Loch Awe. The bedrooms are all *en suite* and functionally furnished and equipped. The sitting-room, from which there are views over the loch, has an open fire for when the weather demands. Evening meals are available, and vegetarians can be catered for by request. Packed lunches can also be provided. This peaceful spot is a wonderful place for hill-walking, bird-watching and fishing.

OWNERS: Donald and Sheila Bannister OPEN: May to Oct ROOMS: 1 double, 2 twin; all rooms with bath/shower and tea/coffee; lounge with TV TERMS: single occupancy £19–£21, twin/double £38–£42; dinner £13; deposit required CARDS: MasterCard, Visa DETAILS: no children under 13; dogs by arrangement; no smoking; car park; garden

FORT AUGUSTUS Highland — map 11

Old Pier House

Fort Augustus PH32 4BX TEL: (01320) 366418 FAX: (01320) 366770
on A82 Fort William to Inverness road at north end of village

Old Pier House stands on the shores of Loch Ness, a few minutes from the centre of Fort Augustus. The property includes a farm, occupying an entire peninsula, with highland cattle and a riding centre. Boats, canoes and mountain bikes are also available for hire. The house, built over a hundred years ago, is a low whitewashed building with a large patio overlooking the loch. Décor is simple, floors and furniture are pine, there is a large, light, comfortable lounge, and the house is guaranteed to be warm thanks to open fires plus central heating.

Breakfast is served in the combined kitchen/dining-room, and evening meals can be arranged except during July and August. The small bedrooms all have *en suite* facilities, and help-yourself hot drinks are available in the dining-room at all times. The atmosphere is informal and very friendly, and Jenny Mackenzie speaks several languages. The minimum stay is three nights in July and August.

OWNER: Jenny Mackenzie OPEN: Apr to Oct ROOMS: 2 double, 1 twin, 1 family; all rooms with bath/shower; lounge with TV TERMS: single occupancy £30–£50, twin/double £40–£60, family room £50–£90; dinner £17.50; deposit: £50 CARDS: none DETAILS: no children under 5; no dogs; no smoking; car park; garden

FORT WILLIAM Highland **map 11**

Glenlochy Guest House

Nevis Bridge, Fort William PH33 6PF TEL: (01397) 702909
on A82, ½m N of town centre

Glenlochy was built as a whisky distillery manager's residence in 1930 and is opposite the old distillery itself, which has now been converted into accommodation. It is immaculately kept and well run, and hill-walkers should note that the West Highland Way ends in the grounds. The house is also convenient for the town centre. The bedrooms, seven of which are on the ground floor, are on the small side and functional, there is a comfortable lounge, and individual tables in the breakfast room are well spaced. There are two self-catering units in a wing of the house, which are ideal for families, and sometimes are used as an overflow for the guesthouse.

OWNERS: Mr and Mrs D. Macbeth OPEN: all year exc Christmas ROOMS: 7 double, 6 with bath/shower, 1 with wash-basin; 3 twin, 2 with bath/shower, 1 with wash-basin; 2 family, both with bath/shower; tea/coffee and TV in all bedrooms; lounge with TV TERMS: single occupancy £20–£48, twin/double £32–£50, family room £40–£65; deposit: £10 per person CARDS: Delta, MasterCard, Visa DETAILS: children welcome; no dogs; smoking in lounge only; car park; garden

The Grange

Grange Road, Fort William PH33 6JF TEL: (01397) 705516

This interesting Victorian house, restored by the present owners, stands in a superb position above the town, near Loch Linnhe. It is on a quiet residential road and has an attractive garden. The bedrooms are spacious, beautifully furnished and decorated, each in individual style, and have lovely views – one room has a turret with a window seat overlooking the garden and loch. The drawing-room has an attractive carved wooden fireplace, which came from a hunting lodge. Breakfasts, in the words of one reader, are 'excellent' and are served in the dining-room at individual tables. The Campbells are friendly, cheerful people and greet guests with a complimentary sherry.

OWNERS: John and Joan Campbell OPEN: Mar to Nov ROOMS: 3 double, all with bath/shower, tea/coffee and TV; lounge with TV TERMS: double £66–£70; deposit £20 per person CARDS: none DETAILS: children welcome; no dogs; no smoking; car park; garden

FYVIE Aberdeenshire map 11

Meikle Camaloun

Fyvie AB53 8JY TEL: (01651) 891319
on A947, 2m N of Fyvie and 6m S of Turriff

This attractive and well-kept stone house is approached up a long driveway from the main road. Part of a 200-acre farm, it stands in a neat garden with an old monkey puzzle tree and enjoys views of open countryside. The house is decorated in a variety of wallpapers, and the two bedrooms are fresh and simply furnished, one with *en suite* facilities, the other with a private bathroom. Breakfast is served in the dining-room, and there is a large lounge for guests' use. Fyvie Castle is one of several in the area.

OWNERS: Mr and Mrs W.Wyness OPEN: Mar to Nov ROOMS: 1 double with private bathroom; 1 twin, with bath; tea/coffee and TV in both bedrooms; lounge TERMS: single occupancy £25–£28, twin/double £44–£50 CARDS: none DETAILS: no children; no dogs; no smoking; car park; garden

GARTLY Aberdeenshire map 11

Faich-Hill Farmhouse

Gartly AB54 4RR TEL: (01466) 720240
just off A97, 5m S of Huntly; find Gartly church (not in centre of village), take farm road behind cottage next to church

Faich-Hill is a traditional granite farmhouse, in an isolated location at the end of a long driveway. It forms one side of on an immaculately kept farmyard, with views of rolling hills and farmland, and has been in the Grant family since 1884. The entrance to the house is through the conservatory, where there is lots of literature and brochures on what to do in the area. The two bedrooms are comfortably furnished; one is a twin-bedded room with *en suite* shower, the other a double room with a private bathroom. There is also a cosy TV lounge. The local area is rich with castles and historic houses and gardens.

OWNERS: Margaret and Theo Grant OPEN: May to Oct ROOMS: 1 double, with private bathroom; 1 twin, with shower; lounge with TV TERMS: single occupancy £25, twin/double £36; deposit: £30 CARDS: none DETAILS: no children under 5; no dogs; no smoking; car park; garden

---

If we know a B&B has an alcohol licence, we say so. Most unlicensed B&Bs that offer evening meals allow guests to bring their own wine to dinner. If you wish to do this, ask the B&B when you book.

GARTOCHARN **Dumbarton & Clydebank** **map 11**

Ardoch Cottage

Gartocharn G83 8NE TEL/FAX: (01389) 830452
on A811 between Drymen and Balloch south of Loch Lomond

Views over farmland to Ben Lomond from all three of the *en suite* rooms are a plus at this small whitewashed cottage built in the 1790s. The Lindsays write that it was once a tollhouse on the old military road running between Stirling and Dumbarton castles. The bedrooms, on the other side of the house from the road, are very quiet; one is on the ground floor. A warm and friendly atmosphere pervades: one visitor was impressed with 'help-yourself hot drinks' available in the dining-room, where evening meals (as well as breakfast) are served at 7–7.30pm. A reporter notes that heating in bedrooms is ample, even on cooler summer days and the comfortable sitting-room with its TV has a log fire. Loch Lomond is nearby, and Stirling and Glasgow are within easy reach.

OWNERS: Mabel and Paul Lindsay OPEN: all year ROOMS: 2 double, 1 twin; all rooms with shower; lounge with TV TERMS: single occupancy £35–£40, twin/double £48–£54; children's reductions; dinner £16–£18; deposit: £10 CARDS: MasterCard, Visa DETAILS: children welcome; dogs welcome; no smoking; car park; garden

GIFFORD **East Lothian** **map 11**

Eaglescairnie Mains

Gifford EH41 4HN TEL/FAX: (01620) 810491
from Haddington take B6368 for 4 miles, through Bolton, then take left fork signposted Eaglescairnie, house is ½m on left

This interesting eighteenth-century farmhouse is set in unspoilt, peaceful countryside about a mile from Gifford. The Williamses have won a national conservation award for their work on the 350-acre mostly sheep and arable farm, and have marked walking routes around it. The house is spacious and has been beautifully decorated. There is a large drawing-room and three pretty bedrooms, two of which are *en suite*. Breakfast is served at one table in a small conservatory off the kitchen. Eaglescairnie is an excellent base for exploring the Borders and is not far from Edinburgh. There is also a hard tennis court for guests' use, and packed lunches can be provided.

OWNER: Barbara Williams OPEN: all year exc Christmas ROOMS: 2 double, both with bath and shower; 1 twin, with private bathroom; tea/coffee in all bedrooms; lounge with TV TERMS: single occupancy £20–£30, twin/double £36–£44; children's reductions; deposit: £10 per person CARDS: none DETAILS: children welcome; no smoking in bedrooms or dining-room; car park; garden; games room; tennis

If there are any bedrooms with TV, or with tea/coffee-making facilities, we mention this in the details at the end of an entry.

GLASGOW Glasgow **map 11**

Kirklee Hotel

11 Kensington Gate, Glasgow G12 9LG
TEL: (0141) 334 5555 FAX: (0141) 339 3828

Since the arrival of new owners Douglas and Rosemary Rogen in late 1996, the house has undergone extensive redecoration. They have continued the practice of serving breakfast in the bedrooms, which all have adequate tables and chairs, as well as TV, telephone, trouser press and *en suite* bathrooms. Kirklee Hotel is an attractive red sandstone terraced building in a quiet, residential crescent, within one of the city's conservation areas, and close to the centre. It was built in 1904 for a shipping magnate, and retains many period features, such as the wood-panelled hall, staircase and original drawing-room, and the lounge has been renovated to expose the original parquet floor. The hotel has a restricted licence, and drinks may be served in the lounge or bedrooms.

OWNERS: Douglas and Rosemary Rogen OPEN: all year exc Christmas ROOMS: 4 double, 2 twin, 3 family; all rooms with bath/shower, tea/coffee and TV; lounge with TV TERMS: single occupancy £48, twin/double £64, family room £75–£90; children's reductions according to age; deposit: £20 or credit card details CARDS: Amex, Delta, Diners, MasterCard, Visa DETAILS: children welcome; no dogs; garden

Scott's Guest House

417 North Woodside Road, Kelvinbridge, Glasgow G20 6NN
TEL: (0141) 339 3750

This stone terraced house is on a quiet cul-de-sac just off the Great Western Road, only a ten-minute walk from the university and Botanical Gardens. All the bedrooms have TV, and most have tea/coffee-making facilities and either *en suite* showers or private bathrooms. Guests have the use of a comfortably furnished lounge, and take breakfast at separate tables in the pleasant first-floor dining-room overlooking Kelvin Park. The guesthouse provides good-value accommodation in a convenient location; Kelvinbridge underground station is opposite.

OWNERS: Robert and Kay Scott OPEN: all year ROOMS: 1 single, with private bathroom; 4 double, 3 with shower, 1 with private bathroom; 2 twin, 1 with private bathroom, 1 with wash-basin; 1 family; tea/coffee in most bedrooms; TV in all bedrooms and lounge TERMS: single £17–£20, single occupancy £20–£25, twin/double £30–£35, family room £45–£50; deposit required CARDS: none DETAILS: children welcome; dogs welcome; no smoking in some rooms; car park

The Town House

4 Hughenden Terrace, Glasgow G12 9XR
TEL: (0141) 357 0862 FAX: (0141) 339 9605

Bill and Charlotte Thow continue to maintain high standards at, and improve where possible, this delightful Victorian town house, built in

1882. It has its own attractive small garden, and is located in a quiet residential street close by Glasgow's West End, with its shops, art galleries and restaurants. The rooms are grandly proportioned, some are positively enormous – one family room has a fire certificate for twelve people – and all have *en suite* shower-rooms. There are some lovely original ceiling decorations and cornices, and the décor is muted and relaxing. Lots of reading material can be found in the comfortable lounge, good Scottish breakfasts are served in the original dining-room, and evening meals are also available by arrangement.

OWNERS: Bill and Charlotte Thow OPEN: all year exc Christmas ROOMS: 2 double, 6 twin, 2 family; all rooms with shower, tea/coffee and TV; lounge TERMS: single £58, twin/double £68, family room £78–£88; children's reductions according to age when sharing with parents; dinner £25; deposit: £20 per room CARDS: MasterCard, Switch, Visa DETAILS: children welcome; no dogs; no smoking in dining-room; garden

GOLSPIE Highland map 11

Deo Greine

Backies, Golspie KW10 6SE TEL: (01408) 633106

take A9 north from Golspie for ¾m, turn left under railway bridge, after 1m turn right at T-junction by public telephone; Deo Greine is second left

Deo Greine is a crofthouse in the old community of Backies, in a secluded location on the edge of moorland, and has lovely views. Nelly Grant, originally from Belgium, is a great character, has enormous energy and is an excellent cook: breakfast and dinner are served, and her food is a mixture of French, English and Scottish. The size of the interior is quite surprising, and the house is in immaculate order. Three of the four *en suite* bedrooms are on the ground floor. There is a popular sun lounge which leads on to a patio, another comfortably furnished lounge with a piano, and a separate smoking-room. Dunrobin Castle is nearby, along with many other interesting historical sites.

OWNER: Nelly Grant OPEN: Apr to Oct ROOMS: 1 double, 2 twin, 1 family; all rooms with bath/shower and tea/coffee; lounge with TV TERMS: twin/double £36, family room £42–£48; dinner £11; deposit required CARDS: none DETAILS: children welcome; smoking in 1 sitting-room only; car park; garden

GRANTOWN-ON-SPEY Highland map 11

Culdearn House

Woodlands Terrace, Grantown-on-Spey PH26 3JU
TEL: (01479) 872106 FAX: (01479) 873641

This imposing, granite-built Victorian house sits just on the outskirts of Grantown-on-Spey in its own garden. The Littles are welcoming hosts who provide every comfort, good service and attention to detail. They take pride in their Scottish cooking, offering a substantial Highland breakfast, and dinner, which is included in the room price, using local produce wherever possible. Meals are served at individual tables in the elegant dining-room. The lounge is warm and relaxing and all the bedrooms are well equipped and have *en suite* facilities. Since the last edition of the *Guide*, the public areas have undergone complete refurbishment. Grantown-on-Spey is an excellent base for many activities, such as bird-watching, visiting the malt whisky distilleries, golf and fishing.

OWNERS: Alasdair and Isobel Little OPEN: Mar to mid-Oct ROOMS: 1 single, 5 double, 3 twin; all rooms with bath/shower, tea/coffee and TV; 1 room suitable for wheelchair-users; lounge TERMS: D,B&B single £45–£60, twin/double £90–£120; deposit required CARDS: Amex, Delta, Diners, MasterCard, Switch, Visa DETAILS: no children under 10; no dogs; no smoking in dining-room; car park; garden

Kinross House

Woodside Avenue, Grantown-on-Spey PH26 3JR
TEL: (01479) 872042 FAX: (01479) 873504

This Victorian stone-built villa is located in a peaceful residential road in the centre of Grantown-on-Spey. The bedrooms are bright, warm and spacious, and the ground floor twin bedroom is suitable for ambulant disabled guests. One twin room has a double and single bed. Traditional evening meals are served by David Elder, wearing his McIntosh kilt. Coffee is served after dinner in the guests' sitting-room, which is warmed by a log fire on cooler evenings.

OWNERS: David and Katherine Elder OPEN: Apr to Oct ROOMS: 2 single, 1 with shower, 1 with wash-basin; 1 double with shower; 3 twin, all with shower; tea/coffee and TV in all bedrooms TERMS: single £21–£30, twin/double £46–£54, family room £44–£52; dinner £14.50; deposit: £25 per person CARDS: Delta, MasterCard, Visa DETAILS: no children; no dogs; no smoking; car park; garden

GRIMSAY Western Isles **map 11**

Glendale

7 Kallin, Grimsay HS62 5HY TEL: (01870) 602029

This simple, neat house is on Grimsay, one of the small islands between North Uist and Benbecula. It overlooks the tiny, picturesque fishing port of Kallin, and the rocky inlets along the coast. Mrs MacLeod is a very friendly host, and uses locally caught shrimps, crabs and lobsters in her home-cooked evening meals. The comfortable accommodation comprises two twin-bedded rooms on the ground floor, one with *en suite* bath and shower, one with a private shower-room, and a larger first-floor double room with *en suite* shower and good views.

OWNER: Mrs C. MacLeod OPEN: all year exc Christmas ROOMS: 1 double, with shower and TV; 2 twin, 1 with bath/shower, 1 with private bathroom; tea/coffee in all bedrooms; lounge TERMS: single occupancy £18–£20, twin/double £30–£36, family room from £36; children's reductions; dinner £12; deposit: £10 CARDS: none DETAILS: children welcome; no dogs; no smoking in bedrooms; car park; garden

HOUGHARRY Western Isles **map 11**

Sgeir Ruadh

Hougharry, North Uist HS6 5DL TEL: (01876) 510312
17m from ferry; take A867 to Clachan, then turn right on to A865, after 8m turn left to Hougharry (Hogha Gearraidh)

Sgeir Ruadh stands on the edge of a lovely sandy beach on the Balranald Bird Reserve, and is a popular place for walkers and bird-watchers. Corncrakes can be seen from here in the spring and summer. It is a modern house offering comfortable accommodation in small bedrooms, and breakfast and evening meals are served in the large dining-room/lounge which overlooks the beach. The Simpsons are a welcoming, cheerful couple. There is no licence but guests may bring their own wine to dinner, and packed lunches can be provided.

OWNER: Kathy Simpson OPEN: all year ROOMS: 1 single, 1 double, 1 twin; all rooms with bath/shower and tea/coffee; lounge with TV TERMS: single £16, single occupancy £18, twin/double £32; reductions for children sharing with parents; dinner £12; deposit required CARDS: none DETAILS: children welcome; dogs in bedrooms only; no smoking; car park; garden

INNERLEITHEN Borders **map 11**

Caddon View Guest House

14 Pirn Road, Innerleithen EH44 6HH TEL: (01896) 830208
on A72, 6½m S of Peebles, on right just before leaving Innerleithen

Once a doctor's house, this large, stone Victorian building is set back a little from the main road on the edge of town and has views across the Tweed Valley. The Djellils took over in summer 1996 and offer a friendly welcome to guests. They have also redecorated the house, adding *en suite* showers to most rooms, and a sauna which guests may use without charge. Amar Djellil is an enthusiastic cook and serves four-course evening meals (these must be booked in advance) that might include dishes such as salmon with beurre blanc, or chicken with tarragon in a cream and white wine sauce. Dinner takes place at individual tables in the dining-room, spilling over if necessary into the conservatory, which is where the breakfast buffet items are served. Places to visit in Innerleithen include St Ronan's Well and Robert Smail's Printing works.

OWNERS: Amar and Elena Djellil OPEN: Apr to mid-Jan ROOMS: 3 double, 2 with shower, 1 with private bathroom; 2 twin, both with shower; 1 family, with shower; tea/coffee and TV in all bedrooms; lounge TERMS: single occupancy £25–£30, twin/double £40–£50, family room from £40; children under 2 free, half-price for ages 3–11; dinner £13.50, less for children CARDS: none DETAILS: children welcome; no dogs; smoking in guest lounge only; car park; garden

---

Any smoking restrictions that we know of are given in the details at the end of the entry.

INVERASDALE Highland

Knotts Landing

12 Coast, Inverasdale IV22 2LR TEL: (01445) 781331
on B8057, 5m N of Poolewe

One visitor writes she was surprised 'to pay so little for such comfort and hospitality' at this small house with its lovely views of water and mountains. It is reached down a narrow road which follows the west side of Loch Ewe five miles from Poolewe. Most of the accommodation has been redecorated (including new carpets) since the last edition of the *Guide*, and the house is even more spick and span than before; as we went to press there were plans to make the double and twin rooms *en suite*. Residents' have the use of a TV lounge, and breakfast and evening meals are served in the small dining-room.

OWNER: Sandra Maclean OPEN: all year exc Christmas ROOMS: 1 single, 1 double, 1 twin; all rooms with wash-basin, tea/coffee and TV; lounge with TV TERMS: single/ single occupancy £13, twin/double £26; half-price for children under 12; dinner £10 CARDS: none DETAILS: children welcome; no dogs; no smoking; car park; garden

INVERNESS Highland map 11

Clisham House

43 Fairfield Road, Inverness IV3 5QP TEL/FAX: (01463) 239965

This substantial stone house, formerly the bishop's residence, stands in its own grounds in a quiet neighbourhood. Large *en suite* bedrooms have separately controlled heating, the comfortable lounge has a TV, and breakfast is served at individual tables. Owner Rhoda Beaton is friendly and welcoming. A short walk away are the town centre with a good choice of pubs and restaurants and the Caledonian Canal footpath.

OWNER: Rhoda Beaton OPEN: all year ROOMS: 2 double, 2 family; all rooms with shower and TV; lounge with TV TERMS: double £44, family room from £44 CARDS: none DETAILS: children welcome; no dogs; no smoking in dining-room or lounge; car park; garden

---

Craigside Lodge

4 Gordon Terrace, Inverness IV2 3HD
TEL: (01463) 231576 FAX: (01463) 713409
from town centre take Castle St, first left, then 3 first-lefts

Craigside Lodge is an attractive detached Victorian house standing above the castle on a quiet, narrow residential road. It is only a few minutes' walk from the centre of town and has lovely views over the castle and river. The Skinners, who are friendly and welcoming, continue to improve the facilities of the house. The *en suite* bedrooms are comfortable and attractive; most have showers and one has shower and bath. Both the pretty breakfast room on the lower-ground floor and large lounge have good views. The car park has room for just three cars, but there is also parking available in a lay-by across the street.

OWNERS: Mr and Mrs W. Skinner OPEN: all year ROOMS: 3 double, 3 twin; all rooms with bath/shower, tea/coffee and TV; lounge TERMS: single occupancy £20–£22, twin/double £40; half-price for children under 11; deposit: credit card details CARDS: Delta, MasterCard, Visa DETAILS: children welcome; no dogs; no smoking in bedrooms; car park

Culduthel Lodge

14 Culduthel Road, Inverness IV2 4AG TEL/FAX: (01463) 240089
from town centre take Castle St to Culduthel Rd

Elegance, a spacious country-house feel and a high level of comfort are the qualities that draw visitors to this listed Georgian guesthouse within easy reach of the town centre. All the bedrooms have *en suite* facilities plus amenities such as telephone, TV, CD and cassette system, hair dryer and – upon arrival – a welcoming glass of sherry. Guests are also offered complimentary newspapers of their choice, and there is a 24-hour laundry service. In fine weather drinks or soup and sandwiches are served on the garden terrace, otherwise in the drawing-room, or – if preferred – in guests' bedrooms. Dinner consists of a variety of traditional Scottish dishes prepared by Marion Bonsor, and is served in the attractively laid-out dining-room with its wonderful views over the River Ness and the hills beyond. The house continues to offer a high standard of accommodation.

OWNERS: David and Marion Bonsor OPEN: all year exc Christmas ROOMS: 1 single, 7 double, 2 twin, 1 four-poster, 1 family; all rooms with either shower or bath and shower; tea/coffee and TV in all bedrooms; lounge TERMS: single £45, single occupancy £50–£65, twin/double £75–£80, four-poster £80–£90, family room £80–£85; reductions for children sharing with parents; dinner £18; deposit: £30–£50 CARDS: MasterCard, Visa DETAILS: children welcome (but only children over 10 years at dinner); no dogs in public rooms; no smoking in bedrooms and dining-room; car park; garden

Millwood House

NEW ENTRY

36 Old Mill Road, Inverness IV2 3HR
TEL: (01463) 237254 FAX: (01463) 719400

Millwood House is located in a residential area just ten minutes' walk from the town centre. The Lees are welcoming, friendly people and like their guests to feel at home. The three bedrooms are well equipped; two are on the ground floor overlooking the pretty, colourful garden, which has chairs and a hammock for guests' use, and in summer afternoon tea can be taken outside. A long, narrow picture-lined corridor leads to the combined dining/sitting-room. In the dining-area, guests sit around one table for breakfast, while the spacious sitting-area has an open fire and plenty of books, plus information packs and videos about local places to visit.

OWNERS: Gillian and Bill Lee OPEN: Apr to Oct ROOMS: 2 double, both with shower; 1 twin, with private bathroom; tea/coffee and TV in all bedrooms; lounge with TV TERMS: single occupancy £30–£35, twin/double £50–£54; deposit: £25 CARDS: MasterCard, Visa DETAILS: no children under 12; no dogs; no smoking; car park; garden

Old Rectory

9 Southside Road, Inverness IV2 3BG TEL: (01463) 220969

The Old Rectory is a small, attractive, stone house with pretty gardens both to the front and rear of the property. The décor is regularly updated and the furnishings changed, the pretty bedrooms are all *en suite*, and there is a comfortable lounge. Breakfast is served at individual tables in the attractive dining-room, which has a Victorian fireplace. The house is about five minutes' walk from the town centre.

OWNERS: John and Neina Lister OPEN: all year exc Christmas ROOMS: 2 double, 2 twin; all rooms with shower, tea/coffee and TV; lounge TERMS: twin/double £38–£40; deposit required CARDS: Delta, MasterCard, Visa DETAILS: no children under 8; no dogs; no smoking; car park; garden

Sealladh Sona

3 Whinpark, Canal Road, Muirtown, Inverness IV3 6NQ
TEL/FAX: (01463) 239209
take A862 from Inverness to Beauly, turn left after crossing Caledonian Canal bridge, then ¾m after lock gates take narrow entrance to Whinpark

Readers have been unanimous in their praise of this B&B: the Cooks are 'warm-hearted and hospitable' as well as 'very professional', the food is 'excellent', the location is 'ideal', and even the beds are 'extremely comfortable'. Standing beside the Caledonian Canal on a very quiet, narrow street, Sealladh Sona is an attractive stone-built Victorian cottage which the Cooks have fully and tastefully renovated. The town centre is about a 15-minute stroll away, and there are beautiful walks along the canal. The pretty twin *en suite* rooms are on the first floor, and the double, also *en suite*, is on the ground floor. The entrance opens into the cosy sitting-room. Breakfasts are much praised and offer a great deal of choice: besides usual items such as porridge, bacon and egg, you may find black pudding, hot fruit compôte, poached smoked haddock, and – for vegetarians – rice with vegetables cooked on the griddle and served with poached egg and baked beans. A complimentary nightcap is offered to guests.

OWNER: Marjory W. Cook OPEN: all year exc Christmas ROOMS: 1 double, 2 twin; all rooms with bath/shower, tea/coffee and TV; lounge TERMS: single occupancy £26–£32, twin/double £46–£52; babies free, reductions for children sharing with parents CARDS: Delta, MasterCard, Visa DETAILS: children welcome; no dogs; no smoking; car park

Trafford Bank

NEW ENTRY

96 Fairfield Road, Inverness IV3 5LL TEL: (01463) 241414

This substantial house, standing in its own garden, was once home to the Bishop of Inverness. The McKenzies are genial and energetic hosts and will collect people from the railway station or airport if required. One visitor commented, 'Not only did Peter drive us to the railway station for 6am, he made breakfast first.' All the rooms are spacious and comfortable, the bedrooms *en suite* and supplied with fresh fruit and flowers, and evening meals are served by arrangement in the dining-room. Trafford Bank is very close to the Caledonian Canal, and about 15 minutes' walk from the town centre. At the time of going to press, the McKenzies were planning to add another bedroom.

OWNERS: Peter and Caroline McKenzie OPEN: all year ROOMS: 4 double, 1 twin; all rooms with bath/shower, tea/coffee and TV; lounge TERMS: single occupancy £35–£40, twin/double £50–£55; children's reductions; dinner £17.50 CARDS: Amex, MasterCard, Visa DETAILS: children welcome; dogs welcome in bedrooms only; no smoking; car park; garden

ISLE OF COLONSAY Argyll & Bute map 11

Seaview

NEW ENTRY

Isle of Colonsay PA61 7YR TEL/FAX: (01951) 200315

This renovated working croft on the west coast of the island has spectacular views from the conservatory room at the front and the three simple bedrooms also have fine sea views. There is a shared bathroom on the ground floor, and at the time of going to press the Lawsons were planning to add *en suite* showers to two bedrooms. It is a comfortable, cheerful place, with laundry facilities and bicycle hire, and Annie Lawson provides excellent home-cooked evening meals. Colonsay has wonderful sandy beaches, moorland, cliffs and lochs, and is a great place for walking, cycling, fishing and bird-watching. There are many historic and prehistoric sites, and over 600 species of plants and 200 species of birds have been recorded on the island. The ferry visits only three times a week, so it is advisable to book for a few nights. Self-catering accommodation is also available.

OWNERS: Bill and Annie Lawson OPEN: Easter to mid-Oct ROOMS: 1 double, 2 twin; tea/coffee in all bedrooms; lounge with TV TERMS: single occupancy £22, twin/double £44; children's reductions by arrangement; dinner £15; deposit: £20 per room CARDS: none DETAILS: children welcome; dogs by arrangement; no smoking; car park; garden

---

To find an entry in the Guide, *go to the maps at the back of the book. Entries are plotted on the maps under their closest village, hamlet or city, except in London, where they are listed by name of B&B. After choosing your localities, go to the relevant section of the book (England, Scotland, Wales etc.), where localities are listed in alphabetical order (by B&B name order in London). There is also an index at the back of the book.*

ISLE ORNSAY Highland **map 11**

Tawny Croft

Isle Ornsay, Sleat, Isle of Skye IV43 8QS TEL/FAX: (01471) 833325

When Roger and Pat Cottis moved to this whitewashed old croft just outside the village of Isle Ornsay in 1993, they extended it to incorporate a large lounge with a conservatory and two *en suite* bedrooms, each with double and single beds, to accommodate couples or families. The conservatory has comfortable chairs, a wood burning stove and lovely views. There is a good selection of wildlife books and a telescope is provided, and the island where Gavin Maxwell, author of *Ring of Bright Water*, lived can be seen from here. Both of the small bedrooms look out over the Sound of Sleat and are equipped with binoculars. Roger and Pat organise guided wildlife tours with associated videos shown in the evening. Dinners are served, with vegetarian choices and children's portions available on request; packed lunches can also be provided. Bookings are taken for a minimum of two nights' stay.

OWNERS: Roger and Pat Cottis OPEN: all year exc Christmas ROOMS: 2 double/family, both with bath and shower; tea/coffee in both bedrooms; lounge with TV TERMS: double £50; family room £48–£56; half-price for children under 10; dinner £10; deposit: £20 CARDS: none DETAILS: children welcome; no dogs; no smoking; car park; garden

JEDBURGH Borders **map 11**

Hundalee House

Jedburgh TD8 6PA TEL: (01835) 863011
off A68, 1m S of Jedburgh

Set in ten acres of mature gardens and woodland, this attractive stone-built house with its mullioned windows dating from the eighteenth century lies about a quarter-mile off the main road and enjoys wonderful views over Jed Water and across to the Cheviot Hills. Despite many interests apart from bed and breakfast, Mrs Whittaker maintains a stylish establishment, and the well-kept grounds have picnic benches for guests' use. Each of the five bedrooms has its own colour scheme – traditional flowery patterns and stripes predominate – and one sports an enormous four-poster. The Whittakers were planning to add two family suites by summer 1998. Traditional Scottish breakfast has come in for praise from readers.

OWNERS: Alan and Sheila Whittaker OPEN: Mar to Nov ROOMS: 1 double, with bath/shower; 2 twin, 1 with bath/shower, 1 with wash-basin; 1 four-poster, with bath/shower; 1 family, with wash-basin; tea/coffee and TV in all bedrooms TERMS: single occupancy £25–£35, twin/double £36–£40, four-poster £40–£45, family room £36–£56; children's reductions according to age; deposit required CARDS: none DETAILS: children welcome; no dogs; no smoking; car park; garden

KEITH Moray

map 11

Haughs Farm Guest House

The Haughs, Keith AB55 6QN TEL: (01542) 882238
off A96 Aberdeen to Inverness road, ½ W of Keith

Haughs Farm Guest House is part of a mixed farm of some 165 acres producing rotational crops, beef cattle and sheep. The house itself dates from 1614, and fine views are enjoyed from the south-facing conservatory-style dining-room, only marred a little by the expanses of the distillery warehouses which lie below the house. James Scott Skinner, the famous fiddler and composer, was a regular guest here, settling his B&B account with the composition of a hornpipe. The bedrooms are large and are either *en suite* or have private bathrooms. Although the main entrance is up a steep flight of stairs, there is another entrance for those having difficulty with steps. Dinners are served at 6.30pm, and must be pre-booked. Transportation can be provided by prior arrangement for visitors arriving at Keith by train.

OWNERS: Peter and Jean Jackson OPEN: Easter to Oct ROOMS: 3 double, 2 with bath/shower, 1 with private bathroom; 2 twin, 1 with bath/shower, 1 with private bathroom; tea/coffee and TV in all bedrooms; lounge with TV TERMS: single occupancy £22–£25, twin/double £34–£40; reductions for children sharing with parents; dinner £11.50; deposit: £15 per person CARDS: none DETAILS: children welcome; no dogs; no smoking in bedrooms; car park; garden

KILMALUAG Highland

map 11

Trodaidh View

NEW ENTRY

4 Balmacquien, Kilmaluag, Isle of Skye IV51 9UM TEL: (01470) 522343
off A855, 6m N of Staffin

On the northern coast of Skye, this little whitewashed croft set well away from the road has a dramatic location facing the sea and looking out towards the Outer Hebrides. Guests can walk from the house right down to the shore. The present house is quite old, built on the site of an even older original thatched-roof croft: Mr Campbell is the fifth generation of his family to live here. The two attic-type bedrooms are very small, but bright and immaculate, and share a bathroom downstairs. Mrs Campbell is a cheerful host who offers home-made evening meals, if arranged in advance, served in the lounge-cum-dining-room.

OWNER: Mrs N. Campbell OPEN: all year ROOMS: 1 double, 1 family; both rooms with wash-basin, tea/coffee and TV; lounge with TV TERMS: single occupancy £18–£20, twin/double £28–£30, family room £36–£40; dinner £6.50 to £13 CARDS: none DETAILS: children welcome; dogs welcome; car park; garden

Many B&Bs are in remote places, and although in many cases we provide directions, it is always advisable to ask for clear instructions when booking.

KILMARTIN Argyll & Bute map 11

Tibertich NEW ENTRY

Kilmartin PA31 8RQ TEL/FAX: (01546) 810281
off the A816, 2½m N of Kilmartin

A long, rough driveway winding up the hillside leads to this whitewashed house, originally a croft, in a peaceful setting. Part of a working sheep farm, Tibertich is also a wonderful place for observing wildlife and walking, with fantastic views of the islands just over the brow of the hill. Mrs Caulton is a delightfully welcoming lady, and has furnished the house with simple taste. The three bedrooms are upstairs and share a bathroom; there is a lounge where guests may read or watch TV, and a dining-room where breakfasts are served. Nearby are a number of sites of archaeological and historical interest, including the iron-age fort of Dunadd, Kilmartin Church and Carnasserie Castle. Self-catering cottages are also available.

OWNER: Barbara L. Caulton OPEN: Mar to Nov ROOMS: 1 single, 1 double, 1 twin; lounge with TV TERMS: single/single occupancy £14, twin/double £28; half-price for children under 10 CARDS: none DETAILS: children welcome; no dogs; no smoking; car park; garden

KILMUIR Highland map 11

Kilmuir House

Kilmuir, by Uig, Isle of Skye IV51 9YN TEL: (01470) 542262
on A855 Uig to Staffin road, 5m N of Uig

This attractive whitewashed former manse stands on the Trotternish peninsula, in a walled three-quarter-acre garden, overlooking Loch Snizort and the hills of the Outer Hebrides. Roy and Sally Phelps bought the house in a derelict state and have renovated it extensively to create a comfortable family home. The spacious rooms are furnished with antiques. Two bedrooms are on the first floor with lovely views, and there is a room suitable for families on the ground floor. Dinner (available if booked in advance) and breakfast make good use of home-grown vegetables and their own free-range eggs. Vegetarians and special diets are catered for and guests may bring their own wine to dinner. Packed lunches are also available. Nearby attractions include the Skye Museum of Island Life, Flora MacDonald's grave, the site of Bonnie Prince Charlie's first landing in Skye and the ruins of Duntulm Castle.

OWNER: Sally Phelps OPEN: all year exc Christmas ROOMS: 2 double, 1 twin; lounge with TV TERMS: single occupancy £20–£25, twin/double £34–£35; children's reductions according to age; dinner £10 CARDS: none DETAILS: children welcome; no dogs; no smoking; car park; garden

---

'NEW ENTRY' indicates that a B&B was not in the previous edition (although its owners may have been, at a different address).

KINCRAIG Highland

map 11

March House

NEW ENTRY

Lagganlia, nr Kincraig PH21 1NG TEL: (01540) 651388

from Kincraig follow signs to Feshiebridge, turn right after phone box

March House resembles a Swiss mountain chalet and is set in peaceful, unspoilt scenery between the Cairngorm Mountains and the Caledonian pine forest. It is simply furnished and has an informal atmosphere. One large room with a central wood-burning stove comprises both lounge and dining-room. The Hayeses have a reputation for good food: meals use the best of local produce and vegetables and herbs from their garden. There is mountain bike hire, a ski store and a drying-room, and the area offers many opportunities for hill-walking, mountain-biking, bird-watching, fishing, and both cross-country and down-hill skiing. One-night bookings are not accepted in July and August.

OWNER: Caroline Hayes OPEN: Jan to Oct ROOMS: 2 double, 1 with bath/shower, 1 with private bathroom; 2 twin, both with bath/shower; 2 family, both with bath/shower; tea/coffee in all bedrooms; lounge TERMS: single £20–£26, twin/double £40–£44, family room £40–£64; children's reductions; dinner £15; deposit: £40 CARDS: Visa DETAILS: children welcome; dogs welcome; no smoking in bedrooms; car park; garden

KINGARTH Argyll & Bute

map 11

New Farm Farmhouse

Mount Stuart, Kingarth, Isle of Bute PA20 9NA TEL/FAX: (01700) 831646

Since opening their farmhouse in 1995 as a simple B&B, the Howards have enjoyed great success. Their reputation for good Scottish cooking has spread throughout the island, and, space allowing, several dinner sittings are arranged every evening. New Farm, a 1,000-acre sheep and cattle farm, lies a couple of miles outside the small village of Kingarth. The farmhouse has been imaginatively decorated and furnished, and there is a pretty front garden. Lunch is also served, and packed lunches are available. Nearby attractions include Mount Stuart, a spectacular Victorian Gothic house, which is open to the public.

OWNER: Carole Howard OPEN: all year ROOMS: 2 double, 1 with bath, 1 with wash-basin; 1 family with wash-basin; tea/coffee in all bedrooms; lounge TERMS: single occupancy £17.50–£22.50, double £35–£45, family room £17.50–£22.50; dinner £15; deposit required CARDS: none DETAILS: children welcome; dogs welcome in kennels; no smoking in bedrooms and dining-room; car park; garden

---

If you are forced to turn up later than planned, please telephone to warn the proprietor. It is always best to book a room in advance, even in winter. B&Bs with few rooms may close at short notice for periods not specified in the details.

KINGUSSIE Highland **map 11**

Bhuna Monadh

NEW ENTRY

85 High Street, Kingussie PH21 1HX TEL/FAX: (01540) 661186

Bhuna Monadh, meaning 'foot of the mountain', is a neat, stone-built listed house in the middle of Kingussie – one of the first houses built in the village. It was derelict when Joan Gibson bought it, and she had virtually to rebuild it. Now it is attractively decorated and furnished, with rugs on bare wooden floors throughout most of the house, and two *en suite* bedrooms on the first floor. There is a small dining-area at the back of the house, where breakfast is served. Dinner is also available by arrangement, there is no licence, but guests may bring their own wine. Kingussie is a good base for hill-walking and bird- and wildlife-watching.

OWNER: Joan Gibson OPEN: all year ROOMS: 1 double, 1 twin; both rooms with shower, tea/coffee and TV; lounge with TV TERMS: single occupancy £17–£20, twin/double £34–£40; children under 2 free, half-price for children under 12; dinner £10.50; deposit required CARDS: none DETAILS: children welcome; dogs welcome by arrangement only; no smoking; car park

Osprey Hotel

Ruthven Road, Kingussie PH21 1EN TEL/FAX: (01540) 661510
at south end of the main street

This attractive, granite-built small hotel lies near the centre of the village of Kingussie overlooking the beautiful memorial gardens. Bedrooms are small and cheerful, with most having been recently redecorated and carpeted, and the Burrows are welcoming and enthusiastic hosts. The Osprey is licensed, and guests are served drinks in the two small lounges; one leads through to the dining-room, with its tartan tablecloths and curtains. Scottish cuisine predominates, with much use made of local produce, and over 70 bins feature on the wine list. Packed lunches can be provided, and nearby attractions include golf, clay-pigeon-shooting, skiing in the Cairngorms (usually December to May), walking and fishing.

OWNERS: Robert and Aileen Burrow OPEN: all year exc Christmas ROOMS: 1 single, with bath/shower; 4 double, 3 with bath/shower, 1 with private bathroom; 3 twin, all with bath/shower; all rooms with tea/coffee and TV; 2 lounges TERMS: single £27–£39, single occupancy £34–£46, twin/double £48–£72; half-price for children under 14; dinner £21; deposit: £25 CARDS: Amex, MasterCard, Visa DETAILS: children welcome; dogs welcome; smoking in lounges only; car park; garden

'Bath / shower' in the details under each entry means that the rooms have en suite *facilities. 'Private bathroom' signifies that a room has a bathroom for its exclusive use. The B&B may have other, shared bathroom facilities as well. We list 'wash-basins' for rooms that have them but do not have* en suite *or private facilities.*

KINLOCHBERVIE Highland

map 11

Old School Restaurant

Inshegra, Kinlochbervie IV27 4RH TEL/FAX: (01971) 521383
on B801, on N shore of Loch Inchard halfway between Rhiconich (on A838) and Kinlochbervie

This combined licensed restaurant and guesthouse on the northern shore of Loch Inchard makes much of its former incarnation as a schoolhouse, with writing slates for placemats and the menu chalked up on a blackboard. It is open for lunch and dinner, also to non-residents, and specialises in seafood, although vegetarians are also catered for. Children's helpings are offered, and packed lunches are also available. The restaurant is in the main stone building, which dates from 1879, while the well-equipped bedrooms and a tiny sitting-room are in a modern annexe. Most of the bedrooms are *en suite*, all have TV and telephone and views of either the loch or mountains.

OWNERS: Tom and Margaret Burt OPEN: all year exc Christmas ROOMS: 1 single, with shower; 2 double, both with shower; 3 twin, 1 with shower, 2 with wash-basin; tea/coffee and TV in all bedrooms; lounge TERMS: single £29, single occupancy £29–£36, twin/double £48–£58; £10 for children in family room; dinner £15 to £17 CARDS: MasterCard, Switch, Visa DETAILS: children welcome; dogs welcome by arrangement only; no smoking in dining-room; car park; garden

KIRKAPOL Argyll & Bute

map 11

Kirkapol Guest House

NEW ENTRY

Gott Bay, Kirkapol, Isle of Tiree PA77 6TW TEL/FAX: (01879) 220729

This distinctive white building was once an old church, and was converted impressively into a guesthouse by Grahame Street some eight years ago. The bedrooms are simple and functional, each with *en suite* facilities and TVs. Evening meals are available by arrangement, and are served in the long, high-ceilinged dining-room, which also has an honesty bar. Beyond the dining-room is the lounge, with TV. The guesthouse stands just a few yards away from the beach of Gott Bay, has lovely views and is a couple of miles from the ferry terminal. A courtesy car service from the ferry or airport, which is six miles away, can be arranged.

OWNERS: Grahame and Nora Street OPEN: all year exc Christmas ROOMS: 2 single, 2 double, 2 twin; all rooms with shower, tea/coffee and TV; lounge with TV TERMS: single/single occupancy £24, twin/double £42; dinner £12–£13; deposit: 1 night's charge CARDS: none DETAILS: no children; no dogs; no smoking; car park; garden

---

We state at the end of an entry whether children are welcome, and explain any age restrictions. If there are reduced rates for children, this is mentioned; if no reductions are specified, assume you will have to pay full rates for children.

KIRKCUDBRIGHT Dumfries & Galloway map 11

Gladstone House NEW ENTRY

48 High Street, Kirkcudbright DG6 4JX TEL/FAX: (01557) 331734

Kirkcudbright's High Street is actually a quiet residential street set back from the bustle of shops and cars, close to the old castle. This unpretentious building in a Georgian terrace has three *en suite* double bedrooms at the front of the house with dormer windows, and one also has a sitting-area with windows to the back of the house. Breakfast is taken at separate tables in the ground-floor dining-room, and the lounge is a large, attractive room on the first floor. The house is bright and cheerful, comfortably appointed and thoughtfully furnished with some antique pieces, and the atmosphere is warm and friendly. Afternoon teas are served in the small garden at the back of the house.

OWNERS: Sue and Jim Westbrook OPEN: all year exc 31 Dec ROOMS: 3 double, all with bath/shower, tea/coffee and TV; lounge TERMS: single occupancy £30–£35, double £50–£58; deposit required CARDS: MasterCard, Visa DETAILS: no children under 12; no dogs; no smoking; garden

KIRKTON OF GLENISLA Angus map 11

Glenmarkie Farmhouse

Kirkton of Glenisla PH11 8QB TEL/FAX: (01575) 582341

take B951 to Glenisla then follow signs to Glenmarkie Riding Centre for 3m

Glenmarkie Farmhouse and Riding Centre is in a remote location, at the end of a rough three-mile track, which follows a picturesque glen. The attractive whitewashed building was originally built as servants' quarters for the nearby lodge, and is ideal for an away-from-it-all-type holiday in a warm, informal, relaxed atmosphere. The bedrooms are small and quite simple, and there is a cosy lounge and dining-room, where Simon Evans, who trained in hotel management at the Savoy in London, serves lunch and dinner. While he takes care of accommodation, Sally runs the Riding Centre, catering for all standards of riders for both hacking and trekking. This is also a good base for skiing (cross-country and downhill), fishing, stalking and shooting, and bird-watching.

OWNERS: Simon and Sally Evans OPEN: Easter to Nov ROOMS: 2 double, 1 with bath, 1 with wash-basin; 1 twin, with wash-basin; lounge with TV TERMS: single occupancy £18.50, twin/double £37; half-price for children under 12; dinner £13.50; deposit: £20 CARDS: none DETAILS: children welcome; dogs welcome; smoking in lounge only; car park; garden

---

The end details for each entry state whether or not dogs are allowed, but it is always best to check when booking.

KIRKWALL Orkney **map 11**

Briar Lea

10 Dundas Crescent, Kirkwall KW15 1JQ TEL: (01856) 872747

This old stone house stands in its own garden very close to the town centre. It has a friendly, homely atmosphere and offers simple accommodation. The Fletts are local people and very knowledgeable about the area. There are two spacious twin-bedded rooms and two small singles, one of which is on the ground floor. The breakfast room also has a sitting-area. There is much of architectural interest in the town, including St Magnus Cathedral. Bird-watching and loch-fishing can be enjoyed close by.

OWNERS: Mr and Mrs Arthur Flett OPEN: all year ROOMS: 2 single, both with wash-basin; 2 twin, both with private bathroom; tea/coffee in all bedrooms; lounge with TV TERMS: single/single occupancy £17, twin £34; children's reductions by arrangement; deposit: £10 CARDS: none DETAILS: children welcome; no dogs; no smoking; car park; garden

Leckmelm NEW ENTRY

Annfield Crescent, Kirkwall KW15 1NS TEL: (01856) 873917

This very comfortable modern house is in a quiet part of Kirkwall, about 15 minutes' walk from the centre. It has an attractive garden, with a cannon on the rear lawn, and a patio area, and has views of Kirkwall Bay and the North Isles. The Scotts are a very welcoming couple and are happy to advise about local places of interest. Mrs Scott, a retired teacher, is a good cook and offers guests a home-baked local delicacy called 'fatty cutties' for breakfast. The three bedrooms share a bathroom, and guests have use of a games room with a pool table.

OWNERS: John and Margaret Scott OPEN: all year exc Christmas ROOMS: 1 single, 1 double, 1 twin; tea/coffee and TV in all bedrooms; lounge with TV TERMS: single/single occupancy £16–£17, twin/double £30–£32 CARDS: none DETAILS: children welcome; no dogs; no smoking; car park; garden

KIRRIEMUIR Angus **map 11**

Purgavie Farmhouse NEW ENTRY

Lintrathen, Kirriemuir DD8 5HZ TEL/FAX: (01575) 560213
on B951, 6m W of Kirriemuir; farm is signposted from road

This old farmhouse stands at the foot of Glen Isla six miles from Kirriemuir, and has good views of the surrounding glens. The Clark family have farmed here since 1902, and now produce potatoes and barley, with sheep and cattle on the hills. Mrs Clark's evening meals make good use of seasonal produce, and she is happy to discuss preferences with guests. The spacious bedrooms are either *en suite* or have a private bathroom, and have hairdryers, electric blankets and clock radios as well as TVs. Guests may relax in the conservatory.

Kirriemuir was the childhood home of J.M. Barrie, and is only a few miles from Glamis Castle, where the Queen Mother lived as a child and where Princess Margaret was born. Purgavie Farm is a good base for fishing, skiing, pony-trekking and walking. Self-catering accommodation is also available.

OWNER: Mrs Moira Clark OPEN: all year ROOMS: 1 twin, with bath/shower; 2 family, 1 with bath/shower, 1 with private bathroom; tea/coffee and TV in all bedrooms; lounge with TV TERMS: single occupancy £23–£25, twin £36–£40, family room from £36; half-price for children under 14; dinner £11; deposit: £15 per person CARDS: none DETAILS: children welcome; well-behaved dogs welcome; no smoking in bedrooms or dining-room; car park; garden

LARGS North Ayrshire **map 11**

South Whittlieburn Farm

Brisbane Glen, Largs KA30 8SN TEL/FAX: (01475) 675881

turn right off A78 ½m NE of Largs, signposted Brisbane Glen Rd; after 2¼m farm is second on left

Mary Watson is constantly upgrading the guests' accommodation, and now the three clean, fresh bedrooms at this old whitewashed farmhouse are all *en suite*. Set in a pretty valley with good views of the hills, South Whittlieburn is part of a working sheep farm and also provides stabling for horses. Guests are welcome to look round the farm and help with feeding the lambs. The TV lounge has also been freshly decorated and furnished, and there is a sitting-area in the breakfast room. Facilities for campers and caravaners are available at the farm. About two miles away is the resort town of Largs, which has a good selection of restaurants and bars.

OWNER: Mary Watson OPEN: all year exc Christmas ROOMS: 1 double, 1 twin, 1 family; 2 rooms with shower, 1 with bath and shower; tea/coffee and TV in all bedrooms; lounge with TV TERMS: single occupancy £19.50, twin/double £37, family room from £39; children's reductions by arrangement CARDS: none DETAILS: children welcome; no dogs; smoking in lounge only; car park; garden

LERWICK Shetland **map 11**

Leeskol

NEW ENTRY

4 Scalloway Road, Lerwick ZE1 0BT TEL: (01595) 693135

Leeskol is a small bungalow in central Lerwick, with a very pretty and colourful garden, and wonderful views of the hills and sea. Mrs Black, who was born only a few streets away, is a cheerful and friendly lady who makes her guests feel at home. The comfortable sitting-room, open to residents 24 hours a day, has a breakfast table in the window overlooking the garden towards the sea. The simple bedrooms all have tea- and coffee-making facilities, and the two upstairs share a shower-room.

OWNER: Betty Black OPEN: all year ROOMS: 3 twin, 1 with bath; 1 room suitable for wheelchair-users; tea/coffee in all rooms; lounge with TV TERMS: single occupancy £20, twin £36; deposit required for stays more than 5 nights CARDS: none DETAILS: children welcome; no dogs; no smoking in bedrooms; garden

Whinrig

12 Burgh Road, Lerwick ZE1 0LB TEL: (01595) 693554

Whinrig is a neat house located in a quiet cul-de-sac only a few minutes from shops and museums. All the immaculate, small bedrooms are on the ground floor and are comfortably furnished. One twin room has an *en suite* shower, another has a shower but is not fully *en suite*, and shares a bathroom with a double. Besides a guest lounge, there is separate dining-room where breakfast is served. The compact, beautifully kept garden, with its tables and chairs for sitting outside on fine days, affords views of the sea. The Giffords are a welcoming couple.

OWNER: Mrs W. Gifford OPEN: all year exc Christmas and New Year ROOMS: 1 double, with wash-basin; 2 twin, 1 with shower; tea/coffee and TV in all bedrooms; lounge TERMS: single occupancy £18, twin/double £34–£36; deposit required CARDS: none DETAILS: no children; no dogs; no smoking; car park; garden

LEVERBURGH Western Isles **map 11**

St Kilda House

Leverburgh, Isle of Harris HS5 3UB TEL: (01859) 520419
off A859, 21m S of Tarbert

St Kilda stands on a quiet, narrow road, on the edge of Leverburgh – An-t-Ob in Gaelic – just above the shoreline, and enjoys wonderful views of inlets and the many small islands that dot the coastline. From the late 1880s to the early 1930s it was the local schoolhouse, and when the present owners moved here in 1992 it was in a state of dereliction. The scene now couldn't be more different: the two *en suite* bedrooms are well appointed and extremely comfortable; the twin room overlooks the sea and the double has a king-sized bed and both a bath and extra-large shower. Besides a sitting-room with TV, there is a minute dining-room facing the sea, where first-class breakfasts and five-course dinners are served (dinner is included in room prices). Sue and Jim take particular pride in their cooking, making as much as possible themselves, including yoghurt and bread. Vegetarians can be catered for with advance notice. It is preferred that guests book for a minimum of three nights.

OWNERS: Sue Massey and Jim Shaw OPEN: May to Sept ROOMS: 1 double, 1 twin, one with bath, one with bath and shower; tea/coffee and TV in both bedrooms; lounge with TV TERMS: D,B&B single occupancy £55, twin/double £90; deposit required CARDS: none DETAILS: children welcome; no dogs; no smoking; garden

Shieldaig House

NEW ENTRY

Leverburgh, Isle of Harris HS5 3TY TEL: (01859) 520378

Shieldaig House, an old whitewashed cottage on a hillside on the edge of the village, was renovated and opened as a relaxed and informal guesthouse in 1997 by Elaine and Ken Whettall. The bedrooms are compact, but are freshly and simply decorated, and there is a small lounge-cum-dining-room where lunch and dinner are served. Menus feature local ingredients and there is a separate vegetarian menu. Bicycles and fishing equipment are available for free hire, boat trips to nearby islands can be arranged, and maps and local information can be provided.

OWNERS: Elaine and Ken Whettall OPEN: all year ROOMS: 2 double, 1 twin/family; tea/coffee in all bedrooms; lounge TERMS: single occupancy £25, twin/family £36; children's reductions according to age; dinner £9; deposit: 10% CARDS: none DETAILS: children welcome; dogs welcome; no smoking; car park; garden

LINLITHGOW West Lothian **map 11**

Thornton

NEW ENTRY

Edinburgh Road, Linlithgow EH49 6AA TEL: (01506) 844216

This large, attractive house dating from 1870 has a happy, welcoming atmosphere, and has received many favourable reports from *Guide* readers. Thornton has been gradually extended over the years, and the guest accommodation is at the more modern end of the house, which has its own entrance via the dining/sitting-room. There are two attractive, well-equipped *en suite* bedrooms, and a lovely garden. A canal runs behind the property, and it is a pleasant walk to follow its banks into the centre of historic Linlithgow.

OWNERS: Rob and Jill Inglis OPEN: all year exc Christmas ROOMS: 1 double, with bath/shower; 1 twin, with shower; tea/coffee and TV in both bedrooms; lounge with TV TERMS: single occupancy £25–£30, twin/double £40–£50 CARDS: none DETAILS: no children under 10; no dogs; no smoking; car park; garden

LOCHBOISDALE Western Isles **map 11**

Brae Lea House

Lasgair, Lochboisdale, South Uist HS8 5TH TEL/FAX: (01878) 700497
½m along main road from ferry terminal, turn right at Lasgair

Brae Lea House is on the edge of town, overlooking the loch, and at low tide it is possible to take a short cut to the town centre and ferry. All the plain, simple bedrooms are on the ground floor and are *en suite*; most have nice views down to the water and to the hills, as does the large lounge. Two bedrooms have been adapted to accommodate wheelchairs, and a ramp has been installed at the back of the house. Work has also been done to the outside of the house, and a large car park has been added. Evening meals are served by arrangement. Mrs Murray is happy to provide breakfast early for guests catching ferries, and will also arrange to pick guests up from the ferry.

OWNERS: Patsy and George Murray OPEN: all year ROOMS: 2 double, 2 twin, 2 family; all rooms with bath/shower and tea/coffee; 2 rooms suitable for wheelchair-users; lounge with TV TERMS: single occupancy £25–£30, twin/double £50–£60, family room £50–£70; children under 3 free, half-price for ages 5–12; dinner £12 CARDS: none DETAILS: children welcome; dogs welcome; car park; garden; sauna

Loch-Side Cottage

NEW ENTRY

Lochboisdale, South Uist HS8 5TH TEL: (01878) 700472

This small pebble-dashed house is just off the road on the edge of a small sea loch. At the time of going to press, the two bedrooms had private bathrooms but the owners were planning to add *en suite* facilities. There is also a comfortable lounge. Mrs MacDonald will prepare evening meals if pre-booked, and Mr MacDonald is happy to take guests out fishing. Loch-Side Cottage is close to the ferry terminal.

OWNERS: Mr and Mrs Alastair MacDonald OPEN: all year exc Christmas ROOMS: 1 double, 1 twin; both rooms with private bathroom and tea/coffee; lounge with TV TERMS: single occupancy £15–£17, twin/double £30; reductions for children under 12; dinner £10 CARDS: none DETAILS: children welcome; dogs welcome; car park; garden

LOCHCARNAN Western Isles map 11

Orasay Inn

Lochcarnan, South Uist HS8 5PD
TEL: (01870) 610298 FAX: (01870) 610390
off A865, on NE coast of South Uist

Orasay Inn is located on the north-eastern coast of South Uist, and makes a good base for exploring North and South Uist and Benbecula. It is a small hotel, offering simple accommodation and a warm and friendly welcome, plus a restaurant (open to non-residents) which specialises in seafood. The dining-room has views across the Minch to the mountains of South Uist, and there is a cosy residents' lounge/bar with peat fire, plus a separate bar for non-residents. Wheelchair access to both the restaurant and accommodation has been improved with the addition of ramps, and there is now a WC suitable for wheelchair-users. Nearby Loch Bee is popular for windsurfing; guests can also enjoy the wild life, unspoilt beaches, fishing and the archaeological sites.

OWNERS: Alan and Isobel Graham OPEN: all year ROOMS: 2 single, 3 double, 2 twin, 2 family; all rooms with bath/shower; 2 rooms suitable for wheelchair-users; tea/coffee and TV in all bedrooms; lounge with TV TERMS: single £25–£29, single occupancy £25–£38, twin/double £46–£70; dinner £10 CARDS: Delta, MasterCard, Switch, Visa DETAILS: children welcome; dogs by arrangement (not in public areas); no smoking in dining-room and some bedrooms; car park; garden

LOCHDON Argyll & Bute **map 11**

Gorsten Farm House

NEW ENTRY

Gorten, Lochdon, Isle of Mull PA64 6AP TEL/FAX: (01680) 812332
turn left off A849 at Gorten, signposted after 1½m

When the road ends at the end of Loch Don, the Gorsten Farm property begins. There are two gates between this point and reaching the farmhouse, with possibly sheep and cattle to encounter on the way. The house stands in the middle of the peninsula, almost surrounded by two-and-a-half miles of rocky coastline, and its 400 acres of farmland encompass the entire end of the point. Bedrooms are simply and comfortably furnished, and all have lovely sea views. Rosemarie Auld is an attentive host and offers evening meals if arranged in advance, served in the conservatory-style dining-room. This is an away-from-it-all location, and a great place for nature and walking.

OWNER: Rosemarie Auld OPEN: all year exc Christmas ROOMS: 1 double, 2 twin; all rooms with bath/shower and tea/coffee; lounge with TV TERMS: single occupancy £30–£36, twin/double £40–£50; 25% reduction for children 2 to 10; dinner £15; deposit: 1 night's charge CARDS: none DETAILS: children welcome; no dogs; no smoking; car park; garden

LOCHDONHEAD Argyll & Bute **map 11**

Old Mill Cottage

Lochdonhead, Isle of Mull PA64 6AP TEL/FAX: (01680) 812442
on A849, 3m S from ferry at Craignure

Old Mill Cottage can be found just off the road in the village of Lochdonhead. It is an attractive, long, low whitewashed cottage, converted and extended by Jim and Jenny Smith when they moved here in 1994. Jim is an experienced chef, having previously worked at the Craignure Inn, and before that in Paris, and the Cottage has established a reputation for good food, served in the charming, intimate licensed restaurant. The three bedrooms, all on the ground-floor, are simply furnished, and guests can be assured of a warm welcome from the Smiths.

OWNERS: James and Jennifer Smith OPEN: all year exc Christmas ROOMS: 1 double, with bath/shower; 2 twin, 1 with bath/shower, 1 with private bathroom; 1 room suitable for wheelchair-users; tea/coffee and TV in all bedrooms; lounge TERMS: single occupancy £35, twin/double £50, family room from £50; half-price for children; dinner £25; deposit required CARDS: Delta, MasterCard, Visa DETAILS: children welcome; no dogs in restaurant or lounge; smoking in lounge only; car park; garden

If a B&B offers off-street car parking, we note 'car park' at the end of the entry. If nearby on-street parking must be used, in most cases we give details in the descriptive text.

LOCH ERIBOLL Highland map 11

Port-na-Con House

Loch Eriboll IV27 4UN TEL/FAX: (01971) 511367
just off A838, 7m SE of Durness

Port-na-Con, originally a customs house and harbour store, is in a beautiful position on the west side of Loch Eriboll, down a long driveway off the A838. It was converted and modernised in 1984 to a small, comfortable whitewashed guesthouse with its own little beach. The small bedrooms are clean and comfortable, one *en suite*, the other two with private bathroom, and all have loch views. There is a first-floor lounge, with plenty of local books and maps. Evening meals make good use of local produce and are also available to non-residents. Port-na-Con is licensed, vegetarians and other special requirements are catered for with notice, and packed lunches can also be provided. There is a nine-hole golf course in nearby Durness, and the Blacks can provide air for divers.

OWNERS: Ken and Lesley Black OPEN: Mar to Oct ROOMS: 1 double with private bathroom; 1 twin with shower; 1 family with private bathroom; tea/coffee in all bedrooms; lounge TERMS: single occupancy £23.50–£25, twin/double £35–£38, family room from £35; dinner £12; deposit: £10 per person CARDS: MasterCard, Visa DETAILS: children welcome; dogs welcome; no smoking; car park; garden

LOCHINVER Highland map 11

The Albannach

Baddidarroch, Lochinver IV27 4LP TEL/FAX: (01571) 844407
off A837, ½m W of Lochinver

Most of this house dates back to the nineteenth century, but parts are more than 200 years old. It stands in a peaceful position half a mile from the fishing village of Lochinver, and offers all that is best in Highland hospitality. The 1990s addition to the house is the conservatory, where guests can sit and enjoy a drink while admiring the spectacular views across the bay to the mountains of Assynt. The character of the house has been enhanced by sympathetic renovation to provide unusual and comfortable accommodation. One room has a four-poster bed and has been decorated with a Highland theme, and a fifth, larger bedroom has been converted from an adjoining building. TV is available in rooms on request. The superb meals are included in the price and are served in the wood-panelled candlelit dining-room, which is also open to non-residents. Lesley cooks and Colin serves, often sporting a kilt.

OWNERS: Colin Craig and Lesley Crosfield OPEN: Mar to Dec ROOMS: 2 double, 2 twin, 1 four-poster; all rooms with bath and shower and tea/coffee; lounge TERMS: D,B&B single occupancy £74–£85, twin/double/four-poster £114–£130; deposit: £50 per room CARDS: MasterCard, Visa DETAILS: no children under 5; no dogs; no smoking; car park; garden

LOCHMADDY Western Isles map 11

Stag Lodge

NEW ENTRY

Lochmaddy, North Uist HS6 5AE
TEL: (01876) 500364 FAX: (01876) 500417

Once upon a time this attractive whitewashed building on a quiet side road was Lochmaddy's first post office, and later the local grocery store. Renovated by the present owners, it offers glimpses of the sea in front and rolling countryside to the rear, and is only a few minutes' walk from the ferry terminal. Each bedroom's décor has an individual Scottish clan tartan theme, and all have *en suite* showers. As the *Guide* went to press, another room that would be suitable for disabled visitors was under construction. The licensed restaurant, which is open to non-residents, offers a wide variety of dishes; room service is also available to 9pm. Sea-fishing can be arranged, and an abseiling and canoeing centre is nearby.

OWNERS: Jock and Jacqueline Handyside OPEN: all year ROOMS: 2 double, 2 twin; all rooms with shower, tea/coffee and TV; lounge with TV TERMS: single occupancy £21.50–£26.50, twin/double £43; children under 3 breakfast price only, half-price for ages 3–9; dinner £9–£16; deposit required CARDS: none DETAILS: children welcome; no dogs in dining-room; smoking in lounge only; car park; garden

LOCHRANZA North Ayrshire map 11

Apple Lodge

Lochranza, Isle of Arran KA27 8HJ TEL/FAX: (01770) 830229

The Boyds have transformed the former village manse into a place of elegance and comfort, with antique furniture in the sitting- and dining-rooms. The spacious bedrooms have been attractively decorated, and as the *Guide* went to press the twin room was being converted into *en suite*. There is also a ground-floor suite, with access to the garden, which incorporates bedroom, bathroom and sitting-room. The dining-room has been extended to incorporate two rooms, and meals are served at separate tables. Evening meals, including vegetarian options, are available using local produce and home-grown herbs. The house is a mile from the ferry to Kintyre.

OWNERS: John and Jeannie Boyd OPEN: all year exc Christmas ROOMS: 3 double, 1 twin; all rooms with bath/shower, tea/coffee and TV; lounge TERMS: single occupancy £35–£42, twin/double £50–£56, suite £64–£68; dinner £15; deposit: £25 per person CARDS: none DETAILS: no children under 12; no dogs; no smoking in bedrooms or dining-room; car park; garden

Butt Lodge Hotel

Lochranza, Isle of Arran KA27 8JF TEL: (01770) 830240

Butt Lodge stands in two acres of gardens on the edge of the village of Lochranza in a quiet rural spot under the hills, and not far from the ferry to Kintyre. A pleasant whitewashed building, built in the late nineteenth century as a shooting lodge, it is now a hotel with a cosy, friendly atmosphere. The bedrooms are fresh and clean, are frequently redecorated, and all have *en suite* facilities. Dinner is served at 7.30 in the pretty licensed dining-room, and the large, comfortable sitting-room has an open log fire. Next to the hotel is a golf course, and deer can often be seen grazing nearby.

OWNERS: Mr and Mrs P. Price OPEN: Apr to Oct ROOMS: 4 double, 2 twin; all rooms with bath/shower and tea/coffee; lounge with TV TERMS: twin/double £48–£56; dinner £14; deposit required CARDS: Delta, MasterCard, Visa DETAILS: no children; no dogs; no smoking; car park; garden

LONGFORMACUS Borders **map 11**

Eildon Cottage

Longformacus, nr Duns TD11 3PB TEL: (01361) 890230
off A6105 / B6355, 6m W of Duns

Eildon Cottage is way off the beaten track in an unspoilt moorland setting and doubles as the post office for the tiny village of Longformacus. However, the Southern Upland Way passes the front of the house, so it is a popular stopping-off place for hikers on their way from coast to coast. It is a charming, extremely comfortable house, very attractively decorated and furnished, with delightfully welcoming hosts. There is a pretty sitting-room with a round table in the bay window for breakfast, and evening meals on request; vegetarians are catered for. Fishing is available on the River Dye, and it is a short distance to Duns for a golf course.

OWNER: Margaret Amos OPEN: all year exc Christmas and New Year ROOMS: 1 double, with private bathroom; 1 twin, with bath/shower; 1 family, with bath/shower; tea/coffee and TV in all bedrooms; lounge with TV TERMS: single occupancy £18–£20, twin/double £36–£38, family room £54–£56; children's reductions; dinner £10–£12; deposit required CARDS: none DETAILS: children welcome; dogs welcome; no smoking in bedrooms; car park; garden

LONGHOPE Orkney **map 11**

Burnhouse Farm

Longhope, South Walls, Hoy KW16 3PA TEL: (01856) 701263
from Lyness ferry terminal follow directions for Longhope, take first right, signposted Burnhouse farm

This small farmhouse, standing on a hill just above Longhope, with lovely views towards Lyness, has a welcoming, friendly atmosphere. Leslye Budge looks after the accommodation, while husband John, a mechanic for the Longhope lifeboat crew and a voluntary fireman, as well as being a farmer, is happy to point guests in the direction of local attractions, which include a Martello tower and archaeological sites. There are two simple, spacious, comfortable ground-floor bedrooms furnished in pine and guests share the large sitting/dining-room with the family. Hoy is a wonderful place for walks, bird-watching and spectacular scenery, including the Old Man of Hoy. Families with children are very welcome.

OWNER: Leslye Budge OPEN: all year exc Christmas ROOMS: 1 twin, 1 family; both rooms with private bathroom, tea/coffee and TV; lounge with TV TERMS: single occupancy £16–£18, twin £32–£36, family room from £32; children under 2 free; dinner £9 CARDS: none DETAILS: children welcome; dogs welcome by arrangement; smoking in sun porch only; car park; garden

LUNNING Shetland map 11

Skeo Green

Lunning ZE2 9QB TEL: (01806) 577302
16m N of Lerwick (ask for directions when booking)

Skeo Green is a large whitewashed house – previously two semi-detached crofts – standing at the very end of a narrow road in a beautiful and isolated spot close to the sea. It offers simple accommodation, with just one double bedroom. Optional evening meals, taken in the family dining-room, are discussed with guests beforehand; a sample menu might include poached salmon with dill yoghurt dressing, served with Shetland-style potatoes, salad and oatcakes, and followed by baked apples with almond paste and home-made custard. Both Mr and Mrs Ford are artists, with Barbara sculpting, and Roger, who also teaches in a school, painting. They work out of their studio, which adjoins the house, and both this room and a dark room are available to guests. The house is full of books, and is an excellent base for walkers, fishermen and bird-watchers.

OWNER: Barbara Ford OPEN: all year ROOMS: 1 double; lounge with TV TERMS: single occupancy £16; double £32; half-price for children under 14; dinner £6–£10; deposit: £6 per night CARDS: none DETAILS: children welcome; no dogs; no smoking; car park; garden

LYNESS Orkney map 11

Stoneyquoy Farm

Lyness, Hoy KW16 3NY TEL/FAX: (01856) 791234
3m from Lyness Pier towards Longhope

'Extremely comfortable with excellent food' was how one visitor summed up his stay at this traditional farm with its low stone buildings and slate roofs, sheltered garden and views over Longhope Bay. Both of the small bedrooms – which are in an extension to the house – are *en suite*. The house is open-plan and guests are welcome to share the kitchen (where they can make tea or coffee when they wish), sun porch and sitting-room with the family, enjoying the open peat fire on cooler evenings. Louise Budge, who comes from Holland, describes her home-cooked dinners as 'plain and wholesome', and she is happy to plan meals with guests who are staying a few days. Arthur Budge is pleased to give guests a tour of the 200-acre beef farm. Plenty of advice is available on good walks in the area and places to visit, and guests may borrow bicycles. Hoy is the largest outer island of the Orkneys and has a large RSPB reserve.

OWNERS: Arthur and Louise Budge   OPEN: all year exc Christmas   ROOMS: 1 double, 1 twin; both rooms with shower; lounge with TV   TERMS: single occupancy £16–£18, twin/double £32–£34; reductions for children according to age; dinner £9; deposit: £2.50 per person per night   CARDS: none   DETAILS: children welcome; no dogs; no smoking; car park; garden

MACHRIHANISH   Argyll & Bute   map 11

East Trodigal Cottage

Machrihanish PA28 6PT   TEL: (01586) 810305
take A83 from Tarbert to Campbeltown, then A843 to Macrihanish

A pretty stream runs round the garden of this whitewashed house and up the glen to a little ruined church and graveyard. The house, which stands on the Campbeltown road just outside Machrihanish, has been delightfully decorated and simply furnished. One room serves as both sitting-room and breakfast room, and there are two bedrooms, each with *en suite* bath and shower. Machrihanish golf course, the local airport (with regular services from Glasgow) and a chapel are very close by, while Campbeltown, Mull of Kintyre Lighthouse and Saddell Abbey are within easy reach. A babysitting service is offered, and tea and coffee trays that come with home-made cakes can be supplied on request.

OWNER: Linda Peacock   OPEN: Apr to Oct   ROOMS: 1 double, 1 family, both with bath/shower and TV   TERMS: single occupancy £18–£20, twin/double £32–£36, family room £16–£18; children under 2 free, half-price for ages 2–12   CARDS: none   DETAILS: children welcome; dogs welcome; no smoking; car park; garden

MELROSE   Borders   map 11

Dunfermline House

Buccleuch Street, Melrose TD6 9LB   TEL/FAX: (01896) 822148

Dunfermline House, a small stone building, has been prettily decorated throughout and offers clean, comfortable accommodation. It is efficiently and professionally run, yet still has a welcoming and friendly atmosphere. There is a cosy lounge and an attractive dining-room, where breakfast is served. Packed lunches can also be provided. The house stands right in the centre of Melrose, about 50 yards from the abbey. The property does not have off-street parking, but there is a public car park close by.

OWNERS: Susan and Ian Graham   OPEN: all year   ROOMS: 1 single, with private bathroom; 2 double, both with bath/shower; 2 twin, both with bath/shower; tea/coffee and TV in all bedrooms; lounge with TV   TERMS: single £22–£24, twin/double £44–£48; deposit: £10 per person   CARDS: none   DETAILS: children welcome; no dogs; no smoking

MELVAIG Highland map 11

Rua Reidh Lighthouse NEW ENTRY

Rua Reidh, Melvaig IV21 2EA TEL/FAX: (01445) 771263

The Lighthouse is in about a remote a spot as can be found: Melvaig is at the end of eight miles of single-track road from Gairloch, then it's another three miles of private, twisty, sometimes steep and bumpy lane to the end of the point, affording spectacular views of Skye and the Outer Hebrides. Accommodation is in the old lighthouse-keeper's house, a substantial building on a wild rocky clifftop next to the still operational light tower. It lay derelict for four years before being rescued in 1989 by the present owners, who have gradually been improving the property ever since. They offer a wide variety of accommodation in a friendly and informal atmosphere, combining hostel-type rooms, comfortable *en suite* bedrooms, catered meals, including teas for non-residents, and a kitchen where guests can cook their own meals. Rock-climbing, abseiling and guided walks are all offered with qualified guides, and the area is great for watching seals, occasionally whales and dolphins, and for walking.

OWNERS: Fran Cree and Chris Barrett OPEN: all year ROOMS: 1 double, with bath/shower; 2 twin, 1 with bath/shower, 1 with wash-basin; 2 family, 1 with bath/shower, 1 with wash-basin; 1 room suitable for wheelchair-users; tea/coffee in all bedrooms; TV in some bedrooms TERMS: single occupancy £18–£25, twin/double/family £28–£36; children under 2 free, reductions for children sharing with parents; dinner £10; deposit: 20% or credit card CARDS: Delta, MasterCard, Switch, Visa DETAILS: children welcome; dogs by arrangement; no smoking; car park

MELVICH Highland map 11

The Sheiling

Melvich KW14 7YJ TEL/FAX: (01641) 531256
on A836, 15m W of Thurso

This small, pebble-dashed house stands above the main road on the edge of Melvich with panoramic views over the River Halladale to the Atlantic. The Campbells, who were born and brought up in the area, built the Sheiling as a family home. An enthusiastic reporter described Joan Campbell as 'a bright and cheerful hostess'. All three bedrooms are on the ground floor; two face the front and the one at the back enjoys the afternoon sun. Each has *en suite* shower and use of the separate bathroom. There is a comfortable lounge and an attractive dining-room, where guests sit at one large table for breakfast, overlooking the beach. Across the road there is a walkway down to the beach, and visitors can enjoy walks on the Campbells' private land. Dinner is no longer served, but there are two pubs and a hotel nearby serving bar meals. At the time of going to press, the Campbells were planning to convert the third bedroom to include *en suite* facilities.

OWNERS: Hugh and Joan Campbell OPEN: March to Oct ROOMS: 3 double, 2 with shower, 1 with private bathroom; tea/coffee in all bedrooms; lounge with TV TERMS:

single occupancy £30–£46, twin/double £44–£48; deposit: £10 CARDS: none DETAILS: children welcome; no dogs in dining-room or lounge; no smoking; car park; garden

MOFFAT Dumfries & Galloway **map 11**

Alba House

20 Beechgrove, Moffat DG10 9RS TEL/FAX: (01683) 220418
last turning on right before exiting town, going N, on A701

Evelyn and Jake Lindsay's listed terraced house is, in the words of one visitor, an 'unusual and fascinating' place, reflecting their interests in birds and bird-watching, pottery and pictures. They provide a friendly atmosphere and maintain a high standard of comfort: one couple felt they were 'staying with friends rather than as paying guests'. Built in 1731, the house is on a quiet street on the edge of the town, with a pretty terraced garden overlooking fields and the Annan Valley. The three *en suite* bedrooms are spacious and well appointed; breakfast is served in the attractive dining-room, which has an inglenook fireplace. Many sporting facilities are available nearby, including tennis courts and an 18-hole golf course. Visitors have the use of a washing machine and drying facilities.

OWNERS: Evelyn and Jake Lindsay OPEN: all year exc Christmas ROOMS: 1 double, 1 twin, 1 four-poster; all rooms with bath and shower, tea/coffee and TV; lounge with TV TERMS: single occupancy £25–£30, twin/double £40–£50, four-poster £50–£60; children under 5 free CARDS: none DETAILS: children welcome; no dogs; no smoking; car park; garden

Ericstane

Moffat DG10 9LT TEL: (01683) 220127
at end of narrow road following River Annan, 4m N of Moffat

Ericstane farm lies in an idyllic, secluded valley overlooking fields of sheep and the River Annan, and surrounded by the rolling Moffat hills. It is a typical hill sheep farm, covering 800 acres, tended by Mrs Jackson, while Mr Jackson takes care of the accommodation. The farmhouse itself is an attractive, old, rambling building, which has been extensively modernised while retaining many of its original features, such as its pine doors, and its décor includes a fine collection of old paintings and prints. The two large, comfortable bedrooms, both *en suite*, face the front. Breakfast, which features home-made bread, is served at one end of the sitting/dining-room.

OWNER: R.H. Jackson OPEN: all year ROOMS: 1 double, 1 twin; both rooms with bath/shower, tea/coffee and TV; lounge with TV TERMS: single occupancy £23, twin/double £36; deposit required CARDS: none DETAILS: children welcome; dogs welcome; car park; garden

The end details for each entry state whether or not dogs are allowed, but it is always best to check when booking.

Fernhill

Grange Road, Moffat DG10 9HT TEL: (01683) 220077

The Gourlays are gracious, hospitable hosts who have the knack of always making their guests feel welcome. Their comfortably furnished and extremely well-maintained house, with its trinkets, ornaments and pictures, stands at the top of a small rise at the end of a quiet residential street. Both bedrooms have *en suite* facilities. Breakfast is served in the pretty dining-room, which has a sitting-area off it overlooking the colourful and beautifully kept garden. Mrs Gourlay tells us the garden was featured on BBC TV in 1997 and occasioned much interest in Moffat. Guests also have the use of another lounge, which has a TV. The car park is locked at night.

OWNERS: Mr and Mrs A.N. Gourlay OPEN: Apr to Sept ROOMS: 1 double, 1 twin; both rooms with bath/shower, tea/coffee and TV; lounge with TV TERMS: single occupancy £20–£25, twin/double £36; deposit required CARDS: none DETAILS: no children; no dogs; smoking in lounge only; car park; garden

Thai-Ville

3 Dundanion Place, Moffat DG10 9GD TEL: (01683) 220922
entering town from south, turn right at war memorial on High St, continue up Old Well Rd to 'Thai-Ville' sign

Located in a quiet residential street, this small modern bungalow offers two very comfortable *en suite* twin rooms, a warm welcome and extremely convenient access to Moffat: the town centre is just a few minutes' walk away. The house – named 'Thai-Ville' after the Batys' many visits to Thailand – is full of ornaments and trinkets, and has a strictly no-smoking policy throughout. One of the bedrooms, Mrs Baty writes, is suitable for the less able (and for wheelchair-users, with help). Breakfast is served at one table in the dining-room, and guests are encouraged to mark their menu choices the night before, especially if they want porridge or kippers. Besides a full, cooked breakfast, a continental option is also available, and special diets can be catered for with prior notice.

OWNER: Eileen Baty OPEN: Apr to Oct ROOMS: 2 twin, both with bath and shower, tea/coffee and TV; lounge with TV TERMS: single occupancy £35, twin £37; deposit: £10 CARDS: none DETAILS: no children; dogs by arrangement; no smoking; car park; garden

MUCKLE ROE Shetland — map 11

Westayre

NEW ENTRY

Muckle Roe ZE2 9QW TEL: (01806) 522368
4½m S of Brae; last house on Muckle Roe

Set in a spectacular position, overlooking water, cliffs and hills, and close to the shore, Westayre is a small, modern croft house. The round-shaped island of Muckle Roe is linked to the mainland by a rather treacherous-looking narrow bridge, and the croft is at the very end of the road, which goes almost halfway around the island. Further exploration can be made on foot: to sandy beaches, over moorland to rugged headlands and the former old settlement of The Hams, or out to the lighthouse. Mr Wood was born on Muckle Roe and his great-grandfather farmed the land on which the croft now stands, which was fairly recently built by the Woods; the land supports about 60 sheep. Mrs Wood maintains a delightfully colourful garden – no mean feat in Shetland's climate. She is a most welcoming, hospitable lady, and offers extremely comfortable and well-appointed accommodation. The restful lounge has an open peat fire, and a pretty table set in the window is where breakfast and good home-cooked evening meals are served.

OWNERS: Elsie and Ivor Wood OPEN: Mar to Dec ROOMS: 1 double, 1 twin; both rooms with bath/shower, tea/coffee and TV; lounge with TV TERMS: single occupancy £16–£18, twin/double £32–£36; babies free, reductions for children aged 1–12; dinner £9 CARDS: none DETAILS: children welcome; no dogs; no smoking; car park; garden

MUIR OF AIRD Western Isles **map 11**

Lennox Cottage

Muir of Aird, Isle of Benbecula PA88 5LA TEL: (01870) 602965

Owner Emma Macdonald was born nearby in one of the island's oldest houses, which has connections with Bonnie Prince Charlie. She is a warm, friendly host and offers guests home-baked cakes on arrival. The accommodation is simple and the bedrooms are comfortably appointed – two have *en suite* facilities, the other has a private bathroom – and the cosy lounge has an open fire. Good home-cooked meals are served in the kitchen. Muir of Aird is close to a golf course, beaches and trout lochs, and makes an excellent base for exploring both South and North Uist.

OWNER: Emma Macdonald OPEN: all year exc Christmas ROOMS: 2 double, 1 with bath/shower, 1 with private bathroom; 1 twin, with bath/shower; tea/coffee and TV in all bedrooms; lounge with TV TERMS: single occupancy £30, twin/double £36–£38; dinner £10 CARDS: none DETAILS: no children under 8; no dogs; no smoking; car park; garden

NENTHORN Borders **map 11**

Whitehill Farm

Nenthorn TD5 7RZ TEL/FAX: (01573) 470203

take A6089 from Kelso towards Edinburgh; farm is next right after passing through Nenthorn

This early-Victorian farmhouse on a working farm is in an attractive location with marvellous views of the Cheviots. It is a comfortable, tastefully decorated house with a large, pleasant lounge, and a front-facing dining-room where evening meals are served. The two single rooms are very spacious and share a bathroom with one of the twin-bedded rooms, while the other twin has an *en suite* shower-room.

Guests are welcome to explore the farm and there is access to tracks for walks. The area is full of history and has an abundance of castles and old houses, including nearby Floors Castle. Packed lunches are provided for fishing parties.

OWNERS: David and Betty Smith OPEN: all year exc Christmas and New Year ROOMS: 2 single, both with wash-basin; 2 twin, 1 with shower, 1 with wash-basin; tea/coffee in all bedrooms; lounge with TV TERMS: single £22, single occupancy £27–£28, twin £44–£46; children's reductions; dinner £14 CARDS: none DETAILS: children welcome; dogs welcome; no smoking in bedrooms; car park; garden

NEWBURGH Fife map 11

Ninewells Farmhouse NEW ENTRY

Woodriffe Road, Newburgh KY14 6EY TEL/FAX: (01337) 840307

from Newburgh take A913 W, turn left into Woodriffe Rd; continue 1m to farm

This attractive old farmhouse is in a truly rural location, about a mile outside the small town of Newburgh, and has glorious views over the River Tay. It is part of a 400-acre working cattle and arable farm, and the house has a delightful walled garden. The Bairds are extremely friendly and welcoming people, and guests feel at home here. Pretty stencilling decorates many of the walls, and the bedrooms are comfortable and unfussy. The guests' lounge is an enormous conservatory-type room with views all round, where visitors are offered a welcoming tea or coffee with home-baked biscuits or scones. Breakfast is served at one table in the dining-room.

OWNERS: Barbara and Gavin Baird OPEN: Apr to Oct ROOMS: 1 double, with shower; 1 twin, with private bathroom; 1 family, with private bathroom; lounge with TV TERMS: single occupancy £20–£23, twin/double £34–£46; family from £34 CARDS: none DETAILS: no children under 7; no dogs; no smoking; car park; garden

NEWTON STEWART Dumfries & Galloway map 11

Oakbank

Crosbie Road, Newton Stewart DG8 6JB
TEL: (01671) 402822 FAX: (01671) 403050

This Victorian stone-built house stands on a hill above the town in its own large garden with a croquet lawn, and commands fine views. It is attractively decorated and furnished, with a fine collection of prints, and the rooms are spacious and comfortable. Unusual slanting bay windows in the main rooms make the most of the scenery. There is a comfortable sitting-room, and dinner is served by arrangement at one table in the dining-room. Sheila Limbrey is happy to cater for any dietary needs. Logan Botanical Gardens and Wigtown Bay Nature Reserve are nearby.

OWNER: Sheila Limbrey OPEN: all year exc Christmas ROOMS: 2 double, 1 with bath/shower, 1 with private bathroom; 1 twin, with bath/shower; tea/coffee and TV in all bedrooms; lounge with TV TERMS: single occupancy £20, twin/double £18–£20; dinner £11 CARDS: none DETAILS: no children; dogs welcome; no smoking; car park; garden

NORTH ERRADALE Highland

map 11

Little Lodge

North Erradale, Gairloch IV21 2DS TEL: (01445) 771237
on B8021 Gairloch to Melvaig road, ¼m beyond turning to North Erradale

This attractive whitewashed crofthouse stands alone on a wild moorland peninsula overlooking the Minch to Skye and the Torridon Mountains. Di and Inge are welcoming, friendly and unobtrusive hosts, and guests immediately feel at home. The sitting-room has an open fire, exposed stone walls, and painstakingly stripped original wood panelling. Good home-cooked meals (including vegetables and herbs from the garden), a highlight of a stay at Little Lodge, are served in the sun-room, which has windows all round. (Note that room rates include dinner.) The bedrooms are very comfortable; one is on the ground floor. Sheep, goats and hens occupy the land surrounding the croft.

OWNERS: Inge Ford and Di Johnson OPEN: Apr to Oct ROOMS: 2 double, 1 twin; all rooms with shower and tea/coffee; lounge with TV TERMS: D,B&B twin/double £45–£48; deposit: £50 CARDS: none DETAILS: no children; no dogs; no smoking; car park; garden

OBAN Argyll & Bute

map 11

Argyll Villa

NEW ENTRY

Albert Road, Oban PA34 5EJ TEL: (01631) 566897

Set in a pretty terraced garden with seating that guests can use on fine days, and enjoying lovely views over Oban Bay, Argyll Villa is in a very central position. Steps through the garden lead to the street below, which in turn is only a couple of streets below the centre of town. It is a substantial early-Victorian house, comfortably furnished, including quilts made by Maggie McGill, who is a most welcoming host.

OWNERS: Mac and Maggie McGill OPEN: all year exc Christmas ROOMS: 2 double, 1 with bath/shower; 1 twin; tea/coffee and TV in all bedrooms TERMS: single occupancy £25–£30, twin/double £36–£50; deposit: £20 CARDS: none DETAILS: no children; no dogs; no smoking; car park; garden

Don-Muir

Pulpit Hill, Oban PA34 4LX TEL: (01631) 564536 FAX: (01631) 563739

Don-Muir is a modern villa-style house on a hill in a residential area of Oban. It has a well-kept front garden, with pleasant hillside views behind. Mrs Robertson is a friendly host, and is constantly seeking to maintain and improve the house. The three ground-floor bedrooms are on the small side, while the two on the first-floor are more spacious. They are all comfortably furnished, as is the ground-floor lounge. Breakfasts, and evening meals by arrangement, are served in a small dining-room at the back of the house. Oban is the starting point for ferries to the Inner and Outer Hebrides.

OWNERS: Peigi and Malcolm Robertson OPEN: Feb to Oct ROOMS: 1 single, with wash-basin; 3 double, all with bath/shower; 1 twin, with WC and wash-basin; tea/coffee and TV in all bedrooms; lounge TERMS: single £16–£18, single occupancy £25, twin/double £34–£38; dinner £12.50; children's reductions; deposit: £5 per person CARDS: none DETAILS: children welcome; dogs welcome; smoking in lounge only; car park; garden

---

Dungrianach

Pulpit Hill, Oban PA34 4LU TEL/FAX: (01631) 562840

Dungrianach (a Gaelic word meaning 'the sunny house') occupies a fine position in Oban, in a quiet and peaceful location with superb views over the Sound of Mull. The late-Victorian house, situated in a large, mature and beautifully maintained garden, is immaculately kept, attractively furnished and decorated, and has spacious rooms. Guests have use of a bright TV lounge and breakfast is served at one table in the dining-room. Dungrianach is only five minutes' walk from the ferry to the islands.

OWNERS: Mike and Elaine Robertson OPEN: Easter to Sept ROOMS: 1 double, 1 twin, both with shower, tea/coffee and TV; lounge TERMS: single occupancy £35, twin/double £40; deposit: £20 CARDS: none DETAILS: children welcome; dogs welcome; car park; garden

---

Heatherfield House NEW ENTRY

Albert Road, Oban PA34 5EJ TEL/FAX: (01631) 562681

Excellent food is a main reason for visiting this former manse, which dates from 1878 and enjoys some fine views over Oban Bay. Another plus is its convenient location, just a short way up the hill from the centre of town. The bedrooms are comfortable and well appointed, but it is the restaurant that counts: to stay here and not to eat would be, for most visitors, unthinkable. Alasdair Robertson's expertise in the kitchen, which has earned him entries in *The Good Food Guide*, yields dishes such as lobster poached in herb broth, minted breast of duckling, and casserole of venison with pineapple and green peppercorns; herbs are home-grown, ingredients are mostly locally supplied, and much of the food is home-cured or baked. The room rate is reduced if dinner is included. High teas are offered for children.

OWNERS: Alasdair and Jane Robertson OPEN: all year ROOMS: 3 double, 1 twin; all rooms with bath/shower, tea/coffee and TV; lounge TERMS: single occupancy £37.50, twin/double £60; children's reductions by arrangement; dinner £16.50–£27; deposit:

£30 per room or credit card details CARDS: MasterCard, Visa DETAILS: children welcome; small dogs welcome in bedrooms only; smoking in lounge only; car park; garden *(The Good Food Guide)*

Lorne View

Ardconnel Road, Oban PA34 5DW TEL: (01631) 565500

Lorne View is a small terraced house with views over Oban Bay. It stands in a quiet street on a hillside above the centre of town, which is only a few minutes' walk away, and is close to the famous McCaig's Tower. The three bedrooms are small and attractively decorated, and each has its own shower unit, tea-making facilities and TV. The two double rooms, one of which has a wonderful view, are on the second floor, and the twin-bedded room is on the first floor next to the bathroom. There is a small lounge/dining-room where evening meals are served by arrangement. Mrs Maclean is a very welcoming host, and her husband is coxswain of the Oban lifeboat.

OWNER: Elizabeth Maclean OPEN: all year exc Christmas ROOMS: 2 double, 1 twin; all rooms with shower, tea/coffee and TV; lounge TERMS: single occupancy £30–£36, twin/double £68–£76; dinner £12; deposit: £20 CARDS: none DETAILS: children welcome; dogs by arrangement; no smoking in lounge

OLD DAILLY South Ayrshire **map 11**

Hawkhill Farm

Old Dailly KA26 9RD TEL: (01465) 871232
take B734 from Girvan to Old Dailly, left crossroads, ½m to farm

Once a coaching-inn, Hawkhill is now a working farm where wheat, barley and other crops are grown and which supports a small herd of naturally reared beef cattle. Besides offering a warm welcome, Mrs Kyle takes the trouble to fill the house with attractive flower arrangements and to provide home-baked bread and biscuits for her visitors. The two bedrooms are spacious and share a bathroom, and the attractive first-floor sitting-room with its log fire is a comfortable place in which to relax or watch TV. Guests are free to use the large garden, and there is a lock-up shed for those who have brought – or arrived on – bikes. Breakfast is taken in the dining-room at what Mrs Kyle describes as 'grannie's large Victorian table', and features home-made preserves along with a choice of cooked dishes based on local produce. Restaurants and pubs for evening meals are a short drive away.

OWNERS: Morton and Isobel Kyle OPEN: Easter to Oct ROOMS: 1 double, 1 twin; both rooms with wash-basin, tea/coffee and TV; lounge with TV TERMS: single occupancy £25, twin/double £42, family room from £34; children's reductions by arrangement; deposit: £10 CARDS: none DETAILS: children welcome; dogs in bedrooms only; smoking in lounge only; car park; garden

OLDMELDRUM Aberdeenshire map 11

Cromlet Hill

South Road, Oldmeldrum AB51 0AB
TEL: (01651) 872315 FAX: (01651) 872164
entering Oldmeldrum on A947 from S, take first left signposted 'town centre' and Inverurie; Cromlet Hill is 200yds on right

Most of this listed Georgian house standing on the outskirts of the old market town of Oldmeldrum dates from around 1805, although it was extended in early Victorian times. It was once home to Sir Patrick Manson, founder of the London School of Tropical Medicine. It is furnished throughout in keeping with its style and history, and has spacious, well-appointed rooms. Guests also have the use of a large, secluded garden and conservatory. Dinner, available by prior arrangement, is served in the dining-room, and guests are welcome to bring their own wine. Aberdeen Airport is just 15 minutes' drive away, and Haddo House, Fyvie Castle, Pitmedden gardens and local distilleries are all within easy reach.

OWNERS: John and Isabel Page OPEN: all year exc Christmas ROOMS: 1 double, 1 twin, 1 family; all rooms with bath and shower, tea/coffee and TV; lounge with TV TERMS: single occupancy £29–£37.50, twin/double £50–£65, family room from £67.50; half-price for children in family room; dinner £17.50; deposit: 20% if booking 2 weeks or more in advance CARDS: none DETAILS: children welcome; no dogs; smoking in lounge only; car park; garden

PEEBLES Borders map 11

Whitestone House

Innerleithen Road, Peebles EH45 8BD TEL: (01721) 720337

This large stone house, on the A72, close to the centre of Peebles, was built in 1892 as a manse and is set in a large, pretty garden with lovely views of the hills. The rooms are of a good size and simply furnished. Margarete Muir continues to redecorate the house, and has deliberately not made any of the rooms *en suite*, as she would prefer to keep the size and shape of the rooms intact, and likes to be able to keep prices down. There are two bathrooms for guests' use. The comfortable sitting/breakfast room has an original black marble fireplace and overlooks the garden. Breakfast is served at one table.

OWNER: Margarete Muir OPEN: all year exc Christmas ROOMS: 1 single, 3 double, 1 twin, 1 family; all rooms with wash-basin and tea/coffee; lounge with TV TERMS: single £16–£17, twin/double £32, family room £40–£50; children's reductions; deposit required for arrival after 6pm CARDS: none DETAILS: children welcome; no dogs; car park; garden

---

If you are forced to turn up later than planned, please telephone to warn the proprietor. It is always best to book a room in advance, even in winter. B&Bs with few rooms may close at short notice for periods not specified in the details.

PERTH Perthshire & Kinross **map 11**

Achnacarry

3 Pitcullen Crescent, Perth PH2 7HT
TEL: (01738) 621421 FAX: (01738) 444110
on A94, on N side of Perth

A warm and comfortable house that offers a friendly welcome, Achnacarry is one of the first in a row of guesthouses in Pitcullen Crescent (part of the A94 Perth to Forfar road). It is about a ten-minute walk from the town centre. Residents have the use of a restful small sitting-room, and the four attractively decorated, well-equipped bedrooms are all either *en suite* or have sole use of a shower-room. Breakfast, as well as evening meals by arrangement, is served in the dining-room, and guests are welcome to bring their own wine to dinner.

OWNERS: Eileen and John Cowan OPEN: all year ROOMS: 1 double, with shower; 1 twin, with private shower-room; 2 family, both with shower; tea/coffee and TV in all bedrooms; lounge with TV TERMS: single occupancy £25–£38, twin/double £39–£45, family room £52–£60; reductions for children sharing with parents; dinner £9.50–£10; deposit: 1 night's charge CARDS: Amex, MasterCard, Visa DETAILS: children welcome; dogs by arrangement; no smoking in dining-room; car park

Pitcullen Guest House

NEW ENTRY

17 Pitcullen Crescent, Perth PH2 7HT
TEL: (01738) 626506 FAX: (01738) 628265

This family-run guesthouse is on the A94 Perth to Forfar road, approximately ten minutes' walk from the town centre. It has a small, well-kept front garden and pleasant views to the back of the house, which the bright, first-floor lounge enjoys. The pretty dining-room is on the ground floor. The bedrooms, one of which is on the ground floor, are attractively decorated and well-maintained, and all have *en suite* or private shower or bath. Nancy Keddie is a warm and welcoming host.

OWNER: Nancy Keddie OPEN: all year ROOMS: 1 single, with private bathroom; 4 double, all with showers; 1 family, with shower; tea/coffee and TV in all bedrooms; lounge TERMS: single £22–£30, single occupancy £25–£30, twin/double £40–£50, family room £50–£70; reductions for children under 2; deposit: £20 CARDS: MasterCard, Visa DETAILS: children welcome; no dogs; no smoking in some rooms and dining-room; car park

Sunbank House Hotel

50 Dundee Road, Perth PH2 7BA
TEL: (01738) 624882 FAX: (01738) 442515

The main part of this very comfortable and professionally run guesthouse dates from 1853, although five of the well-appointed bedrooms, all with good-sized bathrooms, are in a modern ground-floor extension. There is a very attractive, light dining-room, which overlooks the front garden and has fine views to the River Tay and across the city to the Grampian Mountains. The comfortable guests' lounge has a licensed bar. One of the bedrooms is suitable for wheelchair-users, and there are facilities for the disabled on the ground floor.

OWNERS: Gordon and Florence Laing OPEN: all year ROOMS: 5 double, 2 twin, 2 family; all rooms with bath/shower; 1 room suitable for wheelchair-users; tea/coffee and TV in all bedrooms; lounge TERMS: single occupancy £53–£65, twin/double £58–£70, family room £75–£85; children's reductions according to age; dinner £25; deposit required CARDS: MasterCard, Visa DETAILS: children welcome; no dogs; smoking in lounge only; car park; garden

PITLOCHRY Perthshire & Kinross map 11

Arrandale House

Knochfarrie Road, Pitlochry PH16 5DN TEL/FAX: (01796) 472987

This attractive two-storey stone house lies on the edge of Pitlochry in the heart of the Highlands, and offers fine views over the valley to the hills. It dates from the 1860s and was built as a manse for Pitlochry East Church. The house has spacious rooms, some with their original ceilings. The bedrooms have their own sitting-areas, as there is no guests' lounge. Breakfast is served in the dining-room. Woodland walks, golf, pony-trekking, boating and fishing are just some of the attractions nearby.

OWNERS: Atholl and Pat Irvine OPEN: Mar to Nov ROOMS: 1 single, with wash-basin; 3 double, 2 with shower, 1 with wash-basin; 1 twin, with shower; 2 family, both with shower; tea/coffee and TV in all bedrooms TERMS: single £22.50, single occupancy £25–£35, twin/double £45–£50, family room £60–£70; reductions for children CARDS: none DETAILS: children welcome; no dogs; no smoking; car park; garden

Craigatin House NEW ENTRY

165 Atholl Road, Pitlochry PH16 5QL TEL: (01796) 472478

Craigatin House, built by Pitlochry's first doctor, after whom the hospital is named, stands on the northern edge of town in an acre of gardens. The bedrooms are very comfortable, spacious and well-equipped – some have everything including (literally) the kitchen sink. Half of the bedrooms are in the main house, with the remainder in a conversion of the stable wing. The breakfast room has been extended to include the conservatory. Kathy and Peter Stevenson give a warm welcome to their guests.

OWNER: Kathleen Stevenson OPEN: all year ROOMS: 10 double, 4 twin; all rooms with bath/shower; 1 room suitable for wheelchair-users; tea/coffee and TV in all bedrooms TERMS: single occupancy £24–£35, twin/double £36–£52; deposit required CARDS: none DETAILS: children welcome; dogs welcome; no smoking in public areas and some bedrooms; car park; garden

PLOCKTON Highland

map 11

The Shieling

Plockton IV52 8TL TEL: (01599) 544282
on S side of Loch Carron 5m north of Kyle of Lochalsh

A happy atmosphere and an enviable position add to the charm of this low, narrow house standing on a peninsula jutting out into the loch. One side of The Shieling faces the picturesque conservation village of Plockton, while the other reaches down to the water. All three bedrooms are on the ground floor, and the two rooms without *en suite* facilities have fine views across the bay to hills and Duncraig Castle. The large, light-filled lounge has sliding doors to the garden, and is where breakfast is served. The house is just a couple of minutes' walk from the village centre along a footpath on top of a narrow causeway. Guests bringing children should note that only two people are permitted in each bedroom – i.e. only one adult and one child per room.

OWNERS: Mr and Mrs John MacDonald OPEN: Apr to Oct ROOMS: 2 double, 1 with shower, 1 with wash-basin; 1 twin, with wash-basin; tea/coffee in all bedrooms; lounge with TV TERMS: twin/double £36–£44; children's reductions by arrangement; deposit: £10 CARDS: none DETAILS: children welcome; no dogs; smoking in lounge only; car park; garden

PORT APPIN Argyll & Bute

map 11

Lochside Cottage

NEW ENTRY

Fasnacloich, Port Appin PA38 4BJ TEL/FAX: (01631) 730216

Lochside Cottage, a modest whitewashed building, can be found up Glen Creran, which was made famous by Robert Louis Stevenson's *Kidnapped*. From the head of the sea loch, a narrow road runs inland, and the cottage lies one mile beyond the Invercreran Hotel, in a peaceful and beautiful location on the shore of Loch Baile Mhie Chailen. The house has wonderful views across the hills of Glen Etive to the distant mountains of Glencoe, and is tastefully and simply furnished, with spacious, well-appointed bedrooms. The sitting-room, with a log fire, overlooks the loch, and guests sit at one large table for breakfast and delicious home-cooked dinners. Earle and Stella Broadbent are welcoming hosts. Most visitors come for the peace and quiet or the opportunities for outdoor pursuits. From the house one can walk around the loch or climb one of the nearby hills. It is a good base too for touring the west coast, or visiting the Western Isles.

OWNERS: Earle and Stella Broadbent OPEN: all year ROOMS: 1 double, with bath; 2 twin, 1 with bath, 1 with private bathroom; tea/coffee and TV in all bedrooms; lounge TERMS: single occupancy £20–£25, twin/double £40–£50; dinner £17; deposit: £20 per person CARDS: none DETAILS: children welcome; dogs welcome in bedrooms only and not left unattended; no smoking; car park; garden

PORT CHARLOTTE **Argyll & Bute** map 11

Nerabus NEW ENTRY

Port Charlotte, Isle of Islay PA48 7UE TEL/FAX: (01496) 850431
on A847, 2m S of Port Charlotte

This modest-looking, whitewashed former crofthouse was extended some years ago on the sea side of the building. It is only about 100 yards from the beach, and the views from Nerabus are reckoned to be among the best on the island. The hills of Jura are clearly visible, as well as the southernmost part of Islay. The house is quite delightful inside: the large, open, comfortable sitting-room, where breakfast and dinner are also served, has windows all around to take maximum advantage of the views. Meat comes from local farmers and much of the produce is home-grown. Two of the comfortable bedrooms are on the ground floor, two are on the first floor, and all of them are *en suite*. Mrs Lenton-Halsall is a charming and welcoming lady and will arrange for guests to be picked up from the ferry or airport. Nerabus is unlicensed but guests may bring their own wine to dinner. Packed lunches can be provided.

OWNER: Patricia Lenton-Halsall OPEN: all year ROOMS: 1 double, 3 twin; all rooms with bath/shower, tea/coffee and TV; lounge with TV TERMS: single/single occupancy £20, twin/double £40; half-price for children under 14; dinner £10 CARDS: none DETAILS: children welcome; no dogs; no smoking in some areas; car park; garden

PORT ELLEN **Argyll & Bute** map 11

Glenmachrie Farmhouse NEW ENTRY

Port Ellen, Isle of Islay PA42 7AW TEL/FAX: (01496) 302560

This modest whitewashed building stands beside the road six miles from Bowmore and four from Port Ellen, near the airport, Duich Nature Reserve and Machrie Golf Links. It is within walking distance of the Big Strand – seven miles of sandy beach and dunes – and guests are offered fishing on the Whytes' own loch and river. Glenmachrie is a 450-acre mixed farm, with cattle, sheep, ponies and horses, as well as some pure highland cattle. Wildlife abounds in the area, including roe deer, hares, herons, otters, and barnacle and white-fronted geese. The house is comfortably furnished, with bedrooms *en suite* and well equipped, and there are drying facilities for clothes and boots. There are also two sun-rooms, one facing the sunrise and the other the sunset. The Whytes are hospitable and friendly, and will arrange bicycle and car hire and distillery tours. Rachel is a superb cook and makes good use of the farm's own lamb, beef, pork, free-range eggs, salmon and brown trout. Vegetarian choices are available by arrangement. Guests are offered a glass of sherry in the lounge before dinner.

OWNER: Rachel Whyte OPEN: all year ROOMS: 2 double, 3 twin; all rooms with shower, tea/coffee and TV; lounge with TV TERMS: single occupancy £38, twin/double £56; dinner £20; deposit: £10 per person CARDS: none DETAILS: no children under 12; no dogs; no smoking; car park; garden

PORTPATRICK Dumfries & Galloway **map 11**

Carlton House

21 South Crescent, Portpatrick DG9 8JR TEL: (01776) 810253

This terraced nineteenth-century house has one of the best locations in the attractive small seaside town of Portpatrick, on the seafront and right in the centre of town. It is fresh and bright and simply furnished, and some of the bedrooms and the first-floor lounge enjoy spectacular views over the bay and harbour and, on fine days, to the distant hills of Ireland. Breakfast and evening meals are served, and packed lunches can be provided. The Southern Upland Way, a popular walking route which crosses the entire width of Scotland, starts in Portpatrick.

OWNERS: R. and E. Thorburn OPEN: all year ROOMS: 5 double, 4 with bath/shower, 1 with private bathroom; 1 twin, with bath/shower; 1 family, with bath/shower; 1 room suitable for wheelchair-users; tea/coffee and TV in all bedrooms; lounge with TV TERMS: single occupancy £19–£28, twin/double £38–£40, family room £40–£50; reductions for children sharing with parents; dinner £9; deposit: £10 per person CARDS: Mastercard, Visa DETAILS: children welcome; dogs welcome; no smoking in dining-room; car park

---

Melvin Lodge

Dunskey Street, South Crescent, Portpatrick DG9 8LE
TEL: (01776) 810238

Standing in an elevated position just a few minutes' walk away from the beach and the shops and restaurants of Portpatrick, Melvin Lodge has the look of a Victorian villa. It started life as a simple two-room cottage; those two rooms are now the comfortable guest lounge. Some of the ten bedrooms have good sea views, and most have either *en suite* showers or private bathrooms. The atmosphere is warm and friendly; children and pets are welcome, and a babysitting service is available.

OWNERS: Michael and Eileen Pinder OPEN: all year exc Christmas ROOMS: 2 single, both with private bathroom; 3 double, 1 with bath/shower, 2 with private bathroom; 1 twin, with private bathroom; 4 family, 3 with bath/shower, 1 with private bathroom; tea/coffee and TV in all bedrooms; lounge with TV TERMS: single £18, single occupancy £18–£40, twin/double £36–£40, family room from £36; children under 5 free, reductions for older children; deposit: £20 per booking CARDS: none DETAILS: children welcome; dogs welcome; smoking in bedrooms only; car park; garden

---

Any smoking restrictions that we know of are given in the details at the end of the entry.

PORTREE Highland map 11

Almondbank Guest House NEW ENTRY

Viewfield Road, Portree, Isle of Skye IV51 9EU
TEL: (01478) 612696 FAX: (01478) 613114
on the main road into Portree

This comfortable and efficiently run guesthouse is close to the shoreline and faces the bay. Some of the rooms have sea views, including the very spacious lounge. Mrs Nicolson has been running Almondbank for over 20 years, and keeps an immaculate house. All the bedrooms are *en suite* and are fitted with hair dryers and have TVs. The guesthouse is a few minutes' walk into Portree, and a good central location for visiting Skye.

OWNER: Effie Nicolson OPEN: all year ROOMS: 2 double, 2 twin; all rooms with shower, tea/coffee and TV; lounge with TV TERMS: twin/double £53–£65; deposit required CARDS: Delta, MasterCard, Switch, Visa DETAILS: children welcome; dogs welcome; car park; garden

---

Balloch

Viewfield Road, Portree, Isle of Skye IV51 9ES TEL: (01478) 612093

This comfortable villa stands on the main road on the outskirts of Portree. Mrs Macphie runs a very professional guesthouse, which one visitor found 'conveniently placed, beautifully clean and well decorated'. All the bedrooms are *en suite* and well furnished, and there is a large, warm residents' lounge. Breakfast is now served in a separate dining-room with individual tables, and offers a good choice, including traditional Scottish porridge, kippers, Scottish white pudding and oatcakes. Balloch is close to the water and on fine days guests can enjoy the view from the garden.

OWNER: Ena Macphie OPEN: Easter to Oct ROOMS: 3 double, 1 twin; all rooms with shower and tea/coffee; lounge with TV TERMS: single occupancy £30; twin/double £40–£50; deposit required CARDS: none DETAILS: no children; dogs welcome; car park; garden

---

Conusg

Coolin Hills Gardens, Portree, Isle of Skye IV51 9NB TEL: (01478) 612426

Once the stables for a local hunting lodge, this late-Victorian whitewashed house with its attractive gables and tall chimneys was taken over and converted by the Murrays, who themselves hail from Skye, in the early 1970s. It is also where the lodge's coachman and gardener used to live (above the former stables), and now provides guests with simple, comfortable accommodation that includes four bedrooms and a combined breakfast room and lounge. A warm welcome and a peaceful location – the house stands in an elevated position at the edge of Portree – plus fine views of the hills and water all add to the appeal. The town's bus station is a ten-minute walk away.

OWNERS: Catriona and Thomas Murray OPEN: Mar to Oct ROOMS: 2 single, 1double, 1 twin; all rooms with wash-basin and tea/coffee; lounge with TV TERMS: single £16.50–£17, twin/double £33–£34; children's reductions by arrangement; deposit required CARDS: none DETAILS: children welcome; no dogs in dining-room; car park; garden

ROTHESAY Argyll & Bute **map 11**

The Commodore

12 Battery Place, Rothesay, Isle of Bute PA20 9DP
TEL/FAX: (01700) 502178

This three-storey, white terraced guesthouse on the seafront is only a short walk from the town centre and enjoys fine views across Rothesay Bay to the hills beyond. The bedrooms, on the small size, are all *en suite* and are located on the second floor; the front-facing rooms overlook the sea. There is a lounge-cum-breakfast room, and guests are welcome to use the sunny garden at the rear of the house. Mike Spear is both a friendly host and a keen fisherman who can arrange free coarse-fishing for guests, and the B&B offers rod storage, use of freezer for the day's catch, a laundry room and drying facilities. Although the house has no car park, the Spears tell us that guests can park without problem on the street outside. There is a small self-catering cottage within the grounds, as well as a flat in the house.

OWNER: Mike Spear OPEN: all year ROOMS: 4 double, 2 twin; all rooms with bath and shower, tea/coffee and TV; lounge TERMS: single occupancy £22–£30, twin/double £40–£44; children under 5 free, half-price for ages 6–12; deposit required CARDS: none DETAILS: children welcome; small dogs by arrangement only; no smoking in lounge/breakfast room; garden

ST ANDREWS Fife **map 11**

Cadzow Guest House

58 North Street, St Andrews KY16 9AH TEL: (01334) 476933

Cosy and comfortable, Cadzow Guest House is conveniently sited in one of St Andrews' main streets. Shops and restaurants are within easy reach, and – for keen golfers – the Old Course is just ten minutes' walk away. Although small, the bedrooms are bright and light, and most have *en suite* showers. The large basement sitting/breakfast room leads out to the well-kept back garden. The guesthouse is handy too for museums and the university.

OWNERS: Alexander and Elizabeth Small OPEN: Mar to Nov ROOMS: 1 single, with shower; 4 double, 2 with shower, 2 with wash-basin; 2 twin, both with shower; 1 family, with shower; all rooms with tea/coffee and TV; lounge with TV TERMS: single £20–£24, single occupancy £22–£30, twin/double £32–£44, family room £50–£60; half-price for children under 12; deposit: £10 per person CARDS: none DETAILS: children welcome; dogs welcome but not to be left unattended; smoking in lounge only; garden

Glenderran Guest House

9 Murray Park, St Andrews KY16 9AW
TEL: (01334) 477951 FAX: (01334) 477908

This late-Victorian terraced townhouse is right in the middle of St Andrews, only a few minutes' walk from shops, beaches, the university and the world-famous golf course. It has been furnished and decorated with care and taste, and has an air of quiet elegance and comfort. There is a comfortable lounge, stocked with books and magazines, and five comfortable and well-equipped bedrooms; two are single rooms with their own adjacent bathrooms, while the other rooms have *en suite* shower-rooms.

OWNERS: Brian Hitchcock and Derrick Armitage OPEN: all year ROOMS: 2 single, both with private bathroom; 2 double, both with shower; 1 twin with shower; tea/coffee and TV in all rooms; lounge TERMS: single £22–£28, single occupancy £35–£50, twin/double £44–£56; deposit required CARDS: Delta, MasterCard, Switch, Visa DETAILS: no children under 12; no dogs; no smoking

---

Riverview Guest House

Edenside, St Andrews KY16 9SQ TEL/FAX: (01334) 838009
off A91, 2m N of St Andrews

Built in 1990, this purpose-built, motel-style guesthouse has good views over the Eden Estuary and Wildlife Reserve. Each spacious room has its own outdoor access, and all have good-sized shower-rooms and dressing-areas. Guests may sit outside on balconies or in the courtyard in fine weather; three bedrooms are at ground level. Breakfast – traditional Scottish – is served in the dining-room with its neat décor and individual pine tables. With enough notice, the Gatherums can help golfers organise a game at St Andrews or other nearby courses, and Riverview is a good base for visiting the many small fishing villages and beaches along the coast.

OWNERS: David and Stella Gatherum OPEN: all year exc Christmas ROOMS: 2 double, 5 twin; all rooms with shower, tea/coffee and TV; 3 rooms suitable for wheelchair-users TERMS: single occupancy £25–£40, twin/double £45; half-price for children 5–14; deposit: 1 night's stay CARDS: MasterCard, Visa DETAILS: no children under 5; no dogs; no smoking; car park; garden

ST CATHERINES Argyll & Bute map 11

Thistle House

St Catherines PA25 8AZ TEL: (01499) 302209 FAX: (01499) 302531
on A815, 5m S of Cairndow

Thistle House is a Victorian building set in two acres of beautifully kept gardens with magnficent views across Loch Fyne to Inverary and Inverary Castle. The house is immaculate and provides comfortable bedrooms and a pleasant lounge with TV. The front bedrooms have fine loch views and all the rooms have *en suite* shower.

Breakfast – which may include oak-smoked Loch Fyne kippers – has been described as 'excellent'. The house is close to Argyll Wildlife Park and many of the region's most beautiful gardens are nearby.

OWNER: Sandra Cameron   OPEN: Apr to Oct   ROOMS: 2 double, 1 twin, 1 family; all rooms with shower, tea/coffee and TV; lounge   TERMS: single occupancy £30, twin/double £43–£47, family room £52.50–£55.50; reductions for children sharing with parents   CARDS: Delta, MasterCard, Visa   DETAILS: children welcome; no dogs; no smoking in dining-room; car park; garden

ST MARGARET'S HOPE   Orkney   map 11

Bellevue Guest House

St Margaret's Hope, South Ronaldsay KW17 2TL   TEL: (01856) 831294

This stone-built house, a comfortable family home built by Mr Gunn's great-grandfather in 1886, enjoys beautiful views of the attractive fishing village of St Margaret's Hope. The bedrooms are spacious and well appointed. Good home-cooked breakfast, lunch and evening meals, are served in the dining-room at one large table, and there is a residents' lounge with TV. A laundry service is also offered. This area is good for walking, beaches and bird-watching.

OWNER: Evelyn Gunn   OPEN: all year   ROOMS: 1 double, with private bathroom; 1 twin, with wash-basin; 1 family with wash-basin; tea/coffee and TV in all bedrooms; lounge with TV   TERMS: single occupancy £20, twin/double £30–£36, family £40; babies free, half-price for older children sharing with parents; dinner £8 to £10   CARDS: none   DETAILS: children welcome; no dogs; smoking in lounge only; car park; garden

The Creel

Front Road, St Margaret's Hope, South Ronaldsay KW17 2SL
TEL: (01856) 831311

This plain three-storey house at the water's edge in the centre of town draws in visitors chiefly for its excellent food. Menus focus on Orkney specialities – lots of local seafood, plus perhaps pot-roasted North Ronaldsay lamb, and clootie dumpling parfait with Orkney ice-cream, for example – and people come from the mainland to dine here. The Craigies have previously worked in Edinburgh and Los Angeles, and Alan, who does the cooking, originally trained as a baker. The Creel offers three large, attractive *en suite* bedrooms, one with an open fire and two with sea views. Guests on the top floor have use of a small kitchen, and there is a small residents' lounge. The restaurant is licensed and serves dinner from 7 to 9pm; bookings are recommended.

OWNERS: Alan and Joyce Craigie   OPEN: Apr to mid-Oct, weekends in winter exc Jan   ROOMS: 1 double, 2 twin; all rooms with bath/shower; lounge   TERMS: twin/double £50–£60; children's reductions; dinner £25; deposit: £50   CARDS: MasterCard, Visa   DETAILS: children welcome; no dogs; no smoking; car park *(The Good Food Guide)*

SALEN Argyll & Bute — map 11

The Craig

Salen, Isle of Mull PA72 6JG TEL: (01680) 300347

The Craig is a small, friendly bed and breakfast overlooking the Sound of Mull. It is located on the main road between Craignure and Tobermory, and is well placed for exploring the island. The pretty garden has a sun-trap area and extends down to the small stream which borders the property. Bedrooms are simply furnished and the sitting-room has a piano, games, magazines, TV and books. Breakfast is served in the pine-furnished dining-room, and there is a restaurant nearby for evening meals. Salen is close to ferries to the mainland and is served by buses from Craignure.

OWNERS: James and Lorna Mcintyre OPEN: Easter to Oct ROOMS: 1 double, 3 twin; all rooms with wash-basin; lounge with TV TERMS: single occupancy £20–£22, twin/double £34–£36 CARDS: Delta, Diners, Visa DETAILS: children welcome; dogs welcome in bedrooms only; no smoking in dining-room; car park; garden

SANDWICK Orkney — map 11

Netherstove NEW ENTRY

Sandwick KW16 3LS TEL/FAX: (01856) 841625

from Stromness take A965, then take A967 towards Skara Brae, turn on to B9056 towards Bay of Skaill; Netherstove is first on right after the old kirk

Netherstove is a modern beef farm set in a quiet, rural spot with views of the Bay of Skaill. The Pokes give guests a warm welcome and are happy to show them around the farm. The two bedrooms are on the small side and share two bathrooms, and there is a comfortably furnished, spacious lounge with panoramic views of the fields and bay. Tea- and coffee-making facilities are available in the dining-room. Breakfasts are large and evening meals feature home-grown and local produce, and might include the farm's own beef. The Stone Age village of Skara Brae and the Bay of Skaill, which is popular with surfers, are both 15 minutes' walk from the farm, which also offers several self-catering chalets.

OWNER: Ann Poke OPEN: May to Nov ROOMS: 1 double, 1 twin; both rooms with wash-basin; lounge with TV TERMS: single occupancy £18, twin/double £30–£32; deposit required CARDS: none DETAILS: children welcome; no dogs; no smoking; car park; garden

---

To find an entry in the Guide, *go to the maps at the back of the book. Entries are plotted on the maps under their closest village, hamlet or city, except in London, where they are listed by name of B&B. After choosing your localities, go to the relevant section of the book (England, Scotland, Wales etc.), where localities are listed in alphabetical order (by B&B name order in London). There is also an index at the back of the book.*

SANNOX North Ayrshire **map 11**

Gowanlea

Sannox, Isle of Arran KA27 8JD TEL: (01770) 810253
on A841, 5m N of Brodick

This charming old whitewashed house is on the road between Lochranza and Brodick, overlooking the Firth of Clyde. The small, cosy sitting-room and dining-room are at the front of the house. June offers home-cooked evening meals, which are included in the room rates. The accommodation is simple, the three bedrooms sharing one bathroom and one WC. Sannox is an ideal base for fishing, golfing, walking, bird-watching and climbing, and Brodick Castle is nearby.

OWNERS: Christopher and June Warburton OPEN: all year ROOMS: 1 twin, 2 family; tea/coffee in all bedrooms; lounge with TV TERMS: D,B&B twin/family £32–£46 CARDS: none DETAILS: children welcome; dogs welcome; car park; garden

SCADABAY Western Isles **map 11**

Hillhead

NEW ENTRY

6 Scadabay, Harris HS3 3EP TEL: (01859) 511226

Hillhead is one of a small cluster of houses in the tiny hamlet of Scadabay, on the rocky and beautiful east coast of Harris about 15 minutes' drive from Tarbert. The Macleods are a delightful local couple, Mrs Macleod taking care of the bed and breakfast and good home-cooked dinners (which are included in the room price) while Mr Macleod works the family Harris tweed business. Apart from spinning the wool, he does virtually everything, from the time the wool is shorn from his son's sheep to the final woven tweed product. His machinery is of a certain age, but still in excellent working order, and it is fascinating to visit him in his little workshop/sales room set to one side of the house. The accommodation is comfortable, and some of the bedrooms are on the ground floor. Drying and ironing services and babysitting are available. Hillhead makes a great base for loch- and sea-fishing and walking.

OWNERS: William and Ina Macleod OPEN: Apr to Nov ROOMS: 1 single; 2 double, 1 with shower; 1 twin, with shower; 2 family, with wash-basin; tea/coffee in all bedrooms; TV in some bedrooms; lounge with TV TERMS: D,B&B single £26–£28, twin/double £52–£56, family room £52–£56; deposit required CARDS: none DETAILS: children welcome; dogs welcome in bedrooms only; no smoking in lounge or dining-room; car park; garden

---

B&B rates specified in the details at the end of each entry are given (as applicable) for a single room, for single occupancy of a double room, and then per room in the case of two people sharing a double or twin-bedded room, or for a family room. Because double rooms with four-poster beds often cost more, those are listed separately.

SCOURIE Highland map 11

Minch View

Scouriemore, Scourie IV27 4TG TEL: (01971) 502010
off A894, third road on right S of Scourie

Minch View is a simple white house standing among outbuildings at the end of a narrow twisty lane on the outskirts of the village. There are spectacular views over hills and water, and nearby is the old family croft. Two of the small, plainly furnished bedrooms are on the ground floor and are suitable for wheelchair-users, and the large sitting-room has a TV. Dinner, which must be booked ahead, is served at 7pm, and usually includes home-made soup, a roast or fish, and perhaps banoffi pie or trifle. Late suppers too are available, as is an early-morning tea tray, if requested.

OWNER: Christine B. Macdonald OPEN: Mar to Oct ROOMS: 2 double, 1 twin, all rooms with wash-basin; 2 rooms suitable for wheelchair-users; lounge with TV TERMS: single occupancy £20, twin/double £31; children's reductions according to age; dinner £10; deposit required CARDS: none DETAILS: children welcome; dogs welcome; no smoking in bedrooms; car park; garden

Scourie Lodge NEW ENTRY

Scourie IV27 4TE TEL: (01971) 502248

Scourie Lodge, a substantial whitewashed building, lies just above the picturesque bay and harbour in the centre of Scourie. It was built in 1835 by the Duke of Sutherland for his new bride, who didn't like it. Among the famous people who have stayed here are Gladstone, the Queen Mother and J.M. Barrie. The house was eventually abandoned, and bought by a Swiss gentleman, who completely rebuilt it and redesigned the garden, which is now open to the public. The present owners offer three comfortable and spacious double bedrooms, sharing two bathrooms, plus a twin-bedded *en suite* room in the adjoining coach-house. Breakfast and evening meals are served at separate tables in the dining-room, and drying facilities and a babysitting service are available.

OWNER: Penny Hawker OPEN: Mar to mid-Nov ROOMS: 3 double; 1 twin, with bath; tea/coffee and TV in all bedrooms; lounge with TV TERMS: single occupancy £25, twin/double £40–£45; children's reductions according to age CARDS: none DETAILS: children welcome; dogs by arrangement; no smoking; car park; garden

SKIRLING South Lanarkshire map 11

Skirling House NEW ENTRY

Skirling, ML12 6HD TEL/FAX: (01899) 860274
on A72, 2m N of Biggar

This delightful and unusual house facing the village green is in an unspoilt, rural spot well placed for visiting the Border country, Edinburgh and Glasgow. Skirling House started life as a farmhouse and was adapted and added to in 1908 in the 'arts and crafts' style to become a country home for Lord Carmichael. It is full of fascinating architectural details and is spread out in a rambling way, with almost all the rooms facing the garden, beyond which are glimpses of rolling hills. It has been faultlessly furnished and decorated, and exudes an air of tranquillity. Of particular note is the drawing-room, which has a sixteenth-century Florentine ceiling and beautiful built-in cupboards and bookshelves. An open log fire is lit on cooler days. Imaginative four-course evening meals are served in one of the two very attractive dining-rooms (the other one is used mainly for small private parties) and might include dishes such as breast of Barbary duck with a teriyaki sauce or rack of lamb in a pecan herb crust – complemented by a good selection of wines. The bedrooms are spacious, beautifully furnished, and with every comfort. Guests have use of both a croquet lawn and tennis court, and self-catering accommodation is also available.

OWNERS: Bob and Isobel Hunter OPEN: Mar to Dec ROOMS: 1 double, 2 twin; all rooms with either shower or bath and shower; tea/coffee and TV in all bedrooms; lounge TERMS: single occupancy £39, twin/double £55–£58; dinner £17.50; deposit: 50% CARDS: none DETAILS: children welcome; dogs by arrangement; no smoking; car park; garden; tennis

SOUTH GALSON Western Isles map 11

Galson Farm Guest House NEW ENTRY

South Galson, Ness, Isle of Lewis HS2 0SH TEL/FAX: (01851) 850492

This attractive stone-built eighteenth-century farmhouse was once the only house in the area, its land extending to 6,000 acres. Later the land was split up into crofts and the house fell into disrepair. Dorothy and John Russell rescued it from a virtual ruin, and have turned it into a smart guesthouse, filled with plush furniture and every possible amenity. It is set on an 18-acre croft in the north of Lewis, close to the shore with wonderful Atlantic ocean views. Guests have use of two lounges, warmed by peat fires on cold days, and traditional lunch and dinner are available if arranged in advance. This is a wonderful place for fishing, bird-watching and walking.

OWNERS: John and Dorothy Russell OPEN: all year ROOMS: 1 double, 2 twin; all rooms with bath/shower and tea/coffee; 2 lounges, 1 with TV TERMS: single occupancy £35, twin/double £58; dinner £16; deposit required CARDS: MasterCard, Visa DETAILS: children welcome; dogs by arrangement; no smoking; car park; garden

---

We welcome your feedback about B&Bs you have stayed in. Please make use of the report forms at the end of the book – or use your own stationery if you prefer – and mail your report to: The Editors, The Good Bed and Breakfast Guide, *FREEPOST, 2 Marylebone Road, London NW1 1YN. (No stamps are needed if mailed within the UK.) Recommendations for B&Bs for our next edition are very welcome. Please let us know if you need more report forms and we will send you a fresh supply.*

SPEAN BRIDGE Highland map 11

Invergloy House

Spean Bridge PH34 4DY TEL: (01397) 712681
on A82, 5m N of Spean Bridge

Invergloy House stands in 50 acres of grounds with access to Loch Lochy, and has splendid water and mountain views. It was formerly the stables to the big house which was burnt down. It shares part of the driveway with Riverside House (see entry, below), and has the same long, winding approach through woodland and shrubs. The entrance to the house opens into a dining-room with a grand piano; off this and overlooking the loch is the drawing-room, with another piano. Of the four comfortable and attractively decorated bedrooms, three are now *en suite*. Guests can enjoy free fishing on the loch, and there are rowing boats for hire as well as a hard tennis court. Mrs Cairns also rents out caravans for self-catering.

OWNER: Margaret Cairns OPEN: all year ROOMS: 1 single, with wash-basin; 3 twin, all with bath/shower; tea/coffee in all bedrooms; lounge with TV TERMS: single £20, single occupancy £28–£30, twin £40; deposit: £5 per person per night CARDS: none DETAILS: no children under 8; no dogs; no smoking; car park; garden; tennis

---

Old Pines

Spean Bridge, by Fort William PH34 4EG
TEL: (01397) 712324 FAX: (01397) 712433

This delightful restaurant-with-rooms goes from strength to strength, and owners Sukie and Bill Barber are constantly seeking to maintain and improve Old Pines. Despite the name, the long, low, Scandinavian-chalet-style house was built in the early 1980s. It stands in 30 acres of grounds, just 300 yards from the famous Commando Memorial, and has views across the Great Glen and Glen Spean to Aonach Mor and, on a clear day, Ben Nevis. There are eight bedrooms, five of which are suitable for wheelchair-users, each having specially adapted bathrooms. Sukie is an enthusiastic cook, and the food is definitely one of the highlights of a stay here (room rates include dinner), making good use of daily-delivered local produce, plus eggs provided by the Barbers' own chickens and ducks. They also smoke trout and salmon and make all their own bread, pasta, ice-cream and preserves. The dining-room (also open to non-residents) is in a bright conservatory-style room, which has warming log fires, and there are three sitting-rooms with a large collection of books.

OWNERS: Bill and Sukie Barber OPEN: all year exc 2 weeks late Nov ROOMS: 2 single, 1 with shower, 1 with private bathroom; 2 double, both with shower; 2 twin, both with shower; 2 family, both with shower; 5 rooms suitable for wheelchair-users; lounge with TV TERMS: D,B&B single £55–£60, single occupancy £70–£75, twin/double £110–£120, family room £110–£120; children £5 plus food; deposit: £20 CARDS: Amex, Delta, MasterCard, Switch, Visa DETAILS: children welcome; dogs welcome; no smoking; car park; games room; garden *(The Good Food Guide)*

Riverside

Invergloy, Spean Bridge PH34 4DY TEL/FAX: (01397) 712684
on A82, 5m NE of Spean Bridge; entrance on left down driveway signposted Invergloy

'Altogether an elegant and gracious house where we felt completely at home,' wrote one reporter of this modern bungalow close to Loch Lochy. It is approached down a long, winding driveway (shared with Invergloy House; see entry, above), flanked by mature trees and shrubs, and has an attractive garden and pleasant views. There are two large, comfortable bedrooms on the ground floor, one *en suite* and the other with a private bathroom. Guests have their own lounge with an eating-area off it where breakfast is served and from which they can enjoy the view of the garden. Riverside Lodges, three self-catering chalets, are situated in the grounds.

OWNER: Joan Bennet OPEN: all year exc Christmas ROOMS: 1 double, with private bathroom; 1 family, with bath/shower; tea/coffee in both bedrooms; lounge TERMS: single occupancy £26–£28, twin/double £38–£42, family room £38–£42; children's reductions; deposit: £10 CARDS: Visa DETAILS: children welcome; no dogs; no smoking; car park; garden

Tirindrish House

Spean Bridge PH34 4EU TEL: (01397) 712398
on A86, ¾m from Spean Bridge

Tirindrish House stands in 15 acres of grounds and enjoys wonderful views of Ben Nevis. The rear of the house dates from the fifteenth or sixteenth century, and is where two of the large guest bedrooms are located, each with its own staircase and bathroom. The third bedroom is in the front part of the house overlooking the mountains. Guests have use of a sitting-room, and breakfast and evening meals, by arrangement, are served in the attractive dining-room, which is towards the back of the house, past the row of old servants' bells, only one of which is still operational. Self-catering accommodation is also available.

OWNERS: Peter and Jean Wilson OPEN: all year exc Christmas ROOMS: 1 double, 1 twin, 1 family; all rooms with private bathroom, tea/coffee and TV; lounge TERMS: single occupancy £19–£26, twin/double £36–£38, family room £50–£55; children's reductions; dinner £12; deposit: £10 CARDS: none DETAILS: children welcome; dogs welcome; no smoking in bedrooms; car park; garden; tennis

If you intend to spend several days at a B&B, it is worth asking whether there are reduced rates, particularly if the period is midweek or off-season. It is always best to check prices, especially for single occupancy, when booking. If we know of any particular payment stipulations, we mention them in the details at the end of the entry. We asked the proprietors to estimate their 1998 prices in the autumn of 1997, so the rates may have changed since publication. If a deposit is required for an advance booking, this is stated in the details.

STAFFIN Highland **map 11**

Glenview Inn and Restaurant

Culnacnoc, Staffin, Isle of Skye IV51 9JH
TEL: (01470) 562248 FAX: (01470) 562211
12m N of Portree, on A855 between the Old Man of Storr and the Quiraing

The Glenview Inn goes from strength to strength, with an enviable reputation for food, and a welcoming and informal atmosphere. Tables now occupy what used to be the bar, and the restaurant is open for lunch, tea and dinner; meals might include Skye scallops or mussels, wild pigeon or Scotch beef, and cranachan (a Highland dish with oatmeal, whisky, honey and cream). The bedrooms are attractive and comfortable, and the residents' lounge has an open fire. The inn lies just off the road from Portree to Staffin in a Gaelic-speaking area of the Trotternish peninsula, which boasts some spectacular land formations, and interesting finds such as the ichthyosaur at Bearreraig Bay and the dinosaur footprint at Valtos.

OWNERS: Paul and Cathie Booth OPEN: Mar to Oct ROOMS: 1 double, with shower; 1 twin, with shower; 2 four-poster, 1 with bath/shower, 1 with private bathroom; 1 family, with shower; lounge with TV TERMS: all rooms £50–£70; children under 5 free, half-price for children under 12 sharing with parents; dinner £15; deposit required CARDS: Delta, MasterCard, Switch, Visa DETAILS: children welcome; dogs welcome; no smoking in main dining-area and bedrooms; car park; garden

---

Keeper's Cottage

NEW ENTRY

Staffin, Isle of Skye IV51 9JS TEL/FAX: (01470) 562217

Keeper's Cottage was the boyhood home of Mr MacDonald, and his father was the gamekeeper to the estate. It now is an attractive, long, whitewashed building that incorporates the original two-bedroomed house and the old hay barn. The two small and simply furnished guest bedrooms have partial sea views, somewhat blocked by the lodge house in front. There is a cosy sitting-room with open fire, where breakfast is also served. Mrs MacDonald is a delightful, friendly lady, and guests staying here appreciate the homely and informal atmosphere. Her main business is letting three self-catering cottages, located near the house, but she loves having bed and breakfast guests. Keeper's Cottage is only a few yards from the shore and well off the road.

OWNER: Peggy MacDonald OPEN: all year ROOMS: 2 double, both with wash-basin and tea/coffee; lounge with TV TERMS: single occupancy £15–£20, double £30; half-price for children sharing with parents CARDS: none DETAILS: children welcome; dogs welcome; no smoking in bedrooms; car park; garden

---

If a B&B accepts credit cards, we list them in the details at the end of an entry – or specify no cards are accepted if that is so. There may be a surcharge if you pay by credit card. It is always best to check when booking whether the card you want to use will be accepted.

STANLEY Perthshire & Kinross **map 11**

Newmill Farm

Stanley PH1 4QD TEL/FAX: (01738) 828281
from Perth take A9 N; ignore turn-off for Stanley, drive another 1½m up A9, take Tullybelton turn-off

This comfortable stone-built farmhouse dating from around the sixteenth century offers three large, unfussy *en suite* bedrooms. The wide-ranging breakfast menu takes in everything from locally grown fruit and over a dozen cereals to 'eggs just right', potato scones and smokies; 'toast comes with everything' and 'don't forget to ask for the porridge'. Vegetarian options and home-baking feature at evening meals, to which guests may bring their own wine. Those returning from a ramble on a wet day will welcome the use of drying facilities. Glamis Castle and Scone Palace are within striking distance by car.

OWNER: Ann Guthrie OPEN: all year exc Christmas ROOMS: 2 double, 1 twin; all rooms with bath/shower and tea/coffee; TV in most rooms and lounge TERMS: single occupancy £20–£25, twin/double £36; children under 2 free, £6 for ages 2–6, £8 for ages 6–12; dinner £14; deposit by arrangement CARDS: none DETAILS: children welcome; dogs welcome; no smoking; car park; garden

STIRLING Stirling **map 11**

Castlecroft

Ballengeich Road, Stirling FK8 1TN
TEL: (01786) 474933 FAX: (01786) 466716

This modern house, in the shadow of Stirling Castle, enjoys wonderful views, particularly from the lounge, which has windows all the way round and a telescope. The castle can be reached by a series of footpaths, or by the road into the centre of town. There is a large garden with fish ponds and patios with seats and tables for sitting out. The bedrooms are all *en suite*, and the two on the ground floor are particularly suited for wheelchair-users. The accommodation is clean, comfortable and practical, and the house has a rather business-like atmosphere.

OWNERS: Bill and June Salmond OPEN: all year exc Christmas and New Year ROOMS: 3 double, 2 twin, 1 family; all rooms with bath/shower; 2 rooms suitable for wheelchair-users; tea/coffee and TV in all bedrooms; lounge TERMS: single occupancy £32–£42, twin/double £38–£45, family room £50–£60; reductions for children sharing with parents; deposit required CARDS: MasterCard, Visa DETAILS: children welcome; dogs welcome but must not be left unattended; smoking in lounge only; car park; garden

Forth Guest House

23 Forth Place, Riverside, Stirling FK8 1UD
TEL: (01786) 471020 FAX: (01786) 447220

Flowers, hanging baskets and immaculate paintwork single out this middle-terrace Georgian house, which is within five minutes' walk from the town centre. The four smallish bedrooms are all *en suite*, are attractively decorated and offer many amenities. The two top-floor rooms can be connected to make a family suite. The pretty dining-room overlooks the tiny front garden, and there is a small sitting-area at the back of the room. Here breakfast, as well as evening meals (these must be arranged in advance), are served, and there is an honesty bar. The Loudons have now installed air-conditioning in the house.

OWNERS: Sheena and Jim Loudon OPEN: all year ROOMS: 2 double, 2 twin, 2 family; all rooms with bath/shower, tea/coffee and TV; lounge TERMS: single occupancy £30–£40, twin/double £39–£43, family room £19.50–£21.50 per adult plus £10 for each child; dinner £12.50 (£8 for children); deposit: 25% CARDS: Delta, MasterCard, Visa DETAILS: no children under 5; no dogs; no smoking; car park

STORNOWAY Western Isles **map 11**

The Old House

4 Lewis Street, Stornoway, Isle of Lewis HS1 2QH TEL: (01851) 704495

The Old House, with its large, secluded garden, stands on a corner in the middle of Stornoway. When the MacDonalds bought this house nearly a decade ago, they had their work cut out: the building was not even weatherproof and had to be more or less gutted to bring it up to its present comfortable and well-appointed standard. Some original features remain, such as a winding staircase. Mrs MacDonald is a cheerful host and takes pride in running a professional and immaculate guesthouse. The six rooms are comfortable, and there is a TV lounge for guests as well as a dining-room where breakfast is served.

OWNER: Mary MacDonald OPEN: all year ROOMS: 2 single, both with shower; 1 double, with shower; 2 twin, 1 with shower, 1 with private shower-room and wash-basin; 1 family, with shower; TV in all bedrooms and lounge TERMS: single £23, single occupancy £30, twin/double £46, family room £58; half-price for children under 12 sharing with parents CARDS: none DETAILS: children welcome; no dogs; smoking in lounge only; car park; garden

STRANRAER Dumfries & Galloway **map 11**

Kildrochet House

Kildrochet, Stranraer DG9 9BB TEL: (01776) 820216
at junction of A716 and B7077, 3½m S of Stranraer

Built as a dower house by William Adam in 1723, Kildrochet House is an impressive whitewashed building, standing in six acres of attractive gardens with views of the Rhins of Galloway. The house has been lovingly restored and decorated with elegance. Guests have a choice of spacious, comfortable bedrooms and use of a large drawing-room, off which there is another sitting/sun-room with doors leading to the terrace, the garden and a croquet lawn. Dinner, by arrangement, and breakfast are served at separate tables in the dining-room. Kildrochet is an ideal base for the Galloway beaches, walking, bird-watching and the ferry to Ireland.

OWNERS: Mr and Mrs P. Whitworth OPEN: all year ROOMS: 2 double, 1 twin; all rooms with bath/shower and tea/coffee; lounge with TV TERMS: single occupancy £30, twin/double £50; deposit: dinner £15; 10% CARDS: Delta, MasterCard, Visa DETAILS: children welcome; no dogs; no smoking; car park; garden

STRATHAIRD Highland map 11

Strathaird House NEW ENTRY

Strathaird, Isle of Skye IV49 9AU
TEL: (01471) 866269 FAX: (01471) 866320
on B8083 Broadford to Elgol road, 10m W of Broadford

This B&B is really off the beaten track: ten miles of narrow twisty roads from Broadford eventually lead one to Strathaird House. Hidden up a 200-yard tree-lined lane, this large, rambling house stands in a superb position in a partially walled garden with a croquet lawn and lovely vistas down to the sea. It was built 150 years ago, and acquired by John Kubale's father in 1968. The present generation of the family have now renovated it to provide comfortable, no-frills accommodation in a friendly, informal atmosphere. There is a sitting-room with a good selection of books, a drying/ironing-room with tea- and coffee-making facilities, and good home-cooked evening meals are served in the licensed dining-room or in the sun-room, which overlooks the garden. A new restaurant is planned as we go to press. The track to Camasunary Bay begins a quarter of a mile away, and there are scenic walks in every direction, and many species of wildlife to observe.

OWNERS: John and Jenny Kubale OPEN: Easter to Sept ROOMS: 2 single; 1 double; 4 family, 1 with bath/shower, 1 with private bathroom; 1 room suitable for wheelchair-users; lounge TERMS: single £18–£25, single occupancy £20–£27, twin/double £36–£50, family room £36–£50; children's reductions; dinner £15; deposit: £25 per person CARDS: Amex, MasterCard, Visa DETAILS: children welcome; dogs welcome; smoking in lounge only; car park; garden

STRATHAVEN South Lanarkshire map 11

Millwell Farm

Chapelton, Strathaven ML10 6SJ TEL: (01355) 243248
1m off A726 between East Kilbride and Strathaven

Millwell Farm, only 12 miles from Glasgow, is one of the best-value B&Bs in Scotland. The whitewashed farmhouse is on a 96-acre working dairy farm, surrounded by even more peaceful farmland. The accommodation is simple and immaculately clean, and includes a large beamed sitting/dining-room with open fire. The Taylors are delightful, welcoming hosts, and Fred Taylor's porridge is highly recommended, as is his singing. All three simply furnished bedrooms are on the ground floor, and are suitable for disabled guests.

OWNERS: Fred and Betty Taylor OPEN: all year exc Christmas ROOMS: 1 single, 1 double, 1 twin, all with private bathroom; all rooms suitable for wheelchair-users; lounge with TV TERMS: single £12.50, twin/double £25 CARDS: none DETAILS: children welcome; no dogs; car park; garden

STRATHPEFFER Highland **map 11**

Craigvar

The Square, Strathpeffer IV14 9DL TEL: (01997) 421622

Craigvar is a small, stone-built listed house, dating from 1839, and stands in its own well-kept garden in the very centre of the charming Victorian spa village of Strathpeffer, overlooking the square. Margaret Scott strives to give this delightful house a feeling of home combined with the highest standards of accommodation – as one couple commented, 'We consider this B&B to be far superior to some very expensive hotels.' The house retains its original Victorian fireplaces, and the bedrooms are spacious, comfortable and tastefully furnished. The four-poster bedroom has a large bathroom, and the twin a dressing-room area, while the lounge and dining-room have swapped roles and both have been redecorated. An extensive breakfast menu is offered, and the lounge has a piano, and an open fire for cooler days. Many events take place in Strathpeffer, including a Victorian Week in June and the Strathpeffer Games in August. During the peak holiday season a pipe band plays in the square every Saturday evening.

OWNER: Margaret Scott OPEN: all year exc Christmas ROOMS: 1 single, 1 twin, 1 four-poster; all rooms with bath/shower, tea/coffee and TV; lounge TERMS: single £27, twin/double £46–£52, four-poster £46–£52; deposit: £10 per person CARDS: Visa DETAILS: children welcome; no dogs; no smoking in lounge or dining-room; car park; garden

Inver Lodge

Strathpeffer IV14 9DL TEL: (01997) 421392

off A834, 5m W of Dingwall; approaching from Dingwall, take left turn by Spa Pavillion signposted 'Bowling Green'

With good views of wooded hills, this small Victorian house set in three-quarters of an acre of gardens on a quiet road in the centre of Strathpeffer provides simple and comfortable accommodation. Evening meals are available on request; fresh local produce and home-baking are a feature. Soup and sandwiches are also on offer in the evening, which has proved popular with guests who have spent the day taking advantage of the local trout and salmon fishing (which can be arranged at the B&B).

OWNERS: Kate and Alan Derbyshire OPEN: Mar to mid-Dec ROOMS: 1 twin, 1 family; both rooms with wash-basin, tea/coffee and TV; lounge TERMS: single occupancy

£22–£25, twin £30–£32, family room from £30; children under 3 free, £11 for ages 3–10; dinner £11; deposit: 1 night's stay CARDS: Delta, MasterCard, Visa DETAILS: children welcome; no dogs; no smoking; car park; garden

STRATHY Highland

map 11

Catalina

Aultivullin, Strathy Point KW14 7RY
TEL: (01641) 541279 FAX: (01641) 541314
on B836, 24m W of Thurso

Catalina is a remarkable place. It offers only one bedroom, but readers are unanimous in their view that the value is excellent: the 'standard is way above the price charged' in the opinion of one. The guest accommodation occupies an entire ground-level wing of this extended old croft, and comprises a dining-room, sitting-room, twin-bedded room and bathroom, all warmly and comfortably furnished, with a wealth of books and maps. The Salisburys are cheerful and sensitive hosts. The croft stands at the very end of a long, narrow road on a wild and desolate moorland headland that is surrounded on three sides by the Atlantic. Although the sea is out of sight of the house, a short walk will take you to a marvellous viewpoint, and it is possible to walk along the cliffs right round the head. Breakfast and dinner are offered at any time to suit guests, and includes a varied selection of home-cooked dishes; there is no need to pre-book for evening meals. Light hot lunches can also be provided.

OWNERS: Jane and Peter Salisbury OPEN: all year exc Christmas ROOMS: 1 twin, with private bathroom; lounge with TV TERMS: single occupancy £25, twin £34; dinner £10 CARDS: none DETAILS: no children; well-behaved dogs welcome; no smoking; car park; garden

TAIN Highland

map 11

Aldie House

NEW ENTRY

Tain IV19 1LZ TEL/FAX: (01862) 893787
on A9 going N, just before Tain on left

Built in the mid-nineteenth century, Aldie House was once surrounded by a big estate, including the old mill (under renovation as we went to press). The De Deckers on a visit from their native Belgium fell in love with the house, though it was empty and derelict at the time, bought it and transformed it into a comfortable family home with guest accommodation in the front rooms. Nowadays it is an attractive and substantial stone-built edifice, standing in lovely, well-tended gardens. The large, rectangular sitting-room has plenty of books and comfortable chairs, and the bedrooms are spacious, each with *en suite* bath or shower. Mrs De Decker is a good cook, and offers three-course evening meals, served in the dining-room or, if the weather is sunny, in the conservatory. The guesthouse is licensed.

OWNERS: Mr and Mrs De Decker OPEN: all year ROOMS: 1 double, 2 family; 1 room with bath, 2 rooms with shower; TV in all bedrooms; lounge TERMS: single occupancy £26–£30, double £44–£50, family room £60–£65; children under 2 free, half-price for ages 2–10; dinner £13; deposit: 25% CARDS: MasterCard, Visa DETAILS: children welcome; no dogs; smoking in lounge only; car park; garden

THORNHILL Dumfries & Galloway map 11

Drumcruilton NEW ENTRY

Thornhill DG3 5BG TEL/FAX: (01848) 500210
off A702, 4m N of Thornhill

Drumcruilton offers a special blend of warm hospitality and comfort in an informal atmosphere. Dorothy Hill and her husband moved to Scotland from Ireland in the late 1980s to take over this 800-acre farm supporting sheep and cattle, with its fine 150-year-old farmhouse. Only four miles from Thornhill, it is set among beautiful, wild scenery with views of the Lowther Hills, in an area of Scotland that often tends to be overlooked by visitors hurrying on their way further north. Those that find this inviting place come back for more. Dorothy Hill has put much energy into injecting simple elegance into the décor and furnishings of the accommodation, and is happy to provide evening meals by arrangement. The area lends itself to walking – and fishing, shooting and riding can all be arranged.

OWNER: Dorothy Hill OPEN: May to late Nov ROOMS: 2 double, 1 with bath/shower, 1 with private bathroom; 1 twin, with bath/shower; tea/coffee in all bedrooms; lounge with TV TERMS: single occupancy £22–£25, twin/double £40–£44; dinner £15 CARDS: Visa DETAILS: no children under 12; no dogs; smoking in some areas only; car park; garden

THURSO Highland map 11

Ulbster Villa

South Toll, Thurso KW14 8RE TEL: (01847) 893664

This unusual-looking stone-built Victorian villa stands just off the main road on the edge of Thurso, and has been run as a B&B by the same family for 40 years. It is a compact but comfortable house in a lovely, well-tended garden. There are two good-sized bedrooms on the first floor, which is reached by a narrow circular stairway, while the third, *en suite* room is on the ground floor. Guests have use of a sitting-room, beyond which is a built-on sun-lounge where breakfast is served. The ferry from Orkney leaves from nearby Scrabster.

OWNER: Mrs A. McKenzie OPEN: all year exc Christmas and New Year ROOMS: 1 double, with shower; 2 family, both with wash-basin; tea/coffee and TV in double bedroom; lounge with TV TERMS: single occupancy £20, twin/double £35, family room £39; deposit: £10 CARDS: none DETAILS: children welcome; no dogs; smoking in lounge only; car park; garden

---

'NEW ENTRY' indicates that a B&B was not in the previous edition (although its owners may have been, at a different address).

TOBERMORY Argyll & Bute **map 11**

Broomhill

NEW ENTRY

Breadalbane Street, Tobermory, Isle of Mull PA75 6PX
TEL: (01688) 302349

Broomhill is a modest white house standing in its own garden, situated high above the centre of Tobermory and with wonderful views over the bay and hills beyond. The atmosphere is relaxed and informal. Unpretentious yet comfortable, the bedrooms all have sea views; the single room is large enough to be let as a small double when required. The lounge, with its open fire, has plenty of books for visitors to browse through, as well as information about the area. Breakfast is served in the sun-room off the lounge, where hot and cold drinks are available during the day. The garden has chairs for sitting out on fine days, and guests are welcome to use the barbecue.

OWNER: Juliana Ashford OPEN: Apr to late Oct ROOMS: 1 single; 2 double, 1 with bath/shower, 1 with private bathroom; tea/coffee and TV in all bedrooms; lounge TERMS: single/single occupancy £18, double £28–£40; children's reductions; deposit required CARDS: none DETAILS: children welcome; well-behaved dogs welcome; no smoking; car park; garden

---

Fàilte Guest House

Main Street, Tobermory, Isle of Mull PA75 6NU TEL/FAX: (01688) 302495

Fàilte Guest House is continuing the tradition of staying in the family. Having survived two generations, it has now passed to Mairi Barlow from her sister. Standing right in the centre of Tobermory, on the seafront overlooking the bay, it is an attractive terraced building, originally a bank. It is frequently redecorated and all bedrooms are *en suite*. Breakfast is taken in an attractive room facing the sea. There is no lounge, but the bedrooms are spacious and each has a TV.

OWNERS: Mr and Mrs R.B. Barlow OPEN: Easter to mid-Nov ROOMS: 3 double, 3 twin, 1 family; all rooms with bath/shower, tea/coffee and TV TERMS: single occupancy £25–£40, twin/double £40–£56, family room £50–£70; deposit: 20% CARDS: Delta, MasterCard, Visa DETAILS: children welcome but must be supervised; no dogs; no smoking

TONGUE Highland **map 11**

Tigh Aoidh Rhian

NEW ENTRY

Tongue IV27 4XJ TEL: (01847) 611257
1m S of Tongue; B&B signposted

This guesthouse offers excellent value. A former gamekeeper's cottage which has been considerably enlarged, it stands in more than 20 acres of grounds (including a stretch of river) in pretty countryside and with spectacular views of Ben Loyal. It is a pretty whitewashed house surrounded by a garden, and has been attractively decorated and furnished. Stephanie MacKay is a cheerful and welcoming host, and also an excellent cook. Guests eat at separate tables in the dining-room, which opens on to a patio, and the cosy lounge has peat or log fires in winter and panoramic views of Ben Loyal. Tongue, which is halfway between Cape Wrath and John O'Groats, is an excellent base for visiting the north of Scotland with its cliffs, sea lochs, sandy beaches, impressive mountains and wealth of wild life. Tigh Aoidh Rhian is licensed.

OWNER: Stephanie S. Mackay OPEN: all year ROOMS: 2 double, both with shower; 2 twin, 1 with shower, 1 with private bathroom; 2 family, 1 with shower, 1 with private bathroom; tea/coffee in all bedrooms; lounge with TV TERMS: single occupancy £25–£30, twin/double £36–£40, family room from £36; children under 2 free, £5 for ages 2–5, £10 for ages 5–11; dinner £14; deposit: £10 per room CARDS: none DETAILS: children welcome; dogs in bedrooms only; no smoking; car park; garden

ULLAPOOL Highland **map 11**

The Sheiling Guest House

Garve Road, Ullapool IV26 2SX TEL/FAX: (01854) 612947
on A832 at S edge of village

Good views over Loch Broom, private fishing over many square miles, plus a gracious welcome are pluses at this B&B, built by the MacKenzies in the late 1980s on the one-acre sight of their original family home. Three of the seven small but attractive and bright *en suite* bedrooms are on the ground floor. Besides a TV lounge for guests and a split-level breakfast room, there is also a 'Sportsman's Lodge' with a rod room (where fishing gear can be hired for the day), a sauna and shower, a laundry and drying-room. Ullapool has a good selection of hotels and restaurants for evening meals.

OWNERS: Duncan and Mhairi MacKenzie OPEN: all year exc Christmas ROOMS: 4 double, 3 twin; all rooms with bath/shower and tea/coffee; lounge with TV TERMS: single occupancy £20–£30, twin/double £40–£50; half-price for children under 10; deposit: £20 CARDS: none DETAILS: children welcome; no dogs; no smoking; car park; garden

UPPER DIABAIG Highland **map 11**

Upper Diabaig Farm

Upper Diabaig, Achnasheen IV22 2HE TEL: (01445) 790227
take A896 to Torridon then take Diabaig road for 8m

Few bed and breakfasts are situated in such a remote and wildly spectacular location. It is a daunting eight-mile drive from the village of Torridon along a winding and, at times, steep and narrow road to Upper Diabaig, which stands between two freshwater lochs, but this did not stop one reporter calling it 'my favourite B&B'. Less than a mile beyond the house the road drops down to the village of Lower Diabaig, where there are spectacular views across Loch Torridon to the Applecross peninsula. Upper Diabiag Farm is a modern house built beside the ruins of an old croft, and is furnished simply and comfortably. The two first-floor bedrooms share a bathroom, and the ground-floor room has a large, beautifully tiled *en suite* bathroom. Roy Peacock is a farmer and vet, and Brenda prepares good home-cooked food for her guests.

OWNER: Brenda Peacock OPEN: Easter to Oct ROOMS: 1 double, with bath/shower; 2 twin, both with wash-basin; tea/coffee in all bedrooms; lounge with TV TERMS: single occupancy by arrangement; twin/double £31–£36; dinner £13; deposit: £10 CARDS: none DETAILS: no children; no dogs; no smoking; car park; garden

UPPER SCALLOWAY Shetland **map 11**

Hildasay Guest House

NEW ENTRY

Upper Scalloway ZE1 0UP TEL: (01595) 880822

Hildasay is a purpose-built guesthouse with a Scandinavian appearance, on the edge of Scalloway, above the school. Anne Robertson and Elaine Watt, a mother and daughter team, have been offering bed and breakfast here since 1994. The split-level bedrooms are very spacious, each with a sitting-area and bathroom and steps down to the sleeping-area. All bedrooms are on the ground floor, and one is equipped for disabled use. The large, comfortable lounge overlooks the neat garden, and opens on to the dining-area. Both Anne and Elaine's husbands are keen, experienced fishermen and are happy to pass on their knowledge to guests, and boats and fishing equipment are available for hire. Scalloway is the ancient capital of Shetland, and ten minutes by car from Lerwick.

OWNERS: Anne Robertson and Elaine Watt OPEN: all year ROOMS: 3 twin, 1 family; all rooms with shower, tea/coffee and TV; 1 room suitable for wheelchair-users; lounge with TV TERMS: single occupancy £20–£22, twin/double £36–£40, family room £18–£20; children under 3 free, reductions for older children according to age; deposit required for stays of 1 week or more CARDS: none DETAILS: children welcome; no dogs; no smoking in dining-room and lounge; car park; garden

WALSTON South Lanarkshire **map 11**

Walston Mansion Farmhouse

Walston, Carnwath ML11 8NF TEL/FAX: (01899) 810338
off A721, 5m E of Carnwath

Margaret Kirby offers three comfortable rooms – one a four-poster – and home-cooked food at this attractive old stone house in the middle of unspoilt countryside. Just off a narrow minor road, the house has a peaceful setting and lovely hilly views. Children are welcome here, and there is a play area with lots of farm animals, including a goat, and an aviary housing a variety of birds. Guests may relax in a lounge with TV and an open fire. Dinner is served in the separate dining-room.

OWNER: Margaret Kirby OPEN: all year ROOMS: 1 twin, with wash-basin; 1 four-poster, with bath/shower; 1 family, with bath/shower; tea/coffee and TV in all bedrooms; lounge with TV TERMS: single occupancy £16, twin £28–£32, four-poster

£32, family room from £16 per person; children under 14 £9; dinner £7.50; deposit: £10 per booking CARDS: none DETAILS: children welcome; no dogs in dining-room or lounge; no smoking in dining-room; car park; garden

WATERNISH Highland map 11

Lismore

Waternish, Isle of Skye IV55 8GE TEL: (01470) 592318
take A850 towards Dunvegan from A87, turn right on to B886; Lismore is second house on left after approx 2m

Lismore stands on the clifftop high above Lochbay on the Waternish peninsula, looking out towards the Western Isles. The view must be one of the finest on Skye, and sunsets are particularly memorable here. To take advantage of this, the Dames added a sun-lounge to the front of the house, which is where breakfast and, by arrangement, evening meals are served. The two simple, and charmingly decorated bedrooms are in the old part of the croft, both on the ground floor, with a shared bathroom. Vegetarians can be catered for.

OWNERS: Bill and Janet Dame OPEN: Apr to Oct ROOMS: 1 double, 1 family; both rooms with wash-basin and tea/coffee; lounge with TV TERMS: single occupancy £18.50, twin/double £32, family room £16; half-price for children sharing with parents; dinner £10 to £15; deposit: 20% CARDS: none DETAILS: children welcome; no dogs; no smoking; car park; garden

WHITEKIRK East Lothian map 11

Whitekirk Mains

Whitekirk EH42 1XS TEL: (01620) 870245 FAX: (01620) 870330
from A1 from Edinburgh take A198 just after East Linton

The creeper-clad, Georgian front of the house, along with pretty gardens, adds to the attractiveness of this old farmhouse located near the village church. Parts of the house – which is on a working farm – date back to the fifteenth century, though the amenities for visitors are certainly more modern than that and make for a comfortable stay. The twin bedrooms all have *en suite* showers as well as TVs and tea- and coffee-making facilities. Guests have use of two comfortable sitting-rooms; smoking is permitted in the smaller one. The Tuers also own an 18-hole golf course and restaurant close to the house, and within ten miles of Whitekirk are a dozen other golf courses.

OWNER: Mrs J. Tuer OPEN: Mar to Oct ROOMS: 3 twin, all with shower, tea/coffee and TV; lounge TERMS: single occupancy £25, twin/double £40–£44, family £40–£44 plus £5 for each child sharing with parents (babies are free) CARDS: MasterCard, Switch, Visa DETAILS: children welcome; no dogs; smoking in 1 lounge only; car park; garden

---

Any smoking restrictions that we know of are given in the details at the end of the entry.

WHITING BAY North Ayrshire **map 11**

Royal Hotel

Shore Road, Whiting Bay, Isle of Arran KA27 8PZ TEL/FAX: (01770) 700286

This traditional sandstone building, dating from 1895, is next to the school and immediately opposite the beach in the small village of Whiting Bay, a few miles south of Brodick. It has been extensively modernised and decorated, and Brenda and Brian Wilson are charming, hospitable hosts who provide an excellent service, including good home-cooked evening meals. Both the lounge and large dining-room overlook the Firth of Clyde. The ground-floor bedroom has a private bathroom, while the other rooms are on the first floor, and all have *en suite* showers. There are also a couple of shared bathrooms, one with a whirlpool bath. One of the front-facing rooms has its own small sitting-room which can take additional beds to be converted into a family room, and another has a four-poster bed. The hotel also has extensive car- and boat-parking facilities.

OWNERS: Brian and Brenda Wilson OPEN: Mar to Nov ROOMS: 1 single, 3 double, 2 twin, 1 four-poster; all rooms with bath/shower, tea/coffee and TV; lounge TERMS: single/single occupancy £22, twin/double £44; children's reductions; dinner £13 CARDS: none DETAILS: children welcome; no dogs in public rooms; no smoking in dining-room; car park; garden

WICK Highland **map 11**

Bilbster House

Bilbster, Wick KW1 5TB TEL: (01955) 621212
from Wick take A882 for 5m, turn right at line of trees

This genteel country house dates from the mid-eighteenth century, and was extensively renovated when the Stewarts bought it in the 1970s. The grounds are a green oasis in the middle of the flat surrounding landscape, and the house itself stands in a delightful, somewhat overgrown, mature walled garden, with a stream to one side. Since the last edition of the *Guide*, Ian Stewart has taken over the running of the house from his parents, and has continued improving both house and garden. All three bedrooms are spacious and furnished in an old fashioned-way; each has a hair-dryer, electric blankets and shoe-cleaning facilities. The large, comfortable drawing-room has a TV, and the attractive dining-room has small tables covered with crisply laundered tablecloths, flowers, linen napkins and silver cutlery. Evening meals are available only from October to Easter.

OWNER: Ian Stewart OPEN: all year exc Christmas (Oct to Easter by prior arrangement only) ROOMS: 2 double, 1 with bath/shower, 1 with private bathroom; 1 twin, with bath/shower; tea/coffee in all bedrooms; lounge with TV TERMS: single occupancy £14.50–£15.50, twin/double £29–£31; children under 5 free, half-price for ages 8–12; dinner £8 (from Oct to Easter only) CARDS: none DETAILS: children welcome; dogs welcome; smoking in lounge only; car park; garden

Wales

ABERCELYN, BALA

ABERAERON Ceredigion **map 4**

Hazeldene NEW ENTRY

South Road, Aberaeron SA46 0DP TEL: (01545) 570652

This large, white-painted Victorian house, less than a mile from the beach, was built at the turn of the century by Captain James William Evans, a retired sailor. It retains some interesting original architectural features, such as the plaster ceilings, wide entrance steps, arched entryway, and an elegant front-facing verandah. Owners Jackie and John Lewis have refurbished the house to a high standard. They are a friendly, interesting, Welsh-speaking couple, who go out of their way to ensure guests enjoy their stay and offer assistance with local information. The three bedrooms are luxuriously and traditionally furnished with rich carpets and fabrics. The master bedroom has a king-sized waterbed, and there is a separate luxury bathroom with a jacuzzi. The spacious, homely lounge has satellite TV, there is a dining-room, and other facilities include a paved sunbathing garden, a fitness area and a solarium. Good-value three-course dinners are served by arrangement, vegetarians can be catered for with notice, and Hazeldene is licensed. Breakfasts are either a substantial continental version or a traditional cooked one.

OWNERS: John and Jackie Lewis OPEN: Apr to Oct ROOMS: 2 double, 1 twin; all rooms with shower; lounge with TV TERMS: single occupancy £20–£26, twin/double £36–£48; dinner £12; deposit: 10% CARDS: MasterCard, Visa DETAILS: no children under 12; no dogs; no smoking; car park; garden

ABERCEGIR Powys **map 4**

Yr Hen Felin NEW ENTRY

Abercegir SY20 8NR TEL: (01650) 511868

off A489 4m E of Machynlleth; turn right after phone box in centre of village, go over wooden bridge; house on right

This beautifully restored mill was making blankets until the 1960s and now offers luxurious accommodation in a unique setting on the banks of the River Gwydol. The character of the old mill has been retained in many original features, such as stripped pine floors, oak beams and the mill wheel. The bedrooms have antique furniture and comfortable beds and are strikingly decorated, each having a theme based on its view and named accordingly: Pen-y-Bont ('bridge end'), Swn-yr-Afon ('sound of the river') and Bryn Glas ('green hills'). The sitting-room with TV is an inviting spot in which to relax. It is warmed by a wood-burning stove on cool evenings, and there is an interesting collection of clocks and china. This is an idyllic spot, and guests are encouraged to enjoy the one-and-a-half acres of gardens or stroll along the river and admire the wide variety of wildlife, including herons and rare nesting birds. Barry and Jill Stevens extend a warm welcome and are happy to help their guests in every way to ensure a comfortable stay.

OWNER: Barry Stevens OPEN: all year exc Christmas ROOMS: 1 double, 2 twin; all rooms with shower; lounge with TV TERMS: single occupancy £25, twin/double £38; deposit: 25% CARDS: none DETAILS: no children under 12; no dogs; no smoking; car park; garden

ABERGAVENNY Monmouthshire map 4

Pentre House NEW ENTRY

Brecon Road, Abergavenny NP7 7EW TEL/FAX: (01873) 853435
off A40 towards Brecon; past hospital, then garage, left at next crossroads

This nineteenth-century house stands in one-and-a-half acres of secluded gardens. It has been extensively refurbished and the three bedrooms, all on the first floor, are light and bright and have antique furniture. The dining-room, where 'excellent' breakfasts are served, has lots of books to browse through and a portfolio of local information. On cold days, a wood-burning stove warms the cosy lounge, which leads out on to a pretty terrace overlooking the garden. This is an ideal spot for nature-lovers, as there are several walks to be taken from the house, including one up the nearby Sugar Loaf Mountain, and the River Usk is a pleasant ten-minute stroll away. Plenty of places to eat can be found in the town centre, about a mile away.

OWNER: Lynda Reardon Smith OPEN: all year exc Christmas ROOMS: 2 double, 1 twin, 1 family; all rooms with wash-basin, tea/coffee and TV; lounge with TV TERMS: single occupancy £20–£25, twin/double £30–£36, family room £24–£36; dinner £10; deposit: £5 per person CARDS: none DETAILS: children welcome; dogs £2 per night; smoking in lounge only; car park; garden

ABERHAFESP Powys map 4

Dyffryn Farm

Aberhafesp SY16 3JD TEL: (01686) 688817 FAX: (01686) 688324
just off B4568, 3m W of Newtown

This beautifully restored half-timbered barn stands in a lovely garden on the banks of a stream, on a 100-acre beef farm. This is a magical place for families. Supervised children are welcome to wander around the farm, and there is an outside play-area, as well as a nature trail with plenty of wildlife to be seen. Other children's facilities include cots, high chairs and a babysitting service. The elegant bedrooms are furnished in country style and have *en suite* facilities and TV. Breakfast and dinner are served in the beamed dining-room at a large oval table. Guests may bring their own wine to dinner as there is no licence, and vegetarian and other special dietary needs can be catered for with notice. The very comfortable lounge overlooks the stream and adjoining farmyard. Dave and Sue Jones make guests feel at home, and this is a delightful spot from which to explore nearby places of interest, including the upland lakes of Llyn Mawr Nature Reserve. Pony-trekking can be arranged at a nearby farm, and packed lunches can be provided.

OWNERS: David and Sue Jones OPEN: all year exc Christmas ROOMS: 2 double, 1 twin, 1 family; all rooms with bath/shower, tea/coffee and TV; lounge with TV TERMS: twin/double £44–£48, family room £60–£70; dinner £13; deposit required CARDS: none DETAILS: children welcome; no dogs; no smoking; car park; garden

ABERYSTWYTH Ceredigion **map 4**

Glyn-Garth

South Road, Aberystwyth SY23 1JS TEL: (01970) 615050

The Evanses have been running their B&B for over 40 years, and continue to maintain a high standard. Their double-fronted Victorian house, located within the walls of the old castle, offers 11 prettily decorated bedrooms, most of them of a good size and some with *en suite* facilities. The guest lounge with TV is a comfortable place to relax in, and breakfast is served in a separate dining-room, which now has new pine furniture and a blue décor. The castle and the sea are just a stone's-throw away. Although there is no car park, unrestricted street parking is available nearby.

OWNER: Elizabeth Evans OPEN: all year exc Christmas ROOMS: 2 single, both with wash-basin; 6 double, 4 with bath/shower, 2 with wash-basin; 1 twin, with wash-basin; 2 family, both with bath/shower; tea/coffee and TV in most bedrooms; lounge with TV TERMS: single £19, single occupancy £28–£34, twin/double £38–£48, family room £60–£70; children's reductions by arrangement; deposit required CARDS: none DETAILS: children welcome; no dogs; no smoking

Sinclair Guest House

43 Portland Street, Aberystwyth SY23 2DX TEL/FAX: (01970) 615158

This late-Victorian four-storey terraced house is centrally situated in a tree-lined street close to the seafront and the town centre. It retains much of its period character and original features, including leaded windows, tiled entrance, stripped pine doors and fireplaces. The well-proportioned bedrooms are all on the ground floor, most have fireplaces and all are smartly decorated with wicker and pine furniture. Guests also have use of a lounge and conservatory, and the Wards are a down-to-earth friendly couple who instantly make guests feel at home in their good-value guesthouse. They no longer serve evening meals, but there are plenty of places to eat in the town.

OWNERS: Sarah and Lester Ward OPEN: all year exc Christmas ROOMS: 1 double, 2 twin; all rooms with bath/shower, tea/coffee and TV; lounge TERMS: single occupancy £30, twin/double £45; deposit: £10 per room per night CARDS: none DETAILS: no children; no dogs; no smoking

Yr Hafod

1 South Marine Terrace, Aberystwyth SY23 1JX TEL: (01970) 617579

Just a five-minute walk from the train and bus stations, and sited right on the sea front at the south end of the promenade between the harbour and castle, Yr Hafod provides excellent-value accommodation in a very convenient location. Pine furniture and colour-co-ordinated fabrics add to the charm of the bedrooms; the top-floor rooms with their sloping ceilings are particularly attractive. Some of the rooms have sea views. Guests have the use of a lounge with TV, and breakfasts are served in the bright and airy dining-room. A number of cafés, pubs and restaurants are nearby. On-street parking is free and unrestricted.

OWNER: John Evans OPEN: all year exc Christmas ROOMS: 2 single, both with wash-basin; 2 double, 1 with bath/shower, 1 with wash-basin; 1 twin, with bath/shower; 2 family, both with wash-basin; tea/coffee and TV in all bedrooms; lounge with TV TERMS: single £18–£19, single occupancy £23–£40, twin/double £34–£44, family room £45–£51; deposit: 50%–60% of 1 night's charge CARDS: none DETAILS: children welcome; no dogs; no smoking

BALA Gwynedd **map 7**

Abercelyn

Llanycil, Bala LL23 7YF TEL: (01678) 521109 FAX: (01678) 520556
on B494 on W shore of Bala Lake, 1m SW of Bala

Dating from the early eighteenth century, this beautiful old rectory is set in seven acres of landscaped grounds at the edge of Bala Lake in Snowdonia National Park. Many original features – marble fireplaces, window-seats and a Georgian staircase, for example – add to the charm of the house, which has been stylishly modernised. The bedrooms have been decorated with designer fabrics and furnished with pine and antiques. Breakfasts featuring home-baked bread and home-made preserves are served in the main house in the dining-room, which overlooks the garden and a waterfall. Mrs Cunningham arranges walking tours through this lovely area; guests have the use of drying facilities, and may request packed lunches. Fergus the border terrier is a friendly favourite with visitors. Rooms must be booked for a minimum of two nights in July and August.

OWNER: Judy Cunningham OPEN: all year exc Christmas ROOMS: 2 double, 1 with bath, 1 with shower; 1 twin, with private bathroom; tea/coffee in all bedrooms; lounge with TV TERMS: single occupancy £22.50–£25, twin/double £37–£49; £10 for children under 12 sharing with parents; deposit: £18.50 CARDS: none DETAILS: children welcome; no dogs; no smoking; car park; garden

---

If a B&B offers off-street car parking, we note 'car park' at the end of the entry. If nearby on-street parking must be used, in most cases we give details in the descriptive text.

BARMOUTH Gwynedd

map 7

Bryn Melyn Hotel

Panorama Road, Barmouth LL42 1DQ
TEL: (01341) 280556 FAX: (01341) 280276
off A496, ½m E of town centre

Approached by a fairly steep uphill road, this small hotel with its pretty terraced garden has fine views to Cader Iris across the estuary. It is in a quiet position about 15 minutes' walk from the town centre and beach. The comfortable bedrooms are decorated with floral wallpaper and co-ordinated bedspreads and curtains, and all have either *en suite* shower facilities or private bathroom, plus facilities such as direct-dial telephones. Guests may relax in the TV lounge, conservatory, or well-stocked bar. Breakfasts and evening meals – which include a selection of vegetarian dishes – are served in the licensed restaurant, which is also open non-residents.

OWNERS: David and Carol Clay OPEN: Mar to mid-Nov ROOMS: 5 double, all with shower; 3 twin, 2 with shower, 1 with private bathroom; 1 family, with shower; tea/coffee and TV in all bedrooms; lounge with TV TERMS: single occupancy £37, twin/double £58, family room £66; children's reductions by arrangement; dinner £15; deposit: £25 CARDS: Amex, Diners, MasterCard, Visa DETAILS: no children under 7; dogs by arrangement; no smoking in restaurant; car park; garden

The Sandpiper

7 Marine Parade, Barmouth LL42 1NA TEL: (01341) 280318
on seafront, opposite Barmouth Sands

Susan and John Palmer have been taking good care of their visitors for over ten years in their sea-front guesthouse: many of their guests return every year, and it is advisable to make reservations early for the summer months. Note that one-night bookings are not accepted during the peak season and weekends. The Sandpiper offers a TV-free lounge on the top floor for those who wish to relax or read, and a dozen well-maintained and decorated bedrooms; the front ones have good views, and one room on the ground floor is suitable for wheelchair-users. Substantial breakfasts are served in a room overlooking the sea, and Barmouth has plenty of eating-places for evening meals. Free on-street parking is available outside.

OWNERS: Susan and John Palmer OPEN: Mar to Oct ROOMS: 3 single, all with wash-basin; 5 double, 3 with bath/shower, 2 with wash-basin; 4 family, 3 with bath/shower, 1 with wash-basin; 1 room suitable for wheelchair-users; tea/coffee and TV in all bedrooms; lounge TERMS: single £14.50–£15.50, twin/double £27–£40; half-price for children sharing with 2 adults; deposit: 1 night's charge CARDS: none DETAILS: children welcome; no dogs; no smoking in breakfast room; garden

If you are forced to turn up later than planned, please telephone to warn the proprietor. It is always best to book a room in advance, even in winter. B&Bs with few rooms may close at short notice for periods not specified in the details.

Wavecrest Hotel

NEW ENTRY

8 Marine Parade, Barmouth LL42 1NA TEL/FAX: (01341) 280330

This family-run seafront hotel has been carefully restored in keeping with its Victorian origins, and is furnished mostly with antique pine and decorated in soft pastels. The majority of the bedrooms are of a good size, most have *en suite* facilities, and many have views of Cardigan Bay and the mountains of Snowdonia; antique washstands, armchairs, cotton sheets and pretty floral bedcovers add to the comfort factor. Breakfasts and well-cooked and -presented dinners are served in the predominately pink dining-room at individual tables set with linen tablecloths and fine china. The food is complemented by a good selection of wines; a wide choice of other beverages including unusual sherries is available from the bar. A well-furnished lounge on the first floor provides a quiet spot in which to relax. The Jarmans are charming hosts who are dedicated to extending high standards of comfort to their guests – one of whom wrote us that Wavecrest 'was a real find'. Free parking is available on the street outside.

OWNERS: Shelagh and Eric Jarman OPEN: Apr to Oct ROOMS: 2 single, both with wash-basin; 4 double, 3 with bath/shower, 1 with private bathroom; 2 twin, both with bath/shower; 2 family, both with bath/shower; tea/coffee and TV in all bedrooms; lounge TERMS: single £16–£18, single occupancy £23–£35, twin/double £36–£50, family room £45–£58; children's reductions; dinner £16; deposit by arrangement CARDS: Delta, MasterCard, Visa DETAILS: children welcome; dogs welcome with own bedding and not to be left unattended in bedrooms; no smoking

BENLLECH Isle of Anglesey **map 7**

Belvoir

8 Lon Fferam, Benllech LL74 8RL TEL: (01248) 852907
off A5205, 7m N of Britannia Bridge

Valerie and Robert Evans provide a friendly, homely atmosphere at their modern house in a quiet residential street, just a few minutes' walk from the sandy beach. One bedroom is on the first floor, with lovely sea and mountain views, while the ground-floor room looks out over the garden and has an adjacent private bathroom. Both are well furnished and have comfortable beds, radio alarm clocks and TV. There is a sitting-room for guests' use, plus a conservatory, where excellent breakfasts are served; featuring home-made marmalade and local Anglesey honey. Belvoir is well placed for exploring Anglesey.

OWNER: Valerie Evans OPEN: Apr to Oct ROOMS: 2 double, both with private bathroom, tea/coffee and TV; lounge TERMS: single occupancy £25, twin/double £34–£36 CARDS: none DETAILS: no children under 12; no dogs; no smoking; car park

---

The end details for each entry state whether or not dogs are allowed, but it is always best to check when booking.

BETWS-Y-COED Conwy **map 7**

Ferns Guest House

NEW ENTRY

Betws-y-Coed LL24 0AN TEL/FAX: (01690) 710587
on main A5 road through village

This Victorian Welsh-stone spacious house stands back off the main road in a pretty garden and is within walking distance of the centre of the village. The Roobottoms are 'warm, friendly, welcoming hosts' who provide 'very beautiful accommodation and excellent cooking'. The nine bedrooms are individually decorated, some with antique furnishings, some with a fun theme featuring teddy-bear pictures and clowns. Breakfasts and pre-booked evening meals are served in the dining-room, with its rich wood furniture, flower arrangements and attractive pictures. The well-appointed lounge is a good place to relax in.

OWNERS: Teresa and Keith Roobottom OPEN: all year exc Christmas and Boxing Day ROOMS: 1 single, 6 double, 1 twin, 1 family; all rooms with bath/shower, tea/coffee and TV; lounge with TV TERMS: single/single occupancy £20–£25, twin/double £36–£42, family room £18–£21 per person; dinner £12; deposit: 1 night's charge CARDS: none DETAILS: no children under 4; no dogs; no smoking; car park; garden

Fron Heulog

Pont-y-Pair, Betws-y-Coed LL24 0BL TEL/FAX: (01690) 710736
turn off A5 in village over stone bridge on to B5106, then take first left along river bank for 150yds

This large Victorian stone building is in a quiet location just outside Betws-y-Coed. It was lovingly restored by local craftsmen a few years ago; the operation was overseen by the owners, who wanted to ensure the period charm was retained. Inside, however, modern comforts prevail. There are three lounges, a small library stocked with plenty of local information, and a furnished verandah with south-facing views over a wooded valley. The comfortable bedrooms are well equipped, and all have *en suite* bath and shower. Breakfasts are large, with a help-yourself buffet followed by a generous cooked breakfast, and evening meals, with a menu suited to guests' requirements, are available by arrangement. Betws-y-Coed is a good base for walkers and tourists, and the Whittinghams are very knowledgeable about the area and happy to assist with itinerary planning. The house operates a strict no-smoking and no-pets policy.

OWNERS: Peter and Jean Whittingham OPEN: all year ROOMS: 2 double, 1 twin; all rooms with bath/shower, tea/coffee and TV; 3 lounges, 1 with TV TERMS: single occupancy £24–£39, twin/double £40–£52; dinner £15; deposit required CARDS: none DETAILS: no children under 12; no dogs; no smoking; car park; games room; garden

If we know a B&B has an alcohol licence, we say so. Most unlicensed B&Bs that offer evening meals allow guests to bring their own wine to dinner. If you wish to do this, ask the B&B when you book.

Park Hill Hotel

NEW ENTRY

Llanrwst Road, Betws-y-Coed LL24 0HD TEL/FAX: (01690) 710540

This imposing Welsh-stone hotel is set in an acre of lush gardens overlooking the River Conwy and a nine-hole golf course. The village is only a few minutes' walk away. There are two lounges, both elegantly furnished and with a fine display of interesting paintings, as well as a sun lounge. The well-appointed bedrooms are furnished in rich mahogany; one has a four-poster bed, and most have superb views. Dinner, which makes good use of local supplies, is served from 7 to 7.45 in the attractive dining-room at separate tables set with white tablecloths and fine china, and there is a small, well-stocked bar. The Bovairds have created a genuine welcoming atmosphere in their small family-run hotel, which also boasts a heated indoor swimming-pool with jacuzzi at one end, plus a sauna.

OWNERS: James and Elizabeth Bovaird OPEN: all year ROOMS: 2 single, both with private bathroom; 6 double, 2 twin, 1 four-poster, all with bath/shower; tea/coffee and TV in all bedrooms; lounge with TV TERMS: single £18.50–£19.50, single occupancy £31.50–£46, twin/double £51–£55, four-poster £60–£62, family room £66.50–£82.50; half-price for children 6–12 sharing with parents; dinner £14.50; deposit: £20 CARDS: Amex, Delta, Diners, MasterCard, Switch, Visa DETAILS: no children under 6; no dogs; no smoking in dining-room; car park; garden; swimming-pool

Swn-y-Dwr

NEW ENTRY

Pentrefelin, Betws-y-Coed LL24 0BB TEL: (01690) 710648

Swn-y-Dwr translates into English as 'sound of water', an appropriate name for this 120-year-old detached house adorned with pretty window boxes, which is in a peaceful location by the river. It has been tastefully refurbished and the décor throughout is light and bright. The three bedrooms have traditional furniture, duvets and *en suite* shower facilities, and one of the rooms overlooks the river. The comfortable lounge also has a river view and is a tranquil spot to unwind after a busy day sightseeing. Mr and Mrs McGregor are a friendly couple who extend a warm welcome and provide a generous breakfast, enough to set you up for the day. There are several pubs and restaurants in the pretty village of Betws-y-Coed.

OWNER: Sue McGregor OPEN: all year ROOMS: 3 double, 1 twin; all rooms with shower, tea/coffee and TV; lounge with TV TERMS: single occupancy £17–£20, twin/double £34; deposit: 1 night's charge CARDS: none DETAILS: no children; no dogs; no smoking; car park; garden

---

'Bath / shower' in the details under each entry means that the rooms have en suite *facilities. 'Private bathroom' signifies that a room has a bathroom for its exclusive use. The B&B may have other, shared bathroom facilities as well. We list 'wash-basins' for rooms that have them but do not have* en suite *or private facilities.*

BORTH Ceredigion **map 4**

Hafan Wen

Borth SY24 5JA TEL: (01970) 871739
on B4353, 6m N of Aberystwyth, 1m N of lifeboat station

Guests are greeted with hot drinks on arrival at this seafront terraced guesthouse. Bedrooms are simple and bright; one is on the ground floor and has an adjacent bathroom, and the first-floor sitting-room has a large picture window with sea views. Breakfast is the only meal served, but there are several eating-places within easy walking distance. Golfers have a choice of two courses both very near the house, and the beach at Borth stretches for four miles.

OWNERS: Christine and David Cox OPEN: all year exc Christmas ROOMS: 2 double, 1 with private bathroom; lounge with TV TERMS: single occupancy £16, twin/double £32; deposit: £5 CARDS: none DETAILS: no children; dogs welcome; smoking in lounge only; car park

BRECHFA Carmarthenshire **map 4**

Glasfryn Guest House NEW ENTRY

Brechfa SA32 7QY TEL/FAX: (01267) 202306
in centre of village on B4310

Located in a pretty village on the edge of the Brechfa Forest, this turn-of-the-century whitewashed house offers good-quality accommodation and food. Three comfortable bedrooms are attractively decorated and have been furnished in stripped pine; each is either *en suite* or with a private bathroom. Breakfasts and tastefully presented evening meals are served in the licensed conservatory-cum-dining-room, which is also open to non-residents and where children have their own menu. Joyce and Derek Hart are a friendly couple who provide a warm welcome to guests. The market town of Carmarthen is ten miles to the south-west through the Towy Valley.

OWNER: Joyce Hart OPEN: all year ROOMS: 2 double, 1 with bath/shower, 1 with private bathroom; 1 twin, with bath/shower; tea/coffee and TV in all bedrooms; lounge with TV TERMS: single occupancy £25, twin/double £46; half-price for children sharing with parents; dinner £12; deposit: 20% CARDS: none DETAILS: children welcome; small dogs by arrangement; car park; garden

BRECON Powys **map 4**

Pickwick House NEW ENTRY

St John's Road, Brecon LD3 9DS
TEL: (01874) 624322 FAX: (01874) 624700

This handsome Edwardian house is on a quiet side-street between the castle and the cathedral, just five minutes' walk from the centre of the tenth-century market town of Brecon. The house is beautifully maintained and has all modern comforts, yet retains its original character in features such as stained-glass windows and tiled floors. Isobel Stephen extends a traditional Welsh welcome, greeting guests with tea and home-made bara brith (a traditional Welsh fruitbread), served in the lounge, which has TV, books, games and jigsaw puzzles, and is warmed in winter by a log fire. There is a varied breakfast menu and an excellent choice for evening meals, with a menu featuring Welsh lamb, local salmon and trout, and delicious home-made desserts. Meals are served around an antique mahogany table in the dining-room or, in summer, in the conservatory. Dinners must be pre-booked, and vegetarians can be catered for with notice. There are drying and secure storage facilities for walkers and cyclists.

OWNER: Isobel Stephen OPEN: Easter to Oct ROOMS: 3 double/family, 2 with bath/shower, 1 with private bathroom; tea/coffee in all bedrooms; lounge with TV TERMS: single occupancy £26–£28, double/family £40–£44; dinner £10; deposit: £10 per person CARDS: none DETAILS: children welcome by arrangement; no dogs; no smoking; car park; garden

BUILTH WELLS Powys — map 4

Querida

43 Garth Road, Builth Wells LD2 3AR TEL: (01982) 553642

Mrs Hammond continues to offer good-value accommodation in her spotlessly clean home, greeting arriving guests with a hot drink and, on baking days, Welsh teacakes. Querida is a modest and friendly house within walking distance of shops and other amenities in the pretty market town of Builth Wells. The smallish, simply furnished bedrooms provide a comfortable night's stay, and there are two bathrooms for guests' use, as well as a lounge. Traditional cooked breakfasts are substantial.

OWNER: Mrs C.M. Hammond OPEN: all year ROOMS: 2 double, 1 twin; all rooms with wash-basin and tea/coffee; lounge with TV TERMS: single occupancy £15–£20, twin/double £28–£30; reductions for children sharing with parents; deposit required CARDS: none DETAILS: children welcome; dogs welcome; smoking permitted in certain rooms only; car park

CAERNARFON Gwynedd — map 7

Isfryn

11 Church Street, Caernarfon LL55 1SW TEL/FAX: (01286) 675628

from main entrance to castle take Castle St to bottom, turn left 20 metres after archway into Church St; Isfryn 100yds on right

Just a stroll away from the castle and town centre, Isfryn is a white-painted Victorian house set within the old town walls on a one-way street. Four of the light and spacious bedrooms are *en suite*, and guests have the use of a neat and comfortable lounge, which is also bright and airy. Dishes such as home-made pâté to start, followed by Welsh lamb escalopes, and lemon and brandy-sauce pancakes with home-made ice-cream may feature on the three-course dinner menu. Dinners are served at 6pm in the dining-room at individual tables; vegetarian options are available if pre-arranged, and guests are welcome to bring their own wine. A free public car park is nearby.

OWNERS: Mr and Mrs G. Bailey OPEN: Mar to Oct ROOMS: 1 single, with wash-basin; 1 double, with bath/shower; 1 twin, with wash-basin; 3 family, all with bath/shower; tea/coffee and TV in all bedrooms; lounge with TV TERMS: single £18, twin/double £36–£40, family room from £40; reductions for children under 12 sharing with parents; dinner £17.50; deposit: 1 night's charge CARDS: none DETAILS: children welcome; small dogs by arrangement; no smoking in lounge or dining-room

White House

NEW ENTRY

Llanfaglan, Caernarfon LL54 5RA TEL: (01286) 673003

take A487 S from Caernarfon, over roundabout, then after 50yds turn right, signposted Llanfaglan; proceed 1½m, turn right and house is last on left before sea

The tranquil location of the appropriately white-painted White House – overlooking the Foryd Bay and the Isle of Anglesey – makes it the perfect spot for bird-watchers, anglers and walkers. The house is spotlessly maintained, with the bedrooms and lounge offering splendid views. Two bedrooms have *en suite* facilities and one has a private bathroom. An outdoor swimming-pool is in use in summer, and the Caernarfon Golf Course is one mile away.

OWNER: R.W. Bayles OPEN: Mar to Nov ROOMS: 2 double, 1 with bath/shower, 1 with private bathroom; 2 twin, both with bath/shower; tea/coffee and TV in all bedrooms; lounge TERMS: single occupancy £22–£24, twin/double £36–£40; babies free, half-price for children under 12; deposit: £10 per room CARDS: none DETAILS: children welcome; dogs welcome in bedrooms only; no smoking; car park; garden; swimming-pool

CAERWYS Flintshire

map 7

Plas Penucha

NEW ENTRY

Caerwys CH7 5BH TEL: (01352) 720210

from N on B5122, take first right in village, left after ⅔m at crossroads; house is 1m on left

This unique and interesting hall-style farmhouse has been in the same family since it was built over 400 years ago. It has two acres of grounds with a rock garden and many species of rhododendron. Guests entering the reception hall are greeted with the Welsh message 'Aelwyd a Gymhell' ('A welcoming hearth beckons') carved into the oak beam over the fireplace. The house is beautifully furnished with antiques, and some of the rooms are decorated with unusual arts-and-crafts-style wallpaper. There are four good-sized bedrooms. The dining-room, built over an old spring, and the lounge, with its original Elizabethan panelling intact, are in the oldest part of the house. Log fires are lit on cool evenings, books and jigsaw puzzles are provided, and there is TV and radio. Breakfasts and pre-booked evening meals are available, and vegetarian choices can be provided with notice. Mrs Price is a charming host who has created a peaceful atmosphere for guests in her lovely home.

OWNERS: Mrs N. Price OPEN: all year ROOMS: 2 double, 1 with bath/shower, 1 with private bathroom; 3 twin, 2 with bath/shower, 1 with wash-basin; tea/coffee in all bedrooms; TV in 1 bedroom and lounge TERMS: single occupancy £18.50, twin/double £37; children under 3 free, 25% reduction for ages 3–14; dinner £10.50; deposit: £10 CARDS: none DETAILS: children welcome; dogs by arrangement; no smoking; car park; garden

CAPEL DEWI Carmarthenshire **map 4**

Farm Retreats

Capel Dewi Uchaf Farm, Capel Dewi SA32 8AY
TEL: (01267) 290799 FAX: (01267) 290003
off B4300, 4m E of Carmarthen

Fredena Burns has been offering B&B in this 500-year-old farmhouse since 1992 and continues to ensure that old-world charm is cleverly interlaced with all the modern comforts. Exposed stone walls, a mediaeval door and inglenook fireplaces add to the appeal, while bedrooms decorated in traditional country-style boast cotton sheets and embroidered white bedspreads, and the huge, comfortable lounge has a piano and a guitar for the musically inclined. The family room consists of a suite with a double and single room (and bathroom) in an adjacent cottage. A dining-room decorated like a baronial hall is where breakfast and evening meals (at 8pm) featuring fresh farmhouse cuisine are served; after dinner coffee and liqueurs are taken in the lounge. There is a short wine list, and vegetarians can be catered for with advance notice. The B&B has its own fishing rights on the Towy River

OWNER: Fredena Burns OPEN: all year exc Christmas ROOMS: 3 double, 2 with bath/shower, 1 with private bathroom; 1 family, with private bathroom; tea/coffee and TV in all bedrooms; lounge with TV TERMS: single occupancy £35.25, double £50, family from £50; reductions for children sharing with parents; dinner £25; deposit required CARDS: none DETAILS: children welcome; no dogs; no smoking; car park; garden

CAREW Pembrokeshire **map 4**

Old Stable Cottage

Carew SA70 8SL TEL: (01646) 651889
turn off A477 6m W of Kilgetty on to A4075; cottage is close to entrance to Carew Castle

High standards continue at this charming cottage-conversion of the stables and cart house originally belonging to neighbouring Carew Castle. Original stone walls, exposed brickwork, hand-woven rugs and old pine furniture add to the warmth of the atmosphere. Guests can relax in the enormous lounge with its comfortable sofas, teak beams, and pair of bread ovens in the original fireplace. A cast-iron spiral staircase leads up to the bedrooms: the twin-bedded room is small, the others more spacious. Wholesome breakfasts and evening meals, to which guests may bring their own wine, are cooked on the Aga and served in the conservatory dining-room overlooking the pretty walled garden. The Fielders, in the words of one visitor, are 'caring, attentive' hosts. There is very limited off-street parking, though on-street parking has no restrictions.

OWNERS: Lionel and Joyce Fielder OPEN: Mar to end Nov ROOMS: 1 double, 1 twin, 1 family; all rooms with bath/shower, tea/coffee and TV; lounge TERMS: single occupancy £38, twin/double £48, family room £65–£70; dinner £17.50 CARDS: none DETAILS: no children under 10; no dogs; no smoking; games room; garden

CEFN-DDWYSARN Gwynedd **map 7**

Cwm Hwylfod

Cefn-ddwysarn LL23 7LN TEL/FAX: (01678) 530310

heading NE from Bala on A494, after 3m turn right at phone box in Cefn-ddwysarn; take 4th small turning on left, pass farmhouse and go through 2 gates

Set in the middle of superb walking country, and handy for the water sports at Bala, this 400-year-old whitewashed farmhouse offers a friendly welcome, and is especially suitable for families with children. Wellington boots of all sizes are provided, and children enjoy accompanying Edward Best on his rounds of this working sheep farm. Facilities for washing and drying are also available, and there is also a good selection of toys and board games. The three bedrooms share two bathrooms and have traditional furniture. Breakfasts and evening meals make good use of local farm supplies: free-range eggs feature at breakfast, and evening meals might include Welsh lamb or home-made beef and onion pie. Joan Best is also happy to prepare food for babies and toddlers, and will cater for vegetarian and other diets if requested in advance.

OWNERS: Edward and Joan Best OPEN: all year exc Christmas ROOMS: 2 twin, 1 family; all rooms with wash-basin and tea/coffee; lounge with TV TERMS: single occupancy £16–£18, twin/double £32–£36, family room from £32; reductions for children under 10; dinner £10 CARDS: none DETAILS: children welcome; no dogs; no smoking; car park; garden

COLWYN BAY Conwy **map 7**

Holcombe Hotel

9 Grosvenor Road, Colwyn Bay LL29 7YF TEL/FAX: (01492) 530423

This small family-run hotel is in a quiet residential area, yet near the town centre and seafront, and just off the A55. The comfortable bedrooms are well proportioned and all have *en suite* facilities. Two are on the ground floor and are suitable for wheelchair-users. Several original features remain, such as the stained glass in the hallway, and fireplaces, including one in the guests' lounge. Evening meals are available and the hotel is licensed, although guests may bring their own wine to dinner if they wish. Vegetarians can be catered for with notice and children's helpings are provided.

OWNER: Eira Wyn Wellings   OPEN: all year exc Christmas   ROOMS: 1 single, 3 double, 3 twin, 1 family; all rooms with bath/shower, tea/coffee and TV; 2 rooms suitable for wheelchair-users; lounge with TV   TERMS: single £18–£20, single occupancy £30, twin/double £36–£42, family room £54–£60; children under 4 free, half-price for older children; dinner £8; deposit: 15%   CARDS: none   DETAILS: children welcome; no dogs; no smoking in dining-room; car park; garden

St Margaret's Hotel

NEW ENTRY

Princes Drive, Colwyn Bay LL29 8RP   TEL: (01492) 532718

This spacious double-fronted Edwardian building, five minutes from the station, has been a hotel since opening in 1908. Monica and Geoffrey Copley have refurbished it to a high standard; the bedrooms are freshly decorated with pretty pastel wallpapers, and have new furniture and firm beds. There are two lounges, one with a small bar and the other a good-size sunny conservatory. The Copleys have been in the hotel and catering trade since 1969, and provide good four-course dinners with delicious home-made puddings at modest prices. Children's portions are available, and vegetarians can be catered for with advance notice. The town centre and beautiful beaches are within walking distance.

OWNERS: Monica and Geoffrey Copley   OPEN: all year exc Nov   ROOMS: 1 single, 6 double, 2 twin, 1 family; all rooms with bath/shower, tea/coffee and TV; lounge with TV   TERMS: single/single occupancy £18.50–£21.50, twin/double £37–£43, family room £40–£60; children under 5 free, reductions for ages 5–16; dinner £10; deposit: £10 per person   CARDS: MasterCard, Visa   DETAILS: children welcome; no dogs in public rooms; no smoking in dining-room and 1 lounge; car park; garden

CONWY   Conwy   map 7

Town House

18 Rosehill Street, Conwy LL32 8LD   TEL: (01492) 596454

opposite castle car park

Elaine Priestley offers a warm welcome and a homely atmosphere at this 150-year-old stone house overlooking the castle, and only a short walk from the town centre. The house is well maintained, and the bedrooms are spotless and prettily decorated with patterned wallpapers. Three of the rooms now have *en suite* showers, while the others have use of private bathrooms. Breakfast is served in the bright dining-room at separate pine tables. There are six free parking spaces for guests opposite the house. The visitors' entrance to the castle is very near by.

OWNER: Elaine Priestley   OPEN: all year   ROOMS: 5 double, 2 with shower, 3 with private bathroom; 1 family, with shower; tea/coffee and TV in all bedrooms   TERMS:

single occupancy £16.50, twin/double £25–£33, family room £33–£43 CARDS: Amex, Delta, MasterCard, Visa DETAILS: no children under 4; small dogs welcome with own bedding; no smoking; car park

CRICCIETH Gwynedd map 7

Trefaes

Y Maes, Criccieth LL52 0AE TEL: (01766) 523204 FAX: (01766) 523013
on B4411 Caernarfon road

This Edwardian house is on the edge of the village green and has views of the castle and the sea. It was originally the residence of a builder, who had constructed Lloyd George's house and he based Trefaes on the same plans. It stands in mature terraced gardens with a summer-house, and though the house has been tastefully modernised, it retains the lovely stained-glass front door and original pine doors inside. A chaise longue graces the hallway, along with other interesting antiques, and the guests' sitting-room is cosy, while bedrooms are decorated in different colour schemes – one pink, one green, one gold. Pat Clayton is a vegetarian and an excellent cook, offering an extensive and innovative vegetarian dinner menu, but also provides a range of chicken and fish dishes, and a full Welsh breakfast. Pat has two friendly black labradors. Local attractions include Criccieth Castle, the Ffestiniog railway and Portmeirion.

OWNER: Patricia Clayton OPEN: all year exc Christmas ROOMS: 2 double, 1 twin; all rooms with shower, tea/coffee and TV; lounge TERMS: single occupancy £23–£25, twin/double £40–£44; 33% reduction for children from 12–15; dinner £14; deposit: £10 per person CARDS: none DETAILS: no children under 12; dogs welcome; no smoking in dining-room; car park; garden

DALE Pembrokeshire map 4

Post House Hotel NEW ENTRY

Dale SA62 3RE TEL: (01646) 636201
from Haverfordwest take B4327 to Dale; in village keep sea on left, turn right after the Griffin pub; B&B 100yds on right

This comfortable family-run small hotel, built in the 1920s, is situated in Dale, a pretty, unspoilt village by the sea. The Pembrokeshire Coast Path and the ferry to the National Nature Reserve islands of Skokholm and Skomer are nearby. The bedrooms are bright and spacious, have attractive fitted furnishings and are decorated in soft pastel shades. One of the twin rooms is very large, with its own sitting-room and bathroom, and overlooks the sea. Breakfasts and good-value home-styled cooked evening meals are served in the licensed dining-room at individual tables, and there is a warm and inviting lounge, plus a conservatory, for guests to use. Vegetarians can be catered for with advance notice. The Rileys have been running their B&B since the early '80s, and are a friendly and welcoming couple.

OWNERS: Laurence and Christine Riley OPEN: all year exc Christmas ROOMS: 3 double, 2 twin; all rooms with bath/shower and tea/coffee; TV in 1 bedroom and lounge TERMS: single occupancy £25–£35, twin/double £45–£55; dinner £9.50; deposit: £20 per person CARDS: none DETAILS: no children under 11; no dogs; no smoking in bedrooms; car park; garden

DINGESTOW Monmouthshire — map 2

Cider Mill

Lower Pen-y-Clawdd Farm, Dingestow NP5 4BG
TEL: (01600) 740223/740677
on A40 between Raglan and Monmouth; turn off at Granada services across cattle-grid into farm drive

The approach to this 100-acre sheep and cattle farm is directly off a main road, but the seventeenth-century farmhouse is set back so traffic noise is not a problem. The cider mill itself is an adjacent building and dates from the same period. The accommodation is simple and good value and has a laid-back atmosphere. Guests, including supervised children, are welcome to wander around the farmyard, which is inhabited by ducks, chickens, white peacocks and friendly dogs. The spacious bedrooms have brass and mahogany antique beds, and there are several other items of antique furniture throughout the house, including a chaise longue and a beautiful dresser. Breakfasts only are served, but there are several pubs that do evening meals within easy driving distance.

OWNER: Averil Bayliss OPEN: all year ROOMS: 1 double, 1 family; both rooms with wash-basin and tea/coffee; lounge with TV TERMS: single occupancy £18–£22, twin/double £34–£38, family room £42–£50; half-price for children sharing with parents CARDS: none DETAILS: children welcome; dogs welcome; no smoking; car park; garden

DOLGELLAU Gwynedd — map 7

Bryn yr Odyn — NEW ENTRY

Maescaled, Dolgellau LL40 1UG TEL/FAX: (01341) 423470
from Dolgellau town centre take Tywyn / Fairbourne Rd for ½m

This Welsh long-house dating from the seventeenth century stands on the edge of town in an acre and a half of landscaped gardens with a stream running through them. The three bedrooms are individually decorated; one has a Spanish theme, with floral wallpaper, colourful fans and rugs, while another is beamed and white-clad, and the third boasts a Welsh woven bed quilt; all have armchairs and TV. There are no *en suite* facilities, but two bathrooms are exclusively for guests' use, one of which has a power-shower. Mr and Mrs Jones make their guests welcome in the family lounge with its inglenook fireplace; Mr Jones is a local historian who is happy to share his knowledge with interested visitors. 'High quality and value' is how one reader summed up his stay.

OWNERS: Robert and Rita Gwyn Jones OPEN: all year ROOMS: 1 double, 2 twin; all rooms with wash-basin, tea/coffee and TV; lounge with TV TERMS: single occupancy £20–£24, twin/double £34–£40; children's reductions; deposit: 1 night's charge CARDS: none DETAILS: children by arrangement; no dogs; no smoking; car park; garden

Ivy House

Finsbury Square, Dolgellau LL40 1RF
TEL: (01341) 422535 FAX: (01341) 422689

Ivy House is a large, three-storey granite semi-detached building situated close to the town centre. The licensed restaurant is open to the general public (dinner is served from 5 to 9.30pm), but guests have plenty of space to themselves, as the owners live in a neighbouring property. Bedrooms are decorated to a high standard in soft pastel shades, and there is a lounge for guests' use. The evening menu is fairly extensive, ranging from simple dishes to four-course meals. The house is licensed, with a short wine list, and a small cellar bar. Dolgellau is at the foot of Cader Idris in Snowdonia National Park and makes an ideal base for walking or pony-trekking.

OWNERS: James and Margaret Bamford OPEN: all year exc Christmas ROOMS: 3 double, 2 with shower, 1 with wash-basin; 2 twin, 1 with shower, 1 with wash-basin; 1 family, with wash-basin; tea/coffee and TV in all bedrooms; lounge with TV TERMS: single occupancy £22–£30, twin/double £37, family room from £37; children's reductions according to age; deposit: £10 per person CARDS: Amex, Delta, MasterCard, Switch, Visa DETAILS: children welcome; dogs welcome; garden

DOLWYDDELAN Conwy

map 7

Bryn Tirion Farm

Dolwyddelan LL25 0JD TEL: (01690) 750366
off A470, 5m SW of Betws-y-Coed

This farmhouse is in a magnificent setting overlooking the Lledr Valley and has within its grounds 900-year-old Dolwyddelan Castle. Caroline and Robert Price are cheerful and energetic people, and offer simple, functional accommodation which is well suited to walkers and nature lovers. The three bedrooms have firm beds. Breakfast is served in the dining-room/lounge, and there is a tea-shop adjacent to the property which sells home-made cakes and snacks, as well as tickets to the castle. Camping and caravans are available on the farm.

OWNER: Caroline Price OPEN: all year exc Christmas and New Year ROOMS: 1 double, 1 twin, 1 family; all rooms with wash-basin and tea/coffee; lounge with TV TERMS: twin/double £30, family from £30; children's reductions according to age; deposit required CARDS: none DETAILS: children welcome; no dogs; no smoking; car park

If there are any bedrooms with TV, or with tea / coffee-making facilities, we mention this in the details at the end of an entry.

FELINFACH Powys

map 4

Trehenry Farm

NEW ENTRY

Felinfach LD3 0UN TEL/FAX: (01874) 754312

take A470 from Brecon, after 4½m turn left at Felinfach; Trehenry is signposted on right

This welcoming eighteenth-century Welsh-stone farmhouse has stunning views of the Black Mountains and Brecon Beacons. It is part of a 200-acre mixed farm that sits in a remote area. The warm and comfortable bedrooms have traditional furnishings; there are two lounges for guests, both with wood-burning stoves. Generous farmhouse breakfasts, and evening meals if booked ahead, are served in the bright dining-room, and a barbecue is available to residents. In the opinion of one visitor, 'this is the best B&B . . . in the Brecon area'.

OWNER: Theresa Jones OPEN: all year exc Christmas ROOMS: 1 double, 1 twin, 1 family; all rooms with bath/shower; lounge with TV TERMS: single/single occupancy £25–£35, twin/double £40, family room £50–£60; half-price for children sharing with parents; dinner £12.50; deposit: 1 night's charge CARDS: none DETAILS: children welcome; no dogs; no smoking; car park; garden

FISHGUARD Pembrokeshire

map 4

Manor House Hotel

NEW ENTRY

Main Street, Fishguard SA65 9HG TEL/FAX: (01348) 873260

This stylish Georgian building with its eclectic assortment of antiques and other collectables is located on the picturesque main street of the town, and has views over the harbour and sea. The atmosphere is pleasant and informal, and the Davieses are happy to help guests plan itineraries. Some of the bedrooms are themed: for example, the Edwardian Room is very large and is furnished in keeping with that era, while the Victorian Room boasts an art-deco wardrobe and bed. All the bedrooms have interesting displays of paintings and books, and most have sitting-areas; antiques and books feature in the elegant lounge too. Guests may stroll out into the pretty walled garden with its panoramic views; on warm days breakfast and pre-dinner drinks are served on the patio. Breakfast times are flexible, and readers have praised the imaginative candlelit dinners that are served in the restaurant, which is open to non-residents. Menus might offer the likes of cockle cakes in a spicy coconut sauce, organic Welsh black beef in a Guinness gravy with dumplings, followed by Manor House gooseberry flan. There is free on-street parking, as well as a public car park nearby.

OWNERS: Beatrix and Ralph Davies OPEN: all year exc Christmas and 3 weeks in winter ROOMS: 1 single, 4 double, 2 twin; all rooms with bath/shower, tea/coffee and TV; lounge TERMS: single £25–£26, single occupancy £28–£40, twin/double £44–£55; children's reductions by arrangement; dinner £18; deposit: credit card details or cheque CARDS: Delta, Diners, MasterCard, Switch, Visa DETAILS: children welcome; dogs by arrangement; no smoking in restaurant; garden

GELLILYDAN Gwynedd

map 7

Tyddyn Du

Gellilydan LL41 4RB TEL/FAX: (01766) 590281
off A470 near junction with A487, ½m from Gellilydan village

Reporters continue to endorse the warm welcome and comfortable accommodation at this delightful seventeenth-century farmhouse in the Snowdonia National Park. It has been tastefully restored, retaining the exposed stone walls, an inglenook fireplace, kettle and cauldron cranes, and Welsh slate walls in the dining-room. Bedrooms have exposed beams, antique German pine furniture, and views of the hills and mountains. The former stable has been converted into a suite with two double bedrooms and a whirlpool bath, and the Bwthyn cottage adjoining the farmhouse is especially suitable for families. Tyddyn Du is part of a working farm with plenty of friendly animals, and guests are welcome to help at feeding-time, and collect their own freshly laid eggs for breakfast. Guests can relax in the luxurious sitting-room, where log fires burn on cool evenings. Candlelit dinners are served by arrangement and feature traditional farmhouse cooking using local produce. Vegetarian choices can be provided and guests may bring their own wine to dinner. There are many places of interest in the area, including the Ffestiniog railway, Llechwedd Slate Caverns and the Italianate village at Portmeirion.

OWNERS: Paula and Meredydd Williams OPEN: all year ROOMS: 1 double, with bath/shower; 1 twin, with wash-basin; 2 family, all with bath/shower; tea/coffee and TV in all bedrooms; lounge with TV TERMS: twin/double £36–£39, family room £46–£50; children's reductions according to age; dinner £12; deposit required CARDS: none DETAILS: children welcome; dogs welcome; no smoking; car park; garden

GOODWICK Pembrokeshire

map 4

Ivybridge

NEW ENTRY

Drim Mill, Dyffryn, Goodwick SA64 0FT
TEL: (01348) 875366 and 872623 FAX: (01348) 872338
off A487 Fishguard to St David's road; 1m W of Fishguard

This tastefully converted mill and adjoining cottages is in the outskirts of Fishguard, close to the port for ferries to Ireland. Bedrooms have modern pine furniture, and three of them are in an annexe, ideal for guests who like a little more privacy. There are two sitting-areas: a spacious beamed lounge with a fireplace on the ground floor, and a smaller lounge on the first floor. Guests also have use of a heated indoor swimming-pool and whirlpool, a sunbed and a games room with chess, darts and a pool table. Some rooms have been adapted for wheelchair access. Breakfast is served in the bright dining-room, and pre-booked evening meals are also available, with vegetarian options by arrangement. Ivybridge is licensed. This is an ideal spot for visiting historical Fishguard and the beautiful coastline, with its wide variety of bird-life.

OWNERS: Colin Phillips OPEN: all year exc Christmas ROOMS: 1 single, 5 double, 2 twin, 4 family; all rooms with bath/shower, tea/coffee and TV; 2 rooms suitable for wheelchair-users; lounge with TV TERMS: single £19.50, twin/double £39–£47, family room from £39; dinner £11.50; deposit required CARDS: Delta, MasterCard, Switch, Visa DETAILS: children welcome; dogs welcome; car park; games room; garden; swimming-pool

HAY-ON-WYE Powys **map 5**

Brookfield Guesthouse

Brook Street, Hay-on-Wye, HR3 5BQ TEL: (01497) 820518

This partly creeper-clad stone-built house with origins in the seventeenth century has tremendous architectural character. Exposed beams, a Queen Anne door and some horse-hair and plaster walls all add to the charm, and more recent add-ons – such as the electrical fixtures produced by a local craftsman – are in keeping with the rest. The guest lounge has an open fire, TV and piano, and the simple, very neat bedrooms are tastefully decorated; the *en suite* family room is enormous. Hay-on-Wye is famous for its book and craft shops, and is set in beautiful countryside.

OWNERS: David and Cheryl Price OPEN: all year exc Christmas ROOMS: 3 double, all with wash-basin; 2 twin, both with wash-basin; 2 family, 1 with shower, 1 with wash-basin; tea/coffee in all bedrooms; TV in 1 family room; 1 room suitable for wheelchair-users; lounge with TV TERMS: single occupancy £18–£20, twin/double £30–£35, family room £45–£60; deposit: £10 per room CARDS: none DETAILS: no children under 5; no dogs; smoking downstairs only; car park

HOLYHEAD Isle of Anglesey **map 7**

Roselea

26 Holborn Road, Holyhead LL65 2AT TEL/FAX: (01407) 764391

Improvements are ongoing at his welcoming guesthouse: new carpets have been laid on the stairs, and the dining-room has new farmhouse-style chairs. The house is just a few minutes from the ferry to Ireland, and Mrs Foxley – whom one visitor found 'kind without being intrusive' – will await guests arriving on the late ferry as long as prior notice is given. Colourful floral displays at the front of the house in summer cause passers-by to pause and admire. Within, the house is immaculate, and the guest lounge warm and comfortable, with plenty of books as well as a TV. Breakfasts are substantial, and Holyhead has a wide range of establishments for eating out in the evenings.

OWNER: Mrs S. Foxley OPEN: all year exc Christmas ROOMS: 1 double, 1 twin, 1 family; all rooms with wash-basin, tea/coffee and TV; lounge with TV TERMS: single occupancy £20–£28, twin/double £28–£30, family room from £14 per person; reductions for children sharing with parents; deposit usually required CARDS: none DETAILS: children welcome; no dogs; smoking in designated area only

LITTLE HAVEN Pembrokeshire **map 4**

Whitegates

Little Haven SA62 3LA TEL: (01437) 781552 FAX: (01437) 781386
off B4341, 7m W of Haverfordwest

Ostriches are something of a passion with Richard Llewellin, who invites guests at this 150-year B&B to 'meet the birds' at his hatchery. Set in an elevated position with good views over St Brides Bay and the village, Whitegates offers five bedrooms, most of them of a good size and all but one with a harbour view. One bedroom is on the ground floor. There is also an outdoor swimming-pool, and for the less energetically inclined a lounge with TV and video. Four-course evening meals (which must be pre-booked), as well as breakfast, are served at separate tables in the dining-room. Out-of-season 'Gastronomic Weekends' with the emphasis on traditional Welsh cooking are held for couples and parties of up to ten. One-night bookings are not accepted in July and August.

OWNERS: Richard and Marion Llewellin OPEN: all year ROOMS: 3 double, 2 with bath/shower, 1 with private bathroom; 1 twin, with private bathroom; 1 family, with bath/shower; tea/coffee in all bedrooms; lounge with TV TERMS: single occupancy £25–£30; twin/double £41–£48; family £50–£60; children's reductions by arrangement; dinner £17.50; deposit required, or credit card details CARDS: MasterCard, Visa DETAILS: children welcome; no dogs in public rooms; no smoking in bedrooms; car park; garden; swimming-pool

LLANANNO Powys **map 4**

Bwlch Farm

Llananno LD1 6TT TEL/FAX: (01597) 840366
from Llandrindod Wells take A483 towards Newtown, turn left towards Bwlch-y-sarnau 1½m N of Llanbister, then first left

This wonderful away-from-it-all farmhouse with its eight acres of grounds is set in the hills overlooking the Ithon Valley. The three bedrooms all have their original cruck beams dating from the sixteenth century; two of the rooms are *en suite* and one has a private bathroom. Original flagstone floors, a mixture of traditional and antique furniture and a log fire in the sitting-room add to the atmosphere. Candlelit three-course dinners are served from 7pm, and guests are welcome to bring their own wine. Glyndwr's Way passes nearby, making this an ideal base for walkers, and a wide variety of birdlife can be seen around the garden. Stabling for two horses can be provided, and self-catering accommodation is available.

OWNERS: Roy and Dorothy Taylor OPEN: Easter to late Oct ROOMS: 2 double, 1 with shower, 1 with private bathroom; 1 twin, with shower; tea/coffee in all bedrooms; lounge with TV TERMS: single occupancy £21, twin/double £37; children's reductions by arrangement; dinner £10.50; deposit: £10 CARDS: none DETAILS: children welcome; well-behaved dogs welcome; no smoking in bedrooms; car park; garden

LLANBEDR Gwynedd map 7

Plas y Bryn Hall

Llanbedr LL45 2DX TEL: (01341) 241520 FAX: (01341) 241214
off A496, 3m S of Harlech

Approached by a long drive, this Edwardian stone house with a black and white Tudor-style front stands in an acre of beautiful landscaped gardens with views of Cardigan Bay and the mountains. It is full of character, furnished mostly with antiques, and original features include an attractive ceiling rose and cornices. Janis and Alan, originally from London, are a charming couple who welcome guests into their home as their friends. Guests are free to come and go as they please and are encouraged to ask for recommendations for walks and drives nearby. The two bedrooms are well appointed; one has a comfortable antique iron bed, its own bathroom and fine views over the water. A sitting-room is also available to guests. Hearty breakfasts are served and recommendations for local eating-places are happily given. Shell Island beach is a mile away, Harlech is three miles and Rhinog Uplands, described as one of Britain's last true wildernesses, is within easy driving distance.

OWNERS: Alan and Janis Redshaw OPEN: all year exc Christmas ROOMS: 2 double, 1 with bath, 1 with private bathroom; tea/coffee and TV in both bedrooms; lounge TERMS: double £36–£44; deposit required CARDS: none DETAILS: no children; no dogs; no smoking; car park; garden

LLANDDERFEL Gwynedd map 7

Bronwylfa Guest House NEW ENTRY

Llandderfel LL23 7HG TEL/FAX: (01678) 530207
6m W off A5, or 4m E from Bala

This impressive Victorian country house is approached up a long private drive bordered by trees, and has superb views of surrounding countryside. The old-fashioned conservatory overlooks a large, well-tended mature garden, with its interesting shrubs and a rare tulip tree. High ceilings, wool carpets and rich floral-flocked wallpaper in the bedrooms all enhance the Victorian effect; rooms are spacious and have good views, and one is in a small cottage opposite the house – ideal for those who value privacy. Excellent breakfasts – including home-made preserves – are served in the elegant dining-room, which is furnished in yew. Lesley Andrews is a warm and friendly host who greets guests with tea and cakes upon arrival.

OWNER: Lesley Andrews OPEN: all year exc Christmas ROOMS: 2 double, both with bath/shower; 1 twin, with bath/shower; 1 family, with private bathroom; tea/coffee and TV in all bedrooms; lounge with TV TERMS: single occupancy £24–£30; twin/double £37–£45, family room £45–£60; children's reductions according to age; deposit: £10 minimum CARDS: none DETAILS: children welcome; dogs welcome in 1 bedroom only; no smoking; car park; garden

LLANDDEW Powys map 4

Old Rectory

NEW ENTRY

Llanddew LD3 9SS TEL: (01874) 622058
in centre of village, 1½m N of Brecon

Built in 1867, the Old Rectory stands in a peaceful position in two acres of grounds overlooking a thirteenth-century church and the Brecon Beacons. It is a lovely old house, impeccably kept and furnished with antiques, and guests are well looked after by the charming owner, Val Williams. The three attractive bedrooms are of a good size: two have *en suite* facilities and one a private bathroom; all have armchairs and TV. Guests are welcome to enjoy the garden and croquet lawn. Of special interest are the ruins of the 800-year-old Llanddew Castle. Breakfast only is served, but there are venues for evening meals close by. Self-catering accommodation is also available.

OWNER: Mrs V. Williams OPEN: all year exc Christmas ROOMS: 1 double, with shower; 1 twin, with shower; 1 family, with private bathroom; tea/coffee and TV in all bedrooms; lounge TERMS: single occupancy £26, twin/double £40, family room from £20 per person; £12 for children under 12; deposit: £20 CARDS: none DETAILS: children welcome; no dogs; smoking in lounge only; car park; garden

LLANDECWYN Gwynedd map 7

Tegfan

Llandecwyn, nr Talsarnau LL47 6YG TEL: (01766) 771354
on A496, 1m N of Talsarnau

This neat detached house in a peaceful setting, just two miles from Porthmadog, stands in a pretty garden and has views over hills where sheep graze and beyond to the sea. Bedrooms are well decorated and furnished in pine. The separate annexe room has its own bathroom and would be ideal for a family or anyone wanting a little extra privacy. Roy King has developed a mini theme park in the rock face with two small railway engines and trucks to represent the scenic railway at Porthmadog, together with figures of the various wildlife found in the area, such as badgers and colourful butterflies. Excellent breakfasts are served on Portmeirion china in the dining-room, which has a great view. Note that one-night bookings are not taken.

OWNER: Roy King OPEN: all year exc Christmas ROOMS: 3 double, 1 with bath/shower, 2 with wash-basin; 1 twin, with private bathroom; 1 family; lounge with TV TERMS: single occupancy £18–£22, twin/double £32–£40; deposit: 25% CARDS: none DETAILS: no children; no dogs; smoking in annexe room only; car park; garden

We state at the end of an entry whether children are welcome, and explain any age restrictions. If there are reduced rates for children, this is mentioned; if no reductions are specified, assume you will have to pay full rates for children.

LLANDRINDOD WELLS Powys map 4

Charis

Pentrosfa, Llandrindod Wells LD1 5AL TEL/FAX: (01597) 824732
off A483, S of town centre

This large, beautifully maintained Edwardian house, on a quiet residential road, has an interesting turret-style entrance. Guests are treated as friends and warm Welsh hospitality is guaranteed. Delicious breakfasts are served in the dining-room, which overlooks the garden and has a one-handed clock. Bedrooms are spacious and have tall, elegant windows that allow plenty of light and give lovely views of the surrounding hills. The décor is in soft colours, and the beds have firm mattresses and pretty floral duvets.There is a lounge with TV and in summer guests may enjoy use of the well-tended garden at the rear of the house.

OWNER: Pat Gimson OPEN: all year exc Christmas ROOMS: 3 double, 1 twin, 1 family; all rooms with shower, tea/coffee and TV; lounge with TV TERMS: single occupancy £18, twin/double £32–£34, family room £45–£48; children under 5 free in family room; deposit: 10% CARDS: none DETAILS: children welcome; dogs by arrangement; no smoking; car park; garden

LLANDUDNO Conwy map 7

Amber Court

West Parade, Llandudno LL30 2BD TEL: (01492) 874521

Panoramic views and consistent high standards have guests returning often to this detached Victorian house in a quiet area of town. Ann Pickup is an interior designer and has decorated the bedrooms beautifully in soft greens, pinks, beige and peach. Each room is comfortably furnished and has a firm bed, its own wash-basin and WC, and the front rooms have sea views. There is a lovely marble fireplace in the lounge, which is shared with Ann, who is a charming host, and the hall has an antique carved sideboard. There is no car park, but Amber Court is on a quiet road with ample parking space.

OWNER: Ann Pickup OPEN: Mar to Nov ROOMS: 2 double, 2 twin; all rooms with wash-basin, tea/coffee and TV; lounge with TV TERMS: single occupancy £20–£30, twin/double £34–£42; children's reductions according to age CARDS: none DETAILS: no children under 7; no dogs; no smoking; garden

Beach Cove

8 Church Walks, Llandudno LL30 2HD TEL: (01492) 879638

Bob and Karen continue to maintain high standards in this Victorian guesthouse, well situated for the beaches and the town centre. It is in excellent decorative order, warm and comfortable, and the bedrooms are bright and airy. The dining-room, where excellent breakfasts and home-cooked traditional dinners are served, is now on the ground floor. Vegetarians can be catered for by arrangement, and although the house is unlicensed guests may bring their own wine. Bob Carroll has a good sense of humour and enjoys a chat with his guests. The Carrolls also own a self-catering cottage on Great Orme Head, and they can provide plenty of information on the local area.

OWNERS: Bob and Karen Carroll OPEN: all year exc Christmas ROOMS: 2 single, 1 with shower, 1 with wash-basin; 5 double, all with shower; 1 four-poster, with shower; tea/coffee and TV in all bedrooms; 1 room suitable for wheelchair-users; lounge with TV TERMS: single £15–£25, single occupancy £20–£25, double £36–£56, four-poster £40–£60; children £8–£10; dinner £10; deposit: £30 CARDS: none DETAILS: children welcome; no dogs; no smoking in 1 bedroom, dining-room and lounge; garden

Bryn-y-Mor

NEW ENTRY

25 North Parade, Llandudno LL30 2LP TEL: (01492) 876790

This five-storey Victorian hotel stands in an elevated position overlooking the bay and mountains. Upon taking over the business a few years ago, the Sherlocks refurbished the property to a high standard, installing new carpets, curtains and furnishings. The bedrooms are of a good size, all have armchairs, *en suite* facilities, radio-alarms and TVs; some have sea views. Breakfast and home-styled evening meals are served in the licensed dining-room, which leads to a large terrace facing the bay. Vegetarians can be catered for, and children have their own menu. Visitors receive a warm welcome, are offered tea or coffee and biscuits on arrival, and are given their own keys. There is a well-stocked bar, plus a lounge where guests can read or watch TV.

OWNERS: Brian and Fay Sherlock OPEN: all year ROOMS: 8 double, 1 twin, 2 family; all rooms with bath/shower, tea/coffee and TV; lounge with TV TERMS: single occupancy £30–£36, twin/double £40, family room £60–£72; dinner £12; deposit: £20 per person CARDS: Amex, Delta, Diners, MasterCard, Switch, Visa DETAILS: children welcome; no dogs; no smoking; garden

The Lighthouse

Marine Drive, Great Ormes Head, Llandudno LL30 2XD
TEL/FAX: (01492) 876819

from seafront in Llandudno follow signs for Great Orme Scenic Route for 2m

The approach to this spectacular listed building is via an exciting drive up the Great Orme, a headland rising to over 600 feet. The cost of a stay here is above the normal limit for B&Bs in the *Guide*, but this one does provide an exceptional experience. A fully operational lighthouse until the mid-'80s, it has been converted and furnished by John Callin to a high standard. Guests are fascinated upon arrival by the entrance hall with its 19-foot pitch-pine panelling and gallery; early-birds can watch the sunrise from the glass-walled lamp room; those wishing to relax can make use of the lounge where log fires burn on cool evenings; and breakfasters in the dining-room will look out over a 360-foot sheer drop to the sea. Bedrooms have *en suite* showers and are decorated to a high standard. Single-night bookings are accepted throughout the year, except for Friday and Saturday, which must be booked together.

OWNER: John Woodman Callin OPEN: all year exc Christmas ROOMS: 2 double, 1 family; all rooms with shower and TV; 1 room suitable for wheelchair-users; lounge with TV TERMS: single occupancy £39.50–£44.50, double £79–£89, family room from £79 plus children's charge; children under 3 free, half-price for ages 3–12 sharing with parents; deposit: 50% of final account CARDS: none DETAILS: children welcome; no dogs; no smoking; car park; garden

LLANDYBIE Carmarthenshire map 4

Glynhir Mansion NEW ENTRY

Llandybie SA18 2TD TEL: (01269) 850438 FAX: (01269) 851275
2m E of Llandybie, between Ammanford and Llandeilo

Beautiful gardens, a walled orchard, woodland walks, a 30-foot waterfall, peacocks and free-roaming pot-bellied pigs are all part of the estate where this rambling early-eighteenth-century house is set, at the foot of the Black Mountain. The atmosphere is informal, and families, artists and nature lovers all feel at home here. One reader called Glynhir 'a rare thing – a peaceful idyll in this hectic world'. The spacious, clean and comfortable bedrooms are furnished with antique and traditional pieces; three of the rooms have *en suite* facilities and two have private bathrooms. (Owing to fire regulations, the B&B tells us, only six guests total are accepted at one time.) The lounge and dining-room are in the Queen Anne end of the house, and guests also have the use of a flower-filled conservatory. Breakfasts and evening meals are served family-style: platters of food are brought to the table and guests may help themselves to as much as they want. Glynhir is licensed. Self-catering accommodation is also available.

OWNERS: Miss K.C.L., Mr J.W.B. and Mrs C.H.J. Jenkins OPEN: Mar to Nov ROOMS: 1 single, with wash-basin; 5 double, 1 with bath, 2 with shower, 2 with private bathroom; 1 twin, with wash-basin; lounge with TV TERMS: single/single occupancy £16.50–£21, twin/double £33–£42, family room from £33 per adult; reductions for children and babies free; dinner £12.50; deposit: £25 minimum CARDS: MasterCard, Switch, Visa DETAILS: children welcome; dogs in kennelling only; car park; garden

LLANFAIR Gwynedd map 7

Fron Deg NEW ENTRY

Llanfair LL46 2RE TEL: (01766) 780448
from Harlech take A496 S for 1m, then left on staggered crossroad

This attractive 200-year-old Virginia-creeper-clad stone house just outside the hamlet of Llanfair stands in an elevated position, and enjoys sea views. From across the road a footpath leads down to a quiet, sandy beach. Tasteful restoration, traditional furniture and antiques – including a huge oak-carved cabinet in the dining-room – add to the charm of Fron Deg, along with a warm and homely ambience. The twin room has private facilities, and the double and single share a bathroom. Pre-booked evening meals are available, featuring traditional dishes such as home-made steak and kidney pie, lots of fresh vegetables, followed by Ann Jones's speciality dessert, bread-and-butter pudding. Guests may relax in a comfortable lounge with TV, the only place in the house where smoking is permitted.

OWNER: Ann Jones OPEN: Mar to Oct ROOMS: 1 single, with wash-basin; 1 double, with wash-basin; 1 twin, with bath/shower; tea/coffee in all bedrooms; lounge with TV TERMS: single £17, single occupancy £30, twin/double £30; children under 5 free, reductions for older children; dinner £8; deposit by arrangement CARDS: none DETAILS: children welcome; dogs by arrangement; smoking in lounge only; car park; garden

LLANFAIR CAEREINION Powys map 7

Bryn Penarth

Llanfair Caereinion SY21 0BZ TEL/FAX: (01938) 810535
just off B4389, 1m S of Llanfair Caereinion

Bryn Penarth is a large, red-brick farmhouse, built in 1830, set in an acre of well-kept gardens and 46 acres of farmland in an elevated position with outstanding views of the countryside and the Berwyn Mountains. Inside it is beautifully maintained and traditionally furnished; the bedrooms are decorated in Victorian style and all have either private bathrooms or are *en suite*. A sitting-room has an open fireplace with a wood-burning stove and TV, and a sun-room, where breakfast is sometimes served, overlooks the garden. There is a separate beamed dining-room where breakfast and pre-arranged home-cooked dinners are taken around one table. Vegetarian choices and children's helpings can be provided with notice, and guests may bring their own wine to dinner. At the time of going to press, the owner was planning to convert the private bathrooms to *en suite*.

OWNER: Ivernia Watkin OPEN: all year exc Christmas ROOMS: 1 single, with private bathroom; 3 double, 2 with bath/shower, 1 with private bathroom; 1 twin, with private bathroom; tea/coffee in all bedrooms; TV in most bedrooms and lounge TERMS: single £18–£20, single occupancy £16–£25, twin/double £32–£36, four-poster £36–£40; half-price for children under 16; dinner £10 CARDS: none DETAILS: children welcome; no dogs in dining-room; no smoking in bedrooms and dining-room; car park; garden

Cwmllwynog

Llanfair Caereinion SY21 0HF TEL: (01938) 810791
from Llanfair Caereinion take B4385 towards Melin-y-ddol and take second turning left; from A458, turn on to B4385 and take first turning right

A warm welcome awaits guests at this traditional seventeenth-century Welsh farmhouse. It is on a working dairy farm in a tranquil and secluded location just outside the tiny hamlet of Melin-y-ddol, and may be difficult to find, so it is best to phone for directions. The large bedrooms are traditionally furnished and well equipped. There are sturdy beams throughout and the oak-panelled lounge has a huge stone fireplace with a wood-burning stove, and a fine collection of Portmeirion china is displayed on a splendid Welsh dresser. The house is surrounded with tubs and hanging baskets full of flowers, and the spacious, well-tended garden has a stream running past at the bottom, and supplies produce for Joyce Cornes's home-cooked meals. She also makes her own bread and puddings. Vegetarians can be catered for and guests may bring their own wine to dinner.

OWNERS: Joyce Cornes OPEN: all year exc Christmas ROOMS: 1 double, with shower; 1 twin, with private bathroom; tea/coffee and TV in both bedrooms; lounge with TV TERMS: single occupancy £20, twin/double £36; dinner £10 CARDS: none DETAILS: children welcome; dogs by arrangement; smoking downstairs only; car park; garden

LLANFAIR DYFFRYN CLWYD Denbighshire **map 7**

Plas Uchaf NEW ENTRY

Graigadwywynt, Llanfair Dyffryn Clwyd LL15 2TF TEL: (01824) 705794
take A525 S of Ruthin; at Llanfair Dyffryn Clwyd turn right towards Pwllglas; take next left, signposted Graigadwywynt; proceed 2m along narrow road; Plas Uchaf is first left after hamlet

Plas Uchaf is a beautifully kept stone property in a remote and peaceful location approached by a narrow two-mile lane. It was built in the sixteenth century as a hall house, and retains the high Jacobean chimneys and a wealth of oak beams. Restoration was undertaken in the seventeenth century by Thomas Goodman, whose uncle, Gabriel Goodman, was the Dean of Westminster and assisted Bishop William Morgan in his translation of the Bible into Welsh. The large and lofty bedrooms are furnished in keeping with the character of the house, and one has its own sitting-room. Guests have the use of a good-sized lounge and a small snug room – with settee and books – tucked in a narrow stairway to the loft of the galleried landing. According to one visitor, 'Sian Jones and her family are perfect hosts – very welcoming and friendly but not intrusive.' The Joneses are Welsh-speaking and have two young sons.

OWNER: Sian Jones OPEN: all year exc Christmas ROOMS: 1 double, 1 twin, 1 family; all rooms with bath/shower, tea/coffee and TV; lounge with TV TERMS: single occupancy £17–£20, twin/double £30–£34, family from £30; half-price for children sharing with parents CARDS: none DETAILS: children welcome; no dogs; no smoking; car park; garden

LLANFAIRFECHAN Conwy **map 7**

Plas Heulog NEW ENTRY

Mount Road, Llanfairfechan LL33 0HA TEL/FAX: (01248) 680019

This mountainside retreat, built in 1896, is approached by a steep, narrow lane and stands in the foothills of the Carneddau Mountains with spectacular views of Snowdonia, the Isle of Anglesey, and the sea – it is best to phone for directions. 'One of the most beautiful locations we have ever stayed at in Wales,' wrote one reporter. Plas Heulog is Welsh for 'sunny mansion', and the house has lots of character and interesting architectural features. The bedrooms are in an elevated annexe, reached by several stairs, and all have scenic views. Breakfasts and pre-booked dinners are served in the panelled dining-room/lounge where there are plenty of books to browse through, and a log fire. Beautiful surroundings, a variety of wildlife, and mountain hikes make this area a paradise for nature-lovers and walkers. Owners Kathleen and Peter Coleman, originally from Devon, have created a peaceful, friendly ambience and are happy to help guests with information on walks and places to visit in the area. Plas Heulog has secure bicycle storage and a drying-room, cots and high-chairs for young children, and a courtesy car service from the station. Horse riding and bicycle hire can be arranged. One-night bookings are not taken over bank holidays.

OWNERS: Kathleen and Peter Coleman OPEN: all year ROOMS: 4 double, 6 twin; all rooms with bath/shower, tea/coffee; lounge with TV TERMS: single occupancy £17.50–£25, twin/double £35–£40; children under 5 free, other reductions according to age; dinner £9.50; deposit: 1 night's charge CARDS: Delta, MasterCard, Visa DETAILS: children welcome; dogs by arrangement; no smoking; car park; garden

LLANFIHANGEL GLYN MYFYR Conwy map 7

Old Rectory

Llanfihangel Glyn Myfyr, nr Corwen LL21 9UN
TEL: (01490) 420568 FAX: (01490) 420773
just off B5105 Cerrigydrudion to Ruthin road

The Old Rectory is a Grade II-listed building standing in three acres of beautiful gardens. The surrounding valley, through which runs the River Alwen, is home to many species of wildlife, including some rare birds. The house is impeccably maintained and well furnished. The three bedrooms, all with lovely views, are individually decorated, and have half-tester or coronet beds. The elegant drawing-room has an open fire and lots of books, games and maps, and the main bathroom has a whirlpool bath; bathrobes are provided. TVs are available for the bedrooms on request. This establishment is an ideal base for hill-walking and mountain climbing; the Hugheses will supply route maps. Fishing on the River Alwen can be arranged, and water activities are available at the nearby Brenig reservoir.

OWNERS: Elwyn and Jenny Hughes OPEN: all year exc Christmas ROOMS: 3 family, all with wash-basin and tea/coffee; lounge with TV TERMS: single occupancy £24; family room from £40; children under 5 free, £10 for ages 5–14; deposit required CARDS: none DETAILS: children welcome; no dogs; smoking in lounge only; car park; garden

---

Many B&Bs are in remote places, and although in many cases we provide directions, it is always advisable to ask for clear instructions when booking.

LLANGOLLEN Denbighshire map 7

Adanhurst

Abbey Road, Llangollen LL20 8SS TEL: (01978) 860562
opposite Pavilion entrance

Adanhurst is an attractive modern bungalow on a main road a ten-minute walk from the town centre. It stands in a large lawned garden and has good rear views of the River Dee and the steam railway line. Annie and Mike Pearce extend a friendly welcome, and guests may share the lounge with the family on most occasions if they so request. The bedrooms are clean and comfortable; the twin now has *en suite* facilities. Breakfast is served in the breakfast room.

OWNER: Annie Pearce OPEN: all year ROOMS: 2 double; 1 twin, with shower; tea/coffee in all bedrooms; TV in double bedrooms TERMS: single occupancy £20–£25, twin/double £32–£35; deposit by arrangement CARDS: none DETAILS: children by arrangement; dogs by arrangement; no smoking; car park; garden

Hendy Isa NEW ENTRY

Llangollen LL20 8DE TEL: (01978) 861232
from Llangollen take A542 Horseshoe Pass and Ruthin road, first left after Abbey ruins, continue 200 metres up lane

This 150-year-old spacious house with recent additions is approached by a quiet lane and surrounded by beautiful open countryside. Two of the four family-sized bedrooms are on the ground floor; all have modern stylish furnishings, including armchairs, mini-bar and TV. Family rooms can also be booked as doubles or twins. Breakfast is served at separate tables in the dining-room, and packed lunches can be provided. The Llangollen Canal and Steam Railway are close by, and visitors planning on attending the annual international musical Eisteddfod in July should reserve early. 'The Jeffreys were very welcoming and helpful,' writes one summer visitor, who adds that 'breakfast was delicious'.

OWNERS: Eira and Phil Jeffreys OPEN: all year exc Christmas ROOMS: 4 family, all with bath and shower, tea/coffee and TV; lounge with TV TERMS: single occupancy £32–£40, family room £16–£20 per adult; children under 2 free, reductions for older children; deposit: £10 per person CARDS: none DETAILS: children welcome; no dogs; no smoking; car park; garden

---

If you intend to spend several days at a B&B, it is worth asking whether there are reduced rates, particularly if the period is midweek or off-season. It is always best to check prices, especially for single occupancy, when booking. If we know of any particular payment stipulations, we mention them in the details at the end of the entry. We asked the proprietors to estimate their 1998 prices in the autumn of 1997, so the rates may have changed since publication. If a deposit is required for an advance booking, this is stated in the details.

LLANGOVAN Monmouthshire **map 2**

Court St Lawrence

NEW ENTRY

Llangovan NP5 4BT TEL: (01291) 690279
take B4293 towards Monmouth, exit left towards Llansoy, after village take right fork towards Monmouth, house is 1½m along by prominent pine tree

This elegant country house, surrounded by glorious countryside, has magnificent gardens which are open to the public under the National Garden Scheme, as well as tennis courts and a heated swimmimg-pool. The interior is spacious and luxuriously furnished with antiques, and the ambience is unpretentious and welcoming. Susan Inkin is a gracious host who enjoys sharing her home with guests and serves substantial breakfasts in a sunny gallery overlooking the gardens. On warm, sunny mornings, breakfast can be taken by the pool. Three spacious bedrooms are decorated in pastel colours and furnished with armchairs and TV. The drawing-room has a log fire and there is also a library. Two- or four-course evening meals are served by arrangement in the large dining-room; vegetarians can be catered for with notice, and guests may bring their own wine. This is a wonderful base for exploring the Monmouthshire border country and is within easy reach of the Wye Valley and the Forest of Dean.

OWNER: Susan Inkin OPEN: all year exc Christmas ROOMS: 2 double, 2 twin; all rooms with private bathroom, tea/coffee and TV; lounge with TV TERMS: single occupancy £30, twin/double £55; dinner £20; deposit required CARDS: none DETAILS: no children under 8; no dogs; no smoking upstairs; car park; games room; garden; swimming-pool; tennis

LLANIGON Powys **map 4**

Old Post Office

Llanigon, nr Hay-on-Wye HR3 5QA TEL: (01497) 820008
from Hay-on-Wye take B4350 Brecon road for ½m, turn left signposted Llanigon; after 1½m turn left just before school; house on right

Just two miles from Hay-on-Wye, this characterful seventeenth-century house retains many of its original features, such as thick stone walls, heavy beams and a winding oak staircase. It also has the advantage of being set in the Brecon Beacons National Park and not far from Offa's Dyke, and is a good base for walkers. Bedrooms have rich floral matching fabrics and original polished board floors; one has a king-sized bed. Breakfast – which is entirely vegetarian, and includes home-made jams – is served at one table in the warm-hued dining-room with its stone fireplace and pretty Welsh dresser full of china. Guests can relax in a comfortable sitting-room with large couches and a TV.

OWNERS: Linda Webb and James Moore OPEN: all year exc Jan ROOMS: 2 double, 1 with shower, 1 with wash-basin; 1 twin, with shower; tea/coffee in all bedrooms; lounge with TV TERMS: single occupancy £17–£25, twin/double £30–£40; reductions for children sharing with parents; deposit: 1 night's charge CARDS: none DETAILS: children welcome; dogs by arrangement; no smoking; car park

LLANRHAEADR-YM-MOCHNANT Powys map 7

Bron Heulog

Waterfall Road, Llanrhaeadr-ym-Mochnant SY10 0JX TEL: (01691) 780521
off B4580, 4m N of Llanfyllin; in village turn in to Waterfall Rd; first large house on right

This spacious Victorian house, built in 1860 as a doctor's residence, stands in one-and-a-half acres of gardens, just four miles from the spectacular Pistyll Rhaeadr Waterfall, the highest in Wales. The hospitable Ken and Karon Raines restored the house themselves in period style, retaining original features such as the fireplaces and the curved oak staircase. Bedrooms have been decorated in soft blues and pinks, with pretty wallpapers, attractive curtains and quality modern furnishings. They are quite large, all are *en suite* and one has a four-poster bed, which was built by the owners. Breakfasts are good and substantial, dinner is served by arrangement, and vegetarians can be catered for with advance notice. Bron Heulog is not licensed but guests are welcome to bring their own wine. Pony-trekking and fishing can be arranged and Ken Raines is a qualified paragliding instructor.

OWNERS: Ken and Karon Raines OPEN: all year ROOMS: 1 double, 1 twin, 1 four-poster; all rooms with shower, tea/coffee and TV; lounge with TV TERMS: single occupancy £23–£25, twin/double £38–£42, four-poster £21; dinner £12; deposit: £25 CARDS: Delta, MasterCard, Switch, Visa DETAILS: no children under 10; no dogs; no smoking; car park; garden

Llys Morgan

Llanrhaeadr-ym-Mochnant SY10 0JZ TEL: (01691) 780345
off B4580, 4m N of Llanfyllin; in village near square and adjacent to church

Formerly the village vicarage, this sixteenth-century house these days offers a warm welcome, excellent meals and five good-sized guest bedrooms. There are also two lounges, one with a fire for chilly evenings, and the other with satellite TV, plus a games room with a snooker table. On warm days guests may enjoy the garden and walled patio. Reasonably priced 'excellent' home-cooked meals, if pre-arranged, are served in the dining-room; it is here that seven Bibles are set into the fireplace – a reminder that in this house the Bible was translated into Welsh in 1588. The owners tell us that only six guests are accepted at any one time because of fire regulations.

OWNER: Mrs J. Morgan OPEN: all year exc Christmas ROOMS: 3 double, 1 with bath/shower, 2 with wash-basin; 1 twin, with bath/shower; 1 family, with bath/shower; tea/coffee in all bedrooms; lounge with TV TERMS: single occupancy £15–£16.50, twin/

double £30–£33; half-price for children under 12 sharing with parents; dinner £8 CARDS: none DETAILS: children welcome; no dogs; car park; games room; garden

LLANRUG Gwynedd map 7

Lakeside

Llanrug LL55 4ED TEL: (01286) 870065
from Llanrug follow signs to Bryn Bras Castle, go under arch of castle and up hill for 600yds

This eighteenth-century Welsh-stone house was originally the gamekeeper's cottage for nearby Bryn Bras Castle. It is surrounded by six acres of woods (inhabited by dogs, peacocks, geese, chickens, quail and Taran the eagle owl) and a landscaped garden. There is a lake in the grounds, and guests have use of a two-seater canoe. Mountain bikes are also available for hire. Lakeside is a nature and animal lover's paradise, adjacent to Snowdonia National Park, and lovely walks can be taken from the door of the cottage. The luxurious bedrooms are decorated in light shades and have quality fabrics and furnishings. The elegant beamed lounge has a log fire burning on cool days, and breakfast is served in the dining-room. Vegetarians can be catered for with advance notice. A ground-floor suite is available, and requires a minimum three-nights' booking. Two self-catering properties are available.

OWNER: Lyn Kane OPEN: all year ROOMS: 1 double, with shower; 1 twin, with wash-basin; 1 family, with wash-basin; tea/coffee and TV in all bedrooms; lounge with TV TERMS: single occupancy £30–£35, double (suite) £30–£40, twin/family room £40–£50; half-price for children sharing with parents; deposit: £30 CARDS: none DETAILS: children welcome; dogs by arrangement; no smoking; car park; garden

LLANRWST Conwy map 7

Awelon NEW ENTRY

Plas Isa, Llanrwst LL26 0EE TEL: (01492) 640047
150yds off A470 in N part of town

This good-value mid-terrace guesthouse is tucked away in a quiet cul-de-sac in a neat garden not far from the town centre. The whitewashed outer walls of the house are three feet thick and over 400 years old – they once were part of stables belonging to the estate of William Salesbury, who translated the New Testament into Welsh in the sixteenth century. The interior, however, was restored in the 1930s, and is clean and comfortable. The bedrooms are decorated with soft pastel wallpapers, and have modern furnishings and firm beds. The two doubles share a bathroom, and the twin can be used as a family room. There is a guest lounge with TV, and a dining-room where breakfasts are served at separate tables.

OWNER: Eleanore Roberts OPEN: Mar to Oct ROOMS: 2 double; 1 twin, with shower; tea/coffee and TV in all bedrooms; lounge with TV TERMS: single occupancy £18–£20, twin/double £31–£36; half-price for children sharing with parents; deposit: £10–£20 CARDS: none DETAILS: no children under 5; small dogs welcome; smoking in lounge only; car park; garden

White Cottage

Maenan Hall, Maenan, Llanrwst LL26 0UL TEL: (01492) 640346
just off A470, 2m N of Llanwrst and 15m S of Llandudno

This delightful creeper-covered cottage stands in a pretty garden in the large grounds of Maenan Hall. The cottage provides a high standard of accommodation in a friendly home-from-home atmosphere. Kathleen is a cheerful hostess who greets guests with a cup of tea and is happy to provide local information. There is a lounge/dining-room, where huge breakfasts are served, featuring home-baked bread and home-made jams and marmalade. The comfortable bedrooms share a bathroom and separate WC. The River Conwy is across the field and the Bodnant Gardens are close by.

OWNERS: Kathy and Bryn Vaughan Williams OPEN: all year exc Christmas ROOMS: 1 double, 1 twin; both rooms with wash-basin and tea/coffee; lounge with TV TERMS: single occupancy £25, twin/double £33; deposit: £5 per person per night CARDS: none DETAILS: children welcome; dogs welcome; no smoking; car park; garden

LLWYNGWRIL Gwynedd **map 7**

Pentre Bach

NEW ENTRY

Llwyngwril LL37 2JU TEL: (01341) 250294 FAX: (01341) 250885
from Dolgellau take A493 S 12m to Llwyngwril, then over stone bridge on right

The friendly couple who run Pentre Bach have won awards for their cooking, and food plays an important role here. Candelit dinners often feature fresh organic produce from the garden and local fish and meats; menus might include Glamorgan sausage with spicy apple sauce, or stuffed trout with honey, followed by the house speciality, Pentre Bach crumble. Vegetarians can be catered for with prior notice; there is no alcohol licence, but guests may bring their own wine. Parts of the house date from the eighteenth century; it stands in four and a half acres of grounds, and is approached up a tree-lined drive. It enjoys splendid views of Cardigan Bay, especially when there is a fine sunset. There is no guest lounge, but the three good-sized bedrooms are all well furnished and decorated, with *en suite* facilities, TVs and armchairs; the twin room has a single and double bed. Table tennis can be played in a barn on the property. Visitors arriving by train can arrange to be met.

OWNERS: Mr and Mrs N. Smyth OPEN: all year exc Christmas ROOMS: 2 double, 1 twin; all rooms with bath/shower, tea/coffee and TV TERMS: single occupancy £26–£48, twin/double £40–£52; dinner £14; deposit: £15 per person CARDS: Delta, Master Card, Switch, Visa DETAILS: no children under 12; no dogs; no smoking; car park; garden

LLYSWEN Powys map 4

Oakfield NEW ENTRY

Llyswen, Brecon LD3 0UR TEL: (01874) 754301
on A470 in village, 8m NE of Brecon

Visitors feel instantly at home in this pre-World War I house, which stands in an attractive garden and has views of the distant Black Mountains. Guests are warmly greeted with a hot drink on arrival by Betty Phillips, who provides good-value accommodation in her spotlessly clean home. Bedrooms have traditional furnishings and comfortable beds. Breakfasts only are served, but there are eating-establishments in the area for dinner. A ten-minute walk brings you to the river, and the area is good for salmon and trout fishing.

OWNERS: Mr and Mrs Phillips OPEN: Mar to Oct ROOMS: 2 double, 1 with bath/shower, 1 with private bathroom; 1 twin, with private bathroom; tea/coffee in all bedrooms; lounge with TV TERMS: single occupancy £15–£18, twin/double £30–£36; children's reductions; deposit required CARDS: none DETAILS: children welcome; no dogs; no smoking; car park; garden

MAMHILAD Monmouthshire map 4

Ty-Cooke Farm

Mamhilad NP4 8QZ TEL: (01873) 880382
on minor road heading NW from A4042, 2m N of Pontypool

This pleasant, well-maintained three-storey farmhouse dates back to the eighteenth century. It is part of a working mixed farm, which guests are invited to explore. The three bedrooms share a bathroom. Guests have the use of a roomy lounge, which contains a beautifully carved fireplace from close-by Maindiff Court. Other nearby places of interest include the Monmouthshire and Brecon Canal, Raglan Castle and the Roman Baths at Caerleon. A pub within walking distance offers evening meals.

OWNER: Marion Price OPEN: all year exc Christmas ROOMS: 1 double, 1 twin, 1 family; all rooms with wash-basin; lounge with TV TERMS: single occupancy £20, twin/double £36; £10 for children under 12 CARDS: none DETAILS: children welcome; no dogs; no smoking; car park; garden

MENAI BRIDGE Isle of Anglesey map 7

Bwthyn NEW ENTRY

Brynafon, Menai Bridge LL59 5HA TEL/FAX: (01248) 713119
in village turn by post office into Water St, follow road round past slipway, then second right

Bwthyn is Welsh for 'dear little house', and is an excellent description of this small, pretty terraced house with its distinctive white door and stained-glass panels. It is a stone's-throw from the Menai Straits, and two miles from train and coach stations. Mrs Abas offers a warm welcome to visitors. There is no guest lounge, but the two pretty bedrooms have armchairs, TV and *en suite* facilities. Breakfasts, served in the conservatory/dining-room, include a traditional cooked platter featuring locally made pork and chestnut sausages, as well as healthy alternatives such as whole-grain cereals, fresh fruit and yoghurt. Imaginative four-course evening meals are also available, and one of Mrs Abas's speciality desserts, chocolate and coffee mousse, will usually be on the menu. Vegetarians are well catered for, and guests are welcome to bring their own wine. A pleasant walk from the house can be taken along the shoreline of the Straits to a causeway leading to Church Island and the tiny fourteenth-century Church of St Tisilio's. Two nights minimum must be booked in July and August, and at least four nights at Easter and the spring bank holiday. Limited off-street parking is available, and must be arranged in advance.

OWNER: Rosemary A. Abas OPEN: all year exc Christmas ROOMS: 2 double, 1 with bath/shower, 1 with shower; tea/coffee and TV in both bedrooms TERMS: single occupancy £20–£24, double £30–£32; dinner £12.50; deposit: 1 night's stay CARDS: none DETAILS: no children; no dogs; no smoking; car park

MONTGOMERY Powys — map 7

Beeches

New Road, Montgomery SY15 6UJ TEL/FAX: (01686) 668663
off B4388, just N of town

This two-storey modern brick house on the edge of town has views of the castle and the Severn Valley. It has a conservatory at one end and a large landscaped garden, but the views are best enjoyed from the first-floor lounge with its balcony. The Thomases are friendly and hospitable hosts. The four bedrooms are spacious and beautifully decorated with colour-co-ordinated fabrics and wallpapers; one is on the ground floor with a shower-room opposite. Traditional breakfasts are served in the elegant dining-room and vegetarians can be catered for. Dinner can be taken if booked in advance and there are several eating places within walking distance in the town centre. Offa's Dyke path is nearby.

OWNERS: Basil and Hilary Thomas OPEN: all year ROOMS: 1 double, with shower; 2 twin, 1 with shower, 1 with private bathroom; tea/coffee and TV in all bedrooms TERMS: single occupancy £20–£22, twin/double £36–£40; babies free, children's reductions according to age; dinner £10; deposit: £10 per room CARDS: none DETAILS: children welcome; no dogs; no smoking; car park; garden

B&B rates specified in the details at the end of each entry are given (as applicable) for a single room, for single occupancy of a double room, and then per room in the case of two people sharing a double or twin-bedded room, or for a family room. Because double rooms with four-poster beds often cost more, those are listed separately.

MOYLEGROVE Pembrokeshire **map 4**

Old Vicarage

Moylegrove SA43 3BN TEL: (01239) 881231 FAX: (01239) 881341
600yds S of Moylegrove just past the church on road to Glanrhyd

David and Patricia Phillips took over this lovely old Edwardian house in summer 1997, and have been enjoying their new business very much. The interior remains much the same as before, as the previous owners have left many of the furnishings and various items that add to the charm and atmosphere of the house. It is set in an acre of gardens, and there are paddocks and views down to the coastal village of Moylegrove and out to sea. Bedrooms are large, decorated in Edwardian mode, with co-ordinated fabrics and friezes set against pastel walls. One is a suite leading out to a patio. Log fires burn on cool days in the lounge and dining-room, which both have good views of Cardigan Bay and the valley. Dinners are served by prior arrangement and make good use of local produce; there is now a drinks licence.

OWNERS: Patricia and David Phillips OPEN: Mar to Nov ROOMS: 2 double, 1 twin; all rooms with shower and tea/coffee; lounge with TV TERMS: single occupancy £32, twin/double £48; dinner £19; deposit: £20 per room CARDS: none DETAILS: no children; no dogs; no smoking; car park; garden

NEATH Neath Port Talbot **map 4**

Cwmbach Cottages

Cwmbach Road, Cadoxton, Neath SA10 8AH
TEL: (01639) 639825 and 641436
exit M4 J43 on to A465; after 3m at Aberdulais roundabout take first left signposted Cadoxton; after ½m turn right opposite church; proceed ½m

Standing in a pretty garden which has two ornamental ponds and a Japanese-style bridge, this tasteful conversion of six miners' cottages offers five comfortable *en suite* bedrooms. All have satellite TV, and one is suitable for wheelchair-users. Guests are welcome to sit out on the patio on pleasant days, or relax in the lounge. Breakfast is served in a separate dining-room. A golf course is just 200 yards away, and nearby is Neath Gorge with its dramatic series of waterfalls. Self-catering accommodation is planned.

OWNER: Lynda Morgan OPEN: all year ROOMS: 3 double, 1 twin, 1 family; all rooms with bath/shower; 1 room suitable for wheelchair-users; tea/coffee and TV in all bedrooms; lounge with TV TERMS: single occupancy £26, twin/double £42, family room £42 plus £8 per child CARDS: none DETAILS: children welcome; no dogs; smoking in lounge only; car park; garden

---

If a B&B accepts credit cards, we list them in the details at the end of an entry – or specify no cards are accepted if that is so. There may be a surcharge if you pay by credit card. It is always best to check when booking whether the card you want to use will be accepted.

NEWPORT Newport — map 2

Kepe Lodge

46A Caerau Road, Newport NP9 4HH TEL/FAX: (01633) 262351

Carole Blyth took over Kepe Lodge in June 1997 and has refurbished the house considerably. Carole was born in Newport and has been in the catering industry for many years. She is a helpful, considerate host, and happy to assist guests with information on the area. Breakfasts and pre-booked evening meals are served in the separate dining-room, but for guests wanting to eat out there are plenty of places in the nearby town centre. Although Kepe Lodge is centrally located, it is in a quiet position, tucked away off the main road, surrounded by lovely gardens with roses round the lawn.

OWNER: Carole Blyth OPEN: all year ROOMS: 5 single, 2 with private bathroom, 3 with wash-basin; 1 double, with shower; 2 twin, both with shower; tea/coffee and TV in all bedrooms; lounge TERMS: single £25–£48, twin/double £50; dinner £7 CARDS: none DETAILS: children welcome; no dogs; no smoking; car park; garden

NEWPORT Pembrokeshire — map 4

Grove Park Guest House — NEW ENTRY

Pen-y-Bont, Newport SA42 0LT TEL: (01239) 820122

This small double-fronted guesthouse was built in 1879 for a sea captain and his family, and is only 100 yards from the beach and Pembrokeshire Coastal Path. Although tastefully restored, the house retains its original character and Victorian theme. The bedrooms are a good size and are furnished with antiques, two have lovely views and one is in the garden house. The sitting-room has comfortable sofas and chairs and is a good room to relax in. Breakfast, which includes home-made preserves, and imaginative three-course dinners using fresh local produce are served on lace tablecloths and fine china in the nostalgic dining-room. This is a peaceful spot and well placed to explore the beautiful area. The nearby Nevern Estuary is a listed nature reserve.

OWNERS: Mrs A. King and Mr M. Powell OPEN: all year exc Christmas ROOMS: 4 double, 3 with bath/shower, 1 with wash-basin; 1 twin, with wash-basin; tea/coffee and TV in all rooms; lounge TERMS: single occupancy £19–£26.50, twin/double £38–£43; half-price for children under 12 in winter; dinner £13.50; deposit required CARDS: none DETAILS: children welcome; dogs by arrangement; no smoking; car park

Llysmeddyg

East Street, Newport SA42 0SY TEL: (01239) 820008
on A487 between Fishguard and Cardigan

This spacious listed Georgian house in the small coastal town of Newport in Pembrokeshire was originally built as a coaching-inn.

The house is kept in first-class condition by Ian and Penny Ross, who are happy to share with guests their extensive knowledge of the area. The roomy bedrooms are furnished with antiques, as well as armchairs to relax in; the front rooms have views of Carn Ingli. Log fires burn in the lounge and dining-room on cool days, adding to the welcoming atmosphere. Guests also have the use of a games room with table tennis. Three-course home-cooked dinners (with vegetarian options if pre-arranged) are served at 7.45pm; or, if guests prefer, soup and sandwiches are available until 10pm. Llysmeddyg is licensed. Self-catering accommodation is also offered.

OWNERS: Ian and Penny Ross OPEN: all year exc Christmas ROOMS: 1 single, with wash-basin; 2 double, 1 with shower, 1 with wash-basin; 2 twin, both with wash-basin; tea/coffee in all bedrooms; lounge with TV TERMS: single £18.50; twin/double £37–£42; dinner £13.50; deposit: £10 per person CARDS: none DETAILS: children welcome by arrangement; no dogs; no smoking; car park; games room; garden

PENCELLI Powys map 4

Cambrian Cruisers Marina

Ty Newydd, Pencelli LD3 7LJ TEL/FAX: (01874) 665315
on B4558, 4m SE of Brecon

Cambrian Cruisers offers a unique combination holiday for those who wish to combine a stay in a farmhouse with a few days afloat in a narrow boat on the Monmouthshire and Brecon Canal (or choose just one or the other). Lying beneath Pen-y-Fan, the highest of the Brecon Beacons, the whitewashed eighteenth-century house offers four comfortably furnished *en suite* bedrooms as well as a conservatory for guests. On pleasant days visitors may be tempted to relax in the garden, where seating overlooks the canal. Breakfast only is served, but there are numerous eating-places a short drive away, and packed lunches can be provided. Day boat hire, as well as cycling, pony-trekking and fishing, can be arranged.

OWNERS: Peter and Ruth Griffiths OPEN: Mar to Oct ROOMS: 2 double, 1 twin, 1 family; all rooms with bath/shower, tea/coffee and TV; lounge TERMS: single occupancy £22, twin/double £36, family room £42–£45; children's reductions by arrangement; deposit: £10 CARDS: none DETAILS: children welcome; no dogs; smoking in conservatory only; car park; garden

PENMACHNO Conwy map 7

Penmachno Hall NEW ENTRY

Penmachno LL24 0PU TEL/FAX: (01690) 760207
through village on B4406, at Eagles Hotel follow signs 'Ty Mawr'

A stream flows through the two acres of private grounds surrounding this large former rectory. The beautiful area is well suited for nature lovers and there are good walks through the hills and many waterfalls to admire. The four spacious bedrooms, all *en suite*, are quite luxurious and have locally hand-made furniture and quilts. There are four sitting-rooms, including a garden room/conservatory and a library. Food plays an important role here: Modwena is an excellent cook and often uses home-grown vegetables, local salmon and lamb on her menus, and occasionally a Chinese chef is called upon to create an authentic Far Eastern banquet. The Cutlers usually join guests for dinner. A house-party atmosphere with a warm and friendly ambience prevails, and the hall is licensed. The Penmachno woollen mill is nearby, and Mount Snowdon is a short drive away.

OWNERS: Modwena and Ian Cutler OPEN: all year exc Christmas and New Year ROOMS: 1 double, 3 twin; all rooms with bath/shower; lounge with TV TERMS: single occupancy £30, twin/double £50; dinner £15 CARDS: MasterCard, Visa DETAILS: children welcome; no dogs; no smoking in bedrooms and dining-room; car park; garden

PENTRE HALKYN Flintshire **map 7**

The Hall

Lygan-y-Wern, Pentre Halkyn CH8 8BD
TEL: (01352) 780215 FAX: (01352) 780187
leave A55 2m SE of Holywell, on B5123 follow signs to Bagillt for ¼m to large house on left

This tall sixteenth-century building overlooking the Dee Estuary stands in 13 acres of grounds, which guests are welcome to explore. They will, however, no longer encounter the bantams, ducks and hens mentioned in the previous edition of the *Guide*, thanks to the unfortunate attentions of a fox. The house and grounds retain many original features – flagstone floors, a listed dovecote and (strictly to be viewed, not used) outdoor privies dating from the seventeenth century. The two very large and comfortable bedrooms share a bathroom and are decorated in pine. Breakfasts are served in the lounge/dining-room; venues for evening meals can be found close by. Mrs Vernon extends a warm welcome, and offers guests a hot drink upon arrival.

OWNER: Davinia Vernon OPEN: all year ROOMS: 2 twin, both with wash-basin and tea/coffee; lounge with TV TERMS: single occupancy £20, twin £36 CARDS: MasterCard, Visa DETAILS: no children under 5; no dogs; no smoking; car park; garden

PENYBONTFAWR Powys **map 7**

Glyndwr

Penybontfawr, nr Oswestry SY10 0NT TEL: (01691) 860430
just off B4396 in centre of village

This whitewashed seventeenth-century stone cottage, adorned with hanging baskets, is easily found on the main street next to the stone bridge over the River Barrog. Enid Henderson is a friendly and helpful host who greets guests with a hot drink on arrival and is happy to share her knowledge of the area, and she keeps an immaculate house. The traditionally beamed sitting/dining-room is warmed by an open fire on cold days, while in fine weather the riverside patio and garden may tempt guests outdoors. Evening meals prepared with local ingredients are served, with vegetarian options by arrangement, and guests may bring their own wine to dinner. Two of the bedrooms are in the main house and for those who value privacy an adjoining self-catering cottage that sleeps two is available. Penybontfawr is in the heart of the Tanat Valley in the Berwyn Mountains, and is an excellent location for walkers and cyclists.

OWNER: Enid Henderson OPEN: all year exc Christmas ROOMS: 2 double, 1 with bath/shower, 1 with private bathroom; 1 twin, with bath/shower; tea/coffee in all bedrooms; lounge with TV TERMS: single occupancy £25, twin/double £40; half-price for children under 12; dinner £12; deposit required CARDS: none DETAILS: children welcome; no dogs; no smoking; car park; garden

PRESTATYN Denbighshire map 7

Traeth Ganol

41 Beach Road West, Prestatyn LL19 7LL
TEL: (01745) 853594 FAX: (01745) 886687
follow brown tourist signs to Nova Centre and Beaches; past Nova into the cul-de-sac

A handy location, good food, comfortable rooms, and a pleasant and relaxed atmosphere all add to the attractiveness of this small hotel/restaurant. Traeth Ganol is right on the seafront, in a quiet cul-de-sac yet close to the town centre, a leisure centre and golf courses. Bedrooms are spacious and well appointed; six are family rooms and three are suitable for wheelchair-users. Breakfasts and excellent evening meals are served in the restaurant, which is licensed and open to non-residents.

OWNERS: Chris and Jo Groves OPEN: all year ROOMS: 1 single, 1 double, 1 twin, 6 family; all rooms with bath/shower, tea/coffee and TV; 3 rooms suitable for wheelchair-users; lounge TERMS: single £35–£54, single occupancy £45–£54, twin/double £52–£60, family room £70–£84; babies under 1 free; dinner £12.50; deposit: £25 CARDS: Delta, MasterCard, Switch, Visa DETAILS: children welcome; guide dogs only; smoking in bar only; car park; garden

PRESTEIGNE Powys map 4

Carmel Court NEW ENTRY

King's Turning, Presteigne LD8 2LD TEL: (01544) 267986
on E edge of town, off B4362

Built in 1810, Carmel Court was formerly a Carmelite monastery, and the adjacent chapel, which is cared for by Mr and Mrs Monaghan, is still in use. There are some religious artifacts about the house, including old photographs of nuns in full habit, wielding hods and crawling over the roof gables – which one visitor found 'a delight'. The spacious bedrooms are located in various areas of this rambling old house, and are furnished with a mixture of interesting pieces. Some are in a converted outbuilding, and two ground-floor rooms have wheelchair access. There are two lounges, one with a TV, one with a piano which musically inclined guests are welcome to play. Breakfast is served in the separate dining-room, and for evening meals guests will find a number of eating places in town. The atmosphere is relaxed, children are welcome – there is a play area for them in the walled garden – and the labrador dogs are friendly. Self-catering accommodation is also available.

OWNERS: Marenée and Terence Monaghan OPEN: all year exc Christmas ROOMS: 1 single; 2 double, 1 with private bathroom, 1 with wash-basin; 1 twin; 2 family, 1 with private bathroom; 2 rooms suitable for wheelchair-users; tea/coffee in all bedrooms; TV in some bedrooms and lounge TERMS: single £16.50, single occupancy £20–£25, twin/double £33–£35, family room £42–£52; half-price for children under 10; deposit: £5 per room per day CARDS: none DETAILS: children welcome; dogs by arrangement; no smoking in bedrooms or breakfast rooms; car park; games room; garden

RHAYADER Powys map 4

Glyn Gwy

Rhayader LD6 5LE TEL: (01597) 810441
on A470, 3½m N of Rhayader

One visitor after a four-night stay wrote to say that Glyn Gwy is the 'sort of place [that] makes us glad we use your guide', citing food and setting as particular strong points. An attractive early-Victorian house, it is surrounded by 14 acres of beautiful parkland on the banks of the River Wye, affording good walks and stunning views. Fishing for guests can be arranged. Bedrooms are spacious, and two overlook the river. There are two lounges, one with TV, and one with a log fire where smoking is permitted. The guesthouse is licensed and evening meals, if pre-arranged, can be provided.

OWNER: Mrs M.A. Moorsom OPEN: Easter to end Oct ROOMS: 2 double, both with wash-basin; 1 twin, with private bathroom; tea/coffee in all bedrooms; lounge with TV TERMS: single occupancy £19, twin/double £38; half-price for children under 11; dinner £9.50–£12; deposit: £19 CARDS: none DETAILS: children welcome; no dogs; smoking in smoking-room only; car park; garden

Raveloe

Doldowlod, Rhayader LD1 6NN TEL/FAX: (01597) 810851
on A470, 3m S of Rhayader

This modern ranch-style bungalow, built with Forest of Dean stone, overlooks lovely countryside and the hills beyond. Rob and Julia are welcoming hosts, greeting guests with hot or cold drinks. The lounge is equipped with satellite TV and a CD player for guests to use, and is warmed by an electric fire. The neat bedrooms are decorated in light pastel shades. One double bedroom is in a granny flat which has its own kitchen and TV. Evening meals are no longer available but there is a restaurant within two minutes' walk that serves good food.

OWNER: Julia Wilson OPEN: all year ROOMS: 3 double, 1 with shower, 1 with wash-basin; 1 twin, with wash-basin; tea/coffee and TV in 1 bedroom; lounge with TV TERMS: single occupancy £20–£25, twin/double £30–£36; babies free, £4.50 for children under 5, £9 for ages 6–12 CARDS: none DETAILS: children welcome; dogs to be kept on leads at all times; no smoking; car park; garden

RHOOSE Vale of Glamorgan — map 4

Welford Court Guest House — NEW ENTRY

Port Road West, Rhoose CF62 3BT TEL/FAX: (01446) 722460
on A4226, on brow of hill 1m E of Cardiff Airport

This modernised 250-year-old farmhouse stands in open countryside, about a mile from Cardiff Airport. For a modest charge, guests may leave their car here while they are away. There are eight clean and functional bedrooms, all with armchairs, TVs and *en suite* facilities. Very good-value home-cooked dinners – including vegetarian choices with advance notice – are available. Margaret and Terry Prince are a congenial couple who have been in business since summer 1997, and continue to upgrade their property. Welford Court is a good base for the city of Cardiff, as well as the airport.

OWNERS: Mr and Mrs T. Prince OPEN: all year exc Christmas ROOMS: 4 single, 2 twin, 2 family; all rooms with bath/shower; tea/coffee and TV in some bedrooms; 1 room suitable for wheelchair-users; lounge with TV TERMS: single £20–£24, single occupancy £25–£30, twin/double £40–£48, family room from £40; children under 4 free; dinner £4; deposit required CARDS: none DETAILS: children welcome; no dogs; smoking downstairs only; car park; garden

RHYDLEWIS Ceredigion — map 4

Broniwan — NEW ENTRY

Rhydlewis SA44 5PF TEL/FAX: (01239) 851261
at Rhydlewis Post Office take signed direction to Pentregat, keeping shop on right; then first lane on right and first drive on right

This pretty grey-stone house with pine panelled windows is part of a small farm inhabited by hens, cows, Jenny the tame dairy cow and Flossie the dog. It is approached up a quiet lane which in spring is bordered by waves of daffodils. Traditional and antique furniture provide an elegant touch to the interior, and paintings and woollen tapestries enhance the three prettily decorated bedrooms. The cosy lounge has a wood stove, TV and lots of books. Dinners as well as breakfasts are served in the separate dining-room, and feature home-produced meat and organic vegetables from the garden; vegetarian dishes are a speciality of the house, and with advance notice most diets can be catered for. Guests are welcome to explore the farm; maps are provided, and Flossie enjoys showing visitors around.

OWNERS: Carole and Allen Jacobs OPEN: all year ROOMS: 1 single, with wash-basin; 1 double, with private bathroom; 1 twin, with shower; tea/coffee in all bedrooms; lounge with TV TERMS: single/single occupancy £19–£21, twin/double £38–£42; half-price for children from 7–11; dinner £12; deposit: 10% CARDS: none DETAILS: no children under 7; dogs welcome; no smoking; car park; garden

RHYL Denbighshire map 7

Romsley Guest House

8 Butterton Road, Rhyl LL18 1RF TEL: (01745) 330300

The atmosphere at Romsley Guest House is homely, and the down-to-earth owners, Sheila and Charles Bill, are pleasant and helpful. They continue to upgrade and refurbish their immaculate house, and offer six well-maintained, colour-co-ordinated bedrooms. One has a four-poster bed, and the three double rooms can be booked for families. Guests have the use of a comfortable lounge with TV, and chess-lovers can play with a slate set made locally. Excellent-value evening meals can be booked, and are served in the dining-room; the house is licensed. There is no central heating, but rooms have individual heaters which can be controlled by guests. Unrestricted on-street parking is available nearby.

OWNERS: Charles and Sheila Bill OPEN: all year exc Christmas; closed occasionally other times (phone to check) ROOMS: 2 single, 3 double, 1 four-poster; all rooms with wash-basin, tea/coffee and TV; lounge with TV TERMS: single £14, single occupancy £16–£20, double £28, four-poster £32; children under 3 free, half-price for ages 3–10 sharing with parents; dinner £6 (less for children); deposit: 1 night's charge per person CARDS: none DETAILS: children welcome; no dogs; no smoking in dining-room

ST CLEARS Carmarthenshire map 4

Old Board School NEW ENTRY

High Street, St Clears SA33 4DY TEL: (01994) 231572

The school was built in 1847, on a hillside in the small village of St Clears, close to Laugharne, birthplace of Dylan Thomas. It is now a spacious guesthouse, with rich, modern furniture and beautifully decorated. Most of the guest bedrooms have *en suite* facilities. Generous breakfasts are served, and there is a good restaurant nearby. Pendine and the sandy beaches are just four miles away.

OWNER: Verona Williams OPEN: all year ROOMS: 1 single; 2 double, 1 with shower; 2 twin, both with shower; 2 family, both with bath/shower; tea/coffee and TV in all bedrooms TERMS: single £20–£25, single occupancy £25, twin/double £38, family room £48–£55; children under 3 free; deposit required CARDS: none DETAILS: children welcome; no dogs; no smoking; car park; garden

The end details for each entry state whether or not dogs are allowed, but it is always best to check when booking.

ST DAVID'S Pembrokeshire **map 4**

Craig-y-Mor

Whitesands, St David's SA62 6PT TEL: (01437) 720431
from St David's take B4583 to Whitesands beach and turn left at golf course

This chalet-style house, located adjacent to a golf course and within walking distance of the impressive Whitesands beach and the coastal path, offers three good-sized bedrooms. All have *en suite* showers and TVs, as well as sitting-areas with good views over the bay. Some of the beds have cosy Welsh blankets. The atmosphere is informal, and, although there is no lounge, guests are welcome to use a kitchen area. Ramsey Island Nature Reserve is a short boat ride away.

OWNER: Muriel Barton OPEN: all year exc Christmas ROOMS: 1 double, 1 twin, 1 family; all rooms with shower and TV TERMS: twin/double £34; family from £34; children under 5 free sharing with parents; deposit: £10 CARDS: none DETAILS: children welcome; no dogs; no smoking; car park

SAUNDERSFOOT Pembrokeshire **map 4**

Primrose Cottage

Stammers Road, Saundersfoot SA69 9HH TEL: (01834) 811080
three houses up from Saundersfoot post office

This well-maintained Victorian cottage, which has been tastefully modernised, stands behind neat railings in the centre of the village, close to the harbour and beaches. Two friendly labradors are often on hand to extend their own greeting. The small, comfortable bedrooms are immaculately kept; the double has an *en suite* shower, and the twin can be adapted for use as a family room; guests with babies will need to provide their own cots. Dinners can be provided on request, but a wide selection of alternative venues are nearby. Council-run parking is available in the close vicinity.

OWNERS: Malcolm and Jennifer Quinn OPEN: most of the year (check by phone) ROOMS: 1 single; 1 double, with bath/shower; 1 twin, with private bathroom; tea/coffee in all bedrooms; lounge with TV TERMS: single £15, single occupancy £16, twin/double £32–£33; children under 3 free, half-price for ages 3–10; deposit required CARDS: none DETAILS: children welcome; well-behaved dogs welcome; smoking in lounge only; garden

Sandyhill Guest House

Tenby Road, Saundersfoot SA69 9DR TEL: (01834) 813165
on A487, 3m S of junction with A477, opposite nursery

Sandyhill was built as a two-up two-down farmhouse in the seventeenth century, but has had various alterations and additions over the years since then. The bedrooms, one of which is on the ground floor, are warm and comfortable, and have double-glazing to minimise traffic noise. Peggy and David Edwards are a friendly, welcoming couple who take pride in their house and offer a high standard of accommodation. The lounge has a convivial atmosphere and a licensed bar, and the attractive garden has a swimming-pool for guests' use. Saundersfoot and Tenby beaches are less than five minutes' drive away.

OWNERS: Peggy and David Edwards OPEN: Easter to Sept ROOMS: 4 double, 3 with bath/shower; 1 family, with bath/shower; tea/coffee and TV in all bedrooms; lounge TERMS: single occupancy £22–£28, twin/double £32–£38, family room £47.50; half-price for children sharing with parents; dinner £9; deposit: 10% CARDS: none DETAILS: no children under 5; dogs welcome in bedrooms only; smoking in bar area only; car park; garden; swimming-pool

SOLVA Pembrokeshire — map 4

Min Yr Afon

11 Y Gribin, Solva SA62 6UY TEL: (01437) 721752
take A487 NW from Haverfordwest for 10m, then turn down hill into Solva and sharp left before bridge

Julia Hann welcomes guests with a hot drink and biscuits on arrival at this delightful 200-year-old whitewashed cottage, with its colourful array of flowers, in the pretty harbour village of Solva. Bedrooms are daintily decorated, have sloping ceilings, and one has an ornamental brass bed with a lace canopy. Two rooms are in an annexe, and one of these is suitable for the partially disabled. Breakfasts are taken in the main house in the cosy beamed dining-room with its collections of dried flowers, patchwork pillows and tapestry. A terrace garden and boat mooring is now available to guests. The coastal path is only 150 yards away, and a fully working woollen mill is close by.

OWNERS: David and Julia Hann OPEN: all year exc Christmas ROOMS: 2 double, both with bath/shower; 1 twin, with bath/shower; tea/coffee and TV in all bedrooms; lounge with TV TERMS: single occupancy £20, twin/double £33; deposit: £10 CARDS: none DETAILS: no children; no dogs; car park; garden

SOUTHGATE Swansea — map 4

Heatherlands — NEW ENTRY

1 Hael Lane, Southgate SA3 2AP TEL: (01792) 233256
from Swansea take A4067 S to sign to South Gower, turn right on to B4436, then left in Pennard

Located in an officially designated area of outstanding beauty, this attractive property stands on the edge of open fields, near cliffs, the sea and sandy beaches. Mr and Mrs Churchill have been in business since the early '70s, and many of their guests are regulars. The house is beautifully kept and furnished to a high standard. Bedrooms are decorated in soft peach and pink pastels and have armchairs. Breakfasts are served in the beamed dining-room, and guests have the use of a sun-lounge overlooking the tranquil garden. Mumbles is only five miles sway, and there is an 18-hole golf course nearby.

OWNER: Joyce Churchill OPEN: all year exc Christmas ROOMS: 2 double, 1 with shower, 1 with private bathroom; 1 twin, with private bathroom; tea/coffee and TV in 3 bedrooms; lounge with TV TERMS: single occupancy £21–£23, twin/double £37–£39; half-price for children over 8 sharing with parents; deposit required CARDS: none DETAILS: no children under 8; no dogs; no smoking; car park; garden

SWANSEA Swansea **map 4**

Alexandra House

366 Mumbles Road, Swansea SA3 5TN
TEL: (01792) 406406 FAX: (01792) 405605

Alexandra House stands on the seafront overlooking Swansea Bay, just outside the town centre, and five minutes' walk from Mumbles Village. It is beautifully maintained and Christine Llewellyn offers a warm welcome to her guests. The bedrooms are tastefully decorated with co-ordinated pastel fabrics and have antique pine furniture; all have *en suite* shower. The guests' lounge, which has been extended, also has some interesting antiques. Excellent breakfasts are served in the bright basement dining-room. The bus into the city centre stops right outside.

OWNER: Christine Llewellyn OPEN: all year exc Christmas ROOMS: 3 double, 1 twin, 1 family; all rooms with shower, tea/coffee and TV; lounge with TV TERMS: single occupancy £25, twin/double £40, family room £40; deposit required CARDS: none DETAILS: no children under 5; no dogs; smoking in lounge only; car park; garden

Uplands Court

134 Eaton Crescent, Uplands, Swansea SA1 4QR
TEL/FAX: (01792) 473046

This child-friendly B&B is conveniently located in a peaceful residential area about a half-mile from the city centre, and close to bus routes. It is a large Edwardian house, offering eight simple but immaculate guest bedrooms; four have *en suite* facilities. Plenty of toys, the availability of high chairs and cots, and some constraints set on smoking make this a good place for families. Breakfast is served in the dining-room and guests can relax in the TV lounge, where there is a licensed bar. Although there is no car park, nearby on-street parking is free and unrestricted.

OWNERS: Susan and Allan Gray OPEN: all year ROOMS: 4 single, 1 with bath/shower, 2 with wash-basin; 2 double, 1 with bath/shower, 1 with wash-basin; 2 family, both with bath/shower; tea/coffee and TV in all bedrooms; lounge with TV TERMS: single £16–£22, single occupancy £18–£25, twin/double £32–£38, family room £38–£48; children up to 3 free, half-price for ages 3–14; deposit: 10% CARDS: MasterCard, Visa DETAILS: children welcome; no dogs; smoking in some rooms only

If any bedrooms are suitable for wheelchair-users, we mention this in the details at the end of the entry.

TALYBONT Powys map 4

Llansantffraed House NEW ENTRY

Talybont LD3 7YF TEL: (01874) 676229 FAX: (01874) 676432
on A40, 6m E of Brecon and just W of Llansantffraed church

This distinctive pink Georgian manor-house sits back from the road in its own beautiful garden, and has splendid views of the River Usk and the Brecon Beacons. On pleasant days guests will find the garden a wonderful place to relax in, or may wish to make use of the tennis court or swimming-pool. The two bedrooms are huge: the double has a king-sized bed and *en suite* shower and bath, while the twin has its own private bathroom. Breakfasts are served in the dining-room or, weather allowing, the conservatory, and there is a guest lounge. Astrid Inglis is happy to arrange visits to private gardens. Bookings normally have to be a minimum of two nights.

OWNER: Astrid Inglis OPEN: Mar to Oct ROOMS: 1 double, with bath/shower; 1 twin, with private bathroom; tea/coffee in both bedrooms; lounge with TV TERMS: single occupancy £25, twin/double £50 CARDS: none DETAILS: children by arrangement; no dogs; no smoking; car park; garden; swimming-pool; tennis

TENBY Pembrokeshire map 4

High Seas

8 The Norton, Tenby SA70 8AA TEL/FAX: (01834) 843611

Built in the early 1800s, this elegant terraced house stands in a quiet position overlooking the sea. It is well proportioned and maintained, and the atmosphere is welcoming. The bedrooms are reached by an original staircase; most have views over the North Beach, one has an antique brass bed and another a half-tester. The large first-floor lounge with its baby grand piano has panoramic views of the bay. An original fireplace and casement shutters can be found in the dining-room, where breakfast is served at individual tables. Tenby has a good selection of eating-places for evening meals.

OWNERS: Mr and Mrs J. Macdonald OPEN: Apr to Oct ROOMS: 4 double, 3 with bath/shower, 1 with wash-basin; 1 twin, with wash-basin; 1 family, with private bathroom; tea/coffee and TV in all bedrooms; lounge TERMS: single occupancy £18–£22, twin/double £36–£44, family room £40–£50; children under 5 free CARDS: none DETAILS: children welcome; no dogs

TINTERN Monmouthshire map 2

Old Rectory

Tintern NP6 6SG TEL: (01291) 689519 FAX: (0374) 570395
on A466 Chepstow to Monmouth road

Wendy and Kevin Taylor took over this lovely old former Church of Wales residence on the main road through Tintern in spring 1996, and have done much in the way of refurbishing. Bedrooms have new carpets, new beds and antique pine furniture; two now have *en suite* bath or shower. The comfortable sitting-room still has its two welcoming log-burning fires. Optional evening meals – thought 'excellent value' by one reader – are served at 7.30pm, and menus might include a choice of Welsh lamb chops with wine and mushrooms, and home-made vegetable lasagne, with perhaps blackcurrant tart or raspberry bombe (a house speciality) for dessert. A snack menu is also available. This is a very child-friendly B&B, and cots, high chairs, baby-sitting and children's meals can be arranged. The house benefits from having its own source of natural spring water, and has fine views of the Wye Valley.

OWNERS: Wendy and Kevin Taylor OPEN: all year exc Christmas ROOMS: 2 double, 1 with bath/shower, 1 with wash-basin; 2 twin, 1 with bath/shower, 1 with wash-basin; tea/coffee and TV in all bedrooms; lounge TERMS: single occupancy £25–£30, twin/double £34–£38; children under 2 free, £8 for ages 2–12 sharing with parents; dinner £12; deposit: £5 per person per night CARDS: none DETAILS: children welcome; no dogs in public rooms or left unattended in bedrooms; no smoking; car park; garden

TRETOWER Powys **map 4**

The Firs

Tretower NP8 1RF TEL/FAX: (01874) 730780
off A479, 3m NW of Crickhowell

Set in a secluded position not far from Tretower Court and Castle, this 300-year-old country house retains many of its original features. There are wooden beams and a stone spiral staircase, as well as antique furniture such as a grandfather clock and a beautiful seventeenth-century sideboard. Three of the five smallish but spotless bedrooms have *en suite* facilities; one is on the ground floor. Guests have the use of a lounge with TV. Evening meals are not provided, but some good restaurants can be found in and near Crickhowell, including the *Good Food Guide*-recommended Bear Hotel and the Nantyffin Cider Mill.

OWNER: Mary Eckley OPEN: all year ROOMS: 4 double, 2 with shower, 2 with wash-basin; 1 family, with shower; tea/coffee in most bedrooms; TV in some bedrooms and lounge TERMS: single occupancy £18.50; twin/double £37–£45, family room £40; reductions for children sharing with parents; deposit required CARDS: none DETAILS: children welcome; dogs by arrangement; car park; garden

WELSHPOOL Powys **map 7**

Gungrog House

Rhallt, Welshpool SY21 9HS TEL: (01938) 553381 FAX: (01938) 556224
off A483, 1½m N of Welshpool

A friendly bearded collie greets visitors to this spacious sixteenth-century farmhouse on a 21-acre smallholding just outside Welshpool. It is set in a lovely garden with magnificent views over the Severn

Valley; there are roses round the door and horses in the paddock. The two bedrooms are traditionally furnished and have oak floors and their own individual bathrooms. Breakfast is taken in the large beamed dining-room. Both Powis Castle and Offa's Dyke are nearby.

OWNERS: Stan and Eira Jones OPEN: all year exc Christmas ROOMS: 1 double, 1 family; both rooms with bath/shower and tea/coffee; lounge with TV TERMS: double £44; half-price for children under 12 CARDS: none DETAILS: children welcome; no dogs; no smoking; car park; garden

---

Montgomery House

43 Salop Road, Welshpool SY21 7DX TEL: (01938) 552693

This handsome Welsh-stone house is conveniently located within easy walking distance of the shops and restaurants of Welshpool, and Angela Kaye continues to offer a high standard of accommodation. The bedrooms, all on the second floor, are average in size and the bedding is in Laura Ashley patterns. All rooms have wash-basins, tea- and coffee-making facilities and TVs. Good breakfasts are served in the cosy dining-room. The Welshpool and Llanfair Light Railway terminus is nearby, the Montgomery canal runs not far from the house, and it is a couple of miles to Powis Castle. There is a large public car park to the rear of the house, and a pub immediately opposite serves evening meals.

OWNER: Angela Kaye OPEN: all year exc Christmas ROOMS: 1 twin, 3 family; all rooms with wash-basin, tea/coffee and TV TERMS: single occupancy £18, twin/double £30, family room £40–£50; children £10 CARDS: none DETAILS: children welcome; no dogs; no smoking in dining-room

---

Tynllwyn Farm

Welshpool SY21 9BW TEL: (01938) 553175

signposted off A490, 1m N of Welshpool

This large modernised farmhouse dating from 1861 has wonderful views of the Severn Valley and Long Mountain. Tynllwyn is mainly a beef and sheep farm, but also has chickens, peacocks, pheasants, ducks, geese and a goat, and there are a pond and a fountain in the garden. Bedrooms are spacious and traditionally furnished, and one double room now has an *en suite* shower. The lounge has an interesting plate collection, and in winter is warmed by an open log fire. Farmhouse-style dinners are served if pre-booked and make good use of home-produce such as honey and eggs. Children's helpings, vegetarian meals and packed lunches are available by arrangement. There is a market in Welshpool every Monday.

OWNER: Freda Emberton OPEN: all year exc Christmas ROOMS: 1 single, with wash-basin; 1 double, with shower; 1 twin, with wash-basin; 1 family, with wash-basin; tea/coffee and TV in all bedrooms; lounge with TV TERMS: single £15.50–£20, twin/double £31–£35, family room from £31; dinner £9 CARDS: none DETAILS: children welcome; dogs by arrangement; no smoking in dining-room; car park; garden

Channel Islands

BORDEAUX Guernsey

map 1

Bordeaux Guesthouse

Roques Barrées Road, Bordeaux Bay, Vale GY3 5LX
TEL: (01481) 47461 FAX: (01481) 43669
at north end of island, 50 metres inland from Bordeaux Bay

This 200-year-old former farmhouse was taken over by Frances Laing and Valerie Wade, both qualified nurses, in January 1997, since when they have been busy upgrading and refurbishing the property. The bedrooms are in excellent decorative order, three have four-poster beds and three are on the ground floor. The guest lounge has a honey-coloured fireplace and new furniture, and the dining-room, which also has been refurbished, retains its Victorian fireplace; there is also a small bar. Home-cooked evening meals are served by arrangement, and vegetarians can be catered for. The bus to St Peter Port stops outside the guesthouse, and arrangements can be made to meet guests at the airport or harbour. No one-night bookings are taken.

OWNERS: Frances Laing and Valerie Wade OPEN: all year exc Christmas ROOMS: 1 double, with bath/shower; 1 twin, with private bathroom; 3 four-poster, 2 with bath/shower, 1 with private bathroom; 3 family, all with bath/shower; tea/coffee and TV in all bedrooms; lounge with TV TERMS: single occupancy £25–£30, twin/double/four-poster £36–£46, family room £45–£69; dinner £8; deposit: £50 per person per week CARDS: none DETAILS: children welcome; no dogs; no smoking; car park; garden

FOREST Guernsey

map 1

Tudor Lodge Deer Farm

Forest Road, Forest GY8 0AG TEL: (01481) 37849 FAX: (01481) 35662

Tudor Lodge is on the south of the island, in a very peaceful area overlooking Petit Bot Bay, and is surrounded by woods and meadows, yet within walking distance of shops and restaurants. The house dates from the mid-eighteenth century and is furnished in keeping with its period. Bedrooms are comfortable and well equipped, and the lounge and dining-room are both warmed by log fires on cold days. There is also a large conservatory, filled with plants and fruit trees. In summer the Galliennes also run a tea-shop, serving light lunch, morning coffee and afternoon tea. Breakfast is a generous selection.

OWNERS: John and Jackie Gallienne OPEN: all year exc Christmas ROOMS: 1 double, 2 twin, 2 family; all rooms with bath, tea/coffee and TV; lounge TERMS: single occupancy £32–£35, twin/double £50–£60, family room £62.50–£75; half-price for children over 12; deposit: £50 CARDS: none DETAILS: no children under 12; guide dogs only; no smoking in dining-room; car park; garden

If we know a B&B has an alcohol licence, we say so. Most unlicensed B&Bs that offer evening meals allow guests to bring their own wine to dinner. If you wish to do this, ask the B&B when you book.

ROZEL BAY Jersey — map 1

La Petite Chaire

Rozel Bay JE3 6AN TEL: (01534) 862682 FAX: (01534) 865005

Rozel Bay is a quiet spot in the north-east corner of Jersey, and La Petite Chaire, a former coach-house, can be found next to its picturesque harbour, 100 yards from the sheltered beach, where fishing and water sports are available. Breakfast and modestly priced dinners are served in the spacious dining-room, and guests can relax with a drink in the bar or outside on the terrace on sunny days. There is also a comfortable TV lounge. Bedrooms are decorated in light pastel shades, and have modern fitted furniture; six are on the ground floor. Boat trips and car hire can be arranged, and Augress Manor, the Jersey zoo, is a short distance inland. Two self-catering units are available.

OWNERS: Sergio and Maureen Michieli OPEN: mid-Apr to early Oct ROOMS: 1 single; 8 double, 1 with private bathroom; 2 twin; 2 family; lounge with TV TERMS: single/single occupancy £41–£43, twin/double £52–£56; half-price for children under 5, one-third off for ages 5–10; dinner £6.50; deposit: £30 per person per week CARDS: MasterCard, Visa DETAILS: children welcome; dogs by arrangement; car park; garden

ST HELIER Jersey — map 1

La Bonne Vie

Roseville Street, St Helier JE2 4PL
TEL: (01534) 35955 FAX: (01534) 33357

This tastefully modernised Victorian house, built in the 1890s for a wealthy local merchant, is just a stone's throw from the beach, and five minutes' walk from the town centre. In summer the outside of the house is livened up with colourful baskets and window boxes. Inside, the house is beautifully maintained and decorated by Carol Hetherington. All the bedrooms have their own heated towel rack, and use of a private bathroom; two rooms have antique brass beds, and two have hand-built French four-posters. Breakfast is served in the large, elegant dining-room. The guest lounge has an Adam-style open fireplace, a library and a selection of games. The beach has a tidal pool to allow safe bathing at all times.

OWNERS: Mr and Mrs R. Hetherington OPEN: all year ROOMS: 2 single, 8 double, 1 twin, 2 four-poster; all rooms with private bathroom, tea/coffee and TV; lounge with TV TERMS: single £17.50–£25, single occupancy £35–£50, twin/double £35–£50, four-poster £40–£55; 25% reduction for children over 8; deposit: £25 per person CARDS: Diners, MasterCard, Visa DETAILS: children welcome; no dogs; smoking in lounge only; garden

---

If you are forced to turn up later than planned, please telephone to warn the proprietor. It is always best to book a room in advance, even in winter. B&Bs with few rooms may close at short notice for periods not specified in the details.

La Sirene

23 Clarendon Road, St Helier JE2 3YS
TEL: (01534) 23364 FAX: (01534) 509727

This bright house with its jaunty pink shutters is situated on a quiet residential road. The Hitchmoughs are a friendly couple, and Sandy is a cabaret singer who can obtain half-price tickets for guests when she is on the bill at a local venue. The house is well maintained, with a high standard of décor and furnishings. The comfortable bedrooms are decorated in bright colours, and guests have access to the house at all times. There is a pleasant lounge, and a licensed dining-room where breakfast and freshly prepared evening meals are served; vegetarians can be catered for with advance notice. In low season bookings must be for a minimum of two nights, and in the high season for a week.

OWNERS: Sandy and Lawrence Hitchmough OPEN: all year ROOMS: 2 single, 4 double, 2 twin, 1 family; all rooms with shower, tea/coffee and TV; lounge with TV TERMS: single £14–£21, twin/double/family £28–£42; children's reductions; dinner £5; deposit: £25 per person CARDS: none DETAILS: no children under 5; no dogs; no smoking in dining-room at meal times

ST MARTIN Guernsey **map 1**

Santi Villa Guest House

La Rue Maze, St Martin GY4 6LJ TEL: (01481) 37332 FAX: (01481) 36764

Santi Villa is an attractive Victorian building, set in a large garden, not far from Moulin Huet Bay, where Renoir painted some of his famous works. The house is tastefully decorated, bedrooms are clean and comfortable, and most of them have *en suite* facilities. The beamed lounge has a TV, breakfast is served in the dining-room, and there is a small reading room. Guests also have use of the garden, if they wish to sunbathe or make use of the picnic tables provided.

OWNERS: Ken and Marie Finch OPEN: all year ROOMS: 1 double, with wash-basin; 1 twin, with bath/shower; 4 family, 3 with bath/shower, 1 with private bathroom; tea/coffee in all bedrooms; lounge with TV TERMS: single occupancy £20–£30, twin/double £30–£50, family room from £30; half-price for children under 12 sharing with parents; deposit: £20 per person per week CARDS: none DETAILS: children welcome; guide dogs only; no smoking; car park; garden

ST MARTIN Jersey **map 1**

Le Relais de St Martin

St Martins House, St Martin JE3 6UG
TEL: (01534) 853271 FAX: (01534) 855241

With parts dating from before 1400, this impeccably maintained Jersey granite house is one of the oldest on the island. It stands in large grounds, with a swimming-pool and a boules pitch, and has beaches nearby, and the famous Gerald Durrell zoo is only two miles away. Breakfasts and good-value evening meals, using fresh local ingredients and fruit from the garden, are served at separate tables in the dining-room. There is a lounge with TV and a bar with a billiard table. The Gicquels are accommodating hosts, and many visitors return on a regular basis to enjoy the warm hospitality extended by the owners. Self-catering units are also available.

OWNERS: Mr and Mrs J. Gicquel OPEN: Easter to end Oct ROOMS: 3 single, 4 double, 4 family; all rooms with bath/shower, tea/coffee and TV; lounge with TV TERMS: twin/double/family £42–£54; reductions for children sharing family room; dinner £9.50; deposit: £30 per person per week or 1 night's charge CARDS: Delta, MasterCard, Visa DETAILS: children welcome; guide dogs only; no smoking in dining-room; car park; garden; swimming-pool

ST OUEN Jersey — map 1

Lecq Farm Guest House

Leoville, St Ouen JE3 2BU TEL: (01534) 481745

Lecq Farm is a seventeenth-century Jersey longhouse, with a large, mature landscaped garden, and surrounded by peaceful countryside. It is run by the Renoufs, who have been offering bed and breakfast here since the mid-1960s, and is a very popular place, so early booking is advised. The two bedrooms are comfortable and of a good size, and the family room has an *en suite* shower. Guests have use of a lounge and separate dining-room, both with fireplaces built from local granite. There are several pubs nearby, and a frequent bus service into town.

OWNERS: Mr and Mrs D.C. Renouf OPEN: Mar to Oct ROOMS: 1 double, with wash-basin; 1 family, with shower; tea/coffee in both bedrooms; lounge with TV TERMS: single occupancy £15–£16, double £30–£32, family room from £30; deposit: £10 per person CARDS: none DETAILS: children welcome; dogs welcome; no smoking in dining-room; car park; garden

ST PETER PORT Guernsey — map 1

Marine Hotel

Well Road, St Peter Port GY1 1WS
TEL: (01481) 724978 FAX: (01481) 711729

Margaret and Arthur Clegg have reached a decade of offering good-value accommodation in a friendly atmosphere at their small hotel, 30 metres from the seafront and marina of the picturesque town of St Peter Port. The shops and starting point for island bus tours are also close by. Bedrooms are well appointed and spotlessly clean, and are decorated in light pastel shades; most also have sea views. TV can be provided for a modest charge, although there is a TV in the lounge, as well as a good selection of books. Guests also have use of the patio, which makes a pleasant place in which to relax on sunny days. Breakfast is a traditional English affair.

OWNERS: Arthur and Margaret Clegg OPEN: all year ROOMS: 1 single, 4 double, 3 twin, 3 family; all rooms with private bathroom and tea/coffee; lounge with TV TERMS: single £15.50–£25.50, twin/double £31–£48; half-price for children under 5, 25% reduction for ages 5-10 sharing with parents; deposit: £30 per person CARDS: MasterCard, Visa DETAILS: children welcome; no dogs; no smoking in dining-room or TV lounge; garden

SARK Sark **map 1**

Hivernage

Sark GY9 0SA TEL: (01481) 832000 FAX: (01481) 832472

Hivernage, which means 'winter retreat', is situated on the west coast of the island. Visitors arrive on Sark by boat, and then can be brought here on a tractor. The house is well-maintained, and bedrooms are spotlessly clean, comfortable, and most have sea views. There is also a guests' lounge, conservatory and a peaceful garden. Hivernage has been in Marilyn Carré's family since 1914. She is a congenial host, and provides excellent home-cooked dinners using local produce, in the licensed dining-room. Guests wishing to explore the island can walk or hire a bicycle, and boat and horse-and-carriage trips can be arranged.

OWNER: Marilyn Carré OPEN: Apr to Sept ROOMS: 2 single, 1 with bath/shower, 1 with wash-basin; 2 double, 1 with bath/shower, 1 with wash-basin; 2 twin, 1 with bath/shower, 1 with wash-basin; 1 family, with wash-basin; tea/coffee and TV in all bedrooms TERMS: single £29–£31, single occupancy £29–£41, twin/double £58–£62, family room £87–£93; children's reductions by arrangement CARDS: none DETAILS: no children under 3; no dogs; garden

Le Petit Coin

Le Petit Coin de la Tour, Sark GY9 0SF
TEL: (01481) 832077 FAX: (01481) 832603

Ann and Tom Long continue to offer a warm welcome at their attractive bungalow, in the north of Sark. The bright bedrooms all have sea views and share a bathroom, except one twin-bedded room which has *en suite* facilities. There is also a cosy lounge for guests' use. Tom is an excellent cook, and imaginative dinners are available; the house is unlicensed, but guests may bring their own wine. The Longs also share their house with their pets – Monty the friendly black labrador, and three cats.

OWNERS: Tom and Ann Long OPEN: all year ROOMS: 1 single, with wash-basin; 1 double, with wash-basin; 2 twin, 1 with bath/shower, 1 with wash-basin TERMS: single/single occupancy £18–£24, twin/double £36–£48; half-price for children under 11; dinner £10; deposit: £5 per person per night CARDS: none DETAILS: children welcome; no dogs in dining-room; smoking in lounge only; garden

Any smoking restrictions that we know of are given in the details at the end of the entry.

Les Quatre Vents

Sark GY9 0SE TEL: (01481) 832247 FAX: (01481) 832332

Standing in its own grounds close to the harbour, shops and beaches, this friendly family-run guesthouse is spotlessly clean and well maintained. Two of the fresh and bright bedrooms are on the ground floor, and all have pretty duvets and sea views. The lounge is a good place to relax in the evening, and there is a dining-room where breakfast and pre-arranged evening meals are served at separate tables. The garden, with seating, is also available for guests' use. Sylvia Godwin's daughter has a horse-and-carriage business, and visitors can watch the horses being groomed.

OWNER: Sylvia Godwin OPEN: all year exc Christmas ROOMS: 1 single, 1 double, both with private bathroom; 1 twin, 1 family, both with shower; tea/coffee and TV in all bedrooms; lounge TERMS: single £20, single occupancy £30, twin/double £40, family room £40–£60; children's reductions by arrangement; dinner £15; deposit: £5 per day CARDS: none DETAILS: children welcome; dogs welcome; no smoking in bedrooms or dining-room; garden

Indexes

Index 1

B&Bs by county and town or village

LONDON
Avonmore Hotel 17
Bickenhall Hotel 17
Collin House 17
Concorde Hotel 18
Enrico Hotel 18
La Gaffe 18
Harlingford Hotel 19
Lincoln House Hotel 19
Melrose House 20
Mentone Hotel 20
Oxford House Hotel 20
Parkland Walk Guest House 21
Parkwood Hotel 21
Romany House Hotel 22
17 Ovington Street 22
Swiss House Hotel 22
Terstan Hotel 23
Thanet Hotel 23
25 Eglington Road 24
Vicarage Private Hotel 24
Westminster House Hotel 24

ENGLAND

BATH & N.E. SOMERSET

BATH *Bloomfield House* 47
Cranleigh 48
Greenways 48
Haydon House 48
Leighton House 49
Meadowland 49
Somerset House 50
Wellsgate 50
BATHFORD *Eagle House* 51
HINTON CHARTERHOUSE *Green Lane House* 203
MONKTON COMBE *Dundas Lock Cottage* 267

BEDFORDSHIRE

LUTON *Belzayne Guest House* 246

BERKSHIRE

COOKHAM DEAN *Primrose Hill* 124
LAMBOURN WOODLANDS *Lodge Down* 227
MAIDENHEAD *Beehive Manor* 251
READING *Rainbow Lodge* 297
TWYFORD *The Hermitage* 376
WARGRAVE *Windy Brow* 383
WINDSOR *Beaumont Lodge* 408
Langton House 408

BRISTOL

BRISTOL *Lawns Guest House* 81

BUCKINGHAMSHIRE

FRIETH *Little Parmoor Farm* 168
GAYHURST *Mill Farm* 171
KINGSEY *Foxhill* 221
MURSLEY *Richmond Lodge* 271

CAMBRIDGESHIRE

CAMBRIDGE *De Freville House* 96
Netley Lodge 97
ELY *Black Hostelry* 153
Springfields 153
SWAFFHAM BULBECK *The Old Rectory* 355
WANSFORD *Stoneacre* 383
WATERBEACH *Berry House* 386
WITCHFORD *Clare Farm House* 411

CHESHIRE

CHESTER *Chester Town House* 107
Holly House Guest House 107
Mitchell's of Chester 107
GAWSWORTH *Rough Hey Farm* 171
HARGRAVE *Greenlooms Cottage* 184
MACCLESFIELD *Chadwick House* 250
MACCLESFIELD FOREST *Hardingland Farm* 250
MALPAS *Laurel Farm* 252
MOBBERLEY *Laburnum Cottage Guest House* 266
NANTWICH *Stoke Grange Farm* 272
TARVIN *Grove House* 358
TILSTON *Tilston Lodge* 367

WEAVERHAM *Beechwood House* 388
WILLINGTON *Roughlow Farm* 401

CO DURHAM

BARNARD CASTLE *Marwood View* 44
CORNFORTH *Ash House* 126
COTHERSTONE *Glendale* 128
DURHAM *Georgian Town House* 146
STAINDROP *Fawn Lea* 343

CORNWALL

BOTALLACK *Manor Farm* 68
CRACKINGTON HAVEN *Nancemellan* 130
Trevigue Farm 130
Treworgie Barton 131
CRAFTHOLE *The Bungalow* 131
CREED *Creed House* 133
FOWEY *Carneggan House* 163
Lanherriot Farm 163
KINGSAND *Cliff House* 220
LADOCK *Bissick Old Mill* 226
LITTLE PETHERICK *Molesworth Manor* 238
LIZARD *Lizard Hotel* 240
LOOE *Marwinthy Guest House* 242
MALPAS *Woodbury* 253
MARAZION *Castle Gayer* 254
MEVAGISSEY *Southcliffe* 261
MORWENSTOW *Old Vicarage* 268
MOUNT *Mount Pleasant* 269
NEWLYN EAST *Degembris Farmhouse* 274
Trewerry Mill 275
PADSTOW *Dower House* 283
Khandalla 284
PELYNT *Trenderway Farm* 285
PENRYN *Clare House* 286
PENTEWAN *Polrudden Farm* 287
PENZANCE *Lombard House* 288
PERRANPORTH *Morgans of Perranporth* 288
PERRANUTHNOE *Ednovean Farm* 289
PORT ISAAC *Archer Farm* 294
PORTLOE *Tregain* 295
ST HILARY *Ennys* 313
ST IVES *The Count House* 314
Sunrise Guest House 314
ST JUST *Penrose House* 315
ST MAWES *Braganza* 317
ST MEWAN *Poltarrow Farm* 318
TINTAGEL *Ferny Park* 367
Ye Olde Malthouse 368
TRESILLIAN *Manor Cottage* 373
Polsue Manor Farm 374
VERYAN *Broom Parc* 380
WIDEGATES *Coombe Farm* 400
ZENNOR *Tregeraint House* 425

CUMBRIA

AMBLESIDE *Cherry Garth* 36
Fern Cottage 36
Old Vicarage 36
Riverside Lodge 37
ARNSIDE *Willowfield* 38
BOWNESS-ON-WINDERMERE *Elim House* 72
Fairfield 72
Storrs Gate House 73
BROUGHTON IN FURNESS *Garner House* 84
CALDBECK *Swaledale Watch* 96
CARLISLE *Avondale* 98
Blackwell Farm 98
Courtfield House 99
Fern Lee 99
Howard House 99
CATLOWDY *Bessiestown Farm* 102
COCKERMOUTH *Wythop Mill Cottage* 119
CONISTON *Arrowfield Country Guest House* 122
Cruachan 123
Townson Ground 123
CROOK *Birksey Brow* 135
DENT *Stone Close* 142
FAR SAWREY *West Vale* 156
GRANGE-OVER-SANDS *Somerset House* 174
Thornfield House 174
GRASMERE *Rothay Lodge* 175
GRAYRIGG *Punchbowl House* 175
HAVERIGG *Dunelm Cottage* 189
IVEGILL *Streethead Farmhouse* 212
KENDAL *Holmfield* 214
KESWICK *Abacourt Guest House* 216
Berkeley Guest House 216
Claremont House 217

KIRKBY STEPHEN *Fletcher House* 223
KIRKBY THORE *Bridge End Farm* 224
MILLOM *Buckman Brow House* 264
NEAR SAWREY *Buckle Yeat* 272
PENRITH *Barco House* 286
ST BEES *Tomlin Guest House* 312
SEDBERGH *Holmecroft* 323
Marshall House 323
TALKIN *Hullerbank* 357
THIRLMERE *Brackenrigg* 363
THRELKELD *Blease Farm* 365
THURSBY *How End Farm* 366
TROUTBECK *Yew Grove* 374
WINDERMERE *The Archway* 406
Boston House 407
Kirkwood Guest House 407
Villa Lodge 408

DERBYSHIRE

ALPORT *Rock House* 33
BRADWELL *Stoney Ridge* 75
BUXTON *Coningsby* 93
Grosvenor House 93
Hawthorn Farm Guest House 93
Netherdale 94
Stoneridge 94
CHESTERFIELD *Abigail's Guest House* 108
Sheeplea Cottage Farm 108
CLIFTON *Collycroft Farm* 117
DETHICK *Manor Farmhouse* 142
GLOSSOP *Stanley Farm* 172
HARTINGTON *Manifold House* 186
Raikes Farm 186
HOLMESFIELD *Horsleygate Hall* 205
LANGWITH *Blue Barn Farm* 229
LITTLE LONGSTONE *The Hollow* 237
MATLOCK *Bradvilla* 257
Kensington Villa 258
Sunnybank 258
ROWLAND *Holly Cottage* 307
SHOTTLE *Dannah Farm* 331
Shottle Hall 331
TANSLEY *Packhorse Farm* 358

DEVON

ASHWATER *Renson Mill* 39
AVETON GIFFORD *Court Barton Farmhouse* 40
AXMINSTER *Millbrook Farm* 41
BARNSTAPLE *Bradiford Cottage* 45
BERRYNARBOR *Sloley Farm* 56
BICKINGTON *Penpark* 60
BIDEFORD *Lower Winsford House* 61
BOVEY TRACEY *Front House Lodge* 72
BRANSCOMBE *Hole Mill* 78
BUCKFASTLEIGH *Kilbury Manor Farm* 86
BUCKLAND MONACHORUM *Store Cottage* 86
CHAGFORD *Glendarah House* 103
CHERITON BISHOP *Horselake Farm* 106
CHIVELSTONE *South Allington House* 113
CHUDLEIGH *Oakfield* 114
COMBE MARTIN *Holdstone Farm* 121
CROYDE *Combas Farm* 137
DARTMOUTH *Broome Court* 139
Campbells 139
Ford House 140
Hedley House 140
DAWLISH *Oak Cottage* 141
DREWSTEIGNTON *Ford House* 145
EAST PRAWLE *Hines Hill* 150
EXETER *The Edwardian* 155
Raffles Hotel 156
FENITON *Colestocks House* 158
FREMINGTON *Muddlebridge House* 166
GULWORTHY *Hele Farm* 180
HARTLAND *West Titchberry Farm* 187
HEASLEY MILL *Heasley House* 194
JACOBSTOWE *Higher Cadham Farm* 213
KENTISBURY *Bridwick Farm* 215
KILMINGTON *White Hall* 218
KINGSBRIDGE *Galleons Reach* 220
LYNTON *Fernleigh* 249
Valley House 249
MAIDENCOMBE *The Beehive* 251
NORTH BOVEY *Gate House* 276
NORTHLEIGH *The Pantiles* 277
OAKFORD *Newhouse Farm* 279
PETER TAVY *The Barn* 290
Churchtown 290

PLYMOUTH *Park View* 292
Rosaland Hotel 293
PRINCETOWN *Duchy House* 296
RINGMORE *Aymer House* 300
SALCOMBE *Sunningdale* 318
SHALDON *Virginia Cottage* 325
SHEEPWASH *Half Moon Inn* 327
SIDMOUTH *Old Farmhouse* 333
STARCROSS *The Old Vicarage* 345
STOCKLAND *Kings Arms Inn* 348
STOKE GABRIEL *Red Slipper* 348
TAVISTOCK *April Cottage* 360
TIVERTON *Hornhill* 368
TORQUAY *Fairmount House Hotel* 369
Mulberry House 370
Walnut House 370
TOTNES *Old Forge* 371
WEARE GIFFARD *Burnards* 388
WEST BUCKLAND *Huxtable Farm* 391
WHIMPLE *Down House* 398
WIDECOMBE IN THE MOOR *Rutherford House* 400
YELVERTON *Cider House* 420

DORSET

AFFPUDDLE *Old Vicarage* 29
BOURNEMOUTH *Parklands Hotel* 70
Sandhurst 70
BRADFORD PEVERELL *Dower House* 75
BUCKLAND NEWTON *Holyleas House* 87
CHIDEOCK *Chimneys* 110
COMPTON ABBAS *Old Forge* 122
COOMBE KEYNES *April Thatch* 124
FIFEHEAD MAGDALEN *Apple Tree Cottage* 159
HAZELBURY BRYAN *Droop Farm* 193
HERMITAGE *Almshouse Farm* 199
HOOKE *Watermeadow House* 207
LANGTON MATRAVERS *Maycroft* 229
LYDLINCH *Holebrook Farm* 247
LYME REGIS *Rashwood Lodge* 247
The Red House 248
Willow Cottage 248
MARNHULL *Lovells Court* 256
Old Bank 256
Old Lamb House 256
MORETON *Vartrees House* 268
NETHERBURY *Heritage* 273
POOLE *ITP Lodge* 294
SANDFORD ORCAS *The Alders* 321
STURMINSTER NEWTON *Stourcastle Lodge* 353
WIMBORNE MINSTER *Acacia House* 402
Ashton Lodge 402
WINFRITH NEWBURGH *Manor House* 409
WOOL *East Burton House* 415
WOOTTON FITZPAINE *Rowan House* 416
YETMINSTER *Manor Farmhouse* 421

EAST RIDING OF YORKSHIRE

BEVERLEY *Eastgate Guest House* 59
BRIDLINGTON *Etherleigh* 79
Glen Alan Hotel 80
The Ryburn 80
FLAMBOROUGH *Revidge* 161

EAST SUSSEX

ARLINGTON *Bates Green* 38
BATTLE *Abbey View* 51
Kitchenham Farm 52
BERWICK *Dawes House* 56
BRIGHTON *Franklins* 80
BURWASH *Villiers* 91
CROWHURST *Brakes Coppice Farm* 136
DANEHILL *Sliders Farm* 138
EASTBOURNE *Beachy Rise* 148
ETCHINGHAM *King John's Lodge* 154
FRANT *Henley Farm* 165
Old Parsonage 166
IDEN *Barons Grange* 210
LEWES *Millers* 233
RYE *Cadborough Farm* 308
Half House 309
Jeake's House 309
Little Orchard House 309
Old Vicarage 310
Playden Cottage 310
WESTDEAN *Old Parsonage* 393
WINCHELSEA *Cleveland House* 404
St Anthony's House 404

ESSEX

BARDFIELD END GREEN *Wellcroft* 43
BOXTED *Round Hill House* 73
BRAN END *Elmcroft Guest House* 77
CASTLE HEDINGHAM *Pannells Ash* 101
CHELMSFORD *Aarandale Guest House* 105
COLCHESTER *Four Sevens Guest House* 120
Old Manse 120
DEDHAM *May's Barn Farm* 141
FRINTON-ON-SEA *Uplands Guest House* 168
GREAT DUNMOW *Homelye Farm* 176
HARWICH *Reids of Harwich* 187
HATFIELD PEVEREL *The Wick* 188
MARGARET RODING *Greys* 255
NEWNEY GREEN *Moor Hall* 275
SOUTHEND-ON-SEA *Pebbles Guest House* 340
STEEPLE BUMPSTEAD *Yew Tree House* 347
THAXTED *Folly House* 362
TOPPESFIELD *Ollivers Farm* 369
WRABNESS *Dimbols Farm* 418

GLOUCESTERSHIRE

ASTON MAGNA *Newlands Farmhouse* 40
BOURTON-ON-THE-WATER *Larch House* 71
Windrush Farm 71
CHELTENHAM *Hannaford's* 106
CHIPPING CAMPDEN *Rosary Cottage* 112
Sparlings 112
CHURCHAM *Edgewood House* 114
CIRENCESTER *Wimborne House* 115
EBRINGTON *Holly House* 152
FRAMPTON ON SEVERN *Old School House* 165
GLOUCESTER *Lulworth Guest House* 172
HAZLETON *Windrush House* 193
HIGHNAM *Linton Farm* 202
KEMPLEY *The Granary* 213
MEYSEY HAMPTON *Old Rectory* 262
MINCHINHAMPTON *Hunters Lodge* 264
MITCHELDEAN *Gunn Mill House* 266
NORTHLEACH *Market House* 277
ST BRIAVELS *Cinderhill House* 313
SLAD *Chessed* 336
STAUNTON *Mayfield Cottage* 346
STOW-ON-THE-WOLD *Tall Trees* 350
Wyck Hill Lodge 350
TEWKESBURY *Two Back of Avon* 362
UPPER ODDINGTON *Orchard Cottage* 377
WINCHCOMBE *Gower House* 403
The Homestead 403
WOODCHESTER *Southfield House* 413

GREATER MANCHESTER

ALTRINCHAM *Marron Guest House* 35
SALE *Brooklands Luxury Lodge* 319
Cornerstones 319

HAMPSHIRE

BARTON ON SEA *Bank Cottage* 46
BASHLEY *Yew Tree Farm* 46
BROCKENHURST *Caters Cottage* 83
BURLEY *Holmans* 90
CADNAM *Walnut Cottage* 95
DOWNTON *Cottage Bed & Breakfast* 144
EAST MEON *Drayton Cottage* 150
FLEET *8 Chinnock Close* 161
FORDINGBRIDGE *Green Patch* 162
KING'S SOMBORNE *How Park Farm* 222
LYMINGTON *Wheatsheaf House* 248
MILFORD ON SEA *Seawinds* 263
NETHER WALLOP *The Great Barn* 274
ODIHAM *Poland Mill* 279
PICKET HILL *Picket Hill House* 291
PORTSMOUTH *Fortitude Cottage* 295
RINGWOOD *Little Forest Lodge* 300
Moortown Lodge 301
ROCKBOURNE *Shearings* 303

ROMSEY *Spursholt House* 305
SHIPTON BELLINGER *Parsonage Farm* 330
SWAY *Kingfishers* 356
UPPER CLATFORD *Malt Cottage* 376
WEST MEON *Home Paddocks* 395
WINCHESTER *Brymer House* 404
Dellbrook 405
East View 405
54 St Cross Road 406
Florum House Hotel 406

HEREFORD & WORCESTER

BEOLEY *Cherrypit* 55
BREDWARDINE *Bredwardine Hall* 78
BROADWAY *Barn House* 81
Leasow House 82
Whiteacres 82
BROBURY *Brobury House* 83
BYFORD *Old Rectory* 95
CLIFTON-UPON-TEME *Pitlands Farm* 117
COLLINGTON *The Granary* 120
CUSOP *Lansdowne House* 137
EVESHAM *Brookside* 154
Church House 155
FRITH COMMON *Hunthouse Farm* 169
GREAT MALVERN *Elm Bank* 177
HEREFORD *Charades* 198
Chesley House 198
Grafton Villa Farm 198
KIMBOLTON *Lower Bache House* 219
KINNERSLEY *Upper Newton Farmhouse* 223
LEYSTERS *Hills Farm* 232
LITTLE WITLEY *Ribston House* 238
LLANWARNE *The Lawns* 240
MALVERN WELLS *Mellbreak* 253
Old Vicarage 253
OMBERSLEY *Eden Farm* 281
PERSHORE *The Barn* 289
ROSS-ON-WYE *The Arches* 305
Benhall Farm 306
Lumleys Guest House 306
UPTON SNODSBURY *Upton House* 379
WIGMORE *Queen's House* 401
WORCESTER *Burgage House* 416
40 Britannia Square 417

HERTFORDSHIRE

ST ALBANS *Care Inns* 312

ISLE OF WIGHT

COWES *Northlands* 129
EAST COWES *Crossways House* 149
FRESHWATER *Brookside Forge Hotel* 167
Yarlands Country House 167
GURNARD *Hillbrow* 181
MOTTISTONE *Mottistone Manor Farm* 269
ST LAWRENCE *Lisle Combe* 315
SHALFLEET *Orchard Cottage* 325
Shalfleet House 326
WOOTTON BRIDGE *Bridge House* 415
Oakenshore 416

ISLES OF SCILLY

BRYHER *Bank Cottage* 85
Soleil D'or 85
ST AGNES *Coastguards* 311
Covean Cottage 311
ST MARTIN'S *Glenmoor Cottage* 316
Polreath 317
ST MARY'S *The Boathouse* 317

KENT

BETHERSDEN *Little Hodgeham* 58
BIDDENDEN *River Hall Coach House* 60
CANTERBURY *Oriel Lodge* 97
Zan Stel Lodge 97
CHARING *Barnfield* 104
CRANBROOK *Folly Hill Cottage* 132
The Oast 132
DOVER *Linden Guest House* 143
Tower House 143
FARNINGHAM *The Bakery* 156
FAVERSHAM *Frith Farm House* 157
The Granary 157
FOUR ELMS *Knowlands* 163
FRITTENDEN *Maplehurst Mill* 169
Old Rectory 170
GOUDHURST *Mill House* 173
West Winchet 173
GREAT CHART *Worten House* 176
HADLOW *Leavers Oast* 181
HAWKHURST *Conghurst Farm* 190

HEADCORN *Vine Farm* 194
HIGH HALDEN *Hales Place* 201
HUNTON *The Woolhouse* 209
LEYBOURNE *Woodgate* 233
LINTON *Hill Place* 236
White Lodge 236
MAIDSTONE *Willington Court* 252
MARDEN *Merzie Meadows* 254
PENSHURST *Swale Cottage* 287
PLAXTOL *Jordans* 292
RYARSH *Heavers* 308
ST MARGARET'S AT CLIFFE *Merzenich Guest House* 316
SELLING *Owens Court Farm* 324
SHEPHERDSWELL *Sunshine Cottage* 328
SISSINGHURST *Camden Lodge* 334
SITTINGBOURNE *The Beaumont* 335
SOUTHBOROUGH *Number Ten* 339
TENTERDEN *Brattle House* 361
TESTON *Court Lodge Farm* 362
TOY'S HILL *Corner Cottage* 372
Heath House 372
TUNBRIDGE WELLS *Danehurst House Hotel* 375
WEST MALLING *Scott House* 395
WHITSTABLE *Windyridge* 400
WISSENDEN *Old Stables* 410
WORMSHILL *Saywell Farm House* 417
WYE *Wife of Bath* 419

LANCASHIRE

BLACKPOOL *Beaucliffe Hotel* 63
Grosvenor View 63
Sunray 64
CARNFORTH *Thwaite End Farm* 100
CLITHEROE *Brooklyn* 118
LANCASTER *Edenbreck House* 227
Elsinore House 228
MORECAMBE *Yacht Bay View* 268
SILVERDALE *Limes Village Guest House* 333
SLAIDBURN *Pages Farm* 336
WARTON *Cotestones Farm* 385

LEICESTERSHIRE

BURTON LAZARS *The Grange* 91
CASTLE DONINGTON *Weaver's Lodge* 101
FOXTON *Old Manse* 164
LOUGHBOROUGH *Charnwood Lodge* 243
Highbury Guest House 243
SHEARSBY *Knaptoft House Farm / The Greenway* 326

LINCOLNSHIRE

BASSINGTHORPE *Sycamore Farm* 47
BOSTON *Fairfield Guest House* 68
BOURNE *Bourne Eau House* 69
Mullions 69
BUSLINGTHORPE *East Farm House* 92
EAST BARKWITH *Bodkin Lodge* 147
FILLINGHAM *Church Farm* 159
LEGBOURNE *Gordon House* 231
LINCOLN *Carline Guest House* 235
Lindum View Guest House 235
POINTON *Greenoaks* 293
SARACEN'S HEAD *Pipwell Manor* 321
SPALDING *Bedford Court* 342
STAMFORD *Martins* 344
STURTON BY STOW *Gallows Dale Farm* 353
SWINHOPE *Hoe Hill* 356
TALLINGTON *The Old Mill* 357

MERSEYSIDE

LIVERPOOL *Blenheim Guest House* 239

N.E. LINCOLNSHIRE

CLEETHORPES *Brentwood Guest House* 116

NORFOLK

AYLSHAM *Old Bank House* 41
BACONSTHORPE *Chestnut Farmhouse* 42
BINHAM *Field House* 61
CASTLE ACRE *Willow Cottage* 100
CLINT GREEN *Clinton House* 118
CROMER *Beachcomber* 135
DOWNHAM MARKET *Dial House* 143
ELSING *Bartles Lodge* 152
FINCHAM *Rose Cottage* 160
FRAMLINGHAM EARL *Oakfield* 165
GREAT SNORING *Red House* 177
GREAT YARMOUTH *Senglea Lodge* 178
HEMSBY *Old Station House* 195

HORSEY *Old Chapel* 208
HUNSTANTON *Sutton House* 209
KING'S LYNN *Fairlight Lodge* 222
MENDHAM *Weston House Farm* 260
MUNDFORD *Colveston Manor* 270
NEATISHEAD *Regency Guest House* 273
NORWICH *Linden House* 278
PULHAM MARKET *Old Bakery* 297
SAXLINGHAM THORPE *The Lodge* 322
SHERINGHAM *Fairlawns* 330
Oak Lodge 330
SPORLE *Corfield House* 343
STARSTON *Starston Hall* 346
TAVERHAM *Foxwood* 360
THELNETHAM *Lodge Farmhouse* 363
THOMPSON *Thatched House* 364
THRANDESTON *Abbey Farm* 365
WALTON HIGHWAY *Maple Lodge* 381
Stratton Farm 381
WATERDEN *The Old Rectory* 387
WELLS-NEXT-THE-SEA *The Normans* 389
The Warren 390
WINTERTON-ON-SEA *Tower Cottage* 410
WROXHAM *Garden Cottage* 419

NORTH YORKSHIRE

ALDFIELD *Bay Tree Farm* 31
BEDALE *Hyperion House* 52
Southfield 53
BLUBBERHOUSES *Scaife Hall Farm* 65
BRAFFERTON *Laurel Farm* 76
BULMER *Grange Farm* 88
Lower Barn 88
CHOP GATE *Hillend Farm* 113
COXWOLD *School House* 129
EAST WITTON *Dale View* 151
EASINGWOLD *Old Vicarage* 147
FYLINGTHORPE *Croft Farm* 170
GOATHLAND *Glendale House* 173
GREENHOW HILL *Mole End* 179
HANLITH *Coachman's Cottage* 183
HARROGATE *The Alexander* 184
Knabbs Ash 185
Lynton House 185
HAWES *Brandymires* 189
Tarney Fors Farm House 190
HELMSLEY *Stilworth House* 195
HUTTON-LE-HOLE *Hammer & Hand* 210
KETTLEWELL *The Elms* 218
KNARESBOROUGH *Balaka* 225
Grove House 225
LEYBURN *Secret Garden House* 234
LITTON *Park Bottom* 239
LOVESOME HILL *Lovesome Hill Farm* 244
PATELEY BRIDGE *Bruce House Farm* 284
PICKERING *Bramwood Guest House* 291
RICHMOND *The Old Brewery* 299
West End 299
RIPON *Bishopton Grove House* 301
ROBIN HOOD'S BAY *Devon House* 302
SCARBOROUGH *Lyncris Manor* 323
SETTLE *Whitefriars* 324
SHERIFF HUTTON *Hall Farm* 329
SINNINGTON *Riverside Farm* 334
SKIPTON *Low Skibeden Farm House* 335
SLEIGHTS *Dalegarths* 337
SLINGSBY *The Hall* 338
SOUTH KILVINGTON *Thornborough House Farm* 340
STARBOTTON *Bushey Lodge Farm* 345
SUMMER BRIDGE *Clough House Farm* 354
THORALBY *Low Green House* 364
TOSSIDE *Sandy Laithe* 371
WEST BURTON *The Grange* 392
WEST WITTON *Ivy Dene* 397
WHITBY *Grantley House* 398
Grove Hotel 398
Lansbury Guest House 399
YORK *Abbeyfields* 421
Burton Villa 421
Curzon Lodge & Stable Cottages 422
Dairy Guesthouse 422
Holgate Bridge Hotel 423
Holmwood House 423
23 St Mary's 424

NORTHAMPTONSHIRE

CHACOMBE *Berry Furze* 103

NORTHAMPTON *St Georges Private Hotel* 276
OLD *Wold Farm* 280
WOLLASTON *Duckmire* 412

NORTHUMBERLAND

ALNMOUTH *Bilton Barns* 32
The Grange 33
ALNWICK *Charlton House* 33
BAMBURGH *Glenander* 43
Greengates 43
BEADNELL *Shepherds Cottage* 52
BELLINGHAM *Westfield House* 54
BELSAY *Bounder House* 55
BERWICK-UPON-TWEED *Dervaig Guest House* 57
Funnywayt'mekalivin 57
3 Scott's Place 58
CHESWICK *Ladythorne House* 109
CORBRIDGE *Clive House* 125
Town Barns 125
CROOKHAM *Coach House* 136
FORD *Estate House* 162
HALTWHISTLE *Ald White Craig Farm* 182
HARTBURN *Baker's Chest* 185
HAYDON BRIDGE *Geeswood House* 192
HEXHAM *East Peterel Field Farm* 199
Middlemarch 200
West Close House 200
HOLY ISLAND *Britannia House* 206
North View 206
Rose Villa 207
KIRKHARLE *Shieldhall* 224
KIRKWHELPINGTON *Cornhills Farmhouse* 225
LESBURY *Hawkhill Farmhouse* 232
ROTHBURY *Silverton Lodge* 306
SLALEY *Rye Hill Farm* 337
THROPTON *Thropton Demesne Farmhouse* 366
TWEEDMOUTH *Old Vicarage* 375
WARK *Low Stead* 384

NOTTINGHAMSHIRE

BABWORTH *Barns Country Guest House* 42
BLIDWORTH *Holly Lodge* 65
COTGRAVE *Jerico Farm* 127
GRINGLEY ON THE HILL *Old Vicarage* 179
LOWDHAM *Old School Mews* 244
WEST BRIDGFORD *Gallery Hotel* 391

N.W. SOMERSET

NAILSEA *Highdale Guest House* 271

OXFORDSHIRE

BLADON *Manor Farmhouse* 64
BURFORD *Chevrons* 89
HENLEY-ON-THAMES *Alftrudis* 195
Lenwade 196
The Rise 196
Watermans 197
OXFORD *Chestnuts* 282
Cotswold House 282
The Gables 282
Norham Guesthouse 283
SHENINGTON *Sugarswell Farm* 328
TAYNTON *Coombe Brook Lodge* 361
WOODSTOCK *Holmwood* 414
Pine Trees 414

RUTLAND

UPPINGHAM *Rutland House* 378

SHROPSHIRE

BOMERE HEATH *Fitz Manor* 66
BROSELEY *Broseley Guest House* 84
BUILDWAS *Bridge House* 87
Hill View Farm 88
CHURCH STRETTON *Brookfields Guest House* 115
CLUN *Old Farmhouse, Woodside* 119
IRONBRIDGE *Wharfage Cottage* 212
KNOCKIN *Top Farmhouse* 226
LLANYMYNECH *Hospitality* 241
LUDLOW *Number Twenty Eight* 246
MUCH WENLOCK *Walton House* 270
SHREWSBURY *Anton Guest House* 332
Fieldside 332
STREFFORD *Strefford Hall* 352
TREFONEN *The Pentre* 373

WEM *Foxleigh House* 390
WHITCHURCH *Dearnford Hall* 399

SOMERSET

ALLERFORD *Fern Cottage* 31
BEERCROCOMBE *Frog Street Farm* 53
Whittles Farm 54
BISCOMBE *Merlands* 62
BRIDGWATER *Cokerhurst Farm* 79
BURNHAM-ON-SEA *Priors Mead* 90
CHARD *Yew Tree Cottage* 104
COMBWICH *Moxhill Farmhouse* 121
CREWKERNE *Broadview Gardens* 134
DULVERTON *Town Mills* 145
DUNSTER *Dollons House* 146
Spears Cross Hotel 146
EAST COKER *Holywell House* 148
GREENHAM *Greenham Hall* 178
HENSTRIDGE *Quiet Corner Farm* 197
HOLFORD *Quantock House* 204
HORSINGTON *Manor Farm House* 208
KILVE *Old Mill* 219
MARTOCK *Wychwood* 257
MIDDLE CHINNOCK *Chinnock House* 262
MINEHEAD *Hindon Farm* 265
MISTERTON *Dryclose* 265
ROADWATER *Wood Advent Farm* 302
RODE *Irondale House* 303
SHEPTON MALLET *Bowlish House* 329
SOMERTON *The Lynch* 339
Still Cottage 339
SPAXTON *Gatesmoor* 342
STAPLEHAY *West Amberd Cottage* 344
STOKE ST GREGORY *Slough Court* 350
TAUNTON *Forde House* 359
Huntersmead 359
Orchard House 359
VELLOW *Curdon Mill* 379
WATERROW *Pare Mill* 387
WELLS *Infield House* 389
WEST PORLOCK *Bales Mead* 396
West Porlock House 396
WHEDDON CROSS *Raleigh Manor* 397
WIVELISCOMBE *Alpine House* 411
YEOVIL *Sunnymede* 420

SOUTH GLOUCESTERSHIRE

ALMONDSBURY *Abbotts Way Guest House* 32
RUDGEWAY *Friezecroft* 307
TORMARTON *Chestnut Farm* 369

SOUTH YORKSHIRE

CASTLETON *Bargate Cottage* 102
PENISTONE *Aldermans Head Manor* 285
SHEFFIELD *Holme Lane Farm* 327

STAFFORDSHIRE

ALSTONEFIELD *Stanshope Hall* 34
BLYTHE BRIDGE *The Limes* 66
CHEADLE *Ley Fields Farm* 104
CHEDDLETON *Choir Cottage* 105
ILAM *Beechenhill Farm* 211
LICHFIELD *Gaialands* 234
MAYFIELD *Lichfield House* 259
OAKAMOOR *Bank House* 278
STOKE-ON-TRENT *Corrie Guesthouse* 349
Westfield House 349

SUFFOLK

ACTON *Durham Cottage* 29
ALDEBURGH *Brightside* 30
Ocean House 30
Wateringfield 30
BEYTON *Manorhouse* 59
BRAMFIELD *Broad Oak Farm* 76
BURY ST EDMUNDS *South Hill House* 92
CLARE *Ship Stores* 115
CLAYDON *Redbrae* 116
CORTON *Church Farm* 127
FELIXSTOWE *Primrose Gate* 158
GREAT THURLOW *Old Vicarage* 177
HIGHAM *The Bauble* 201
HINTLESHAM *College Farm* 202
HITCHAM *Hill Farmhouse* 203
HOLBROOK *Highfield* 204
IPSWICH *Burlington Lodge* 211
KERSEY *Fair View* 216
KETTLEBURGH *Church Farm* 217
LAVENHAM *Meathe House* 230
LONG MELFORD *1 Westropps* 242

LOWESTOFT *Coventry House* 245
Longshore Guest House 245
MENDLESHAM GREEN *Cherry Tree Farm* 260
OTLEY *Bowerfield House* 281
SNAPE *Flemings Lodge* 338
SOUTHWOLD *Acton Lodge* 341
SUDBURY *St Faiths Villa* 354
WANGFORD *Hill House* 382
Poplar Hall 382

SURREY

CHIDDINGFOLD *Greenaway* 110
CRANLEIGH *Bookers Lee* 133
HASLEMERE *Deerfell* 188
WEST CLANDON *Ways Cottage* 393
WOKING *Knap Hill Manor* 412

TYNE & WEAR

SUNDERLAND *Mayfield Hotel* 355

WARWICKSHIRE

BINTON *Gravelside* 62
DARLINGSCOTT *Lower Farm* 138
HAMPTON LUCY *Sandbarn Farm* 183
KENILWORTH *Ferndale* 214
Victoria Lodge Hotel 215
LONG COMPTON *Butler's Road Farm* 241
LOXLEY *Loxley Farm* 245
MAXSTOKE *Old Rectory* 259
STRATFORD-UPON-AVON *32 College Street* 351
Victoria Spa Lodge 351
Woodstock 352
UPPER QUINTON *Winton House* 378
WARWICK *Avon Guest House* 385
Forth House 386

WEST MIDLANDS

COVENTRY *Abigail Guest House* 128
Crest Guest House 129
HAMPTON IN ARDEN *The Hollies* 182

WEST SUSSEX

ARDINGLY *Old Knowles* 37
BARNHAM *Tamarisk Cottage* 44
BOSHAM *Critchfield House* 67
Kenwood 67
White Barn 68
CHICHESTER *Chichester Lodge* 109
CHIDHAM *Easton House* 111
Old Rectory 111
CHILGROVE *Post Office Cottage* 112
COPTHORNE *Linchens* 125
EAST WITTERING *Bayside* 151
FINDON *Findon Tower* 160
PETWORTH *Old Railway Station* 290
REDFORD *Redford Cottage* 298
ROGATE *Cumbers House* 304
Mizzards Farm 304
TROTTON *Trotton Farm* 374
WALBERTON *Berrycroft* 381
WARNHAM *Glebe End* 384
WEST CHILTINGTON *New House Farm* 392
WEST HOATHLY *Coneybury* 394
WINEHAM *Frylands* 409
WOODMANCOTE *Eaton Thorne House* 413
Tithe Barn 413
WORTHING *Delmar Hotel* 418

WEST YORKSHIRE

BRAMHOPE *The Cottages* 77
HAWORTH *Hill Top* 191
Hole Farm 191
Moorfield Guest House 192
HOLMFIRTH *Holme Castle* 205
HUDDERSFIELD *The Mallows* 209
LEEDS *118 Grovehall Drive* 231
OLDFIELD *Far Two Laws Farm* 280
SOWERBY BRIDGE *Park Villa Guesthouse* 341

WILTSHIRE

ALTON BARNES *Newtown House* 35
ASHTON KEYNES *Two Cove House* 39
BERWICK ST JAMES *The Mill House* 57
BRADFORD-ON-AVON *Bradford Old Windmill* 74
Priory Steps 74
BURCOMBE *Manor Farm* 89
CORSHAM *Pickwick Lodge Farm* 126
CROCKERTON *Tanhouse Cottage* 134

DOWNTON *The Warren* 144
EAST KNOYLE *Moors Farmhouse* 149
GRITTLETON *Church House* 180
KINGSDOWN *Owl House* 221
LANDFORD *Landsbrook Farm* 228
LEA *Winkworth Farm* 230
LIMPLEY STOKE *Avonside* 234
LITTLE LANGFORD *Little Langford Farmhouse* 237
MARLBOROUGH *Clench Farmhouse* 255
MERE *Chetcombe House* 261
MIDDLE WINTERSLOW *Beadles* 263
MONKTON FARLEIGH *Fern Cottage* 267
POULSHOT *Middle Green Farm* 296
REDLYNCH *Templemans Old Farmhouse* 298
SALISBURY *Farthings* 319
Hayburn Wyke 320
Old Bakery 320
Stratford Lodge 321
STERT *Spout Cottage* 347
UPPER MINETY *Flisteridge Cottage* 377
WADSWICK *Manor Farm* 380
WEST GRAFTON *Rosegarth* 394
ZEALS *Stag Cottage* 424

SCOTLAND

ABERDEEN

ABERDEEN *Aberdeen Springdale Guest House* 429
Ewood House 429

ABERDEENSHIRE

ABOYNE *Hazlehurst Lodge* 431
Struan Hall 431
BANCHORY *The Old West Manse* 442
BANFF *Eden House* 442
FYVIE *Meikle Camaloun* 470
GARTLY *Faich-Hill Farmhouse* 470
OLDMELDRUM *Cromlet Hill* 506

ANGUS

ABERLEMNO *Wood of Auldbar* 430
ARBROATH *Farmhouse Kitchen* 434
BRECHIN *Doniford* 444
KIRKTON OF GLENISLA *Glenmarkie Farmhouse* 486
KIRRIEMUIR *Purgavie Farmhouse* 487

ARGYLL & BUTE

ARDNADAM *Lochside* 435
ARINAGOUR *Garden House* 436
Taigh Solas 436
ASCOG *Ascog Farm* 437
BALEPHETRISH *Sandy Cove* 439
BALLYGRANT *Kilmeny Farmhouse* 440
CALGARY *Calgary Farmhouse Hotel* 447
CAMPBELTOWN *Balegreggan Country House* 449
Sandiway 449
CARDROSS *Kirkton House* 450
CARRADALE *Dunvalanree Guest House* 450
CONNEL *Dunfuinary* 453
Ronebhal Guest House 454
CRAIGNURE *Inverlussa* 454
CRAOBH HAVEN *Buidhe Lodge* 455
DALMALLY *Orchy Bank* 457
DERVAIG *Ardrioch Farm Guest House* 458
Balmacara 459
DUNOON *Abbot's Brae* 460
FIONNPHORT *Achaban House* 467
Dungrianach 468
FORD *Tigh an Lodan* 468
ISLE OF COLONSAY *Seaview* 479
KILMARTIN *Tibertich* 482
KINGARTH *New Farm Farmhouse* 483
KIRKAPOL *Kirkapol Guest House* 485
LOCHDON *Gorsten Farm House* 492
LOCHDONHEAD *Old Mill Cottage* 492
MACHRIHANISH *East Trodigal Cottage* 497
OBAN *Argyll Villa* 503
Don-Muir 503
Dungrianach 504
Heatherfield House 504
Lorne View 505
PORT APPIN *Lochside Cottage* 509
PORT CHARLOTTE *Nerabus* 510

PORT ELLEN *Glenmachrie Farmhouse* 510
ROTHESAY *The Commodore* 513
ST CATHERINES *Thistle House* 514
SALEN *The Craig* 516
TOBERMORY *Broomhill* 529
Fàilte Guest House 529

BORDERS

ANCRUM *Ancrum Craig Guest House* 433
DARNICK *The Gables* 457
INNERLEITHEN *Caddon View Guest House* 475
JEDBURGH *Hundalee House* 480
LONGFORMACUS *Eildon Cottage* 495
MELROSE *Dunfermline House* 497
NENTHORN *Whitehill Farm* 501
PEEBLES *Whitestone House* 506

DUMBARTON & CLYDEBANK

GARTOCHARN *Ardoch Cottage* 471

DUMFRIES & GALLOWAY

DALBEATTIE *Briardale House* 456
KIRKCUDBRIGHT *Gladstone House* 486
MOFFAT *Alba House* 499
Ericstane 499
Fernhill 500
Thai-Ville 500
NEWTON STEWART *Oakbank* 502
PORTPATRICK *Carlton House* 511
Melvin Lodge 511
STRANRAER *Kildrochet House* 524
THORNHILL *Drumcruilton* 528

EAST LOTHIAN

GIFFORD *Eaglescairnie Mains* 471
WHITEKIRK *Whitekirk Mains* 532

EDINBURGH

EDINBURGH *Ashlyn Guest House* 461
Bonnington Guest House 462
Classic House 462
Gloria's Place 462
Hopetoun Guest House 463
17 Abercromby Place 463
Sibbet House 464
Sonas Guest House 464
The Town House 464
Turret Guest House 465

FALKIRK

DENNY *Lochend Farm* 458

FIFE

ABERDOUR *Hawkcraig House* 429
ANSTRUTHER *The Hermitage* 434
AUCHTERMUCHTY *Ardchoille Farm* 438
CRAIL *Selcraig House* 454
NEWBURGH *Ninewells Farmhouse* 502
ST ANDREWS *Cadzow Guest House* 513
Glenderran Guest House 514
Riverview Guest House 514

GLASGOW

GLASGOW *Kirklee Hotel* 472
Scott's Guest House 472
The Town House 472

HIGHLAND

ACHARACLE *Ardshealach Lodge* 432
ARDINDREAN *Taigh Na Mara* 435
ARISAIG *Old Library Lodge* 437
BALLACHULISH *Home Farm* 439
Lyn-Leven Guest House 440
BOAT OF GARTEN *Heathbank* 443
Old Ferryman's House 443
BROADFORD *Corry Lodge* 445
BRORA *Inverbrora Farm* 446
Lynwood 446
Tigh Fada 447
CARRBRIDGE *Féith Mho'r Country House* 451
DORNOCH *Trevose Guest House* 459
DRUMNADROCHIT *Glenkirk* 460
ERBUSAIG *Old Schoolhouse* 466
FESHIEBRIDGE *Balcraggan House* 467
FORT AUGUSTUS *Old Pier House* 468
FORT WILLIAM *Glenlochy Guest House* 469
The Grange 469
GOLSPIE *Deo Greine* 473
GRANTOWN-ON-SPEY *Culdearn House* 473
Kinross House 474
INVERASDALE *Knotts Landing* 476
INVERNESS *Clisham House* 476

Craigside Lodge 476
Culduthel Lodge 477
Millwood House 477
Old Rectory 478
Sealladh Sona 478
Trafford Bank 479
ISLE ORNSAY *Tawny Croft* 480
KILMALUAG *Trodaidh View* 481
KILMUIR *Kilmuir House* 482
KINCRAIG *March House* 483
KINGUSSIE *Bhuna Monadh* 484
Osprey Hotel 484
KINLOCHBERVIE *Old School Restaurant* 485
LOCH ERIBOLL *Port-na-Con House* 493
LOCHINVER *The Albannach* 493
MELVAIG *Rua Reidh Lighthouse* 498
MELVICH *The Sheiling* 498
NORTH ERRADALE *Little Lodge* 503
PLOCKTON *The Shieling* 509
PORTREE *Almondbank Guest House* 512
Balloch 512
Conusg 512
SCOURIE *Minch View* 518
Scourie Lodge 518
SPEAN BRIDGE *Invergloy House* 520
Old Pines 520
Riverside 521
Tirindrish House 521
STAFFIN *Glenview Inn and Restaurant* 522
Keeper's Cottage 522
STRATHAIRD *Strathaird House* 525
STRATHPEFFER *Craigvar* 526
Inver Lodge 526
STRATHY *Catalina* 527
TAIN *Aldie House* 527
THURSO *Ulbster Villa* 528
TONGUE *Tigh Aoidh Rhian* 529
ULLAPOOL *The Sheiling Guest House* 530
UPPER DIABAIG *Upper Diabaig Farm* 530
WATERNISH *Lismore* 532
WICK *Bilbster House* 533

MIDLOTHIAN

FALA *Fala Hall Farm* 466

MORAY

ELGIN *The Croft* 465
KEITH *Haughs Farm Guest House* 481

NORTH AYRSHIRE

BRODICK *Glencloy Farmhouse* 445
LARGS *South Whittlieburn Farm* 488
LOCHRANZA *Apple Lodge* 494
Butt Lodge Hotel 494
SANNOX *Gowanlea* 517
WHITING BAY *Royal Hotel* 533

NORTH LANARKSHIRE

AIRDRIE *Easter Glentore Farm* 433

ORKNEY

CLEATON *Cleaton House Hotel* 453
KIRKWALL *Briar Lea* 487
Leckmelm 487
LONGHOPE *Burnhouse Farm* 495
LYNESS *Stoneyquoy Farm* 496
ST MARGARET'S HOPE *Bellevue Guest House* 515
The Creel 515
SANDWICK *Netherstove* 516

PERTHSHIRE & KINROSS

BLAIR ATHOLL *Woodlands* 443
PERTH *Achnacarry* 507
Pitcullen Guest House 507
Sunbank House Hotel 507
PITLOCHRY *Arrandale House* 508
Craigatin House 508
STANLEY *Newmill Farm* 523

SHETLAND

LERWICK *Leeskol* 488
Whinrig 489
LUNNING *Skeo Green* 496
MUCKLE ROE *Westayre* 500
UPPER SCALLOWAY *Hildasay Guest House* 531

SOUTH AYRSHIRE

AYR *The Crescent* 438
Windsor Hotel 439
OLD DAILLY *Hawkhill Farm* 505

SOUTH LANARKSHIRE

ABINGTON *Craighead Farm* 430
DUNSYRE *Dunsyre Mains* 461

SKIRLING *Skirling House* 518
STRATHAVEN *Millwell Farm* 525
WALSTON *Walston Mansion Farmhouse* 531

STIRLING

BALQUHIDDER *Calea Sona* 441
Monachyle Mhor 441
CALLANDER *Leny House* 448
The Priory 448
CRIANLARICH *Ewich House* 456
DRYMEN *Dunleen* 460
STIRLING *Castlecroft* 523
Forth Guest House 523

WEST LOTHIAN

LINLITHGOW *Thornton* 490

WESTERN ISLES

ACHMORE *Cleascro Guest House* 432
BREASCLETE *Eshcol Guest House* 444
CASTLEBAY *Ceol Mara* 451
Terra Nova 451
Tigh-na-Mara 452
CLADDACH KIRKIBOST *Sealladh Traigh* 452
GRIMSAY *Glendale* 474
HOUGHARRY *Sgeir Ruadh* 475
LEVERBURGH *St Kilda House* 489
Shieldaig House 490
LOCHBOISDALE *Brae Lea House* 490
Loch-Side Cottage 491
LOCHCARNAN *Orasay Inn* 491
LOCHMADDY *Stag Lodge* 494
MUIR OF AIRD *Lennox Cottage* 501
SCADABAY *Hillhead* 517
SOUTH GALSON *Galson Farm Guest House* 519
STORNOWAY *The Old House* 524

WALES

CARMARTHENSHIRE

BRECHFA *Glasfryn Guest House* 545
CAPEL DEWI *Farm Retreats* 548
LLANDYBIE *Glynhir Mansion* 562
ST CLEARS *Old Board School* 580

CEREDIGION

ABERAERON *Hazeldene* 537
ABERYSTWYTH *Glyn-Garth* 539
Sinclair Guest House 539
Yr Hafod 540
BORTH *Hafan Wen* 545
RHYDLEWIS *Broniwan* 579

CONWY

BETWS-Y-COED *Ferns Guest House* 543
Fron Heulog 543
Park Hill Hotel 544
Swn-y-Dwr 544
COLWYN BAY *Holcombe Hotel* 549
St Margaret's Hotel 550
CONWY *Town House* 550
DOLWYDDELAN *Bryn Tirion Farm* 553
LLANDUDNO *Amber Court* 560
Beach Cove 560
Bryn-y-Mor 561
The Lighthouse 561
LLANFAIRFECHAN *Plas Heulog* 564
LLANFIHANGEL GLYN MYFYR *Old Rectory* 565
LLANRWST *Awelon* 569
White Cottage 570
PENMACHNO *Penmachno Hall* 575

DENBIGHSHIRE

LLANFAIR DYFFRYN CLWYD *Plas Uchaf* 564
LLANGOLLEN *Adanhurst* 566
Hendy Isa 566
PRESTATYN *Traeth Ganol* 577
RHYL *Romsley Guest House* 580

FLINTSHIRE

CAERWYS *Plas Penucha* 547
PENTRE HALKYN *The Hall* 576

GWYNEDD

BALA *Abercelyn* 540
BARMOUTH *Bryn Melyn Hotel* 541
The Sandpiper 541
Wavecrest Hotel 542
CAERNARFON *Isfryn* 546
White House 547
CEFN-DDWYSARN *Cwm Hwylfod* 549
CRICCIETH *Trefaes* 551
DOLGELLAU *Bryn yr Odyn* 552
Ivy House 553

GELLILYDAN *Tyddyn Du* 555
LLANBEDR *Plas y Bryn Hall* 558
LLANDDERFEL *Bronwylfa Guest House* 558
LLANDECWYN *Tegfan* 559
LLANFAIR *Fron Deg* 562
LLANRUG *Lakeside* 569
LLWYNGWRIL *Pentre Bach* 570

ISLE OF ANGLESEY

BENLLECH *Belvoir* 542
HOLYHEAD *Roselea* 556
MENAI BRIDGE *Bwthyn* 571

MONMOUTHSHIRE

ABERGAVENNY *Pentre House* 538
DINGESTOW *Cider Mill* 552
LLANGOVAN *Court St Lawrence* 567
MAMHILAD *Ty-Cooke Farm* 571
TINTERN *Old Rectory* 584

NEATH PORT TALBOT

NEATH *Cwmbach Cottages* 573

NEWPORT

NEWPORT *Kepe Lodge* 574

PEMBROKESHIRE

CAREW *Old Stable Cottage* 548
DALE *Post House Hotel* 551
FISHGUARD *Manor House Hotel* 554
GOODWICK *Ivybridge* 555
LITTLE HAVEN *Whitegates* 557
MOYLEGROVE *Old Vicarage* 573
NEWPORT *Grove Park Guest House* 574
Llysmeddyg 574
ST DAVID'S *Craig-y-Mor* 581
SAUNDERSFOOT *Primrose Cottage* 581
Sandyhill Guest House 581
SOLVA *Min Yr Afon* 582
TENBY *High Seas* 584

POWYS

ABERCEGIR *Yr Hen Felin* 537
ABERHAFESP *Dyffryn Farm* 538
BRECON *Pickwick House* 545
BUILTH WELLS *Querida* 546
FELINFACH *Trehenry Farm* 554
HAY-ON-WYE *Brookfield Guesthouse* 556
LLANANNO *Bwlch Farm* 557
LLANDDEW *Old Rectory* 559
LLANDRINDOD WELLS *Charis* 560
LLANFAIR CAEREINION *Bryn Penarth* 563
Cwmllwynog 563
LLANIGON *Old Post Office* 567
LLANRHAEADR-YM-MOCHNANT *Bron Heulog* 568
Llys Morgan 568
LLYSWEN *Oakfield* 571
MONTGOMERY *Beeches* 572
PENCELLI *Cambrian Cruisers Marina* 575
PENYBONTFAWR *Glyndwr* 576
PRESTEIGNE *Carmel Court* 577
RHAYADER *Glyn Gwy* 578
Raveloe 578
TALYBONT *Llansantffraed House* 584
TRETOWER *The Firs* 585
WELSHPOOL *Gungrog House* 585
Montgomery House 586
Tynllwyn Farm 586

SWANSEA

SOUTHGATE *Heatherlands* 582
SWANSEA *Alexandra House* 583
Uplands Court 583

VALE OF GLAMORGAN

RHOOSE *Welford Court Guest House* 579

THE CHANNEL ISLANDS

GUERNSEY

BORDEAUX *Bordeaux Guesthouse* 589
FOREST *Tudor Lodge Deer Farm* 589
ST MARTIN *Santi Villa Guest House* 591
ST PETER PORT *Marine Hotel* 592

JERSEY

ROZEL BAY *La Petite Chaire* 590
ST HELIER *La Bonne Vie* 590
La Sirene 591
ST MARTIN *Le Relais de St Martin* 591
ST OUEN *Lecq Farm Guest House* 592

SARK

SARK *Hivernage* 593
Le Petit Coin 593
Les Quatre Vents 594

Index 2

B&Bs by name

Aarandale Guest House Chelmsford 105
Abacourt Guest House Keswick 216
Abbey Farm Thrandeston 365
Abbeyfields York 421
Abbey View Battle 51
Abbot's Brae Dunoon 460
Abbotts Way Guest House Almondsbury 32
Abercelyn Bala 540
Aberdeen Springdale Guest House Aberdeen 429
Abigail Guest House Coventry 128
Abigail's Guest House Chesterfield 108
Acacia House Wimborne Minster 402
Achaban House Fionnphort 467
Achnacarry Perth 507
Acton Lodge Southwold 341
Adanhurst Llangollen 566
Alba House Moffat 499
The Albannach Lochinver 493
Ald White Craig Farm Haltwhistle 182
Aldermans Head Manor Penistone 285
The Alders Sandford Orcas 321
Aldie House Tain 527
The Alexander Harrogate 184
Alexandra House Swansea 583
Alftrudis Henley-on-Thames 195
Almondbank Guest House Portree 512
Almshouse Farm Hermitage 199
Alpine House Wiveliscombe 411
Amber Court Llandudno 560
Ancrum Craig Guest House Ancrum 433
Anton Guest House Shrewsbury 332
Apple Lodge Lochranza 494
Apple Tree Cottage Fifehead Magdalen 159
April Cottage Tavistock 360
April Thatch Coombe Keynes 124
Archer Farm Port Isaac 294
The Arches Ross-on-Wye 305
The Archway Windermere 406
Ardchoille Farm Auchtermuchty 438
Ardoch Cottage Gartocharn 471
Ardrioch Farm Guest House Dervaig 458
Ardshealach Lodge Acharacle 432
Argyll Villa Oban 503
Arrandale House Pitlochry 508
Arrowfield Country Guest House Coniston 122
Ascog Farm Ascog 437
Ash House Cornforth 126
Ashlyn Guest House Edinburgh 461
Ashton Lodge Wimborne Minster 402
Avon Guest House Warwick 385
Avondale Carlisle 98
Avonmore Hotel London 17
Avonside Limpley Stoke 234
Awelon Llanrwst 569
Ayrmer House Ringmore 300
Baker's Chest Hartburn 185
The Bakery Farningham 156
Balaka Knaresborough 225
Balcraggan House Feshiebridge 467
Balegreggan Country House Campbeltown 449
Bales Mead West Porlock 396
Balloch Portree 512
Balmacara Dervaig 459
Bank Cottage Barton on Sea 46
Bank Cottage Bryher 85
Bank House Oakamoor 278
Barco House Penrith 286

Bargate Cottage Castleton 102
The Barn Pershore 289
The Barn Peter Tavy 290
Barnfield Charing 104
Barn House Broadway 81
Barns Country Guest House Babworth 42
Barons Grange Iden 210
Bartles Lodge Elsing 152
Bates Green Arlington 38
The Bauble Higham 201
Bayside East Wittering 151
Bay Tree Farm Aldfield 31
Beachcomber Cromer 135
Beach Cove Llandudno 560
Beachy Rise Eastbourne 148
Beadles Middle Winterslow 263
Beaucliffe Hotel Blackpool 63
The Beaumont Sittingbourne 335
Beaumont Lodge Windsor 408
Bedford Court Spalding 342
Beechenhill Farm Ilam 211
Beeches Montgomery 572
Beechwood House Weaverham 388
The Beehive Maidencombe 251
Beehive Manor Maidenhead 251
Bellevue Guest House St Margaret's Hope 515
Belvoir Benllech 542
Belzayne Guest House Luton 246
Benhall Farm Ross-on-Wye 306
Berkeley Guest House Keswick 216
Berrycroft Walberton 381
Berry Furze Chacombe 103
Berry House Waterbeach 386
Bessiestown Farm Catlowdy 102
Bhuna Monadh Kingussie 484
Bickenhall Hotel London 17
Bilbster House Wick 533
Bilton Barns Alnmouth 32
Birksey Brow Crook 135
Bishopton Grove House Ripon 301
Bissick Old Mill Ladock 226
Black Hostelry Ely 153
Blackwell Farm Carlisle 98
Blease Farm Threlkeld 365
Blenheim Guest House Liverpool 239
Bloomfield House Bath 47
Blue Barn Farm Langwith 229
The Boathouse St Mary's 317
Bodkin Lodge East Barkwith 147
La Bonne Vie St Helier 590
Bonnington Guest House Edinburgh 462
Bookers Lee Cranleigh 133
Bordeaux Guesthouse Bordeaux 589
Boston House Windermere 407
Bounder House Belsay 55
Bourne Eau House Bourne 69
Bowerfield House Otley 281
Bowlish House Shepton Mallet 329
Brackenrigg Thirlmere 363
Bradford Old Windmill Bradford-on-Avon 74
Bradiford Cottage Barnstaple 45
Bradvilla Matlock 257
Brae Lea House Lochboisdale 490
Braganza St Mawes 317
Brakes Coppice Farm Crowhurst 136
Bramwood Guest House Pickering 291
Brandymires Hawes 189
Brattle House Tenterden 361
Bredwardine Hall Bredwardine 78
Brentwood Guest House Cleethorpes 116
Briar Lea Kirkwall 487
Briardale House Dalbeattie 456
Bridge End Farm Kirkby Thore 224
Bridge House Buildwas 87
Bridge House Wootton Bridge 415
Bridwick Farm Kentisbury 215
Brightside Aldeburgh 30
Britannia House Holy Island 206
Broad Oak Farm Bramfield 76
Broadview Gardens Crewkerne 134
Brobury House Brobury 83
Bron Heulog Llanrhaeadr-ym-Mochnant 568
Broniwan Rhydlewis 579
Bronwylfa Guest House Llandderfel 558

Brookfield Guesthouse Hay-on-Wye 556
Brookfields Guest House Church Stretton 115
Brooklands Luxury Lodge Sale 319
Brooklyn Clitheroe 118
Brookside Evesham 154
Brookside Forge Hotel Freshwater 167
Broome Court Dartmouth 139
Broomhill Tobermory 529
Broom Parc Veryan 380
Broseley Guest House Broseley 84
Bruce House Farm Pateley Bridge 284
Brymer House Winchester 404
Bryn Melyn Hotel Barmouth 541
Bryn Penarth Llanfair Caereinion 563
Bryn Tirion Farm Dolwyddelan 553
Bryn yr Odyn Dolgellau 552
Bryn-y-Mor Llandudno 561
Buckle Yeat Near Sawrey 272
Buckman Brow House Millom 264
Buidhe Lodge Craobh Haven 455
The Bungalow Crafthole 131
Burgage House Worcester 416
Burlington Lodge Ipswich 211
Burnards Weare Giffard 388
Burnhouse Farm Longhope 495
Burton Villa York 421
Bushey Lodge Farm Starbotton 345
Butler's Road Farm Long Compton 241
Butt Lodge Hotel Lochranza 494
Bwlch Farm Llananno 557
Bwthyn Menai Bridge 571
Cadborough Farm Rye 308
Caddon View Guest House Innerleithen 475
Cadzow Guest House St Andrews 513
Calea Sona Balquhidder 441
Calgary Farmhouse Hotel Calgary 447
Cambrian Cruisers Marina Pencelli 575
Camden Lodge Sissinghurst 334
Campbells Dartmouth 139
Care Inns St Albans 312
Carline Guest House Lincoln 235
Carlton House Portpatrick 511
Carmel Court Presteigne 577
Carneggan House Fowey 163
Castle Gayer Marazion 254
Castlecroft Stirling 523
Catalina Strathy 527
Caters Cottage Brockenhurst 83
Ceol Mara Castlebay 451
Chadwick House Macclesfield 250
Charades Hereford 198
Charis Llandrindod Wells 560
Charlton House Alnwick 33
Charnwood Lodge Loughborough 243
Cherry Garth Ambleside 36
Cherry Tree Farm Mendlesham Green 260
Cherrypit Beoley 55
Chesley House Hereford 198
Chessed Slad 336
Chester Town House Chester 107
Chestnut Farm Tormarton 369
Chestnut Farmhouse Baconsthorpe 42
Chestnuts Oxford 282
Chetcombe House Mere 261
Chevrons Burford 89
Chichester Lodge Chichester 109
Chimneys Chideock 110
Chinnock House Middle Chinnock 262
Choir Cottage Cheddleton 105
Church Farm Corton 127
Church Farm Fillingham 159
Church Farm Kettleburgh 217
Church House Evesham 155
Church House Grittleton 180
Churchtown Peter Tavy 290
Cider House Yelverton 420
Cider Mill Dingestow 552
Cinderhill House St Briavels 313
Clare Farm House Witchford 411
Clare House Penryn 286
Claremont House Keswick 217
Classic House Edinburgh 462

Cleascro Guest House Achmore 432
Cleaton House Hotel Cleaton 453
Clench Farmhouse Marlborough 255
Cleveland House Winchelsea 404
Cliff House Kingsand 220
Clinton House Clint Green 118
Clisham House Inverness 476
Clive House Corbridge 125
Clough House Farm Summer Bridge 354
Coach House Crookham 136
Coachman's Cottage Hanlith 183
Coastguards St Agnes 311
Cokerhurst Farm Bridgwater 79
Colestocks House Feniton 158
College Farm Hintlesham 202
Collin House London 17
Collycroft Farm Clifton 117
Colveston Manor Mundford 270
Combas Farm Croyde 137
The Commodore Rothesay 513
Concorde Hotel London 18
Coneybury West Hoathly 394
Conghurst Farm Hawkhurst 190
Coningsby Buxton 93
Conusg Portree 512
Coombe Brook Lodge Taynton 361
Coombe Farm Widegates 400
Corfield House Sporle 343
Corner Cottage Toy's Hill 372
Cornerstones Sale 319
Cornhills Farmhouse Kirkwhelpington 225
Corrie Guesthouse Stoke-on-Trent 349
Corry Lodge Broadford 445
Cotestones Farm Warton 385
Cotswold House Oxford 282
Cottage Bed & Breakfast Downton 144
The Cottages Bramhope 77
The Count House St Ives 314
Court Barton Farmhouse Aveton Gifford 40
Court Lodge Farm Teston 362
Court St Lawrence Llangovan 567
Courtfield House Carlisle 99
Covean Cottage St Agnes 311
Coventry House Lowestoft 245
The Craig Salen 516
Craigatin House Pitlochry 508
Craighead Farm Abington 430
Craigside Lodge Inverness 476
Craigvar Strathpeffer 526
Craig-y-Mor St David's 581
Cranleigh Bath 48
Creed House Creed 133
The Creel St Margaret's Hope 515
The Crescent Ayr 438
Crest Guest House Coventry 129
Critchfield House Bosham 67
The Croft Elgin 465
Croft Farm Fylingthorpe 170
Cromlet Hill Oldmeldrum 506
Crossways House East Cowes 149
Cruachan Coniston 123
Culdearn House Grantown-on-Spey 473
Culduthel Lodge Inverness 477
Cumbers House Rogate 304
Curdon Mill Vellow 379
Curzon Lodge & Stable Cottages York 422
Cwm Hwylfod Cefn-ddwysarn 549
Cwmbach Cottages Neath 573
Cwmllwynog Llanfair Caereinion 563
Dairy Guesthouse York 422
Dalegarths Sleights 337
Dale View East Witton 151
Danehurst House Hotel Tunbridge Wells 375
Dannah Farm Shottle 331
Dawes House Berwick 56
Dearnford Hall Whitchurch 399
Deerfell Haslemere 188
De Freville House Cambridge 96
Degembris Farmhouse Newlyn East 274
Dellbrook Winchester 405
Delmar Hotel Worthing 418
Deo Greine Golspie 473
Dervaig Guest House Berwick-upon-Tweed 57
Devon House Robin Hood's Bay 302
Dial House Downham Market 143
Dimbols Farm Wrabness 418

Dollons House Dunster 146
Doniford Brechin 444
Don-Muir Oban 503
Dower House Bradford Peverell 75
Dower House Padstow 283
Down House Whimple 398
Drayton Cottage East Meon 150
Droop Farm Hazelbury Bryan 193
Drumcruilton Thornhill 528
Dryclose Misterton 265
Duchy House Princetown 296
Duckmire Wollaston 412
Dundas Lock Cottage Monkton Combe 267
Dunelm Cottage Haverigg 189
Dunfermline House Melrose 497
Dunfuinary Connel 453
Dungrianach Fionnphort 468
Dungrianach Oban 504
Dunleen Drymen 460
Dunsyre Mains Dunsyre 461
Dunvalanree Guest House Carradale 450
Durham Cottage Acton 29
Dyffryn Farm Aberhafesp 538
Eagle House Bathford 51
Eaglescairnie Mains Gifford 471
East Burton House Wool 415
East Farm House Buslingthorpe 92
East Peterel Field Farm Hexham 199
East Trodigal Cottage Machrihanish 497
East View Winchester 405
Easter Glentore Farm Airdrie 433
Eastgate Guest House Beverley 59
Easton House Chidham 111
Eaton Thorne House Woodmancote 413
Eden Farm Ombersley 281
Eden House Banff 442
Edenbreck House Lancaster 227
Edgewood House Churcham 114
Ednovean Farm Perranuthnoe 289
The Edwardian Exeter 155
8 Chinnock Close Fleet 161
Eildon Cottage Longformacus 495
Elim House Bowness-on-Windermere 72
Elm Bank Great Malvern 177
Elmcroft Guest House Bran End 77
The Elms Kettlewell 218
Elsinore House Lancaster 228
Ennys St Hilary 313
Enrico Hotel London 18
Ericstane Moffat 499
Eshcol Guest House Breasclete 444
Estate House Ford 162
Etherleigh Bridlington 79
Ewich House Crianlarich 456
Ewood House Aberdeen 429
Faich-Hill Farmhouse Gartly 470
Fàilte Guest House Tobermory 529
Fair View Kersey 216
Fairfield Bowness-on-Windermere 72
Fairfield Guest House Boston 68
Fairlawns Sheringham 330
Fairlight Lodge King's Lynn 222
Fairmount House Hotel Torquay 369
Fala Hall Farm Fala 466
Far Two Laws Farm Oldfield 280
Farmhouse Kitchen Arbroath 434
Farm Retreats Capel Dewi 548
Farthings Salisbury 319
Fawn Lea Staindrop 343
Féith Mho'r Country House Carrbridge 451
Fern Cottage Allerford 31
Fern Cottage Ambleside 36
Fern Cottage Monkton Farleigh 267
Ferndale Kenilworth 214
Fernhill Moffat 500
Fern Lee Carlisle 99
Fernleigh Lynton 249
Ferns Guest House Betws-y-Coed 543
Ferny Park Tintagel 367
Field House Binham 61
Fieldside Shrewsbury 332
54 St Cross Road Winchester 406
Findon Tower Findon 160
The Firs Tretower 585

Fitz Manor Bomere Heath 66
Flemings Lodge Snape 338
Fletcher House Kirkby Stephen 223
Flisteridge Cottage Upper Minety 377
Florum House Hotel Winchester 406
Folly Hill Cottage Cranbrook 132
Folly House Thaxted 362
Forde House Taunton 359
Ford House Dartmouth 140
Ford House Drewsteignton 145
Forth Guest House Stirling 523
Forth House Warwick 386
Fortitude Cottage Portsmouth 295
40 Britannia Square Worcester 417
Four Sevens Guest House Colchester 120
Foxhill Kingsey 221
Foxleigh House Wem 390
Foxwood Taverham 360
Franklins Brighton 80
Friezecroft Rudgeway 307
Frith Farm House Faversham 157
Frog Street Farm Beercrocombe 53
Fron Deg Llanfair 562
Fron Heulog Betws-y-Coed 543
Front House Lodge Bovey Tracey 72
Frylands Wineham 409
Funnywayt'mekalivin Berwick-upon-Tweed 57
The Gables Darnick 457
The Gables Oxford 282
La Gaffe London 18
Gaialands Lichfield 234
Galleons Reach Kingsbridge 220
Gallery Hotel West Bridgford 391
Gallows Dale Farm Sturton by Stow 353
Galson Farm Guest House South Galson 519
Garden Cottage Wroxham 419
Garden House Arinagour 436
Garner House Broughton in Furness 84
Gate House North Bovey 276
Gatesmoor Spaxton 342
Geeswood House Haydon Bridge 192
Georgian Town House Durham 146
Gladstone House Kirkcudbright 486
Glasfryn Guest House Brechfa 545
Glebe End Warnham 384
Glen Alan Hotel Bridlington 80
Glenander Bamburgh 43
Glencloy Farmhouse Brodick 445
Glendale Cotherstone 128
Glendale Grimsay 474
Glendale House Goathland 173
Glendarah House Chagford 103
Glenderran Guest House St Andrews 514
Glenkirk Drumnadrochit 460
Glenlochy Guest House Fort William 469
Glenmachrie Farmhouse Port Ellen 510
Glenmarkie Farmhouse Kirkton of Glenisla 486
Glenmoor Cottage St Martin's 316
Glenview Inn and Restaurant Staffin 522
Gloria's Place Edinburgh 462
Glyndwr Penybontfawr 576
Glyn-Garth Aberystwyth 539
Glyn Gwy Rhayader 578
Glynhir Mansion Llandybie 562
Gordon House Legbourne 231
Gorsten Farm House Lochdon 492
Gowanlea Sannox 517
Gower House Winchcombe 403
Grafton Villa Farm Hereford 198
The Granary Collington 120
The Granary Faversham 157
The Granary Kempley 213
The Grange Alnmouth 33
The Grange Burton Lazars 91
The Grange Fort William 469
The Grange West Burton 392
Grange Farm Bulmer 88
Grantley House Whitby 398
Gravelside Binton 62
The Great Barn Nether Wallop 274

Greenaway Chiddingfold 110
Greengates Bamburgh 43
Greenham Hall Greenham 178
Green Lane House Hinton Charterhouse 203
Greenlooms Cottage Hargrave 184
Greenoaks Pointon 293
Green Patch Fordingbridge 162
Greenways Bath 48
Greys Margaret Roding 255
Grosvenor House Buxton 93
Grosvenor View Blackpool 63
Grove Hotel Whitby 398
Grove House Knaresborough 225
Grove House Tarvin 358
Grove Park Guest House Newport 574
Gungrog House Welshpool 585
Gunn Mill House Mitcheldean 266
Hafan Wen Borth 545
Hales Place High Halden 201
Half House Rye 309
Half Moon Inn Sheepwash 327
The Hall Pentre Halkyn 576
The Hall Slingsby 338
Hall Farm Sheriff Hutton 329
Hammer & Hand Hutton-le-Hole 210
Hannaford's Cheltenham 106
Hardingland Farm Macclesfield Forest 250
Harlingford Hotel London 19
Haughs Farm Guest House Keith 481
Hawkcraig House Aberdour 429
Hawkhill Farm Old Dailly 505
Hawkhill Farmhouse Lesbury 232
Hawthorn Farm Guest House Buxton 93
Hayburn Wyke Salisbury 320
Haydon House Bath 48
Hazeldene Aberaeron 537
Hazlehurst Lodge Aboyne 431
Heasley House Heasley Mill 194
Heath House Toy's Hill 372
Heathbank Boat of Garten 443
Heatherfield House Oban 504
Heatherlands Southgate 582
Heavers Ryarsh 308
Hedley House Dartmouth 140
Hele Farm Gulworthy 180
Hendy Isa Llangollen 566
Henley Farm Frant 165
Heritage Netherbury 273
The Hermitage Anstruther 434
The Hermitage Twyford 376
Highbury Guest House Loughborough 243
Highdale Guest House Nailsea 271
Higher Cadham Farm Jacobstowe 213
Highfield Holbrook 204
High Seas Tenby 584
Hildasay Guest House Upper Scalloway 531
Hillbrow Gurnard 181
Hillend Farm Chop Gate 113
Hill Farmhouse Hitcham 203
Hillhead Scadabay 517
Hill House Wangford 382
Hill Place Linton 236
Hills Farm Leysters 232
Hill Top Haworth 191
Hill View Farm Buildwas 88
Hindon Farm Minehead 265
Hines Hill East Prawle 150
Hivernage Sark 593
Hoe Hill Swinhope 356
Holcombe Hotel Colwyn Bay 549
Holdstone Farm Combe Martin 121
Holebrook Farm Lydlinch 247
Hole Farm Haworth 191
Hole Mill Branscombe 78
Holgate Bridge Hotel York 423
The Hollies Hampton in Arden 182
The Hollow Little Longstone 237
Holly Cottage Rowland 307
Holly House Ebrington 152
Holly House Guest House Chester 107
Holly Lodge Blidworth 65
Holmans Burley 90
Holme Castle Holmfirth 205
Holmecroft Sedbergh 323
Holme Lane Farm Sheffield 327
Holmfield Kendal 214
Holmwood Woodstock 414
Holmwood House York 423

Holyleas House Buckland Newton 87
Holywell House East Coker 148
Home Farm Ballachulish 439
Homelye Farm Great Dunmow 176
Home Paddocks West Meon 395
The Homestead Winchcombe 403
Hopetoun Guest House Edinburgh 463
Hornhill Tiverton 368
Horselake Farm Cheriton Bishop 106
Horsleygate Hall Holmesfield 205
Hospitality Llanymynech 241
Howard House Carlisle 99
How End Farm Thursby 366
How Park Farm King's Somborne 222
Hullerbank Talkin 357
Hundalee House Jedburgh 480
Hunters Lodge Minchinhampton 264
Huntersmead Taunton 359
Hunthouse Farm Frith Common 169
Huxtable Farm West Buckland 391
Hyperion House Bedale 52
Infield House Wells 389
Inverbrora Farm Brora 446
Invergloy House Spean Bridge 520
Inver Lodge Strathpeffer 526
Inverlussa Craignure 454
Irondale House Rode 303
Isfryn Caernarfon 546
ITP Lodge Poole 294
Ivybridge Goodwick 555
Ivy Dene West Witton 397
Ivy House Dolgellau 553
Jeake's House Rye 309
Jerico Farm Cotgrave 127
Jordans Plaxtol 292
Keeper's Cottage Staffin 522
Kensington Villa Matlock 258
Kenwood Bosham 67
Kepe Lodge Newport 574
Khandalla Padstow 284
Kilbury Manor Farm Buckfastleigh 86
Kildrochet House Stranraer 524
Kilmeny Farmhouse Ballygrant 440
Kilmuir House Kilmuir 482
Kingfishers Sway 356
King John's Lodge Etchingham 154
Kings Arms Inn Stockland 348
Kinross House Grantown-on-Spey 474
Kirkapol Guest House Kirkapol 485
Kirklee Hotel Glasgow 472
Kirkton House Cardross 450
Kirkwood Guest House Windermere 407
Kitchenham Farm Battle 52
Knabbs Ash Harrogate 185
Knap Hill Manor Woking 412
Knaptoft House Farm / The Greenway Shearsby 326
Knotts Landing Inverasdale 476
Knowlands Four Elms 163
Laburnum Cottage Guest House Mobberley 266
Ladythorne House Cheswick 109
Lakeside Llanrug 569
Landsbrook Farm Landford 228
Langton House Windsor 408
Lanherriot Farm Fowey 163
Lansbury Guest House Whitby 399
Lansdowne House Cusop 137
Larch House Bourton-on-the-Water 71
Laurel Farm Brafferton 76
Laurel Farm Malpas 252
The Lawns Llanwarne 240
Lawns Guest House Bristol 81
Leasow House Broadway 82
Leavers Oast Hadlow 181
Leckmelm Kirkwall 487
Lecq Farm Guest House St Ouen 592
Leeskol Lerwick 488
Leighton House Bath 49
Lennox Cottage Muir Of Aird 501
Lenwade Henley-on-Thames 196
Leny House Callander 448
Ley Fields Farm Cheadle 104
Lichfield House Mayfield 259

The Lighthouse Llandudno 561
The Limes Blythe Bridge 66
Limes Village Guest House Silverdale 333
Linchens Copthorne 125
Lincoln House Hotel London 19
Linden Guest House Dover 143
Linden House Norwich 278
Lindum View Guest House Lincoln 235
Linton Farm Highnam 202
Lisle Combe St Lawrence 315
Lismore Waternish 532
Little Forest Lodge Ringwood 300
Little Hodgeham Bethersden 58
Little Langford Farmhouse Little Langford 237
Little Lodge North Erradale 503
Little Orchard House Rye 309
Little Parmoor Farm Frieth 168
Lizard Hotel Lizard 240
Llansantffraed House Talybont 584
Llys Morgan Llanrhaeadr-ym-Mochnant 568
Llysmeddyg Newport 574
Lochend Farm Denny 458
Lochside Ardnadam 435
Loch-Side Cottage Lochboisdale 491
Lochside Cottage Port Appin 509
The Lodge Saxlingham Thorpe 322
Lodge Down Lambourn Woodlands 227
Lodge Farmhouse Thelnetham 363
Lombard House Penzance 288
Longshore Guest House Lowestoft 245
Lorne View Oban 505
Lovells Court Marnhull 256
Lower Bache House Kimbolton 219
Lower Barn Bulmer 88
Lower Farm Darlingscott 138
Lower Winsford House Bideford 61
Lovesome Hill Farm Lovesome Hill 244
Low Green House Thoralby 364
Low Skibeden Farm House Skipton 335
Low Stead Wark 384
Loxley Farm Loxley 245
Lulworth Guest House Gloucester 172
Lumleys Guest House Ross-on-Wye 306
The Lynch Somerton 339
Lyncris Manor Scarborough 323
Lyn-Leven Guest House Ballachulish 440
Lynton House Harrogate 185
Lynwood Brora 446
The Mallows Huddersfield 209
Malt Cottage Upper Clatford 376
Manifold House Hartington 186
Manor Cottage Tresillian 373
Manor Farm Botallack 68
Manor Farm Burcombe 89
Manor Farm Wadswick 380
Manor Farmhouse Bladon 64
Manor Farmhouse Dethick 142
Manor Farm House Horsington 208
Manor Farmhouse Yetminster 421
Manorhouse Beyton 59
Manor House Winfrith Newburgh 409
Manor House Hotel Fishguard 554
Maplehurst Mill Frittenden 169
Maple Lodge Walton Highway 381
March House Kincraig 483
Marine Hotel St Peter Port 592
Market House Northleach 277
Marron Guest House Altrincham 35
Marshall House Sedbergh 323
Martins Stamford 344
Marwinthy Guest House Looe 242
Marwood View Barnard Castle 44
Maycroft Langton Matravers 229
Mayfield Cottage Staunton 346
Mayfield Hotel Sunderland 355
May's Barn Farm Dedham 141
Meadowland Bath 49
Meathe House Lavenham 230
Meikle Camaloun Fyvie 470
Mellbreak Malvern Wells 253
Melrose House London 20

Melvin Lodge Portpatrick 511
Mentone Hotel London 20
Merlands Biscombe 62
Merzenich Guest House St Margaret's at Cliffe 316
Merzie Meadows Marden 254
Middle Green Farm Poulshot 296
Middlemarch Hexham 200
Millbrook Farm Axminster 41
Mill Farm Gayhurst 171
The Mill House Berwick St James 57
Mill House Goudhurst 173
Millers Lewes 233
Millwell Farm Strathaven 525
Millwood House Inverness 477
Minch View Scourie 518
Min Yr Afon Solva 582
Mitchell's of Chester Chester 107
Mizzards Farm Rogate 304
Mole End Greenhow Hill 179
Molesworth Manor Little Petherick 238
Monachyle Mhor Balquhidder 441
Montgomery House Welshpool 586
Moorfield Guest House Haworth 192
Moor Hall Newney Green 275
Moors Farmhouse East Knoyle 149
Moortown Lodge Ringwood 301
Morgans of Perranporth Perranporth 288
Mottistone Manor Farm Mottistone 269
Mount Pleasant Mount 269
Moxhill Farmhouse Combwich 121
Muddlebridge House Fremington 166
Mulberry House Torquay 370
Mullions Bourne 69
Nancemellan Crackington Haven 130
Nerabus Port Charlotte 510
Netherdale Buxton 94
Netherstove Sandwick 516
Netley Lodge Cambridge 97
New Farm Farmhouse Kingarth 483
Newhouse Farm Oakford 279
New House Farm West Chiltington 392
Newlands Farmhouse Aston Magna 40
Newmill Farm Stanley 523
Newtown House Alton Barnes 35
Ninewells Farmhouse Newburgh 502
Norham Guesthouse Oxford 283
The Normans Wells-next-the-Sea 389
North View Holy Island 206
Northlands Cowes 129
Number Ten Southborough 339
Number Twenty Eight Ludlow 246
Oakbank Newton Stewart 502
Oak Cottage Dawlish 141
Oakenshore Wootton Bridge 416
Oakfield Chudleigh 114
Oakfield Framlingham Earl 165
Oakfield Llyswen 571
Oak Lodge Sheringham 330
The Oast Cranbrook 132
Ocean House Aldeburgh 30
Old Bakery Pulham Market 297
Old Bakery Salisbury 320
Old Bank House Aylsham 41
Old Bank Marnhull 256
Old Board School St Clears 580
The Old Brewery Richmond 299
Old Chapel Horsey 208
Ye Olde Malthouse Tintagel 368
Old Farmhouse Sidmouth 333
Old Farmhouse, Woodside Clun 119
Old Ferryman's House Boat of Garten 443
Old Forge Compton Abbas 122
Old Forge Totnes 371
The Old House Stornoway 524
Old Knowles Ardingly 37
Old Lamb House Marnhull 256
Old Library Lodge Arisaig 437
Old Manse Colchester 120
Old Manse Foxton 164
Old Mill Kilve 219
The Old Mill Tallington 357
Old Mill Cottage Lochdonhead 492

Old Parsonage Frant 166
Old Parsonage Westdean 393
Old Pier House Fort Augustus 468
Old Pines Spean Bridge 520
Old Post Office Llanigon 567
Old Railway Station Petworth 290
Old Rectory Byford 95
Old Rectory Chidham 111
Old Rectory Frittenden 170
Old Rectory Inverness 478
Old Rectory Llanddew 559
Old Rectory Llanfihangel Glyn Myfyr 565
Old Rectory Maxstoke 259
Old Rectory Meysey Hampton 262
The Old Rectory Swaffham Bulbeck 355
Old Rectory Tintern 584
The Old Rectory Waterden 387
Old Schoolhouse Erbusaig 466
Old School House Frampton on Severn 165
Old School Mews Lowdham 244
Old School Restaurant Kinlochbervie 485
Old Stable Cottage Carew 548
Old Stables Wissenden 410
Old Station House Hemsby 195
Old Vicarage Affpuddle 29
Old Vicarage Ambleside 36
Old Vicarage Easingwold 147
Old Vicarage Great Thurlow 177
Old Vicarage Gringley on the Hill 179
Old Vicarage Malvern Wells 253
Old Vicarage Morwenstow 268
Old Vicarage Moylegrove 573
Old Vicarage Rye 310
The Old Vicarage Starcross 345
Old Vicarage Tweedmouth 375
The Old West Manse Banchory 442
Ollivers Farm Toppesfield 369
118 Grovehall Drive Leeds 231
1 Westropps Long Melford 242
Orasay Inn Lochcarnan 491
Orchard Cottage Shalfleet 325
Orchard Cottage Upper Oddington 377
Orchard House Taunton 359
Orchy Bank Dalmally 457
Oriel Lodge Canterbury 97
Osprey Hotel Kingussie 484
Owens Court Farm Selling 324
Owl House Kingsdown 221
Oxford House Hotel London 20
Packhorse Farm Tansley 358
Pages Farm Slaidburn 336
Pannells Ash Castle Hedingham 101
The Pantiles Northleigh 277
Pare Mill Waterrow 387
Park Bottom Litton 239
Park Hill Hotel Betws-y-Coed 544
Parkland Walk Guest House London 21
Parklands Hotel Bournemouth 70
Park View Plymouth 292
Park Villa Guesthouse Sowerby Bridge 341
Parkwood Hotel London 21
Parsonage Farm Shipton Bellinger 330
Pebbles Guest House Southend-on-Sea 340
Penmachno Hall Penmachno 575
Penpark Bickington 60
Penrose House St Just 315
The Pentre Trefonen 373
Pentre Bach Llwyngwril 570
Pentre House Abergavenny 538
Le Petit Coin Sark 593
La Petite Chaire Rozel Bay 590
Picket Hill House Picket Hill 291
Pickwick House Brecon 545
Pickwick Lodge Farm Corsham 126
Pine Trees Woodstock 414
Pipwell Manor Saracen's Head 321
Pitcullen Guest House Perth 507
Pitlands Farm Clifton-upon-Teme 117
Plas Heulog Llanfairfechan 564
Plas Penucha Caerwys 547
Plas Uchaf Llanfair Dyffryn Clwyd 564
Plas y Bryn Hall Llanbedr 558
Playden Cottage Rye 310
Poland Mill Odiham 279

Polreath St Martin's 317
Polrudden Farm Pentewan 287
Polsue Manor Farm Tresillian 374
Poltarrow Farm St Mewan 318
Poplar Hall Wangford 382
Port-na-Con House Loch Eriboll 493
Post House Hotel Dale 551
Post Office Cottage Chilgrove 112
Primrose Cottage Saundersfoot 581
Primrose Gate Felixstowe 158
Primrose Hill Cookham Dean 124
Priors Mead Burnham-on-Sea 90
The Priory Callander 448
Priory Steps Bradford-on-Avon 74
Punchbowl House Grayrigg 175
Purgavie Farmhouse Kirriemuir 487
Quantock House Holford 204
Les Quatre Vents Sark 594
Queen's House Wigmore 401
Querida Builth Wells 546
Quiet Corner Farm Henstridge 197
Raffles Hotel Exeter 156
Raikes Farm Hartington 186
Rainbow Lodge Reading 297
Raleigh Manor Wheddon Cross 397
Rashwood Lodge Lyme Regis 247
Raveloe Rhayader 578
Red House Great Snoring 177
The Red House Lyme Regis 248
Red Slipper Stoke Gabriel 348
Redbrae Claydon 116
Redford Cottage Redford 298
Regency Guest House Neatishead 273
Reids of Harwich Harwich 187
Le Relais de St Martin St Martin 591
Renson Mill Ashwater 39
Revidge Flamborough 161
Ribston House Little Witley 238
Richmond Lodge Mursley 271
The Rise Henley-on-Thames 196
River Hall Coach House Biddenden 60
Riverside Spean Bridge 521
Riverside Farm Sinnington 334
Riverside Lodge Ambleside 37
Riverview Guest House St Andrews 514
Rock House Alport 33
Romany House Hotel London 22
Romsley Guest House Rhyl 580
Ronebhal Guest House Connel 454
Rosaland Hotel Plymouth 293
Rosary Cottage Chipping Campden 112
Rose Cottage Fincham 160
Rosegarth West Grafton 394
Roselea Holyhead 556
Rose Villa Holy Island 207
Rothay Lodge Grasmere 175
Rough Hey Farm Gawsworth 171
Roughlow Farm Willington 401
Round Hill House Boxted 73
Rowan House Wootton Fitzpaine 416
Royal Hotel Whiting Bay 533
Rua Reidh Lighthouse Melvaig 498
Rutherford House Widecombe in the Moor 400
Rutland House Uppingham 378
The Ryburn Bridlington 80
Rye Hill Farm Slaley 337
St Anthony's House Winchelsea 404
St Faiths Villa Sudbury 354
St Georges Private Hotel Northampton 276
St Kilda House Leverburgh 489
St Margaret's Hotel Colwyn Bay 550
Sandbarn Farm Hampton Lucy 183
Sandhurst Bournemouth 70
Sandiway Campbeltown 449
The Sandpiper Barmouth 541
Sandy Cove Balephetrish 439
Sandyhill Guest House Saundersfoot 581
Sandy Laithe Tosside 371
Santi Villa Guest House St Martin 591
Saywell Farm House Wormshill 417

Scaife Hall Farm Blubberhouses 65
School House Coxwold 129
Scott House West Malling 395
Scott's Guest House Glasgow 472
Scourie Lodge Scourie 518
Sealladh Sona Inverness 478
Sealladh Traigh Claddach Kirkibost 452
Seaview Isle of Colonsay 479
Seawinds Milford on Sea 263
Secret Garden House Leyburn 234
Selcraig House Crail 454
Senglea Lodge Great Yarmouth 178
17 Abercromby Place Edinburgh 463
17 Ovington Street London 22
Sgeir Ruadh Hougharry 475
Shalfleet House Shalfleet 326
Shearings Rockbourne 303
Sheeplea Cottage Farm Chesterfield 108
The Sheiling Melvich 498
The Sheiling Guest House Ullapool 530
Shepherds Cottage Beadnell 52
Shieldaig House Leverburgh 490
Shieldhall Kirkharle 224
The Shieling Plockton 509
Ship Stores Clare 115
Shottle Hall Shottle 331
Sibbet House Edinburgh 464
Silverton Lodge Rothbury 306
Sinclair Guest House Aberystwyth 539
La Sirene St Helier 591
Skeo Green Lunning 496
Skirling House Skirling 518
Sliders Farm Danehill 138
Sloley Farm Berrynarbor 56
Slough Court Stoke St Gregory 350
Soleil D'or Bryher 85
Somerset House Bath 50
Somerset House Grange-over-Sands 174
Sonas Guest House Edinburgh 464
South Allington House Chivelstone 113
Southcliffe Mevagissey 261
Southfield Bedale 53
Southfield House Woodchester 413
South Hill House Bury St Edmunds 92
Sparlings Chipping Campden 112
South Whittlieburn Farm Largs 488
Spears Cross Hotel Dunster 146
Spout Cottage Stert 347
Springfields Ely 153
Spursholt House Romsey 305
Stag Cottage Zeals 424
Stag Lodge Lochmaddy 494
Stanley Farm Glossop 172
Stanshope Hall Alstonefield 34
Starston Hall Starston 346
Still Cottage Somerton 339
Stilworth House Helmsley 195
Stoke Grange Farm Nantwich 272
Stoneacre Wansford 383
Stone Close Dent 142
Stoneridge Buxton 94
Stoneyquoy Farm Lyness 496
Stoney Ridge Bradwell 75
Store Cottage Buckland Monachorum 86
Storrs Gate House Bowness-on-Windermere 73
Stourcastle Lodge Sturminster Newton 353
Stratford Lodge Salisbury 321
Strathaird House Strathaird 525
Stratton Farm Walton Highway 381
Streethead Farmhouse Ivegill 212
Strefford Hall Strefford 352
Struan Hall Aboyne 431
Sugarswell Farm Shenington 328
Sunbank House Hotel Perth 507
Sunningdale Salcombe 318
Sunnybank Matlock 258
Sunnymede Yeovil 420
Sunray Blackpool 64
Sunrise Guest House St Ives 314
Sunshine Cottage Shepherdswell 328
Sutton House Hunstanton 209
Swale Cottage Penshurst 287
Swaledale Watch Caldbeck 96

Swiss House Hotel London 22
Swn-y-Dwr Betws-y-Coed 544
Sycamore Farm Bassingthorpe 47
Taigh Na Mara Ardindrean 435
Taigh Solas Arinagour 436
Tall Trees Stow-on-the-wold 350
Tamarisk Cottage Barnham 44
Tanhouse Cottage Crockerton 134
Tarney Fors Farm House Hawes 190
Tawny Croft Isle Ornsay 480
Tegfan Llandecwyn 559
Templemans Old Farmhouse Redlynch 298
Terra Nova Castlebay 451
Terstan Hotel London 23
Thai-Ville Moffat 500
Thanet Hotel London 23
Thatched House Thompson 364
32 College Street Stratford-upon-Avon 351
Thistle House St Catherines 514
Thornborough House Farm South Kilvington 340
Thornfield House Grange-over-sands 174
Thornton Linlithgow 490
3 Scott's Place Berwick-upon-tweed 58
Thropton Demesne Farmhouse Thropton 366
Thwaite End Farm Carnforth 100
Tibertich Kilmartin 482
Tigh an Lodan Ford 468
Tigh Aoidh Rhian Tongue 529
Tigh Fada Brora 447
Tigh-na-Mara Castlebay 452
Tilston Lodge Tilston 367
Tirindrish House Spean Bridge 521
Tithe Barn Woodmancote 413
Tomlin Guest House St Bees 312
Top Farmhouse Knockin 226
Tower Cottage Winterton-on-sea 410
Tower House Dover 143
Town Barns Corbridge 125
Town House Conwy 550
The Town House Edinburgh 464
The Town House Glasgow 472
Town Mills Dulverton 145
Townson Ground Coniston 123
Traeth Ganol Prestatyn 577
Trafford Bank Inverness 479
Trefaes Criccieth 551
Tregain Portloe 295
Tregeraint House Zennor 425
Trehenry Farm Felinfach 554
Trenderway Farm Pelynt 285
Trevigue Farm Crackington Haven 130
Trevose Guest House Dornoch 459
Trewerry Mill Newlyn East 275
Treworgie Barton Crackington Haven 131
Trodaidh View Kilmaluag 481
Trotton Farm Trotton 374
Tudor Lodge Deer Farm Forest 589
Turret Guest House Edinburgh 465
25 Eglington Road London 24
23 St Mary's York 424
Two Back of Avon Tewkesbury 362
Two Cove House Ashton Keynes 39
Ty-Cooke Farm Mamhilad 571
Tyddyn Du Gellilydan 555
Tynllwyn Farm Welshpool 586
Ulbster Villa Thurso 528
Uplands Court Swansea 583
Uplands Guest House Frinton-on-Sea 168
Upper Diabaig Farm Upper Diabaig 530
Upper Newton Farmhouse Kinnersley 223
Upton House Upton Snodsbury 379
Valley House Lynton 249
Vartrees House Moreton 268
Vicarage Private Hotel London 24
Victoria Lodge Hotel Kenilworth 215
Victoria Spa Lodge Stratford-upon-Avon 351
Villa Lodge Windermere 408
Villiers Burwash 91
Vine Farm Headcorn 194

Virginia Cottage Shaldon 325
Walnut Cottage Cadnam 95
Walnut House Torquay 370
Walston Mansion Farmhouse Walston 531
Walton House Much Wenlock 270
The Warren Downton 144
The Warren Wells-next-the-Sea 390
Wateringfield Aldeburgh 30
Watermans Henley-on-Thames 197
Watermeadow House Hooke 207
Wavecrest Hotel Barmouth 542
Ways Cottage West Clandon 393
Weaver's Lodge Castle Donington 101
Welford Court Guest House Rhoose 579
Wellcroft Bardfield End Green 43
Wellsgate Bath 50
West Amberd Cottage Staplehay 344
Westayre Muckle Roe 500
West Close House Hexham 200
West End Richmond 299
Westfield House Bellingham 54
Westfield House Stoke-on-Trent 349
Westminster House Hotel London 24
Weston House Farm Mendham 260
West Porlock House West Porlock 396
West Titchberry Farm Hartland 187
West Vale Far Sawrey 156
West Winchet Goudhurst 173
Wharfage Cottage Ironbridge 212
Wheatsheaf House Lymington 248
Whinrig Lerwick 489
Whiteacres Broadway 82
White Barn Bosham 68
White Cottage Llanrwst 570
Whitefriars Settle 324
Whitegates Little Haven 557
White Hall Kilmington 218
Whitehill Farm Nenthorn 501
White House Caernarfon 547
Whitekirk Mains Whitekirk 532
White Lodge Linton 236
Whitestone House Peebles 506
Whittles Farm Beercrocombe 54
The Wick Hatfield Peverel 188
Wife of Bath Wye 419
Willington Court Maidstone 252
Willow Cottage Castle Acre 100
Willow Cottage Lyme Regis 248
Willowfield Arnside 38
Wimborne House Cirencester 115
Windrush Farm Bourton-on-the-Water 71
Windrush House Hazleton 193
Windsor Hotel Ayr 439
Windy Brow Wargrave 383
Windyridge Whitstable 400
Winkworth Farm Lea 230
Winton House Upper Quinton 378
Wold Farm Old 280
Wood Advent Farm Roadwater 302
Wood of Auldbar Aberlemno 430
Woodbury Malpas 253
Woodgate Leybourne 233
Woodlands Blair Atholl 443
Woodstock Stratford-upon-Avon 352
The Woolhouse Hunton 209
Worten House Great Chart 176
Wychwood Martock 257
Wyck Hill Lodge Stow-on-the-Wold 350
Wythop Mill Cottage Cockermouth 119
Yacht Bay View Morecambe 268
Yarlands Country House Freshwater 167
Ye Olde Malthouse Tintagel 368
Yew Grove Troutbeck 374
Yew Tree Cottage Chard 104
Yew Tree Farm Bashley 46
Yew Tree House Steeple Bumpstead 347
Yr Hafod Aberystwyth 540
Yr Hen Felin Abercegir 537
Zan Stel Lodge Canterbury 97

Report form BB98

To: *The Good Bed and Breakfast Guide,*
Consumers' Association
FREEPOST, 2 Marylebone Road,
London NW1 1YN

Report on:

Address:

Date of visit:

Please tick appropriate box:

☐ Should continue as a main entry

☐ Should be considered as a main entry for future editions

☐ Should not be included

My reasons are:

please continue overleaf

I am not connected in any way with the owners

Name and address (BLOCK CAPITALS):

Signed:

☐ Please send some more report forms (*tick if appropriate*)

Report form BB98

To: *The Good Bed and Breakfast Guide,*
Consumers' Association
FREEPOST, 2 Marylebone Road,
London NW1 1YN

Report on:

Address:

Date of visit:

Please tick appropriate box:

☐ Should continue as a main entry

☐ Should be considered as a main entry for future editions

☐ Should not be included

My reasons are:

please continue overleaf

I am not connected in any way with the owners

Name and address (BLOCK CAPITALS):

Signed:

☐ Please send some more report forms (*tick if appropriate*)

Report form BB98

To: *The Good Bed and Breakfast Guide,*
Consumers' Association
FREEPOST, 2 Marylebone Road,
London NW1 1YN

Report on:

Address:

Date of visit:

Please tick appropriate box:

- ☐ Should continue as a main entry
- ☐ Should be considered as a main entry for future editions
- ☐ Should not be included

My reasons are:

please continue overleaf

I am not connected in any way with the owners

Name and address (BLOCK CAPITALS):

Signed:

☐ Please send some more report forms (*tick if appropriate*)

Report form BB98

To: *The Good Bed and Breakfast Guide,*
Consumers' Association
FREEPOST, 2 Marylebone Road,
London NW1 1YN

Report on:

Address:

Date of visit:

Please tick appropriate box:

☐ Should continue as a main entry

☐ Should be considered as a main entry for future editions

☐ Should not be included

My reasons are:

please continue overleaf

I am not connected in any way with the owners

Name and address (BLOCK CAPITALS):

Signed:

☐ Please send some more report forms (*tick if appropriate*)

Maps

KEY MAP

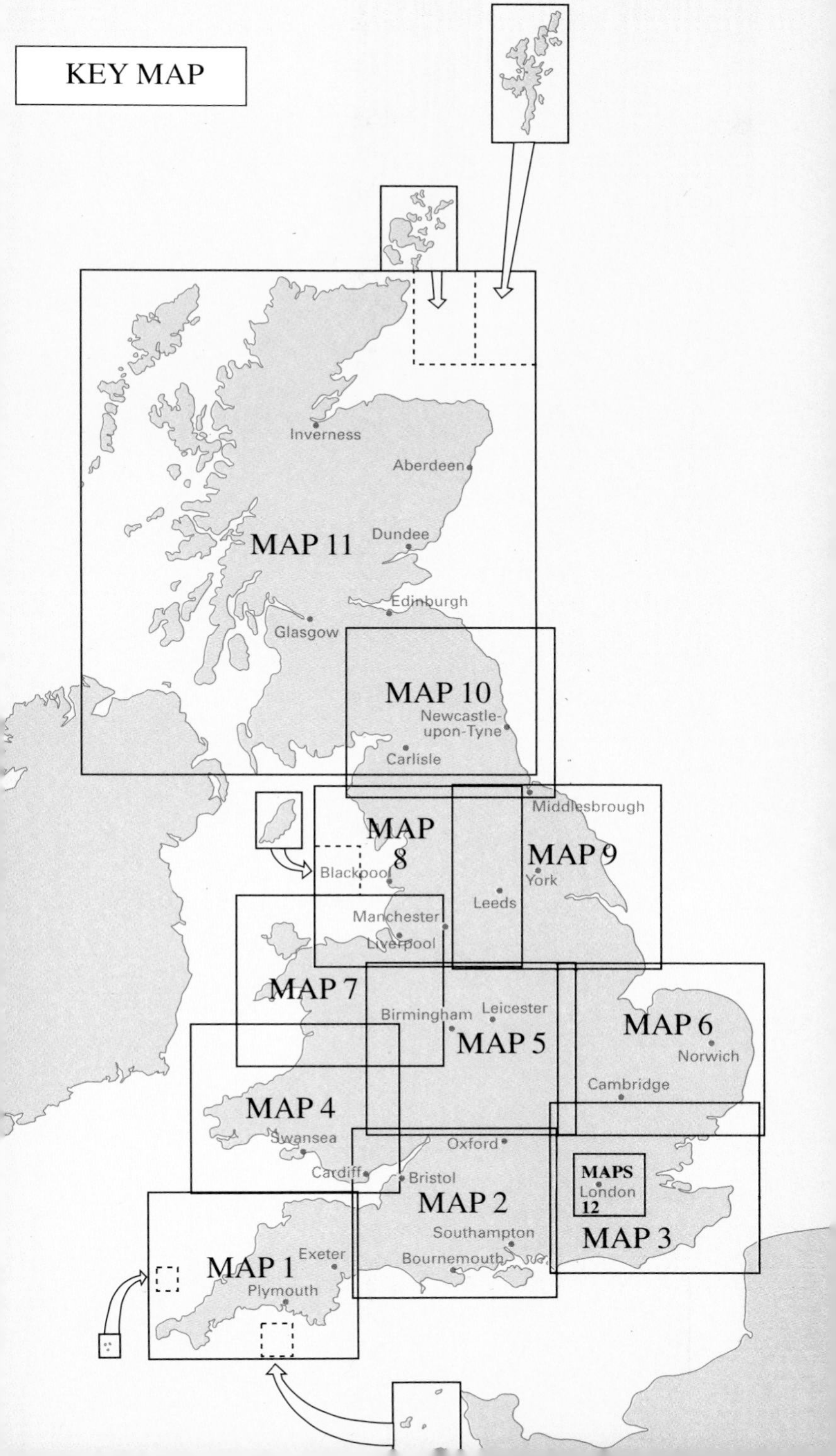
MAP 11
Inverness
Aberdeen
Dundee
Edinburgh
Glasgow
MAP 10
Newcastle-upon-Tyne
Carlisle
Middlesbrough
MAP 8
Blackpool
MAP 9
York
Leeds
Manchester
Liverpool
MAP 7
Birmingham
Leicester
MAP 5
MAP 6
Norwich
Cambridge
MAP 4
Swansea
Cardiff
Oxford
Bristol
MAP 2
MAPS 12
London
MAP 3
Southampton
Bournemouth
Exeter
MAP 1
Plymouth

4

MAP 1

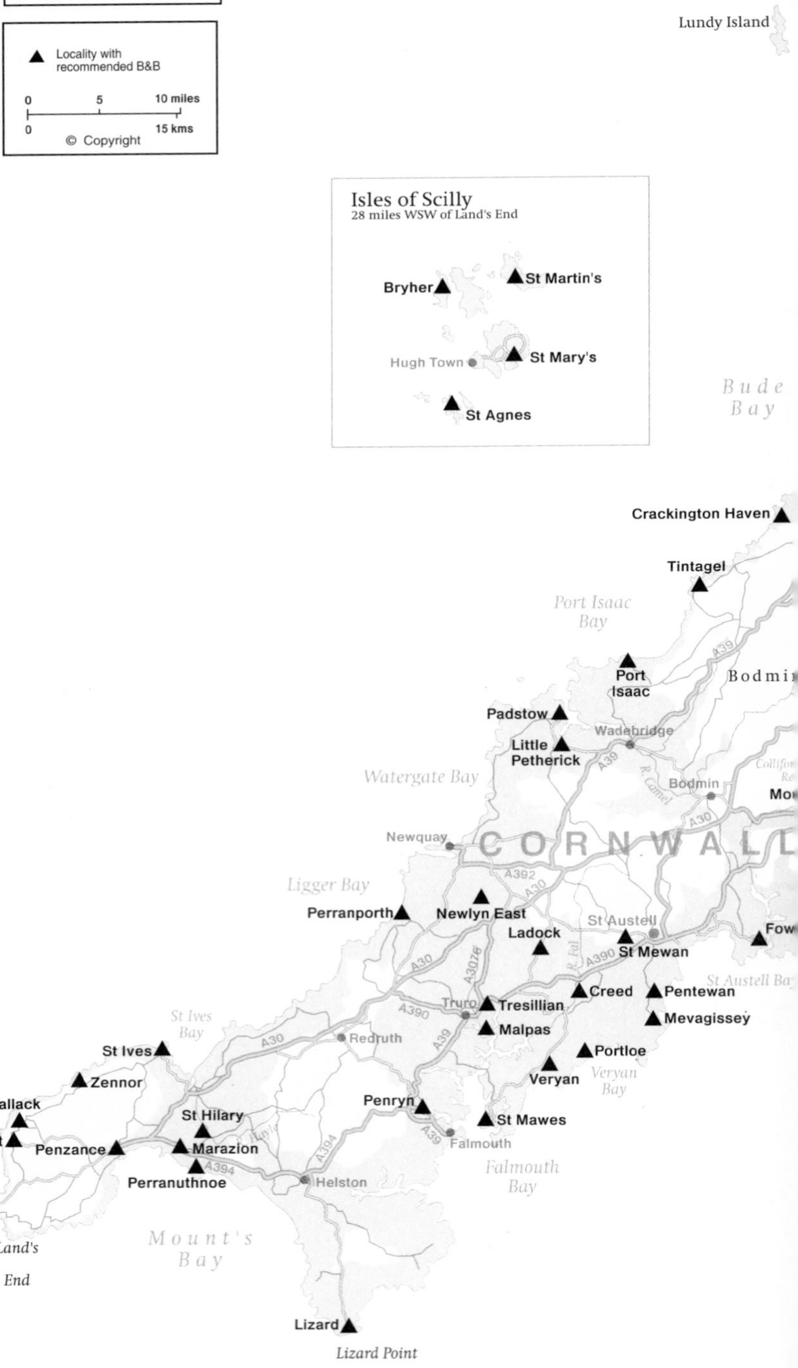

Locality with recommended B&B
0
5
10 miles
0
15 kms
© Copyright
Lundy Island
Isles of Scilly
28 miles WSW of Land's End
Bryher
St Martin's
Hugh Town
St Mary's
St Agnes
Bude Bay
Crackington Haven
Tintagel
Port Isaac Bay
A39
Port Isaac
Padstow
Wadebridge
Little Petherick
A39
R. Camel
Watergate Bay
Bodmin
A30
Newquay
CORNWALL
A392
A30
Ligger Bay
Perranporth
Newlyn East
Ladock
St Austell
St Mewan
A390
R. Fal
A30
A3076
Creed
Pentewan
Truro
Tresillian
A390
Mevagissey
Malpas
St Ives Bay
A30
Redruth
A39
Portloe
St Ives
Veryan
Veryan Bay
Zennor
Botallack
Penryn
St Hilary
St Mawes
St Just
Penzance
Marazion
A39
Falmouth
A394
A394
Perranuthnoe
Helston
Falmouth Bay
Mount's Bay
Land's End
Lizard
Lizard Point

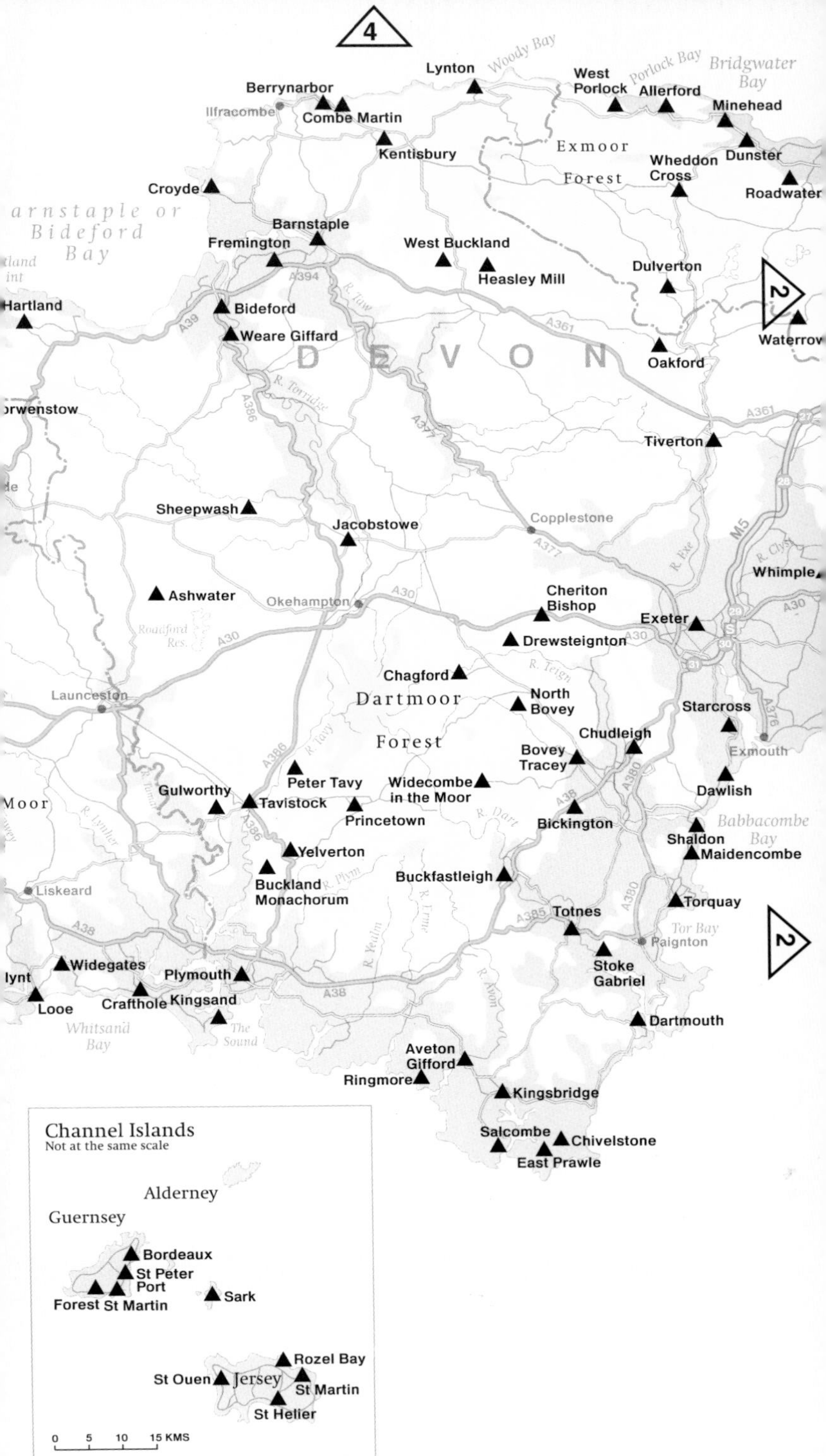
4
Lynton
Woody Bay
West Porlock
Porlock Bay
Allerford
Bridgwater Bay
Minehead
Berrynarbor
Ilfracombe
Combe Martin
Kentisbury
Exmoor Forest
Dunster
Wheddon Cross
Roadwater
Croyde
Barnstaple or Bideford Bay
Barnstaple
Fremington
West Buckland
Heasley Mill
Dulverton
2
A394
R. Taw
Hartland
Bideford
A39
Weare Giffard
A361
Waterrow
DEVON
Oakford
R. Torridge
A386
A377
A361
Tiverton
Sheepwash
Jacobstowe
Copplestone
A377
M5
R. Exe
R. Clyst
Whimple
Ashwater
Okehampton
A30
Cheriton Bishop
Roadford Res.
A30
Exeter
Drewsteignton
A30
R. Teign
Chagford
Launceston
Dartmoor Forest
North Bovey
Starcross
Chudleigh
A376
Exmouth
Bovey Tracey
A386
R. Tavy
Peter Tavy
Widecombe in the Moor
A380
Dawlish
Gulworthy
Tavistock
Princetown
R. Tamar
R. Lynher
A38
Bickington
Babbacombe Bay
R. Dart
Shaldon
Maidencombe
A386
Yelverton
Buckland Monachorum
R. Plym
Buckfastleigh
Liskeard
R. Erme
R. Yealm
A385
Totnes
A380
Torquay
Tor Bay
Paignton
2
A38
Widegates
Plymouth
R. Avon
Stoke Gabriel
Looe
Crafthole
Kingsand
A38
Whitsand Bay
The Sound
Dartmouth
Aveton Gifford
Ringmore
Kingsbridge
Salcombe
Chivelstone
East Prawle
Channel Islands
Not at the same scale
Alderney
Guernsey
Bordeaux
St Peter Port
Sark
Forest
St Martin
Rozel Bay
St Ouen
Jersey
St Martin
St Helier
0 5 10 15 KMS

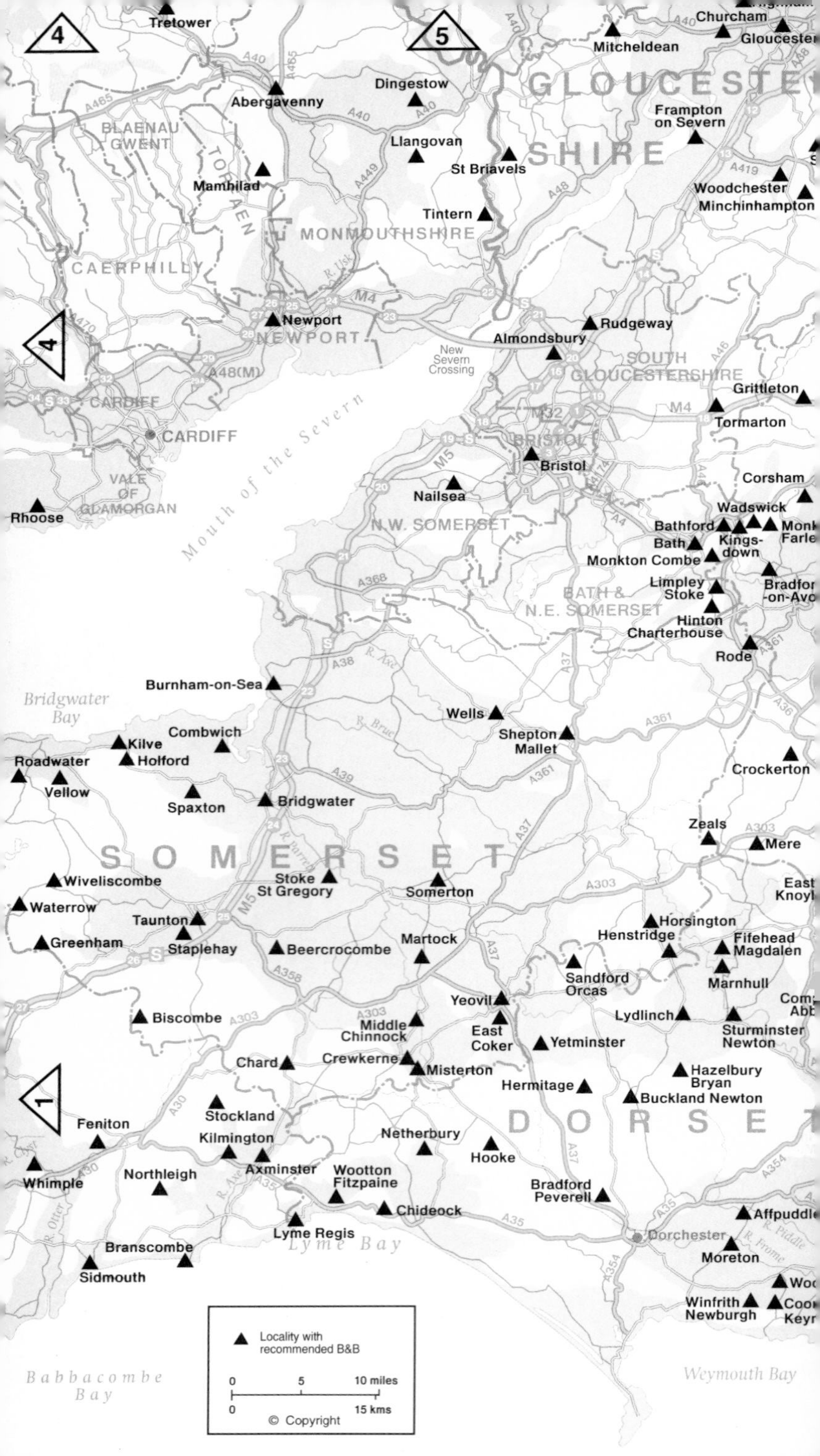
4
Tretower
5
Mitcheldean
Churcham
Gloucester
GLOUCESTER
SHIRE
A40
A465
Abergavenny
Dingestow
Frampton
on Severn
BLAENAU
GWENT
TORFAEN
Llangovan
St Briavels
A449
A48
A419
Woodchester
Minchinhampton
Mamhilad
Tintern
MONMOUTHSHIRE
CAERPHILLY
R. Usk
M4
Newport
NEWPORT
Rudgeway
A470
Almondsbury
New
Severn
Crossing
SOUTH
GLOUCESTERSHIRE
A46
A48(M)
CARDIFF
Grittleton
Tormarton
M32
Mouth of the Severn
BRISTOL
Bristol
M5
VALE
OF
GLAMORGAN
Nailsea
Corsham
Rhoose
Wadswick
N.W. SOMERSET
A4
Bathford
Bath
Kings-
down
Monkton Combe
Limpley
Stoke
A368
BATH &
N.E. SOMERSET
Hinton
Charterhouse
A37
Rode
A38
R. Axe
Burnham-on-Sea
Bridgwater
Bay
Wells
R. Brue
Shepton
Mallet
A361
A36
Combwich
Kilve
Holford
Roadwater
Vellow
Crockerton
A39
Spaxton
Bridgwater
Zeals
A303
Mere
SOMERSET
R. Parrett
Stoke
St Gregory
Wiveliscombe
Somerton
Waterrow
Taunton
Horsington
Henstridge
Fifehead
Magdalen
Greenham
Staplehay
Beercrocombe
Martock
Sandford
Orcas
Marnhull
A358
Yeovil
Middle
Chinnock
East
Coker
Lydlinch
Sturminster
Newton
Biscombe
Yetminster
Chard
Crewkerne
Misterton
Hazelbury
Bryan
Hermitage
Buckland Newton
1
Stockland
DORSET
Feniton
A30
Netherbury
Kilmington
Hooke
Axminster
R. Axe
Whimple
Northleigh
Wootton
Fitzpaine
Bradford
Peverell
A354
R. Otter
A35
Chideock
Affpuddle
Lyme Regis
Lyme Bay
Dorchester
R. Piddle
R. Frome
Moreton
Branscombe
Sidmouth
Winfrith
Newburgh
Locality with
recommended B&B
0
5
10 miles
15 kms
© Copyright
Babbacombe
Bay
Weymouth Bay

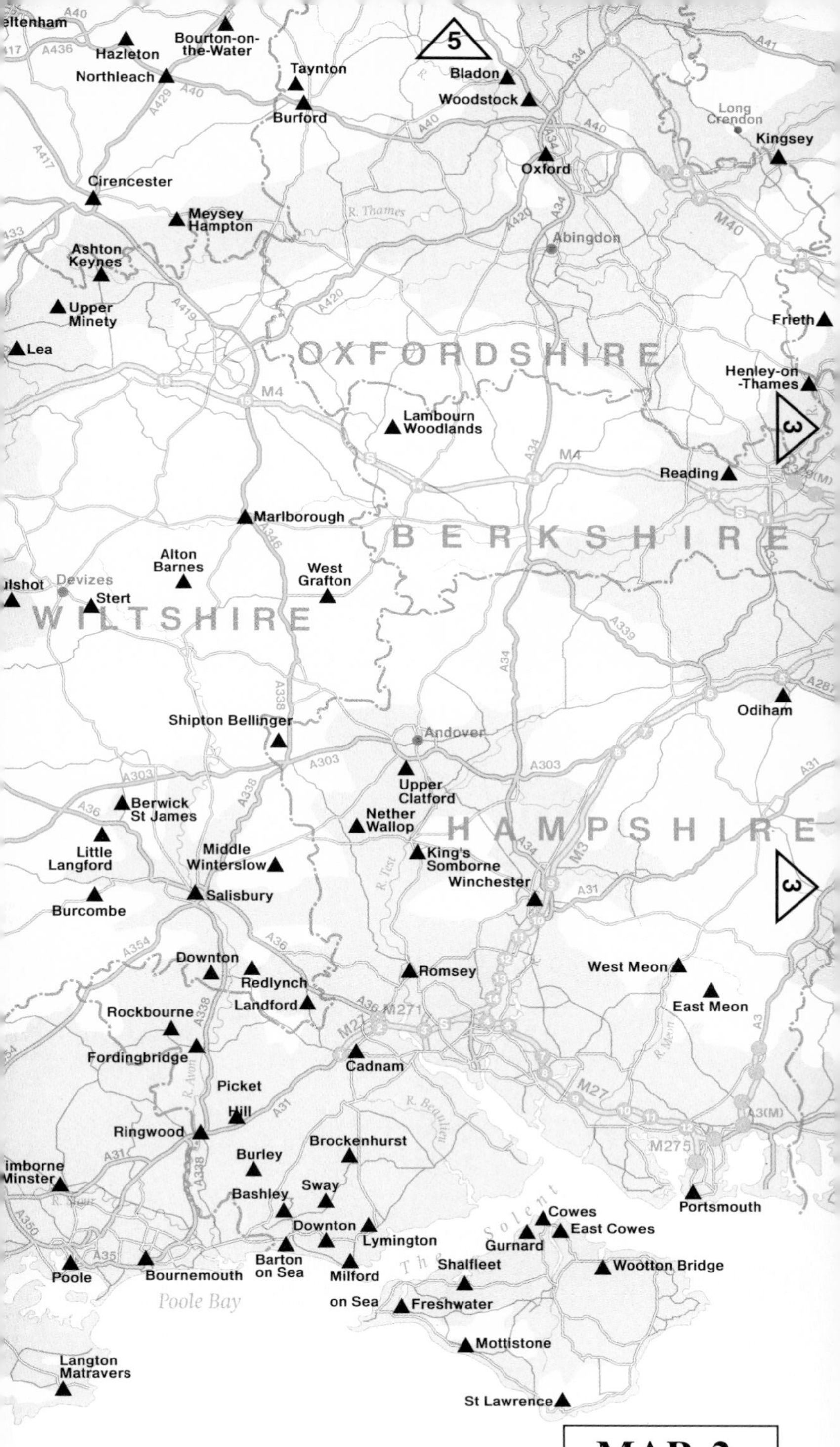

eltenham
Hazleton
Bourton-on-the-Water
Northleach
Taynton
Burford
5
Bladon
Woodstock
Long Crendon
Kingsey
Oxford
Cirencester
Meysey Hampton
R. Thames
Abingdon
Ashton Keynes
Upper Minety
Lea
Frieth
OXFORDSHIRE
Henley-on-Thames
Lambourn Woodlands
3
Reading
Marlborough
BERKSHIRE
Alton Barnes
West Grafton
ulshot
Devizes
Stert
WILTSHIRE
Odiham
Shipton Bellinger
Andover
Upper Clatford
Berwick St James
Nether Wallop
HAMPSHIRE
Little Langford
Middle Winterslow
King's Somborne
Winchester
3
Burcombe
Salisbury
Downton
Redlynch
Romsey
West Meon
East Meon
Landford
Rockbourne
Fordingbridge
Cadnam
Picket Hill
Ringwood
Brockenhurst
Burley
imborne Minster
Sway
Bashley
Portsmouth
Downton
Lymington
Cowes
East Cowes
Gurnard
Poole
Bournemouth
Barton on Sea
Milford on Sea
Shalfleet
Wootton Bridge
Poole Bay
Freshwater
The Solent
Mottistone
Langton Matravers
St Lawrence

MAP 2

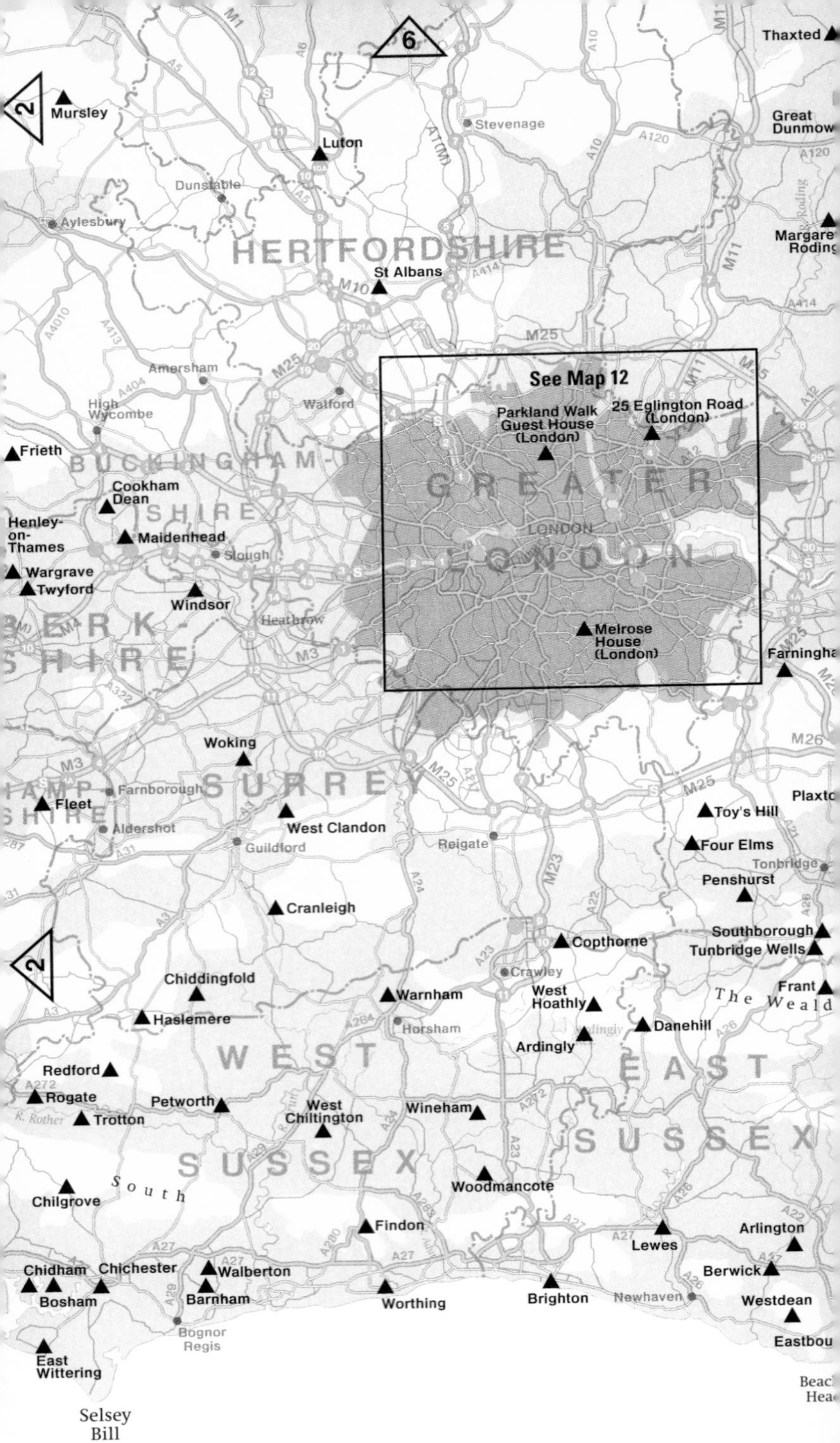
6
2
Thaxted
Mursley
Luton
Stevenage
Great Dunmow
Dunstable
Aylesbury
HERTFORDSHIRE
Margaret Roding
St Albans
M10
M25
Amersham
Watford
See Map 12
Parkland Walk Guest House (London)
25 Eglington Road (London)
High Wycombe
Frieth
BUCKINGHAMSHIRE
Cookham Dean
GREATER LONDON
LONDON
Henley-on-Thames
Maidenhead
Slough
Wargrave
Twyford
Windsor
Heathrow
BERKSHIRE
Melrose House (London)
Farningham
M3
M26
Woking
SURREY
Farnborough
Fleet
West Clandon
Aldershot
Guildford
Reigate
Toy's Hill
Four Elms
Tonbridge
Penshurst
Cranleigh
Copthorne
Southborough
Tunbridge Wells
2
Crawley
Chiddingfold
Warnham
West Hoathly
Frant
The Weald
Haslemere
Horsham
Danehill
Ardingly
WEST
EAST
Redford
Rogate
Petworth
West Chiltington
Wineham
Trotton
R. Rother
SUSSEX
SUSSEX
Woodmancote
South
Chilgrove
Findon
Lewes
Arlington
Chidham
Chichester
Walberton
Berwick
Bosham
Barnham
Worthing
Brighton
Newhaven
Westdean
Bognor Regis
Eastbou
East Wittering
Selsey Bill

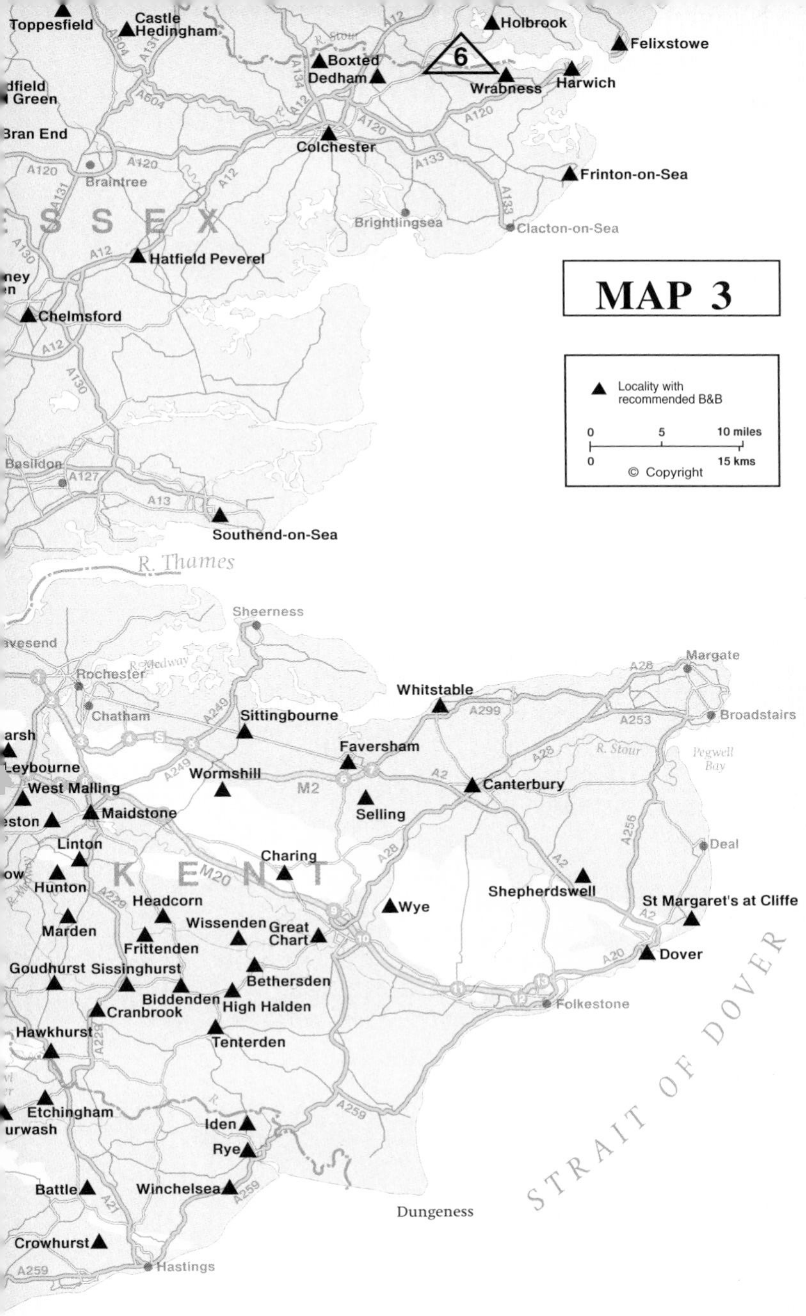
MAP 3
Locality with recommended B&B
0 5 10 miles
0 15 kms
© Copyright
Toppesfield
Castle Hedingham
Holbrook
Felixstowe
Boxted
Dedham
6
Wrabness
Harwich
Colchester
Frinton-on-Sea
Braintree
Brightlingsea
Clacton-on-Sea
Hatfield Peverel
Chelmsford
Basildon
Southend-on-Sea
R. Thames
Sheerness
Rochester
Chatham
Margate
Whitstable
Broadstairs
Sittingbourne
Faversham
Pegwell Bay
Leybourne
West Malling
Wormshill
Canterbury
Maidstone
Selling
Linton
Charing
Deal
KENT
Hunton
Shepherdswell
Headcorn
Wye
St Margaret's at Cliffe
Marden
Wissenden
Great Chart
Frittenden
Dover
Goudhurst
Sissinghurst
Bethersden
Biddenden
High Halden
Folkestone
Cranbrook
Hawkhurst
Tenterden
Etchingham
Iden
Rye
Battle
Winchelsea
Dungeness
Crowhurst
Hastings
STRAIT OF DOVER

7

MAP 4

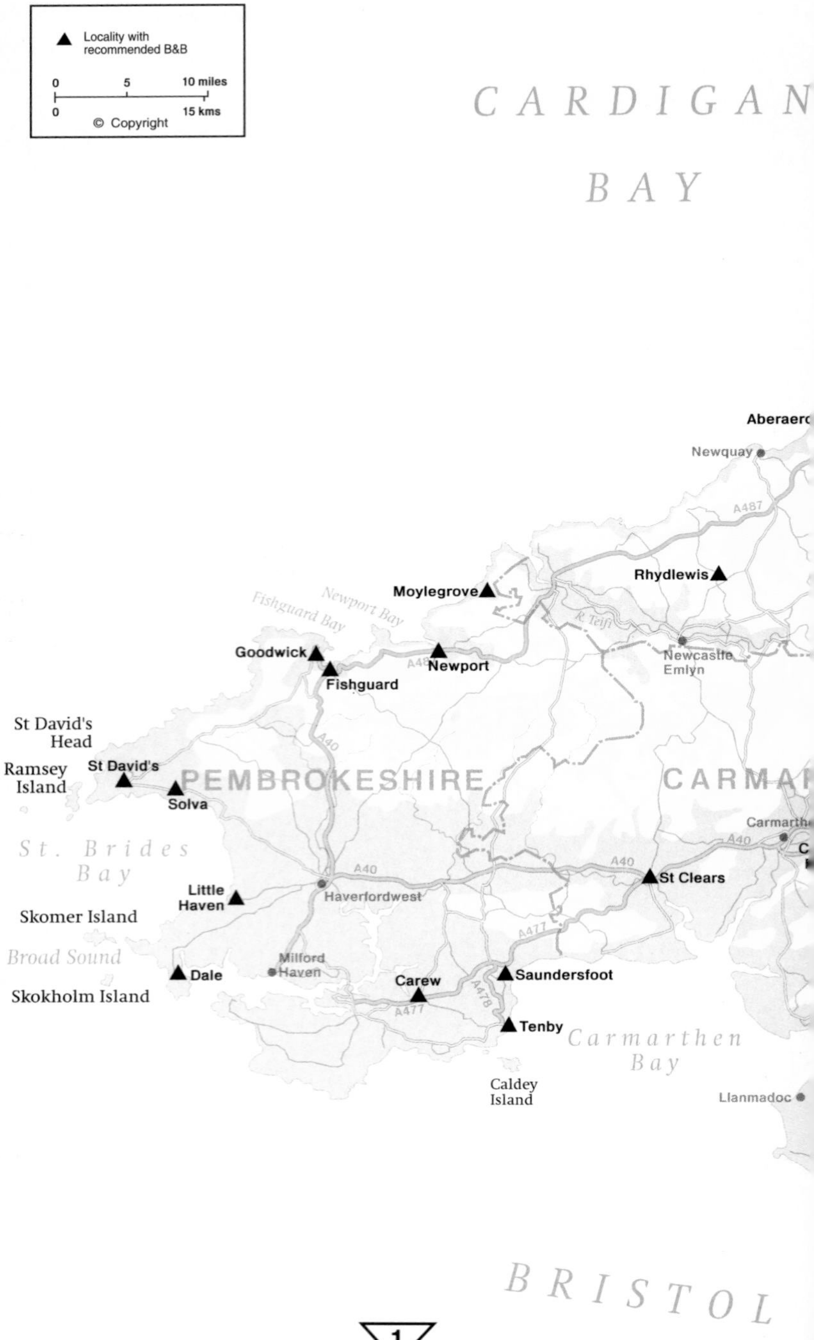

Locality with recommended B&B
0 5 10 miles
0 15 kms
© Copyright
CARDIGAN BAY
Aberaerc
Newquay
A487
Rhydlewis
Moylegrove
Newport Bay
Fishguard Bay
R. Teifi
Goodwick
Newport
A487
Fishguard
Newcastle Emlyn
A40
St David's Head
Ramsey Island
St David's
Solva
PEMBROKESHIRE
CARMA
Carmarth
St. Brides Bay
A40
A40
A40
St Clears
Little Haven
Haverfordwest
Skomer Island
A477
Broad Sound
Milford Haven
Dale
Saundersfoot
Skokholm Island
Carew
A478
A477
Tenby
Carmarthen Bay
Caldey Island
Llanmadoc
BRISTOL

1

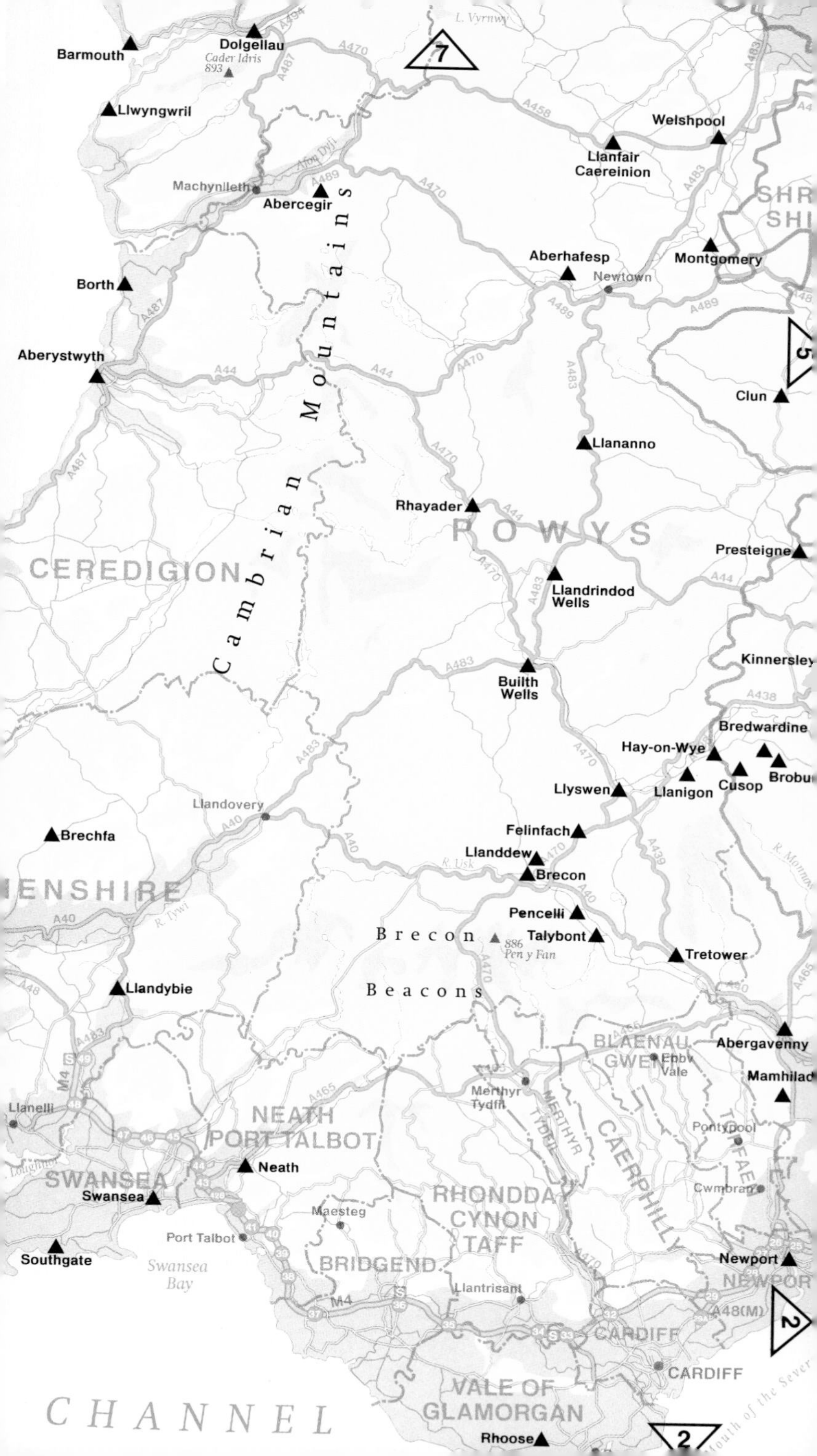

L. Vyrnwy
7
Barmouth
Dolgellau
Cader Idris
893
Llwyngwril
Welshpool
Llanfair
Caereinion
Machynlleth
Abercegir
Afon Dyfi
Aberhafesp
Montgomery
Newtown
Borth
Cambrian Mountains
Aberystwyth
5
Clun
Llananno
Rhayader
POWYS
CEREDIGION
Presteigne
Llandrindod
Wells
Builth
Wells
Kinnersley
Bredwardine
Hay-on-Wye
Llanigon
Cusop
Llyswen
Llandovery
Brechfa
Felinfach
Llanddew
R. Usk
Brecon
Pencelli
Talybont
Brecon
886
Pen y Fan
Beacons
Tretower
Llandybie
Abergavenny
Mamhilad
BLAENAU
GWENT
Ebbw
Vale
Merthyr
Tydfil
MERTHYR
TYDFIL
CAERPHILLY
Pontypool
TORFAEN
Llanelli
NEATH
PORT TALBOT
Neath
SWANSEA
Swansea
Cwmbran
RHONDDA
CYNON
TAFF
Maesteg
Port Talbot
Southgate
Swansea
Bay
BRIDGEND
Newport
Llantrisant
CARDIFF
CARDIFF
2
VALE OF
GLAMORGAN
CHANNEL
Rhoose
2

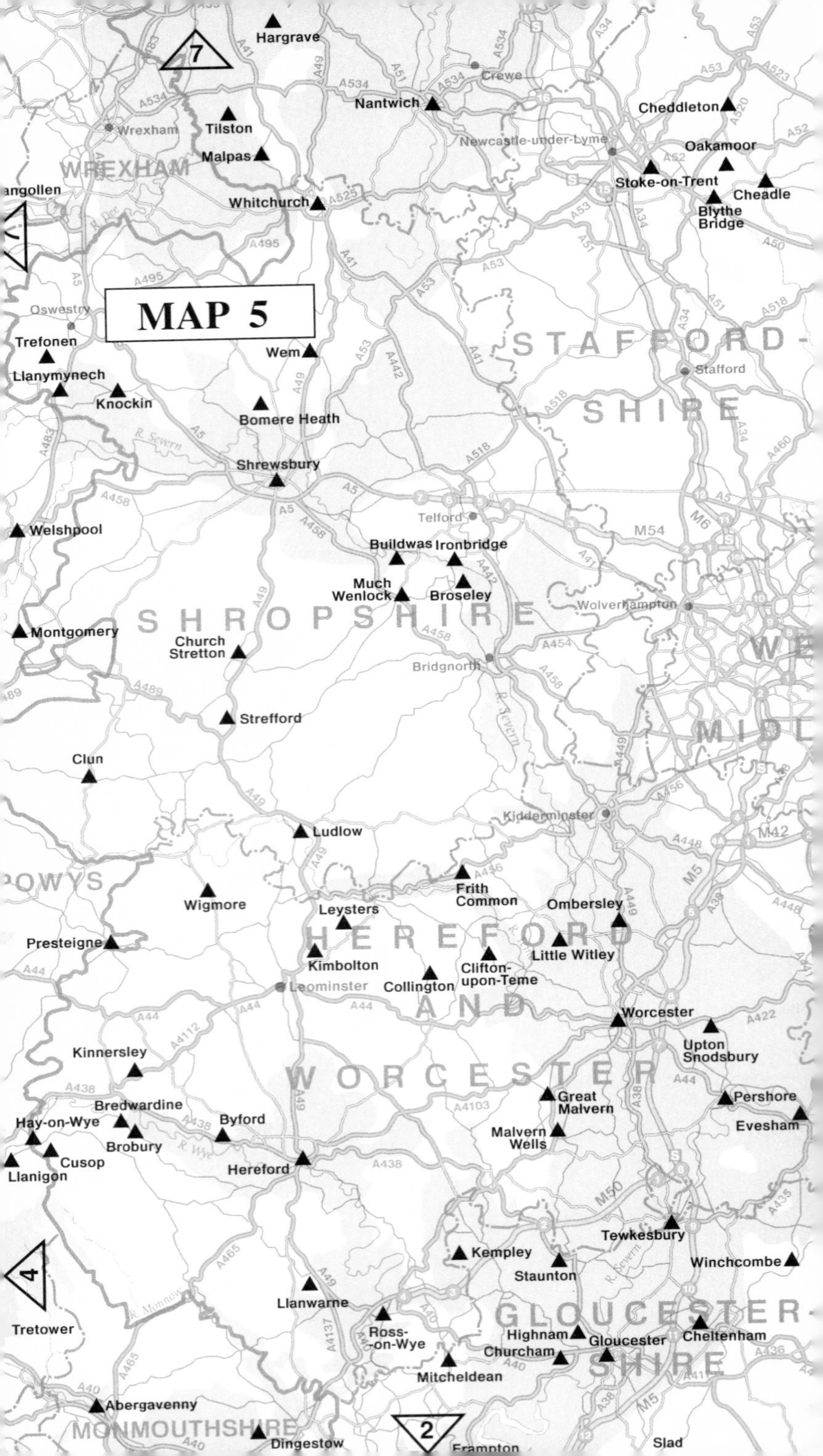
MAP 5
7
4
2
Hargrave
Crewe
Nantwich
Cheddleton
Wrexham
Tilston
Malpas
Newcastle-under-Lyme
Oakamoor
WREXHAM
Stoke-on-Trent
Cheadle
Llangollen
Whitchurch
Blythe Bridge
Oswestry
Trefonen
Llanymynech
Knockin
Wem
Bomere Heath
STAFFORD-
SHIRE
Stafford
R. Severn
Shrewsbury
Telford
M54
Welshpool
Buildwas
Ironbridge
Much Wenlock
Broseley
Wolverhampton
SHROPSHIRE
Montgomery
Church Stretton
Bridgnorth
Strefford
MIDL
Clun
Kidderminster
Ludlow
M42
POWYS
Wigmore
Frith Common
Ombersley
Leysters
Presteigne
HEREFORD
Little Witley
Kimbolton
Clifton-upon-Teme
Collington
Leominster
AND
Worcester
Upton Snodsbury
Kinnersley
WORCESTER
Great Malvern
Pershore
Bredwardine
Hay-on-Wye
Byford
Evesham
Malvern Wells
Brobury
Cusop
Llanigon
Hereford
R. Wye
M50
Tewkesbury
Kempley
Winchcombe
Staunton
R. Monnow
Llanwarne
GLOUCESTER-
SHIRE
Tretower
Ross-on-Wye
Highnam
Gloucester
Cheltenham
Churcham
Mitcheldean
Abergavenny
MONMOUTHSHIRE
Dingestow
Frampton
Slad
M5
M6

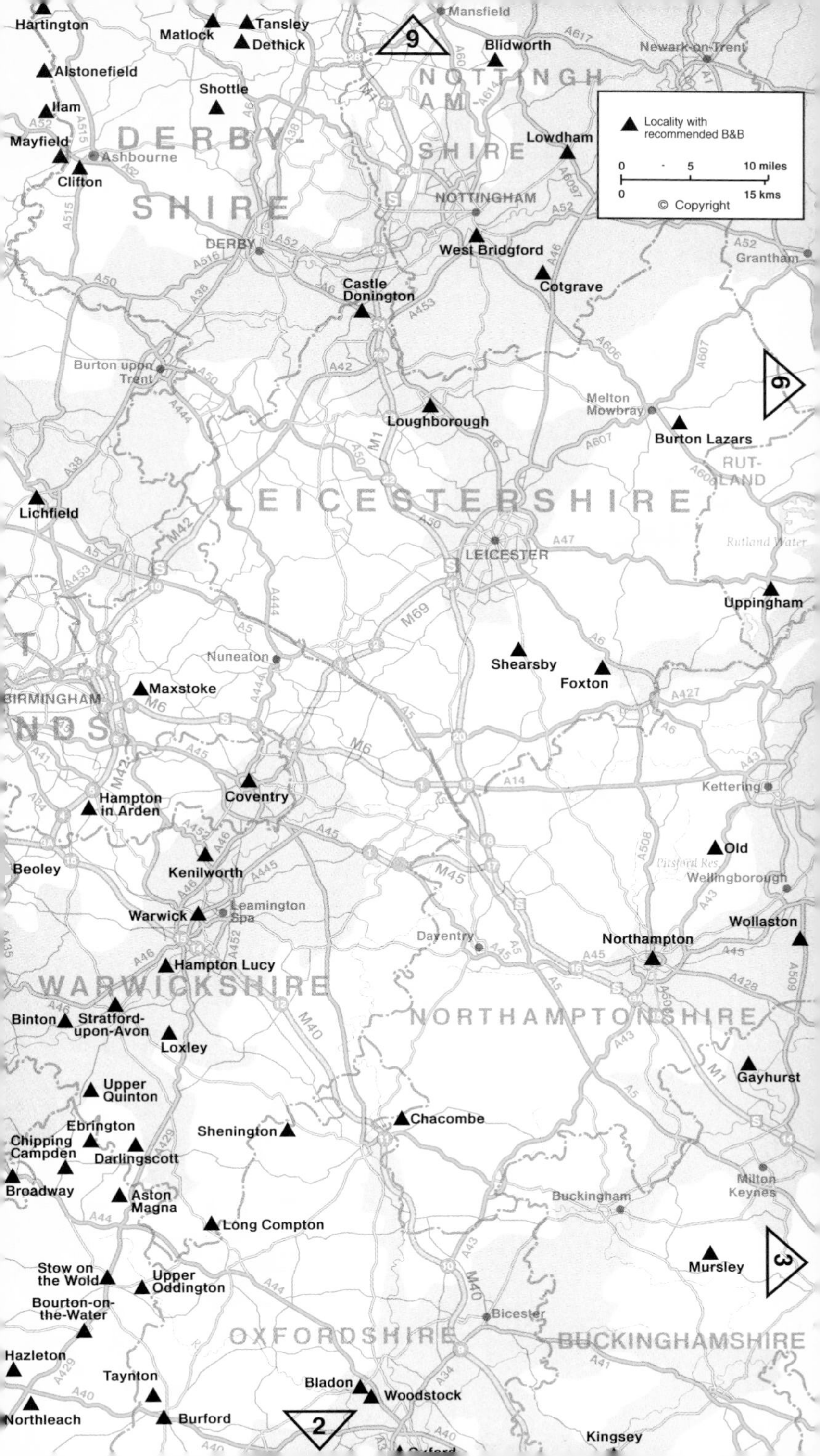

9
Locality with recommended B&B
0 5 10 miles
0 15 kms
© Copyright
DERBYSHIRE
NOTTINGHAMSHIRE
LEICESTERSHIRE
RUTLAND
WARWICKSHIRE
NORTHAMPTONSHIRE
OXFORDSHIRE
BUCKINGHAMSHIRE
Hartington
Matlock
Tansley
Dethick
Mansfield
Blidworth
Newark-on-Trent
Alstonefield
Shottle
Ilam
Mayfield
Ashbourne
Clifton
Lowdham
NOTTINGHAM
DERBY
West Bridgford
Grantham
Cotgrave
Castle Donington
Burton upon Trent
6
Melton Mowbray
Burton Lazars
Loughborough
Lichfield
LEICESTER
Rutland Water
Uppingham
Nuneaton
Shearsby
Foxton
Maxstoke
BIRMINGHAM
Kettering
Coventry
Hampton in Arden
Old
Pitsford Res.
Wellingborough
Beoley
Kenilworth
Warwick
Leamington Spa
Wollaston
Daventry
Northampton
Hampton Lucy
Binton
Stratford-upon-Avon
Loxley
Gayhurst
Upper Quinton
Ebrington
Chacombe
Chipping Campden
Shenington
Darlingscott
Broadway
Aston Magna
Milton Keynes
Buckingham
Long Compton
Mursley
3
Stow on the Wold
Upper Oddington
Bourton-on-the-Water
Bicester
Hazleton
Taynton
Bladon
Woodstock
Northleach
Burford
2
Kingsey

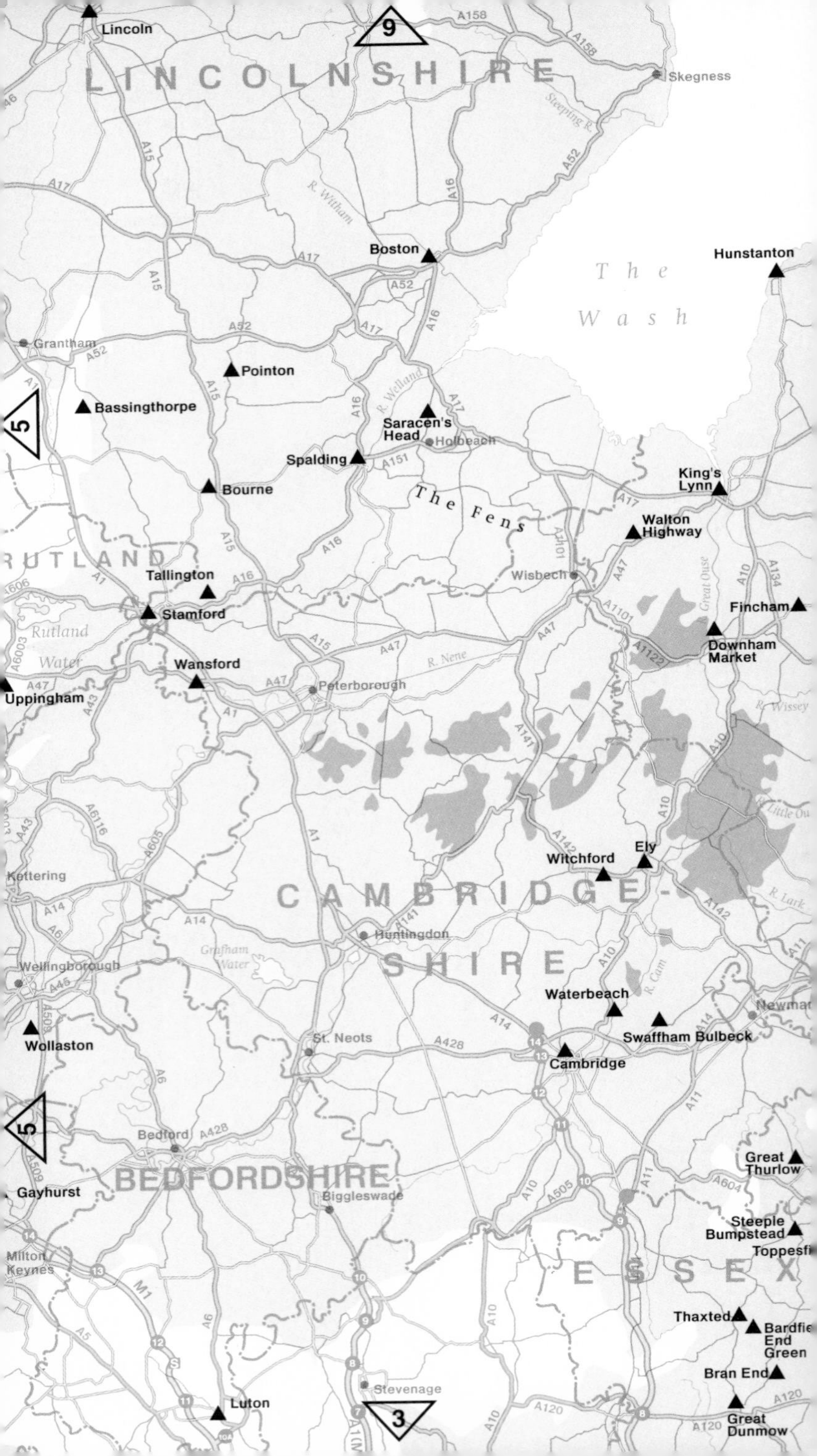
9
Lincoln
LINCOLNSHIRE
Skegness
Steeping R.
R. Witham
Boston
Hunstanton
The Wash
Grantham
Pointon
Bassingthorpe
5
R. Welland
Saracen's Head
Holbeach
Spalding
Bourne
The Fens
King's Lynn
Walton Highway
RUTLAND
Tallington
Wisbech
Great Ouse
Fincham
Stamford
Rutland Water
Downham Market
Wansford
R. Nene
Peterborough
Uppingham
R. Wissey
R. Little Ouse
Kettering
Witchford
Ely
CAMBRIDGE-SHIRE
R. Lark
Huntingdon
Grafham Water
Wellingborough
R. Cam
Waterbeach
Wollaston
St. Neots
Swaffham Bulbeck
Cambridge
5
Bedford
BEDFORDSHIRE
Great Thurlow
Gayhurst
Biggleswade
Steeple Bumpstead
Milton Keynes
ESSEX
Thaxted
Bran End
Stevenage
Luton
3
Great Dunmow
A158
A52
A16
A17
A15
A151
A1101
A1122
A47
A141
A142
A10
A134
A1
A6
A14
A45
A428
A509
A43
A605
A6116
A6003
A606
A505
A11
A604
A120
A5
M1

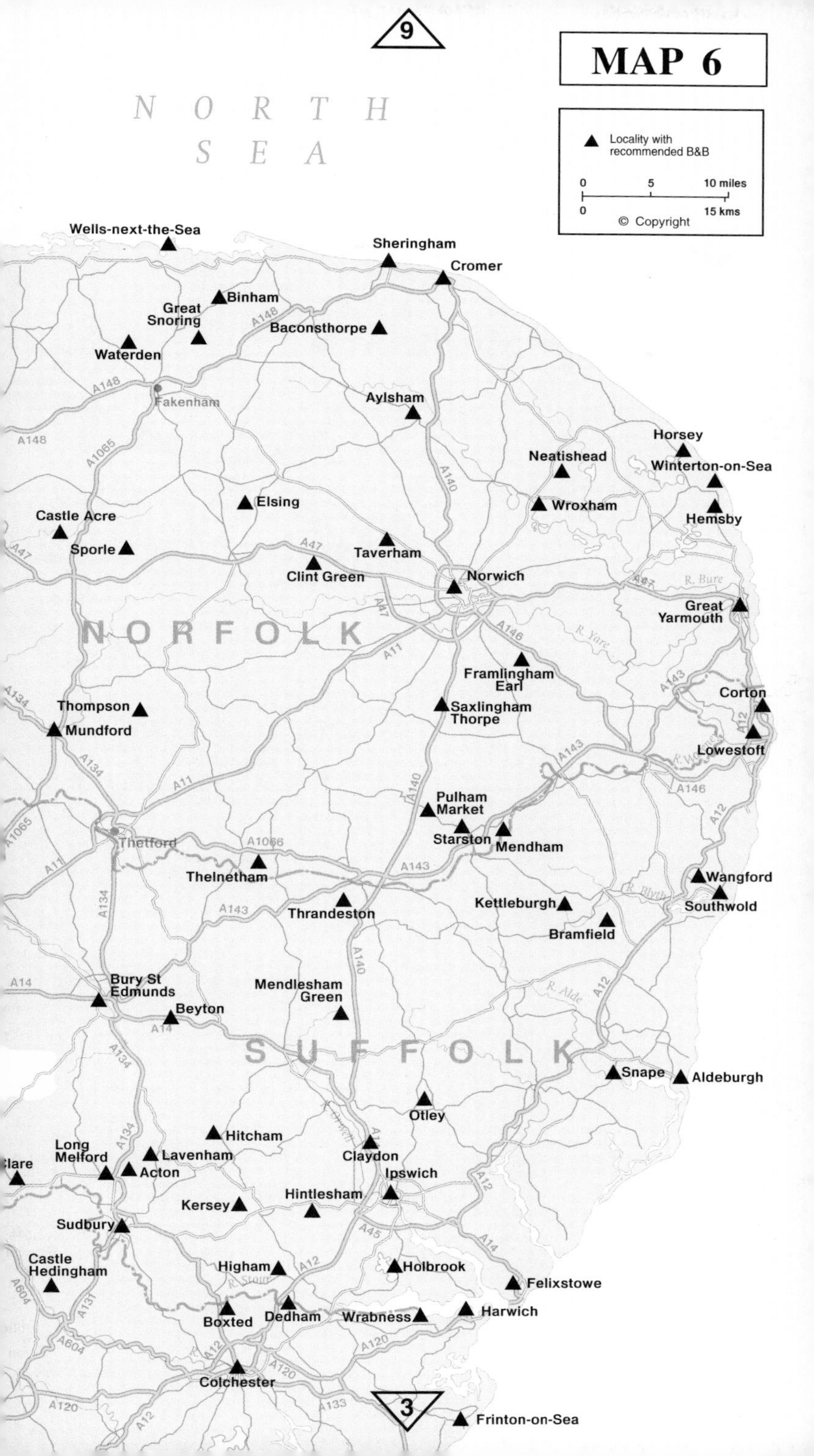
MAP 6
9
3
NORTH SEA
Locality with recommended B&B
0 5 10 miles
0 15 kms
© Copyright
NORFOLK
SUFFOLK
Wells-next-the-Sea
Sheringham
Cromer
Binham
Great Snoring
Baconsthorpe
Waterden
Fakenham
Aylsham
Horsey
Neatishead
Winterton-on-Sea
Wroxham
Hemsby
Elsing
Castle Acre
Sporle
Taverham
Clint Green
Norwich
Great Yarmouth
R. Bure
R. Yare
Framlingham Earl
Corton
Thompson
Saxlingham Thorpe
Mundford
Lowestoft
R. Waveney
Pulham Market
Starston
Mendham
Thetford
Thelnetham
Wangford
Southwold
R. Blyth
Thrandeston
Kettleburgh
Bramfield
Bury St Edmunds
Mendlesham Green
Beyton
R. Alde
Snape
Aldeburgh
Otley
Hitcham
Claydon
R. Orwell
Long Melford
Lavenham
Clare
Acton
Ipswich
Hintlesham
Kersey
Sudbury
Castle Hedingham
Higham
Holbrook
R. Stour
Felixstowe
Boxted
Dedham
Wrabness
Harwich
Colchester
Frinton-on-Sea
A148
A1065
A47
A140
A146
A11
A143
A134
A12
A14
A1066
A45
A131
A604
A120
A133

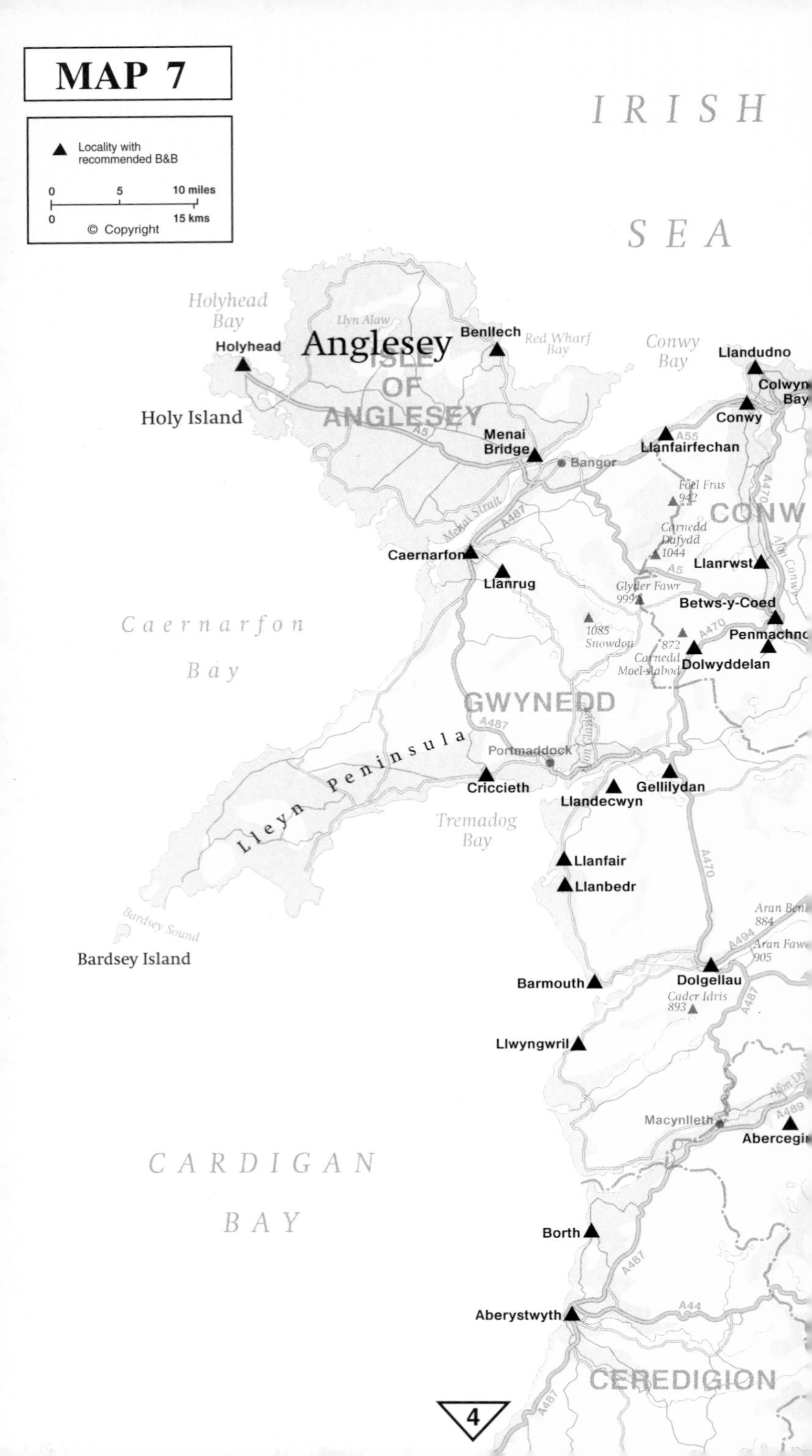
MAP 7
Locality with recommended B&B
0 5 10 miles
0 15 kms
© Copyright
IRISH
SEA
Holyhead Bay
Llyn Alaw
Holyhead
Anglesey
ISLE OF ANGLESEY
Benllech
Red Wharf Bay
Conwy Bay
Llandudno
Colwyn Bay
Conwy
Holy Island
A5
Menai Bridge
Bangor
Llanfairfechan
A55
Foel Fras 942
Menai Strait
A487
Carnedd Dafydd 1044
A470
Caernarfon
Llanrug
A5
Llanrwst
Afon Conwy
Glyder Fawr 999
Betws-y-Coed
Caernarfon
Bay
1085 Snowdon
872
Carnedd Moel-siabod
A470
Penmachno
Dolwyddelan
GWYNEDD
A487
Lleyn Peninsula
Portmaddock
Afon Glaslyn
Criccieth
Llandecwyn
Gellilydan
Tremadog Bay
Llanfair
Llanbedr
A470
Bardsey Sound
Bardsey Island
A494
Barmouth
Dolgellau
Cader Idris 893
A487
Llwyngwril
Macynlleth
A489
CARDIGAN
BAY
Borth
A487
Aberystwyth
A44
CEREDIGION
A487
4

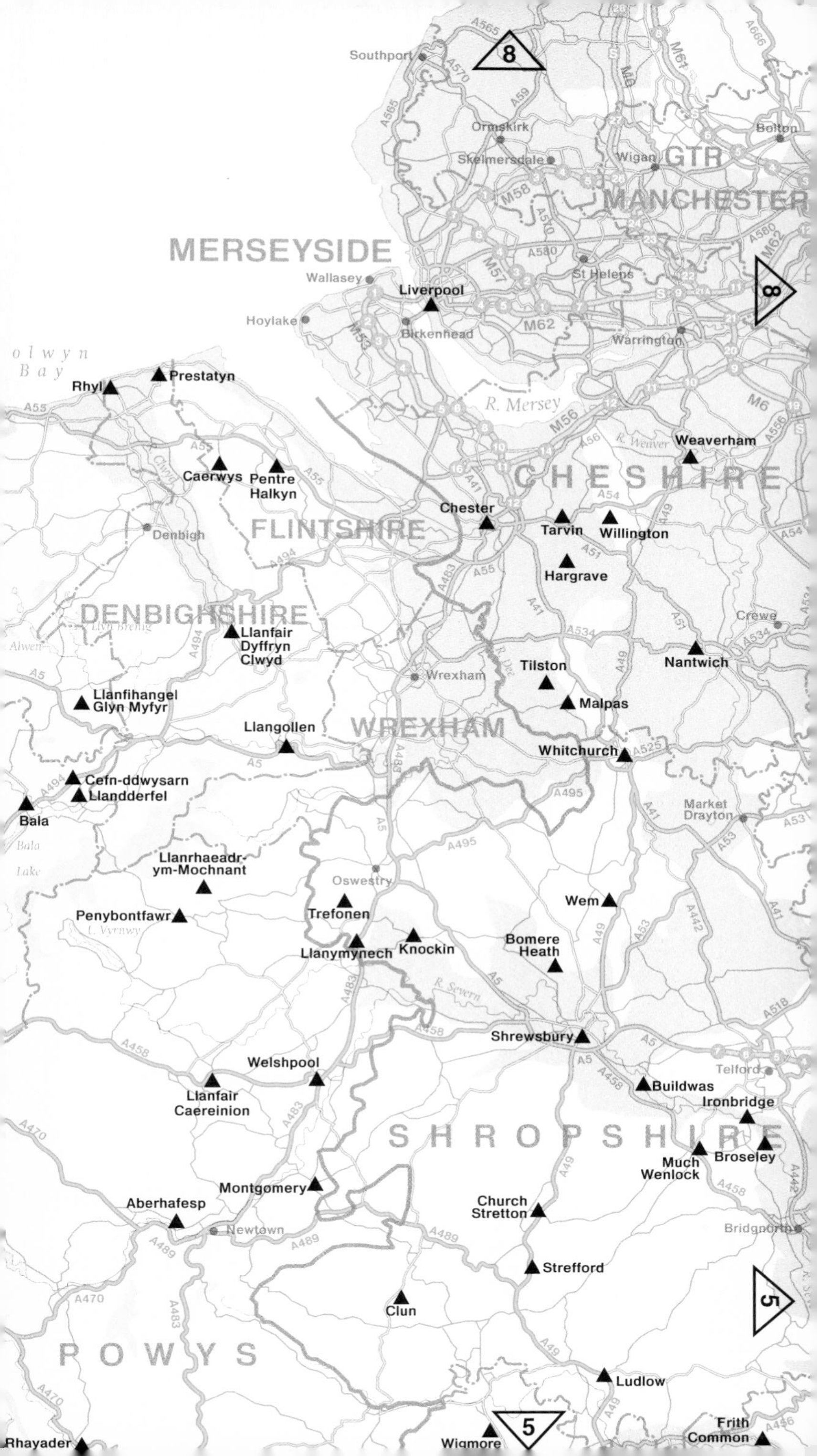

8
8
5
5
MERSEYSIDE
GTR MANCHESTER
CHESHIRE
FLINTSHIRE
DENBIGHSHIRE
WREXHAM
SHROPSHIRE
POWYS
Southport
Ormskirk
Skelmersdale
Wigan
Bolton
Wallasey
Liverpool
Hoylake
Birkenhead
St Helens
Warrington
R. Mersey
R. Weaver
Colwyn Bay
Rhyl
Prestatyn
Caerwys
Pentre Halkyn
Denbigh
Chester
Tarvin
Willington
Weaverham
Hargrave
Crewe
Nantwich
Llyn Brenig
Alwen
Llanfair Dyffryn Clwyd
Wrexham
Tilston
Malpas
R. Dee
Llanfihangel Glyn Myfyr
Llangollen
Whitchurch
Cefn-ddwysarn
Llandderfel
Bala
Bala Lake
Market Drayton
Llanrhaeadr-ym-Mochnant
Oswestry
Penybontfawr
L. Vyrnwy
Trefonen
Wem
Llanymynech
Knockin
Bomere Heath
R. Severn
Shrewsbury
Telford
Buildwas
Ironbridge
Welshpool
Llanfair Caereinion
Much Wenlock
Broseley
Montgomery
Aberhafesp
Newtown
Church Stretton
Bridgnorth
Strefford
Clun
Ludlow
Rhayader
Wigmore
Frith Common

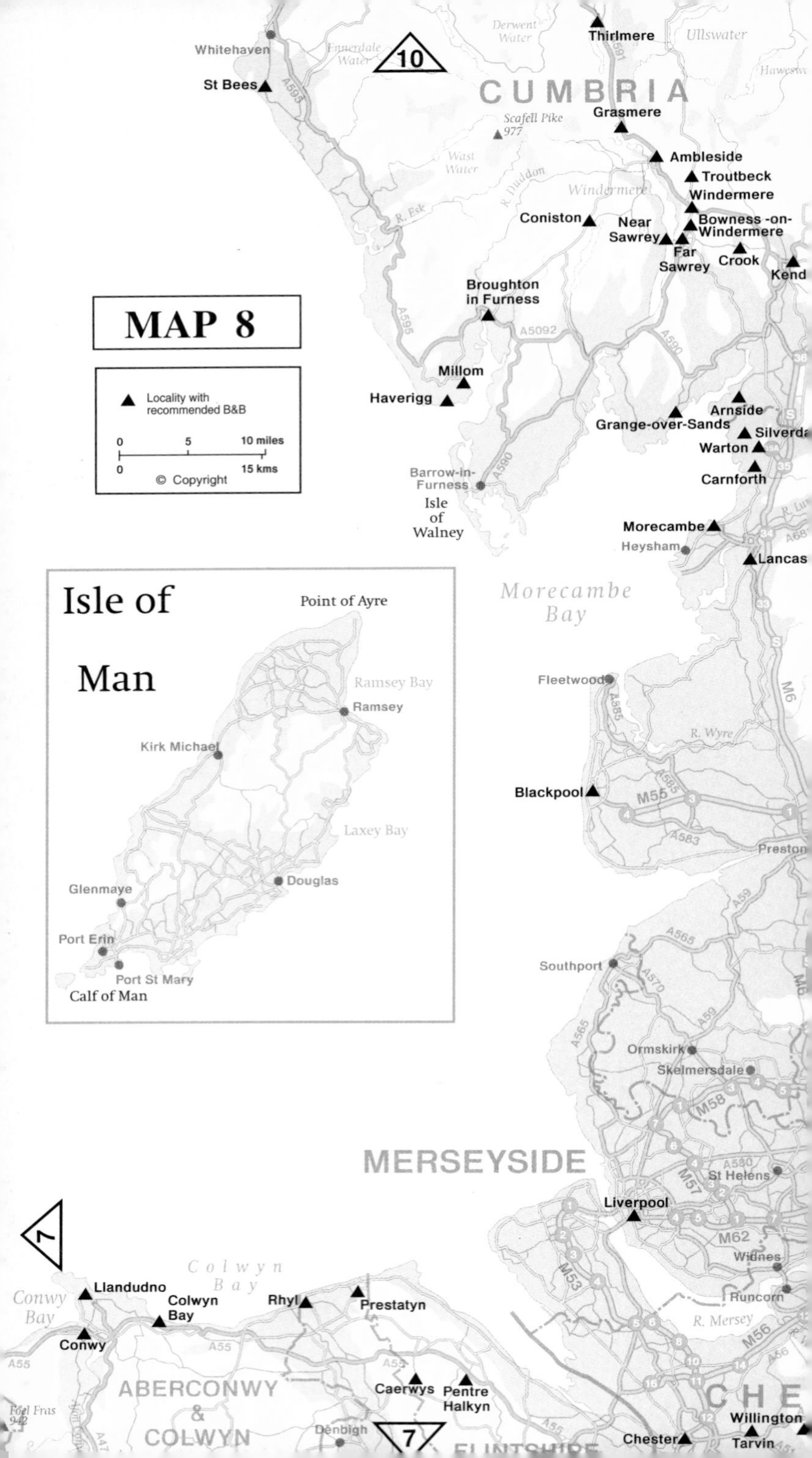

MAP 8
Locality with recommended B&B
0 5 10 miles
0 15 kms
© Copyright
10
7
7
CUMBRIA
Whitehaven
St Bees
Ennerdale Water
Derwent Water
Thirlmere
Ullswater
Scafell Pike 977
Wast Water
Grasmere
Ambleside
Troutbeck
Windermere
Windermere
Bowness -on-Windermere
Coniston
Near Sawrey
Far Sawrey
Crook
Kend
R. Duddon
R. Esk
Broughton in Furness
A5092
A590
A595
A593
A591
Millom
Haverigg
Arnside
Grange-over-Sands
Silverd
Warton
Carnforth
Barrow-in-Furness
Isle of Walney
Morecambe
Heysham
Lancas
Morecambe Bay
Isle of Man
Point of Ayre
Ramsey Bay
Ramsey
Kirk Michael
Laxey Bay
Douglas
Glenmaye
Port Erin
Port St Mary
Calf of Man
Fleetwood
A585
R. Wyre
M6
Blackpool
M55
A583
Preston
A59
A565
Southport
A570
Ormskirk
Skelmersdale
M58
MERSEYSIDE
A580
St Helens
M57
Liverpool
M62
Widnes
M53
Runcorn
R. Mersey
M56
Colwyn Bay
Conwy Bay
Llandudno
Colwyn Bay
Rhyl
Prestatyn
Conwy
A55
ABERCONWY & COLWYN
Caerwys
Pentre Halkyn
Denbigh
Foel Fras 942
FLINTSHIRE
CHE
Willington
Tarvin
Chester

Cotherstone
Staindrop
Barnard Castle
10
Darlington
Kirkby Stephen
Richmond
Lovesome Hill
Grayrigg
Northallerton
Sedbergh
Hawes
West Witton
Leyburn
Thoralby
West Burton
Bedale
Dent
Yorkshire
Dales
East Witton
South Kilvington
6
Kirkby Lonsdale
NORTH
YORKSHIRE
Starbotton
Kettlewell
Litton
Horton in Ribblesdale
Ripon
Aldfield
Brafferton
Pateley Bridge
Greenhow Hill
Settle
Hanlith
Summer Bridge
Knaresborough
Tosside
Harrogate
Skipton
Blubberhouses
Slaidburn
Clitheroe
ANCASHIRE
Oldfield
Haworth
Bramhope
Leeds
Bradford
Burnley
WEST
Blackburn
Accrington
Sowerby Bridge
Dewsbury
Wakefield
YORKSHIRE
Huddersfield
Heywood
Bolton
Holmfirth
GREATER
MANCHESTER
SOUTH
Penistone
MANCHESTER
Eccles
YORKSHIRE
Glossop
Rotherham
Sale
Stockport
Derwent Res.
Warrington
Altrincham
Ladybower Res.
Sheffield
Castleton
Bradwell
Mobberley
Northwich
Holmesfield
Weaverham
Rowland
Buxton
Macclesfield
Little Longstone
Chesterfield
Macclesfield Forest
Gawsworth
5

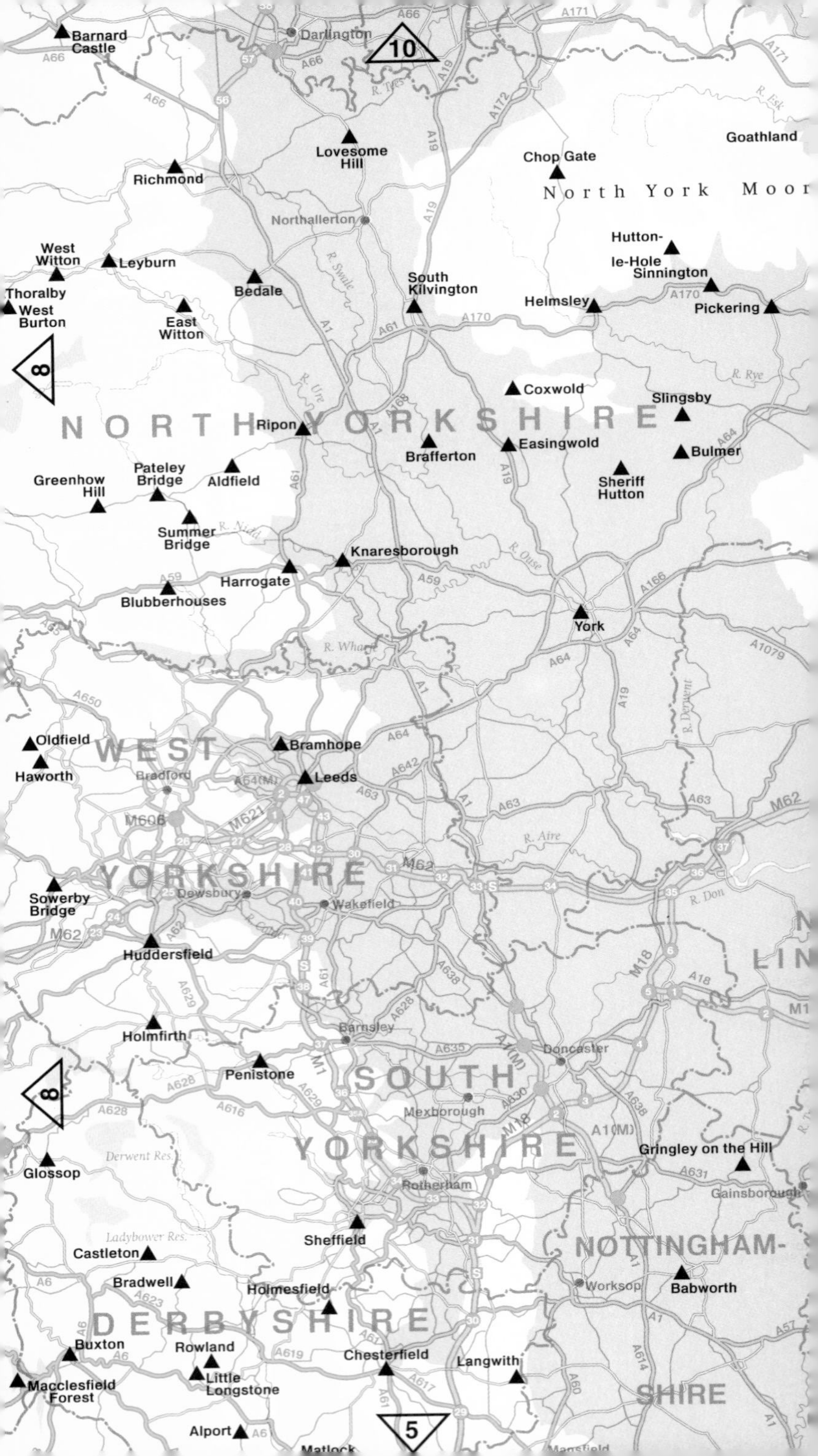
Barnard Castle
Darlington
10
Goathland
Lovesome Hill
Chop Gate
Richmond
North York Moor
Northallerton
Hutton-le-Hole
West Witton
Leyburn
Sinnington
Bedale
South Kilvington
Thoralby
West Burton
East Witton
Helmsley
Pickering
8
Coxwold
Slingsby
NORTH YORKSHIRE
Ripon
Easingwold
Brafferton
Bulmer
Sheriff Hutton
Pateley Bridge
Greenhow Hill
Aldfield
Summer Bridge
Knaresborough
Harrogate
Blubberhouses
York
Oldfield
Haworth
Bramhope
Leeds
WEST YORKSHIRE
Bradford
Sowerby Bridge
Dewsbury
Wakefield
Huddersfield
Holmfirth
Barnsley
Doncaster
Penistone
SOUTH YORKSHIRE
Mexborough
Glossop
Gringley on the Hill
Rotherham
Gainsborough
Sheffield
Castleton
NOTTINGHAMSHIRE
Bradwell
Worksop
Babworth
Holmesfield
DERBYSHIRE
Buxton
Rowland
Chesterfield
Langwith
Little Longstone
Macclesfield Forest
Alport
5
Matlock
Derwent Res.
Ladybower Res.
R. Tees
R. Swale
R. Ure
R. Nidd
R. Ouse
R. Wharfe
R. Rye
R. Esk
R. Derwent
R. Aire
R. Don
R. Calder
A1
A19
A59
A61
A64
A170
A62
A628
A629
A616
A6
M1
M18
M62
A1(M)

MAP 9

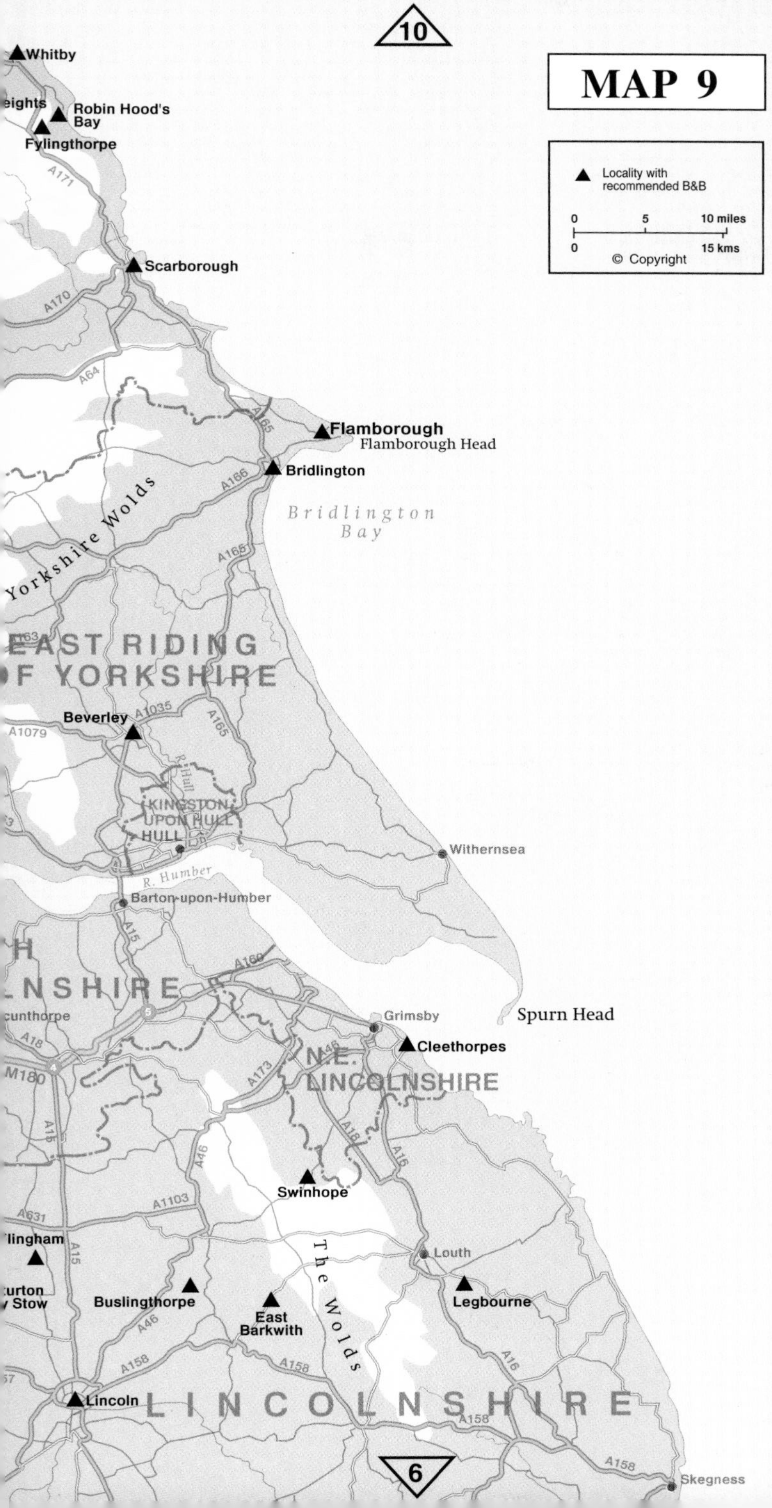
10
Locality with recommended B&B
0
5
10 miles
0
15 kms
© Copyright
Whitby
eights
Robin Hood's Bay
Fylingthorpe
A171
Scarborough
A170
A64
A165
Flamborough
Flamborough Head
Bridlington
A166
Bridlington Bay
Yorkshire Wolds
A165
EAST RIDING OF YORKSHIRE
Beverley
A1035
A1079
A165
R. Hull
KINGSTON UPON HULL
HULL
Withernsea
R. Humber
Barton-upon-Humber
A15
A160
NSHIRE
cunthorpe
A18
M180
Spurn Head
Grimsby
Cleethorpes
N.E. LINCOLNSHIRE
A173
A18
A16
A46
A15
Swinhope
A1103
A631
lingham
A15
urton
Stow
Buslingthorpe
East Barkwith
The Wolds
Louth
Legbourne
A46
A158
A158
A16
Lincoln
LINCOLNSHIRE
A158
A158
Skegness
6

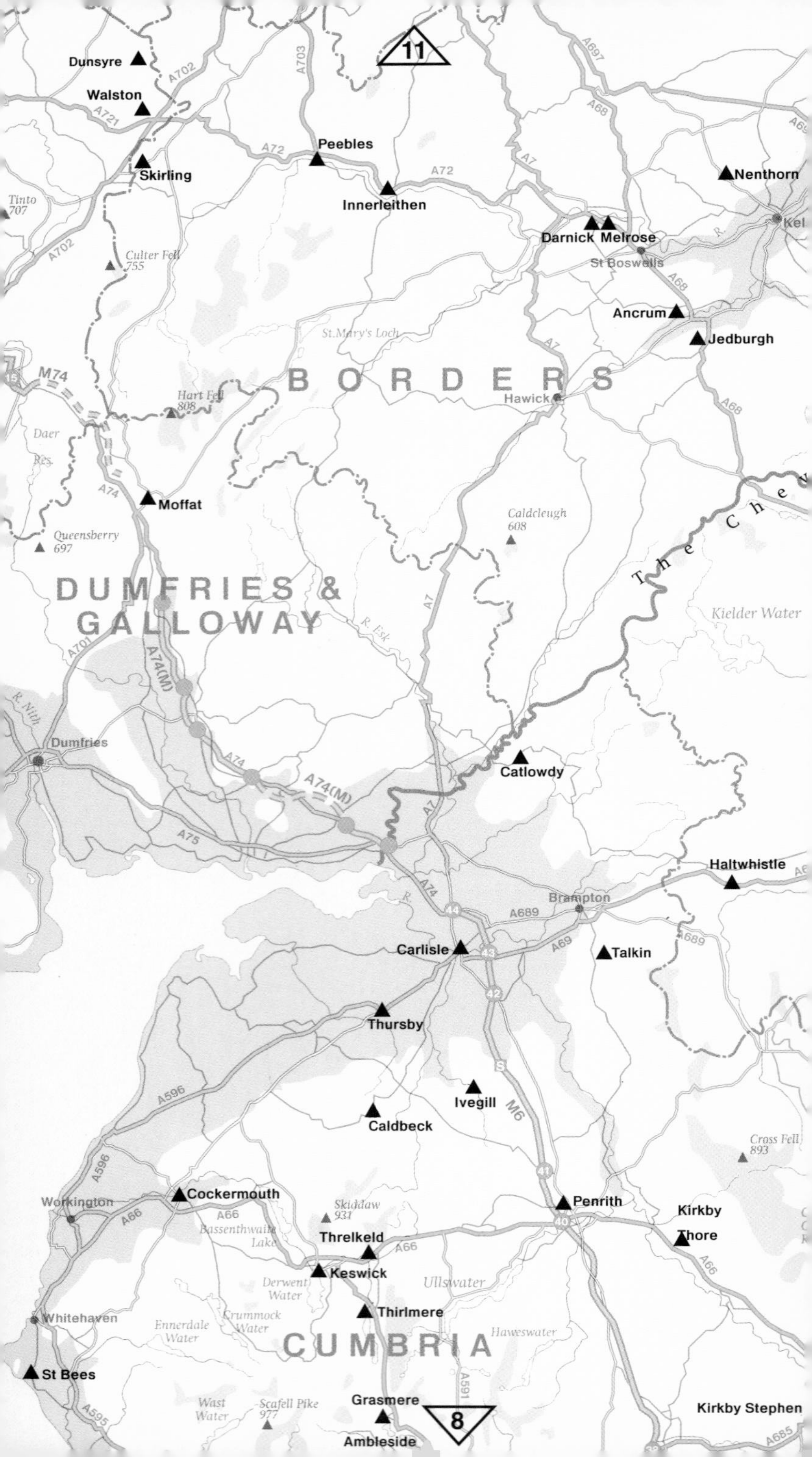
11
Dunsyre
Walston
Skirling
Peebles
Innerleithen
Tinto 707
Culter Fell 755
Darnick
Melrose
St Boswells
Nenthorn
Ancrum
Jedburgh
St.Mary's Loch
BORDERS
Hawick
Hart Fell 808
Daer Res.
Moffat
Queensberry 697
Caldcleugh 608
The Chev
Kielder Water
DUMFRIES & GALLOWAY
R. Esk
R. Nith
Dumfries
Catlowdy
Haltwhistle
Brampton
Carlisle
Talkin
Thursby
Ivegill
Caldbeck
Cross Fell 893
Workington
Cockermouth
Skiddaw 931
Penrith
Kirkby Thore
Bassenthwaite Lake
Threlkeld
Keswick
Derwent Water
Ullswater
Thirlmere
Whitehaven
Ennerdale Water
Crummock Water
Haweswater
CUMBRIA
St Bees
Wast Water
Scafell Pike 977
Grasmere
Ambleside
8
Kirkby Stephen
M74
A74
A74(M)
A75
A7
A68
A72
A702
A703
A721
A697
A701
A689
A69
A596
A586
A66
A591
A595
A685
M6

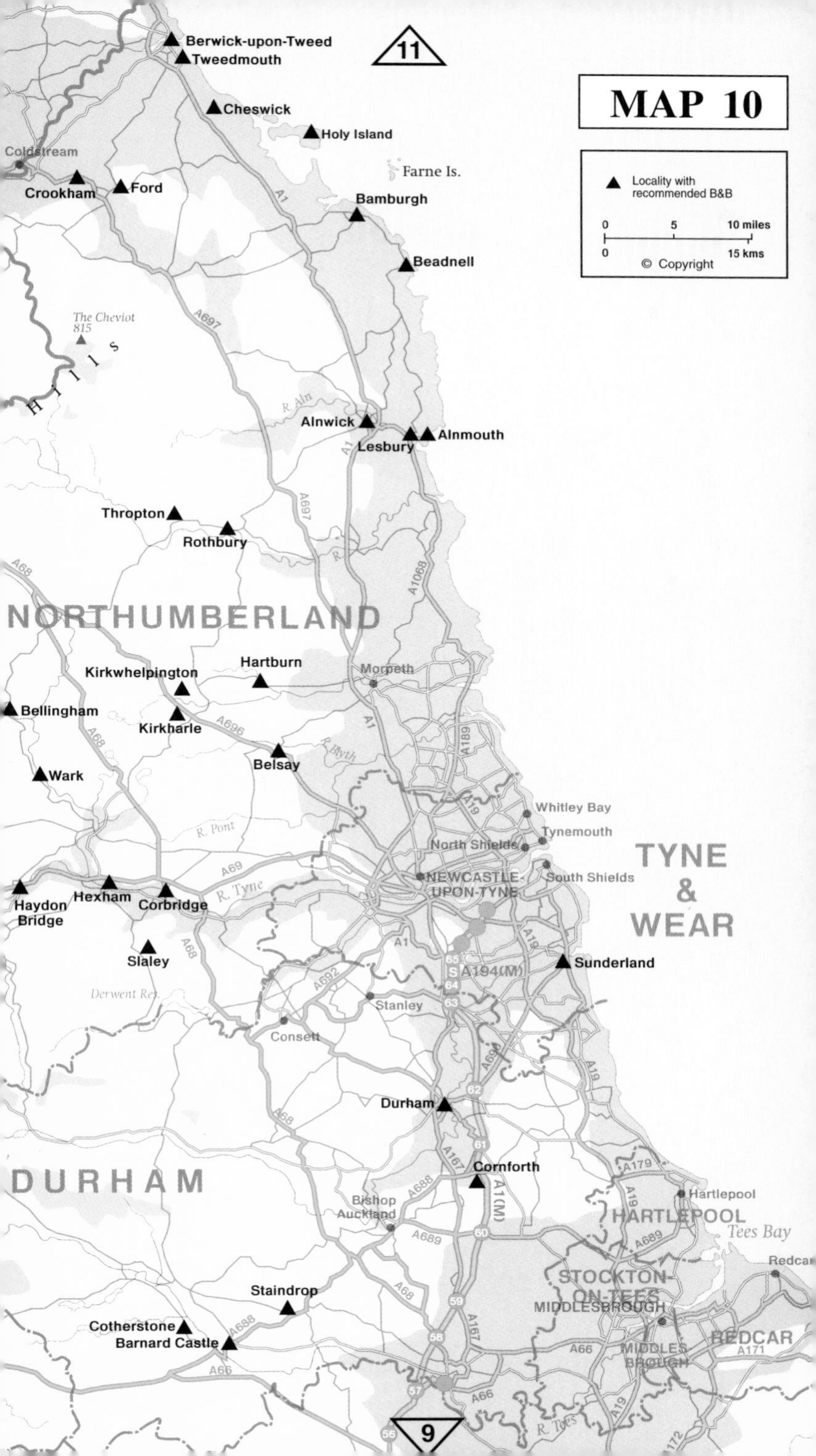

11
MAP 10
Locality with recommended B&B
0 5 10 miles
0 15 kms
© Copyright
Berwick-upon-Tweed
Tweedmouth
Cheswick
Holy Island
Farne Is.
Coldstream
Crookham
Ford
Bamburgh
Beadnell
The Cheviot 815
Alnwick
Lesbury
Alnmouth
Thropton
Rothbury
NORTHUMBERLAND
Hartburn
Kirkwhelpington
Morpeth
Bellingham
Kirkharle
Belsay
Wark
Whitley Bay
Tynemouth
North Shields
TYNE & WEAR
South Shields
NEWCASTLE-UPON-TYNE
Haydon Bridge
Hexham
Corbridge
Slaley
Sunderland
Derwent Res.
Stanley
Consett
Durham
Cornforth
DURHAM
Bishop Auckland
Hartlepool
HARTLEPOOL
Tees Bay
Redcar
STOCKTON-ON-TEES
MIDDLESBROUGH
REDCAR
Staindrop
Cotherstone
Barnard Castle
R. Tees
9

Locality with recommended B&B
0 20 miles
0 20 kms
© Copyright
10
10
ARGYLL & BUTE
PERTHSHIRE & KINROSS
DUNDEE
STIRLING
FIFE
EAST LOTHIAN
MIDLOTHIAN
WEST LOTHIAN
NORTH LANARKSHIRE
SOUTH LANARKSHIRE
NORTH AYRSHIRE
EAST AYRSHIRE
SOUTH AYRSHIRE
DUMFRIES & GALLOWAY
BORDERS
NORTHUMBERLAND
TYNE & WEAR
CUMBRIA
DURHAM
Southern Uplands
Balephetrish
Kirkapol
Calgary
Dervaig
Salen
Craignure
Lochdon
Lochdonhead
Island of Mull
Fionnphort
Port Appin
Connel
Oban
Dalmally
Crianlarich
Balquhidder
Callander
Stanley
Perth
Arbroath
Newburgh
St Andrews
Crail
Anstruther
Auchtermuchty
Craobh Haven
Ford
Kilmartin
Inveraray
St Catherines
Thornhill
Stirling
Drymen
Gartocharn
Cardross
Denny
Aberdour
Whitekirk
Isle of Colonsay
Ardnadam
Dunoon
Linlithgow
Edinburgh
Gifford
Glasgow
Airdrie
Fala
Ballygrant
Port Charlotte
Islay
Port Ellen
Rothesay
Ascog
Kingarth
Largs
Longformacus
Berwick-upon-Tweed
Tweedmouth
Cheswick
Holy Island
Lochranza
Sannox
Carradale
Brodick
Dunsyre
Peebles
Walston
Nenthorn
Crookham
Ford
Bamburgh
Beadnell
Strathaven
Skirling
Innerleithen
Darnick
Melrose
Kelso
Whiting Bay
Ayr
Abington
Ancrum
Jedburgh
Machrihanish
Campbeltown
Alnwick
Lesbury
Alnmouth
Moffat
Thropton
Rothbury
Old Dailly
Kirkwhelpington
Hartburn
Bellingham
Kirkharle
Belsay
Catlowdy
Haltwhistle
Hexham
Corbridge
Newton Stewart
Dalbeattie
Haydon Bridge
Slaley
Stranraer
Portpatrick
Kirkcudbright
Carlisle
Talkin
Sunderland
Thursby
Caldbeck
Ivegill
Durham
Hartlepool
NEWCASTLE UPON TYNE
Greenock
Paisley
Motherwell
Kilmarnock
Falkirk
Dunfermline
Kirkcaldy
Leith
Hawick
Dumfries
Morpeth
Whitley Bay
Firth of Forth
Firth of Lorn
Sound of Jura
Solway Firth
Luce Bay
Kilbrannan Sound
Ochil Hills
Sidlaw Hills
Lammermuir Hills
The Cheviot Hills
Grampia
Tiree
Coll
Iona
Jura
Colonsay
Oronsay
Gigha
Isle of Arran
Mull of Kintyre
Mull of Oa
Farne Is.
Fife Ness

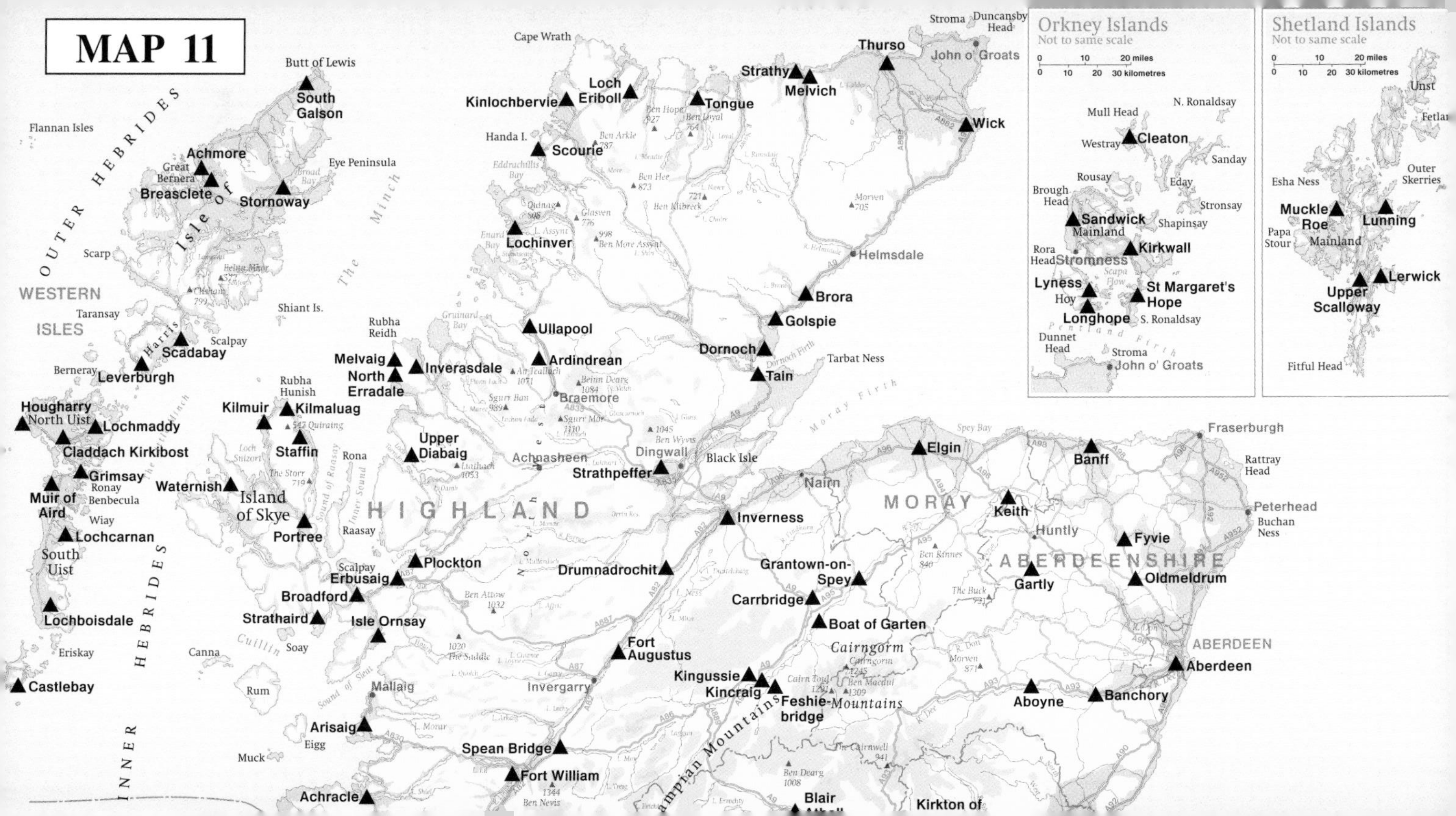
MAP 11
OUTER HEBRIDES
WESTERN ISLES
INNER HEBRIDES
Isle of Lewis
Flannan Isles
Butt of Lewis
South Galson
Achmore
Great Bernera
Breasclete
Stornoway
Eye Peninsula
Scarp
Taransay
Harris
Scadabay
Scalpay
Berneray
Leverburgh
Shiant Is.
The Minch
Hougharry
North Uist
Lochmaddy
Claddach Kirkibost
Grimsay
Ronay
Muir of Aird
Benbecula
Wiay
Lochcarnan
South Uist
Lochboisdale
Eriskay
Castlebay
Canna
Rum
Soay
Eigg
Muck
Rubha Hunish
Kilmuir
Kilmaluag
Staffin
Waternish
Island of Skye
Portree
Raasay
Rona
Sound of Raasay
Inner Sound
Cuillin
Strathaird
Broadford
Scalpay
Erbusaig
Isle Ornsay
Sound of Sleat
Mallaig
Arisaig
Achracle
Rubha Reidh
Melvaig
North Erradale
Inverasdale
Upper Diabaig
Plockton
HIGHLAND
North West
Cape Wrath
Kinlochbervie
Loch Eriboll
Tongue
Strathy
Melvich
Thurso
John o' Groats
Stroma
Duncansby Head
Wick
Handa I.
Scourie
Lochinver
Ullapool
Ardindrean
Braemore
Achnasheen
Strathpeffer
Dingwall
Black Isle
Helmsdale
Brora
Golspie
Dornoch
Tain
Dornoch Firth
Tarbat Ness
Moray Firth
Inverness
Drumnadrochit
Fort Augustus
Invergarry
Spean Bridge
Fort William
Ben Nevis
Kingussie
Kincraig
Feshie-bridge
Carrbridge
Grantown-on-Spey
Boat of Garten
Cairngorm Mountains
Grampian Mountains
Blair Atholl
Kirkton of
Nairn
MORAY
Elgin
Spey Bay
Keith
Huntly
Banff
Fraserburgh
Rattray Head
Peterhead
Buchan Ness
ABERDEENSHIRE
Gartly
Fyvie
Oldmeldrum
Aboyne
Banchory
ABERDEEN
Aberdeen
Orkney Islands
Not to same scale
0 10 20 miles
0 10 20 30 kilometres
Mull Head
N. Ronaldsay
Westray
Cleaton
Sanday
Rousay
Eday
Brough Head
Sandwick
Mainland
Shapinsay
Stronsay
Rora Head
Stromness
Kirkwall
Scapa Flow
Lyness
Hoy
St Margaret's Hope
Longhope
S. Ronaldsay
Pentland Firth
Dunnet Head
Stroma
John o' Groats
Shetland Islands
Not to same scale
0 10 20 miles
0 10 20 30 kilometres
Unst
Fetlar
Esha Ness
Outer Skerries
Muckle Roe
Lunning
Papa Stour
Mainland
Upper Scalloway
Lerwick
Fitful Head

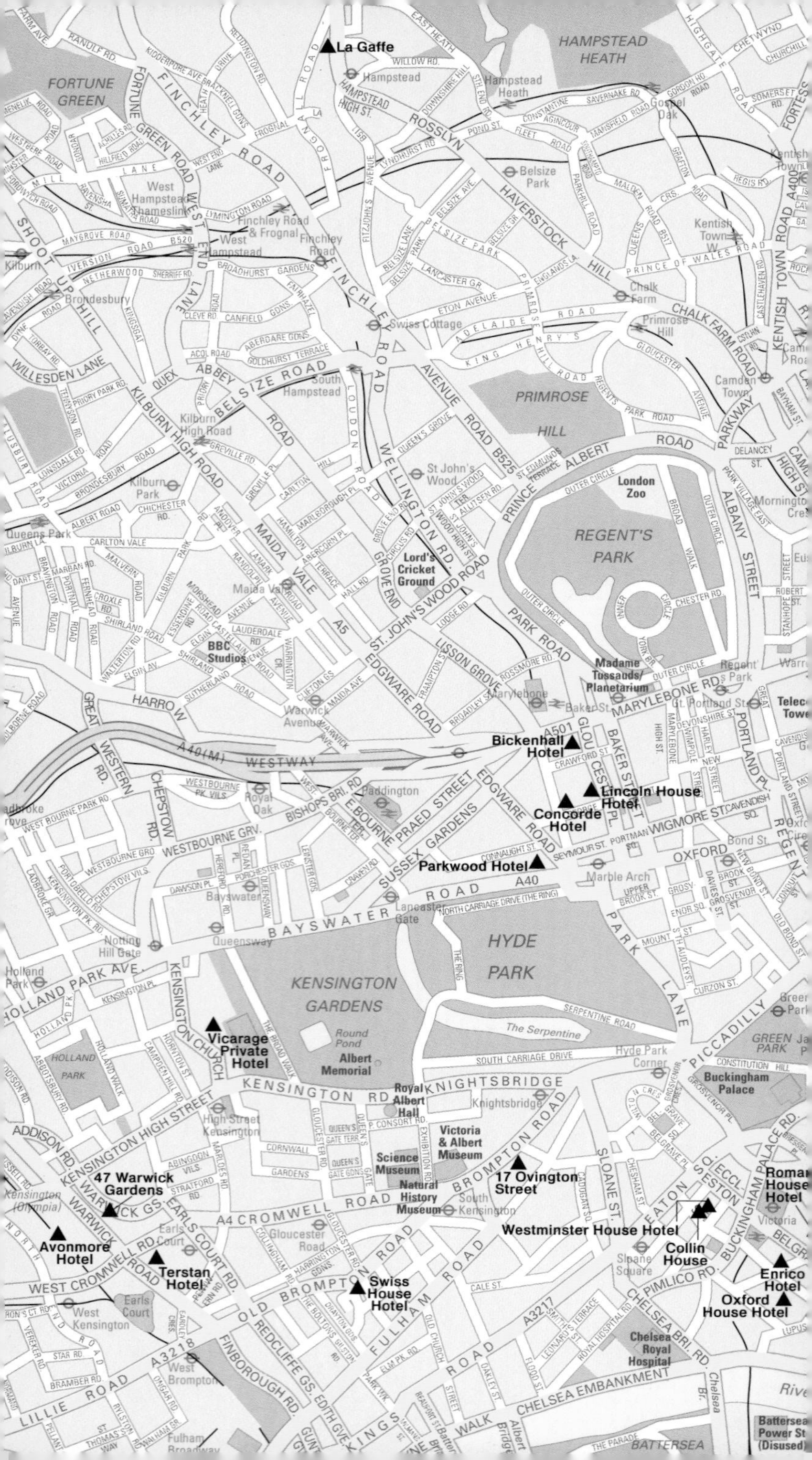
La Gaffe
HAMPSTEAD HEATH
FORTUNE GREEN
Hampstead
Hampstead Heath
Gospel Oak
Belsize Park
Kentish Town
Chalk Farm
Primrose Hill
Camden Town
West Hampstead
Finchley Road & Frognal
Finchley Road
Kilburn
Brondesbury
Swiss Cottage
South Hampstead
Kilburn High Road
Kilburn Park
Queens Park
St John's Wood
PRIMROSE HILL
London Zoo
REGENT'S PARK
Lord's Cricket Ground
Maida Vale
BBC Studios
Madame Tussauds/ Planetarium
Marylebone
Baker St.
Regent's Park
Gt. Portland St.
Warwick Avenue
Bickenhall Hotel
Lincoln House Hotel
Concorde Hotel
Paddington
Royal Oak
Parkwood Hotel
Marble Arch
Bond St.
Bayswater
Lancaster Gate
Queensway
Notting Hill Gate
Holland Park
HYDE PARK
KENSINGTON GARDENS
Round Pond
Albert Memorial
The Serpentine
Vicarage Private Hotel
HOLLAND PARK
Hyde Park Corner
GREEN PARK
Green Park
Buckingham Palace
Royal Albert Hall
Knightsbridge
High Street Kensington
Victoria & Albert Museum
Science Museum
Natural History Museum
South Kensington
17 Ovington Street
47 Warwick Gardens
Kensington (Olympia)
Avonmore Hotel
Earls Court
Terstan Hotel
Gloucester Road
Westminster House Hotel
Collin House
Roman House Hotel
Victoria
Sloane Square
Enrico Hotel
Oxford House Hotel
Swiss House Hotel
West Kensington
West Brompton
Chelsea Royal Hospital
Fulham Broadway
Battersea Power St (Disused)
BATTERSEA
FINCHLEY ROAD
HAVERSTOCK HILL
KILBURN HIGH ROAD
MAIDA VALE
EDGWARE ROAD
ST. JOHN'S WOOD ROAD
PRINCE ALBERT ROAD
MARYLEBONE RD.
A40(M) WESTWAY
BAYSWATER ROAD
PARK LANE
OXFORD
PICCADILLY
KENSINGTON HIGH STREET
KENSINGTON RD.
KNIGHTSBRIDGE
BROMPTON ROAD
A4 CROMWELL ROAD
FULHAM ROAD
KINGS ROAD
CHELSEA EMBANKMENT
SLOANE ST.
BUCKINGHAM PALACE RD.
LILLIE ROAD
WEST CROMWELL ROAD
HOLLAND PARK AVE.
WILLESDEN LANE
SHOOT UP HILL
BELSIZE ROAD
ABBEY ROAD
WELLINGTON RD.
AVENUE ROAD
KENTISH TOWN ROAD
PARKWAY
ALBANY STREET
BAKER STREET
PORTLAND PL.
WIGMORE ST.
PRAED STREET
SUSSEX GARDENS
WESTBOURNE GRV.
HARROW ROAD
CHEPSTOW RD.
WESTERN RD.

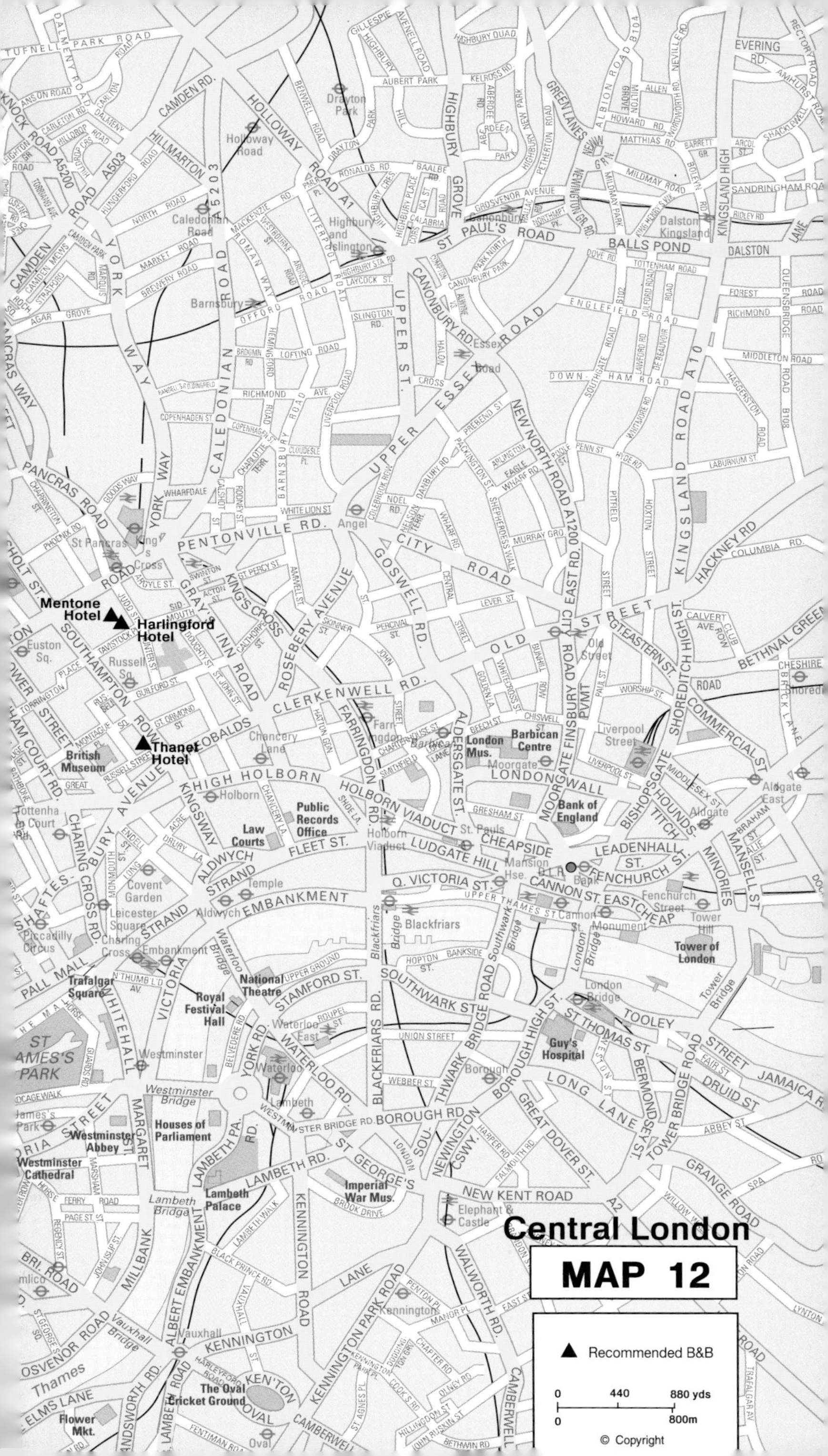
Central London
MAP 12
Recommended B&B
0
440
880 yds
0
800m
© Copyright
Mentone Hotel
Harlingford Hotel
Thanet Hotel
British Museum
Russell Sq.
Euston Sq.
St Pancras
King's Cross
Angel
Barnsbury
Caledonian Road
Holloway Road
Drayton Park
Highbury and Islington
Canonbury
Essex Road
Dalston Kingsland
Old Street
Liverpool Street
Barbican Centre
London Mus.
Moorgate
Bank of England
Public Records Office
Law Courts
Chancery Lane
Holborn
Farringdon
St. Pauls
Mansion Hse.
Bank
Cannon St.
Monument
Fenchurch Street
Tower Hill
Tower of London
Aldgate
Aldgate East
Covent Garden
Leicester Square
Piccadilly Circus
Charing Cross
Embankment
Temple
Aldwych
Blackfriars
Trafalgar Square
National Theatre
Royal Festival Hall
Waterloo East
Waterloo
Westminster
St James's Park
Houses of Parliament
Westminster Abbey
Westminster Cathedral
Lambeth Palace
Lambeth North
Imperial War Mus.
Elephant & Castle
Borough
London Bridge
Guy's Hospital
Tower Bridge
Kennington
Vauxhall
The Oval Cricket Ground
Oval
Flower Mkt.
Thames
Pentonville Rd.
City Road
Upper St.
Holborn Viaduct
Fleet St.
Strand
Embankment
Southwark St.
Borough Rd
New Kent Road
Kennington Road
Kennington Park Road
Walworth Rd.
Tooley Street
Long Lane
Balls Pond Road
St Paul's Road
Old Street
Clerkenwell Rd.
High Holborn
Cheapside
Leadenhall St.
Fenchurch St.
London Wall
Commercial St
Kingsland Road A10
New North Road
Essex Road
Caledonian Road
York Way
Gray's Inn Road
Euston Road
Southampton Row
Kingsway
Charing Cross Rd.
Victoria Embankment
Whitehall
Millbank
Albert Embankment
Lambeth Road
Great Dover St.
Tower Bridge Road
Jamaica Road
Grange Road
Camberwell
Highbury Grove
Holloway Road A1
Green Lanes
Hackney Rd
Bethnal Green
Evering Rd.
Amhurst Road
Tufnell Park Road

Report form BB98

To: *The Good Bed and Breakfast Guide,*
Consumers' Association
FREEPOST, 2 Marylebone Road,
London NW1 1YN

Report on:

Address:

Date of visit:

Please tick appropriate box:

☐ Should continue as a main entry

☐ Should be considered as a main entry for future editions

☐ Should not be included

My reasons are:

please continue overleaf

I am not connected in any way with the owners

Name and address (BLOCK CAPITALS):

Signed:

☐ Please send some more report forms (*tick if appropriate*)

Report form BB98

To: *The Good Bed and Breakfast Guide,*
Consumers' Association
FREEPOST, 2 Marylebone Road,
London NW1 1YN

Report on:

Address:

Date of visit:

Please tick appropriate box:

☐ Should continue as a main entry

☐ Should be considered as a main entry for future editions

☐ Should not be included

My reasons are:

please continue overleaf

I am not connected in any way with the owners

Name and address (BLOCK CAPITALS):

Signed:

☐ Please send some more report forms (*tick if appropriate*)

Report form BB98

To: *The Good Bed and Breakfast Guide,*
Consumers' Association
FREEPOST, 2 Marylebone Road,
London NW1 1YN

Report on:

Address:

Date of visit:

Please tick appropriate box:

- ☐ Should continue as a main entry
- ☐ Should be considered as a main entry for future editions
- ☐ Should not be included

My reasons are:

please continue overleaf

I am not connected in any way with the owners

Name and address (BLOCK CAPITALS):

Signed:

☐ Please send some more report forms (*tick if appropriate*)